R197.00

D0831185

by
Diners Club
INTERNATIONAL

2015
SOUTH AFRICAN

WINE
GUIDE

35th ANNIVERSARY
EDITION

John Platter SA Wine Guide (Pty) Ltd
www.wineonaplatter.com

PUBLISHER

Jean-Pierre Rossouw

EDITOR

Philip van Zyl

ASSOCIATE EDITORS

Tim James, Wendy Toerien, Cathy van Zyl

TASTERS

Angela Lloyd; Master of Wine Cathy van Zyl; Cape Wine Masters Winnie Bowman, Greg de Bruyn, Tim James, Christine Rudman and Meryl Weaver; David Biggs, David Clarke (2014 edition), Christian Eedes (2014 edition), Joanne Gibson, Higgo Jacobs, Cathy Marston, Fiona McDonald, Ingrid Motteux, Khuselo Mputa (2010 edition), Gregory Mutambe, Jörg Pfützner, James Pietersen (2014 edition) & Dave Swingler.

COPYWRITERS

Greg de Bruyn, Christian Eedes, Joanne Gibson, Tim James, Angela Lloyd, Cathy Marston, Fiona McDonald, Christine Rudman, Dave Swingler, Wendy Toerien, Cathy van Zyl & Meryl Weaver

COORDINATORS

Ina de Villiers (information) & Christina Harvett (wine & tasting)

DATABASE & QR CODES

Sean de Kock, Ben van Rensburg (Modern Web Presence)

TYPESETTING & MAPS

Gawie du Toit

ADVERTISING

Highbury Safika Media ▪ Tel +27 (0)21-416-0141

SALES & ADMINISTRATION

Christine Parent +27 (0)28-316-3049 ▪ Tel: +27 (0)28-316-3049 ▪ Fax: +27 (0)28-316-1048 ▪ Email: office@wineonaplatter.com

© John Platter SA Wine Guide (Pty) Ltd 2015
PO Box 537, Hermanus 7200
Tel: +27 (0)28-316-3049 ▪ Fax: +27 (0)28-316-1048
Email: office@wineonaplatter.com

🌐 Wineonaplatter.com
📘 Facebook.com/wineonaplatter
🐦 Twitter.com/wineonaplatter ▪ @wineonaplatter

Contents

A Word from Diners Club

Welcome to the 2015 Diners Club Platter's Wine Guide.

For 35 years Platter's has been the undisputed leading guide to South African wines, and with good reason. Every new edition is filled with information, hints and tips that are invaluable to wine experts and novices alike.

This year the guide contains info on more than 7,000 wines from 961 producers, merchants and brands, to ensure that you are never at a loss for a well-informed choice.

Cheers to another vintage year!

Ebrahim Matthews
Managing Director, Diners Club South Africa

South African Wine: Rejuvenation and Discovery

Governor Jan van Riebeeck oversaw the Cape's first vinification in February 1659. Fast-forward 356 years, and the industry which he founded has an air of rejuvenation and discovery about it, as well as a renewed sense of purpose, with the arrival of young blood and new brooms at all levels.

The shift coincides with a wider trend: the growing influence of Generation Y, whose more senior members (born in the 1980s) are reckoned to be the largest economically empowered population age segment in South Africa, touching every industry — including wine — over the next 10 years.

Youthful hands are now at the helm of VinPro, the independent advisory company which since 2003 has been assisting some 3,600 grape producers and wine cellars. The chief executive is a dynamic young former agricultural banking professional. His small team of experts are mostly of an age, equally qualified, similarly enthused, noticeably driven.

Wines of South Africa (WOSA), the organisation tasked with marketing Brand SA overseas, has fresh leadership, too. The new chair is also owner of a boutique wine farm, and comes to the post as the former CEO of a major bank (awarded for innovation), recently appointed chair of a SA-created mobile social network, and founder of a start-ups investment and advisory company.

There are high expectations that these and other new incumbents will forge ahead with initiatives integral to the success and sustainability of the industry.

Recently, various stakeholders drafted 'a new roadmap' for SA wine, the Wine Industry Strategic Framework. It lists six essential development areas: economic empowerment, collective marketing, social upliftment, knowledge and information, technology innovation and transfer, and human resources training.

Strong focuses will be on job creation, increasing foreign exchange earnings and developing infrastructure. A structure to forge a closer relationship with government and facilitate open, sustained interaction among government, producers and labour has been mooted.

Young guns, niche wines

The number of high-end, small-volume, niche wines being produced by Millennial winemakers under their own labels is rising. Qualified, travelled, au fait with both Old and New World techniques and styles, some work for progressive wineries which allow them to vinify small quantities under their own brand. Others consult for boutique producers, giving them even more opportunity to trawl the winelands for special parcels for their own labels.

This confident new generation is walking the walk, long talked about, that vineyards are where fine-wine is made. At the same time, they are educating and inspiring growers to spend time and money on obtaining the best quality fruit possible, knowing they'll be financially rewarded.

Farming smart

The larger-volume cellars are following suit. While continuing to feed big and buyers-own brands, they are introducing interesting own-label bottlings, from new varieties to single-vineyard selections to trending low-alcohol and slightly sweeter wines.

New-generation viticulturists and vintners are also encouraging their growers to 'farm smart'. The thinking: 'Grow grapes to slot into one of the five levels: the absolutely exquisite and artisanal; high priced (HP); medium priced; entry level; and bulk. There is a place for each. But we need to develop that top level because that's what gives a face to SA wines.'

The injunction: 'Our top growers must be paid more; the gap between the lower four tiers and the price per ton for those top-quality grapes and resultant wines that reflect a sense of place and authentic identity should be greater.'

Old vines, new sites

The search for good grapes by young independents has led to the production of acclaimed premium wines, often featuring chenin blanc, from resurrected vines of rare maturity. This has lent impetus to a project to record and preserve all SA's still-viable old vines (35+ years). Halfway along, some 1,500 ha have been tagged, sparking the thought that SA may have the largest volume of surviving old vines worldwide.

The search for venerable parcels has exposed exciting hillside and mountainside sites offering cool growing conditions in often warmer regions: Piekenierskloof (Citrusdal), Piketberg (Swartland), Witzenberg (Ceres/Tulbagh/Wolsely), Langeberg (Robertson/Ashton), Riviersonderend (Napier). Maritime examples include Skurfberg (West Coast) and Malgas (Cape South Coast).

Difficulties in cultivating on steep slopes, in rocky soils and under windy conditions have in turn prompted exploratory alternative vine training methods. Some are adopting the 'poled vine' system, essentially a bushvine lifted and supported by a single thick, round stake.

'New old' varieties

Accepting and embracing SA's warm dry climate, viticulturists, growers and winemakers are increasingly focusing on Mediterranean varieties.

Following on Rhône-style blends featuring shiraz, mourvèdre and grenache noir, and distinctive new multi-variety blends featuring marsanne, roussanne, grenache blanc and other denizens of southern France, come sorties into Spain, Portugal and Greece.

Top local fortified-wine producers are right on trend with their Portuguese counterparts in using classic 'port' varieties to make unfortified wines. The better new-generation bottlings, often featuring touriga nacional, tinta barocca and/or tinta roriz/tempranillo, show the benefit of inspanning these pedigreed grapes suited to SA's climate.

Portugal's verdelho has also taken root here, as has Spain's macabeo. Another 25 carefully selected new varieties will be planted on a Paardeberg farm next year. Among them: assyrtiko, xinomavro and aghiorghitiko from Greece; mencía from Spain; poulsard from France's Jura. The resultant wines in 4-6 years will be open to all for assessment.

Modern wine the traditional way

Young winemakers, working with the right varieties on appropriate sites, are increasingly willing and able to adopt the old non-interventionist 'natural' way of making wine.

Keeping it simple includes open tanks (often resurrected old concrete 'kuipe') and open barrels for fermentation; whole-berry fermentation; natural (wild) yeasts; less, if any, sulphur; older and larger barrels (300/500L instead of 225); minimal pumping and racking; no filtering/fining.

The aim: freshness, purity of fruit, natural acidity, ripe tannins and subtler (if any) wood influence. The result: more distinctive, individual, authentic wines.

Smorgasbord of styles

Classic, versatile, some say still-undervalued, chenin blanc continues its strong comeback, showing its strengths particularly in old-vine wines, serious blends and appealing, food-friendly bottlings, both barrel fermented and unwooded.

SA's fine Bordeaux-style white and red blends are joined by serious chenin-led originals. The Rhône-influenced red blend category is expanded by shiraz-based combinations with Mediterranean varieties for fresh, 'crunchy' wines.

Rosés are returning: not the sweet wines of yore, but dry, crisp, complex single-varietal versions from pinotage, merlot and shiraz, or blends of Mediterranean grapes.

Ethical, sustainable practices

Internationally recognised accreditation from industry and other acknowledged organisations such as Agricultural Ethical Trade Initiative (WIETA), Integrated Production of Wine (IPW) and Biodiversity & Wine Initiative (BWI) for ethical trading and production and environmentally sustainable practices is increasingly sought after. Membership of WIETA alone doubled in 2014.

However, monitoring remains a daunting task, possibly weakening impact and credibility. Hence support of and endorsement by larger bodies (including WOSA) for farms forming spin-off associations, such as the recent Premium Independent Wineries of South Africa (PIWOSA). Its ethics charter encapsulates what SA's ethical wine production is all about.

Transformation

While industry bodies concentrate on the big picture – including substantial black-owned brand representation on industry boards such as WOSA – individual wineries facilitate black empowerment initiatives through staff trusts, shareholdings, ownership of winemaking facilities and more.

The Cape Winemakers Guild (CWG) has expanded its well-established Oenology Protégé Programme (mentoring student winemakers through internships with its members) with a similar programme for viticulture, assisted by the VinPro Foundation.

The Women in Wine initiative aims to provide opportunities and training for black women, 'the backbone of South Africa', while the Pinotage Youth Development Programme last year sent its first intake into the industry. The curriculum collaborates with partner wineries to provide practical on-the-job training.

Total wine experience

The last wine industry survey showed wine tourism's contribution to SA's overall tourism revenue as R4.6 billion. At the first Cape Town Wine Tourism Symposium, held last year, the City of Cape Town's Tourism Product Development representative highlighted wine tourism as a key area for the next five years.

A wine-and-food culture is growing. Top-notch wine farm restaurants are on the increase, as are gourmet wine-and-food tastings, dégustation menus and novel wine pairings (chocolate, ice-cream, biltong, nougat). Pop-up restaurants, sometimes accompanied by live music performances are trending.

Social media & constant contact

A little tardily, perhaps, SA wine is going digital and online in a big way. Some small entrepreneurial producers go to market solely by way of websites and social media accounts. QR (quick response) codes on back labels direct smartphone users to websites for information and orders.

Winemakers and winelovers are communicating directly with via Twitter and Instagram, among other platforms. Wines launches, special events, exclusive offers and one-off wine experiences are increasingly announced via digital channels, spurring the not-so-tech-savvy or constantly-in-touch to get connected.

New (and not-so-new) wine drinkers are buying less but better. Integral to the purchase decision are the wine's backstory and its underlying authenticity/integrity.

In a wired world, sharing a good experience is the work of but a second. So too is a bad. That's a sobering thought for all industry players but an invitation, too, to connoisseurs and novices alike to join in the conversation.

Editor's Note

Andrew McDowall, who succeeded the guide's co-founder John Platter as publisher in 1998, retired last November and passed the reins to wine-and-food man Jean-Pierre Rossouw (also originator and publisher of Rossouw's Restaurant Guide, now Platter's sibling publication in the Diners Club South Africa stable.) Under JP's baton a number of improvements have been introduced for this, the 35th edition, notably a revamped logo and cover design; crisper page layouts with larger, more legible type; stricter good-value parameters; and a new Hidden Gem category, with associated icon (🍐), highlighting a limited number of wines especially worthy of note – interesting, attractive, unusual, unique, representative of an important trend etc.

Unchanged are our aim and approach, namely to taste, rate and describe as many as possible South African-made wines available during the currency of the book, both locally and overseas.

Much as we'd like to, the number of individual wines precludes us from re-tasting/rating vintages which have been submitted previously yet will still be available for sale during the book's currency. Only wines which last year were reviewed as tank or barrel samples, and thus rated provisionally (or considered too young and unformed to rate), or wines we believe we may have miscalled last time, are revisited for the current book. New and previously untasted vintages are, of course, reviewed as normal.

A-Z directory & Ratings Summary

It bears repeating that the rankings reflected in the book are the result of a process beginning towards the end of June, when we mobilise our team of tasters. The results of their work are reflected in the A–Z section, along with news about the wineries and winemakers, general information about products, vinification facilities, vineyards, amenities available to visitors and more. (Scores for all wines in the A-Z are also listed separately for convenience in the section named This Year's Ratings Summarised on page 547.)

For visitors in search of wine-route information, we've incorporated GPS coordinates for as many as possible of the wineries open to the public at set hours or by appointment. The maps have again been fully updated, along with the quick-lookup tables which furnish key visitor information about the wineries of a particular area, such as whether or not they are open on weekends and public holidays, offer meals or refreshments, specifically cater for children, or are friendly to individuals with reduced mobility.

Our initiative to provide professionally conducted audits of winetasting areas, cellar tours and other visitor facilities in the winelands in conjunction with accessibility specialist Disability Solutions is highlighted on page 606.

Our wine ranking system remains the same as last year. We cover the full spectrum, from wines we consider 'somewhat less than ordinary' (and award 0 stars, equivalent to 50–59 on the 100-point scale) to 'superlative South African classics', worthy of a full 5 stars (95-100 points). Wines rated ★★★★ or higher are usually listed first in each entry. Vintages deviating from the general rating are individually starred in the text. Very good/promising wines and more modest examples (★★★☆ or fewer) are included in the 'run-on' listings at the end of entries. Good-value wines are highlighted with the ⊘ icon for easy identification. See also How to Use the Guide on page 20.

Pre-bottling samples

Because of deadlines, many wines in the guide are tasted freshly bottled or as works-in-progress; any considered unrateable as a result are noted as such in the text. It's worth mentioning that we taste from the end of June to end-August. Except for the bottlings assessed for five stars (see About the Wines of the Year on page 16), all wines are tasted 'sighted' (with labels exposed) and the name of the producer known.

Sighted tasting has been the preferred approach since the inception of the guide. The reason is that we wish to remain true to the essence of this project – that of being a wine guide and not a wine competition. Platter's 'reason for being' is to inform winelovers about wines and wineries. To best do this, our tasters are encouraged to learn as much as possible about their allocated wines and wineries, and winemakers are asked to provide background information along with tasting samples. Understanding what producers intend to achieve is far more difficult when wines are assessed blind, because then perforce you are assessing only the organoleptic qualities of what's in the glass. Since we understand the intention of the winery, we can assess how successfully the intent manifests in the glass. The more we know about the sites, the soils, the winemaking and the philosophy of the winery, the better we can assess the final product in terms of character, style and quality – and tell you about it. Our scores are the considered opinion of wine experts who understand the responsibility of adducing a star rating to a product as changeable as wine.

Tracking wines' performance

Another reason for sighted tasting is that the guide aspires responsibly to track the performance of the wines under review over successive vintages, to consider them against one another and to highlight those vintages which are particularly successful (and ones that are less so). This is why, for the better scoring wines, there is a 'general' or 'track record' rating in the left margin plus a 'vintage-specific' rating, if applicable, in brackets beside the particular vintage in the wine description.

It's worth noting that, as a control, we also double-blind taste hundreds of wines in the course of our assessments. In these corroborative reviews, tasters have no information about the wine save what's in the glass.

Because of the subjective element associated with wine assessment, we strongly recommend you view our rankings as adjuncts to the tasting notes rather than as oracular pronouncements. And we continue to urge you, in the words of a local winery's marketing slogan, to 'trust your taste'.

Wines featured in this edition were assessed by a team whose professionalism and unflagging enthusiasm we gratefully acknowledge. Their initials appear below the wines they tasted, as follows: Angela Lloyd (AL); Master of Wine Cathy van Zyl (CvZ); Cape Wine Masters Winnie Bowman (WB), Greg de Bruyn (GdB), Tim James (TJ), Christine Rudman (CR) and Meryl Weaver (MW); also David Biggs (DB), Higgo Jacobs (HJ),

Cathy Marston (CM), Fiona McDonald (FM), Ingrid Motteux (IM), Gregory Mutambe (GM), Jörg Pfützner (JPf), Dave Swingler (DS) and newcomer Joanne Gibson (JG). For potted biographies of the tasters, see page 17.

A splendid team

Warm thanks to the rest of the splendid team, specially to associate editors Tim James (also proofreader) and Wendy Toerien; copywriters Greg de Bruyn, Christian Eedes, Joanne Gibson, Tim James, Angela Lloyd, Cathy Marston, Fiona McDonald, Christine Rudman, Dave Swingler, Wendy Toerien, Cathy van Zyl and Meryl Weaver; information coordinator Ina de Villiers; wine coordinator Christina Harvett and assistants Janus Barnard, Yolandi Barnard, Courtney North, JC Rademeyer, MF Schoeman, Wilhelm Schultz, Carlo Valente and Michelle Waldeck; database trainer Ina Smith; map and typesetting guru Gawie du Toit; Highbury Safika Media for advertising sales; Christine Parent for book sales and administration; Lara Philp and Johan Rademan of Vineyard Connection for the use of their excellent facilities; Angela Lloyd for indexing; Lauren de Kock for fact-checking; Mark Whyte and XtraSmile Couriers; Danie Pretorius and the Brandy Foundation; Ben van Rensburg (Modern Web Presence) for the QR code; and the ever-helpful SAWIS. Special thanks to Sean 'Anything Is Possible' de Kock for 24 x 7 help with the database, intranet and website.

Most of all, loving thanks to Cathy, wife and associate editor, who somehow juggles a day job, Platter's and at least half-dozen other roles and responsibilities with style, grace, humour and truly baffling efficiency; and to son Luke, turning 18 and on course to get his Private Pilot Licence.

Certainly not least, sincere thanks to South Africa's wine producers and negociants, without whose support the book could not be produced.

Finally, an invitation to join us on the web, Facebook and Twitter (see page 2 for details), and to look for our brand-new app on the App Store.

Philip van Zyl

Winery of the Year

Sadie Family Wines

Introducing the Winery of the Year for 2010 (coincidentally the guide's 30th anniversary year), we noted that Swartland-based Sadie Family Wines and its prime mover Eben Sadie 'continue to set the benchmarks and retain their status as a true Cape icon. Given their propensity for questioning, tweaking, and looking beyond the horizon, expect them to continue leading from the front for many years to come'.

Which is exactly what they've done, and continue doing - as prominent role players in the influential Swartland Independent Producers organisation and internationally raved-about Swartland Revolution weekend, and crucially as producers of consistently superlative wines. After this year's stringent selection process, they are the only winery to emerge with three maximum 5 star ratings for the 2015 edition.

Two of the top-rated wines are from the more recent Old Vine Series, a remarkable and important collection of terroir expressions, some of them featuring ancient vines and fascinating, sometimes long-overlooked grape varieties. But the Sadies' original Signature Wines, Columella and Palladius, whose quality and drama helped kick-start the Swartland 'revolution' and set the bar for South Africa, are not neglected — intricate, intriguing Palladius being the third of the Sadie 5 stars this edition.

We're delighted to honour Sadie Family Wines as our Winery of the Year for a second time. May they continue to question, tweak, look over the horizon and, yes, lead from the front for many years to come.

Red and White Wines of the Year

Five Stars & Red Wine Of The Year

De Trafford Blueprint Syrah 2012

One of two varietal shirazes/syrahs made by De Trafford co-owner and winemaker David Trafford, its name alluding to David's architect training, Blueprint is mostly from neighbouring property Keermont, the balance from a block on home-farm Mont Fleur aptly named 'Tip Top'. Yields are small (4-6 t/ha). David being one of the vignerons practising natural winemaking years before it became de rigueur, Blueprint Syrah is spontaneously fermented, aged in only older oak (21 months) and bottled unfined and unfiltered. Like most of David's bottlings, Blueprint '12 is no shrinking violet but the power is sheathed and the wine shows wonderful harmony and freshness.

Five Stars & White Wine Of The Year

DeMorgenzon Reserve Chardonnay 2013

Owners Hylton and Wendy Appelbaum retained only venerable chenin vines in their redevelopment of DeMorgenzon estate in the heights above Stellenboschkloof, which meant the newly planted varieties were always going to have to compete for pride of place in the line-up. Cellarmaster Carl van der Merwe reveals that vintages '11 and '12 of the chardonnay were deemed good enough for the stellar Maestro White blend. With in-barrel '14 also 'looking very good', the team was convinced to add the Chardonnay '13 to the prestige Reserve range — an inspired decision indeed! Another 6 ha of the variety are being planted, 'making our confidence very clear!'

Wines of the Year

Five Stars

Cabernet Franc
☐ Warwick 2011

Cabernet Sauvignon
☐ Groot Constantia 2012
☐ Le Riche Reserve 2011
☐ Nederburg II Centuries 2010
☐ Oldenburg 2011
☐ Stark-Condé Three Pines 2012

Cinsaut
☐ Sadie Family Pofadder 2013

Petit Verdot
☐ Stellenbosch Vineyards Flagship 2010

Pinotage
☐ Flagstone Time Manner Place 2012
☐ Kanonkop Black Label 2012

Pinot Noir
☐ Creation Reserve 2013
☐ Crystallum Cuvée Cinéma 2013
☐ Newton Johnson Family Vineyards 2013
☐ Sumaridge 2012

Shiraz/Syrah
☐ Boekenhoutskloof 2012
☐ Boschendal Cecil John Reserve 2012
☐ De Trafford Blueprint 2012
☐ Fable 2012
☐ Porseleinberg 2012

Red Blends
☐ Delaire Graff Botmaskop 2012
☐ Ernie Els CWG Auction Reserve 2012
☐ Hartenberg The Mackenzie 2011
☐ Thelema Rabelais 2010
☐ Vilafonté Series C 2011

Chardonnay
☐ DeMorgenzon Reserve 2013
☐ Iona 2013
☐ Richard Kershaw Elgin Clonal Selection 2013
☐ Sterhuis Barrel Selection 2012

Chenin Blanc
☐ Alheit Magnetic North Mountain Makstok 2013

☐ Fram 2013
☐ Kaapzicht The 1947 2013

Grenache Blanc
☐ Foundry 2013

Sauvignon Blanc
☐ Buitenverwachting Husseys Vlei 2013
☐ Diners Club Bartho Eksteen CWG Auction Reserve Vloekskoot 2013
☐ Reyneke Reserve White 2013

Semillon
☐ Vergelegen Reserve 2013

White Blends
☐ Constantia Uitsig Constantia White 2013
☐ David & Nadia Sadie Aristargos 2013
☐ DeMorgenzon Maestro White 2013
☐ Flagstone Treaty Tree Reserve 2013
☐ Miles Mossop Saskia 2012
☐ Oak Valley Mountain Reserve White 2010
☐ Sadie Family Palladius 2012
☐ Sadie Family Skerpioen 2013

Méthode Cap Classique
☐ Graham Beck Blanc de Blancs Brut 2009

Dessert Wine, Unfortified
☐ Delheim Edelspatz Noble Late Harvest 2013
☐ Mullineux Straw Wine 2013

Dessert Wine, Fortified
☐ Nuy White Muscadel 2013

Port-Style
☐ Boplaas Cape Tawny Vintners Reserve NV
☐ De Krans Cape Vintage Reserve 2012

Brandy
☐ Boplaas Potstill 20 Years
☐ KWV 12 Year Old Barrel Select
☐ KWV 15 Year Old Alambic
☐ KWV 20 Year Old
☐ Oude Meester Souverein
☐ Van Ryn 12 Year Distillers Reserve
☐ Van Ryn 20 Year Collectors Reserve
☐ Van Ryn Au.Ra

Highly Recommended

Cabernet Franc
☐ Raats 2012

Cabernet Sauvignon
☐ Boekenhoutskloof 2012
☐ Buitenverwachting 2012
☐ Cederberg Five Generations 2012
☐ Delaire Graff Reserve 2012
☐ Delaire Graff Laurence Graff Reserve 2011
☐ Ernie Els Proprietor's 2012
☐ Laibach Widow's Block 2012
☐ Le Riche Auction Reserve 2011
☐ Neil Ellis Vineyard Selection 2011
☐ Vergelegen Reserve 2009
☐ Vergelegen V 2011
☐ Waterford 2011

Grenache Noir
☐ Sadie Family Soldaat 2013

Pinotage
☐ Beeslaar 2012
☐ Beyerskloof Diesel 2012
☐ Chateau Naudé Le Vin de François 2012
☐ Spioenkop 1900 2013

Pinot Noir
☐ Botanica Mary Delany Collection 2013
☐ Chamonix Reserve 2013
☐ Newton Johnson Windansea 2013
☐ Stark-Condé Round Mountain 2013
☐ Storm Moya's 2012
☐ Winery of Good Hope Radford Dale Freedom 2013

Shiraz/Syrah
☐ Cederberg CWG Auction Reserve Teen die Hoog 2012
☐ Eagles' Nest 2011
☐ Fairview Eenzaamheid 2012
☐ Fairview Jakkalsfontein 2012
☐ Groote Post 2013
☐ Hartenberg Gravel Hill 2010
☐ Hartenberg CWG Auction Reserve 2011
☐ Hartenberg The Stork 2011
☐ Haskell Vineyards Pillars 2011
☐ Hidden Valley Shipwreck 2009
☐ Keermont Topside 2012
☐ Luddite 2010
☐ Mont Destin Destiny 2010
☐ Mullineux Schist 2012
☐ Mullineux 2012
☐ Reyneke Reserve Red 2012
☐ Saronsberg 2012

☐ Sijnn 2012
☐ Simonsig Merindol 2012
☐ Super Single Vineyards Mount Sutherland 2012

Red Blends
☐ Bellingham Bernard Series Small Barrel SMV 2012
☐ Buitenverwachting Christine 2010
☐ Chamonix Troika 2012
☐ Dalla Cia Teano 2011
☐ David & Nadia Sadie Elpidios 2012
☐ De Toren Fusion V 2012
☐ De Trafford Elevation 393 2010
☐ Eikendal Classique 2012
☐ Ernie Els Signature 2011
☐ Fleur du Cap Laszlo 2009
☐ Grangehurst CWG Auction Reserve 2009
☐ Grangehurst CWG Cape Reserve 2009
☐ Haskell Vineyards Haskell II 2010
☐ Hermanuspietersfontein Die Arnoldus 2010
☐ Hillcrest Hornfels 2012
☐ Jordan CWG Auction Reserve Sophia 2011
☐ Kanonkop Paul Sauer 2011
☐ Keet First Verse 2011
☐ La Motte Pierneef Shiraz-Viognier 2012
☐ Longridge Ekliptika 2012
☐ Miles Mossop Max 2010
☐ Morgenster 2011
☐ Mvemve Raats MR de Compostella 2012
☐ Nederburg Ingenuity Italian Blend 2011, 2012
☐ Nederburg Ingenuity Spanish Blend 2012
☐ Newton Johnson Granum 2012
☐ Nico van der Merwe Mas Nicolas 2009
☐ Raka Five Maidens 2011
☐ Rust en Vrede 1694 Classification 2010, 2011
☐ Sadie Family Columella 2012
☐ Saronsberg Full Circle 2011, 2012
☐ Savage Red 2012
☐ Spier CWG Frans Smit Auction Reserve 2010
☐ Val de Vie 1783 2009
☐ Vergelegen DNA 2010
☐ Vergelegen GVB 2009
☐ Vilafonté Series M 2011
☐ Warwick Trilogy 2011

Chardonnay
☐ Bouchard Finlayson Kaaimansgat/Crocodile's Lair 2013
☐ Chamonix Reserve 2013
☐ Crystallum Clay Shales 2013
☐ De Wetshof Bateleur 2012
☐ De Wetshof The Site 2013

Highly recommended —Chardonnay *(continued)*

- ☐ GlenWood Grand Duc 2012
- ☐ Hamilton Russell 2013
- ☐ Jordan CWG Auction Reserve 2013
- ☐ Môreson Mercator 2013
- ☐ Newton Johnson Family Vineyards 2013
- ☐ Paul Cluver 2013
- ☐ Restless River 2011, 2012
- ☐ Springfield Méthode Ancienne 2011
- ☐ Springfield Wild Yeast 2012
- ☐ Sumaridge 2012
- ☐ Warwick White Lady 2013

Chenin Blanc

- ☐ Beaumont Hope Marguerite 2013
- ☐ Bosman Optenhorst 2012
- ☐ Botanica Mary Delany Collection 2013
- ☐ Cederberg Five Generations 2012
- ☐ DeMorgenzon Reserve 2013
- ☐ Edgebaston David Finlayson Old Vine 2013
- ☐ Intellego Elementis Skin Contact 2013
- ☐ Jean Daneel Signature 2013
- ☐ Keermont Riverside 2013
- ☐ Ken Forrester The FMC 2012
- ☐ Kleine Zalze Family Reserve 2013
- ☐ Miles Mossop The Introduction 2012
- ☐ Mullineux Quartz 2013
- ☐ Opstal Carl Everson 2013
- ☐ Sadie Family Skurfberg 2013
- ☐ Spioenkop 2013
- ☐ Stellenrust 49 Barrel Fermented 2013
- ☐ Windmeul Reserve 2013

Riesling

- ☐ Spioenkop 2013

Sauvignon Blanc

- ☐ Cederberg David Nieuwoudt Ghost Corner 2013
- ☐ Cederberg David Nieuwoudt Ghost Corner Wild Ferment 2013
- ☐ Diemersdal 8 Rows 2014
- ☐ Flagstone Free Run 2012
- ☐ Graham Beck Pheasants' Run 2014
- ☐ Jean Daneel Signature 2013
- ☐ Klein Constantia Block 382 2012
- ☐ Kleine Zalze Family Reserve 2013
- ☐ Nederburg Private Bin D234 2013

Semillon

- ☐ Cederberg David Nieuwoudt Ghost Corner CWG Auction Reserve 2013
- ☐ Constantia Uitsig 2013
- ☐ Sadie Family Kokerboom 2013

Viognier

- ☐ Eagles' Nest 2013

White Blends

- ☐ Alheit Cartology 2013
- ☐ Avondale Cyclus 2012
- ☐ Chamonix Reserve White 2013
- ☐ Cape Point CWG Auction Reserve White 2013
- ☐ Cape Point Isliedh 2013
- ☐ Cederberg David Nieuwoudt Ghost Corner The Bowline 2013
- ☐ Dornier Donatus 2013
- ☐ Fable Jackal Bird 2013
- ☐ Hughes Family Nativo White 2013
- ☐ Mullineux White 2013
- ☐ Nederburg Ingenuity White 013
- ☐ Nitida Coronata Integration 2013
- ☐ Rall White 2013
- ☐ Sadie Family 'T Voetpad 2013
- ☐ Savage White 2013
- ☐ Simonsig CWG The Red Ox Chenin Blanc-Roussanne 2013
- ☐ Steenberg Magna Carta 2012
- ☐ Thorne & Daughters Rocking Horse 2013
- ☐ Tokara Director's Reserve White 2013
- ☐ Vergelegen GVB White 2013

Méthode Cap Classique

- ☐ Avondale Armilla Blanc de Blancs 2009
- ☐ Colmant Brut Chardonnay NV
- ☐ Graham Beck Cuvée Clive 2009
- ☐ House of GM&AHRENS Vintage Cuvée 2010
- ☐ Klein Constantia Brut 2011
- ☐ Silverthorn Jewel Box 2010
- ☐ Silverthorn The Green Man 2011

Dessert Wine, Unfortified

- ☐ Buitenverwachting 1769 2012, 2013
- ☐ Druk My Niet C68 Puella 2013
- ☐ Fairview La Beryl Blanc 2013
- ☐ Fleur du Cap Noble Late Harvest 2013
- ☐ Keermont Fleurfontein 2012
- ☐ Lourensford Semillon Noble Late Harvest 2012
- ☐ Meinert Semillon Straw Wine 2013
- ☐ Miles Mossop Kika 2013
- ☐ Namaqua Noble Late Harvest 2013
- ☐ Nederburg Edelkeur 2013
- ☐ Nederburg Eminence 2013
- ☐ Nederburg Winemaster's Reserve Noble Late Harvest 2013
- ☐ Tokara Reserve Noble Late Harvest 2013

Port-Style

- ☐ Boplaas Cape Vintage Reserve 2011
- ☐ De Krans Cape Tawny Limited Release NV

Hidden Gems

Cabernet Sauvignon
- ☐ Ameera 2012
- ☐ De Wet 2013

Carignan
- ☐ Three Foxes 2012

Cinsaut
- ☐ Rico Suter 2012

Grenache Noir
- ☐ BLANKbottle Familiemoord 2013
- ☐ Waverley Hills 2013

Malbec
- ☐ Fairview La Capra 2013

Merlot
- ☐ Boland Five Climates Single Varietal 2012
- ☐ Drostdy-Hof Core 2014
- ☐ Rosendal 2012
- ☐ Waterstone Pride of Kings 2013

Pinotage
- ☐ Allée Bleue Starlette 2013
- ☐ Franschhoek Cellar Stone Bridge 2013
- ☐ Tulbagh Winery Porter Mill Station 2013
- ☐ Waterstone Africa Five Collection 2009
- ☐ Waterstone Pride of Kings 2011

Pinot Noir
- ☐ Baleia Bay 2012
- ☐ Matzikama Organic The Tidal Phase 2014

Shiraz/Syrah
- ☐ Cape Point Splattered Toad 2013
- ☐ Nieuwedrift 2012
- ☐ Waterstone Pride of Kings 2013

Red Blends
- ☐ Ameera Duel Cabernet Sauvignon-Shiraz 2013
- ☐ De Wet Merlot-Cabernet Sauvignon 2013
- ☐ Groot Parys Pinotage-Chenin Blanc 2014
- ☐ Napier Lion Creek Cabernet Sauvignon-Shiraz 2012
- ☐ Rickety Bridge Foundation Stone 2013

Rosé & Blanc De Noir
- ☐ Allée Bleue Starlette 2014
- ☐ BLANKbottle Lippe 2013
- ☐ Dornier Cocoa Hill 2014
- ☐ Goedverwacht 2014
- ☐ Wolftrap 2014

Chardonnay
- ☐ Bellpost 2013
- ☐ Franschhoek Cellar Our Town Hall 2014
- ☐ Olsen 2013
- ☐ Spier Signature 2014
- ☐ Stonewall 2013
- ☐ Van Loveren Christina Van Loveren 2013

Chenin Blanc
- ☐ Boland Five Climates Single Varietal 2014
- ☐ Olsen 2014
- ☐ Simonsig 2014
- ☐ Spier Signature 2014
- ☐ Stellenrust Premium 2014

Clairette Blanche
- ☐ Three Foxes 2013

Sauvignon Blanc
- ☐ Foothills 2013
- ☐ Imbuko Du Plevaux Private Collection 2014

White Blends
- ☐ Fijndraai Family Reserve VCR 2012
- ☐ Waterstone Cape Discovery Magic NV
- ☐ Zonnebloem Blanc de Blanc 2014

Méthode Cap Classique
- ☐ Bramon Chardonnay 2012
- ☐ Nitida Matriarch in Red 2012

Other Sparkling
- ☐ Scali Ancestor 2013

Dessert Wine, Fortified
- ☐ Aan de Doorns Red Muscadel 2012

Buy Now, Drink Later

Cabernet Franc
- ☐ Hermanuspietersfontein Swartskaap 2011
- ☐ Mont du Toit Les Coteaux 2012

Cabernet Sauvignon
- ☐ Bartinney 2011
- ☐ Cederberg Private Cellar 2012
- ☐ Edgebaston David Finlayson 'GS' 2012
- ☐ Eikendal 2012
- ☐ Flagstone Music Room 2012
- ☐ Kanonkop 2011
- ☐ La Motte Classic Collection 2012
- ☐ Overgaauw 2012
- ☐ Spier 21 Gables 2011
- ☐ Springfield Whole Berry 2012
- ☐ Stark-Condé 2012
- ☐ Stony Brook Ghost Gum 2009
- ☐ Strydom 2012
- ☐ Thelema 2010

☐ Tokara 2012
☐ Villiera 2012
☐ Vriesenhof 2010
☐ Webersburg 2012

Grenache Noir

☐ Spice Route 2012
☐ Woolworths Nederburg 2013

Malbec

☐ Druk My Niet 2011

Merlot

☐ Barton 2012
☐ Eagles' Nest 2010
☐ Eikendal 2012
☐ Laibach Claypot 2012

Petit Verdot

☐ Nederburg Private Bin R104 2010

Pinotage

☐ Allée Bleue 2012
☐ Delheim Vera Cruz 2012
☐ DeWaal CT de Waal 2011
☐ Flagstone Writer's Block 2012
☐ Groot Constantia 2012
☐ L'Avenir Single Block 2012
☐ Reyneke 2012
☐ Tokara 2012

Pinot Noir

☐ Catherine Marshall Barrel Reserve 2012
☐ Cederberg David Nieuwoudt Ghost Corner 2013
☐ Edgebaston David Finlayson Reserve 2012
☐ Groote Post Kapokberg 2013
☐ Whalehaven 2012
☐ Winery of Good Hope Radford Dale AD 2012

Shiraz/Syrah

☐ Andreas 2012
☐ Cederberg Private Cellar 2012
☐ Delheim Vera Cruz 2012
☐ DeMorgenzon Reserve 2012
☐ Diners Club Bartho Eksteen CWG Auction Reserve Sluitsteen 2012
☐ Fairview Cyril Back 2012
☐ Flagstone Dark Horse 2011
☐ Graham Beck The Ridge 2012
☐ Hilton The Dalmatian 2011
☐ Joostenberg 2012
☐ Keermont Annual Release 2012
☐ La Motte Classic Collection 2012
☐ Mullineux Granite 2012
☐ Mullineux Iron 2012
☐ Muratie Ronnie Melck 2011

☐ Raka Biography 2011
☐ Saxenburg Private Collection 2011
☐ Stark-Condé Three Pines 2012
☐ Strandveld 2011

Touriga Nacional

☐ Sijnn 2012

Red Blends

☐ Bartinney Elevage 2010
☐ Barton Winemakers Reserve 2011
☐ Beau Constantia Lucca 2012
☐ Beaumont Vitruvian 2011
☐ Bellevue Tumara 2007
☐ Dornier Founders CMD 2012
☐ Druk My Niet Invictus 2011
☐ Du Toitskloof Heroes Journey 2 Bordeaux Blend 2011
☐ Epicurean 2010
☐ Groot Constantia Gouverneurs Reserve 2011
☐ Hermanuspietersfontein Die Martha 2011
☐ Hidden Valley Hidden Secret 2012
☐ Hughes Family Nativo Red 2011
☐ Knorhoek Pantére Bordeaux Blend 2011
☐ Lourensford Reserve Red 2011
☐ Luddite Saboteur 2010
☐ Mellasat Tempranillo-Cabernet Sauvignon 2011
☐ Mont du Toit 2008
☐ Mulderbosch Faithful Hound 2012
☐ Muratie Ansela van de Caab 2011
☐ Nederburg The Brew Master 2011
☐ Nederburg The Motorcycle Marvel 2011
☐ Nico van der Merwe Red 2009
☐ Overgaauw Tria Corda 2012
☐ Rainbow's End Family Reserve Bordeaux Blend 2011
☐ Remhoogte Sir Thomas Cullinan 2011
☐ Reyneke Cornerstone 2012
☐ Spice Route Chakalaka 2012
☐ Strandveld The Navigator 2012
☐ Tokara Director's Reserve 2011
☐ Waterford The Jem 2010
☐ Windmeul Cape Blend 2013

Chardonnay

☐ Baleia Bay 2013
☐ Bergsig 2013
☐ De Wetshof Finesse 2013
☐ Eikendal Reserve 2013
☐ Glen Carlou Quartz Stone 2013
☐ Rupert & Rothschild Baroness Nadine 2012
☐ Saxenburg Private Collection 2013
☐ Thelema Ed's Reserve Dry White 2013
☐ Whalehaven 2012

Chenin Blanc
- ☐ Boland Cellar Reserve 2013
- ☐ Mulderbosch Single Vineyard - Block A 2013
- ☐ Mullineux Schist 2013
- ☐ Nederburg The Anchorman 2013
- ☐ Reyneke 2013
- ☐ Spice Route 2013
- ☐ Spioenkop 1900 2013
- ☐ Villiera Traditional Barrel Fermented 2014

Sauvignon Blanc
- ☐ Groote Post Kapokberg 2013
- ☐ Reyneke 2013
- ☐ Villiera Bush Vine 2014

Semillon
- ☐ Cederberg David Nieuwoudt Ghost Corner 2012
- ☐ Fairview Oom Pagel 2012
- ☐ GlenWood Vigneron's Selection 2013

- ☐ Mullineux CWG Auction Reserve The Gris 2013

White Blends
- ☐ Bergsig Icarus 2013
- ☐ Bizoe Henriëtta 2013
- ☐ Fairview Nurok 2013
- ☐ Momento Chenin Blanc-Verdelho 2013
- ☐ Mulderbosch Faithful Hound White 2013
- ☐ Nico van der Merwe White 2013

Méthode Cap Classique
- ☐ Villiera Brut Natural 2010

Dessert Wine, Unfortified
- ☐ Hermanuspietersfontein Sauvignon Blanc No 2 2013

Dessert Wine, Fortified
- ☐ Klawer Hanepoot 2009

Port-Style
- ☐ Boplaas Cape Vintage 2012

About the Wines of the Year

In the course of tasting and rating potentially 7,000 wines for this edition, the members of our team individually identified a limited number of bottlings showing exceptional quality. These were entered into a second round of tasting, open only to market-ready wines (i.e. no pre-bottling samples), available during the currency of the book. The short-listed wines were tasted blind (without sight of the label) by an assembled panel, which this year included expert tasters from outside Platter's team. The wines regarded as superlative in a South African context were awarded the guide's highest rating, namely five stars. These standouts are listed above under the heading Five Stars.

The highest-scoring five star wines were subjected to a further evaluation to determine the overall top scorers. The two wines which emerged from the stringent selection represent the pinnacle of SA winemaking and are the joint recipients of the sought-after accolade: Wines of the Year.

The wines which did not make the five star selection, but are extremely fine and collectible in their own right, are listed immediately below the Five Stars under the heading Highly Recommended.

Implicit in wines of this calibre is the potential to improve with further bottle-maturation — say 8–10 years, perhaps more, in the case of the reds and fortifieds, and around 4-6 years for the whites. (Proper storage is, of course, vital for sound maturation.) During the cycle of tasting, our team identified a number of bottlings, over and above the candidate five stars, which show particular potential for cellaring. These ageworthy wines are listed separately under the heading Buy Now, Drink Later.

Also listed is a selection of wines which tasters feel are particularly worthy of note — interesting, attractive, unusual, unique, representative of an important trend etc. These Hidden Gems are also included in the A-Z directory and highlighted with this icon: 🍇

Finally, there is the prestigious 'super award', Winery of the Year, in recognition of a winegrowing team who, in the opinion of the editor, are ambassadors par excellence for South African wine.

Further details about all releases listed in the Wines of the Year section will be found under the names of the relevant producers in the A-Z directory. The five star tasting is audited by Grant Thornton South Africa.

Tasters for this Edition

David Biggs

David discovered wine as an art student back in the 1960s and has been writing about it for more than 30 years. He was appointed wine columnist for the Cape Argus newspaper in 1979, and qualified officially as a wine judge in 2000. In 2001 he received a scroll of honour from the Cape Wine & Spirit Education Trust in recognition of his contribution to wine education in South Africa. David has been a judge in every Veritas competition since its inception, is a founder member of the Wine-of-the-Month tasting panel, and regularly judges at the Muscadel Championship and Terroir Wine Awards. In 2011 he was named a Living Legend of the wine industry. David has written several books on wine and cocktails, is a regular contributor to Good Taste magazine and runs the wine website www.davidbiggsonline.com.

Winifred Bowman

A qualified physiotherapist and biomedical scientist, and holder of a PhD in Education, Winnie developed an interest in wine during her student days at Stellenbosch University and later through frequent travels to international winegrowing areas. She is a Cape Wine Master (and chair of the Institute of Cape Wine Masters), and judges wine regularly at local and international competitions. She also presents corporate and private wine tastings, teaches and writes about wine and food. Wine is Winnie's passion and she enjoys every moment talking about or tasting it.

Greg de Bruyn

Greg is an architect by profession, practising in and around the Cape wine industry. He allowed wine to beguile him into leaving Johannesburg in 1999 to seek his future amongst the vines, first to establish and run a wine estate, and later as a specialist consultant in winery construction. He qualified as a wine judge in 1996 and a Cape Wine Master in 2000. Greg has sat on many of the major South African competitions and assessment panels, and has contributed to several publications and websites.

Joanne Gibson

Newly graduated and covering local politics for a community newspaper, Joanne was invited to the Gauteng launch of Springfield Estate. After hearing co-owner Abrie Bruwer wax lyrical about his soils, his vines, his family heritage, she was hooked on everything that goes into a good bottle of wine. She left Johannesburg for Cape Town, politics for wine, and received her Level 4 Diploma from the Wine & Spirit Education Trust in 2003 while working for Harpers Wine & Spirit in London. Named South African Wine Writer of the Year in 2009, and shortlisted in the 2010, 2012 and 2013 Louis Roederer International Wine Writers' Awards, she is the Sunday Times wine columnist, freelance contributor to numerous wine publications, and multitasking mother of two.

Higgo Jacobs

Hailing from Calitzdorp, to some the port-wine capital of South Africa, Higgo graduated from the University of Stellenbosch with a law degree in 2002, but was constantly taking on wine roles with local vineyards, eventually spending nine years on either side of the cellar door: first making wine, then marketing and exporting it. Today, certified with the Court of Master Sommeliers (UK), he is co-founder of the South African Sommelier Association (SASA) and consults on a selection of hospitality wine programs, and to the wine industry at large. Higgo is a senior judge at the International Wine Challenge (IWC), and tastes for various local publications and competitions.

Tim James

With a home-base on Grape.co.za, Tim, a Cape Wine Master, contributes to various publications, including the local Mail & Guardian and the London-based World of Fine Wine. His wine journalism has won him a number of wine-writing awards. As to wine-judging, he prefers a contextual, descriptive approach and doesn't participate in large-format competitions, but has been a taster (and associate editor) for this guide for many years. Tim's book, Wines of the new South Africa: Tradition and Revolution, was published in 2013.

Angela Lloyd

Writing, lecturing, broadcasting and making wine are some of Angela's undertakings during her more than 30 years' professional involvement with wine. Even so, it is still just one interest in her life though closely allied to another, cooking. When not tied to her laptop, Angela loves the outdoors: she grows vegetables, fruit and indigenous flowers in her and her husband's garden, while her daily walks with Syrah, their black Labrador, keep them both fit. Reading, cinema, theatre, music, rugby and cricket are other interests crammed into a busy life.

Cathy Marston

Cathy hails from Yorkshire, UK, and after completing her degree in English at Cambridge University, she joined Adnams Wine Merchants, passing all the Wine & Spirit Education Trust (WSET) exams, culminating in a diploma. She came to South Africa in 2001, and opened and ran The Nose Restaurant & Wine Bar, selling it after seven successful years. Cathy now concentrates on tasting, writing for local and international publications, and, increasingly, on wine education and edutainment events. She is an associate of the Institute of Wines & Spirits and is the Approved Programme Provider in Africa for the Wine & Spirit Education Trust. Her first book, Love Your Wine, was published last year.

Fiona McDonald

Travel is supposed to broaden the mind, and Fiona, former editor of Wine magazine for eight years, has had her wine mind broadened by having been a long-serving jury president of a number of international wine competitions: Decanter World Wine Awards, International Wine Challenge, International Wine & Spirit Competition and Concours Mondial de Bruxelles. Initially trained as a news journalist, she got into wine by happy accident, helping to organise The Mercury Wine Week in between reportage and newsroom management as the night news editor on the Durban broadsheet. Currently freelancing, Fiona edits Cheers and Whisky magazines as well as contributing to a range of publications and websites.

Ingrid Motteux

Enjoying wine with meals (the result of an Afro-Belgian childhood) led to Ingrid sitting her first wine exam at 23, unlocking a great love for the subject. During a decade spent setting up nuclear medicine departments in London and Hong Kong, she completed the UK WSET Diploma. Returning to South Africa, she explored various aspects of the local industry (working as a vineyard labourer, writer and lecturer) and attained the Cape WSET Wine Judge certification. An associate of the

Institute of Wines & Spirits, Ingrid judges for the International Wine Challenge and runs Winewise, an independent wine consultancy servicing some of Africa's top safari lodges.

Gregory Mutambe

Encouraged to follow his father into accounting, Gregory instead found himself on a journey into wine and food, first as a winemaking assistant at Mukuyu, one of the handful of wineries in his home country, Zimbabwe, and later as a Cape Wine Academy student in Gauteng. Currently he is the sommelier at Cape Town's 12 Apostles Hotel & Spa, overseeing an award-winning winelist. Gregory has judged for the South African Airways, Nederburg Auction and Best Value Wine selections, and twice been a finalist in the Bollinger Exceptional Wine Service Awards. He is enrolled in the Cape Wine Master and University of South Africa B. Comm. programmes, his aim being to become a wine economist.

Jörg Pfützner

German-born Jörg is an internationally trained and certified sommelier living in South Africa. Having worked at top restaurants in Hamburg and Cape Town, he started his own businesses: The Riesling Club, whose members have access to top European bottlings; and Fine Wine Events, which celebrates wine with specifically themed fine-wine and food tastings and festivals. Since completing his postgraduate diploma in Wine Business Management, Jörg continues to present and lecture locally and abroad, as well as manage a group of private cellars.

Christine Rudman

Christine's love affair with wine started when she joined Stellenbosch Farmers' Winery after a Johannesburg FMCG marketing career. Enrolling in the Cape Wine Academy, she achieved her Cape Wine Master qualification in 1986; left SFW to run the CWA for seven years; and has since been occupied with consultancy work, wine-judging, lecturing and writing. She has a wine column in Die Burger and Beeld, regularly contributes to Classic Wine and has published two editions of A Guide to the Winelands of the Cape. She travels widely, tastes on a variety of local and international panels and looks forward to working with wine for years to come.

Dave Swingler

A taster for this guide for eighteen editions to date, Dave over the years has consulted to restaurants, game lodges and convention centres, taught wine courses and contributed to radio, print and other media. He is co-author of One Hundred Wines — An Insider's Guide to South African Wine, and drinks contributor to Posh Nosh. Dave is a long-standing member of the International Wine & Food Society, the South African consultant for its Annual Vintage Chart, and cellarmaster of the Cape Town branch. A psychiatrist by day, he's intrigued by language in general and its application to wine in particular.

Cathy van Zyl

Cathy started her wine journey on a bicycle: she asked her husband to ride South Africa's famed Argus Cycle Tour with her; he accepted if she attended a wine course with him. She has since notched up 16 more Cycle Tours and gone on to pass the Master of Wine examination. Cathy judges locally and internationally, has recently taken on the position of chair of the Institute of Masters of Wine's education committee, occasionally contributes to wine journals and web sites around the world, but spends most of her wine-time as associate editor of this guide.

Meryl Weaver

The Cape winelands lured Meryl away from her legal career and, more than 20 years later, she remains firmly under their spell. She has conducted wine presentations abroad on SA wine on behalf of Wines of South Africa, lectures for the Cape Wine Academy, tastes and writes about wine, and judges for various wine competitions and magazines. Meryl qualified as a Cape Wine Master and has graduated with distinction from the Wine Judging Academy. She ensures, however, that the vinous learning curve continues by visiting wine-producing countries, combining some of her other passions, food and travel.

How to use this Guide

Note: The example text used here is illustrative and not complete. See A–Z for full details.

Producer's name

Our track-record-based rating system
See next page for an explanation

Listings of wines available during the currency of the book

Wine name, vintage, colour & style

Location: nearest major centre to winery, vyd, head office
Map: See Maps section for winery's position
WO: Wine of Origin geographical unit, region, district or ward; wines described/rated bear the first-mentioned WO certification unless noted

T = Telephone number
F= Fax number

Unless noted, red wines wooded; whites unoaked

Symbols
See next page for a complete list

Other attractions or activities available on the property

Bartinney Private Cellar

Owners Michael and Rose Jordaan are branchi
Helshoogte Pass. Their new venture is a wine b
known bakery and deli. For oeno-adviser Ronell
a unique situation and micro-climate which she

★★★★ **Cabernet Sauvignon** 🔞 Upfront a
velvety plummy softness with more than a hint
improve.

★★★★☆ **Elevage** 🔞 Not new, but our first
polished black fruit nose, darkly concentrated bi
around black cherry fruit with plushy tannins &

★★★★ **Chardonnay** Deliciously creamy nose
Rich, rounded flavours of lime cheesecake, ging
improve, like **11**.

★★★★☆ **Sauvignon Blanc** Masses of interes
Restrained elegance takes its time to open up to
acidity & complex finish. Banghoek WO, like Cha

Location/map: Stellenbosch ▪ WO: Stellenbosch/Bang
Closed all pub hols ▪ Cellar tours by appt ▪ Bartinney \
▪ Owner(s) Rose & Michael Jordaan ▪ Winemaker(s) R
2010) ▪ 27ha/±17ha (cab, chard, sauv) ▪ 118t/4,000
Suite 231 Private Bag X5061 Stellenbosch 7599 ▪ info
018° 55' 56.79" ▪ **T +27 (0)21-885-1013** ▪ F +27 (

Barton Vineyards

French-trained winemaker PJ Gœyer brings a w
between Bot River and popular coastal resort H
tempt visitors, as well as a delectable line up c
range of activities for the energetic on a 200 ha w

★★★★ **Shiraz-Cabernet Sauvignon** 🔞 D
vours than **09**, & deep, crushed velvet texture. S
years ahead.

Merlot Next awaited. **Reserve 11** 🆕 ★★★☆
⊘ ★★★★☆ **Sauvignon Blanc 12** ★★★. Sau
🆕 ★★. — MW

Location: Bot River ▪ Map: Elgin, Walker Bay & Bot Riv
cellar tours Mon-Fri 9–5 Sat 10–4 ▪ Closed Easter Sur
olives & proteas ▪ Barton Villas (see Accommodation s
winemaker(s)/viticulturist(s) PJ Gœyer (Oct 2010) ▪ 20
sauv, sem) ▪ 120t/20,000cs own label 40% red 50% v
bartonvineyards.co.za ▪ www.bartonvineyards.co.za ▪
▪ F +27 (0)28-284-9776

from their boutique wine estate perched atop
e heart of Stellenbosch, forming part of a well-
rroir is everything, and she believes the farm has
to capture in every bottle.

Brief introduction/news update

f blackberries & cassis on **10**. Spiced fruitcake &
. Well-integrated tannins & oak, should

All wines dry unless noted

outstanding cab-based Bordeaux blend reveals
colate edge. **09** minty overtones wrapped
erfumes. A keeper. WO Stellenbosch, like Cab.
★★★★) with butterscotch, peaches & melons.
its & lemon curd before involved finish. Sure to

Abbreviations
See next page for a list of abbreviations

Taster/s initials

eal in stellar **13**, improving year on year.
s mouthful of citrus with flinty minerality, zesty
y. — CM

Tastings, sales & cellar tour times (closed
Saturdays & Sundays but open public holidays
unless noted)

Est 2006 ▪ 1stB 2008 ▪ Tasting & sales Mon-Fri 10-4 ▪
Mon-Sat 11-9 (cnr Church & Bird Str, Stellenbosch)
id (consultant) ▪ Viticulturist(s) Ryno Maree (Oct
abel 70% red 30% white ▪ BWI champion ▪ Postnet
ney.co.za ▪ www.bartinney.co.za ▪ S 33° 55' 34.66" E
5-2852

Names of owner, winemaker, viticulturist &
consultant/s; year/month of appointment in
brackets

Production, in tons and/or 6-bottle cases (cs)
and red:white ratio

Postal & email address, website
(see www.wineonaplatter.com for social media
details)

f experience to this small-scale family winery
us. There is a new Bordeaux-style red blend to
produce, luxury 4-star accommodation, and a
g farm, rich in biodiversity.

10 a little riper, with more truffly, gamey fla-
ut with sufficient form, freshness for now or

az Rosé 12 ⓧ ★★★. **Chenin Blanc 12**
n Blanc-Semillon 12 ⊘ ★★★★. **Blanc 12**

Date established

: Walker Bay ▪ Est 2001 ▪ 1stB 2003 ▪ Tasting, sales &
5 & Jan 1 ▪ Lavender products, olive oil, marinated
▪ Owner(s) Peter J Neill ▪ Cellarmaster(s)/
na (cab, malbec, merlot, mourv, pinot, shiraz, chenin,
)% rosé ▪ IPW ▪ PO Box 100 Bot River 7185 ▪ info@
5' 43.8" E 019° 10' 29.2" ▪ T +27 (0)28-284-9283

Total hectares/hectares under vine (not necessarily in production); main varieties planted

GPS coordinates, based on Datum WGS 84

How to use this Guide

Our Track-Record-Based Rating System

General rating   ★★★★ **Caldera**
For 4-star or better wines, we give the 'track-record rating' over two or more vintages in the margin.

Vintage-specific rating   **06** (★★★☆)
Any differences from the general rating are noted in brackets beside the particular vintage

★★★★★	95–100 / 18–20 pts	Superlative. A South African classic
★★★★☆	90–94 / 17–17.5 pts	Outstanding
★★★★	86–89 / 16–16.5 pts	Excellent
★★★☆	83–85 / 15.5 pts	Very good/promising
★★★	80–82 / 15 pts	Characterful, appealing
★★☆	77–79 / 14.5 pts	Good everyday drinking
★★	73–76 / 14 pts	Pleasant drinking
★☆	70–72 / 13 pts	Casual quaffing
★	65–69 / 12 pts	Plain and simple
☆	60–64 / 11 pts	Very ordinary
No star	50–59 / 10 pts	Somewhat less than ordinary

Symbols

Winery symbols

- ⓠ   Open for tasting (no fee unless noted)
- 🅟🅕   Restaurant/refreshments
- ⌂   Accommodation
- 📷   Other tourist attractions/amenities on the property
- 🥡   Bring your own (BYO) picnic
- ⑧   Child friendly
- ♿   Wheelchair friendly (see page 606)
- (NEW)   New winery

Wine symbols

- ⊘   Good value
- (NEW)   New wine
- Ⓧ   Wine still selling, not retasted
- ♁   Organic
- ◎   Biodynamic
- ⊕   Hidden gem

Abbreviations

% alc	Percentage alcohol by volume	NLH	Noble Late Harvest
1stB	First bottled vintage	NV	Non-vintage. Year of harvest not
BEE	Black Economic Empowerment		stated on label
BWI	Biodiversity & Wine Initiative	RS	Residual sugar
BYO	Bring your own (wine, picnic)	SAA	South African Airways (selected for
Cs	Cases		First or Premium Class)
CWG	Cape Winemakers Guild	SLH	Special Late Harvest
CWM	Cape Wine Master	Veritas	SA National Bottled Wine Show
Est	Date established	WIETA	Agricultural Ethical Trade Initiative
g/l	Grams per litre	WO	Wine of Origin
IPW	Integrated Production of Wine		
IWC	International Wine Challenge		
IWSC	International Wine & Spirit	cabernet/cab	cabernet sauvignon
	Competition	pinot	pinot noir
LBV	Late Bottled Vintage	chenin	chenin blanc
Malo	Malolactic fermentation	sauvignon/sauv	sauvignon blanc
MCC	Méthode cap classique	touriga	touriga nacional
MW	Master of Wine	tinta	tinta barocca

AA Badenhorst Family Wines

Adi Badenhorst, co-owner and winemaker at the Badenhorst family's Kalmoesfontein farm on the Perdeberg, has a healthy appreciation for the classics. As a result, his table wines from Rhône varieties and chenin are masterly, refined and textured. But he never strays too far from the fun side, so there's always something interesting in the cellar, like a non-disgorged sparkling inspired by France's méthode ancestrale, and the vin jaune-meets-Spain solera-aged white. His latest fascination is with vermouth, and a work-in-progress is flavoured with kalmoes, an indigenous plant known for its medicinal properties. Those lucky enough to get a seat at his monthly Saturday morning tastings are certain to be offered a sip — in the name of research.

AA Badenhorst range

★★★★☆ **CWG Auction Reserve Kalmoesfontein Ramnasgras Cinsault** (NEW) Translucent **12** wonderfully smooth, pure & persistent, with slight nudge of grape tannin. From 58 year old bushvines, fermented in concrete, pressed into old casks. Moderate 13% alcohol & proper dryness (1.5 g/l sugar) will please classicists.

★★★★☆ **Kalmoesfontein Raaigras Grenache** (NEW) 'Oldest grenache vineyard in SA, 1951' says Adi Badenhorst. **12** bone-dry, less than 14% alcohol, as all these. Intense strawberry, raspberry aromas, crystalline flavours lifted by pleasing touch astringency. Grenache with attitude!

★★★★☆ **Red** Larger & older oak blend for effortless, savoury contemplation; typically from all or several of shiraz, cinsault, tinta, grenache, mourvèdre. **11** has them all. Emphatically dry yet packed with fruit; elegant & long like light-footed **10** (without mourvèdre), seamless **09** (no tinta).

★★★★☆ **CWG Auction Reserve Kalmoesfontein Dassiekop Steen** (NEW) From 60+ year old terraced chenin vineyard on neighbour PA Rossouw's farm, bunch-pressed & bottled directly from old 3,000L cask. **12** bouquet of wet slate & clay followed by exceptionally steely palate; pure, poised, with unrelenting subtle saline finish.

★★★★☆ **White** Fruit source shifts from 100% Voor Paardeberg to 17%, majority Swartland, **12** remains an exceptional, intricate (10-way) chenin (48%) blend showing myriad white & yellow fruits, savoury notes. Full & rich, but with same underlying minerality as showier **11**. Fermented/aged in 60+ year old casks.

★★★★ **Funky White Wine** Latest release (only 1,000 375 ml bottles a year) of NV from 11 varieties, aged in solera. Nutty, salty & 'umami' savouriness, biting acidity & ultra-dry length. Fino-esque but no fortification or flor as in Spain. Enjoy young to preserve its thrilling freshness.

Not retasted: **Méthode Ancestrale 13** ★★★★

Secateurs range

★★★★ **Red Blend** ⊘ New bottling of **12**, 8-way combo versus previous' 5 varieties, still large older oak only. Fruit-filled, slightly meaty, grape tannin bite & modest 12.5% alcohol make it as drinkable as ever.

★★★★ **Chenin Blanc** ⊘ 28 different Swartland/Perdeberg parcels; mostly natural ferment in concrete tanks & old casks. New bottling of multi-layered **13** wonderful concentration, savoury grip & persistence; similar masterly balance to **12**.

Also tasted: **Rosé 14** ★★★★ — CvZ

Location: Malmesbury ▪ Map/WO: Swartland ▪ Est 2007 ▪ 1stB 2006 ▪ Tasting, sales & tours by appt ▪ Closed all pub hols ▪ Conferences ▪ Function venue for 130 people ▪ Conservation area ▪ Guest cottages ▪ Owner(s) Adi & Hein Badenhorst ▪ Winemaker(s) Adi Badenhorst (2006), with Jasper Wickens (2008) ▪ Viticulturist(s) Pierre Rossouw (Jan 1975) ▪ 60ha/23ha (cinsaut, grenache, shiraz, chard, chenin, rouss) ▪ 40,000cs own label 60% red 40% white ▪ PO Box 1177 Malmesbury 7299 ▪ adi@iafrica.com ▪ www.aabadenhorst.com ▪ S 33° 32' 38.01" E 018° 49' 7.42" ▪ F +27 (0)21-794-5196 ▪ **T +27 (0)82-373-5038**

Aaldering Vineyards & Wines

Dutch businessman Fons Aaldering and wife Marianne acquired this Devon Valley estate in 2004 with the explicit intention of developing it into one of the best in the country. A new cellar helmed by Guillaume Nell, previously at Cavalli, has been in operation since the 2012 harvest and the property also recently opened three luxury Cape Dutch lodges to the public.

★★★★ **Pinotage** 11 (★★★★) offers dark fruit & spicy oak notes, pleasingly well-managed tannins, & no great depth of flavour. The big alcohol glows somewhat warmly. Perhaps less intense than **10**, but less rustic than **09** (★★★).

★★★★ **Shiraz** Enticing aromas on **11** lead on to a balanced (though slightly oaky) palate with sweet, concentrated fruit, integrated tannins & a fairly dry finish despite the well disguised big alcohol.

★★★★ **Cabernet Sauvignon-Merlot** Time should be on the side of big, burly **11** (★★★★), integrating the spicy oak, the well-managed tannins &, hopefully, the big acidity. Like **10**, shows red & black fruit.

★★★★ **Pinotage Blanc** Interesting & delicious as well as unusual blanc de noir. **13** palest gold-pink, hints at pinotage's banana. Creamily rich but fresh; easy but not trivial. Mostly natural ferment. **12** (★★★★) was quirky maiden.

★★★★ **Sauvignon Blanc** Nothing too obvious or aggressive on harmonious **13**. Succulent, fresh acidity; tropical ripeness there, but finishes with a greenish hint.

Rosé (NEW) ★★★ Bone-dry, rather acidic & modestly oaked **13** from pinotage. More austere, less harmonious than the paler Blanc. Also tasted: **Chardonnay 13** ★★★★ Not tasted: **Lady M.** — TJ

Location/map/WO: Stellenbosch ▪ Est 2004 ▪ 1stB 2007 ▪ Tasting & sales Mon-Thu 9-5 Fri 9-3 Sat (Nov-Apr) 9-3 ▪ Closed all pub hols ▪ Cellar tours by appt ▪ 3 luxury lodges ▪ Owner(s) Marianne & Fons Aaldering ▪ Winemaker(s)/viticulturist(s) Guillaume Nell (Oct 2014) ▪ 20ha/19.7ha (cab, merlot, ptage, syrah, chard, sauv) ▪ ±120t/±18,300cs own label 70% red 30% white ▪ IPW ▪ PO Box 1068 Stellenbosch 7599 ▪ estate@aaldering.co.za ▪ www.aaldering.co.za ▪ S 33° 55' 9.81" E 018° 49' 8.14" ▪ **T +27 (0)21-865-2495**

Aan de Doorns Cellar

Now into its seventh decade, grower-owned Aan de Doorns Cellar outside Worcester vinifies some 30,000 tons from 1,400 hectares spread over more than 20 farms. Production mostly goes to its partner FirstCape, the hugely successful supplier of entry-level wines to UK supermarkets, but around 20,000 cases (and counting) of appealing, modesty priced wines are available under the own label.

★★★★ **Muscat d'Alexandrie** (V) Honey, sultanas & jasmine - the whole scented nine yards in **12** fortified. Unctuous yet fresh. Light (for style) alcohol extends the sunset sipping. No **11**.

Pinotage ★★★ Pleasing cherry notes with vanilla oak accompaniment in smooth, easy-drinking **13** pre-bottling sample. **Colombar Semi-Sweet** Preview too unformed to rate. **Red Muscadel** (V) ★★★★ Out-to-please fortified **12**, now bottled, offers copious tealeaf, muscat temptations. Very sweet & smooth but not too heavy. Also tasted: **Chenin Blanc 14** ★★ **Sauvignon Blanc 14** ★★ **Cape Ruby** (V) **12** ★★★★ Not retasted: **Doornroodt 12** ★★★ **Sparkling Demi Sec NV** ★★★ Not tasted: **Blanc de Noir**. — AL

Location/map/WO: Worcester ▪ Est 1954 ▪ Tasting & sales Mon–Fri 8–5 Sat 10-1 ▪ Closed all pub hols ▪ Tours during harvest by appt ▪ Owner(s) 58 members ▪ Cellarmaster(s) Johan Morkel (Nov 1993) ▪ Winemaker(s) Gert van Deventer (Sept 1997) & Ryno Booysen (Jan 2007) ▪ Viticulturist(s) Pierre Snyman ▪ 1,494ha (cab, ptage, chard, chenin, cbard) ▪ 30,868t/22,400cs own label ▪ PO Box 235 Worcester 6849 ▪ info@aandedoorns.co.za ▪ www.aandedoorns.co.za ▪ S 33° 41' 47.0" E 019° 29' 26.2" F +27 (0)23-347-4629 ▪ **T +27 (0)23-347-2301**

☐ **Abbotsdale** *see* Bryan MacRobert Wines

☐ **Abbotsville** *see* Org de Rac

Abbottshill

The famine of new vintages from Cameron and Dianne Bain's boutique winery on Swartland's hallowed Perdeberg (up-and-comer Bryan MacRobert a neighbour) was about to turn to feast at press time with a pair of red blends from '11/'12 due for release. 'The one has a 50% mourvèdre content and is tasting outstanding at the moment.'

Shiraz ⊘ **★★★** Now **NV** (blend of **10** & **11**). In the glass, salty meat, cloves, black pepper & dark cherries unfold to show intriguingly different & tasty wine. Not retasted: **Cabernet Sauvignon 09** **★★★** Not tasted: **Shiraz-Cabernet Sauvignon**, **Bosstok Boogie**, **Rosé**. — DB

Location/WO: Malmesbury ▪ Map: Swartland ▪ Est/1stB 2004 ▪ Tasting, sales & tours by appt ▪ BYO picnic ▪ Owner(s) Dynadeals One (Pty) Ltd ▪ Winemaker(s)/viticulturist(s) CA Bain ▪ 112ha/10ha (cab, mourv, shiraz) ▪ 1,250cs own label 100% red ▪ PO Box 433 Malmesbury 7299 ▪ cameron@empa.co.za ▪ S 33° 29' 26.4" E 018° 39' 25.3" ▪ **T +27 (0)82-492-0692**

Abingdon Wine Estate

Conveniently just 2 km off the Johannesburg-Durban artery in the KwaZulu-Natal Midlands lie Abingdon's cellar and vines (the only certified single-vineyards in the province). Pioneer owners Ian and Jane Smorthwaite saw the potential in the altitude (1,150 m) and cooler temperatures offsetting KZN's usual humidity, and have developed a passionate media, restaurant and customer following for their handcrafted wines. Demand continues to outstrip supply.

Location: Lions River ▪ Map: KwaZulu-Natal ▪ Est 2004 ▪ 1stB 2007 ▪ Tasting room & restaurant open Sat/Sun & pub hols 10-5 for personalised tastings & fresh country meals ▪ Weekday visits by appt ▪ Weddings & corporate functions ▪ Owner(s) Ian & Jane Smorthwaite ▪ Winemaker(s)/viticulturist(s) Ian Smorthwaite ▪ 7ha/3ha (cab, shiraz, chard, sauv, viog) ▪ Lions River KZN Midlands ▪ jane@abingdonestate.co.za, ian@abingdonestate.co.za ▪ www.abingdonestate.co.za ▪ S 29° 26' 36.71" E 030° 09' 14.18" ▪ F +27 (0)86-572-6877 ▪ **T +27 (0)33-234-4335/+27 (0)83-463-8503 (Jane)**

Accolade Wines South Africa

Owned by Champ Private Equity of Australia, Accolade Wines South Africa is part of the global drinks company Accolade Wines, whose portfolio contains some of the world's best-known wine brands. The SA business, based in Stellenbosch, is responsible for the no. 1 selling UK brand Kumala, the Fish Hoek range of single varietals, and the highly regarded Flagstone pinnacle wines, all separately listed.

Stellenbosch ▪ Owner(s) Champ Private Equity based in Australia ▪ Winemaker(s) Bruce Jack, Gerhard Swart, Ben Jordaan & Karen Bruwer ▪ Viticulturist(s) Chris Keet ▪ 6.4m cs own label ▪ PO Box 769 Stellenbosch 7599 ▪ flagstone@accolade-wines.com ▪ www.accolade-wines.com ▪ F +27 (0)21-852-5085 ▪ **T +27 (0)21-852-5052**

Adoro Wines

Adoro Wines, sibling of single malt Scotch whisky producer Benriach, was born of the view that blended wine is greater than the sum of its parts. It owns no vines but has long-term relationships with grape growers in a wide variety of regions. Each parcel is vinified separately, giving vintner Ian Naudé a multitude of elements with which to build his compositions.

★★★★☆ Red Blend New look at **07** proves longevity of this multi-region blend. Shiraz (24%) adds meat, smoke & spice notes to blackcurrant backbone of cab & ripe plum softness of merlot, fruit still vibrant despite time in all-new oak & bottle-age. Follows soft & accessible **06** (**★★★★**).

★★★★ Sauvignon Blanc ⊘ **10** (**★★★★**) steely but not as penetrating as **09**, thanks to fleshy fruit & the softening effect of bottle-maturation at the cellar.

★★★★☆ Naudé White Decidedly idiosyncratic blend, intended for ageing; chalky chenin-led **10** (**★★★★**), retasted, boasts a smooth lanolin texture & savoury cucumber/pak choi finish. **09** was mostly semillon & sauvignon, dash chenin.

★★★★☆ **Natural Sweet Mourvèdre** Beloved of sommeliers, retasted **10** is made for cheese, with rich black cherry concentration to handle strong flavours & high acidity (8 g/l) to cut through fat (& wine's good few grams sugar). Swartland fruit, unwooded, tannins barely noticeable. **09** (★★★★) was unsubtle (atypical for this producer). — JG

Location: Stellenbosch ▪ WO: Western Cape ▪ Est 2005 ▪ 1stB 2004 ▪ Closed to public ▪ Owner(s) Intra International ▪ Winemaker(s) Ian Naudé (May 2005) ▪ Viticulturist(s) Lucas de Kock (Aug 2005) ▪ 40% red 60% white ▪ PO Box 982 Stellenbosch 7599 ▪ adorowines@iafrica.com ▪ www.adorowines.co.za ▪ F +27 (0)86-682-0628 ▪ **T +27 (0)83-630-3794**

Aeternitas Wines

If home is where the heart is, then it's where the cellar is too! At least if you are husband and wife team Johan and Michelle Grimbeek, who handcraft wine in their suburban garage near Strand beach between their day jobs - he as winemaker for Kanu, she as MD of the Cape Wine Academy.

★★★★ **Syrah** ⓥ Plush & utterly moreish, **08** heaped with sweet mulberry fruit, shows poise & finesse despite 15% alcohol. Wild ferment, like **07** (★★★★).

Blanc ⓥ ★★★★ **10** from chenin billows summer fruit, shows amazing balance considering ripeness, oak & 14% alcohol. — DS

Location: Strand ▪ Map: Helderberg ▪ WO: Swartland ▪ Est 2005 ▪ 1stB 2007 ▪ Tasting by appt ▪ Closed all pub hols ▪ Owner(s) Johan & Michelle Grimbeek ▪ Cellarmaster(s)/winemaker(s) Johan Grimbeek (Jan 2002) ▪ Viticulturist(s) Various ▪ 4t/640cs own label 50% red 45% white 5% rosé + 8,000cs for clients ▪ 21 Livingstone Street, Strand 7140 ▪ aeternitaswines@telkomsa.net ▪ S 34° 6' 3.3" E 018° 49' 35.6" ▪ **T +27 (0)82-714-2095**

☐ **A Few Good Men** *see* Riebeek Cellars
☐ **Africa** *see* Waterstone Wines
☐ **Africa Five** *see* Waterstone Wines
☐ **African Dawn** *see* Rooiberg Winery
☐ **African Gold** *see* Old Bridge Wines

African Pride Wines

Spreading Brand South Africa across the globe, to far-flung corners like Iceland and Latvia, and many less exotic territories, this large-scale export venture has recently looked inwards and taken on the local market too. Grapes and wines are widely sourced by a team led by the very experienced Mike Graham, winemaker since inception in 2002.

Lady Anne Barnard range
Syrah ★★★★ Complex red fruit, spice notes from year in oak, malleable tannins & moderate alcohol make for a refreshing glassful in **12**. WO Coastal. Also tasted: **Cabernet Sauvignon 12** ★★★ **Sauvignon Blanc 14** ★★★★

Cape Grace Sugarbird range
Pinotage ★☆ Melange soft berry fruit, light tannic grip on unoaked, early-drinking **13**. Also tasted: **Chenin Blanc 14** ★★ Not retasted: **Shiraz 12** ★★★

Footprint Long Walk range
Cabernet Sauvignon ★★ Black plums, herby nuance on sweet-fruited **13** ready for drinking. Unoaked, as all in this range. **Merlot-Pinotage** ★★ Cheerful 55/45 blend in **13**, packed with berries & joie de vivre. **Sauvignon Blanc** ★★★ Gooseberry, grassy **14** is zesty, with appealing black-currant lift on the finish, fair intensity. Also tasted: **Merlot 13** ★★ **Shiraz 13** ★★ **Pinotage Rosé 14** ★★ **Chardonnay 14** ★★ **Chenin Blanc-Semillon 14** ★★ — CvZ

Location: Constantia ▪ WO: Western Cape/Coastal/Elgin ▪ Est/1stB 2002 ▪ Closed to public ▪ Owner(s) Afrifresh Group ▪ Winemaker(s) Mike Graham (May 2002) ▪ 480,000cs ▪ PO Box 518 Constantia 7848 ▪ info@africanpridewines.co.za ▪ www.africanpridewines.co.za ▪ F +27 (0)21-887-2204 ▪ **T +27 (0)21-887-2204**

☐ **African Roots** *see* Seven Sisters
☐ **African Star** *see* Stellar Winery
☐ **African Terroir** *see* Jacques Germanier

African Wines & Spirits

Wholesaling and marketing company owned by Edward Snell & Co, and responsible for entry-level label Craighall.

Cape Town ▪ Est 1999 ▪ Closed to public ▪ Owner(s) Edward Snell & Co ▪ Directors D Asherson, DV Hooper, IV Hooper, JM Pousson, B Coppen & A Kruger ▪ 40% red 60% white ▪ PO Box 318 Paarden Eiland ▪ iainh@esnell.co.za ▪ F +27 (0)21-510-4560/+27 (0)86-682-4922 ▪ **T +27 (0)21-506-2600**

☐ **Agaat** *see* Truter Family Wines

Akkerdal Wine Estate   ⓠ ⌂

Engaging owner, winemaker and viticulturist Pieter Hanekom cultivates a range of unusual grape varieties, although only some of these are used at his own Franschhoek boutique winery. He utilises both electronic social media platforms and personal interaction with visitors to the farm to enlighten winelovers about these cultivars and promote the enjoyment of his characterful creations.

Limited Releases

★★★★ **Kallie's Dream** ⓠ Shiraz-led blend, rest mourvèdre, grenache, carignan, viognier. Pure & very expressive **10** with red fruit permeated with fresh acidity & fine spicy tannins.

★★★★ **TDT** ⓠ **12** unusual blend of tempranillo, durif & tannat has intriguing dark perfumed fruit & supple tannins. Succulent, balanced but still youthful, with potential. Step up on **10** (★★★★). No **11**.

Akkerdal range

★★★★ **Syrah** ⓠ **12**, with dash of mourvèdre, mid-2013 still tight but dry tannins & oak (18 months) revealed underlying seriousness. Needed cellar time to reveal all its charms.

★★★★ **Wild Boar** ⓠ **09** conforms to no conventional template, with 5 different varieties including roobernet & tempranillo. Fruit driven but not facile, with fresh acidity, dry finish. No **07**, **08**.

Not retasted: **Merlot 12** ★★★★ **Petit Noir 10 Passion Reserve 11** ★★★ **Sophie's Blush 13** ★★★★ Not tasted: **Kallie's Dream Red**, **Sauvignon Blanc**. — MW

Location/map/WO: Franschhoek ▪ Est 2000 ▪ 1stB 2001 ▪ Tasting & sales Mon-Fri 10-4 ▪ Fee R20pp ▪ Closed all pub hols ▪ Self-catering chalet ▪ Owner(s)/cellarmaster(s)/winemaker(s) Pieter Hanekom ▪ Viticulturist(s) Pieter Hanekom, advised by Eben Archer, Bennie Liebenberg & Dawid Saayman ▪ 18ha (barbera, cab f, carignan, durif, grenache, malbec, merlot, mourv, p verdot, roobernet, shiraz, tannat, tempranillo, chard, nouvelle, sauv, sem, viog) ▪ 6,000cs own label 95% red 4% white 1% rosé ▪ IPW, WIETA ▪ PO Box 36 La Motte 7691 ▪ wine@akkerdal.co.za ▪ www.akkerdal.co.za ▪ S 33° 52' 50.9" E 019° 3' 3.8" ▪ F +27 (0)21-876-3189 ▪ **T +27 (0)21-876-3481/+27 (0)82-442-1746**

Akkerdraai   ⓠ ⊚

As managing director, Salie de Swardt grew Media24 into Africa's leading media publishing company, and retirement to his Helderberg farm has seen him focus on boutique winemaking with other lofty ambitions — Platter's five stars. With consultant Ronell Wiid, Diners Club Winemaker of the Year, he has shepherded a yet untasted Bordeaux red into bottle, 'because my friends asked'. Could this be it?

★★★★ **Cabernet Sauvignon** ⊘ Tighter than sleek **09** & classy **08**, **11** has similar dense blackcurrant fruit & cassis richness, so should also age with benefit 3+ years. **10** sold out untasted. — CvZ

Location/map: Stellenbosch ▪ WO: Western Cape ▪ Est 1956 ▪ 1stB 2007 ▪ Tasting Mon-Fri 9-5 Sat 9-12.30 ▪ Fee R25, waived on purchase ▪ Closed Easter Fri-Mon, Dec 25 & Jan 1 ▪ Walks/hikes ▪ Owner(s)/cellarmaster(s) Salie de Swardt ▪ Winemaker(s) Ronell Wiid (consultant), with Salie de Swardt (Jan 2013) ▪ Viticulturist(s) Ronell Wiid (consultant) ▪ 1.5ha (cab) ▪ 12t 100% red ▪ PO Box 22 Lynedoch 7603 ▪ saliedes@mweb.co.za ▪ S 33° 59' 53.52" E 018° 49' 50.94" ▪ F +27 (0)86-689-1841 ▪ **T +27 (0)21-881-3861/+27 (0)83-264-1463**

□ **Alexanderfontein** *see* Ormonde Private Cellar

AlexKia Estate

'A marriage of Mediterranean heritage and modern taste' is how Franco and Carla Maestroni describe their wine and rosemary farm – named after granddaughters Alexandra and Chiara – in Robertson's Eilandia Valley.

Chiara Chardonnay ★★★ Unwooded **14** shows complexity in citrus, granadilla, peach & winter melon combo, the ripe flavours underpinned by firm acidity to clean finish. Not tasted: **Alexandra Cabernet Sauvignon**, **Merlot Reserve**. — DB

Location/WO: Robertson ▪ Est 2004 ▪ 1stB 2006 ▪ Tasting by appt at La Verne Wine Boutique, Robertson ▪ Owner(s) Carla Maestroni ▪ Winemaker(s) André van Dyk (Rooiberg) ▪ ±90ha/7ha (cab, chard) ▪ ±70t/10,000cs own label 50% red 50% white + 8,000cs for clients ▪ PO Box 101 Robertson 6705 ▪ franco@alexkia.co.za ▪ www.alexkia.co.za ▪ **T +27 (0)82-575-9578/+27 (0)82-783-9825**

Alheit Vineyards

With a tiny operation founded on genuine passion and minimal initial budget, Chris and Suzaan Alheit are in the Cape's vanguard of a determination to reveal the vinous truths of soil, slope and climate through old vines, whose meagre yields are treated with a respectful minimal intervention in the winery. And ruthless integrity: the second vintage of their Radio Lazarus was blended away, because an imperfectly judged picking time slightly compromised its elegance. 'A tough call,' says Chris ruefully. A second single-vineyard wine has been added (as has the couple's second baby!), and there might be another soon, as well as a blend from young vines on the farm in the Hemel-en-Aarde where the Alheits rent a cellar. Meanwhile, local and international acclaim piles up massively.

★★★★★ **Magnetic North Mountain Makstok** (NEW) Old, ungrafted ('makstok'), dryland chenin from Olifants River. **13** uncompromising & tight, but its web of scent, textures & flavours already combines austerity, profundity, subtle dry power & generous deliciousness. Sweet fruit strained through stone. All these old-oak matured.

★★★★☆ **Cartology 13** from 4 old blocks of chenin, one (12%) of semillon. Scents of warmed stone, fynbos, fruit (with semillon's lanolin & lemon). Triumphant but understated power from start to long, long finish. Already complex layers of sweet, serene flavours in supple, silky harmony. Will develop. Not tasted: **Radio Lazarus**. — TJ

Location: Hermanus ▪ Map: Elgin, Walker Bay & Bot River ▪ WO: Western Cape/Citrusdal Mountain ▪ Est 2010 ▪ 1stB 2011 ▪ Tasting by appt only ▪ Owner(s)/winemaker(s) Chris & Suzaan Alheit ▪ Cellarmaster(s) Chris Alheit ▪ 20t/ 2,000cs own label 100% white ▪ PO Box 711 Hermanus 7200 ▪ chris@alheitvineyards.co.za ▪ www.alheitvineyards. co.za ▪ S 34° 20' 35.56" E 019° 18' 11.30" ▪ **T +27 (0)83-274-6860**

Alkmaar Boutique Vineyard

Bouwer and Janet Nell have embraced the story behind their boutique wine brand - a 19th century school building on their Wellington property, and its Dutch founder, Marinus Stucki. Another local hero, Izak Perold, Wellington-schooled viticulturist and father of pinotage, is the honoured 'Professor'.

The Old School Master ★★★ **11** cab-based Bordeaux blend not ultra-ripe like previous. Generous aromas & flavours of berries, tobacco & spice, with a herbaceous edge. Well built, but no real intensity. **The Old School Mistress** ★★★★ Appropriately, perhaps, shiraz-based **11** with mourvèdre plus touch viognier, more delicate & refined than the Master. Ripe fruited & savoury, judiciously oaked & balanced. Not tasted: **The Old School Professor**, **The Old School Reunion**. — TJ

Location/WO: Wellington ▪ Map: Paarl & Wellington ▪ Est 2001 ▪ 1stB 2005 ▪ Tasting & sales Mon-Fri 10-4 Sat 10-2 ▪ Closed all religious pub hols ▪ Cellar tours by appt ▪ Walks (part of Wellington Wine Walk) ▪ Owner(s) Bouwer & Janet Nell ▪ Winemaker(s) Pieter-Niel Rossouw (Jan 2010, consultant), with Dawid Futhwa (Jan 2010) ▪ Viticulturist(s) Dawid Futhwa (Jan 2003) ▪ 9.9ha (cab, merlot, mourv, p verdot, ptage, shiraz, chard, viog) ▪ 50t/900cs own label

83% red 17% white + 12,000L bulk ▪ PO Box 1273 Blouvlei Road Wellington 7654 ▪ janet@alkmaarwines.co.za ▪ www.alkmaarwines.co.za ▪ S 33° 39' 37.98" E 019° 1' 55.14" ▪ **T +27 (0)21-873-0191**

Allée Bleue Wines

Named after the bluegums lining the avenue to the Franschhoek estate, German-owned Allée Bleue has a diverse portfolio including accommodation, weddings, functions and an extensive cellardoor offering showcasing a 300-year heritage. The delightful wines – note the 'hidden gems' below - are available for tasting at a new venue nearer the cellar and amenities. In its place at the entrance is Marché at Allée Bleue, a 'welcome centre' also offering fresh produce and wine-related merchandise.

Allée Bleue range

★★★★ **Pinotage** Charry savoury notes of smoked meats & coffee **12** from Piekenierskloof give way to cooked black fruit with juicy, integrated tannins. Coriander/biltong spices add interest & appeal.

★★★★ **L'Amour Toujours** ⊘ Flagship blend of cab, cab franc & merlot with a tweak of petit verdot, **10** (★★★★☆) improves on **09**, beautifully integrated & structured. WO Stellenbosch.

★★★★ **Chenin Blanc** ⊘ Smart **13** uses 6% viognier & gentle oak to good effect, adding delicious gingery notes to creamy yellow citrus for well-balanced, satisfying mouthful. Some Walker Bay fruit.

★★★★ **Sauvignon Blanc** ⊘ Lively yellow & green fruit with well-judged acidity on **14** given extra depth & interest by 8% semillon plus time spent on lees.

★★★★ **Isabeau** Ripe tropical notes on **13** blend of chardonnay & semillon with dash of viognier. Toffee, toast & marmalade vie on palate before lengthy, though slightly hot, finish. Walker Bay fruit.

Brut Rosé Méthode Cap Classique ⊘ ★★★☆ Fresh & delightful **12** pink sparkling from mostly pinotage proffers an abundance of red-berried fruit with lively acidity & clean finish. For uncomplicated celebrating. **Also tasted: Shiraz 12** ★★★ **Cabernet Sauvignon–Merlot 12** ★★★☆ **Brut Méthode Cap Classique 11** ★★★☆ **Cape Ruby 13** ★★

Starlette range

Pinotage ⊘ ⊛ ★★★ Delightful **13** shows happy effects of gentle handling & subtle oak in melange of juicy plums, prunes with hints of mint & black olives. **Shiraz Rosé** ⊘ ⊛ ★★★ Truly characterful **14** packs a fruity punch of strawberries & raspberries, sweetness balanced with fresh acidity, helped by 11% sauvignon. **Also tasted: Rouge** ⊘ **13** ★★★ **Blanc** ⊘ **14** ★★★☆ — CM

Location/map: Franschhoek ▪ WO: Franschhoek/Stellenbosch/Walker Bay/Coastal/Western Cape/Banghoek ▪ Est 1690 ▪ 1stB 2001 ▪ Tasting & sales Mon-Fri 9-5 Sat 10-5 Sun 10-4 ▪ Tasting fee R25/4 wines ▪ Cellar tours by appt ▪ Bistro Allée Bleue ▪ Picnics (booking required) ▪ Jungle gym ▪ Tour groups by appt ▪ Gifts ▪ Farm produce ▪ Conferences ▪ Weddings ▪ Allée Bleue Kendall Cottage & Manor House ▪ Owner(s) DAUPHIN Entwicklungs-und Beteiligungs GMH (Germany) ▪ Winemaker(s) Van Zyl du Toit (Jul 2009) ▪ Viticulturist(s) Douw Willemse (Sep 2008) ▪ 135ha/25ha (cab, merlot, ptage, pinot, shiraz, chard, chenin, sauv, sem, viog) ▪ 380t/46,000cs own label 34.5% red 55% white 5% rosé 5% MCC 0.5% fortified ▪ IPW ▪ PO Box 100 Groot Drakenstein 7680 ▪ info@alleebleue.com ▪ www.alleebleue.co.za ▪ S 33°51' 29.0" E 018° 59' 12.9" ▪ F +27 (0)21-874-1850 ▪ **T +27 (0)21-874-1021**

Allegria Vineyards

On Stellenbosch's scenic Polkadraai Hills, Jan and Annemarie Zevenbergen's shiraz grapes are husbanded and vinified by advisers Francois Hanekom and Louis Nel respectively. To taste the resulting wine, check into their luxury guest house or find it on a select winelist.

Shiraz ★★★☆ Pronounced mint, spice & sweet dark chocolate to the black berries on **12**, herbal notes slightly overwhelm the fruit. — CM

Location/map: Stellenbosch ▪ WO: Polkadraai Hills ▪ Est 2005 ▪ 1stB 2010 ▪ Tasting by appt ▪ Allegria Guest House ▪ Owner(s) Jan & Annemarie Zevenbergen ▪ Winemaker(s) Louis Nel (Nov 2009, consultant) ▪ Viticulturist(s) Francois Hanekom (Sep 2009, consultant) ▪ 2ha/0.5ha (shiraz) ▪ ±3,500kg/±160cs own label 100% red ▪ PO Box 24 Vlottenburg 7604 ▪ wine@allegria.co.za ▪ www.allegriavineyards.co.za ▪ S 33° 57' 29.79" E 018° 45' 31.63" ▪ F +27 (0)21-881-3210 ▪ **T +27 (0)21-881-3389**

Allesverloren

The Malan family estate is Swartland's oldest, its name dating from the 18th century when one of its owners returned from a church visit to Stellenbosch to find the property devastated in a raid by San hunters, causing him to exclaim: 'All is lost!' Years ahead of the trend towards unfortified varietal bottlings of grapes traditionally associated with 'port', owner/cellarmaster Danie Malan now has taken the next step by creating the estate's first 'Douro blend'.

★★★★ **Trés Vermelhos** (NEW) Older oak for the (unfortified) 'three reds' souzão, tinta & touriga. Berry pudding, orange zest & black olive notes typical of these varieties, **12** lipsmackingly dry & characterful.

★★★★ **Muscadel** (NEW) Delicious fortified red muscadel from single Kasteelberg vineyard, **13** cascade of aromas & flavours - cranberries, tealeaf, quince, orange & lime - fresh, tangy finale.

Tinta Barocca ★★★ From vines up to 57 years old, step-up **12** richer than previous; black fruit melange, tarry aromas, satisfyingly dry conclusion. Also tasted: **Cabernet Sauvignon 11** ★★★ **Shiraz 12** ★★★★ **Tinta Barocca Rosé 13** ★★★★ Not retasted: **Touriga Nacional 11** ★★★ **Danie's Backyard Blend 11** ★★ Not tasted: **Fine Old Vintage**. — CvZ

Location: Riebeek West ▪ Map/WO: Swartland ▪ Est 1704 ▪ Tasting & sales Mon-Fri 9—5 Sat 9—2 ▪ Fee R20pp ▪ Closed Easter Fri, Dec 25 & Jan 1 ▪ Cellar tours by appt ▪ Pleasant Pheasant Restaurant T +27 (0)22-461-2170 Tue 10.30-3 Wed-Sat 9-3 & 6-10 Sun 9-4 ▪ Facilities for children ▪ Conferences/functions T +27 (0)22-461-2253 ▪ Owner(s) Malan Boerdery Trust ▪ Cellarmaster(s) Danie Malan (Nov 1987) ▪ Winemaker(s) Danie Malan (Nov 1987), with Armand Lacomme (Aug 2012) ▪ 227ha/187ha (cab, shiraz & various port varieties) ▪ 100,000cs own label 100% red ▪ PO Box 23 Riebeek West 7306 ▪ info@allesverloren.co.za ▪ www.allesverloren.co.za ▪ S 33° 21' 32.5" E 018° 52' 24.1" ▪ F +27 (0)22-461-2444 ▪ **T +27 (0)22-461-2589**

☐ **Almara** *see* Southern Sky Wines

Almenkerk Wine Estate

Two years of intense searching led the Belgian/Dutch Van Almenkerk family to this old Elgin apple farm in the early 2000s, some of which they turned to vineyards. Scion Joris, a lawyer, then qualified from Stellenbosch University and took the cellar reins. Now new viticulturist Michael Keown is helping focus on even and full ripening at lower alcohols, a botrytis sauvignon from tricky harvest 2014 is in the offing, maiden petit verdot and mourvèdre are in bottle, and Van Almenkerk patriarch Joep 'became one of our best clients overnight by opening the popular De Brasserie restaurant in Strand'.

Almenkerk Estate range

★★★★ **Petit Verdot Reserve** (NEW) **11** magnums only, from experimental 180 vines. Youthfully unrevealing, mere hints of violet, blueberry fragrance. Nicely built for ageing; typical varietal acidity providing firm thread to rich fruit. Oaked 2 years, older French.

★★★★ **Syrah 11** fuller, firmer than delicate **10**. Deep & resonating dark spice aromas, sweeter flavours with creamy feel currently restrained by dense but balanced tannins. Previous included drop cab franc.

★★★★ **Chardonnay 13** (★★★★) refrains initial buttery, leesy barrel-ferment notes of **12**. Slightly richer, less limy tension leaves more obvious discordant acid/sweet tail. Natural ferment, 30% new oak. Also tasted: **Sauvignon Blanc 13** ★★★★

Hope range (NEW)

Mourvèdre ★★★★ From experimental block of 180 vines. Sold on UK auction with proceeds going to Grabouw AIDS orphanage. **13** & **12** tasted. Former has brighter violet, wild mushroom features, juiciness & well-measured tannins. Latter little calmer, bigger but tasty & balanced.

Lace range

Sauvignon Blanc ★★★ Sound mouthful granadilla, blackcurrant juicy fruit on **13**. Good thrust acid ensures drier taste than few grams sugar might suggest. Also tasted: **Rosé 13** ★★★ Not retasted: **Red Blend 11** ★★★ — AL

Location/WO: Elgin ▪ Map: Elgin, Walker Bay & Bot River ▪ Est 2004 ▪ 1stB 2009 ▪ Tasting, sales & cellar tours Wed-Sun 10-4 (Sep-May) & Tue-Sat 10-4 (May-Sep) ▪ Open pub hols except on Mon/Tue ▪ Meals/picnics by prior booking (min 20 pax) or BYO picnic ▪ Walking/hiking trails ▪ Conservation area ▪ Heliport ▪ Boule court ▪ Owner(s) Van Almenkerk family ▪ Cellarmaster(s) Joris van Almenkerk ▪ Winemaker(s) Joris van Almenkerk, with Danver van Wyk (Feb 2009) ▪ Viticulturist(s) Michael Keown (Jan 2014) & Kevin Watt (consultant) ▪ 104.2ha/15ha (cabs s/f, malbec, merlot, mourv, p verdot, shiraz, chard, sauv, viog) ▪ 100t/1,600cs own label 65% red 30% white 5% rosé ▪ Brands for clients: De Mikke Patron, Pot Luck Club ▪ BWI ▪ PO Box 1129 Grabouw 7160 ▪ info@almenkerk.co.za ▪ www.almenkerk.co.za ▪ S 34° 12' 55" E 019° 01' 57" ▪ F +27 (0)86-523-0877 ▪ **T +27 (0)21-848-9844**

☐ **Alta Casa** *see* Darling Cellars

Alte Neffen Wines

After a 35-year career (Boschendal, Zevenwacht, Solms-Delta), Hilko Hegewisch is 'doing his own wine thing' in Stellenbosch's Devon Valley. His fledgling brand is destined for Germany, where his wine-partner and alte Neffe (literally 'old nephew') Helmut Peters drives sales. In the absence of an official local term for Amarone, they call their vine-dried winemaking style 'Method Kaperone'.

Shiraz ★★★★ Opulent dark fruit, vanilla-laden, ripe, rich & just-dry; **13** smooth & velvety & designed to please. From vine-dried grapes, oak 14 months, 75% new. — CR, CvZ

Location/WO: Stellenbosch ▪ Est/1stB 2013 ▪ Closed to public ▪ Owner(s) Hilko Hegewisch & Helmut Peters ▪ Winemaker(s) Hilko Hegewisch ▪ 55t/1,000cs own label 66.5% red 33.5% white ▪ 22 Van Coppenhagen Street Rozendal Stellenbosch 7600 ▪ hilko@wineclick.co.za ▪ www.alteneffen.co.za ▪ F +27 (0)86-614-5993 ▪ **T +27 (0)21-887-9544**

Alto Wine Estate

The original farm was granted in 1693, but the title 'oldest red wine estate in South Africa' refers to a subdivided portion on which the Malans first made wine in the 1920s. They named it Alto, alluding to the farm's altitude on the slopes of the Helderberg Mountain and their aspirations. Under Lusan Premium Wines ownership, the property maintains its reputation for classically styled red wines, including Alto Rouge, a popular label for more than 50 years.

★★★★ **Cabernet Sauvignon** Super-svelte **11** combines well-defined blackcurrant fruit with ripe, firm tannins, keeps near-15% alcohol in check. Back to best after warmer **10** (★★★★) vintage.

★★★★ **Alto Rouge** ⊘ 4-way blend of mostly cab franc & shiraz. Previewed **12** maintains the tradition: renowned, dependable steakhouse standard. Savoury, with pliable tannins, smooth & flavourful.

Also tasted: **Fine Old Vintage 08** ★★★★ Not retasted: **Shiraz 11** ★★★★ Occasional release: **MPHS**. — DS

Location/map/WO: Stellenbosch ▪ Est 1693 ▪ 1stB 1921 ▪ Tasting & sales Mon-Fri 9—5 Sat/Sun 10—4 ▪ Fee R10 wine/ port tasting ▪ Closed Good Fri & Dec 25 ▪ Pâté & wine pairing R50pp, advance booking required ▪ Hiking trail ▪ MTB track ▪ Owner(s) Lusan Premium Wines ▪ Cellarmaster(s)/winemaker(s) Schalk van der Westhuizen (Jun 2000) ▪ Viticulturist(s) Schalk van der Westhuizen & Danie van Zyl ▪ 191ha/83ha (cabs s/f, merlot, shiraz) ▪ 800t/100,000cs own label 100% red ▪ PO Box 104 Stellenbosch 7599 ▪ info@alto.co.za ▪ www.alto.co.za ▪ S 34° 0' 10.4" E 018° 50' 49.4" ▪ F +27 (0)21-881-3894 ▪ **T +27 (0)21-881-3884**

Altydgedacht Estate

The Parker family have been farming their enviable 400 ha-plus spread, tucked into the suburban edge of Durbanville, since 1852. Fifth-generation Oliver (cellarmaster) and John (viticulturist) have always taken roads less travelled: dry gewürztraminer, varietal barbera, aromatic blends for spicy

food such as the delightful and popular Chatelaine, part of the Tygerberg range, whose recent packaging and label revamp is intended to distinguish it from the rest of the line-up.

Parker Family Reserve range

Pinot Noir 🆕 ★★★★ **13** has lavender & violet scents, sweet cherry fruit; hint of bitter tannin on a generous body. **Weisser Riesling** ★★★★ Intense gewürztraminer-like rose fragrance, gentle acidity, lightish body, atypical but still pleasing **14**. Also tasted: **Méthode Cap Classique Blanc de Blanc 12** ★★★ Not retasted: **Semillon Noble Late Harvest 12** ★★★☆ Not tasted: **Tintoretto**, **The Ollo Estate White**.

Altydgedacht Estate range

★★★★ **Pinotage** Sweet berries, vanilla toffee component on tangy **13**; needs year or two for big tannins to meld, oak to settle.

★★★★ **Sauvignon Blanc** Sweaty, pungent notes on **14** complemented by nettles, green grass. Reined-in fruit on palate with hints of salty minerality. Less strident than **13** (★★★☆).

Chardonnay 🆕 ★★★ Very muted oak on shy, leesy nose, some buttery fruit; **13** quite light & tad brief, otherwise nicely balanced. **Gewürztraminer** ★★★★ **14** floral & dry, appealing, with distinctive rosewater character. Also tasted: **Barbera 13** ★★★☆

Ralph Parker range

Merlot Limited Release ★★★☆ **12** leafy, herbaceous, with tarry notes; generous fruit, riper than previous; tannins still thick, but better managed. Also tasted: **Cabernet Sauvignon Limited Release 12** ★★★ Not retasted: **Shiraz 11** ★★★☆

Tygerberg range

Chatelaine ★★★ Very fragrant riesling, muscat, gewürztraminer blend, near-dry **13** offers litchi fruit, rosepetals, appealing acidity. Perfect for spicy Eastern food. Also tasted: **Cabernet Franc Blanc de Noir 14** ★★★ — GdB

Location/WO: Durbanville ▪ Map: Durbanville, Philadelphia & Darling ▪ Est 1698 ▪ 1stB 1981 ▪ Tasting & sales Mon-Fri 9–5 Sat 9–4 ▪ Closed Easter Fri/Sun, Dec 25 & Jan 1 ▪ Cellar tours by appt ▪ B'fast & light lunches Mon-Sat 9.30-4 (T +27 (0)21-975-7815/eat@altydgedacht.co.za) ▪ Facilities for children ▪ Conferences ▪ Weddings/functions ▪ Conservation area ▪ Owner(s) Parker family ▪ Cellarmaster(s) Oliver Parker (1981) ▪ Winemaker(s) Etienne Louw (Jan 2006) ▪ Viticulturist(s) John Parker (1981) ▪ 412ha/180ha (16 varieties, r/w) ▪ 1,500t total 160t/22,000cs own label 30% red 65% white 5% rosé ▪ PO Box 213 Durbanville 7551 ▪ info@altydgedacht.co.za ▪ www.altydgedacht.co.za ▪ S 33° 50' 46.6" E 018° 37' 26.4" ▪ F +27 (0)86-218-5637 ▪ **T +27 (0)21-976-1295**

Alvi's Drift Private Cellar

Alvi van der Merwe was a medical doctor who always loved working in the vineyards established by his grandfather on the family farm. His brother Johan was a lawyer with a particular interest in business. Linley Schultz was chief winemaker at Distell with a yearning for a brand of his own. Their collaboration has resulted in what they say is 'an authentic family-owned wine business providing great wines at reasonable prices'. Competition successes for their new Albertus Viljoen and established Signature chenins have 'put us on the map as one of SA's leading chenin producers', says Linley.

AD range

★★★★ **Drift Fusion** Ⓥ Suave combo cab, pinotage &, in **09**, shiraz. Berry & clove appeal, supportive tannins, savoury & dry finish despite grain sugar & dash new American oak.

★★★★ **Chardonnay** Back-on-form **13** has ripe peaches & apricots combining with cream on palate, medium bodied, with vanilla & toasted nut nuances from 100% barrel fermentation. Better balanced than syrupy **12** (★★★).

★★★★ **Albertus Viljoen Chenin Blanc** 🆕 Complex, full-bodied **12** fitting tribute to farm's larger-than-life founder, strutting stonefruits, leesy citrus pith & oaky vanilla, all in lovely balance.

For more information, visit wineonaplatter.com

★★★★ **CVC** ⓦ Attractive white blend, aged in 30% new barrels giving vanilla-tinged creamy plushness to **12**'s lemon & white peach. Chardonnay upped to 50%, equal viognier & chenin.

★★★★ **Thornlands Méthode Cap Classique** (NEW) Crisp & dry **NV** sparkling from 70% chardonnay & pinot has fine, persistent bead, with hints of lime & roasted walnut adding intrigue to green apple & lemon notes.

★★★★☆ **Muscat de Frontignan White** ⓦ Alluring fortified dessert, small-oak matured. Copper-hued **10** (★★★★★) 'dry' notes of tealeaf & cherry tobacco, 'moist' honey & fig jam, gingery caramel tail. Endless, unctuous mouthful! Easily trumps last **07**.

Signature range

★★★★ **Viognier** ⓦ Hedonistic **13**'s nectarine & apricot richness enlivened by fresh acidity & careful oaking. Unsubtle but typical & delicious.

Chenin Blanc ⓥ ★★★★ Refreshing **14** has quite ripe, almost honeyed spanspek/melon nose, with citrus flavours & zippy acidity coming to the fore on the palate. **Sauvignon Blanc** ⓥ ★★★☆ Perfect poolside quaffer, **14** bursts with granadilla & gooseberries, ripe & juicy yet crisp & refreshing, with moderate 12% alcohol. Also tasted: **Cabernet Sauvignon 12** ★★★ **Merlot** (NEW) **13** ★★☆ **Pinotage 13** ★★★ **Shiraz 12** ★★★ **Chardonnay-Viognier** ⓥ **13** ★★★★

Naughty Girl range

Sparkling Sahara ★★ Foamy & fun, this muscat-based **NV** is drier than its siblings, with slightly higher alcohol (11.5%), but more attractively fruity than previous. Not retasted: **Sparkling Rosé NV** ★★★ **Sparkling Nude NV** ★★★ — JG

Location/map/WO: Worcester ▪ Est 1928 ▪ 1stB 2004 ▪ Tasting, sales & tours by appt ▪ Closed all pub hols ▪ Farm produce ▪ Owner(s) Bertie, Alvi & Johan van der Merwe ▪ Cellarmaster(s) Henk Swart ▪ Winemaker(s) Henk Swart, Alvi van der Merwe & Linley Schultz, with Anne van Heerden ▪ Viticulturist(s) Pierre Snyman (consultant) & Jan du Toit ▪ 6,000ha/420ha (ptage, shiraz, chard, chenin, muscat de F) ▪ ±7,500t/400,000cs own label ▪ IPW ▪ PO Box 126 Worcester 6850 ▪ info@alvisdrift.co.za ▪ www.alvisdrift.co.za ▪ S 33° 46' 25.8" E 019° 31' 53.7" ▪ F +27 (0)86-654-9425 ▪ T +27 (0)23-340-4117

☐ **Amandalia** *see* Rooiberg Winery

Amani Vineyards

There's a clear aesthetic at this boutique winery on Stellenbosch's Polkadraai Hills, where the grapes off the sustainably farmed vineyards are skilfully vinified by Carmen Stevens & Chris van Reenen. The wines are generally very ripe, richly fruited and powerful yet soft, with a touch of gratifying sweetness; oaking is mostly restrained. Sentiment is not forgotten, with wines named for the children of owners Lynde and Rusty Myers: Kenzie (only in US), Jordan, and the late Forest.

★★★★ **Merlot** ⓦ Powerful, alcoholic **11**, the ultra-ripe sweet fruit also giving plenty of flavour but less freshness, all supported by sensibly restrained oaking. With a lean muscularity allowing for ageing.

★★★★ **Cabernet Franc-Merlot** ⓦ Enticing **10** (★★★★), with drops cab & malbec, less classic than **09**. Fresh, spicy-leafy aromas; succulent flavours with modest savoury grip. WO W Cape.

★★★★ **Forest Myers** ⓦ Amani's ripe charm on **11** from shiraz & mourvèdre, the blend giving some complexity. Typical fruit intensity too, quite soft though powerful; strong acid a bit awkward.

★★★★ **I Am 1** ⓦ Good-natured **11** cab-based Bordeaux blend with a drop of shiraz, offering spicy, sweet-fruited, bright charm in the most restrained & balanced of the reds. Ready, but could keep.

★★★★ **Chardonnay** ⓦ As was lively **11**, **12** (★★★☆) naturally fermented & with only older barrels used for maturation. Easygoing balance of structure & fruit, gently rich, soft textured.

★★★★ **Kamili Chardonnay-Viognier** ⓦ **11** (★★★★) almost semi-sweet, unlike **10**, with easy charm. Structure from chardonnay & light oaking, with viognier's peachy richness, but no intensity.

For more information, visit wineonaplatter.com

Not retasted: **Cabernet Sauvignon 11** ★★★★ **Pinotage 11** ★★★ **Pendana Shiraz 11** ★★★
Poppy Blush 12 ★★ **Sauvignon Blanc 12** ★★★ Occasional release: **Jordan Myers**. — TJ

Location/map: Stellenbosch ▪ WO: Stellenbosch/Upper Hemel-en-Aarde Valley/Western Cape ▪ Tasting by appt only ▪ Owner(s) Lynde & Rusty Myers ▪ Cellarmaster(s) Carmen Stevens (Jul 2005) ▪ Winemaker(s) Chris van Reenen (Jan 2011) ▪ Viticulturist(s) Chris van Reenen (Jan 2011) & Chris Keet (2012, consultant) ▪ 38ha/27.8ha (cabs s/f, merlot, moury, shiraz, chard, sauv, viog) ▪ 235t 76% red 24% white ▪ EnviroWines ▪ PO Box 12422 Die Boord 7613 ▪ wine@amani.co.za ▪ www.amani.co.za ▪ S 33° 57' 54.3" E 018° 43' 59.5" ▪ F +27 (0)21-881-3931 ▪ **T +27 (0)21-881-3930**

☐ **Ama Ulibo** *see* Goedverwacht Wine Estate

Ambeloui Wine Cellar

Nick Christodoulou came to Cape Town's Hout Bay to find a home by the sea. Soon its 'little vineyard' ('ambeloui' in Cypriot) fired a bubbly passion... and a cellar was excavated under the house. Two decades on, the next generation is emerging: son Alexis is taking over the winemaking, daughter Miranda adds exciting new food products to the mix, and a brandy has been distilled.

★★★★☆ **Méthode Cap Classique Rosanne Rosé NV** sparkler from chardonnay (52%) & pinot noir, base wine lightly oaked. Thrilling current release offers subtle red berry flavours, mellifluous texture & a refreshing dry mousse. More yielding than cellarmate, both most satisfying.

★★★★☆ **Méthode Cap Classique** Urbane chardonnay-pinot noir (60/40) bubble, 10% of base wine wooded; rich, aromatic **12** 'Christo' is plush, with a brioche character from extended lees-ageing. **11** 'Max' is tighter. Whatever the name (all family off-spring), these are exquisitely focused, mouthwatering. — DS

Location: Hout Bay ▪ Map: Cape Peninsula ▪ WO: Western Cape ▪ Est 1994 ▪ 1stB 1998 ▪ Tasting by appt ▪ Owner(s) Nick & Ann Christodoulou ▪ Cellarmaster(s)/viticulturist(s) Nick Christodoulou (1994) ▪ Winemaker(s) Nick Christodoulou (1994), with Alexis Christodoulou (2009) ▪ 1ha/0.5ha (pinot, chard) ▪ 15t/3,000cs own label 100% MCC ▪ PO Box 26800 Hout Bay 7872 ▪ wine@ambeloui.co.za ▪ www.ambeloui.co.za ▪ S 34° 0' 49.5" E 018° 22' 55.4" ▪ F +27 (0)88-021-790-7386 ▪ **T +27 (0)21-790-7386/+27 (0)82-460-8399/+27 (0)82-880-1715**

Ameera

With tender loving care, Cape Town lighting business owner Marc Machtelinckx and family are transforming a Cinderella wine and olive property on Stellenbosch's Annandale Road into something of an Ameera ('Princess'). Farming organically, they've nursed the cabernet and shiraz back to health and, with advisers, vinified the first flagship Ameera and early/easy-drinking Duel wines. They've also bought a neighbour's farm and intend to plant it with a white variety for the Duel range. A tasting area beside the farm dam is next.

Ameera range
Cabernet Sauvignon (Ⓥ) ★★★★ Blackcurrant & tobacco, a creamy opulence supported by a streamlined, ultra-smooth texture. **12** drinking well, capable of some cellaring. **Blanc de Noir** ★★ From shiraz, **13** fresh strawberry perfume, dry & light textured, perfect summertime wine.

Duel by Ameera range
Cabernet Sauvignon-Shiraz (Ⓥ) ★★★★ Black plums, liquorice, campfire smoke, Marmite - lots going on in **13**. No oak, but nice grip at the end of a smooth rounded body, delicious drinkability. — CR, CvZ

Location/map/WO: Stellenbosch ▪ Est/1stB 2012 ▪ Tasting & sales Mon-Sat by appt ▪ Fee R30 ▪ Owner(s) Marc Machtelinckx & Kathleen Raemdonck ▪ Winemaker(s) Philip Costandius, Marius Roux (2012/23 vintages, both consultants) & Marc Machtelinckx ▪ 12.5ha/4.5ha (cab, shiraz) ▪ ±35t/1,000cs own label 80% red 20% rosé + 30,000L bulk ▪ PO Box 3949 Somerset West 7129 ▪ wine@ameera.co.za ▪ www.ameera.co.za ▪ S 33° 59' 42.62" E 018° 48' 40.08" ▪ F +27 (0)21-448-8611 ▪ **T +27 (0)21-881-3146**

Anatu Wines

What started as jocular dinner-table talk among friends is today a full-fledged wine business, housed in the old Cordoba cellar on the Helderberg and owned by former Johannesburg bankers André and Freda Hamersma. Though the couple have come a long way since the maiden 2002 crush in a cold room next to Freda's parents' garage in Riebeek-Kasteel, their pursuit remains boutique quantities of 'unique, handcrafted' wines, with a particular focus on blends.

Family Blend range

★★★★☆ **Red** ⓧ Full-bodied **10** (★★★★) mix grenache & shiraz from Wellington & Stellenbosch, concentrated black fruit & good oaking, with warmish finish. Attractive, but misses the complexity of last-tasted **08**.

★★★★ **White** ⓧ **12** (★★★★) chiefly chenin, with grenache blanc & colombard, briefly oaked, is understated, savoury. Intended to be accessible young, but pre-bottling is actually quite esoteric, lacks primary fruit of **11**.

Not retasted: **Rosé 12** ★★★★

Fugue range

★★★★☆ **Red** ⓧ Super debut **10**, shiraz & grenache from Stellenbosch & Wellington, is restrained, combining clean black fruit, meat & wild game aromas. Full-bodied, concentrated fruit flavours with a delicious core of well-judged oak. Alcohol (15.5%) well hidden.

★★★★☆ **White** ⓧ **11** blend of roussanne, chenin & grenache blanc; rich, vibrant & full bodied, waxy ripe-fruit flavours supported by precise oaking & firm minerality. Elegant, with an unflagging end.

Not retasted: **Rosé 12** ★★★ — CE

Location: Stellenbosch ▪ Map: Helderberg ▪ WO: Coastal ▪ Est/1stB 2002 ▪ Tasting, sales & cellar tours by appt ▪ Closed all pub hols ▪ Owner(s) André & Freda Hamersma ▪ 40t/5,600cs own label 40% red 40% white 20% rosé ▪ Other export brand: Sereia ▪ Postnet Suite 246 Private Bag X5061 Stellenbosch 7599 ▪ sales@anatu.co.za ▪ www.anatu.co.za ▪ S 34° 1' 52.20" E 018° 50' 46.73" ▪ F +27 (0)86-577-5019 ▪ **T +27 (0)83-307-9333**

☐ **Anchor Drift** *see* Viljoensdrift Wines & Cruises
☐ **Ancient Earth** *see* Bellingham

Andersons Wines

Owner Ian Anderson planned to retire on his Plettenberg Bay property but now finds himself nurturing promising young sauvignon vines, assisted by Anton Smal of Bramon Wines. Ian names his wine after the endemic Ghost Moth.

Leto Venus Sauvignon Blanc ⓧ ★★★ Bird-marauded **13** preview is deftly handled, shows riper white peach flavours, & more typical Plettenberg racy freshness & seafood compatibility. — GdB

Location/WO: Plettenberg Bay ▪ Map: Klein Karoo & Garden Route ▪ Est 2008 ▪ 1stB 2011 ▪ Tasting by appt ▪ Fee R5/wine ▪ Closed all pub hols ▪ Owner(s) Ian Anderson ▪ Winemaker(s) Anton Smal (Bramon Wines) ▪ Viticulturist(s) Ian Anderson, assisted by Anton Smal ▪ 22ha/2.5ha (sauv) ▪ 5.5t/600cs own label 100% white ▪ PO Box 2564 Plettenberg Bay 6600 ▪ ian@app.co.za ▪ S 33° 59' 17.7" E 023° 27' 15.1" ▪ F +27 (0)44-534-8873 ▪ **T +27 (0)44-534-8873/+27 (0)83-453-3624**

Andreas Wines

Swedish couple Jan and Anita Bokdal realised a lifelong ambition of owning an operational wine farm when they acquired Groenendal in Wellington's Bovlei Valley in 2005. A single shiraz is made from the property's small organically farmed vineyard.

★★★★ **Andreas Shiraz 12** shows warm-climate origin in liqueur-like black berry cordial & mouthcoating extraction. Bold, almost ready to drink but will keep well for up to a decade. — HJ

Location/WO: Wellington ▪ Map: Paarl & Wellington ▪ Est 2003 ▪ 1stB 2004 ▪ Tasting & sales by appt Mon–Fri 9–5 ▪ Closed all pub hols ▪ Cellar tours by appt ▪ Accommodation ▪ Weddings/functions ▪ Owner(s) Jan & Anita Bokdal ▪ Cellarmaster(s)/viticulturist(s) Howard Heughs & Eugenie Potter ▪ Winemaker(s) Howard Heughs & Ettienne Malan (consultant) ▪ 6ha/4.5ha (mourv, shiraz) ▪ 48t/3,168cs own label 100% red ▪ PO Box 892 Wellington 7654 ▪ andreas@ezinet.co.za ▪ www.andreas.co.za ▪ S 33° 37' 52.0" E 019° 2' 50.1" ▪ F +27 (0)86-664-5087 ▪ **T +27 (0)21-873-2286**

Andy Mitchell Wines

Vikki Mitchell and daughter Olivia, a trained chef, are continuing the winemaking legacy of husband and father Andy, who sadly passed away mid-2014 amid preparations for grenache noir plantings and the release of their maiden MCC sparkler. The former sailor and Cape Wine Master sourced grapes widely for their boutique Greyton mountainside operation.

Crooked Path Shiraz ★★★★ Still-youthful **07** from Stellenbosch a full-bodied winter warmer with quiet yet satisfying dark spice & savoury richness. **Nerina Rosé ★★★** From Elgin cab specifically harvested for rosé. **13** deep hued, emphatically dry & flavoursome. **Méthode Cap Classique** ⓜ ★★★☆ Maiden **11** bubbly, chardonnay (ex Franschhoek) & pinot noir (ex Paarl) blend. Light brioche notes, creamy mousse with resoundingly dry conclusion. For 'sunsets & surprises' says winemaker. Also tasted: **Crooked Path Pinot Noir 12 ★★★☆** Not retasted: **Syrah-Grenache-Mourvèdre 12 ★★★** **Walker Bay Chenin Blanc 12 ★★★★** Not tasted: **Elgin Pinot Noir**. — AL

Location: Greyton ▪ Map: Southern Cape ▪ WO: Elgin/Stellenbosch/Western Cape/Walker Bay/Franschhoek-Paarl ▪ Est/1stB 2003 ▪ Tasting, sales & cellar tours by appt ▪ Closed Easter Fri/Sun & Dec 25 ▪ Owner(s) Vikki Mitchell ▪ Winemaker(s) Olivia Mitchell (Jan 2008) ▪ 15t own label 42% red 21% white 13% rosé 24% MCC + 200cs for clients ▪ PO Box 543 Paarden Eiland 7420 ▪ olivia@andymitchellwines.com ▪ www.andymitchellwines.com ▪ S 34° 2' 26.3" E 019° 37' 2.6" ▪ F +27 (0)86-611-2739 ▪ **T +27 (0)28-254-9045**

☐ **Angels Tears** see Grande Provence Heritage Wine Estate
☐ **Ankerman** see uniWines Vineyards

Annandale Wines

Hempies du Toit, owner, winemaker and viticulturist of boutique winery Annandale, traces his heritage in wine back to the earliest days of the Cape settlement. The ever-exuberant rugby legend's rustic estate on the Helderberg is notable for resolutely traditional winemaking and extended barrelling.

★★★★ Cabernet Sauvignon ⓐ Serious-minded & classically styled. A melange of dark cherry & cassis on bold, spicy **04**, bottled after 7 years in barrel & showing similar fine form to previous.

★★★★ Shiraz ⓐ Spicy, oaky complexity adds to black pastille fruit on solid, unshowy & firmly structured **04**. Made to last.

★★★★ Cavalier ⓐ **04** Bordeaux-style blend with shiraz oozes spice & black fruit. Big & sturdy, yet balanced & smooth with lots of life after 7 years in barrel. More complex than **01** (★★★★).

★★★★ Nostalgia ⓐ Tribute to old-style Cape reds & the founders of Alto Estate. From cab, shiraz & cinsaut - latter adding charming wild, raspberry notes in **NV**. From various years, mature but vibrant. Not retasted: **Merlot 05 ★★★★ CVP 04 ★★★★** — WB

Location/map/WO: Stellenbosch ▪ Est/1stB 1996 ▪ Tasting, sales & cellar tours Mon-Sat 9–5 ▪ Fee R20 ▪ Closed Easter Fri-Mon, Ascension Day & Dec 25 ▪ Farm produce ▪ BYO picnic ▪ Owner(s) Hempies du Toit ▪ Winemaker(s)/viticulturist(s) Hempies du Toit (1996) ▪ 72ha/45ha (cabs s/f, merlot, shiraz) ▪ 250t/10,000cs own label 100% red ▪ PO Box 12681 Stellenbosch 7613 ▪ info@annandale.co.za ▪ www.annandale.co.za ▪ S 33° 59' 49.2" E 018° 49' 50.9" ▪ F +27 (0)21-881-3562 ▪ **T +27 (0)21-881-3560**

Annex Kloof Wines

This is a story of three brothers, Thys, Tobie and Hugo Basson, on three Swartland farms, each having vineyards with individual characters and which provide fruit for both big-brand buyers and the range below, made by Hugo. Small private functions are now hosted in a new venue with an outdoor area.

Annex Kloof range

★★★★ Shiraz ⊘ **12** full of ripeness, warmth of Swartland fruit. Rich yet fresh dark spice, earthy flavours backed by lively, chunky tannins allow for current enjoyment with hearty fare & medium-term cellaring.

★★★★ Tulu ⊘ Rhône-style blend led by shiraz with splashes mourvèdre, grenache. Improving on **11** (★★★★), **12** has great depth of spice, roast nuts flavours; richly textured & warmingly long yet unheavy. Good now & for several years.

Also tasted: **Malbec 12** ★★★☆

Xenna range

★★★★ Chenin Blanc ⊘ **14** (★★★☆) echoes spicy pear, green apples character of **13**, with just a bit less concentration, persistence. Remains characterful, dry mouthful. WO W Cape.

Shiraz ⊘ **★★★ 12** rich & ripe, full of spicy warmth; rounded for ready enjoyment. Not retasted: **Cabernet Sauvignon 11** ★★★ **Pinotage 11** ★★★☆ — AL

Location: Malmesbury ▪ Map: Swartland ▪ WO: Swartland/Western Cape ▪ Est/1stB 2006 ▪ AnnexKloof stall on N7: sales daily; tasting Fri 8-5.30 Sat 8-3 Sun 11.30-5.30 ▪ Farm: tasting, sales & cellar tours by appt only ▪ Closed Easter Fri-Mon, Ascension Day, Pentecost, Dec 16/25/26 & Jan 1 ▪ BYO picnic ▪ Walks/hikes ▪ 4x4 trail ▪ Conservation area ▪ Owner(s) Hugo Basson, with brothers Thys & Tobie ▪ Winemaker(s) Hugo Basson (Jan 2006) ▪ 550ha (cab, grenache, malbec, merlot, mourv, ptage, shiraz, chard, chenin, sauv) ▪ 6,000t own label 95% red 5% white ▪ PO Box 772 Malmesbury 7299 ▪ hugo@annexkloofwines.co.za ▪ www.annexkloofwines.co.za ▪ S 33° 30' 39.1" E 018° 48' 22.5" (estate), S 33° 21' 5.69" E 018° 42' 36.87" (farmstall) ▪ F +27 (0)86-569-3957 ▪ **T +27 (0)22-487-3870 (cellar)**

Antebellum Winery

A series of changes at what used to be Meerhof Family Vineyards sees Herman Redelinghuys taking ownership of the cellar and farm on the mountainside above Riebeek-Kasteel in the Swartland. JH ('Stompie') Meyer is still the cellar supremo - with the winery also used by a handful of small-scale vintners, especially other members of the Swartland Independent Producers organisation.

Syrah ★★★ Red-fruited **13** light & airy, with the freshness & modest alcohol of this house. Lighter all round than previous **08** (★★★★), which included mourvèdre, viognier. Just a little tannin, good dry finish. **Syrah-Cinsault-Mourvèdre** ⊛ ★★★★ A little fuller-flavoured but still light feeling, interesting **13** has red fruit & a lean but satisfying dryness. These reds matured in old oak, to allow fruit purity to dominate. Works well & refreshingly with food. Also tasted: **Saffronne Rosé 14** ★★★☆ **Chenin Blanc 13** ★★★★ — TJ

Location: Riebeek-Kasteel ▪ Map/WO: Swartland ▪ Est/1stB 2000 ▪ Tasting & sales by appt only ▪ Owner(s) Herman Redelinghuys ▪ Winemaker(s)/viticulturist(s) Johan Meyer ▪ 20ha (mourv, ptage, shiraz, chenin) ▪ 2,400cs own label 55% red 45% white ▪ PO Box 148 Riebeek Kasteel 7307 ▪ herman@hermanredelinghuys.co.za ▪ www.antebellum.co. za ▪ S 33° 24' 19.8" E 018° 52' 15.0" ▪ F +27 (0)86-683-8132 ▪ **T +27 (0)79-280-0237**

AntHill Wines ⊕

Irrepressible barrel supplier Mark Howell's antennae are finely tuned to finding the odd special parcel of 'good' grapes to vinify for sale to faithful followers. The previously coined Entre Nous name is now reserved for a stand-alone brand 'with others'; AntHill, with construction project manager Hylton Schwenk, 'remains my main focus'.

Cobbold Stone Red Blend ⊛ ★★★☆ **12** merlot-led Bordeaux blend shows cooler Philadelphia provenance in herbaceous nuance; tight chalky-dry tannins need good few years to unfurl & reveal lurking pure fruit. **White Stone Sauvignon Blanc** ⊛ ★★★★ Aptly named **13** from Stellenbosch opens with stony minerality & dusty note, turning into greengage & stonefruit on bone-dry palate. Bright acidity freshens & counteracts the evident alcohol. Not tasted: **Long John Silver Pinot Noir, The Persian Shiraz, Davey Jones Locker, Pieces of 8**. — MW

Location: Somerset West ▪ WO: Stellenbosch/Philadelphia ▪ Est 1999 ▪ 1stB 2000 ▪ Tasting by appt ▪ Owner(s) Mark Howell & Hylton Schwenk ▪ Winemaker(s) Mark Howell (Feb 2000) ▪ 1,200cs own label 60% red 40% white ▪ 19 Immelmal Rd Somerset West 7130 ▪ www@telkomsa.net ▪ S 34° 4' 30.8" E 018° 52' 37.6" ▪ F +27 (0)86-668-4566 ▪ **T +27 (0)82-895-9008**

Anthonij Rupert Wyne

'Wines of extraordinary quality to be enjoyed when ready for the market' is the vision current owner Johann Rupert inherited from his late brother Anthonij over a decade ago, and still espouses at the gracious twin home-farms near Franschhoek. L'Ormarins Estate is the setting for the popular Franschhoek Motor Museum; adjacent, and linked by a pair of new, specially built trams, is Anthonij Rupert Estate, home to two elegant cellardoors: one, nearer the entrance, dedicated to the Protea and Terra del Capo ranges, where an antipasti bar showcases the food-friendliness of the Italian varieties, in particular, and a lounge area offers a taste of 'la dolce vita'; the second at the manor house, where antique furniture and art (and glorious mountains) provide the backdrop for the Cape of Good Hope and Anthonij Rupert flagships.

Location/map: Franschhoek ▪ Est 1714 ▪ 1stB 1982 ▪ Two tasting rooms: Anthonij Rupert Mon-Sat 10–4.30; Terra del Capo Tue-Sun 10-4.30 ▪ Fee R15-R60 per flight ▪ Closed Good Fri & Dec 25 ▪ Antipasti Bar for light meals & refreshments ▪ Cheese, olive oil & honey ▪ Franschhoek Motor Museum T +27 (0)21-874-9020 Mon-Fri 10-4 Sat/Sun 10-3; admittance R60pp, seniors R50 & children (3-12 yrs) R30 ▪ Two specially built trams travel between the motor museum & tasting rooms ▪ Owner(s) Johann Rupert ▪ Winemaker(s) Dawie Botha (Jan 2005), Zanie Viljoen (Jan 2007), Vernon van der Hoven (2012) & Mark van Buuren (2013) ▪ 4 farms: total ±1,100ha/±210ha (cabs s/f, carignan, cinsaut, grenache, marsanne, merlot, mourv, pinot, sangio, shiraz, chard, chenin, pinot grigio, rouss) ▪ ISO 14001:2009 ▪ PO Box 435 Franschhoek 7690 ▪ tasting@rupertwines.com ▪ www.rupertwines.com ▪ S 33° 53' 16.77 E 019° 0' 17.70" (Anthonij Rupert/Cape of Good Hope), S 33° 52' 47.36" E 019° 0' 10.91" (Terra Del Capo/Protea) ▪ F +27 (0)21-874-9111 ▪ **T +27 (0)21-874-9004/+27 (0)21-874-9041 (tasting)**

Anura Vineyards

The Bouma family's dynamic, frog-themed estate in Klapmuts is in a constant state of development and expansion. In the vineyards, an array of classic French varieties vies for space with the southern Mediterranean. Already boasting a restaurant, cheesery, smoke-house and various deli options, the diverse, visitor-friendly attractions are soon to be augmented with a new tasting venue.

LB Series

★★★★ Sangiovese ⓐ Ambitious effort, **10** is fresher, brighter than last-tasted **07**. Thick tannins under cheerful red berry fruit, should soften with time.

★★★★ Shiraz ⓐ Subtle, smooth & rounded, with floral scents & peppery spices, first-release **09** augurs well. Hints of Rhône with solid New World ripeness.

★★★★ Cape Cuvée Was 'Cape Blend'. Smooth **12** leapfrogs never-tasted, sold-out **11**. 100% new oak adds spice to juicy fruit from basket-pressed pinotage (34%), merlot, shiraz & cabs sauvignon & franc. Coastal WO.

Not retasted: **La Traviata 09** ★★★☆

Reserves & Limited Releases

★★★★ Malbec Limited Release ⓐ **10** has last-reviewed **08**'s elegant structure & fruit concentration, with appealing spicy notes & focused finish. Worthy effort.

★★★★ Merlot Reserve ⓐ **10** follows previous form, with plush texture & appealing savoury notes in full-bodied, generously ripe fruit. Dark & deep, yet showing subtle floral fragrances.

★★★★ Petit Verdot Limited Release ⓐ Improving on **08** (★★★☆), **09** has typical inky depth & spicy black fruit. Muscular but showing restraint. Reflects fine vintage, should soften with time in bottle.

★★★★ **Pinotage Reserve** Combo American & French oak adds mocha & caramel notes to ripe black berry flavours of **11**. Dense & dark, velvety smooth, better balanced than **10** (★★★☆).

★★★★ **Syrah Limited Release** Meaty butterscotch & white pepper dominate bold nose on **08**, but palate offers enticing scrub, delicate floral & sweet spicy notes over solid tannin backbone. WO Paarl.

★★★★ **Chardonnay Limited Release 13** is big step up from Anura version, intense & zesty citrus effortlessly handling fermentation (20% natural) & maturation in 70% new French oak.

★★★★ **Sauvignon Blanc Unfiltered Reserve 13**, with tiny new-oaked portion, mainly from Darling, where dryland bushvines yield intense gooseberry flavours with grapefruit finish.

★★★★ **Méthode Cap Classique Brut** Zesty **10** sparkling from chardonnay & pinot noir far less oxidative than **09**, with leesy brioche & creaminess balancing crisp Granny Smith & lemon notes. WO W Cape.

★★★★ **Cape Vintage Reserve** Carefully crafted **10** port-style from Robertson tinta, 32 months in barrel. Fortified with aged brandy, shows traditional grippy spirit, restrained extraction.

Also tasted: **Cabernet Sauvignon Reserve 10** ★★★☆ Not retasted: **Chenin Blanc Limited Release 12** ★★★☆

Anura range

Legato ★★★☆ Merlot (55%) and cab combine harmoniously in unpretentious **12** with ripe plums & blackberries. Smooth if slightly warm finish. Coastal WO. **Viognier Barrel Selection** ★★★ From ripe peachy Swartland grapes, barrel-fermented **13** seems sweeter than 6 g/l RS suggests. Inviting perfume, warm finish. Calls for cheese. Also tasted: **Merlot 12** ★★★ **Pinotage-Syrah 13** ★★★ **Chardonnay 13** ★★★ **Sauvignon Blanc 14** ★★★ Not retasted: **Pinotage 12** ★★★★ **Rosé 13** ★★★ **Cape Ruby Port NV** ★★★

Frog Hill range

Pinotage ★★★☆ Hints of sweet vanilla & banana add to wild berry appeal of **13** quaffer. Also tasted: **Cabernet Sauvignon-Merlot 12** ★★★☆ — JG

Location: Paarl ▪ Map: Paarl & Wellington ▪ WO: Simonsberg-Paarl/Coastal/Western Cape/Paarl ▪ Est 1990 ▪ 1stB 2001 ▪ Tasting, sales & cellar tours daily 9.30–5 ▪ Closed Good Fri, Dec 25 & Jan 1 ▪ Fee R40/cheese & wine ▪ Lilly Pad Restaurant ▪ Tour groups ▪ Farm produce ▪ Conferences ▪ Owner(s) Tymen Bouma ▪ Cellarmaster(s) Tymen Bouma (1990) ▪ Winemaker(s) Johnnie Calitz & Lance Bouma (Jan 2007) ▪ Viticulturist(s) Hannes Kloppers (Oct 1997) ▪ 240ha/120ha (cab, carignan, grenache, malbec, merlot, mourv, nebbiolo, p verdot, ptage, pinot, sangio, shiraz, tempranillo, chard, chenin, nouvelle, pinot gris, sauv, verdelho) ▪ 750t/60,000cs own label 80% red 17% white 2% rosé 1% fortified ▪ PO Box 244 Klapmuts 7625 ▪ info@anura.co.za, wine@anura.co.za ▪ www.anura.co.za ▪ S 33° 48' 41.4" E 018° 53' 19.8" ▪ F +27 (0)21-875-5657 ▪ **T +27 (0)21-875-5360**

Anwilka

This red-wine specialist in a quiet corner of Stellenbosch is owned by the same group as Klein Constantia — including eminent Bordeaux men Bruno Prats and Hubert de Boüard. They were founders of the estate (this year celebrating ten years since the first vintage of Anwilka) and their long experience with making fine red wine remains a great asset. Devotion to the Bordeaux model is far from being the aim, however — witness the increasing role of shiraz in the blend. Malbec is now also being introduced to the vineyards, where a replanting strategy is under way, to complement the expanded and enhanced winemaking facilities.

★★★★ **Petit Frère** 'Little Brother' similar blend to grander sibling but, in **12**, unwooded. Shade less serious than lightly oaked **10** (no **11**) yet as satisfying, with fine tannins, savoury persistence.

★★★★☆ **Anwilka** **11** confirms serious vein noted in **09** (**10** untasted). Now 67% shiraz with cab & drop petit verdot. Youthful & still showing oak, lots of ripe fruit translating into power & firm tannic structure. Deserves good few years to soften, & gain more harmony, charm. WO W Cape. — CvZ

Location: Stellenbosch ▪ WO: Western Cape/Stellenbosch ▪ Est 1997 ▪ 1stB 2005 ▪ Tasting & sales at Klein Constantia ▪ Closed all pub hols ▪ Cellar tours by appt ▪ Owner(s) Zdenek Bakala, Charles Harman, Bruno Prats & Hubert de Boüard ▪ Winemaker(s) Jean du Plessis (Aug 2008) ▪ Viticulturist(s) Piet Neethling, with Johan Wiese (consultant, both 1997) ▪ 48ha/±39ha (cab, merlot, p verdot, shiraz) ▪ 250t/±32,000cs own label 100% red ▪ PO Box 5298 Helderberg 7135 ▪ anwilka@mweb.co.za ▪ www.kleinconstantia.com ▪ F +27 (0)21-842-3983 ▪ **T +27 (0)21-842-3225**

Arendsig Handcrafted Wines

Arendsig co-owner and cellarmaster Lourens van der Westhuizen makes only single-vineyard wines in a boutique cellar on the Robertson family farm, and vinifies on contract for several other small wineries.

Location/map: Robertson ▪ Est/1stB 2004 ▪ Tasting & cellar tours by appt ▪ Tour groups ▪ Picnic baskets to be pre-booked, or BYO picnic ▪ Wedding/function venue ▪ Farmhouse (sleeps up to 10 people) ▪ Owner(s) Lourens & Frikkie van der Westhuizen ▪ Cellarmaster(s)/viticulturist(s) Lourens van der Westhuizen (2004) ▪ 95ha/12ha (cab, shiraz, chard, sauv, viog) ▪ 80t/3,000cs own label 50% red 50% white + 100t/3,000cs for clients ▪ Brands for clients: Esona, Mimosa, Star Hill ▪ PO Box 170 Robertson 6705 ▪ info@arendsig.co.za ▪ www.arendsig.co.za ▪ S 33° 55' 37.9" E 020° 0' 47.6" ▪ F +27 (0)86-535-0693/+27 (0)23-616-2090 ▪ **T +27 (0)84-200-2163/+27 (0)23-616-2835**

Arendskloof

'Only a wine good enough' finds its way into this, the prestige range of Christiaan Groenewald, Diners Club Winemaker of the Year 2013 and owner/winemaker at separately listed Eagle's Cliff Wines-New Cape Wines. The Arendskloof bottlings, well priced and intended to complement good food, are from single-vineyards 'made in a way to try and keep nature in the wines'.

★★★★ **Pinotage 10** improves on flagging **08** with typical acetone & strawberry combo, easy sippability & interesting aloe lift. Ready now but will reward 3+ years cellaring. No **09**.

★★★★ **Tannat-Syrah** Unusual & ambitious blend. **12** (★★★★★) trumps last-tasted **09** (labelled 'Syrah-Tannat'). Spicy black plum & prune, firm but noble tannin (as expected from tannat). **11**, Diners Club Winemaker of the Year 2013 winner, sold out untasted, like **10**.

★★★★ **Pinot Grigio** Seldom-seen quality from this variety in SA. **14** shows producer's 'wet stone' minerality, slightly fuller than vinous **13**. Both weighty & long, savoury for mealtimes.

★★★★ **Sauvignon Blanc** ⊘ Like step-up **13**, **14** flavoursome without overt fruitiness. Elegant & restrained, unusually enduring, delivering texture & precision. WO W Cape, as all these.

Brut Rosé MCC (NEW) ★★★★ Classic & engaging pink dry sparkling, **12** fresh & crisp, lemon sherbet notes from chardonnay, delicate red berry flavours from pinot noir. Year/2 cellaring should add complexity. Not retasted: **Pinot Noir 12** ★★★★ **Chardonnay 13** ★★★ — CvZ

☐ **Arniston Bay** see Stellenbosch Vineyards

Arra Vineyards

Cellarmaster Dee Wentzel concedes the Klapmuts family winery has a relatively low profile but says she and her team are 'very much focused on luring people to the farm.' What to expect when you get there? 'We don't make wines for connoisseurs or critics, but rather for everyday drinking.'

Reserve range

★★★★ **Cabernet Sauvignon** ⓧ Big & bold **09**, smooth textured but ultimately not unbalanced or overdone. Intense cassis, slight earthy note. No **08**.

★★★★ **Shiraz** ⓧ Rich, with layers of flavour - red & black fruit, a hint of vanilla, pepper & spice. **09** bright acidity, crunchy tannins. No **08**.

★★★★ **Viognier** ⓧ Evident oak spice on **11** (★★★★), may still meld with peachy, ginger fruit. Medium bodied, smooth & silky, fruitily dry finish. **09** more expressive; **10** not made.

Not retasted: **Nobility 11** ★★★★

Barrel Select range

★★★★ **Cabernet Sauvignon** ⓥ 08 (★★★★) not as harmonious as **06**. Already quite evolved, with fruit yielding to a more savoury character. No **07**.

★★★★ **Pinotage** ⓥ One to please even non-pinotage lovers. **08** understated, more savoury spice than sweet red fruits; quite dense but fresh, beautifully polished tannins. Subtly oaked (20% new).

★★★★☆ **Shiraz** ⓥ Finesse & balance characterises **08**, with 3% mourvèdre. Layers of flavour including red berries & spice. Medium body, with fresh acidity & fine tannins.

★★★★☆ **Shiraz-Mourvèdre-Viognier** ⓥ Impresses with its poise & complexity. Good concentration & fresh acidity on the palate. Start of some developed character lends further interest to early-drinking **08**.

Not retasted: **Mourvèdre 08 ★★★**

Arra Vineyards range

★★★★ **Cabernet Sauvignon** ⓥ **10** offers real bang for your buck, with a brooding nose, pure dark fruit, fresh acidity & fine tannins. More substance than **09** (★★★★).

★★★★ **Cabernet Sauvignon-Petit Verdot-Merlot** ⓥ **10** over-delivers with plenty of dark fruit, attractive oak. Good concentration, firm but fine tannins. Should keep for a good few years.

Mourvèdre ⓥ ★★★★ Suitably exotic **10** with dark fruit & fynbos plus attractive hint of vanilla. Good concentration, smooth texture. **Chenin Blanc** ⓥ ★★★★ Assertive **11** with oxidative, honeyed concentration; grippy close leaves drier sensation than 4.4 g/l sugar suggests. WO Coastal. Not retasted: **Merlot 10 ★★★ Pinotage 10 ★★★ Shiraz 10 ★★★ Cape Blend 09 ★★★ Shiraz-Mourvèdre 10 ★★★ Shiraz-Cabernet Sauvignon 11 ★★★ Blanc de Noir 13 ★★★ Viognier 12 ★★ Natural Sweet Red Blend 09 ★★★ Natural Sweet Viognier 12 ★★★** — CE

Location: Paarl ▪ Map: Paarl & Wellington ▪ WO: Paarl/Coastal ▪ Est 1998 ▪ 1stB 2001 ▪ Tasting & sales Tue-Sat 9-4.30 ▪ Owner(s) Arra Vineyards (Pty) Ltd ▪ Cellarmaster(s) Dee Wentzel (2006) ▪ Viticulturist(s) Willem Snyman (2014) ▪ 72ha/30ha (cab, merlot, mourv, ptage, ruby cab, shiraz, viog) ▪ 20,000cs ▪ PO Box 298 Klapmuts 7625 ▪ info@arrawines.com ▪ www.arrawines.com ▪ S 33° 49' 25.9" E 018° 51' 47.7" ▪ F +27 (0)21-875-5866 ▪ **T +27 (0)21-875-5363**

Arumdale Cool Climate Wines ⓥ

Now based at Grabouw village, this boutique brand from Elgin operates out of an increasingly popular wine shop, introducing visitors to the handcrafted top range as well as the fun and informal second label, Robin Hood Legendary Wine, listed separately.

St Andrews ⓝⒺⓦ ★★★★ **12** cab/shiraz blend in fruity, pleasant mouthful with good concentration & texture. Cut above everyday glugging. Not retasted: **Pink Shiraz 12 ★★★★ Special LYC Sauvignon Blanc 12 ★★★★** Not tasted: **Shiraz.** — CM

Location/WO: Elgin ▪ Map: Elgin, Walker Bay & Bot River ▪ Est 1962 ▪ 1stB 2003 ▪ Tasting & sales Mon-Fri 10-4 Sat 10-5 Sun 10-4 ▪ Fee R15/5 wines, waived on purchase of 2/more bottles ▪ Closed Easter Fri-Mon, Dec 25/26 & Jan 1 ▪ Owner(s) Mark Simpson ▪ Cellarmaster(s) Ian Nieuwoudt (2012) ▪ Winemaker(s)/viticulturist(s) Ian Nieuwoudt ▪ 90ha/10ha (cab, merlot, shiraz, sauv) ▪ 70t/8,000cs own label 80% red 10% white 10% rosé ▪ PO Box 2 Elgin 7180 ▪ royalwine@arumdale.co.za ▪ www.arumdale.co.za, www.robinhoodlegendarywines.co.za ▪ S 34° 9' 14.51" E 019° 1' 48.22" ▪ F +27 (0)21-859-3430 ▪ **T +27 (0)21-859-3430**

Asara Wine Estate & Hotel ⓥ 🍴 🏠 📷 🅐

The modern name of this historic Stellenbosch property – first granted in 1691 – alludes to the African gods Astar (earth), Asis (sun) and Asase (sky). Under stewardship of estate manager Pete Gottgens since 2010, there have been major changes and improvements, notably the opening of a luxury hotel, cellar and packaging updates, and a tasting venue upgrade. More recent additions include a cookery school, vineyard walks and gardens for the hotel kitchen - all contributing to a memorable - and awarded - winelands experience.

Speciality Collection

★★★★ **Bell Tower Estate Wine 11** first since **07**. Cab-headed Bordeaux quintet offers unshowy tobacco, dark berried notes & grip of firm ripe tannins. Satisfying; but modest concentration suggests more medium- than long-term potential.

★★★★☆ **Avalon** Local take on Italian Amarone style from air/vine-dried shiraz & pinotage, 65/35 in **10** (★★★★). Less striking than **09**, sweet oak (30% new) spice dominating gentle ripe raspberry, flavours. Kick of 16.5% alcohol in tail.

★★★★ **Carillon** ② Elegant Golden botrytis-infused dessert from chenin. Improving on last-tasted **09**, **12** (★★★★☆) lovely peachy purity, juicy flesh enriched but not dimmed by 10 months in older French oak.

Sundried Sauvignon Blanc ⑩ ★★★★ Golden-hued sweet wine from dried grapes. Barrel-fermented **12** unctuous, with lavish ripe peachy flesh, very sweet tail. Also tasted: **Nouveau 14** ★★ **White Cab 14** ★★★

Vineyard Collection

Cabernet Sauvignon ★★★☆ Sound **11** offers forward varietal cassis, dark berry flavours held by firm but unintimidating frame. **Pinotage Rosé** ⑩ ★★★ Sprightly, dry **14**. Lightish but full of spicy wild berries to complement summer dishes or as aperitif. **Chenin Blanc** ⑩ ★★★ Natural ferment in oak adds earthy note to fruit salad ensemble on **13**. Richly textured, slightly grainy dry finish. Also tasted: **Merlot 11** ★★★ **Shiraz 11** ★★★ **Cape Fusion 12** ★★ **Chardonnay Lightly Wooded 13** ★★★ **Sauvignon Blanc 14** ★★★★ Not tasted: **Petit Verdot**.

Classic Collection

Merlot-Cabernet Sauvignon ★★★ Uncomplicated & ready **12**, with straightforward ripe mulberry fruit. WO W Cape. **Sauvignon Blanc-Chardonnay** ★★★ Zingy sauvignon fleshed out with creamy chardonnay, dash chenin. **14** balanced easy-drinker. WO W Cape. Also tasted: **Rosé 14** ★★★ Not retasted: **Shiraz 11** ★★★ **Sauvignon Blanc 13** ★★★ Discontinued: **Merlot**. — AL

Location/map: Stellenbosch • WO: Stellenbosch/Western Cape • Est/1stB 2001 • Tasting Mon-Sat 10-6 Sun 10-4 • Fee R30/3 wines, R50/5 wines • Sales 10-5 • Closed Dec 25 • Tasting centre • Cellar tours by appt • Tour groups • Five star hotel • Raphael's restaurant • Sansibar • Deli • Gift shop • Function & banqueting facilities • Conferences • Weddings • Vineyard walks • Cookery school • Cellarmaster(s) Francois Joubert (Sep 2009) • Winemaker(s) Francois Joubert (Sep 2009), with Sacha Claassen (Aug 2013) • Viticulturist(s) Allan Cockcroft (2013) • 180ha/102ha (cab, merlot, p verdot, chard, sauv) • 1,000t/80,000cs own label 70% red 30% white • IPW • PO Box 882 Stellenbosch 7599 • info@asara.co.za • www.asara.co.za • S 33° 56' 35.00" E 018° 48' 31.00" • F +27 (0)21-888-8001 • **T +27 (0)21-888-8000**

Ashbourne ⑫

The youngest of the trio of distinguished Hemel-en-Aarde Valley wineries owned or co-owned by Anthony Hamilton Russell, Ashbourne offers a trio of wines, all in boutique quantities, two at boutique prices. The red, Ashbourne, was initially 100% pinotage but has evolved into a Cape Blend; the original white, Sandstone, released after four years in bottle, interleaves mainly sauvignon with chardonnay and occasionally semillon. Both have a loyal following globally, a feat being emulated by the more 'democratically priced' Sauvignon Blanc-Chardonnay, which debuted with the 2012 vintage.

★★★★ **Ashbourne 09** in elegant, 'claret' style, though pinotage-led with cab, 3 other Bordeaux varieties accounting for just 14%. Perhaps less concentration than **08** (★★★★★) but oak, tannin trim in balance with fresh raspberry, cassis flavours.

★★★★☆ **Sandstone** A little bottle-age adds complexity, harmony to **09** sauvignon-chardonnay blend (88%/12%), latter naturally fermented in clay amphoras. Food-friendly individual; vinous, textured, with mineral vitality & savoury length.

For more information, visit wineonaplatter.com

Also tasted: **Ashbourne Sauvignon Blanc-Chardonnay 14** ★★★ — AL

Location: Hermanus ▪ Map: Elgin, Walker Bay & Bot River ▪ WO: Hemel-en-Aarde Valley/Walker Bay ▪ Est 1996 ▪ 1stB 2001 ▪ Tasting, sales & tours by appt ▪ Owner(s) Anthony Hamilton Russell ▪ Winemaker(s) Hannes Storm (2004) ▪ Viticulturist(s) Johan Montgomery (2005) ▪ 113ha/24.35ha (cabs s/f, malbec, p verdot, ptage, shiraz, sauv, sem) ▪ 20t/2,000cs own label 50% red 50% white ▪ PO Box 158 Hermanus 7200 ▪ hrv@hermanus.co.za ▪ S 34° 23' 09.25" E 019° 14' 29.90" ▪ F +27 (0)28-312-1797 ▪ **T +27 (0)28-312-3595**

Ashton Kelder

Ashton Kelder pitches its offering as 'something for every vinotype', from grape juice for kids to Reserve wines for sophisticates. The 53-year-old Robertson Valley producer's tasting room has been upgraded to accommodate larger groups, and for employees, ethical performance is being enhanced through WIETA certification for the winery and all 55 owner farms.

Ashton range

Chardonnay Unwooded ★★ Zesty **12** has pear, lemon drop & pineapple appeal. **Chenin Blanc** ★★ **14** light & crisp summer quaffer. **Satynwit** ★★ **14** dry white from chenin, with firm acid & tangy green apple flavour. **Sauvignon Blanc** ★★★ Steps up in **14** with soft acidity, generous fruity flavours. Not retasted: **Cabernet Sauvignon 12** ★★ **Pinotage 12** ★★ **Shiraz 12** ★★★ **Cabernet Sauvignon-Merlot 12** ★★★ **Satynrooi 11** ★★ **Satynrosé 13** ★ **Satynperlé 12** ★★ **Bonica Vin Doux NV** ★ **Red Muscadel 11** ★★

Reserve range

Not retasted: **Chardonnay Limited Release 12** ★★★ Not tasted: **Roodewal.** — DB

Location: Ashton ▪ Map: Robertson ▪ WO: Robertson/Western Cape ▪ Est 1962 ▪ 1stB 1970 ▪ Tasting & sales Mon-Fri 8-5 Sat 10-4 ▪ Closed Easter Fri/Sat & Dec 25/26 ▪ Cellar tours by appt ▪ Facilities for children ▪ Tour groups ▪ Farm produce ▪ Conferences ▪ Owner(s) 55 shareholders ▪ Cellarmaster(s) Sterik de Wet (Oct 2009) ▪ Winemaker(s) Simon Basson (Nov 2007) & Heinrich Coetzee (Sep 2013) ▪ Viticulturist(s) Hennie Visser (Vinpro) ▪ 1,200ha (cab, ruby cab, shiraz, chard, chenin) ▪ 21,079t/±38,000cs own label 50% red 42% white 6% rosé 2% other; bulk & grape juice concentrate ▪ Other export brands: Berryfields, Mountain Stream ▪ ISO 22000, BWI, HACCP, IPW ▪ PO Box 40 Ashton 6715 ▪ info@ashtonkelder.co.za ▪ www.ashtonkelder.co.za ▪ S 33° 50' 12.1" E 020° 1' 48.3" ▪ F +27 (0)23-615-1284 ▪ **T +27 (0)23-615-1135**

Ataraxia Wines

Last year marked a milestone for Kevin Grant; the 10th anniversary of Ataraxia Wines. He is really hopeful it will mark another, long-awaited milestone: the maiden Ataraxia Pinot Noir. Kevin has already bottled three vintages of chardonnay from home fruit, these sold on the Cape Winemakers Guild Auction, so why the delay with his pinot? 'Great pinots have one characteristic in common, palate texture,' he explains; 'something that comes with vine age only; until now mine have been too young.' His 'declassified' version, sold only from the farm, could at last become 'classified'. He believes, with time, the chardonnays and pinots from these higher parts of the Hemel-en-Aarde Valley will be distinguished by their finesse and tension. 'A style that's right up my alley.'

★★★★☆ **Serenity** An undisclosed blend, **11** (★★★★) not so serene or classic as in **10**. Very ripe, a few plummy notes but overall austere, densely tannic. May reach greater harmony with few years. Walker Bay grapes.

★★★★☆ **Chardonnay** Returns to tighter, steelier mode in **13**. Racy lightness contrasted by full & lengthy citrus, nutty flavours. Still an infant with a promising future. 100% home fruit.

★★★★☆ **Sauvignon Blanc 14** (★★★★) still unsettled when tasted early August. Lighter on fruit than splendid **13** with very bracing tail. Walker Bay vines. — AL

Location: Hermanus ▪ Map: Elgin, Walker Bay & Bot River ▪ WO: Western Cape/Hemel-en-Aarde Ridge ▪ Est 2004 ▪ 1stB 2005 ▪ Wine lounge: tasting & sales Mon-Fri 9-4 Sat 10-5 Sun in season only ▪ Fee R15pp for groups of 10 or more, refunded with individual purchase ▪ Closed Easter Fri/Sun, Dec 25 & Jan 1 ▪ Art exhibition ▪ Charcuterie platters available during Dec holiday season ▪ Owner(s) Kevin Grant Wines (Pty) Ltd ▪ Cellarmaster(s)/winemaker(s) Kevin Grant (Sep 2004) ▪ Viticulturist(s) Kevin Grant (Sep 2004) & Francois van Schoor (2013) ▪ 47ha/12ha (pinot, chard) ▪ 83t/12,000cs own label 40% red 60% white ▪ PO Box 603 Hermanus 7200 ▪ info@ataraxiawines.co.za ▪ www. ataraxiawines.co.za ▪ S 34° 20' 27.0" E 019° 18' 30.8" ▪ F +27 (0)28-212-1921 ▪ **T +27 (0)28-212-2007**

☐ **Auberge du Paysan** *see* L'Auberge du Paysan

Auction Crossing Private Cellar

The 1938 cellar at this tiny Hex River Valley winery was refurbished (keeping the traditional open fermenters) and saw its first modern vintage in 2004. Grapes are sourced widely by winemaker Leon Dippenaar — Paarl and Durbanville in the case of the new Syrah, the well-established Syrah-Viognier becoming a best-years-only occasional release.

Syrah ⓃⒺⓌ ★★★★ Spicy dark chocolate on **11** with peppercorns & black fruit. Coffee notes on palate sweep through to fresh, clean finish. **Viognier** ⓐ ★★★ Lightly oaked, flavourful **12** offers pleasantly fruity, spicy savouriness from Durbanville grapes. Occasional release: **Syrah-Viognier**. — CM

Location: De Doorns ▪ Map: Worcester ▪ WO: Western Cape ▪ Est 2003 ▪ 1stB 2004 ▪ Tasting & sales Mon-Fri 9-5 Sat 9-2 ▪ Closed all pub hols ▪ Cellar tours by appt ▪ Bistro 'Inspirati' ▪ Facilities for children ▪ Tour groups ▪ Gifts ▪ Farm produce ▪ Owner(s) De Villiers Graaff, AJ Reyneke & Leon Dippenaar ▪ Cellarmaster(s)/winemaker(s)/viticulturist(s) Leon Dippenaar (Aug 2004) ▪ ±41ha/2ha (mourv, shiraz, viog) ▪ 10t/4,000cs own label 75% red 25% white ▪ The Pines PO Box 5 Hex River 6855 ▪ auctioncrossing@hexvalley.co.za ▪ www.auctioncrossing.co.za ▪ S 33° 29' 42.8" E 019° 34' 32.7" ▪ F +27 (0)23-357-9255 ▪ **T +27 (0)23-357-9655**

Audacia Wines

Envelope-pushing Stellenbosch specialist red-wine boutique Audacia (its Root44 weekend market a huge success), now introduces what co-owner Trevor Strydom notes as a world first: red wine matured with rooibos and honeybush wood as an alternative to sulphites and oak. Developed with Stellenbosch University and patented, the technology drastically reduces the need for preservatives, is more sustainable and eco friendly, contains high levels of antioxidants, no caffeine and low tannin, Trevor says. The resulting debut Merlot 2013, with just 3 mg/l sulphur, is one of 450 officially recognised projects of the World Design Capital Cape Town 2014 initiative.

Merlot No Sulphites Or Preservatives Added ⓃⒺⓌ ★★★ **13** aged with rooibos & honeybush wood chips, giving expected fynbos spiciness to ripe mulberry, plum & strawberry features. **Rouge Noble** ★★★ 70% malbec in improved **NV** 3-way Bordeaux blend. Ripe & red-fruited, light & pleasant sipping. **Jeté** ★★★ Lightly oaked blend, 4 Bordeaux red grapes plus shiraz, roobernet in latest **NV**. Fruity, with a spicy twist, accessibility ensured by few grams sugar. Also tasted: **Merlot 11** ★★☆ **Shiraz 11** ★★★ Not retasted: **Cabernet Franc 10** ★★★ Not tasted: **Cabernet Sauvignon**. — GM

Location/map/WO: Stellenbosch ▪ Est 1930 ▪ Tasting & sales Mon-Fri 9–4 Sat/Sun 11-4 ▪ Fee R20, waived on purchase ▪ Closed pub hols ▪ Root 44 market (food, arts, crafts, jewellery, kiddies area & bar) ▪ Owner(s) Strydom & Harris families ▪ Cellarmaster(s)/winemaker(s)/viticulturist(s) Michael van Niekerk (Aug 2009) ▪ 32ha/20ha (cabs s/f, malbec, merlot, p verdot, roobernet, shiraz) ▪ 120t/18,000cs own label 100% red ▪ IPW ▪ PO Box 13279 Die Boord 7613 ▪ info@audacia.co.za ▪ www.audacia.co.za ▪ S 33° 59' 45.7" E 018° 50' 2.9" ▪ F +27 (0)21-881-3137 ▪ **T +27 (0)21-881-3052**

Aufwaerts Co-operative

A family cooperative, situated on a Breedekloof property in the De Villiers family since the 1800s. Planted with many grape varieties, the estate also features a brandy distillery, declared a National Monument in the 1940s. 'Anybody can visit us by appointment,' says winemaker Hennie de Villiers.

Location: Rawsonville ▪ Map: Breedekloof ▪ Tasting by appt ▪ Winemaker(s) Hennie de Villiers ▪ PO Box 51 Rawsonville 6845 ▪ hanepoot39@gmail.com ▪ S 33° 41' 42.4" E 019° 17' 33.7" ▪ F +27 (0)23-349-1202 ▪ **T +27 (0)23-349-1202**

☐ **Austin** *see* Noble Hill Wine Estate

Autumn Harvest Crackling

Among South Africa's top sellers, these spritzy lower-alcohol wines are made from widely sourced grapes by Distell.

Crisp Perlé Rosé ⊘ ★★☆ Crisp little pink **NV** party wine with a nice acid balance & the perkiness of tiny bubbles. Also in 1.5L bottles, as for Red. **Crisp Perlé White** ★★ Unpretentious **NV** quaffer with extra zing from light fizziness. Just for fun. Also in 1L & 1.5L bottles. **Crisp Perlé Red** ★ Sweet, slightly awkward **NV** rescued by prickle on the palate. Okay for a braai, maybe. — DB

Avondale

At the foot of the Klein Drakenstein mountains, Avondale is owned by the Grieve family, founders of a large health food business. After many years of conventional farming, Johnathan Grieve took up the challenge in 1999 of converting it into a robust and balanced ecosystem that would be sustainable in the long term – he applies a holistic approach combining organic and biodynamic principles with the best modern science has to offer. While Johnathan is viticulturist and general manager, Corné Marais is the long-serving winemaker operating out of an underground cellar that incorporates gravity flow.

★★★★ **Navitas** ⊗ ⊘ Well-assembled, understated **08** is shiraz-led, rest mourvèdre, grenache. Now bottled, it's medium bodied with notes of red fruit & white pepper before a long, dry finish.

★★★★ **Anima** ⊘ Naturally barrel-fermented chenin; **12** matches **10**'s fruit-filled expression, tops **11**'s (★★★☆) oxidative nuance. Ripe apricot & pineapple richness, savoury texture, 20% new oak well integrated into voluptuous & balanced conclusion.

★★★★☆ **Cyclus** ⊘ Exceptional 5-way white blend, native yeast fermented (20% new oak); **12** led by viognier & roussanne (25% each), near-equal chardonnay, chenin & semillon. Intricate, perfumed layers of spring blossom, jasmine & tangerine laced with oak; creamy, round & intense.

★★★★ **Armilla Blanc de Blancs** ⊘ Was 'MCC Brut' & **NV**. Thrilling sparkling from chardonnay. **09** (★★★★☆) greater complexity than last-tasted **NV**, with apple, bruised pear & baked brioche character from part oaking, 2 years on lees as base wine, 3 in bottle. Fresh & tangy, superbly balanced. Delicious now, will develop.

Also tasted: **Samsara** ⊘ 09 ★★★☆ **La Luna** ⊘ 09 ★★★★ **Camissa** ⊘ 13 ★★★ — HJ

Location/WO: Paarl ▪ Map: Paarl & Wellington ▪ Est 1996 ▪ 1stB 1999 ▪ Tasting & sales Mon-Sat by appt ▪ Fee R50pp ▪ Closed Easter Fri-Mon, Dec 25 & Jan 1 ▪ Cellar tours by appt only ▪ Eco tours Wed-Fri 10-4 by appt: R200pp incl MCC on arrival, tour & tasting in vyds, cellar tour ▪ Art exhibit ▪ Child friendly ▪ Owner(s) Grieve family/The Avondale Trust ▪ Winemaker(s) Corné Marais (Oct 2008), with Ivan September (Jan 2012) ▪ Viticulturist(s) Johnathan Grieve (Jul 1999) ▪ 300ha/100ha (cabs s/f, grenache, merlot, mourv, shiraz, chard, chenin, rouss, sem, viog) ▪ 500t/50,000cs own label 50% red 38% white 2% rosé 10% MCC ▪ EU Organic & USDA NOP organic ▪ PO Box 602 Paarl South 7624 ▪ wine@avondalewine. co.za ▪ www.avondalewine.co.za ▪ S 33° 45' 52.9" E 019° 0' 4.7" ▪ F +27 (0)21-863-1534 ▪ **T +27 (0)21-863-1976**

Avondrood Vineyards

The name of this Du Toitskloof family farm was inspired by its beautiful sunsets, perhaps best appreciated – glass in hand - from the veranda of the mountainside guest cottage, one of several visitor attractions and business facilities on or near the estate. Not least, of course, are boutique vintner Albertus van Rensburg's handmade wines.

Location: Rawsonville ▪ Map: Breedekloof ▪ Est/1stB 2005 ▪ Tasting, sales & cellar tours Mon-Fri 8-12 & 1.30-5 Sat by appt (phone +27 (0)82-578-6841) ▪ Closed most pub hols ▪ Refreshments/food-and-wine tastings by appt or BYO picnic ▪ Conferences ▪ Walks/hikes ▪ Facilities for children ▪ Hewn-stone mountain cottage ▪ Owner(s) Albertus van Rensburg ▪ Winemaker(s) Albertus van Rensburg, with Johannes Damane ▪ Viticulturist(s) Pierre Snyman ▪ 80ha (cab, ptage, shiraz, chard, sauv, viog) ▪ 30t/4,200cs own label 40% red 60% white ▪ PO Box 277 Worcester 6849 ▪ vineyards@avondrood.co.za ▪ www.avondrood.co.za ▪ S 33° 43' 32.9" E 019° 20' 18.7" ▪ F +27 (0)86-210-5806 ▪ **T +27 (0)23-349-1858**

Avontuur Estate

Revitalisation of the beautiful winery and racing stud in the Helderberg foothills continues under the new-generation Taberer family. The tasting venue has been upgraded and expanded, and can now accommodate group tastings; the entry-level Vintner's range has been discontinued to better focus on the premium labels; national sales and exports have been expanded; regular events staged at the farm; and educational and community development initiatives continued. The goal, co-owner Michael Taberer says, is an unintimidating people-orientated approach 'without any bling'.

Avontuur Premiere range

★★★★ Dominion Royale (Shiraz Reserve) 11 (★★★☆) not as fleet of foot as **08** or standout **09** (★★★★☆). Stewy, meaty, with savoury black fruit. **10** not made.

Sarabande (Sauvignon Blanc Reserve) ★★★ Pungently aromatic **13** bombshell with khaki bush & farmyard nuances; savoury & resinous palate from brief ageing in older oak; not for keeping, unlike previous. **Above Royalty (Liqueur Wine)** (NEW) **★★★★** Jerepiko-style **09** from shiraz & pinotage, fortified with estate's brandy. Modest sweetness (79 g/l sugar), fiery brandy spirit, primary berry fruit need time to marry & settle down. 375 ml. Also tasted: **Baccarat 09 ★★★★** Not retasted: **Minelli (Pinot Noir Reserve) 10 ★★★ Luna de Miel (Chardonnay Reserve) 10 ★★★**

Avontuur Estate range

★★★★ Brut Cap Classique (Ⓩ) Traditional-method sparkling, **NV** from chardonnay. Aromas of ripe apple, pear & spicy gingerbread; creamy mouthfeel, showing yeasty notes & a good dry finish.

Pinot Noir-Chardonnay (NEW) **★★★** Faintly blushing **14**, fairly neutral flavours & lightish (12% alcohol) food wine, portion oak aged. **Sauvignon Blanc ★★★☆ 14** herbaceous & crisp, with cut grass & nettles. Refreshingly young & vibrant, with positive edginess; outstrips Reserve sibling. Also tasted: **Cabernet Franc 10 ★★★ Pinotage 11 ★★★ Cabernet Sauvignon-Merlot 12 ★★★** Not retasted: **Cabernet Sauvignon 09 ★★★☆** Occasional release: **Above Royalty (Noble Late Harvest)**.

Brandy range

★★★★ 10 Year Private Collection (Ⓩ) 100% potstill from chenin. Sweet apricots, nuts, peardrop & cigar smoke entice on the nose. Rich, with gorgeous depth of flavour; smooth & silky.

Discontinued: **Vintner's range**. — WB, GdB, TJ

Location: Somerset West ▪ Map: Helderberg ▪ WO: Stellenbosch ▪ Est 1850 ▪ 1stB 1990 ▪ Tasting & sales Mon-Fri 8.30–5 Sat/Sun 9–4 ▪ Fee R30/5 wines ▪ Closed Good Fri, Dec 25 & Jan 1 ▪ Cellar tours by appt ▪ Tour groups (up to 20 pax) ▪ Avontuur Estate Restaurant ▪ Function venue ▪ Thoroughbred stud ▪ Owner(s) Taberer family ▪ Winemaker(s) / brandy master(s) Jan van Rooyen (Jan 2011) ▪ Viticulturist(s) Pippa Mickleburgh (Sep 1999) ▪ 110ha/47ha (cabs s/f, merlot, p verdot, ptage, pinot, shiraz, chard, sauv, viog) ▪ 405t/18,000cs own label 60% red 40% white ▪ PO Box 1128 Somerset West 7129 ▪ info@avontuurestate.co.za ▪ www.avontuurestate.co.za ▪ S 34° 1' 33.2" E 018° 49' 23.8" ▪ F +27 (0)21-855-4600 ▪ **T +27 (0)21-855-3450**

Axe Hill

Previous founder-owner of this tiny, acclaimed Calitzdorp winery, the late Tony Mossop, would have heartily endorsed the enthusiasm and commitment of current partner/cellarmaster Mike Neebe. Incumbent since 2009, with Douro experience at Ramos Pinto, he champions Klein Karoo as a region dedicated to authenticity in 'port' production and, more recently, a locus of traditional port varieties in new-look Cape red blends. Given Axe Hill's postage-stamp size, its sustainability is paramount. Hence Mike's pleased to report two new parcels coming onstream. These are set to weight the Machado blend's composition with Portuguese varieties (a minimum of 70% is what proponents like him consider true to the Calitzdorp Blend concept), and only with grapes grown locally.

★★★★ Shiraz 13 (★★★) first since **10**. Ripely rich, with notes of smoked meat mingling with the berry ones. Bold acidity a little unharmonious with the soft structure & sweet-fruited finish.

For more information, visit wineonaplatter.com

★★★★ **Cape Vintage** (symbol) Classic port-style back on top form in **11** (★★★★★). Led by touriga (65%) with dashes souzão & tinta, rich & complex, fine spice & spirity dry grip; cellar with confidence. **10** (★★★★) similar blend, more medicinal, denser. **09**, with souzão (39%) leading touriga & tinta for 1st time, featured herb-sprinkled plump fruit.

Distinta ★★★ **12** from mostly souzão & tinta giving wild element to the ultra-ripe sweet fruitiness. Softly, gently structured & somehow a little blurred in effect. **Cape Late Bottled Vintage** (NEW) ★★★ Spicy **09** has power & some charm, but little of the expected tannic grip (leaving acidity dominant) or fruit intensity - flavour falls away rather quickly. Modest sweetness. Also tasted: **Cape Ruby NV** ★★★★ **Cape White NV** ★★★★ Not retasted: **Dry Red 12** ★★ **Machado 12** ★★★★ — TJ

Location/WO: Calitzdorp ▪ Map: Klein Karoo & Garden Route ▪ Est 1993 ▪ 1stB 1997 ▪ Tasting, sales & cellar tours Mon-Sat by appt ▪ Owner(s) Axe Hill Winery (Pty) Ltd ▪ Cellarmaster(s)/winemaker(s) Mike Neebe (Oct 2007) ▪ Viticulturist(s) Johannes Mellet (Aug 2009, consultant) ▪ ±60ha/1.5ha (grenache, souzão, tinta barocca, tinta roriz, touriga nacional, viog) ▪ ±5t/±1,000cs own label 70% red 30% white ▪ Wesoewer Road Calitzdorp 6660 ▪ info@axehill.co.za ▪ www.axehill.co.za ▪ S 33° 30' 54.6" E 021° 41' 23.0" ▪ F +27 (0)11-447-3219 ▪ **T +27 (0)11-447-4366/ +27 (0)44-213-3585**

Ayama Wines

WWII ace fighter pilot 'Sailor' Malan once chased baboons from plum orchards on Voor Paardeberg's Slent farm, one of the Cape's oldest. Custodians since 2005, Italian viti/vini transplants Attilio Dalpiaz, Michela Sfiligoi and their partners still lose some fruit but respect the property's 330 year history – and its wild inhabitants, also including Cape Leopard. Ayama is Xhosa for 'someone to lean on', so it's fitting that renovations reveal the cellar rests on a pretty solid base: granite rock.

Leopard Spot range

★★★★ **Red** Was 'Shiraz-Pinotage-Mourvèdre', still the (unoaked) varieties in **13** (★★★☆) though riper, more modern than elegant & classic **10**. Flavoursome spicy dark berries, supple tannin. WO W Cape. No **11**, **12**.

White ★★★★ Was 'Chardonnay-Chenin Blanc-Viognier'. **13** is 94% chenin with dabs of the other two grapes. Enticing peachy dried fruit flavours, balanced, tangy & dry. Aperitif or with food. Note: range name was 'Leopard'.

Ayama range

Cabernet Sauvignon ★★★ Unoaked **12** loaded with blackcurrant & zested by brisk acidity. Juicy tannins & bright fruit will tastily partner tomato-based stews & pizza. **Sauvignon Blanc** ★★★★ Now bottled, **13** a notch up. Tropical fruit substance balanced by tangy acid. Feisty & flavoursome, with pleasing moderate alcohol. Also tasted: **Chardonnay 13** ★★★ Not retasted: **Merlot 12** ★★★☆ **Pinotage 12** ★★★ **Shiraz 12** ★★★★ **Chenin Blanc 12** ★★★ Discontinued: **Rosé**, **Viognier**.

Baboon Selection

Baboon's Cuddle Pinotage (NEW) ★★★ Robust **12**'s spicy mulberry flavours enveloped in oak. Still integrating needs time & hearty fare. Ends with an afterglow. **Baboon's Swing Chenin Blanc** (NEW) ★★★ Ripe Golden Delicious apple fruit & crunchy acidity, **13** has a pithy almond undertone which is unusual, appealing & food friendly. **Baboon's Cheek Viognier** (NEW) ★★★ A good foil for Asian/spicy food, **12**'s dried apricot flavours are contained in a dry, leanish, unblowsy body. Also tasted: **Baboon's Back Shiraz 12** ★★☆

Slent range

Cabernet Sauvignon-Merlot (NEW) ★★ Sappy unoaked blend, **12** unpretentious, bright fruited & brisk. Good with pasta. Paarl WO. Also tasted: **Shiraz-Pinotage 13** ★★ Not retasted: **Chenin Blanc-Sauvignon Blanc 12** ★★★

Méthode Cap Classiques

★★★★ **Rosé** ⊘ Dry pink bubbles from pinot noir & 45% chardonnay, 24 months on lees (as for Brut). **11** (★★★★) lovely savoury red berried appeal, with fine mousse & refreshing acidity but shade less balance & panache than **10**. WO W Cape, as for all this range.

★★★★ **Blanc de Blancs 10** zesty sparkler from chardonnay improves on **08** (★★★☆) with richer texture, fruit & toasted brioche profile from 3 years on lees. Poised & lingering, with modest 12% alcohol. **09** sold out untasted.

Also tasted: **Brut** ⊘ **10** ★★★☆ — MW

Location: Paarl • Map: Paarl & Wellington • WO: Voor Paardeberg/Western Cape/Paarl • Est 2005 • 1stB 2006 • Tasting by appt • Closed all pub hols • Meals/refreshments by appt; or BYO picnic • Walks/hikes • Conservation area • Owner(s) Slent Farms (Pty) Ltd (6 partners) • Cellarmaster(s)/winemaker(s) Michela Sfiligoi (2005) • Viticulturist(s) Attilio Dalpiaz (2005) • 172ha/37ha (cab, merlot, ptage, shiraz, chenin, sauv) • 300t/40,000cs own label 40% red 58% white 2% rosé • WIETA • Suite 106 Private Bag X3041 Paarl 7620 • info@slentfarms.com • www.ayama.co.za • S 33° 37' 22.5" E 018° 49' 19" • F +27 (0)21-869-8313 • **T +27 (0)21-869-8313**

☐ **Azania** see Jacques Germanier

Baarsma Wine Group

Stellenbosch-based Baarsma SA is a major exporter of South African wines, shipping wines to most of the major international wine markets. The group's Lyngrove brand is listed separately.

Stellenbosch • Closed to public • Owner(s) Baarsma Wine Group BV • MD Chris Rabie • Cellarmaster(s) Hannes Louw (since Jan 2005) • PO Box 7275 Stellenbosch 7599 • info@baarsma.co.za • www.baarsma.co.za • F +27 (0)21-880-0851 • **T +27 (0)21-880-1221**

BABISA - Born & Bred in South Africa   ⓠ

Born & Bred in South Africa is a lifestyle brand whose various luxury product segments are being rolled out strategically. The Paarl-based wine division works with partner cellars to vinify and bottle wines to spec. CEO Paul Burger says the pair of new wines listed this edition have been bottled-aged and are now ready for release. A second blended red and 'a few whites' will follow in the next year.

Lifestyle range (NEW)

★★★★ **Nicolas** Merlot-led Bordeaux blend from Paarl grapes is a leafy but bold & dense wine. **12** classically styled, with restrained fruit & serious tannin structure destined for a good future.

Cabernet Sauvignon ★★★★ Concentrated dark berries mingle with cedar & vanilla wafts from small component new wood in full-bodied **12**. Serious tannic structure needs year/2 to settle.

Born & Bred in South Africa range
Not tasted: **Valerie Reserve**. — HJ

Location: Paarl • WO: Western Cape • Est 2008 • 1stB 2007 • Tasting by appt • Tours to estates producing BABISA wines by prior arrangement • Owner(s) BABISA Brand Innovation Holdings Ltd • Cellarmaster(s)/winemaker(s)/viticulturist(s) Various • 1,000cs own label 70% red 30% white • PO Box 52185 Waterfront 8002 • wines@babisa.com • www.babisa.com • F +27 (0)86-616-2794 • **T +27 (0)71-232-8840**

☐ **Baboon Selection** see Ayama Wines

Babylon's Peak Private Cellar   ⓠ ⑪ 🖻 🏠 ◎ ⑤

The winery name, derived from the granite thumb on the eastern slope of the Perdeberg, locally known as Babylonstoren, signals that these wines are from some of the highest vineyards in the Swartland. The vines are part of a large farm, in the Basson family since 1919, previously supplying grapes to the big houses. In 2003, 4th-generation scion Stephan, with the 'Swartland revolution' happening all around, set out to make wines on his own account.

Babylon's Peak range

★★★★ SMG Refined, characterful shiraz-based blend from mature vines. Swartland warmth in spicy, clean leather tones, richness & velvet grip of **10**. Own grapes, but WO W Cape.

★★★★ Chenin Blanc ⊘ Concentrated passionfruit, fynbos & guava flavours from dryland bushvines into their 4th decade. **14**'s vibrancy tempered by lees richness; fruitily long, just dry.

Cabernet Sauvignon-Malbec (NEW) ⊘ **★★★★** Swartland's rich, red-earth tones mingle with ripe, dark-berry fruit in **13** 90/10 ensemble. Satisfying without being overly complex; gentle squeeze of tannin & mineral tang in tail add to drinkability. Also tasted: **Shiraz-Carignan** ⊘ **13 ★★★★** Not tasted: **Viognier-Roussanne**. Discontinued: **Syrah**. — AL

Location: Malmesbury ▪ Map/WO: Swartland ▪ Est/1stB 2003 ▪ Tasting, sales & cellar tours by appt ▪ Closed Easter Fri-Mon, Dec 25 & Jan 1 ▪ Pre-booked light refreshments for groups ▪ Olives ▪ BYO picnic ▪ Walking/hiking trails ▪ Conservation area ▪ Self-catering cottage ▪ Dams for fishing ▪ Owner(s) Stephan Basson ▪ Cellarmaster(s)/winemaker(s)/viticulturist(s) Stephan Basson (Jan 2003) ▪ 580ha/230ha (carignan, grenache, mourv, ptage, shiraz, chenin, rouss, viog) ▪ 20,000cs own label 65% red 35% white + 500,000L bulk ▪ PO Box 161 Malmesbury 7299 ▪ info@babylonspeak.co.za ▪ S 33° 33' 40.8" E 018° 48' 38.6" ▪ F +27 (0)86-518-3773 ▪ **T +27 (0)21-300-1052**

Babylonstoren

Babylonstoren is the Paarl showpiece estate established by Koos Bekker, CEO of multinational media group Naspers, and wife Karen Roos, former editor of Elle Decoration. It offers a boutique hotel and spa, restaurants, formal gardens, and a shop selling cheese, bread, olive oil and charcuterie as well as designer homewear. Not forgetting a winery where Charl Coetzee, who joined after stints at Kaapzicht and Clos Malverne, is in charge. It's a complete and certainly upmarket winelands destination.

★★★★ Shiraz Rather heavy-handed charry oak (100% new) spoils underlying floral & red fruit on **12** (**★★★★**). Otherwise nicely balanced for nearly 15% alcohol. Greater harmony possible with year/two. **11**'s wooding more attractive.

★★★★ Chardonnay 12 continues local trend of freshness & well-managed oak (100% new). Complexity from seamless citrus, oatmeal & lees, lifted by a mineral core; plenty more to give. Lighter feel than 14% alcohol suggests.

★★★★ Chenin Blanc All home-grown fruit in persuasive unwooded **14**. Great purity in its layered winter melon & peach fragrance, rich yet zesty & long lasting; fruitily dry.

Babel ★★★★ 13 showing promise behind its youthful veneer. Five Bordeaux varieties, cab-led, with shiraz, in fresher, crunchy style. Tannins & oak carefully judged to allow for improvement over few years. Also tasted: **Mourvèdre Rosé 14 ★★★ Viognier 13 ★★★★** — AL

Location: Paarl ▪ Map: Franschhoek ▪ WO: Simonsberg-Paarl/Western Cape ▪ Est 1692 ▪ 1stB 2011 ▪ Tasting & sales daily 9-5 ▪ Tour groups by appt ▪ Farm shop ▪ Guided garden tours at 10 daily ▪ Hosted wine tasting, cellar tours daily 12-1 ▪ Babylonstoren Farm Hotel ▪ Bakery ▪ Babel Restaurant Wed-Sun 12-4; Garden Greenhouse for teas & light meals Mon-Sun 10-4 ▪ Garden Day Spa ▪ Winemaker(s) Charl Coetzee (Nov 2010), with Klaas Stoffberg (Sep 2013) ▪ Viticulturist(s) Hannes Aucamp (Jan 2010) ▪ 400ha/62ha (cabs s/f, malbec, merlot, mourv, p verdot, pinot, shiraz, chard, chenin, sem, viog) ▪ PO Box 167 Simondium 7670 ▪ cellar@babylonstoren.com ▪ www.babylonstoren.com ▪ S 33° 49' 26.73" E 018° 55' 39.08" ▪ F +27 (0)21-863-1727 ▪ **T +27 (0)21-863-1804**

Baccarat Wines (NEW)

When hoteliers Nic and Ferda Barrow couldn't find blended wines both stylish and easy-drinking for their Oudtshoorn and Cape Town boutique hotels, they got together with family, friends and Paul Gerber, winemaker at Le Lude, their new cap classique bubbly cellar in Franschhoek, to create their own. Paul uses shared cellar space in Stellenboschkloof to vinify these wines.

Cabernet Sauvignon ★★★ Blackcurrants, mulberries, savoury overlay from light oaking, **12** is approachable, unceremonious - uncork now with friends. **Chardonnay-Pinot Noir ★★☆** Delicate pink hue & lots of berries, pinot makes presence felt; **13** technically dry but few grams sugar &

modest alcohol add to affability. WO W Cape. **Chenin Blanc ★★★** Tropical tones, fruit gums, fresh & clean palate; **13** for easy enjoyment. — CR, CvZ

Location: Stellenbosch ▪ WO: Stellenbosch/Western Cape ▪ Est/1stB 2013 ▪ Closed to public ▪ Owner(s) Nic Barrow, Ferda Barrow & Paul Gerber ▪ Winemaker(s) Paul Gerber (2013) ▪ Viticulturist(s) Eben Archer ▪ 30% red 30% white 40% rosé ▪ chantal@barrowtrust.co.za ▪ www.baccaratwines.co.za ▪ F +27 (0)44-279-1793 ▪ **T +27 (0)44-279-1791**

☐ **Back Roads** *see* Black Elephant Vintners

Backsberg Estate Cellars

The back story to this family run Paarl wine farm began with the arrival in Cape Town of CL Back as a penniless immigrant in the early 1900s. Hard work and focus saw his son, the late Sydney Back, ultimately become the doyen of SA winemaking, leading the local renaissance over 60 vintages. His son Michael has handed the reins to the fourth generation, Simon and Jenny, while he concentrates on matters environmental. Backsberg still leads the way, laying claim to being one of only three carbon-neutral wineries worldwide. The Back family feel a burden of care and responsibility, to both the natural environment and people, visitors to the farm and staff alike. See also Tread Lightly by Backsberg.

Flagship - Backsberg Family Reserve range

★★★★ Red Blend ⓥ Cab leads the merlot/shiraz blend in **08**. Rich & spicy, with black fruit. Nutty appeal from prominent oak. Big, firm & ripe with long fruity finish. No **06** or **07**.

★★★★ White Blend ⓥ Chardonnay/roussanne-driven **09**'s waxy overlay complements boldly flavoured yet balanced profile, refreshing acid zing. Drop viognier gives floral lift.

Black Label range

★★★★ Pumphouse Shiraz 11 offers exotic violets (ex drop durif?), nuts & plush ripe black fruit. Supple, yet concentrated. Firm backbone from French & American oak (30% new). Improves on **09** (★★★★). No **10**.

★★★★ Klein Babylons Toren Welcome return of cab & merlot blend, dab petit verdot, last made in **07**. **12**'s genteel silky mouthfeel charms effortlessly. Deep & inviting, with cherry tobacco appeal. Smart oak, 25% new.

★★★★ Elbar ⓥ Malbec & mourvèdre 70% of **07**'s 7-way blend, tasted from barrel previously. Hedgerow fruit, sprinkle of dried herbs, supple oak add savoury flavours, long silky flourish.

★★★★ Hillside Viognier Honeysuckle & peach beauty from Paarl & Elgin fruit on **13**. Part barrel ferment means oak is beautifully supportive. Textured & rich; dry & long with lovely leesy farewell. No **10-12**.

John Martin Sauvignon Blanc ★★★★ Peppery grapefruit on **13**, barrel fermented in 50% new oak. Defined, focused & still vibrant - no rush to drink up. Inc 5% semillon. Coastal WO. Also tasted: **Brut Méthode Cap Classique 10 ★★★★** Not retasted: **Beyond Borders Pinot Noir 10 ★★★★**

Premium range

★★★★ Cabernet Sauvignon ⓥ More serious tone to **11** raises bar on lighter **10** (★★★★). Elegant, refined & harmonious. French oak (20% new) frames optimally ripe black berry fruit.

Shiraz ⓝⓔⓦ **★★★ 13** has dabs (5%) mourvèdre & sangiovese. Smoky, spicy blue fruit appeal with solid grip & fresh appeal. **Dry Red** ⓥ **★★★** Tangy spicy highlights to delightful **NV** (**14**) stalwart blend of cab & merlot with splashes carignan, shiraz, grenache & sangiovese. Generous & vibrantly friendly. 'Comes in 1.5L too!' **Chardonnay ★★★★ 13** a notch more serious & refined. Textured creamy citrus entry with broad mid-palate & long, focused leesy finish. Touch of roussanne (10%). **Chenin Blanc ★★★** Zippy granadilla & melon vibrancy to **14**. Leaner, fresher style. Sound & pleasantly uncomplicated. Also tasted: **Merlot 13 ★★★★ Pinotage 13 ★★★ Rosé NV ★★★ Sauvignon Blanc 14 ★★★ Special Late Harvest 13 ★★★★**

For more information, visit wineonaplatter.com

Kosher range

Merlot ★★★ Improved **14**, appealing mulberry, spice & cocoa oak sheen. Light herb nuance adds dimension. **Pinotage ★★★ 14** raises the bar. Exuberant bright red & blue fruit, with some inky depth & length. Also tasted: **Chardonnay 14 ★★☆ Brut Méthode Cap Classique 10 ★★☆ Kiddush Sacramental Wine 12 ★★**

Fortified range

Pinneau **★★★★** Pineau des Charentes-style fortified & oak-matured chenin **10**, with appealing roasted hazelnut spice. Not retasted: **Cape Ruby NV ★★★☆**

Brandy range

★★★★ Sydney Back 1st Distillation Dark amber on this 20 year old, with rich prune, caramel & clove on the nose. Richly textured, round & well matured, with marmalade, dark chocolate flavours. Loads of oaky vanilla & mature character, but a touch less fresh than the younger brandies. 100% potstill from chenin, as all.

★★★★ Sydney Back Special Release Complex nose of dried fruit & toasty nuts, hint of anise. Dried fruits fill the mouth with apricot, peach & touch of sweet vanilla. Floral notes all the way & hint of orange peel.

Sydney Back Finest Matured **★★★★** Inviting honey, dried apricot & marzipan aromas on the nose. Charming & light footed, with vanilla, toasty nuts, sweet tobacco & caramel. 5-8 years oak maturation. — WB, FM, TJ

Location: Paarl ▪ Map: Franschhoek ▪ WO: Paarl/Western Cape/Elgin/Coastal/Elgin/Paarl ▪ Est 1916 ▪ 1stB 1970 ▪ Tasting & sales Mon–Fri 9–5 Sat/Sun 10–4 ▪ Fee R15 ▪ Open 365 days a year ▪ Cellar tours by appt ▪ Self-guided TV monitor tour of the cellar, brandy cellar, winery & historic corridors ▪ Backsberg Restaurant ▪ Facilities for children ▪ Tour groups ▪ Conferences ▪ Weddings & functions ▪ BYO picnic ▪ Hiking ▪ Mountain biking ▪ Bird watching ▪ Environmental talks ▪ Conservation area ▪ Sunday picnic concerts (summer) ▪ Glass blowing workshops ▪ Owner(s) Michael Back & Simon Back ▪ Winemaker(s) Alicia Rechner (Jun 2012) ▪ Viticulturist(s) Clive Trent (Jul 1992) ▪ 130ha (cab, merlot, shiraz, chard) ▪ 900t/160,000cs own label 65% red 30% white 5% rosé ▪ PO Box 537 Suider-Paarl 7624 ▪ info@backsberg.co.za ▪ www.backsberg.co.za ▪ S 33° 49' 42.9" E 018° 54' 56.9" ▪ F +27 (0)21-875-5144 ▪ **T +27 (0)21-875-5141**

☐ **Badenhorst Family Wines** *see* AA Badenhorst Family Wines

Badgerberg Estate

'Carry on with good farming practices, respect nature and uplift staff as far as possible,' reply Heinz and Lynnette Mederer to our stock question: what happened at your winery since last edition? An intended retirement project, German-toned Badgerberg has morphed into a boutique wine label, aided by technical input from nearby Villiersdorp Cellar and bubbly specialist Matthew Krone. Mostly exported, soupçons are retained for their cellardoor and annual Oktober and Maibaum fests.

Prima ★★★☆ Blend change to merlot (70%) & shiraz sees **13** ramp up a gear. Light thyme edge to bold black fruit. Fresh & spicy, with good length. WO W Cape. **Sauvignon Blanc ★★★ 13**, from own grapes, a step up. Crisp definition & focused flinty varietal expression. Not retasted: **Aquarius Cuvée Brut 10 ★★★☆** — FM

Location/map: Villiersdorp ▪ WO: Overberg/Western Cape ▪ Est 2000 ▪ 1stB 2009 ▪ Tasting & sales by appt ▪ German Octoberfest & Maibaumfest annually ▪ Owner(s) Heinz & Lynnette Mederer ▪ Winemaker(s) J M Crafford & Matthew Krone (MCC consultant) ▪ 35ha/9ha (cab, merlot, shiraz, sauv) ▪ 100t/1,268cs own label 53% red 47% white ▪ PO Box 2605 Somerset West 7129 ▪ info@badgerberg.co.za, lynnettem@badgerberg.co.za ▪ www.badgerberg.co.za ▪ S 33° 57' 07.5" E 19° 19' 29.5" ▪ F +27 (0)86-586-2237 ▪ **T +27 (0)21-852-1150/+27 (0)83-263-2783**

Badsberg Wine Cellar

This large-scale Breedekloof producer and exporter is focused on processing 'quality grapes effectively to make world-class products for the benefit of all our partners'. Its scenic location in a nature conservancy is

consistent with the choice of front-label emblem: the protected March Flower, whose flowering coincides with the ripening of hanepoot, crucial component of the stellar Badslese Natural Sweet.

★★★★ **Chardonnay Sur Lie** ⓥ **12** punches above its price bracket with complex lemon, fennel & floral bouquet, tangy acidity, engaging lime tail. Less buttery than **11** (★★★★), more satisfying.

★★★★★ **Badslese** ⓥ Unwooded Natural Sweet dessert from chenin & muscat d'Alexandrie; only in best years (no **10**, **11**). With muscat portion upped to 30%, **12** (★★★★★) is pure indulgence: melting quince, melon & grape flavours, as scintillating & precise as **09**, our 2012 White Wine of the Year.

★★★★ **Noble Late Harvest** ⓥ Soft & sweet after-dinner treat in 375ml from (unwooded) chenin; **07** lots of good things - honey, apricot, marmalade - to smell & taste; clean & uplifting.

★★★★ **Red Muscadel** ⓥ Consistent fortified sweetie for year-round enjoyment: fireside in winter; on the rocks in summer. Tealeaf-nuanced **13** delivers signature raisin-sweet but balanced slipperiness.

★★★★ **Red Jerepigo** Classy fortified pinotage for the sweet-toothed. **12** producer's signature molasses & caramel overtones, cherry liqueur fruit flavours.

Pinotage-Mocha Fusion ★★★☆ Hedonistic choc & coffee, strawberry cream on smooth & pliable **12**; unwooded & vibrant, good expression of the 'java' style. **Chenin Blanc** ⓥ ★★★ Easy-drinking **14** fresh & appealing summer tipple with sunripe guava & melon flavours, thatchy complexity. **Hanepoot Jerepigo** ★★★★ Spirity uplift from grapey-sweet (but not cloying) **13** fortified dessert with pleasant grapefruit pith taste & texture on finish. Also tasted: **Merlot 12** ★★★ **Perlé Muscato 14** ★★ **Sauvignon Blanc 14** ★★★ **Vin Doux 13** ★★★ **Special Late Harvest 13** ★★★ Not retasted: **Belladonna 11** ★★★★ **Cape Vintage 09** ★★★ Not tasted: **Rosé**, **Noble Late Harvest Limited Edition**. — CvZ

Location: Rawsonville ▪ Map/WO: Breedekloof ▪ Est 1951 ▪ 1stB 1958 ▪ Tasting & sales Mon-Fri 9–5 Sat 10–1 ▪ Fee R20pp for groups of 10+ ▪ Closed all pub hols ▪ Cellar tours Mon-Fri 2-3 (Feb-Mar only) ▪ BYO picnic ▪ Facilities for children ▪ Farm produce ▪ Conferences (40 pax) ▪ Conservation area ▪ Soetes & Soup (Jul) ▪ Owner(s) 26 members ▪ Cellarmaster(s) Willie Burger (1998) ▪ Winemaker(s) Henri Swiegers (2002) & Nicholas Husselman (2011), with Jaco Booysen (Jan 2007) ▪ Viticulturist(s) Nicholas Husselman (2011) ▪ ±1,500ha/±1,300ha (ptage, shiraz, chenin, cbard) ▪ ±23,000t own label 20% red 65% white 10% rosé 5% fortified ▪ ISO 22000:2009 ▪ PO Box 72 Rawsonville 6845 ▪ enquiries@badsberg.co.za ▪ www.badsberg.co.za ▪ S 33° 39' 40.1" E 019° 16' 9.2" ▪ F +27 (0)86-574-6091 ▪ **T +27 (0)23-344-3021**

☐ **Bain's Way** see Wellington Wines
☐ **Bakenskop** see Vinopoly Wines
☐ **Balance** see Overhex Wines International

Baleia Bay

ⓥ ◎

The tiny vineyard on Dassieklip farm near holiday hamlet Vermaaklikheid on the Cape south coast is part of a larger Joubert-family-owned enterprise involving olive groves, Brangus cattle, and Dohne Merino sheep. Encouraged in recent years by limestone-rich soils and cooling ocean breezes to plant a mix of wine varieties, their continuing investment includes a dedicated winemaker/viticulturist and a cellar at Riversdale on the N2 highway, open to visitors. The brand name - 'whale' in Portuguese — invokes nearby St Sebastian Bay, a Southern Right nursery.

★★★★ **Chardonnay** ⓥ Spirited wooding (100% new, 6 months) covers **13**'s kumquat & stonefruit with a duvet of oak, giving a rich breakfast-in-bed effect, complete with honey & toast. Similar to **12** (★★★) but better balanced.

Pinot Noir 🍇 ★★★☆ True expression of variety, with red fruit, spice & meat nuances. **12** lovely layers, bright acidity & long, smooth finish from judicious year in oak. **Shiraz** (NEW) ★★☆ Only 10% new oak for **12**, beguiling smooth, cinnamon-spiced stewed red fruit character. Versatile: for steak dinners or dark choc desserts, say team. **Rosé** (NEW) ⓥ ★★★ Shiraz & tempranillo give pomegranate & strawberry flavours to **14**, few grams sugar balanced by rounded acidity, spicy twist. **Unwooded**

For more information, visit wineonaplatter.com

Chardonnay ⓃⒺⓌ ⊘ ★★★★ Canteloupe & citrus blossom-scented **14** as precise & elegant as its sibling is voluptuous. Also tasted: **Sauvignon Blanc 14** ★★★ — GM

Location: Riversdale ▪ Map: Klein Karoo & Garden Route ▪ WO: Cape South Coast ▪ Est 2009 ▪ 1stB 2011 ▪ Tasting & sales Mon-Fri 9-5 Sat 9-4 ▪ Cellar tours by appt ▪ Olives & oil ▪ Owner(s) Joubert family ▪ Winemaker(s)/viticulturist(s) Jacques Geldenhuys ▪ 1,000ha/9.5ha (pinot, shiraz, tempranillo, chard, sauv) ▪ 80t/600cs own label 60% red 40% white ▪ PO Box 268 Riversdale 6670 ▪ info@baleiabay.co.za ▪ www.baleiabay.co.za ▪ S 34° 6' 36.89" E 021° 15' 18.48" ▪ F +27 (0)86-560-0367 ▪ **T +27 (0)28-713-1367/+27 (0)72-133-2710**

☐ **Balthazar** *see* Roodezandt Wines
☐ **Bandana** *see* Klein Roosboom

Baratok Wines Ⓟ Ⓜ Ⓞ

Baratok owner Alex Boraine exports most of the wines, notably to China, though he recently appointed a local agent. The winery name, 'Friends', is from Hungary, source of most of the oak barrels used for maturation.

Location: Paarl ▪ Map: Paarl & Wellington ▪ Est 2012 ▪ Tasting by appt ▪ Delivery anywhere in South Africa ▪ Closed all pub hols ▪ Restaurant ▪ Tour groups ▪ Farm produce ▪ Conferences ▪ Owner(s)/winemaker(s) Alex Boraine ▪ (cab, cinsaut, grenache, merlot, ptage, shiraz, chard, chenin, sauv, viog) ▪ 27t/200,000L own label 60% red 40% white; 90,000L for clients + 480,000L bulk ▪ Brands for clients: Terre de Papillon, Diamant & Son, Kipepeo, Belle Vallee ▪ PO Box 668 Wellington 7654 ▪ alex@smlwines.com ▪ S 33° 44' 34.93" E 018° 57' 44.98" ▪ **T +27 (0)84-582-6376**

☐ **Barber's Wood** *see* Celestina

Barista Ⓟ

Fifteen years on from the development of what has become a popular – and now hugely commercially valid – style of coffee-toned pinotage, Barista has added a white stablemate from chardonnay. Brand owners Vinimark have been quick to nip rumours in the bud that it has tea overtones…

Pinotage ★★★★ **13** shows more than just the expected coffee bean character: juicy blueberry & cocoa freshness, too, & a smooth glide to smoky mocha tail. **Chardonnay** ⓃⒺⓌ ★★★ Lightly fruited **13**, lemon freshness, citrus appeal, creamy mouthfeel from part barrel ferment. Fun & easy. — WB

Location: Robertson ▪ WO: Western Cape ▪ Est/1stB 2009 ▪ Tasting at Val de Vie ▪ Owner(s) Vinimark ▪ Winemaker(s) Bertus Fourie ▪ 600t/60,000cs own label ▪ PO Box 6223 Paarl 7620 ▪ info@vinimark.co.za ▪ www.baristawine.co.za ▪ F +27 (0)21-886-4708 ▪ **T +27 (0)21-883-8043**

Barnardt Boyes Wines

Stellenbosch negociant business Barnardt Boyes Wines is part of a diverse group of companies, including luxury goods manufacturer Carrol Boyes Functional Art and citrus exporter FruitOne. More specifically, it is a collaboration between FruitOne MD John Boyes (Carrol's brother) and wine industry veteran Neels Barnardt, an old university friend. See also Carrol Boyes Collection.

Premium Blend ★★★ Mainly merlot, with cab, dash shiraz, cab franc, gives retasted **09** a dark berry, slight leafy tone, supported by lively fruit-focused drinkability. **Sauvignon Blanc** ⓃⒺⓌ ★★★ Winter melon nose & flavours, ending fruity-fresh. **12** good palate weight, satisfying, if not complex. Also tasted: **Shiraz-Cabernet Sauvignon 10** ★★ Not retasted: **Pinotage 11** ★★★ — CR

Location: Stellenbosch ▪ WO: Western Cape ▪ Est 2012 ▪ 1stB 2009 ▪ Closed to public ▪ Owner(s) N Barnardt & J Boyes ▪ Winemaker(s) Hendrik Snyman (Jun 2013) ▪ 40,000cs own label 100% red ▪ Other export brands: Le Noe, Carrol Boyes Collection ▪ wim@barnardtboyes.com, neels@barnardtboyes.com ▪ www.barnardtboyes.com ▪ F +27 (0)21-883-3491 ▪ **T +27 (0)21-883-3447**

☐ **Barney Barnato** *see* Douglas Wine Cellar
☐ **Barn Find** *see* Franki's Vineyards
☐ **Barony** *see* Rosendal Winery

Barrydale Winery & Distillery

Jointly owned by Southern Cape Vineyards and Oude Molen Distillery, Barrydale Winery & Distillery is home to internationally awarded Joseph Barry brandies, named after an English tradesman who fostered 19th-century wine and brandy making in Klein Karoo. Just three wines, selected annually on grape quality, are now bottled by winemaker Ferdi Smit, who also nurtures the brandies.

Southern Cape Vineyards range
Barrydale Shiraz (NEW) ★★★ **13** is soft & spicy, with delightful hints of black pepper. Easy, fun, sweet fruited. **Ladismith Chardonnay** (NEW) ★★★ Soft citrus & apple fruit, touch of oak on **14**, rounded from ageing on lees. **Ladismith Chenin Blanc** (NEW) ★★★ Unoaked, bright & cheerful party wine, creamy apple pie flavours, serve **14** well chilled. Not retasted: **Ladismith Ruby Cabernet 11** ★★ **Barrydale Brut Rosé NV** ★★★☆

Brandy range
Joseph Barry Traditional ⓧ ★★★★ 5-year-aged potstill, darker & more auburn of these. Hints of apple, pear, some citrus backed by toasty nut, vanilla & butterscotch. Balanced & smooth, with hint of oak on long finish. **Joseph Barry 10 Year Old** ⓧ ★★★★ Dried fruit, floral wafts with cinnamon on well-matured, rich frame. More forceful, less fruity than Traditional bottling. Dry, lingering finish. — WB, TJ

Location: Barrydale ▪ Map: Klein Karoo & Garden Route ▪ WO: Klein Karoo/Stellenbosch ▪ Est 1941 ▪ 1stB 1976 ▪ Tasting & sales Mon-Fri 9–5 Sat 9–1 ▪ Fee R25 for groups of 5+ ▪ Closed Easter Fri-Mon, Dec 25/26 & Jan 1 ▪ Book ahead for cellar tours ▪ BYO picnic ▪ Conservation area ▪ Owner(s) Southern Cape Vineyards (SCV) & Oude Molen Distillery ▪ Winemaker(s) / distiller Ferdi Smith ▪ ±102ha (cab, merlot, shiraz, chard, cbard, sauv) ▪ 56% red 44% white ▪ PO Box 59 Barrydale 6750 ▪ humanj@scv.co.za ▪ www.barrydalewines.co.za ▪ S 33° 54' 35.83" E 020° 42' 45.20" ▪ F +27 (0)28-572-1541 ▪ **T +27 (0)28-572-1012**

Barry Gould Family Wines

When Barry Gould's day job as an architect got in the way of his winemaking hobby, he took stock of the surplus in his cellar and was left reassured he wasn't about to run out any time soon. 'I will resume this harvest,' he says of the 'hands-on, hands-in, hand-made' wines he crafts in Elgin.

Location: Elgin ▪ Map: Elgin, Walker Bay & Bot River ▪ Est 2003 ▪ 1stB 2004 ▪ Tasting, sales & cellar tours by appt ▪ Closed Good Fri, Dec 25 & Jan 1 ▪ Meals/functions by arrangement (up to 20 pax) ▪ Wildekrans Country House (B&B) + self-catering cottage ▪ Child-friendly ▪ Gifts ▪ Farm produce ▪ Conference venue (20 pax) ▪ 4-day fully guided slackpacking trail ▪ Owner(s) Barry Gould & Alison Green ▪ Cellarmaster(s) Barry Gould (2003) ▪ Winemaker(s) Barry Gould (2003), with family (2004) ▪ Viticulturist(s) Grapes bought in from various sources ▪ ±2t/320cs own label 70% red 30% white ▪ PO Box 7 Elgin 7180 ▪ gould.arc@wildekrans.co.za ▪ S 34° 12' 12.7" E 019° 8' 53.6" ▪ F +27 (0)21-848-9788 ▪ **T +27 (0)21-848-9788/+27 (0)82-901-4896**

Bartinney Private Cellar

Perched high on the slopes of the Helshoogte Pass lies Bartinney Private Cellar, a boutique wine estate owned by Michael and Rose Jordaan who are increasing their biodiversity credentials with new plantings interspersed with native fynbos. The steep, unterraced slopes mean that everything must be done by hand, giving winemaker Ronell Wiid access to parcels of terroir-specific fruit which she shepherds into the bottle with as little intervention as possible.

★★★★ **Cabernet Sauvignon** Elegant & understated **11** (★★★★★) improves on **10** with refined black fruit tempered by savoury Marmite hints, olive tapenade, vanilla & spice. Delightfully gritty texture & clean lengthy finish. 12-18 months French oak, 50% new.

★★★★☆ **Elevage** Poised & polished **10** oozes class & distinction. Cab-led Bordeaux blend from Stellenbosch fruit shows minty notes on nose giving way to plushy black fruit with herbal hints & nicely balanced grippy tannins. Shades of dark chocolate on lengthy finish.

For more information, visit wineonaplatter.com

★★★★☆ **Chardonnay** Classically styled **13** continues form of **12** showing oatmeal, cream & yellow citrus on nose before palate glides delicately into play with pineapples & tropical fruit, balancing oak/acidity & lengthy finish.

★★★★☆ **Sauvignon Blanc** Peaches & cream **14** (★★★★) preview moves on to flinty minerality with green figs & quinces below. Good depth & length but lacks concentrated appeal of **13**. — CM

Location/map: Stellenbosch ▪ WO: Banghoek/Stellenbosch ▪ Est 2006 ▪ 1stB 2008 ▪ Tasting & sales Mon-Fri 10-4 ▪ Closed all pub hols ▪ Cellar tours by appt ▪ Bartinney Wine Bar Mon-Sat 11.30-9 (cnr Church & Bird Str, Stellenbosch) ▪ Owner(s) Rose & Michael Jordaan ▪ Winemaker(s) Ronell Wiid (consultant) ▪ Viticulturist(s) Ryno Maree (Oct 2010) ▪ 27ha/±17ha (cab, chard, sauv) ▪ 118t/4,000cs own label 70% red 30% white ▪ BWI champion ▪ Postnet Suite 231 Private Bag X5061 Stellenbosch 7599 ▪ info@bartinney.co.za ▪ www.bartinney.co.za ▪ S 33°55' 34.66" E 018°55' 56.79" ▪ F +27 (0)21-885-2852 ▪ **T +27 (0)21-885-1013**

Barton Vineyards

Barton is a 200-ha working farm in the hills overlooking the Bot River Valley, rich in biodiversity and offering a range of activities, farm produce and luxury accommodation. Though the own portfolio of stylish wines is still boutique in scale, critical acclaim is resulting in French-trained winemaker PJ Geyer having to expand the cellar facilities to vinify other producers' wines on contract.

★★★★ **Merlot** ⊘ Classy return to form in **12** (★★★★☆), showcasing variety's intensity & elegance. Bordeaux-style complexity with a tight core of fruit & minerality, suavely tailored in fine tannic frame. So harmonious, already tempting, but ageworthy. Rung above **10**. **11** sold out untasted.

★★★★☆ **Winemakers Reserve** Maiden **11** merlot-led Bordeaux blend, now bottled, shows more elegance & balance than barrel sample. Understated, refined core of inky red fruit & violets with cedary nuance. So tailored & sleek, belies its youthful intensity, will age with distinction.

★★★★ **Shiraz-Cabernet Sauvignon** Youthful, harmonious **11** blend has a sappy texture, infused with garrigue scrub, pepper & a touch of cab's clean herbaceousness. Supple structure enhanced by oak.

★★★★ **Sauvignon Blanc-Semillon** **13**'s unwooded 61/39 blend raises the bar on **12** (★★★★☆). Balanced, with refined fruit focus & minerality. An ageworthy, graceful table mate.

Rouge 🆕 ⊘ ★★★★ 4-way blend **12**, shiraz dominates though equal part cab adds pliable structure, & merlot & malbec plump out fruit-filled interest. Flavoursome, firm fleshed & toned yet retains affable drinkability. Balanced & classy quaffer. Also tasted: **Shiraz Rosé 13** ★★★ **Chenin Blanc 13** ★★★☆ **Sauvignon Blanc 13** ★★★★ **Blanc** ⊘ **13** ★★★★ — MW

Location: Bot River ▪ Map: Elgin, Walker Bay & Bot River ▪ WO: Walker Bay ▪ Est 2001 ▪ 1stB 2003 ▪ Tasting, sales & cellar tours Mon-Fri 9–5 Sat 10–4 ▪ Closed Easter Sun, Dec 25 & Jan 1 ▪ Lavender products, olive oil, marinated olives & proteas ▪ Barton Villas ▪ Owner(s) Peter J Neill ▪ Cellarmaster(s)/winemaker(s)/viticulturist(s) PJ Geyer (Oct 2010) ▪ 200ha/30ha (cab, malbec, merlot, mourv, pinot, shiraz, chenin, sauv, sem) ▪ 120t/20,000cs own label 40% red 50% white 10% rosé ▪ IPW ▪ PO Box 100 Bot River 7185 ▪ info@bartonvineyards.co.za ▪ www.bartonvineyards.co.za ▪ S 34°15' 43.8" E 019°10' 29.2" ▪ F +27 (0)28-284-9776 ▪ **T +27 (0)28-284-9283**

☐ **Basco** see Blomendahl Vineyards

Bayede!

Named for the traditional greeting reserved for the Zulu King, HM Goodwill Zwelethini, Bayede! aims to develop a portfolio of luxury products focused on sustainable job creation and promotion of agriculture, textiles, manufacturing, arts, crafts and tourism in South Africa. The bead-adorned wines, integral to what's said to be Africa's first 'royal by appointment' brand, are sourced from seven estates and sold to top-end hotels, boutiques and retail outlets locally and in Europe, Asia and the Americas.

7 Icon Wines

★★★★ **Cabernet Sauvignon** Stately **09** full bodied & elegant, with blackberry, cedar & mint complexity. Like generous **08**, sufficient structure & concentration to improve ±5 years.

For more information, visit wineonaplatter.com

★★★★ **Merlot** Choc/plum-toned **12** step up on **11** (★★★☆). No shrinking violet: mouthfilling & lipsmacking, smooth & polished, with fruit-sweet core, fine oak spicing. WO Groenekloof.

★★★★ **Pinotage Reserve** ⓥ Hinting at blackcurrant & lavender, **10** last edition deserved more time to fully integrate. Stellenbosch WO, like Cab, Shiraz & Chenin.

★★★★ **Chardonnay** Muted & light-footed **13** (★★★☆) from Robertson has similar lemon-cream tones as rounded & full-bodied **12**.

★★★★☆ **Chenin Blanc** Ambitious **13** hedonistic glassful of peaches & limes, vanilla & butter. Emphatically dry & precise, as persistent as savoury **12**.

Also tasted: **Shiraz 11** ★★★ **Sauvignon Blanc 13** ★★★☆

King & Queen range

King Shaka Jubilee ★★★ Bordeaux-style red, mainly cab & merlot. **12** very grippy, leafy (ex 15% cab franc) with decent length & concentration to improve few years. WO Franschhoek. **Queen Thomo Chenin Blanc** ⓃⒺⓦ ★★ Attractive nut & papaya nose let down by overtly leesy palate in **13**. Also tasted: **King Goodwill Shiraz 12** ★★★ Not tasted: **Queen Thomo Sauvignon Blanc, Queen Mantfombi Dry MCC Sparkling Rosé**.

Prince range

Not tasted: **Red, White**.

Shield range

The Prince Cabernet Sauvignon ★★★ Exuberant plummy fruit, coffee notes on **13** early-drinking steakhouse mate. **The Prince Pinotage** ★★ Unforced & honest, fruity **13** has zesty acidity to cut fatty lamb chops. Also tasted: **The Prince Merlot 13** ★★ **The Prince Cabernet Sauvignon-Shiraz-Merlot** Not tasted: **The Prince Chenin Blanc, The Prince Sauvignon Blanc**. — CvZ

Location: Paarl ▪ Map: Paarl & Wellington ▪ WO: Western Cape/Stellenbosch/Groenekloof/Robertson/Franschhoek ▪ Est 2009 ▪ Tasting & sales in showroom/office at 5 Stasie Street, Southern Paarl Mon-Fri or by appt ▪ Fee R30 ▪ Private VIP tastings at Villa Beanto Winelands Estate by appt only ▪ Closed all pub hols ▪ Tour groups by appt ▪ 60% red 30% white 10% rosé ▪ PO Box 7362 Northern Paarl 7623 ▪ anto@bayede.co.za ▪ www.bayede.co.za ▪ S 33° 45′ 54.77″ E 018° 57′ 41.03″ ▪ F +27 (0)21-863-4884 ▪ **T +27 (0)21-863-3406/+27 (0)83-650-3585**

☐ **Bayten** see Buitenverwachting
☐ **BC Wines** see Brandvlei Cellar

Beau Belle

'Start at square one' is the advice given to ex Gauteng property developer Tienie Lindeque and wife Estelle by a brain trust which includes star winemaker Teddy Hall, viticulture guru Eben Archer and designer Rob Taylor, in response to the Stellenbosch-based Lindeques' declared goal of becoming SA's premium shiraz producers. Hence the culling of the entire portfolio and launch, in revamped packaging, of the new labels below. To follow, a third, super-premium shiraz named for great-grandfather George Larsen, 'garagiste winemaker in a time when the term had not yet been coined'.

Beau Belle range ⓃⒺⓦ

★★★★ **The Chapel Shiraz** Cocoa & black pepper, dark hedgerow fruit core. Silky texture, polished tannins, **11**'s overall effect harmonious, well crafted to enjoy & cellar. Ends on a creamy espresso note.

Cooper Shiraz ★★★☆ Plums & brambleberries, deep & richly perfumed, an intriguing caraway seed note in the spicing - **13** very inviting. Succulent palate, vanilla flavoured & just enough grip for food, a bit of ageing. — WB, CR

Location/map/WO: Stellenbosch ▪ Est 2009 ▪ 1stB 2010 ▪ Tasting, sales & cellar tours by appt Mon-Fri 10-5 Sat 10-3 (first & last Sat of month) ▪ Closed Ash Wed, Easter Fri-Sun, Ascension day, Pentecost, Dec 25/26 & Jan 1 ▪ Meals/refreshments for groups of 10-50 by arrangement ▪ Olive oil ▪ BYO picnic ▪ Mountain biking trail ▪ Weddings ▪ Chapel ▪ Special events/functions: contact Estelle at +27 (0)83-419-1761 ▪ Self-catering guest cottage (max 4 people) ▪

Owner(s) Lindeque Family Trust ▪ Directors Tienie & Estelle Lindeque ▪ Cellarmaster(s) Wilhelm van Rooyen (Jan 2014) ▪ Winemaker(s) Teddy Hall (Jan 2014) ▪ Viticulturist(s) Tienie Lindeque (Jan 2014), advised by Johan Pienaar (consultant) ▪ 36ha/23ha (shiraz) ▪ 220t/6,000cs own label 90% red 10% white + 40,000L bulk ▪ PO Box 156 Lynedoch Stellenbosch 7603 ▪ tienie@beaubelle.co.za ▪ www.beaubelle.co.za ▪ S 33° 59' 47.30" E 018° 46' 45.69" ▪ F +27 (0)86-670-6720 ▪ **T +27 (0)21-881-3808/+27 (0)83-522-0100**

Beau Constantia

The Du Preez family winery on Constantiaberg at the northern end of Constantia Valley emerged from the ashes of devastating mountain fires in 2000. With an altitude of around 350 metres, the north-facing vineyards are well sited for ripening red-wine grapes but the white varieties, especially viognier, also do well. Refurbishments see the spa make way for a larger, two-level tasting/sales area (with truly stunning views), additional parking space and an amphitheatre for picnics and functions.

★★★★ **Lucca** Effects of lovely **12** vintage evident in stimulatingly fresh merlot/cab franc pairing. Full of life, spicy concentration but also unshowy. Good potential.

★★★★ **Aidan** Freshly ripe shiraz-based **12** with petit verdot, malbec & merlot betters **11** (★★★★). Mineral, spiced plum flavours conclude with juicy grape tannins.

★★★★ **Cecily** Consistency one attraction of this fresh, pure viognier. Charming honeysuckle, apricot fragrance on dry **13**. Subtly oak enriched (30% new).

Pas de Nom White ★★★ **13** mainly sauvignon augmented with splash semillon, barrelled viognier. Full bodied, dry. These honour viticulturist Japie Bronn. Not tasted: **Pas de Nom Red**. — AL

Location/WO: Constantia ▪ Map: Cape Peninsula ▪ Est 2003 ▪ 1stB 2010 ▪ Tasting & sales Wed-Sun 10-4.30; Mon-Tue 10-4.30 (Sep-Apr) & by appt (May-Aug) ▪ Closed Good Fri, Dec 25/26 & Jan 1 ▪ Owner(s) Dormell Properties 139 (Pty) Ltd ▪ Winemaker(s) Justin van Wyk (Sep 2010) ▪ Viticulturist(s) Japie Bronn (Sep 2002) ▪ 22ha/±11ha (cabs s/f, malbec, merlot, p verdot, shiraz, sauv, sem, viog) ▪ 40t/4,000cs own label 80% red 20% white ▪ 1043 Constantia Main Road Constantia 7806 ▪ winesales@beauconstantia.com ▪ www.beauconstantia.com ▪ S 34° 01' 48.57" E 018° 24' 21.67" ▪ F +27 (0)21-794-0534 ▪ **T +27 (0)21-794-8632**

Beau Joubert Vineyards & Winery

Home to the Joubert family since 1795, through seven generations, this gracious Cape Dutch farm-stead on the Polkadraai Hills, complete with 18th-century manor house, today is part of a joint venture with a group of US families, with American entrepreneur Andrew Hilliard as MD. Lately, upgrades have concentrated on vineyards and cellar facilities, aimed at raising the overall quality profile.

Beau Joubert range

★★★★ **Ambassador** Elegant merlot-led **10** delivers on promise of last year's preview, juicy, with 29% cab for blackcurrant backbone, 2% shiraz adding to spice mix.

Christmas Cabernet ★★★ Worth dashing through the snow for, latest **NV** is smooth & fruity, with milk chocolate sweetness adding to the cheer. **Shiraz** ★★★★ Earthiness of **10** previewed last year still supported by black berry fruit, with a sprinkle of herbs & whiff of smoke. Softening tannins & ample acidity provide structure & balance to mature. Also tasted: **Cabernet Sauvignon 10** ★★★★ **Old Vine Chenin Blanc 13** ★★★ **Sauvignon Blanc 14** ★★ Not tasted: **Rosé, Fat Pig**.

Oak Lane range

Shiraz-Cabernet Sauvignon ★★★ **13** almost cooked berry/fruit pastille nose, fresher cassis on palate, soft tannins & fresh acidity for easy sipping. Also tasted: **Merlot-Cabernet Sauvignon 13** ★★☆ **Chenin Blanc-Sauvignon Blanc 14** ★★★ Discontinued: **Pinot Noir**. — JG

Location/map/WO: Stellenbosch ▪ Est 1695 ▪ 1stB 2000 ▪ Tasting & sales Mon-Fri 8-5 Sat by appt ▪ Closed all pub hols ▪ Cellar tours by appt ▪ BYO picnic ▪ Walks/hikes ▪ Bird watching ▪ Self-catering guest cottage ▪ Owner(s) MD Andrew Hilliard ▪ Cellarmaster(s)/winemaker(s) Christian Kuun (Dec 2006) ▪ Viticulturist(s) Ian Engelbrecht (Nov 2010) ▪ 80ha/40ha (cabs s/f, merlot, pinot, shiraz, chenin, sauv) ▪ 280t/40,000cs own label 60% red 35% white 5% rosé +

10,000L for clients ▪ PO Box 1114 Stellenbosch 7599 ▪ info@beaujoubert.com ▪ www.beaujoubert.com ▪ S 33° 57' 11.6" E 018° 44' 25.5" ▪ F +27 (0)21-881-3377 ▪ **T +27 (0)21-881-3103**

Beaumont Wines

Modestly describing himself as 'cellarmaster (trying to be)', Sebastian Beaumont embodies the motto on his family crest: 'Proud But Not Arrogant'. In fact, he does an outstanding job of overseeing the increasingly individual and elegant wines coming out of this boutique Bot River cellar, now into its third decade of bottling. Making 'the best of Beaumont', Sebastian says, is simply a question of 'letting the vintage express itself'. (This not to minimise the contribution since 2007 of talented winemaker Marelise Jansen van Rensburg.) Expressions to look forward to next time include two 'quirky' new chenins: one demi sec, the other port-style, 'born out of circumstance'. While he cannot reveal details about any future plans, he says there is always something new on the horizons at his family's historic Compagnes Drift farm, from mother Jayne's paintings to very popular barrel lunches.

Beaumont range

★★★★☆ **Mourvèdre** 12 barrel sample, unyielding in youth, too young to rate. 11 (★★★★), previewed last time, seemed shade off benchmark 10, appeared tad weightier & warmer. Minuscule quantities.

★★★★☆ **Ariane** ⓥ Merlot-led Bordeaux blend in 11. Elegant & restrained, with fine-grained tannins framing sappy cassis & red fruit. Poised & harmonious table mate, will reward cellaring.

★★★★☆ **Vitruvian** House's top red showcasing their terroir. 11 a mourvèdre & shiraz blend with pinotage & cab franc (47/32/12/9). Opulent but elegant, savoury & spicy with dark chocolate nuance. Pliable, firm tannins in better balance than brooding 09 (★★★★). No 10.

★★★★ **Shiraz-Mourvèdre** Like 11, tasted from barrel, 12 ample dark & spicy fruit in deftly structured framework. Sappy dry tannins, balanced & juicy. Fruit is the focus, enhanced by older oak.

★★★★★ **Hope Marguerite Chenin Blanc** A Cape classic, from old (36-40 year) vines. More expressive in 13 (★★★★★), intense yet delicate, a scented bouquet of honey, fresh apple & lime. Touch more sugar (7.3 g/l) than 12 & some new oak, but beautifully balanced, with lingering farewell.

★★★★ **Chenin Blanc** Vivacious 14, ripe apple & honey flavours balanced by crunchy fresh acidity. Unoaked, allowing fruit centre stage in a polished performance. Entertaining now & for good few years.

★★★★ **Goutte d'Or** Noble Late Harvest-style chenin, unoaked 14 tank sample exudes glacé pineapple, preserved quince & lime. Intensely sweet but uncloying, dances lithely & lightly across the palate. 375 ml. No 13.

★★★★ **Cape Vintage** Port-style tinta barocca & pinotage, made Portuguese style (foot-crushed grapes, lower sugar & higher alcohol). 09 barrel sample good fruit & peppery tannin grip raises the bar on 08 (★★★).

Also tasted: **Pinotage 13** ★★★★ Not retasted: **Leo's Whole Bunch Chenin Blanc 11** ★★★★

Raoul's range

Constable House Shiraz-Cabernet Sauvignon ★★★★ Classy quaffing 60/40 blend in 12, loads of juicy fruit & freshness but enough structure & underlying seriousness to pair with food or age few years. Nudges next rung up. Also in magnum. Also tasted: **Jackals River White 14** ★★★★ Not retasted: **Red Blend 11** ★★ **Rosé 13** ★★★ — MW

Location/WO: Bot River ▪ Map: Elgin, Walker Bay & Bot River ▪ Est 1750 ▪ 1stB 1994 ▪ Tasting, sales & cellar tours Mon-Fri 9.30—4.30 Sat 10—3 ▪ Fee R25pp for groups of 10+ ▪ Closed Easter Sun, Dec 25 & Jan 1 ▪ Farm produce ▪ Walking/hiking trails ▪ Conservation area ▪ 200-year old watermill ▪ Art/jewellery exhibits ▪ 2 historic self-catering guest cottages ▪ Owner(s) Beaumont family ▪ Cellarmaster(s) Sebastian Beaumont (Jun 2003) ▪ Winemaker(s) Marelise Jansen van Rensburg (Jan 2007) ▪ Viticulturist(s) Sebastian Beaumont (Jun 1999) ▪ 500ha/31ha (mourv, ptage, chenin) ▪ 150t/20,000cs own label 45% red 50% white 5% rosé ▪ BWI, IPW ▪ PO Box 3 Bot River 7185 ▪ info@beaumont. co.za ▪ www.beaumont.co.za ▪ S 34° 13' 27.2" E 019° 12' 24.9" ▪ F +27 (0)28-284-9733 ▪ **T +27 (0)28-284-9194**

For more information, visit wineonaplatter.com

Beeslaar Wines

After 17 years as winemaker, many of those at legendary Stellenbosch red wine property Kanonkop where he continues the legacy of pre-eminent predecessors Beyers Truter and Jan 'Boland' Coetzee, Abrie Beeslaar (and wife Jeanne, mother of pigeon pair Ben and Emma) is investing in a family label. First up: a pinotage. Unsurprising, given his long-term personal affinity for, and professional affiliation with the variety: 'So young and poorly understood, there's much work to be done'.

★★★★☆ **Pinotage** A personal, serious wine from the man who more than filled the shoes of Kanonkop maestro Beyers Truter. Delicious dense dark fruit in **12**, Marmite, a fynbos thread adding interest. Promising longevity is 18 months barrique ageing, half new. — CR, CvZ

Location/WO: Stellenbosch ▪ Est 2011 ▪ 1stB 2012 ▪ Closed to public ▪ Owner(s) Abrie & Jeanne Beeslaar ▪ Cellarmaster(s)/winemaker(s) Abrie Beeslaar (Jul 2011) ▪ Viticulturist(s) Abrie Beeslaar ▪ 5t/750cs own label 100% red ▪ PO Box 93 Elsenburg 7607 ▪ info@beeslaar.co.za ▪ www.beeslaar.co.za ▪ F +27 (0)86-595-9424 ▪ **T +27 (0)83-663-3256/+27 (0)84-255-8686**

Bein Wine Cellar

Former vets, Swiss couple Ingrid and Luca Bein are passionate about their animals (donkeys Poppy and Daisy, dogs and ducks) on their farm in Stellenbosch's Polkadraai Hills, but even more so about their career change to oenology in one of the smallest commercial wine ventures in SA. Precision viticulture is the watchword, identifying and managing micro-terrroirs within their 2.2 ha vineyard, to produce four different styles of their favourite grape, merlot.

★★★★ **Little Merlot 13** (★★★★), with dashes petit verdot & malbec, is nicely ripe, good fruit flavours & subtle oaking, tannins supple & dry. Well crafted, shows structure & presence but shade less serious than **12** & previous.

★★★★☆ **Merlot 13**, with splashes petit verdot & malbec, has lovely dark fruit & violets closely woven into svelte tannin structure. Layers of flavour, 50% new oak unobtrusive. Elegant & classic style that will reward 4-6 years in the cellar. Return to form after **11** (★★★★); **12** sold out untasted.

★★★★☆ **Merlot Reserve** (Ⓟ) Only best vintages & 'best part of our vineyard'. **11** a classic. Elegant, intense, with lovely structure & length, deserves cellaring 6-8 years.

Also tasted: **Pink Merlot 14** ★★★ — MW

Location/map/WO: Stellenbosch ▪ Est 2002 ▪ 1stB 2004 ▪ Tasting, sales & cellar tours Mon-Sat by appt only ▪ Owner(s)/cellarmaster(s)/winemaker(s) Luca & Ingrid Bein ▪ Viticulturist(s) Luca Bein ▪ 3ha/2.2ha (merlot) ▪ 16t/2,400cs own label 80% red 20% rosé ▪ IPW ▪ PO Box 3408 Matieland 7602 ▪ lib@beinwine.com ▪ www.beinwine.com ▪ S 33° 57' 40.0" E 018° 44' 12.0" ▪ F +27 (0)88-021-881-3025 ▪ **T +27 (0)21-881-3025**

Belfield Wines

Despite a childhood spent on his grandparents' Durbanville wine farm, it was the challenge of exploring cool-climate Elgin's red potential rather than 'winemaking passion' that originally engaged Mike Kreft. After expert guidance, he and wife Mel are now doing it all, with international success, in their postage-stamp vineyard, converted-shed cellar and country-chic self-catering cottages.

★★★★ **Magnifica** Cab named for Queen Protea, joined by drops cab franc & merlot in **11**. Juicy red fruits with gentle herb brush & integrated oak (22% new). Complex & sleek, with long finish.

★★★★ **Syrah** Tensile oak frame supports violets & ripe, generous inky blue-fruit succulence of **11** (★★★★), tad lighter bodied & less concentrated than **10**.

★★★★ **Aristata** Merlot heads 3-way Bordeaux blend with dabs cab & cab franc in **11**. Graphite, herbs & pencil shavings show in dense yet softly textured, layered palate. Focused & well defined, it's named for an indigenous aloe. — FM

Location/WO: Elgin ▪ Map: Elgin, Walker Bay & Bot River ▪ Est 2000 ▪ 1stB 2005 ▪ Tasting, sales & tours by appt ▪ Closed Dec 25 ▪ 2 self-catering cottages ▪ Owner(s) Mike & Mel Kreft ▪ Cellarmaster(s)/winemaker(s)/viticulturist(s)

Mike Kreft ▪ 5.5ha/2.5ha (cab, merlot, shiraz) ▪ 17t/2,000cs own label 100% red ▪ PO Box 191 Elgin 7180 ▪ mike@bel-field.co.za ▪ www.belfield.co.za ▪ S 34° 10' 20.9" E 019° 1' 45.8" ▪ F +27 (0)86-613-3108 ▪ **T +27 (0)82-575-1849**

☐ **Belief** *see* Thembi & Co
☐ **Bella Vino** *see* Nicholson Smith
☐ **Bellemore** *see* Bellevue Estate Stellenbosch
☐ **Belle Vallee** *see* Baratok Wines

Bellevue Estate Stellenbosch

Planting pinotage back in 1953, and malbec more recently, continue to pay dividends for family-owned Bellevue. The varieties are 'breaking new ground in export markets', winemaker Wilhelm Kritzinger says, and growing locally through the Woolworths retail network. Bigger news is that a major investor has come on board, and at press time negotiations were under way 'to determine the best way forward, allowing us to grow our in-house brands and benefit the entire Bellevue team'.

PK Morkel range

★★★★ Pinotage Full-bodied **10** preview ticks all boxes, promises good future: quintessential pinotage plum & banana, savoury & spice appeal courtesy 2+ years 50% new oak.

★★★★ Tumara Bordeaux-style red for fine-dining. 5-way blend led by cab (50%) in **07** shows evolved earthy note, red/dark fruit & violets. Firm, with ripe grape tannin melded with oak from 2+ years ageing.

Petit Verdot ★★★ 10 barrel sample shows a full body, firm tannins. Earthy, with subdued fruit, appealing character from 30 months oak, 50% new, some American. 'Pair with fat farm duck.'

Morkel range

★★★★ Malbec As fine as cellarworthy **10**, previewed **11** shows pure concentration of plum fruit, hints of cherry tobacco from aromatic oak. Ample but rounded tannins lead to pleasing spicy finish.

Shiraz ★★★ Spicy mocha, with hints of red fruit & pepper, **13** a smooth delight; drinks easily solo or at the table. Like most of these reds, deft combo French & American oak. Also tasted: **Pinotage 11**
★★★☆ Atticus Cape Blend 10 ★★★ Not retasted: **Eselgraf Single Vineyard Chenin Blanc 13**
★★★☆ Not tasted: **Sauvignon Blanc**. — GM

Location/map: Stellenbosch ▪ WO: Bottelary ▪ Est 1701 ▪ 1stB 1999 ▪ Tasting & sales Mon-Fri 10—4 Sat 10—3 ▪ Closed Good Fri, Dec 25 & Jan 1 ▪ Owner(s) Dirkie Morkel ▪ Winemaker(s) Wilhelm Kritzinger (Feb 2002) & Anneke Potgieter (Feb 2003) ▪ Viticulturist(s) Dirkie Morkel (Jan 1979) ▪ 291ha/151ha (cabs s/f, cinsaut, malbec, merlot, p verdot, ptage, pinot, shiraz, chenin, sauv) ▪ ±750t/±20,000cs own label 97% red 3% white; ±40,000cs for clients; balance in bulkwine & grapes ▪ Export brands: Bellemore, Bellemore Family Selection, Houdamond, Morkel, Tumara ▪ Labels for clients: Cap du Vin, Marks & Spencer, Provoyeur, Pure African, Sizanani, Woolworths ▪ BWI, IPW, WIETA ▪ PO Box 33 Koelenhof 7605 ▪ wilhelm@bellevue.co.za ▪ www.bellevue.co.za ▪ S 33° 52' 48.48" E 018° 45' 50.40" ▪ F +27 (0)21-865-2899 ▪ **T +27 (0)21-865-2055**

Bellingham

An enduring Cape name, founded by French Huguenots as the farm 'Belle en Champ' ('Beautiful Fields'), in 1693, now with a brand home in Franschhoek village undergoing major renovations at press time. An organic shiraz/syrah and ripasso-method pinotage join the portfolio, stratified into the Bernard Series, honouring maverick vintner Bernard Podlashuk, who revitalised the Bellingham estate and started the brand in the 1940s; Tree Series, alluding to the Podlashuks' shady gardens; Insignia, recalling the flavours of the farmhouse kitchen; and Ancient Earth, acknowledging the foundation of the wine industry — its soils.

Bernard Series

★★★★ Bush Vine Pinotage Quintessential pinotage strawberry fruit, no rough edges in bold **13**. Smartly oaked (50% new) & ready, with structure to improve few years. **12** sold out untasted.

For more information, visit wineonaplatter.com

★★★★ **Basket Press Syrah** Seamless & lingering **12** follows in footsteps of well-defined **11**, modern & powerful **10**. Dab of oak (50% new) adds spice, structure for cellaring ±5 years.

★★★★ **Small Barrel SMV** **12** (★★★★☆) repeats successful formula of **11** - shiraz (80%), mourvèdre & viognier, 50% new oak for floral notes & spice - takes step up with purer fruit, more precise tannin structure.

★★★★ **Old Vine Chenin Blanc** Last edition barrel-fermented **12** nudged next level; **13** (★★★★☆) attains it. Well integrated & poised, with white peach & thatch attractions, gravelly grip & tangy lift.

★★★★ **Whole Bunch Roussanne** Rare-in-Cape white grape from Voor Paardeberg delivers restraint, persistence, ageability. Like **12**, **14** (★★★★☆) has food-inviting grip ex lees-ageing, impressive fruit purity. **13** sold out untasted.

★★★★ **Whole Bunch Grenache Blanc-Viognier** The red-wine drinker's white wine? Oak-fermented (60% new) **13** exudes confidence; has the structure (plus 14% alcohol), grip & dry conclusion to be a contender. Includes 20% viognier which, in **12** (★★★★), contributed to a sweet impression.

Organic Syrah (NEW) ⊘ ★★★☆ Vibrant **11**'s bright & pure fruit cossetted by vanilla-sweet oak (50% new) mid-2014. Smooth & long; one to watch. Also tasted: **Hand Picked Viognier 13** ★★★☆

Insignia Series
Pinopasso Pinotage (NEW) ★★☆ Grapes air-dried prior to ferment for extra richness. Balsamic-toned **13** preview gains sweet profile from 10 g/l sugar, plus woody sheen from 100% new oak. Decidedly different. Also tasted: **Mocha Java Merlot 13** ★★ **Citrus Grove Chenin** ⊘ **14** ★★★

Ancient Earth range
Pinotage ★★★ **13** ticks all the pinotage boxes: lush strawberries, mere hint of acetone, fresh finish.
Chardonnay ★★★ Barrel-fermented & -aged (15% new, 9 months) **13** has dollop verdelho for added vivacity. Textbook lemon & spice aromas, flavours, slippery viscosity. WO W Cape. Also tasted: **Cabernet Sauvignon 12** ★★★ **Merlot 13** ★★☆ **Shiraz 12** ★★★ **Sauvignon Blanc 14** ★★★

Tree Series
Berry Bush Rosé ★★ **14** pretty pink sunset tipple with gentle sweetness in tail. From pinotage. WO W Cape. Also tasted: **Big Oak Red** ⊘ **13** ★★★ Not retasted: **Pear Tree White 13** ★★★ — CvZ

Location/map: Franschhoek ▪ WO: Coastal/Western Cape/Voor Paardeberg ▪ Est 1693 ▪ 1stB 1947 ▪ Tasting & sales at Bellingham cellardoor, located at Franschhoek Cellar Mon-Fri 10-5 (Apr-Sep) & 10-6 (Oct-Mar) Sat 10-5 Sun 11-5 ▪ Closed Good Fri, May 1, Jun 16 & Dec 25 ▪ Cheese lunch daily during tasting hours ▪ Owner(s) DGB (Pty) Ltd ▪ Winemaker(s) Niël Groenewald (Jul 2004), with Mario Damon (Jan 2002) ▪ Viticulturist(s) Stephan Joubert (2006) ▪ 4,000t/560,000cs own label 50% red 49% white 1% rosé ▪ ISO 9001:2000, HACCP, IPW, WIETA ▪ PO Box 52 Franschhoek 7690 ▪ bellingham@dgb.co.za ▪ www.bellinghamwines.com ▪ S 33° 54' 16.4" E 019° 6' 40.7" ▪ F +27 (0)21-876-4107 ▪ **T +27 (0)21-876-2086**

Bellpost

Owner Lollies Thiart's sons are integral to this West Coast winery. Koos is the part-time winemaker (he's on the red wine team at Namaqua, nearby) and viticulturist Nico steps into the cellar breach when necessary. The tasting venue has been extended and roadside signage erected to attract more visitors to the cellar between Lutzville and Vredendal.

Ruby Cabernet ★★★☆ Hefty price tag for unfashionable variety (perhaps owner Lollies Thiart's secret weapon!). Asian spice on nose, lovely form on step-up **09**, 15% alcohol well handled. **Chardonnay** ⊘ ★★★☆ No oak trammels the plush citrus fruit on vibrant **13**, showing more elegance than previous. Also tasted: **Merlot 13** ★★★ **Shiraz 09** ★★★ **C'est la Vie 13** ★★★ — CvZ

Location: Vredendal ▪ Map/WO: Olifants River ▪ Est/1stB 2005 ▪ Tasting, sales & cellar tours by appt ▪ Owner(s) Lollies Thiart ▪ Winemaker(s) Koos Thiart (Jan 2005) ▪ Viticulturist(s) Nico Thiart (Jan 2005) ▪ 5ha/2ha (merlot, ruby cab, shiraz, chard, nouvelle, viog) ▪ 12t/1,800cs own label 80% red 20% white ▪ PO Box 39 Vredendal 8160 ▪ bellpost@

starmail.co.za ▪ www.bellpost.co.za ▪ S 31° 36' 24.1" E 018° 25' 0.6" ▪ F +27 (0)27-213-2562 ▪ **T +27 (0)27-213-2562, +27 (0)82-619-2428**

☐ **Bell Tower** *see* Asara Wine Estate & Hotel

Benguela Cove

New owners Nick Rea and Penny Street OBE bought the Benguela Cove property because of its special position at the ocean's edge near Hermanus, which gives a night cooling effect because of the south-eastern breeze, chilled by the Benguela current. Above-average rainfall is another quality factor. Plans include an investment programme to establish Benguela Cove as an international wine producer and luxury wine tourist experience, including artisan shops and new tasting centre.

Premium Selection

★★★★ **Sauvignon Blanc 13** (★★★★) shows flinty freshness, crisp clean fruit profile in light & racy style. Good food partner but hasn't the intensity of **12** preview.

Also tasted: **Shiraz 12** ★★★★ Not tasted: **Cabernet Franc**. In abeyance: **Cabernet Sauvignon, Rosé.** — MW

Location: Hermanus ▪ Map: Elgin, Walker Bay & Bot River ▪ WO: Walker Bay ▪ Est 2004 ▪ 1stB 2007 ▪ Tasting Mon-Sat 10-5 Sun/pub hols 10-4 ▪ Closed Dec 25 ▪ Fee R30pp (Oct-Apr), no charge May-Sep ▪ Sales Mon-Sat 10-5 ▪ Owner(s) Benguela Cove Investments (Pty) Ltd (Penny Streeter OBE) ▪ Winemaker(s) Kevin Grant (2012 Ataraxia) ▪ Viticulturist(s) Paul Wallace (2011, consultant) ▪ 206ha/66ha (cabs s/f, malbec, merlot, p verdot, pinot, shiraz, chard, sauv, sem, viog) ▪ 600t/4,400cs own label 50% red 50% white ▪ PO Box 327 Bellville 7535 ▪ info@benguelacove.co.za ▪ www.benguelacove.co.za ▪ S 34° 20' 45.0" E 019° 8' 15.7" ▪ **T +27 (0)82-499-9774/+27 (0)21-944-1041**

☐ **Ben Hur** *see* Blomendahl Vineyards
☐ **Berg en Dal** *see* Wine-of-the-Month Club

Bergheim

Enthused by food (and cooking), music and wine, general practitioner Edwin Jordaan micro-vinifies in cellar space rented from Mason's Winery on Paarl Mountain. 'Every bottle of wine wants to tell a story about terroir, cultivar and/or harvest,' Edwin says. 'My passion is seeing this happen with minimum interference.'

Bergheim range

★★★★ **Mignon** ⊘ Older-oak-aged **13** (★★★★) is semillon & 35% sauvignon from Franschhoek. Nutty, earthy interest; chalky dryness melds with subtle fruit & pronounced acidity. Slightly less complex, weighty than **12**.

Shiraz ★★★ Wild dark berries, black pepper & rustic farmyard notes on **12**. Dense texture, yet firm tannins & secondary characters provide life & lift. Also tasted: **Pinotage 12** ★★

Couple's Wine range

Not retasted: **Dry Red Ben 08** ★★★★ **Dry White Celia 10** ★★★ — HJ

Location: Paarl ▪ Map: Paarl & Wellington ▪ WO: Paarl/Western Cape/Franschhoek ▪ Est/1stB 2000 ▪ Tasting by appt ▪ Owner(s) Edwin Jordaan ▪ Cellarmaster(s)/winemaker(s) Edwin Jordaan (Jan 2000) ▪ 4-6t/1,000cs own label 66% red 34% white ▪ PO Box 6020 Paarl 7622 ▪ drjordaan@gmail.com ▪ S 33° 45' 20.2" E 018° 57' 42.5" ▪ F +27 (0)21-862-7852 ▪ **T +27 (0)82-923-3115, +27 (0)21-863-1529**

☐ **Bergkelder** *see* Die Bergkelder Wine Centre

Bergsig Estate

Blessed with immense natural beauty, Breedekloof's Bergsig Estate describes itself as 'an innovative family concern with sustainable farming practices and long-term business relationships locally and overseas'. The farm is also blessed with some fully mature vineyards, including 40-year-old riesling

For more information, visit wineonaplatter.com

vines which supply one of three components for the new Icarus White. Cellarmaster De Wet Lategan had wanted to create a partner for Icarus Red since its launch ten years ago, 'it just happened that now was perfect to do so'. The blends' name, De Wet says, reflects the surrounding mountain peaks, his family's passion for flying and their 'driving pursuit for excellence'.

Limited Editions

★★★★ **Cabernet Sauvignon Reserve** ⓥ Lower yield, longer small-oak ageing for this version. Understated but serious **10**, firm but ripe tannins provide excellent balance. Will reward ageing.

Bergsig Estate range

★★★★ **Icarus Red 11** from cab & touriga seduces with sweet blackcurrant & exotic spice profile. Modern & lush, lifted by bright fruit, vibrant acidity, smart oaking. Great balance. Delicious!

★★★★ **Chardonnay 13** back to form after **11** (★★★☆), with creamy oak flavours mingling with lemon cream & lime fruit. Rich & firmly built, tempered by citrus freshness.

★★★★☆ **Icarus White** (NEW) Elegant **13** 3-way chardonnay-led blend with chenin & dollop riesling. Seamless, & framed by a lush structure of mostly new oak, ripe summer fruit & a lipsmacking fresh citrus finish. Destined to give great pleasure.

★★★★ **Cape Vintage** ⓥ Succulent, smooth & spicy port-style from tinta. **04** similar to last-tasted **00**, generously flavoured but not sweet, sufficient fire to warm a winter night.

★★★★ **Cape LBV** ⓥ **03** (★★★★) port-style from touriga a shade shy of **01**. Charms with molasses, nut & coffee bouquet, dusty oak detracts from chocolate-orange end.

Pinotage ★★★☆ Coconut & pinotage's fruit-sweetness on **12**, generous & friendly. **Gewürztraminer** ★★★ 2 vintages reviewed, **13** & **14**. Both floral, jasmine perfume, with few grams sugar for spicy food. **13** shows some development. Delightful, serve chilled. **Sauvignon Blanc** ★★★☆ Preview **14** a notch up with more body & fullness. Shows tangy fruit salad & lively acidity, perfect summer sipping. Also tasted: **Bulldozer Pinotage** ⓥ **13** ★★★ Not retasted: **Cabernet Sauvignon 11** ★★★ **Touriga Nacional 11** ★★★ **The Family Friend 11** ★★★ **Shiraz Rosé 12** ★★ **Chenin Blanc 12** ★★☆ **Cape Ruby NV** ★★★☆ Not tasted: **Bouquet Light, Sauvignon Blanc Brut, Special Late Harvest**. Discontinued: **White River Chenin Blanc**. — WB

Location: Wolseley ▪ Map/WO: Breedekloof ▪ Est 1843 ▪ 1stB 1977 ▪ Tasting & sales Mon–Fri 8–5 Sat & pub hols 9–5 ▪ Fee R20 for groups of 10+ ▪ Closed Good Fri, Dec 25 & Jan 1 ▪ Cellar tours by appt ▪ Bergsig Bistro ▪ Facilities for children ▪ Farm produce ▪ Conferences ▪ Self-guided birdwatching route ▪ Conservation area, visits by appt ▪ Lategan family history & historical artefacts on display ▪ Soetes & Soup (Jul) ▪ Owner(s) Lategan family ▪ Cellarmaster(s) De Wet Lategan (Jan 1989) ▪ Winemaker(s) Chris du Toit (Jul 2003) ▪ Viticulturist(s) Louis & Plum Lategan (1991) ▪ ±400ha/ 253ha (cab, ptage, shiraz, touriga, chard, chenin, sauv) ▪ 3,200t/100,000cs own label 35% red 60% white 4% rosé 1% other + 140,000cs for clients ▪ Other export brand: White River ▪ Brand for clients: Woolworths ▪ BWI, BRC, IPW ▪ PO Box 15 Breërivier 6858 ▪ wine@bergsig.co.za ▪ www.bergsig.co.za ▪ S 33° 31' 7.78" E 019° 11' 37.14" ▪ F +27 (0)23-355-1658 ▪ **T +27 (0)23-355-1603**

Bergwater Winery

Owned by brothers Stephan and Heimie Schoeman, Bergwater in starkly dramatic Prince Albert Valley is the Groot Karoo's first and largest winery, with 63 ha of vineyards and a further ±1,400 ha of nature reserve. Wines, by seasoned Jacques Kruger, are among several visitor attractions, including 4x4 and cycle trails, bass fishing, hiking, an airstrip and accommodation right next to the hanger.

Reserve range

Cabernet Sauvignon ★★★ **12** first since **09**. More harmony, dimension than standard label. Ripe dark fruit; firm backing that will benefit from short ageing. **Sauvignon Blanc** ★★ Marked asparagus, grassy notes on **13**; dry, somewhat acidic tail. Not retasted: **Merlot 09** Tank sample too young to rate. **Shiraz 09** ★★☆ **Royal Reserve 10** ★★ **Rosé 12** ★★

Bergwater range
Cabernet Sauvignon ★★ **12** straightforward blackcurrant flavours; brisk, with green leafy tannins. **Shiraz** (NEW) ★★ Pleasant rustic style **12** has dark spice, hint oak & good freshness. **Rendezvous Red** ★★ Shiraz, merlot & cab blend in no-frills, smooth **12**. First since **08**. Also tasted: **Merlot 12** ★★ **Rendezvous White 13** ★☆ Not retasted: **Muscat d'Alexandrie 12** ★★ **Tinta Barocca 12** ★☆

Sparkling Wine range
Brut Sauvignon Blanc ★★★ Frothy fun in **12** bubbly from sauvignon. Not retasted: **Sparkling Brut Rosé 12** ★★★ — AL

Location: Prince Albert ▪ Map: Klein Karoo & Garden Route ▪ WO: Prince Albert Valley/Western Cape ▪ Est 1999 ▪ 1stB 2003 ▪ Tasting & sales Mon-Thu 8—4.30 Fri 8-4 Sat/Sun 10-3 ▪ Fee R20 ▪ Cellar tours by appt ▪ Meals by prior arrangement ▪ BYO picnic ▪ Gifts ▪ Olives & olive oil ▪ Wedding/conference/function venue (up to 250 pax) ▪ 2 x self-catering guest houses ▪ Gravel airstrip for light aircraft (phone ahead) ▪ Hiking/mountain biking & 4x4 trail by arrangement ▪ Owner(s) Heimie & Stephan Schoeman ▪ Cellarmaster(s)/winemaker(s) Jacques Kruger (Jan 2013) ▪ 1,500ha/63ha (cab, merlot, shiraz, sauv) ▪ ±400-600t ▪ 80% red 15% white 5% rosé + bulk ▪ PO Box 40 Prince Albert 6930 ▪ wine@bergwater.co.za ▪ www.bergwater.com ▪ S 33° 16' 46.3" E 022° 13' 55.7" ▪ F +27 (0)86-541-7335 ▪ **T +27 (0)23-541-1703**

☐ **Bernard Series** see Bellingham
☐ **Bernheim** see Taillard Family Wines

Berrio Wines

Elim winegrower Francis Pratt has entrusted Cederberg cellarmaster David Nieuwoudt (who also owns Elim vineyards) with vinifying his Berrio wines (sauvignon, semillon and shiraz) since 2013 – previously he made them himself. He also sells some of his cool-climate grapes to his colleague up north for Cederberg's acclaimed Ghost Corner range, and there are plans for further collaboration, confides Francis. Meanwhile, he and other vinegrowers on the Agulhas coastal plain conserve local flora and fauna by running their farms as part of the Nuwejaars Wetland Special Management Area.

★★★★ **Sauvignon Blanc** ⊘ Salty-mineral character on **13** (★★★★★) as on **12**, part of an intriguing complexity with blackcurrant, citrus, passionfruit. A little silky richness on the intense palate; bracingly fresh but not aggressively so.

★★★★☆ **Weather Girl** Name tweaked from 'The Weathergirl' with **13**, but still a refined unoaked blend sauvignon & semillon (60:40). Pear, stone, hints of salinity, tangy citrus & a waxy note too. Powerful flavours, & a powerful acid structure to carry them to a clean, forceful conclusion.

Not tasted: **Cabernet Sauvignon**. — TJ

Location/WO: Elim ▪ Map: Southern Cape ▪ Est 1997 ▪ 1stB 2002 ▪ Tasting & sales by appt only ▪ Closed Sun, Easter Fri/Sun, Dec 25/26 & Jan 1 ▪ Owner(s) Francis Pratt ▪ Cellarmaster(s) Francis Pratt (Feb 2009) ▪ Winemaker(s) David Nieuwoudt (2013, Cederberg) ▪ Viticulturist(s) Andrew Teubes (Jan 2006, consultant) ▪ 2,276ha/±30ha (pinot, shiraz, sauv, sem) ▪ ±30t/20,080cs own label 20% red 80% white ▪ Fairtrade ▪ PO Box 622 Bredasdorp 7280 ▪ wine@theberrio.co.za ▪ www.theberrio.co.za ▪ S 34° 37' 17.0" E 019° 48' 32.3" ▪ F +27 (0)86-603-2894 ▪ **T +27 (0)28-482-1880**

☐ **Berryfields** see Ashton Kelder

Beyerskloof

When Beyers Truter (long one of the great characters and great cellarmasters of Cape wine) arrived as a young man at his own tiny Stellenbosch farm way back in 1988, he found nothing at all, he says, except for 'some grass and a donkey. Oh, ja, and some ducks.' The estate – always jointly owned – grew enormously in hectares, in production, and in ambition over the decades that followed, especially when Beyers left Kanonkop, whose renown he had so signally helped establish. His brilliant championing of sometimes-despised pinotage also continued, and this grape is the focus here, appearing in numerous guises. Basically, says Beyers' winemaker son Anri, 'it's what we do best!' Clearly it's also what they love best, and no doubt there's a connection.

★★★★ **Pinotage Reserve** Modern style, gaining polish & chic with each vintage. Sleek, fresh red fruit, well-managed tannins on **12**; smart 30% new French oaking. Drinks well now, can go further 4 years minimum.

★★★★☆ **Diesel Pinotage** Youthful **12** an ageworthy classic. Freshness, complementary oaking (80% new French) & refinement - it has all. Needs 2-3 years for perfumed ripe cherry fruit to emerge from firm yet beautifully polished tannins. Great example of how pinotage responds to TLC & fine vintage.

★★★★☆ **Field Blend** Name refers to cab-merlot vine intermix in vineyard. Latest from standout **09** vintage showing some evolution in its truffly, blood features, savoury tail. But structure & poised acid thread still hold firm. Should easily see 2019 in good shape. **08** (★★★★) lighter year.

★★★★ **Synergy Cape Blend** **12** true to its name: pinotage 54%, equal cab & merlot pull together, provide voluptuous yet mineral-edged fruit, firm yet not harsh frame.

★★★★☆ **Faith** Opulent & showy but **11** has better balance, harmony than **10**. All-new French oak well absorbed in ripe-fruited blend of pinotage & merlot (50/50), cab in usual holding role. Faith in ageability will be rewarded!

Also tasted: Pinotage 13 ★★★☆ Pinotage Dry Rosé 14 ★★★ Chenin Blanc-Pinotage 14 ★★★☆ Not retasted: Cabernet Sauvignon-Merlot 12 ★★★ Lagare Cape Vintage 10 ★★★☆ — AL

Location/map: Stellenbosch ▪ WO: Stellenbosch/Western Cape/Coastal ▪ Est 1988 ▪ 1stB 1989 ▪ Tasting & sales Mon-Fri 9–4 Sat 9.30–4 ▪ Closed Easter Fri-Mon, Dec 25/26 & Jan 1 ▪ Cellar tours by appt ▪ Red Leaf Restaurant ▪ Farm produce ▪ Conferences (30 pax) ▪ Owner(s) Beyers Truter, Simon Halliday & Jan Morgan ▪ Cellarmaster(s) Beyers Truter (Jan 1988) ▪ Winemaker(s) Anri Truter (Jan 2004) & Travis Langley (Jan 2009), with Buddy Hendricks (Jan 2010) ▪ Viticulturist(s) Johan Pienaar (2000, consultant) ▪ 130ha/94ha (cab, merlot, ptage) ▪ 750t/240,000cs own label 96% red 2% white 2% rosé + 10,000cs for clients ▪ Brands for clients: Pick's Pick ▪ WIETA ▪ PO Box 107 Koelenhof 7605 ▪ reception@beyerskloof. co.za ▪ www.beyerskloof.co.za ▪ S 33° 53' 28.0" E 018° 49' 23.6" ▪ F +27 (0)21-865-2683 ▪ **T +27 (0)21-865-2135**

Bezalel-Dyasonsklip Wine Cellar (♀) (🍴) (📷) (♨)

The Bezuidenhout family's farm in Upington offers a variety of attractions (hence its listing on the Northern Cape's Kokerboom Food & Wine Route) including tastings of their boutique wines, recently rebranded. Father-and-son team Inus and Jan-Adriaan also produce 10 Year potstill brandy and an assortment of liqueurs.

Location: Upington ▪ Map: Northern Cape, Free State & North West ▪ Est 1949 (farm)/1997 (cellar) ▪ 1stB 1998 ▪ Tasting, sales & cellar tours Mon-Fri 8.30–6.30 Sat 8–2 ▪ Fee R25-R75pp ▪ Large groups by appt ▪ Closed Easter Fri/Mon & Dec 25 ▪ Green Fig Café: breakfast, lunch & platters ▪ Venue for conferences & weddings (up to 280 pax) ▪ Owner(s) Bezuidenhout family ▪ Cellarmaster(s)/winemaker(s)/viticulturist(s) Inus Bezuidenhout (1989), with Jan-Adriaan Bezuidenhout (2005) ▪ 60ha/44ha (cab, cornifesto, merlot, pinot, ptage, sangio, shiraz, touriga, chard, cbard, gewürz, merbein, sultana) ▪ ±1,000cs own label 100% red ▪ Eurogap certified ▪ PO Dyasonsklip 8805 ▪ info@bezalel.co.za ▪ www.bezalel.co.za ▪ S 28° 36' 28.69" E 021° 6' 19.01" ▪ F +27 (0)54-491-1141 ▪ **T +27 (0)54-491-1325, +27 (0)83-310-4763**

☐ **Big Five** see Jacques Germanier
☐ **Big Flower** see Botanica Wines
☐ **Big Six** see Old Bridge Wines

Bilton Wines (♀) (📷) (♨) (♿)

The Bilton family have farmed the prime Helderberg slopes since the late 1950s. Vegetables and fruit gave way to vines, overseen since 1996 by Mark Bilton, great-grandson of Sir Percy, the entrepreneur honoured in the impressive flagship wine. Winemaker/viticulturist Ruan du Plessis is advised by one of the most experienced vintners in the business, Giorgio Dalla Cia (Dalla Cia Wine & Spirit Company).

Private Collection

★★★★ **The Bilton** (♀) 100% cab, **06** matured 3 years in '500% new oak' produced porty, inky, tannic leviathan, hopefully to emerge with grace.

★★★★☆ **Sir Percy** Cab leads in powerful **09** (★★★★) Bordeaux-style blend with merlot & dab petit verdot. Not as spicy as **08** as mourvèdre omitted. Body & breadth from noticeable oak, all new.

★★★★ **Viognier** Intensity & stature rules on **10** (★★★☆). Big, with oxidative stonefruit, it's less impressive than **08**. No **09**.

Cellar Selection

★★★★☆ **Cabernet Sauvignon** ⓥ **08** cements this label's claim to higher general rating. Structured & firm but beautifully smooth & rich overall. Light cocoa note adds complex nuance to palate.

★★★★ **Shiraz** ⓥ Lovely concentration of **08** on par with **07**. Intense but seamlessly elegant, ripe blue/black berries & char hint from 80% new oak. Silky smooth texture, long rich tail.

Not retasted: **Merlot 08** ★★★

Bilton range

Bonnie Anne ★★★ Fresh, zesty vibrancy on unfussy **14** from sauvignon. Good typicity sees it improve on previous. Not retasted: **Matt Black Red Blend 09** ★★★★ — FM

Location/map/WO: Stellenbosch ▪ Est 1694 ▪ 1stB 1998 ▪ Tasting & sales Mon–Sun 10–5 ▪ Fee R35/6 wines, R50 dark Belgian chocolate & wine pairing (4 wines) ▪ Closed Good Fri, Dec 25/26 & Jan 1 ▪ Cellar tours Mon–Fri by appt ▪ Jungle gym & play area for children ▪ Vineyard walk ▪ Owner(s) Mark Bilton ▪ Winemaker(s) Ruan du Plessis, with Giorgio Dalla Cia (consultant) ▪ Viticulturist(s) Ruan du Plessis (Dec 2004) ▪ 377ha/65ha (cab, merlot, mourv, p verdot, pinot, shiraz, chenin, sauv, viog) ▪ 100t/16,000cs own label 90% red 10% white ▪ IPW, WIETA ▪ PO Box 60 Lynedoch 7603 ▪ info@biltonwines. com ▪ www.biltonwines.com ▪ S 33° 59' 52.9" E 018° 50' 58.3" ▪ F +27 (0)21-881-3721 ▪ **T +27 (0)21-881-3714**

☐ **Birkenhead Estate & Brewery** *see* Walker Bay Vineyards
☐ **Bistro** *see* Zandvliet Wine Estate & Thoroughbred Stud

Bizoe Wines

Bizoe Wines is Somerset West-based boutique winemaker and upscale wine-tour leader Rikus Neethling's premium label, made in rented cellar space. The Syrah is named after his wife, the white blend after his mother. Wine enthusiasts are always welcome to contact him for a private tasting.

★★★★☆ **Henriëtta** Always-impressive Bordeaux white, semillon 70% & sauvignon from Franschhoek & Elgin. Old-wood-fermented **13** tightly wound mid-2014; opens slowly to reveal fresh citrus & floral perfumes; complex mouthful with good oak integration, mineral grip & satisfying dry finish. Only 500 cases.

Estalét Syrah ★★★★ Interesting & individual expression of shiraz, from a Wolseley site. Lavender & fynbos entry to fruit-driven **12**, pleasant confectionery & liquorice flavours, sweet-sour tang of acidity on the finish. — HJ

Location: Somerset West ▪ WO: Western Cape ▪ Est/1stB 2008 ▪ Tasting & sales by appt or during tailor-made tours - booking essential ▪ Fee R1,500pp incl. transport & lunch ▪ Owner(s)/cellarmaster(s)/winemaker(s) Rikus Neethling ▪ Viticulturist(s) Org Viljoen ▪ 2,000cs ▪ Unit 189 Croydon Vineyard Estate Somerset West 7130 ▪ info@bizoe.co.za ▪ www.bizoe.co.za ▪ F +27 (0)86-653-8186 ▪ **T +27 (0)21-843-3307**

Blaauwklippen Vineyards

The peaks of Stellenberg and Helderberg form a craggy backdrop to the venerable Blaauwklippen property — turning 333 this year - on the urban fringe of Stellenbosch, its Dutch name derived from those blue-grey rock faces. Attractions have always been legion: events venue, bistro, weekly Sunday market, new tasting room and, the constant thread, wine. Zinfandel is a unique selling point, and it's always part of the pack for the annual consumer blending competition, now in its fourth decade of staging.

Reserve Single Vineyard range

★★★★ **Shiraz** Delightful, lithe **11** maintains standard of restrained **10**. Graphite edge to generous layered fruit. Textured, with focused, elegant aftertaste.

For more information, visit wineonaplatter.com

★★★★ **Zinfandel** ⓦ Plush & rounded **11** (★★★☆) offers abundant plum, cherry fruit on a lean, focused frame. Spicy but with noticeable alcohol (15.9%). Last-tasted **09** more toned.

Blaauwklippen Vineyard Selection (BVS)
★★★★ **Shiraz 11** (★★★☆) a gentle mouthful of berry compote. Riper & simpler than Rhône-style **07**. **08** - **10** sold out untasted.

★★★★ **Cabriolet** Now bottled, **11** (★★★★) has softened, offering a cornucopia of ripe black fruit. Gently textured six-way blend led by near-equal parts of malbec & merlot. Last-seen **07** remains a standout.

Not retasted: **Zinfandel 10** ★★★☆ **White Zinfandel 12** ★★★

Blaauwklippen Blending Competition (BBC)
Barouche ★★★ Blueberry & graphite spice on light **NV** (**13**) preview of 31st blending competition winner. Shiraz leads zinfandel, malbec & cab franc. Light, juicy & unfussy, like previous.

Blaauwklippen Cultivar Selection
Cabernet Sauvignon ★★★★ **11** keeps up good work of **10** with rounded, rich cassis & toned body. Pleasant concentration & depth. **Red** (ⓝⓔⓦ) ★★☆ Smoky berry notes to **NV** from undisclosed varieties, light inky grip & texture make it a perfect BBQ partner. **Sauvignon Blanc** ★★★ Riper, tropical styled **14** preview improves previous, offering pineapple & guava bounty balanced by flint & zest. Lively, clean acidity. WO W Cape. Also tasted: **Malbec 11** ★★☆ **Merlot 12** ★★★★ **Shiraz 12** ★★★ **Rosé 14** ★★☆ **Chenin Blanc 14** ★★★ Discontinued: **Viognier**.

Noble Late Harvests
★★★★ **Malbec** ⓦ Chalky texture & cherry juice appeal to unusual **12** botrytised dessert that improves on **11** (★★★☆). Spicy, with cranberry tang & clean, fresh dryness. Sweet yet uncloying.

★★★★ **Viognier** ⓦ Sun-dried pineapple & peach on rich, honeyed **12** (★★★★), light & tangy, dry-seeming finish. Last was scented **07**.

★★★★ **Zinfandel** ⓦ Macerated raisin & spicy compote on less sweet **12** (**11** was 316 g sugar!). Good harmony of fruit, sweetness & oak (50% new). Succulent, with long, 'dry' aftertaste.

Aperitif range
★★★★☆ **Before & After** ⓦ Handsome packaging for aptly named berry & spice saturated beauty; cloves, cinnamon, palate silky sweet & very moreish. Fortified to 16% alcohol. **NV**.

Brandy range
★★★★☆ **10 Year Potstilled Brandy** New bottling, from colombard, sauvignon & chenin, vast improvement. Light amber-gold glints entice, floral & tropical fruit notes & a wave of citrus, apricot in reserve. Nutty, spicy oak supports the intense fruit flavours. Elegant balance & subtle texture, with all the mellow, mature notes given a lift on fresh, clean finish.

8 Year Potstilled Brandy ★★★☆ Slightly younger sibling, with fresher flavours but neither the depth nor complexity. Smooth, fragrant, fresh citrus flavours on the finish. Colombard, sauvignon & chenin, 100% potstill, 8 years matured. — WB, FM

Location/map: Stellenbosch ▪ WO: Stellenbosch/Western Cape ▪ Est 1682 ▪ 1stB 1974 ▪ Tasting & sales Mon-Sat 10–6 (summer)/10-5 (winter) Sun/pub hols 10–4 ▪ Wine tasting: R35/5 wines, R55/tour & tasting, R80/unique chocolate & wine experience ▪ Brandy tasting: R10/8 year old, R15/10 year old ▪ Closed Dec 25 & Jan 1 ▪ Food & wine pairing on request ▪ Wine blending on request ▪ Cellar tours 11 & 2 daily, booking advised ▪ Family market every Sun 10-3 (pony rides available) ▪ Bistro ▪ Deli ▪ Facilities for children ▪ Pony & tractor rides Mon-Sat by appt ▪ Gift shop ▪ Conferences ▪ Weddings/functions ▪ Walks/hikes & mountain biking ▪ Distillery: see Gentleman Spirits ▪ Owner(s) Blue Lion GmbH ▪ Winemaker(s) /brandy master(s) Rolf Zeitvogel (Sep 2003), with Albert Basson (Jul 2007) ▪ Viticulturist(s) Christo Hamman (Jan 2009) ▪ 160ha ▪ 500t/60,000cs wine & 650cs (x4-btl) brandy ▪ IPW ▪ PO Box 54 Stellenbosch 7599 ▪ marketing@blaauwklippen.com ▪ www.blaauwklippen.com ▪ S 33° 58′ 23.3″ E 018° 50′ 51.0″ ▪ F +27 (0)21-880-0136 ▪ **T +27 (0)21-880-0133**

☐ **Black Box** *see* Wineways Marketing

Black Elephant Vintners ⓠ

Former Johannesburg investment business partners Kevin Swart ('black' in Afrikaans) and Raymond Ndlovu ('elephant' in Nguni) have ended up in the wine business together. Based in Franschhoek, they collaborate with local winemaker Jacques Wentzel who sources quality grapes for vinification using traditional methods (intended to reflect provenance) for global distribution.

The Back Roads range

★★★★ **Die Middagkrans Malbec** (NEW) Well-structured, fruit-driven **12**, redolent of plums & spice. Natural ferment, unfined/filtered. Clean & vibrant - fatty meat would handle the fine but prominent tannin. Like Petite Sirah, only unobtrusive older oak used.

★★★★ **Matoppie Petite Sirah** (NEW) Inky-purple **13**, with aromas of pepper, blueberries, spice & liquorice. Intensely flavoured, appealingly wild palate, with acidity & tannin to allow for good development.

Die Perdeskoen Pinotage Previously 'The Back Roads Pinotage'. New vintage not ready to taste.

Black Elephant Vintners range

Nicolas Red (NEW) ★★★★ **13** fermented with 30% whole bunches & matured year in older oak. Mostly shiraz with drop of mourvèdre, it's a balanced, uncomplicated, fun wine. **Timothy White** (NEW) ★★★☆ Blend of tank-fermented sauvignon & barrel-fermented semillon & drop of viognier. **14** juicy & fresh - a good summer quaffer. Also tasted: **Two Dogs, a Peacock & a Horse Sauvignon Blanc 14** ★★★ **Timothy White Viognier 13** ★★★★ Not retasted: **Amistad Syrah 12** ★★★☆ — JPf

Location/map/WO: Franschhoek ▪ Est 2013 ▪ 1stB 2012 ▪ Tasting, sales & cellar tours by appt ▪ Fee R25, waived on purchase ▪ Owner(s) Kevin Swart, Raymond Ndlovu & Jacques Wentzel ▪ Winemaker(s) Jacques Wentzel (Jan 2013) ▪ 80t/10,000cs own label 40% red 60% white ▪ IPW ▪ PO Box 686 Franschhoek 7690 ▪ sales@bevintners.co.za, jacques@bevintners.co.za, kevin@bevintners.co.za ▪ www.bevintners.co.za ▪ S 33° 54' 9.00 E 019° 7' 14.00" ▪ **T +27 (0)21-876-2904**

☐ **Black Forest** *see* Louis
☐ **Black Granite** *see* Darling Cellars
☐ **Black Label** *see* Backsberg Estate Cellars

Black Oystercatcher Wines ⓠ 🍽 🏠 📷 🧍 ♿

The Black Oystercatcher home farm is on the windy Agulhas plain at the southernmost tip of Africa, and the conservation-minded Human family have had to adapt to the often extreme climate, diverse and distinctive soil types, and location within the Nuwejaars Wetland Special Management Area. Three new wines from this exceptional cool-climate site missed our tasting deadline: a reserve sauvignon blanc, barrel-fermented botrytis dessert and traditional-method sparkling.

★★★★ **Triton** Mostly shiraz, with splash of cab, **13** reinvents as perfumed, spicy gem laced with cherry, almond & peppery notes. Quite different to cab-merlot driven **10** (★★★★). **11**, **12** not made.

★★★★ **Blanc Fumé** ⓠ Large-oak-fermented sauvignon, from special site within a top block. **10** intensely aromatic, vanilla/nut highlights, glorious rounded mouthfeel ex lees-ageing.

★★★★ **Sauvignon Blanc** Elegant, poised **13** is ripe & round, with appealing twist of nettle & khaki bush spicing gooseberry & granadilla fruit. Generous body & finish, with moderate 13% alcohol.

★★★★☆ **White Pearl** ⊘ Delightful semillon-driven blend with sauvignon, **11** combines best of both. (Older) oak broadens palate but doesn't intrude. Subtle herbaceous notes on waxy-spicy framework, following to almost salty mineral finish.

Also tasted: **Cabernet Sauvignon-Merlot 13** ★★★★ Not retasted: **Rosé 13** ★★★ — GdB

Location/WO: Elim ▪ Map: Southern Cape ▪ Est 1998 ▪ 1stB 2003 ▪ Tasting, sales & cellar tours Mon-Fri 9-5 Sat/Sun 10-2.30 ▪ Closed Good Fri & Dec 24/25 ▪ Restaurant, function & wedding venue: kitchen open Tue-Sun 11-2.30, booking essential ▪ Facilities for children ▪ Tour groups ▪ Conferences ▪ Conservation area ▪ Cycling route ▪ Annual Sauvignon Blanc & Oyster Festival (Dec); peak season programme ▪ Accommodation ▪ Owner(s)/cellarmaster(s)/viticulturist(s) Dirk Human ▪ Winemaker(s) Dirk Human, with Danel Morkel ▪ 1,550ha/18.5ha (cab, merlot, shiraz, sauv, sem) ▪ ±100t/±18,000cs own label 20% red 60% white 20% rosé ▪ BWI, IPW, WIETA ▪ PO Box 199 Bredasdorp 7280 ▪ venue@blackoystercatcher.co.za, wine@blackoystercatcher.co.za, orders@blackoystercatcher.co.za ▪ www. blackoystercatcher.co.za ▪ S 34° 37' 58.0" ▪ E 019° 49' 39.9" ▪ F +27 (0)86-666-7954 ▪ **T +27 (0)28-482-1618**

☐ **Black Pack** *see* Painted Wolf Wines

Black Pearl Vineyards

Since joining her father Lance on Paarl mountainside farm Rhenosterkop in the mid-1990s, energetic American-born Mary-Lou Nash's nature-friendly approach has imbued not only her winemaking but other projects of interest to visitors: distilling brandy, brewing craft beer, growing proteas, husbanding alpacas and Nguni cattle, and opening hiking trails through a tract of endangered renosterveld.

★★★★ **The Mischief Maker Shiraz** ⊘ Classy blend of Swartland shiraz with 15% own mourvèdre, **12** (★★★★☆) shows poise & opulent fruit, appealing Rhône styling. Fuller & bolder than **11** (★★★☆) yet more finessed than **10**. Big future.

★★★★ **Oro** Aromatic, herbaceous nose on **13** shiraz/cab blend leads on to wild fruit & solid tannin. Dense & full-bodied, bit unknit mid-2014, should settle & improve.

★★★★ **Chenin Blanc** ⊘ **13** continues upward from **12** (★★★★). Substantial but understated Swartland old-vine fruit with rich leesy texture. Stylish & focused, shows good potential. — GdB

Location: Paarl ▪ Map: Paarl & Wellington ▪ WO: Coastal/Swartland ▪ Est 1998 ▪ 1stB 2001 ▪ Tasting, sales & tours just about anytime but phone ahead (no credit cards) ▪ Closed Dec 25 ▪ Walks ▪ Lapa & camping facilities ▪ Self-catering cottage ▪ Conservation area ▪ Owner(s) Lance & Mary-Lou Nash ▪ Winemaker(s)/viticulturist(s) Mary-Lou Nash ▪ 240ha/7.2ha (cab, shiraz) ▪ ±5,000cs own label 90% red 10% white ▪ BWI, IPW ▪ PO Box 609 Suider-Paarl 7624 ▪ info@blackpearlwines.com ▪ www.blackpearlwines.com ▪ S 33° 44' 10.5" ▪ E 018° 53' 40.8" ▪ F +27 (0)86-617-8507 ▪ **T +27 (0)83-297-9796/+27 (0)83-395-6999**

☐ **Black Tie** *see* Wineways Marketing

Blackwater Wine

After eight years at high-profile Waterford in Stellenbosch, Francois Haasbroek left at the end of 2012 to concentrate on this, his own project. His approach is to source fruit from under-appreciated vineyards across the winelands, establishing lasting relationships with the growers. As for his winemaking style, he practises minimal intervention – natural acidities, no additives, restrained use of oak, and the like. Appreciating that building a brand is no easy task, he also advises established wineries.

★★★★ **Omerta Carignan** Taut, vibrant **13** refreshing, & unique. Wide spectrum of aromas, flavours - drawing one constantly back to the glass. Older oak. WO Swartland, as was promising **12** (★★★★).

★★★★☆ **Prodigium Pinot Noir** Vibrant, spicy dark fruit leads to creamy yet fresh palate, fruit unobstructed by oak & supported by very finely grained tannin. **13** 25% bunch-fermented, gently extracted; matured in 3rd fill oak, unfiltered & unfined. No additives (as for all these). WO Elgin.

★★★★ **Noir** Shiraz with drops carignan & grenache. **12** is complex, the medium-bodied palate really fresh & untrammelled by new oak; gentle but enough intensity for food. Ex Swartland, like **11** (★★★☆).

★★★★ **The Underdog Chenin Blanc** (NEW) ⊘ Unoaked **14** from Stellenbosch shows crisp apple, green melon & fresh herbs. Promising, fresh palate relatively lean mid-2014; should gain breadth & complexity with cellar-time it deserves.

Also tasted: **Cuvee Terra Lux Pinot Noir 13** ★★★★ **Cultellus Syrah 12** ★★★★ — JPf

Location: Stellenbosch ▪ WO: Swartland/Elgin/Stellenbosch ▪ Est/1stB 2010 ▪ Closed to public ▪ Owner(s) Blackwater Wines & Vines ▪ Cellarmaster(s)/winemaker(s)/viticulturist(s) Francois Haasbroek (Feb 2010) ▪ (carignan, cinsaut, pinot, shiraz, chenin) ▪ 15t/3,000cs own label 70% red 30% white ▪ 1 Trengrove Avenue Uniepark Stellenbosch 7600 ▪ info@blackwaterwine.com ▪ www.blackwaterwine.com ▪ T +27 (0)82-329-8849

Blake Family Wines

With almost 20 years as winemaker in Swartland, Andries Blake knows a thing or two about sourcing prime grapes there, and he and wife Marinda are using that vast knowledge for their new boutique range. Raised on a wine farm, Andries has dreamed of an own label since boyhood (the gemstone wine names reveal just how precious Blake's is to him and his family). Blends are the focus for now ('they're an art form, where a winemaker can showcase flair and skill') but varietal bottlings are a possibility.

★★★★ Amethyst Shiraz-led red blend with pinotage, cab, 24 months new French barrels. Rich & deep **11** has black plum/prune ripeness, tobacco & cocoa notes. Amenable tannins, savoury but ripe.

Tourmaline ★★★☆ White blend of unwooded chenin, oaked chardonnay & viognier. Quince & pineapple, fruit's the hero in **13** giving length & tasty appeal. From bushvine vineyards. — CR, CvZ

Location: Malmesbury ▪ WO: Swartland ▪ Est 2013 ▪ 1stB 2011 ▪ Closed to public ▪ Sales via website ▪ Owner(s) Andries & Marinda Blake ▪ Cellarmaster(s)/winemaker(s) Andries Blake ▪ 5t/750cs own label 40% red 60% white ▪ PO Box 1121 Malmesbury 7299 ▪ info@blakefamilywines.com ▪ www.blakefamilywines.com ▪ T +27 (0)82-922-6162

BLANKbottle

This brand and its qualified winemaker who refuses to be labelled have found a home. After renting space where he could since 2004, Pieter Walser has 'rigged up a cellar' on Lanrust (the old Dellrust farm near Somerset West). Sourcing grapes (currently 50 tons, 35 parcels, 25 varieties) from all corners of the winelands and marketing his quirkily named wines by canny use of the internet and social media, this individualist piques interest, earns trust and tells compelling stories with wines 'driven by quality, adventure, excitement and mystery'. To that one might add 'authenticity'.

★★★★ The Bomb Aptly named **NV** step up on **11** (**★★★☆**). Powerful, ageworthy Stellenbosch cab (80%) & merlot with ample cedary black fruit & fine tannic structure. Fruit intensity & length to match 15.5% alcohol.

★★★★ Breaking Through (NEW) Alluring deep & spicy flavours on shiraz-led melange of Swartland fruit, equal portions mourvèdre, grenache & carignan. **12** creamy, balanced & flavoursome, with fine tannin structure. Natural ferment, older oak only, as all these.

★★★★ Professor Kukurowitz Honours founder of 50+ year old Wellington chenin vineyard. **13** raises bar on **12** (**★★★☆**) with rich & silky layers of spiced apple, greengage & almond balanced by freshening citrus thread.

★★★★ Epileptic Inspiration (NEW) Classy debut **13** from Elgin semillon, barrel fermented. Smooth, waxy texture with rich baked apple & honey flavours lifted by piquant acidity. Vivacious & engaging, with good length. Inspired.

★★★★ Moment of Silence **13** chenin blend with chardonnay & viognier from Wellington. Seamless & aromatic, silk textured (as most of these whites), bit introspective but lovely fruit purity & length.

★★★★ DOK (NEW) Vivacious, tangy **13** trio led by riesling (60%); semillon provides creamy harmony, & splash sauvignon adds zing. Old oak just a platform for symphony of flavours from Elgin. Delicious now & over 4-5 years. **12** (**★★★☆**), labelled 'DOC', is 80% riesling, 10% each semillon & sauvignon. Juicy, lively, tangy - perfect for al fresco fare or summer chilling.

★★★★ The White Bomb (?) **NV** seriously curvaceous (16% alcohol) bellydancer, exuding fragrant opulence & silky charm. Rich & spicy, mainly viognier with chenin, uncloying despite semi-dry styling.

Familiemoord (NEW) (?) **★★★☆ 13** Swartland grenache with loads of spicy new leather & savoury red fruit, flavours as engaging as the name & backstory. Ends happily, & with 3-5 years' lease on life.

2 Klicks Off (NEW) ★★★ Pinot noir from Elgin, **12** red berries & damp leaves, shows some underlying seriousness but somewhat sullen mid-2014, might simply need time to perk up. **Lippe** (NEW) (wine) ★★★☆ 'Lips' a fun name for quite a serious barrel-fermented rosé from grenache & cinsaut. Savoury & dry yet succulent, almost plump cranberry mouthful. **13** made with panache & great with food. WO W Cape. **Kortpad Kaaptoe** (NEW) ★★☆ (Unique?) barrel-fermented fernão pires from Swartland billows variety's pineapple in **13**; somewhat oily texture from year lees-ageing & big alcohol, needs more zing to balance. **What I've Got** (NEW) ★★☆ Nine varieties in perfumed, fruit-filled & summery melange. **12** smooth, crisp & quaffable if not concentrated. WO W Cape. Also tasted: **The Misfit 12** ★★★ **My Koffer 13** ★★★ **Im Hinterhofkabuff 13** ★★★★ Not retasted: **1st Eulogy 11** ★★★ Not tasted: **My Eie Stofpad, The Big Spaniard**. — MW

Location: Somerset West ▪ Map: Helderberg ▪ WO: Swartland/Elgin/Western Cape/Wellington/Breedekloof/Bot River/Stellenbosch ▪ Est 2005 ▪ 1stB 2003 ▪ Tasting & sales Mon-Sat by appt ▪ Sales also via website ▪ Owner(s)/cellarmaster(s)/winemaker(s) Pieter H Walser ▪ Viticulturist(s) Various ▪ 5,000cs own label 50% red 50% white ▪ Lanrust Wine Estate, Winery Road, Somerset West 7129 ▪ pieter@blankbottle.co.za ▪ www.blankbottle.co.za ▪ S 34° 2' 41.1" E 018° 47' 16.0" ▪ F +27 (0)86-503-0974 ▪ **T +27 (0)21-842-2747/+27 (0)82-872-8658**

☐ **Bloem** *see* Noble Hill Wine Estate

Bloemendal Estate

More than 300 years old, and producing wine for almost a third of those, Durbanville's scenic Bloemendal Estate is undergoing a portfolio makeover under consultant Francois Haasbroek, working with well-entrenched wine man Boetman Langevelt and more recent vine man Lombard Loubser (like Francois, with Waterford experience under his belt). Completed are an attractive new tasting area and restaurant in the manor house; ongoing is vineyard rejuvenation, including registration of single-vineyard blocks for the top wines.

Bloemendal Estate range
★★★★ **Syrah** (NEW) Fresh & spicy **12** with lots of dark berry fruit & black pepper. The polished, vibrant palate shows lavender & black olives supported rather than obstructed by oak flavours. Smart wine.

★★★★ **Chardonnay** Last was pleasant **11** (★★★). **13** blends Old & New Worlds; plenty of aroma & flavour, the palate broad yet fresh with a mineral, lemon twist on the finish.

★★★★☆ **Suider Terras Sauvignon Blanc** Intensely aromatic **13** previewed last year, now vastly improved on previous **11** (★★★★☆). Grass, lemongrass, dusty chalk notes. Fresh & tight, the fruit wrapped around a mineral core, unobscured by the subtle oaking (new barrels, but a portion unoaked).

★★★★☆ **Semillon** Last tasted was unwooded **10** (★★★★☆). Clever oaking regime on **13** (66% in new oak, rest in steel) is supportive of the finely chiselled, tight palate & the aromas of ripe apricot, vanilla, green pear. Altogether impressive, with considerable grace & depth.

★★★★☆ **Kanonberg** Now bottled, **13** is a properly dry 70/30 sauvignon & semillon blend. Graceful, expressive & poised, with kaleidoscopic aromas of fruits & minerals. Textured & intense, needing further cellaring to fully open up & integrate the all-new oak.

★★★★ **Semillon Noble Late Harvest** (NEW) Barrel-fermented **13** dessert offers dark rye bread, apricot & integrated toasty oak. The nose slightly closed mid-2014, but shows good potential; round, soft & generous palate well balanced.

Waterlily range
★★★★ **Shiraz 12** (★★★★) attractive freshly crushed black pepper, lilies & cranberry on the nose. Juicy & fresh, with good structure, but a slight bitterness in the finish - not there on **11**.

Cabernet Sauvignon (NEW) ★★★★ **13** shows red pepper, cassis, smoke & herbaceous notes. Juicy, with firm tannin, the modestly oaked palate is more pleasant than complex. **Malbec** (NEW) ★★★★ Slightly unripe blackberry, cherry & plums on **13**'s nose. Firmly structured & lightly oaked, with a warming finish, though just under 14% alcohol. **Pinotage** (NEW) ★★★★ A little spice sprinkling the plum & floral notes of

13. Very firmly built, but the tannins are fine & don't disrupt the easygoing, berried pleasure. Also tasted: **Merlot 12** ★★★ **Rosé Syrah 14** ★★★ **Sauvignon Blanc 14** ★★★☆ — JPf

Location/WO: Durbanville ▪ Map: Durbanville, Philadelphia & Darling ▪ Est 1702 ▪ 1stB 1987 ▪ Tasting & sales Mon-Sat 10–5 Sun 11–3 ▪ Bon Amis Bistro: weddings, evening functions & conferences ▪ Owner(s) Spirito Trade 82 (Pty) Ltd ▪ Winemaker(s) Boetman Langevelt (2006) & Francois Haasbroek (2012, consultant) ▪ Viticulturist(s) Lombard Loubser (2012) ▪ 135ha (cab, malbec, merlot, shiraz, chard, sauv, sem) ▪ PO Box 466 Durbanville 7551 ▪ info@bloemendalwines.co.za ▪ www.bloemendalwines.co.za ▪ S 33° 50′ 22.1″ E 018° 36′ 1.4″ ▪ F +27 (0)86-615-7020 ▪ **T +27 (0)21-975-9591**

Blomendahl Vineyards

Well into its second decade, Blomendahl Vineyards is run by internationally experienced winemaker, negociant and distiller Franz Josef Blomendahl. Through an extensive network, Franz sources grapes across the winelands, notably Stellenbosch, Simonsberg-Paarl and Elgin, where he has a brand home open to the public by appointment.

Ben Hur range
Shiraz ⓥ ★★ Herbaceous seam to wild berry fruit on medium-bodied **07**. Not retasted:
Quadrega 06 ★★★

Estate Collection
Basco Cabernet Sauvignon ⓥ ★★ Hints of cedar & sweet berries, **10** soft & fruity. WO W Cape.
Blue Bay Shiraz ⓥ ★★☆ Ripe, dark fruit in juicy, accessible **06**. Ex West Coast vines. **Môrewag Rosé** ⓥ **09** sweet impression from fruitiness but technically dry & nicely structured. **Môrewag Shiraz** ⓥ ★★★ Natural Sweet **08** had savoury hints last time; sweet, but good grip added balancing savouriness. Not retasted: **Basco Merlot 07** ★★★ **Môrewag Pinotage 06** ★★★ **Basco Pinotage 10** ★★ **Basco Rosé 10** ★★★ **Basco Chardonnay 10** ★★★ **Bonny Bay Bushvine Chenin Blanc 09** ★★☆ **Basco Sauvignon Blanc 09** ★★★☆ **Môrewag Cabernet Sauvignon 08** ★★★

Prime Bin range
Lady in Red Rosé ⓥ ★★★ Attractively different: more 'light red' than 'rosé', **09** had plenty cab fruit for flavour & structure. Simonsberg-Paarl WO. Not retasted: **Cabernet Sauvignon-Merlot 06** ★★★

Bonolo range
Not tasted: **Cabernet Sauvignon**. — DB

Location: Elgin ▪ Map: Elgin, Walker Bay & Bot River ▪ WO: Elgin/Simonsberg-Paarl/Western Cape/Coastal/Stellenbosch ▪ Est 2003 ▪ 1stB 2006 ▪ Tasting by appt ▪ Owner(s) Blomendahl Trust ▪ Cellarmaster(s)/winemaker(s)/viticulturist(s) Franz Josef Blomendahl ▪ 126ha (cab, merlot, ptage, shiraz, chard, chenin) ▪ 480t/70,000cs own label 90% red 10% white ▪ PO Box 52019 Waterfront Cape Town 8002 ▪ info@basco.co.za ▪ www.blomendahl.de ▪ S 34° 13′ 12.2″ E 019° 2′ 28.8″ ▪ F +27 (0)21-859-1411 ▪ **T +27 (0)21-859-2937/+27 (0)72-692-6229**

Blouvlei Wyne

The easy-drinking wines in this range are made at Mont du Toit in Wellington, whose employees are shareholders in the business. Red wines are the focus, made from grapes at the parent farm - white grapes are brought in from elsewhere.

Blouvlei Selection ★★★ Was 'Red'. Delightful **12**, fruity & fun with soft berry flavours. Everyday drinking from undisclosed varieties. Not tasted: **Sauvignon Blanc**. Discontinued: **Rosé**. — WB

Location/WO: Wellington ▪ Map: Paarl & Wellington ▪ Est/1stB 2003 ▪ Tasting, sales & cellar tours Mon-Fri 9-4.30 Sat by appt ▪ Fee R15 ▪ Closed all pub hols ▪ Picnic area by arrangement ▪ Owner(s) BEE Company ▪ Winemaker(s) Abraham Cloete & Chris Roux ▪ Viticulturist(s) Ettienne Barnard (Oct 2010) ▪ ±40ha/28ha (alicante bouschet, cabs s/f, merlot, mourv, p verdot, shiraz, tinta barocca) ▪ ±160t/10,000cs own label 70% red 30% white ▪ IPW ▪ PO Box 817 Wellington 7654 ▪ kelder@montdutoit.co.za ▪ www.montdutoit.co.za ▪ S 33° 39′ 31.3″ E 019° 2′ 2.6″ ▪ F +27 (0)21-864-2737 ▪ **T +27 (0)21-873-7745**

☐ **Blue Bay** *see* Blomendahl Vineyards

Blue Crane Vineyards

After buying the Blue Crane home farm near Tulbagh in 2009, Johannesburg mining businessman (and Singapore racehorse owner) Fred Crabbia's investment in new vines, olive groves and indigenous vegetation has started bearing fruit. Increased wine quantities, a commercially available extra virgin olive oil and pending cellar developments keep daughter Nicolette Barrett and the team busy.

Blue Crane range
Cabernet Sauvignon ★★★ Perfectly correct & particularly pleasant **11**, with dash shiraz, offers black fruit, polish & cedar spice. **Shiraz** ★★★ Sweet black fruit on **11** with soft tannins & hint of spice. Appealing everyday quaffer. Inc splash cab. Also tasted: **Sauvignon Blanc 13** ★★ Not retasted: **Merlot 11** ★★★ Not tasted: **Full Flight**. — CM

Location/WO: Tulbagh ▪ Est 2001 ▪ 1stB 2004 ▪ Closed to public ▪ Sales via website ▪ Owner(s) Fred & Manuela Crabbia ▪ Cellarmaster(s)/winemaker(s) Zia Pienaar ▪ Viticulturist(s) Chris Fox ▪ 138ha/6ha (cab, merlot, shiraz, sauv) ▪ 4,000cs own label 75% red 25% white ▪ BWI ▪ PO Box 306 Tulbagh 6820 ▪ info@bluecrane.co.za ▪ www.bluecrane.co.za ▪ F +27 (0)23-230-0825 ▪ **T +27 (0)23-230-0823**

☐ **Bob's Your Uncle** *see* Boer & Brit

Boekenhoutskloof Winery

It's just over two decades since a group of partners, led by Tim Rands of wine company Vinimark, bought this spectacular property in Franschhoek Valley. Though the home vineyards have not expanded (but are now all organic), Boekenhoutskloof the label and its holdings have grown enormously – in size as well as in reputation as amongst the Cape's finest and most dynamic. So a large volume of grapes is bought in, not least for the great-value sibling brands The Wolftrap and Porcupine Ridge. Helderberg Wijnmakerij in Stellenbosch is also Boekenhoutskloof-owned, as is Porseleinberg in the Swartland - an area which is an ever-growing focus for the roving eye of cellarmaster (and partner) Marc Kent, here from the outset, and a crucial factor in all this growth and all this excellence.

★★★★☆ **Cabernet Sauvignon 12** seduces with lavender perfume & 'femininity' on the palate. Pliant & lissom, it is also powerful & sophisticated. Lengthy (27 months) maturation in new French oak melds seamlessly with dark fruit. As silky & in need of patience as **11** (★★★★★).

★★★★☆ **Syrah 12** (★★★★★) replicates **11**'s light violet whiffs & expressive plum, berry fruit & spice highlights. Trademark precision & nuanced subtlety. Dry, fine tannin partly from the older oak, 27 months. Wellington fruit, as always.

★★★★☆ **The Chocolate Block** Crowd-pleasing bright cherry notes on deservedly successful (75,000+ cases) shiraz-led blend. Generous, pliable & plush, **13** is juicy but with a tannic twist from 16 months in variety French oak. Balanced & rich, with long dry finish. Mainly from Swartland, with 3 other regions. Over-delivers.

★★★★☆ **Semillon** Maintaining the standard, bunch-pressed, barrel-fermented **12** impresses with complexity & integration of fruit & oak (100% new). Cashew nut cream vies with lively citrus & nectarine notes. Full bodied yet fresh from dab sauvignon. Needs time, as did **11**.

★★★★☆ **Noble Late Harvest** ⓧ Inviting sun-baked peach, tart apricot & delicate caramel whiffs hint at great intensity of **10**. Barrel-fermented & -matured semillon (100% new oak) with trademark refined & restrained palate. A fine expression of balanced seduction. — FM

Location/map: Franschhoek ▪ WO: Franschhoek/Coastal/Western Cape ▪ Est 1994 ▪ 1stB 1996 ▪ Tasting & sales by appt only ▪ Closed all pub hols ▪ Owner(s) Boekenhoutskloof Winery (Pty) Ltd ▪ Cellarmaster(s) Marc Kent (1994) ▪ Winemaker(s) Jean Smit, Johan Nesenberend & Elsabé Engelbrecht, with Shaun Meyeridricks ▪ Viticulturist(s) Takkies Cloete ▪ 71ha/6.71ha (cabs s/f, merlot, sem) ▪ 60% red 39% white 1% rosé ▪ BDOCA, BRC, HACCP ▪ PO Box

433 Franschhoek 7690 ▪ info@boekenhoutskloof.co.za ▪ www.boekenhoutskloof.co.za ▪ S 33° 56' 33.0" E 019° 6' 28. 0" ▪ F +27 (0)21-876-3793 ▪ **T +27 (0)21-876-3320**

Boer & Brit

Direct descendants of two major Anglo-Boer War protagonists, 'Boer' Stefan Gerber and 'Brit' Alex Milner now offer tastings of their deftly branded wine label at Peaches & Cream restaurant in Paarl, 'so patrons can also get a meal or even a moerkoffie with their glass of B&B.' On the home front, the Brit has welcomed his first child into the world, leaving the newly married Boer with more marketing trips to 'fun places like south-east Asia' where exports are growing.

Location: Paarl ▪ Map: Paarl & Wellington ▪ Est 2010 ▪ 1stB 2008 ▪ Tasting & sales Mon-Sat at Peaches & Cream restaurant 135 Main Road Paarl ▪ Owner(s) Stefan Gerber & Alexander Milner ▪ Winemaker(s) Stefan Gerber & Alex Milner (both Jul 2010) ▪ 30t own label 60% red 40% white ▪ Other export label: Bob's Your Uncle ▪ PO Box 4 Klapmuts 7625 ▪ alex@boerandbrit.com ▪ www.boerandbrit.com ▪ S33° 45' 6.86" E 018° 57' 43.80" ▪ F +27 (0)86-531-7137 ▪ **T +27 (0)21-863-0940**

☐ **Boland Cellar** *see* Boland Kelder

Boland Kelder

For more than six decades, Paarl's grower-owned Boland Kelder has promoted regional diversity, harnessing the five climatic regions in their catchment area to produce wines of quality and value. First to plant (and bottle, in 2005) nouvelle, pungently aromatic crossing of trebbiano/ugni blanc and crouchen blanc, Boland is relaunching the variety as a 'concept wine' under a Granny Smith label. New international markets are targeted and, with a blueprint in place, the goal is to become 'a national and international leading producer cellar'. Who better to lead the charge than Johan Joubert, returning as cellarmaster after a star-studded decade at Kleine Zalze.

Cellar Reserve range

★★★★ **Shiraz** ⊘ Pronounced black pepper nose on **12** gives way to sweet black fruit coupled with spicy Italian meats. Tannins quite dry & grippy, & will benefit from time or food but lots of potential.

★★★★ **Chenin Blanc** Delicious **13** improves on **12** (★★★★) as natural ferment adds oatmeal to dried fruit & cream. Wonderfully managed oak gives smooth definition & richness to a serious, ageworthy wine.

Also tasted: **Cabernet Sauvignon 11** ★★★☆ **Merlot 11** ★★★☆ **Pinotage 11** ★★★☆ **Chardonnay 12** ★★★☆

Five Climates Single Varietal range

Merlot ⊘ ⊛ ★★★☆ Accessible, affordable **12** gives thoroughly pleasant drinking experience, with bright black fruit, juicy tannins, good texture. **Chenin Blanc** ⊘ ⊛ ★★★☆ **14** continues deserved success of last year's Superquaffer of the Year with grapefruity tang & well-balanced acidity. Should be a summer staple in everyone's fridge. Also tasted: **Cabernet Sauvignon 13** ★★★ **Pinotage 12** ★★★ **Shiraz** ⊘ **12** ★★★★ **Chardonnay 14** ★★★ **Sauvignon Blanc 14** ★★★ **Cape Ruby 10** ★★★ Not retasted: **Red Muscadel 12** ★★★

Cappupino Ccinotage range

Cappupino Ccinotage ★★ Was 'Cappupinoccinotage'. **13** 'coffee pinotage' delivers on the name with lots of sweet java (& berry jam) notes, contrastingly acerbic finish.

Sixty 40 Blend range

Chenin Blanc-Sauvignon Blanc ★★★ Another crowd-pleasing charmer, **14** off-dry but balanced, a happy, fresh 60/40 blend. Also tasted: **Cabernet Sauvignon-Shiraz 13** ★★★

Flutterby range

Merlot ★★ 12's plump fruit followed by markedly dry tannins best enjoyed with rich casseroles. Not retasted: **Sauvignon Blanc 13 ★★** Discontinued: **Rosé**. Range in slim PET (plastic) bottles.

Granny Smith range

Nouvelle ★☆ 13 strident green fruit character, food-inviting banana skin astringency. — CM

Location/WO: Paarl ▪ Map: Paarl & Wellington ▪ Est/1stB 1947 ▪ Tasting & sales Mon-Fri 9–5 Sat & pub hols 9–1 ▪ Closed Easter Fri-Sun, Ascension day, Sep 24, Dec 25/26 & Jan 1 ▪ Cellar tours by appt ▪ Wynvlieg cellar theatre open for venue hire ▪ Owner(s) 76 producing shareholders ▪ Cellarmaster(s) Johan Joubert (Aug 2014) ▪ Winemaker(s) JD Rossouw (Sep 2007) & Bernard Smuts (Dec 2001), with Heidi Dietstein (Dec 2009), Handré Barkhuizen (Dec 2009) & Andrie le Roux (Dec 2012) ▪ Viticulturist(s) Jaco Engelbrecht (Feb 2012) ▪ 1,900ha (cab, merlot, ptage, shiraz, chard, chenin, nouvelle, sauv, viog) ▪ 21,881t/240,000cs own label 50% red 40% white 10% rosé + 400,000cs for clients ▪ Other export brands: Lindenhof, Montestell ▪ WIETA ▪ PO Box 7007 Noorder-Paarl 7623 ▪ lizmar@bolandkelder.co.za ▪ www.bolandkelder.co.za, www.bolandcellar.co.za, www.bolandwines.co.za ▪ S 33° 48' 47.21" E 018° 48' 31.70" (farm), S 33° 41' 19.6" E 018° 57' 20.1" (deli) ▪ F +27 (0)21-862-5379 ▪ **T +27 (0)21-862-6190**

Bon Cap Organic Winery

Seven generations of Du Preez have lived on this Robertson farm, growing wine grapes since the 1920s. Bottling under the Bon Cap label started in 2002, a year the farm received organic status. 'It's still a benefit,' say Roelf and Michelle du Preez, 'although certification costs to international standards increase annually, which is hard for the small producer.'

Bon Cap range

★★★★ Perfect Blend ⊘ Now **NV** from pinotage, cab & dash petit verdot; improves on last, vintage-dated **09 (★★★★)**. Cinnamon, nutmeg & vibrant raspberry/cherry fruit, a silky texture, long tail. Robertson WO.

★★★★ Cape Blend ⊗ Unusual combo pinotage, petit verdot, cab works in polished & fresh **07 (★★★★)**. 1st tasted since **05**. **06** sold out untasted.

Cape Ruby ★★★ **NV** port-style from touriga, sampled pre-bottling. Moist fruitcake styling, richly textured, sweet & luscious, with a nice alcohol grip at the end. Robertson fruit. Not retasted: **Méthode Cap Classique 07 ★★★★** In abeyance: **Viognier**.

Ruins/Green House range

Sauvignon Blanc ★★★ Initial impression of **14** tank sample is gooseberries but the wine's true character is the grapefruit & flinty minerality emerging later, settling into a long finish. Also tasted: **Pinotage 13 ★★★ Rosé 14 ★★★ Chardonnay-Viognier 14 ★★★** Not tasted: **Syrah-Cabernet Sauvignon**. — CR

Location/map: Robertson ▪ WO: Eilandia/Robertson/Stellenbosch ▪ Est 2001 ▪ 1stB 2002 ▪ Tasting & sales Mon-Fri 8–5 Sun 10–4 ▪ Closed Sat due to weddings & functions ▪ Bon Rouge Bistro ▪ Facilities for children ▪ Cheese platters ▪ Sunday buffet ▪ Guest house ▪ Owner(s) Roelf & Michelle du Preez/SHZ Winery (Pty) Ltd ▪ Winemaker(s)/viticulturist(s) Roelf du Preez ▪ 460ha/40ha (cab, p verdot, ptage, pinot, shiraz, chard, cbard, sauv, viog) ▪ 200t/4,000cs own label 61% red 37% white 2% rosé ▪ Other export brand: The Greenhouse ▪ Brands for clients: The UK Societies ▪ Certified organic by SGS ▪ PO Box 356 Robertson 6705 ▪ info@boncap.co.za ▪ www.boncaporganic.co.za ▪ S 33° 47' 1.0" E 019° 40' 53.2" ▪ F +27 (0)23-626-5789 ▪ **T +27 (0)23-626-2073**

Bon Courage Estate

Successive generations have placed their stamp on this storied Robertson riverside property once called Goedemoed. In 1927 Willie Bruwer planted steen and muscadel grapes, while son André expanded when he took over in 1965 and then registered it as Bon Courage Estate in 1983. André created a reputation for sweet wines while his successor, third-generation Jacques, added bubbly and shiraz to the repertoire with increasing critical acclaim and success in recent years.

Inkará range

★★★★ **Cabernet Sauvignon** Intense black berries, liquorice & coffee from new oak (18-24 months) in full-bodied **12**. Tremendous power, dense fruit packed around a solid frame. Impressive now & should reward cellaring 3+ years. Whole-berry ferment (as for Shiraz).

★★★★ **Shiraz 12** (★★★★) complex melange bramble, spiced plum, toasted oak, black tea & pepper. Refreshing acidity lifts ripe, New World profile; oak (50%, American) not quite as harmonious as choc-mint **11**.

Not retasted: **Pinot Noir 10** ★★★

Bon Courage Méthode Cap Classique range

★★★★☆ **Jacques Bruére Cuvée Rosé Brut** Complex salmon-hued sparkling, mainly pinot noir (80%), chardonnay. **08** offers red apple, sour cherry, earth & jasmine; remarkably fresh for its age. Same league as silky **07**, with persistent mousse & length, appetising finish.

★★★★ **Cap Classique Jacques Bruére Brut Reserve Blanc de Blancs** Consistently excellent sparkling chardonnay, **09** pronounced smokiness from 10% barrel fermented/lees-aged component, green apple & lemon acidity. Deserves its upmarket packaging.

★★★★☆ **Cap Classique Jacques Bruére Brut Reserve** Like all-chardonnay version, partly oaked, but extra ±36 months in bottle. Notes of sourdough & salted biscuits, mature palate of cured meats, baked limes & mushrooms on pinot/chardonnay **09** (★★★★) bone-dry sparkling. Misses the zingy freshness of **08** (★★★★★) & **07**.

Bon Courage range

★★★★ **Chardonnay Prestige Cuvée** Barrel/lees-ageing (8 months older oak) noticeable but integrated on juicy **13**. Toasted brioche & citrus blossom perfume, richness enlivened by appetising acidity & minerality. Up a notch on **12** (★★★☆).

★★★★ **Noble Late Harvest** ⊘ Elegant botrytised riesling dessert, unoaked. **11** apricot preserve & chocolate-dipped citrus flavour is succulent, super-concentrated, just misses perfect seam of acidity of **10** (★★★★★).

★★★★ **White Muscadel 14** fortified dessert very youthful, unctuous honey & spice, balanced acidity & long finish. Deserves decade to develop inherent complexity. Improves on very sweet **13**.

Cabernet Sauvignon ★★★☆ Über-ripe **12** displays many characteristic aromas from blackcurrant & prune, to chocolate & tobacco. Rich & supple, with good support from oak. Well-made crowd pleaser. **André's Fame Colombard** ★★★ Bouncy, friendly **14** packed with tropical fruit, white peach & kiwi, good few grams sugar for easy, chilled summer sipping. Also tasted: **Pinotage 13** ★★★ **Shiraz 12** ★★★ **Hillside Red 12** ★★★ **Chardonnay Unwooded 14** ★★ **Gewürztraminer Dry 14** ★★☆ **Sauvignon Blanc 14** ★★☆ **Hillside White 14** ★★☆ **Blush Vin Doux NV** ★★ **Gewürztraminer Special Late Harvest 14** ★★★ **Red Muscadel 14** ★★★☆ **Cape Vintage 13** ★★☆

Like Father Like Son range

Cabernet Sauvignon-Merlot ★★ **13** uncomplicated unwooded red for the BBQ; plenty of juicy black fruit & pleasantly robust tannins. Also tasted: **Chenin Blanc 14** ★★ Not retasted: **Pinotage Rosé 13** ★★ — HJ

Location/map/WO: Robertson ▪ Est 1927 ▪ 1stB 1983 ▪ Tasting & sales Mon-Fri 8—5 Sat 9—3 ▪ Fee R20pp for groups of 10+ ▪ Closed Good Fri, Dec 25 & Jan 1 ▪ Café Maude T +27 (0)23-626-6806 ▪ Facilities for children ▪ Olive oil ▪ Owner(s) André & Jacques Bruwer ▪ Winemaker(s) Jacques Bruwer ▪ Viticulturist(s) André Bruwer ▪ 150ha (cab, pinot, shiraz, chard) ▪ 40% red 50% white 10% rosé ▪ Export brand: Three Rivers ▪ PO Box 589 Robertson 6705 ▪ wine@boncourage.co.za ▪ www.boncourage.co.za ▪ S 33° 50' 43.8" E 019° 57' 38.0" ▪ F +27 (0)23-626-3581 ▪ T +27 (0)23-626-4178

For more information, visit wineonaplatter.com

Bonfoi Estate

Boutique winery Bonfoi is situated on a very old estate in Stellenboschkloof, founded in 1699 and in the Van der Westhuizen family for several generations now. The name, meaning 'Good Faith' was given by two French ladies who purchased the farm in the 18th century.

Location/map: Stellenbosch ▪ Est 1699 ▪ 1stB 1974 ▪ Tasting & sales by appt only ▪ Closed all pub hols ▪ BYO picnic ▪ Walks ▪ Conservation area ▪ Owner(s)/winemaker(s)/viticulturist(s) Johannes van der Westhuizen ▪ 200ha/89ha (cabs s/f, merlot, pinots noir/meunier, ptage, shiraz, chard, chenin, sauv, sem) ▪ 800t/2,000cs own label 60% red 40% white ▪ BWI ▪ PO Box 9 Vlottenburg 7604 ▪ bonfoi@mweb.co.za ▪ www.bonfoiwines.co.za ▪ S 33° 56' 29.1" E 018° 46' 29.8" ▪ F +27 (0)21-881-3807 ▪ **T +27 (0)21-881-3774**

☐ **Bonne Esperance** *see* KWV

Bonnievale Wines

Revamping of wines and visitor attractions continues at the grower-owned cellar outside Bonnievale village. Much of the focus here is on vineyard management, resulting in a portfolio with differing price:quality ratios but the single aim of being 'unpretentious' (the winery's slogan). Top-performing 'winemakers' blocks' are nurtured to produce high-end wines for the Barrel Select label, under guidance of chief winemaker Marthinus Rademeyer. Food-and-wine pairings add further value to a visit.

Barrel Select range

★★★★ Shiraz ⊘ Another step up in **12**, smoky leather, tobacco & savoury spice mingle with dark berry flavours & some dark chocolate, 50% new oak adds complexity. Worth keeping a while, like **11** (**★★★★**).

Also tasted: **Cabernet Sauvignon 12 ★★★** Note: range was 'Vertex Reserve'.

Bonnievale range

Merlot ★★★ Understated but warm & welcoming **13**, savoury dark chocolate notes & hint of oak, plum pudding ripeness on palate with nice spicy exit. **Cabernet Sauvignon-Shiraz ★★☆** Juicy & spicy **13**, soft dark berry flavours, easygoing steakhouse red. **Sauvignon Blanc ★★★** **14** unpretentious & fresh seafood accompaniment, with modest alcohol. Also tasted: **Shiraz 12 ★★ Cabernet Sauvignon-Merlot 13 ★★☆ Chardonnay 14 ★★** Not retasted: **Sauvignon Blanc Brut NV ★★** Discontinued: **Cape Ruby**.

Riggton range

Red ★★ Mixed berries & light texture, unwooded **14** makes for easy, uncomplicated drinking. Also tasted: **Semi Sweet 13** Not retasted: **White 13 ★☆**

Perlé range

Dawn ★☆ Light (9% alcohol) & spritzy **NV**, semi-sweet with a hint of pineapple. Not retasted: **Dusk NV ★** — DB, WB, CR

Location/WO: Bonnievale ▪ Map: Robertson ▪ Est 1951 ▪ 1stB 1977 ▪ Tasting & sales Mon-Fri 9–5 Sat 10–1 ▪ Closed Easter Fri-Mon, Dec 25/26 & Jan 1 ▪ Cheese straws, biltong/droëwors, food & wine pairing ▪ Facilities for children ▪ Tour groups ▪ Conferences (12 pax) ▪ CCC Christmas Market ▪ Owner(s) 110 members ▪ Winemaker(s) Marthinus Rademeyer (Dec 2009), with Jolene le Roux (Aug 2007), Edwin Mathambo (Dec 2012), Mynhardt van der Merwe (Oct 2013) & Jean Aubrey (Jan 2014) ▪ Viticulturist(s) Sakkie Bosman (Nov 2006) ▪ 1,720ha (cab, merlot, shiraz, chard, chenin, cbard, sauv) ▪ 30,000t/90,000cs own label 30% red 55% white 10% perlé 5% juice + 120,000cs for clients ▪ IPW, WIETA ▪ PO Box 206 Bonnievale 6730 ▪ info@bonnievalewines.co.za ▪ www.bonnievalewines.co.za ▪ S 33° 57' 27" E 020° 06' 06" ▪ F +27 (0)23-616-2332 ▪ **T +27 (0)23-616-2795**

☐ **Bonny Bay** *see* Blomendahl Vineyards
☐ **Bonolo** *see* Blomendahl Vineyards

Bon Terroir

Climate, soil and slopes were all just right for growing winegrapes. So thought the founders of this tiny Stellenbosch farm, who celebrated these conditions in its name. It all seemed propitious for red wine, so cabernet (sauvignon and a little franc) it was - still crafted with the eminent Bruwer Raats.

★★★★ **Cabernet Sauvignon** Attractive cassis & tomato cocktail notes on **11** (★★★☆), but fruit struggles to cope with firm tannin structure. Last, conducive-vintage **09** riper, more substantial. — JPf

Location/WO: Stellenbosch ▪ Est 2002 ▪ 1stB 2007 ▪ Closed to public ▪ Owner(s) Agri Marketing Exchange (Pty) Ltd, with shareholder Will-Mag Holdings Ltd ▪ Winemaker(s) Bruwer Raats (2007, consultant) ▪ 15.5ha/4ha (cabs s/f) ▪ 5t/600cs own label 100% red ▪ PO Box 12511 Die Boord 7613 ▪ willie@willmag.co.za ▪ www.bonterroir.co.za ▪ F +27 (0)86-622-8254 ▪ **T +27 (0)82-445-3440**

Bonview Wines

Negociant business Bonview was established in 2011 to produce wine and grape juice for export. Owner Teuns Keuzenkamp has long-term contracts with various Cape cellars, and targets mainly West Africa and China with 'quality wines that are affordable and attuned to the tastes of everyday wine consumers'.

Pegalle range
Not retasted: **Cabernet Sauvignon 11** ★★★ **Merlot 10** ★★ **Shiraz 11** ★★★ — HJ, JP

Location: Somerset West ▪ WO: Stellenbosch/Western Cape ▪ Est 2011 ▪ 1stB 2012 ▪ Closed to public ▪ Owner(s) Teuns Keuzenkamp ▪ 5,700cs own label 95% red 5% white ▪ PO Box 1977 Somerset West 7129 ▪ bonview@telkomsa.net ▪ F +27 (0)86-224-9348 ▪ **T +27 (0)21-887-5812**

Boplaas Family Vineyards

A mistake led to the Nel family's ongoing success with their Portuguese-themed range: in the 1980s, current owner Carel's father Danie ordered shiraz vines but was sent tinta barocca instead. Nothing ventured, nothing gained; knowing this was a 'port' variety, father and son immediately took up the challenge of making top-quality port-style fortified wines. Carel, with daughter Margaux in the cellar, now have their eyes on making world-class (unfortified) table wines from Portuguese varieties. The first such reds have since been joined by a white version. Distilling is a much older heritage; it dates back to the late 19th century when Carel Nel's great-great grandfather, Daniel, exported brandy to England. Today, the extensive Boplaas range culminates with a range of superb brandies.

Heritage Reserve range
★★★★☆ **White Muscadel** Ⓩ Was 'Muscadel'. Limited bottling in exceptional years to honour Nel family association with fortified muscadel since mid-1800s. From white muscadel, fragrant **11** honeyed & rich; delicious now but will reward lengthy cellaring. WO Goudini.

Red Muscadel (NEW) ★★★★☆ Wonderfully fragrant, bright & beautiful grapey flavours with rosepetal perfume, all balanced by lively acidity. **12** fortified cries out for a delicious piece of cheese. 375 ml.

Family Reserve range
★★★★ **Gamka** (NEW) Solid debut **12** from mainly touriga with 22% shiraz in perfumed swirls of flowers, marshmallows & dried plums. Spicy pepper notes take over on the palate with black berries, leather & tar. Calitzdorp, Stellenbosch & Wellington grapes.

★★★★ **Bobbejaanberg Sauvignon Blanc Reserve** Dazzling **14** from Upper Langkloof shows lashings of zippy fruit - tinned grapefruit, pineapple, green figs & pears. Freshening acidity already well integrated, lovely depth of flavour suggests more to come.

Ring of Rocks ★★★★ Sweetly spiced **13** Portuguese-blend of touriga franca & tinta barocca from Stellenbosch pleases with lots of sweet black fruit, firm tannins. Modern, forthright, enjoyable wine.
Not retasted: **Cabernet Sauvignon 09** ★★★ **Pinot Noir Méthode Cap Classique 09** ★★★☆
Not tasted: **Shiraz**, **Cabernet Sauvignon-Shiraz**.

Boplaas range

★★★★ **Cape Portuguese White Blend** ⓝ Unusual & interesting **14** blend of 50% verdelho with chardonnay & sauvignon. Peachily fresh, with good balancing acidity & a rich mid-palate, a great wine for bacalhau or any other fish.

★★★★ **Straw Wine** ⓝ Exuberant aromas & flavours of tinned pineapples, ripe & fresh mangoes & honeyed peach assault the senses on **13** debut. From vine-dried viognier, unwooded, the tropical fruit bomb is balanced by well-judged acidity & zippy finish.

★★★★ **Hanepoot Reserve** ⓐ Fortified dessert from 50+ year old vines planted by Nel patriarch, Oom Danie. 375ml of liquid temptation, poised & persistent, though **13** tad less fresh than last-tasted **11** (★★★★★).

★★★★☆ **Red Muscadel Vintners Reserve** ⓐ Senior citizen **75** suave, engaging, with fully integrated dried fruit flavour, tannin & alcohol.

★★★★ **Red Muscadel** ⓐ **13** puts up a spirited attack which, with time, should mellow pleasingly. Raisins, Karoo dust & spicy flick; similar to zesty **12** (★★★★) tank sample but showing greater weight.

★★★★☆ **Muscadel Reserve** ⓐ Gingery/grapey **10** fortified dessert is beautifully structured with crisp acid, silky fruit & spicy sweetness (213 g/l sugar). Poise in a glass.

★★★★☆ **Cape Vintage Reserve Port 10** included 'Show Selection' in name. **11** shows sleek muscularity in voluptuous mouthful of fruitcake, spicy plum pudding, nutmeg, clove & citrus peel. Fiery alocohol needs time to tame, but concentration ensures development . Tourigas nacional & franca, tinta, souzão. WO W Cape.

★★★★☆ **Cape Tawny Port** ⓐ **NV** from tinta, touriga, souzão. Nutty & spicy from long ageing in barrel, wonderfully balanced, shows mere hint of sweetness on the aftertaste. WO W Cape.

★★★★ **Cape Vintage** Port-style from touriga (80%), tinta & souzão. Pronounced floral notes on **12** vie with orange peel & angelica before slightly thick-textured entry gives way to raisined fruit & dark plums. Smooth but present tannins suggest a good future.

★★★★ **Cape Ruby** Delicious & well-balanced port-style **NV** offers delightful everyday drinking with bright black & red berries, some raisin character & just-warming alcohol. Over-deliverer of note. Tinta, touriga, & souzão (70/20/10).

★★★★★ **Cape Tawny Vintners Reserve** Concentrated nose on latest port-style **NV** with toffee apples, burnt sugar, toasted hazelnuts & a touch of coffee. The taste journey continues with layers of raisined fruit, wonderful oak/alcohol integration & massive finish. WO W Cape, as was previous.

★★★★★ **Cape Tawny Port** ⓐ A tinta, touriga, souzão mix (90/8/2), **97** exceptionally classy. Rich & sleek, with superb spirit integration (±19%) from 12 years in old barrels. W Cape WO.

★★★★ **Chocolate Cape Vintage** ⓐ After hedonistic **09**, port-style tinta (70%), touriga **10** (★★★★) similar lushness, vivid flavours but tannins still obvious when tasted. Should since have knit. WO W Cape.

★★★★☆ **Cape Tawny Reserve** ⓐ Masterly **95** fortified from tinta (90%) & touriga 'made before Calitzdorp even became a WO district' says cellarmaster Carel Nel. 12 years in cask yield complex, intense medley of nuts, toffee, orange marmalade, lingering dry conclusion. 375ml. WO Klein Karoo.

Tinta Barocca ⓥ ★★★★ Juicily gluggable **13** cheers & heartens with lots of black/red fruit & tarry finish. **Tinta Chocolat** ★★★ Well-restrained, 'choc-coffee' styled **13** from tinta barocca is soft & juicy. WO W Cape. **Pinot Noir Brut Sparkling** ★★★ **13** dry bubbly improves with true pretty-in-pink character, delicate red berries & trim acidic bite. Also tasted: **Cabernet Sauvignon** 12 ★★★ **Merlot** 12 ★★★ **Touriga Nacional** 13 ★★★ Not retasted: **Pinotage** 11 ★★☆ **Shiraz** 08 ★★★☆ **Stoepsit Sauvignon Blanc** 13 ★★★ **Hanepoot** 12 ★★★ **Red Muscadel Reserve** 11 ★★★ **White Muscadel** 13 ★★★ **Cape Pink** NV ★★★ **Cape White Port** NV ★★★ Not tasted: **Cape Tawny Show Reserve**. Discontinued: **Chardonnay Unwooded, Moscato Light, Sauvignon Blanc, Viognier**.

Cool Bay range

★★★★ **Sauvignon Blanc Reserve** ⓥ **13** (★★★★), from old Darling bushvines, made for sea-food: crisp & dry with characteristic salty edge, good length. Shade less textured than **12** tank sample. Discontinued: **Sauvignon Blanc**.

Brandy range

★★★★★ **Potstill 20 Years** ⓥ Gold coloured with hint of olive green on rim. Fruitcake, dried apricots, marzipan, sweet prune flavours, mingling with smooth vanilla. Super-complex, elegant & silky palate - both delicate & penetrating - leads to a gorgeous long finish. Just 500 bottles made.

★★★★☆ **Carel Nel 15 Years Reserve** ⓥ Rich amber colour with apricot & peardrop, potpourri wafts. Seductive, rich with caramel, almonds & hint of smoke. Full bodied & mouthfilling, well integrated alcohol. Complex, strikes fine balance between rich fruit & oak. Less ethereal than 20YO, touch less drily refined.

★★★★☆ **Potstill 8 Years** ⓥ Caramel, sweet & smoky oak, fuller bodied with chocolate, dried peaches, pear & apricot. Silky & complex, still youthful, with a clean vanilla finish. Good example of a fresh young serious potstill. 100% potstill, as is 20YO.

★★★★☆ **CWG Auction Reserve Ox Wagon 1880 8 Years Potstill** ⓝⓔⓦ 8 year old unfiltered potstill from colombard. Deep glinting amber, concentrated & complex flavours of marmalade, honey, fragrant dusty Karoo scrub, dried peaches, exotic spice & delightful candied citrus spice. Long, lingering finish.

Carel Nel 5 Years Reserve ⓥ ★★★★ Leafy fresh notes with dried apricot & pear aromas. Rich vanilla complexity, yet delicate & smooth, with a floral dry finish. 40% potstill, as is 15 year old. All of these brandies from colombard, all unfiltered & unfined. **Potstill 10 Years** ⓝⓔⓦ ★★★★ From colombard, 10 year old potstill is bright amber, with dried fruit, floral wafts & cinnamon on well-matured, rich frame. Dry, spicy finish. — WB, CM, TJ

Location: Calitzdorp • Map: Klein Karoo & Garden Route • WO: Calitzdorp/Western Cape/Goudini/Stellenbosch/Upper Langkloof/Klein Karoo/Coastal • Est 1880 • 1stB 1982 • Tasting & sales Mon-Fri 8-5 Sat 9-3 Sun 10-2 • Fee R35pp • Closed Good Fri & Dec 25 • Cellar tours by appt • Facilities for children • Gifts • Farm produce • Walks/hikes • Conservation area • Ring of Rocks • Owner(s) Carel Nel • Cellarmaster(s) Carel Nel (1982) • Winemaker(s) Margaux Nel (Dec 2006) • Viticulturist(s) Pieter Terblanche • 2,300ha/70ha (cab, ptage, shiraz, tinta, touriga, chard, cbard, sauv) • 55% red 45% white • BWI, IPW • PO Box 156 Calitzdorp 6660 • info@boplaas.co.za • www.boplaas.co.za • S 33° 32' 8.0" E 021° 41' 1.9" (Boplaas), S 34° 4' 45.40" E 022° 8' 25.22" (Cool Bay) • F +27 (0)44-213-3750 • **T +27 (0)44-213-3326**

☐ **Borg Family Wines** *see* Painted Wolf Wines
☐ **Born & Bred in South Africa** *see* BABISA - Born & Bred in South Africa

Boschendal Wines   ⓨ ⓘⓘ ⓒ ⓐ ⓑ

Established in 1685 by French Huguenot Jean Le Long, DGB-owned Boschendal is one of South Africa's oldest and best-known estates and, with the stately Groot Drakenstein peaks as a backdrop, one of the most picturesque. Elegant Cape Dutch architecture, ancient oak trees, tasting facilities, wine bar and Le Pique Nique (sun/starlit picnics on the pavillion lawns) contribute to its evergreen appeal. The wine offer caters for every budget and occasion, from everyday enjoyment (note the new S&M and Larone reds and Rose Garden rosé) to limited-release keepers expressing distinctive terroirs.

Cecil John Reserve range

★★★★★ **Shiraz** Accomplished flagship. Restrained **12** less opulently fruited than **11** (★★★★★), shows more of the poise & seamlessness of **10**. Authoritative, with satisfying dryness & grip, judicious 30% new oak provides structure to improve up to a decade.

Reserve Collection

★★★★☆ **Syrah** Was 'Shiraz'. Violets & white pepper, ripe red plums & berries on generous **12**; well-judged tight tannin frame for food or ageing 5+ years. Like **11** (★★★★), departs from 100% new oak for previous vintages, here only 20%.

★★★★ **Grande Reserve** Switches to more conventional shiraz (65%) & cab blend (**11** was petit verdot, shiraz), from Stellenbosch grapes. **12** opens to mix red & black berries, lead pencil & slight leafiness; focused, savoury yet with dense fruit centre, concluding dry.

★★★★ **Chardonnay** ⓧ **12** (★★★★★) good lemon fruit intensity, well-judged wooding (third new) though not quite as persistent as **11** (★★★★★), which improved on **09**. **10** untasted.

★★★★ **Sauvignon Blanc** ⓧ **13** cool green capsicum, fig & nettle, poised & compact with well-judged acidity. Like **12**, has great presence & is a fine-dining companion.

★★★★☆ **Grande Cuvée Méthode Cap Classique Brut** ⓧ Classy **09** chardonnay/pinot noir celebrator has racy bubbles, baked apple & brioche notes from 3 years on lees. Like **08**, rich flavours buoyed by zesty acidity.

★★★★ **Jean Le Long Méthode Cap Classique** ⓧ Bone-dry & mineral sparkling from chardonnay. 'Oystershell' & biscuit tones, **07** shows little of the creaminess expected from 5 years lees-ageing.

★★★★ **Vin d'Or** ⊘ Usually a Natural Sweet, now-bottled **12** (★★★★★) certified as Noble Late Harvest. From riesling & viognier, a step up on **11** chenin/riesling combo; gloriously complex - apricots, marmalade, positive chemical tones of botrytis; sweet melon & papaya palate given verve by lime acidity. WO W Cape.

Also tasted: **Le Grande Pavillion Méthode Cap Classique Brut Rosé NV** ★★★☆ **Grande Cuvée Méthode Cap Classique Brut NV** ★★★☆

Elgin Series

★★★★ **Chardonnay** ⓧ Toast & vanilla overlay, pure lemon core & long, balanced finish the hallmarks of **11**. Deftly oaked (30% new, 11 months), medium bodied, a confident expression.

★★★★☆ **Sauvignon Blanc** ⓧ Accomplished **12** sets a high standard, delivering a smooth, delicate mouthful that is also satisfyingly long & vinous.

Not retasted: **Pinot Noir 12** ★★★☆

1685 range

Shiraz ★★★ Perfumed **12** layered & savoury, very juicy, with enlivening grip & acidity. **S&M** ⓝⓔⓦ ★★★ **12** coffee-toned Rhône blend shiraz (70%) & mourvèdre. Lovely dense fruit & pleasing grip, intense yet accessible, fresh. Partially oaked, 25% new. **Chardonnay** ★★★ Toasty buttery nose, lime & lemon acidity combine with yielding palate & fruit-sweet conclusion to make **13** a real crowd pleaser. WO W Cape. Also tasted: **Merlot 13** ★★★ **Shiraz-Cabernet Sauvignon 12** ★★★ **Chardonnay-Pinot Noir 14** ★★★ **Sauvignon Blanc Grand Vin Blanc 14** ★★★

Boschendal Classics

Larone ⓝⓔⓦ ★★☆ Shiraz & mourvèdre blend named for the 1685 Boschendal homestead. **12** mocha & cream tones, firm tarry flavours to match steak & hearty stews. **Blanc de Noir** ★★★ Merlot, pinotage & shiraz are the noirs in pretty pink, lipsmacking **14**. Cue the oysters or salmon. **Rose Garden Rosé** ⓝⓔⓦ ★★☆ Perfect aperitif enjoyment delivered by sunset-hued **14**, bled from merlot & assorted reds, dry & tangy. **Le Bouquet** ★★☆ Grapey rosewater attraction in **14** from mixed white varieties. Gently sweet but with sufficient grip & pith for solo or spicy foods. WO W Cape. Also tasted: **Lanoy 12** ★★★ **Rachel's Chenin Blanc 14** ★★★ **Boschen Blanc 14** ★★★

Pavillion range

Shiraz-Cabernet Sauvignon ★★☆ **13** bursts with charry fruit; juicy, focused, not overbearing; perfect everyday drinking. WO W Cape. Also tasted: **Pavillion Blanc 14** ★★☆ — CvZ

Location/map: Franschhoek ▪ WO: Coastal/Western Cape/Elgin/Stellenbosch ▪ Est 1685 ▪ 1stB 1975 ▪ Tasting & sales daily 11-5.30 (Oct-Mar) & 11-4.30 (Apr-Sep) ▪ Fee R35pp ▪ Chocolate & wine tasting R65pp, booking essential ▪ Closed Good Fri, May 1, Jun 16 & Dec 25 ▪ Cellar tours daily 10.30, 11.30 & 3 ▪ Cheese platters on request ▪ Restaurant ▪ Facilities for children ▪ Tour groups ▪ Gifts ▪ Museum ▪ Owner(s) DGB (Pty) Ltd ▪ Cellarmaster(s) JC Bekker (1986) ▪ Winemaker(s) Lizelle Gerber (whites, 2006) & Bertho van der Westhuizen (reds, 2012), with Lionel Leibrandt (1999) ▪ Viticulturist(s) Stephan Joubert (2006) ▪ 2,240ha/200ha (shiraz, sauv) ▪ 3,100t/500,000cs own label 32% red 43% white 14% rosé 11% sparkling ▪ WIETA ▪ Private Bag X03 Groot Drakenstein 7680 ▪ cellardoor@dgb.co.za ▪ www. boschendalwines.com ▪ S 33° 52' 27.5" E 018° 58' 34.4" ▪ F +27 (0)21-874-1531 ▪ **T +27 (0)21-870-4200**

☐ **Boschetto** *see* Stellekaya Winery

Boschheim

Involved in international and local wine consulting and winemaking, polymer scientist, phenolic ripeness expert and boutique cellar owner Andy Roediger vinifies for his own label whenever time allows. It's an ever-evolving range, the Stellenbosch-based Cape Wine Master having excellent grape contacts throughout the winelands.

Boschheim range

Mourvèdre ★★★☆ Perfumed **13** has bold & expressive pastille fruit intensity, firm savoury finish, good balance & oak integration. From Paarl vines. **Elemental Shiraz ★★★☆** Vanilla & coffee nuances on **13** combine well with brooding dark fruit & savoury, spicy notes. Fair acidity lifts the palate. WO Paarl. Not retasted: **Cabernet Sauvignon 09 ★★★☆ Pinot Noir 13 ★★★☆ Ella Marie 11 ★★★☆**

Muse range

Calliope (NEW) ★★★☆ 11 almost equal portions cab & shiraz; has earthy elegance, delicate frame. Also tasted: **Cabernet Sauvignon 12 ★★★** — HJ

Location/map: Stellenbosch ▪ WO: Stellenbosch/Paarl/Western Cape ▪ 1stB 2003 ▪ Tasting & sales by appt ▪ Owner(s)/winemaker(s) Andy Roediger ▪ 1,800cs own label 85% red 15% white ▪ PO Box 3202 Matieland 7602 ▪ andy@roedigeragencies.co.za ▪ S 33° 55' 54.9" E 018° 50' 10.5" ▪ F +27 (0)21-886-4731 ▪ **T +27 (0)21-887-0010**

Boschkloof Wines

The personal touch is important to father-and-son team of Jacques and Reneen Borman at this boutique Stellenbosch property. Consequently, visitors often find themselves invited into the cellar for an impromptu tour and barrel tasting, usually of shiraz, the pair's shared not-so-secret passion. If this isn't enough to convince guests to linger, the revamped tasting room and new deck overlooking the vineyards, where they can enjoy the modern Rhône-style fruits of the Bormans' labours, should be.

★★★★ Syrah Opulent, darkly dense **12** (★★★★☆) from small yield has New World structure, Old World complexity. Pepper, prosciutto, scrub, even violets, chocolate, layered & admirable. Also-tasted **11**, similar in style, so no accident, but bit firmer structure.

★★★★ Conclusion Both cabs plus merlot, **11** lavished with care (70% new oak) & it shows. Hint of mint, cassis, cab franc's slight herbaceousness, all add to the complexity. Supple tannin backbone.

Chardonnay ★★★ Peach & almond styling, nice combo fruity/savoury, which makes **13** versatile with food. Round & soft, easily drinkable, fresh finish. Also tasted: **Merlot 11 ★★★★ Cabernet Sauvignon-Merlot 11 ★★★★ Sauvignon Blanc 14 ★★★** Not retasted: **Cabernet Sauvignon 11 ★★★☆** — CR

Location/map: Stellenbosch ▪ WO: Stellenbosch/Western Cape ▪ Est/1stB 1996 ▪ Tasting, sales & cellar tours Mon-Fri 9-5 Sat 10-3 ▪ Fee R30 ▪ Closed Easter Fri-Sun, Dec 25 & Jan 1 ▪ Cheese & charcuterie platters ▪ BYO picnic ▪ Owner(s)/cellarmaster(s) Jacques Borman ▪ Winemaker(s) Reenen Borman (Jun 2010) ▪ Viticulturist(s) Jacques Borman, with Reenen Borman ▪ 30ha/19ha (cabs s/f, merlot, shiraz, chard) ▪ ±100-150t/6-8,000cs own label 90% red 10% white ▪ PO Box 1340 Stellenbosch 7599 ▪ boschkloof@adept.co.za, info@boschkloofwines.com ▪ www.boschkloofwines.com ▪ S 33° 57' 37.0" E 018° 46' 11.8" ▪ F +27 (0)21-881-3032 ▪ **T +27 (0)21-881-3293 (office)/+27 (0)21-881-3268 (cellar)**

For more information, visit wineonaplatter.com

Boschrivier Wines: NJT Boerdery

Paediatrician Theo de Villiers inherited land near Stanford in the 1990s and initially sold off all the grapes. His great-grandfather, however, used to distil 'vaaljapie' in a small cellar on the property and Theo soon felt compelled to grow wine, the latest including an as yet untasted rosé.

Boschrivier range

★★★★ Shiraz ⊗ **11** rich, concentrated but not unbalanced. Dark fruit, attractive oak spice, bright acidity. More convincing than slightly overdone **09** (★★★★). **10** not tasted.

Cabernet Sauvignon (NEW) **★★★☆** Cedar, spearmint & cigarbox, with vanilla toffee from the oak. Medium-bodied, elegant, **12** has firm acidity & structure, wood tad dominant mid-2014. Overberg WO. **Sauvignon Blanc** (NEW) **★★★** Off-dry **14** floral & citrus notes, sugar builds weight on palate but firm acidity keeps it fresh. Very easy drinking, just lacks some focus. Cape South Coast WO. — HJ

Location: Stanford ▪ Map: Elgin, Walker Bay & Bot River ▪ WO: Klein River/Overberg/Cape South Coast ▪ Est 1998 ▪ 1stB 2002 ▪ Tasting & sales Mon-Fri 8-5 Sat 9-5 ▪ Closed Dec 25 ▪ Restaurant ▪ BYO picnic ▪ Gift shop ▪ Farm produce ▪ Conferences (20 pax) ▪ Walking/hiking & 4x4 trails ▪ Self-catering farm house ▪ Owner(s)/viticulturist(s) Theodore de Villiers ▪ Winemaker(s) Mike Dobrovic ▪ 14ha (cab, shiraz) ▪ 7t/ha ±1,950cs own label 68.5% red 21% white 10.5% rosé ▪ Remhoogte Caledon p/a 70 Fairbairn Street Worcester 6850 ▪ drnjtdevilliers@mweb.co.za ▪ www.boschrivierwines.co.za ▪ S 34° 23' 19.4" E 019° 37' 51.0" ▪ F +27 (0)23-342-2215 ▪ **T +27 (0)23-347-3313/2 ext 3; +27 (0)76-736-0351**

Bosman Family Vineyards

The Bosman family, whose roots in Wellington go back to 1798, produced wine continuously on their historic farm Lelienfontein until 1957, when the attention turned to their successful vine nursery. But with winemaking in the DNA, the younger generation was impelled to renovate the old cellar and in 2007, with consultant Corlea Fourie, resume the tradition. That same year a love affair with chenin blanc began, after an eleventh hour 'rethink' by Corlea and team saved the condemned Optenhorst ('Hilltop') vineyard. Subsequently revealed as SA's fourth oldest, its quality left everyone 'speechless'.

Unique Innovation range

★★★★ Adama Red Rich & spicy shiraz-led sextet of Rhône varieties with dash zinfandel/primitivo in **13**. Generous in flavour but not overly dense or heavy; nicely rounded, dry finish. **11**, **12** untasted.

★★★★ Adama White ⊗ **12** unsettled & oaky in youth. Full ripe blend of chenin, chardonnay & 3 others is more vinous than fruity, with balanced weight & freshness. Should benefit from year or 2. No **11**. WO W Cape.

Bosman Family Vineyards range

★★★★☆ Family Cuvée Erfenis Was just 'Erfenis'. Whole greater than parts in **11** five-way blend headed by pinotage. Already hint of evolution in its truffly savouriness; plenty more in store. Beautifully polished, fresh, with oak (best barrels only) complementary.

Not tasted: **30 Rosé**.

Fides range (NEW)

★★★★ Fides From grenache blanc, fermented & left on skins for 3 weeks. **13** muted citrus in aroma, more gold in hue. Still tight, grippy, also tangily fresh. Time should release underlying savoury weight. Very food friendly.

Special Vineyard Selection

★★★★ Pinotage Unusually elegant for warm-climate area. **12** attractive cherry, raspberry fragrance, persuasive flavours lifted by silky feel, balanced freshness. Tannin nip should harmonise in year/two. **11** sold out untasted.

★★★★ Optenhorst Chenin Blanc From 60+ year old vineyard, natural ferment in small French oak, 15% new. Suggestion of oxidative richness thrillingly juxtaposed with mineral vitality on tangily dry **12** (★★★★★). Harmonious & delicious; like **11**, concentration & structure allows lengthy cellaring.

Not retasted: **Cabernet Sauvignon 07 ★★★★** Not tasted: **Dolce Primitivo**. — AL

Location: Wellington ▪ Map: Paarl & Wellington ▪ WO: Wellington/Western Cape ▪ Est 1699 ▪ 1stB 2004 ▪ Tasting by appt ▪ Fee R50pp, waived on purchase ▪ Closed Easter Fri-Mon & Dec 19-Jan 5 ▪ Sales Mon-Thu 8-5 Fri 8-4.30 ▪ Cellar tours by appt ▪ Conservation area ▪ Bosman Release Celebration (Nov) ▪ Owner(s) Bosman family & Adama Workers Trust ▪ Cellarmaster(s) Petrus Bosman (Nov 2003) ▪ Winemaker(s) Corlea Fourie (Nov 2006), with Charlene Ferreira (Nov 2006) ▪ Viticulturist(s) Johan Viljoen (Mar 2014) ▪ 300ha (47 varieties r/w) ▪ 3,000t/20,000cs own label 70% red 25% white 5% rosé ▪ Brands for clients: Checkers; Sainsbury Supermarkets; The Cooperative ▪ BBBEE certificate (level 2), BWI, Fairtrade ▪ PO Box 9 Wellington 7654 ▪ taste@bosmanwines.com ▪ www.bosmanwines.com ▪ S 33° 37' 34.7" E019° 01' 28.9" ▪ F +27 (0)21-873-2517 ▪ **T +27 (0)21-873-3170**

☐ **Bosman's Hill** *see* Saxenburg Wine Farm

Botanica Wines

In 2008, American Ginny Povall decided to put down roots in South Africa and bought Protea Heights, a working flower farm in Devon Valley. She established a luxury guest house on the property and as a longtime wine enthusiast, also set about planting vineyards. While waiting for these to come into production, she sourced grapes from elsewhere — a chenin from Skurfberg near Clanwilliam quickly coming to be recognised as one of South Africa's best. The name 'Botanica' was inspired by an exhibition of 18th century British artist Mary Delany's astonishingly intricate botanical cut-paper collages.

Mary Delany Collection

★★★★★ Pinot Noir Now from Hemel-en-Aarde fruit, fragrantly floral **13** is divinely subtle & elegant. Lavender & red cherries in concentrated harmony, on velvet tannins, revealed in persistently unfurling layers. Consummate form & structure. **12** was ex Elgin.

★★★★★ Chenin Blanc Was 'Old Vine'. **13 (★★★★★)** follows brilliant form of **12**. Delicately nuanced yet profoundly expressive. Ripe tropical fruit laced with salty minerality, bolstered by finely integrated oak. Grapes from Citrusdal Mountain.

Big Flower range

★★★★ Cabernet Sauvignon ⊘ Ripe & generous **13** is accessible & appealing if atypical. Plum pudding fruit, with pepper & tobacco notes on silky tannin structure. Stellenbosch WO. No **10 - 12**.

Rosé 🆕 **★★★★** Hugely appealing pink from petit verdot & wood-fermented chenin. Baked quince, sweet oak spices in **14**. WO W Cape. Not retasted: **Merlot 10 ★★★★** — GdB

Location/map: Stellenbosch ▪ WO: Stellenbosch/Western Cape/Citrusdal Mountain ▪ Est/1stB 2008 ▪ Tasting by appt ▪ Wine sales Mon-Fri 8-5 ▪ Farm produce ▪ Conferences ▪ Walks/hikes ▪ Mountain biking trail ▪ Refreshments offered at Sugarbird Manor guest house ▪ Owner(s) Virginia C Povall ▪ Winemaker(s) Virginia Povall (Jan 2008) ▪ Viticulturist(s) Francois Viljoen ▪ 21.6ha/5ha (cabs s/f, merlot, p verdot, pinot) ▪ PO Box 12523 Die Boord 7613 ▪ ginny@botanicawines.com ▪ www.botanicawines.com ▪ S 33° 54' 18.5" E 018° 49' 25.4" ▪ **T +27 (0)21-865-2313**

Botha Wine Cellar

Being a bulk-wine specialist, this Breedekloof winery has the double advantage of unlimited scope for selection and minimal dependence on sales volumes when setting aside a tiny percentage of quality wines for bottling under its own label. Red-wine cellar extensions have increased capacity, translating into possible additional Reserve wines.

Dassie's Reserve range

Dassie's Rood ⊘ **★★★** Sweet & juicy light red fruit on **12** braai buddy from cinsaut, cab & ruby cab. Uncomplicated, with earthy finish. Not retasted: **Dassie's Rosé 13 ★★ Dassie's Blanc 13 ★★**

Botha range

★★★★ Hanepoot Jerepigo Heady muscat honeysuckle ripeness & sweet ginger to nose & palate of **13** fortified dessert maintains tone & quality of previous. Rich & viscous but not cloying. Lovely balance & palate weight, light on its feet, with long tail.

For more information, visit wineonaplatter.com

Merlot ⊘ ★★★ **13** squishy berry fruit, juicy & generous with dry spicy oak note. Bit rustic & chunky but nice. **Shiraz** ⊘ ★★★ **12** keeps up good work of previous. Soft plum & cherry fruit gently backed by oak. Also tasted: **Pinotage 12** ★★☆ **Chenin Blanc 14** ★★☆ **Chardonnay Brut NV** ★★☆ Not retasted: **Cabernet Sauvignon 09** ★★★ **Light White 13** ★★ **Red Jerepigo 08** ★★★ **Cape Vintage Reserve 10** ★★★ Not tasted: **Sauvignon Blanc**. — FM

Location: Worcester ▪ Map/WO: Breedekloof ▪ Est 1949 ▪ 1stB 1974 ▪ Tasting & sales Mon-Fri 9–5 Sat 10–1 ▪ Closed Easter Fri-Sun, Dec 25/26 & Jan 1 ▪ Cellar tours by appt ▪ BYO picnic ▪ Conservation area ▪ Breedekloof Soetes & Soup festival ▪ Owner(s) Botha Wynkelder (Edms) Bpk ▪ Production manager Johan Linde (Nov 1996) ▪ Cellarmaster(s) Gerrit van Zyl (Nov 2007) ▪ Winemaker(s) Michiel Visser (Nov 1999) & Annamarie van Niekerk (Dec 2008), with Werner Swiegers (Aug 2013) ▪ Viticulturist(s) Jan-Carel Coetzee (Nov 2010) ▪ 1,969ha (cab, merlot, ptage, shiraz, chard, chenin, cbard) ▪ 38,199t/15,000cs own label 75% red 20% white 1% rosé 4% fortified ▪ ISO 22000:2009 ▪ BWI, IPW, WIETA ▪ PO Box 30 PK Botha 6857 ▪ admin@bothakelder.co.za ▪ www.bothakelder.co.za ▪ S 33° 34' 1.5" E 019° 15' 27.5" ▪ F +27 (0)23-355-1615 ▪ **T +27 (0)23-355-1740**

☐ **Bottega Family Wines** *see* Idiom Collection

Bottelary Winery

A budget brand by Perdeberg Winery (see entry for tasting details), mostly exported to China.

Soft Smooth Red ★★ **12** usual cinsaut, shiraz, cab mix, fruity & light, with balanced sweetness. WO W Cape, as most of these. Also tasted: **Merlot 13** ★★ **Rosé NV** ★★ **Chenin Blanc 13** ★☆ **Semi-Sweet 13** ★★ — GdB

Bouchard Finlayson

You can't truly appreciate Peter Finlayson's role at Bouchard Finlayson without understanding that he was the first winemaker in the Hemel-en-Aarde Valley, and a pinot noir advocate from the beginning, especially for its suitability to this particular maritime area. It was Peter's international contacts that brought Paul Bouchard to SA as partner, leading eventually to the Tollman ownership of the property. The viticultural portfolio remains with him, as does sustainability, and over 80% of the estate is currently dedicated to indigenous fynbos. His pinot noir track record speaks for itself, with many local and international awards, including 1989 Diners Club Winemaker of the Year. Ever conscious of the terroir effects, he and Chris Albrecht also produce four chardonnays, each different and admirable.

★★★★☆ **Galpin Peak Pinot Noir** Forthcoming sour cherry, dark fruit, spice & fertile earth on **12** (★★★★), oak very evident (±30% new wood) in toasty coffee notes. Full bodied, ripe New World expression but, like **11**, with a bright core & fine balance. WO Hemel-en-Aarde Valley.

★★★★☆ **Tête de Cuvée Galpin Peak Pinot Noir** ⊘ Barrel selection & double new oak (75%) of siblings. Now bottled & showing the benefit of the extra year, **10**'s dark fruit & mocha, scrub notes reflect a bold version of pinot noir, but keeps the supple polish of the variety at its best.

★★★★☆ **Hannibal** A 6-part marriage of Italian & French varieties, none Bordeaux. **12** (★★★★) über ripe, lacks the elegance & perfume of **10** & standout **11** (★★★★★). Prunes, cherry tomato, spice & liquorice notes, noticeable sweet oak too.

★★★★☆ **Kaaimansgat/Crocodile's Lair Chardonnay** One of Cape's revered chardonnay sites, delivering powerful minerality & crystalline fruit purity; here well supported by judicious oaking, just 17% new on **13**; fresh & elegant as always, with a refinement setting it apart from most recent releases. WO Overberg.

★★★★☆ **Kaaimansgat Chardonnay Limited Edition** **11**'s (★★★★) golden hue reflects 3 years' bottle age; also evident on the nose in savoury complexity, salty roasted nut character. Palate is classy & just becoming slightly tangy with age. Like **10**, probably not for long keeping. Only 50% wooded. WO Overberg.

★★★★ **Missionvale Chardonnay** Butterscotch notes over iodine, soy & marmalade in full-bodied, creamy **12**. Brooding complexity, fine structure & dry tail; different expression to toasty & nutty **11** but no less fine. WO Hemel-en-Aarde Valley.

★★★★ **Sauvignon Blanc Reserve** Different styling to its siblings thanks to 14% semillon, **12** has melon & gooseberry flavours & deepening minerality on the finish, leaves the palate clean & refreshed. No **11**.

★★★★ **Sauvignon Blanc 14** a cool-origin expression, with lime & kiwi, crisp acidity & chalky dry-ness. Wonderful juxtaposition of generous flavour & lean weight. Perfect for solo sipping or with fine food, like personality-packed **13**.

★★★★ **Blanc de Mer** Mostly riesling & 5 others including 20% viognier, **13** heady white peach & citrus blossom bouquet, Granny Smith apple zing & juicy drinkability. Good enough to enjoy on its own. WO Cape South Coast.

Also tasted: **Sans Barrique Chardonnay 13 ★★★★** — HJ

Location: Hermanus ▪ Map: Elgin, Walker Bay & Bot River ▪ WO: Walker Bay/Hemel-en-Aarde Valley/Overberg/Cape South Coast ▪ Est 1989 ▪ 1stB 1991 ▪ Tasting, sales & cellar tours Mon-Fri 9–5 Sat 10–1 ▪ Fee R40pp for groups of 6+ ▪ Closed all pub hols ▪ Cheese & salami platters ▪ Gift shop ▪ BYO picnic ▪ Conservation area ▪ Nature walks by appt (guided & self-guided) ▪ Owner(s) The Tollman Family Trust ▪ Cellarmaster(s)/viticulturist(s) Peter Finlayson (1989) ▪ Winemaker(s) Peter Finlayson (1989), with Chris Albrecht (Nov 2010) ▪ 125ha/22ha (barbera, nebbiolo, pinot, sangio, chard, sauv) ▪ 190t/33,000cs own label 25% red 75% white ▪ BWI, IPW, PO Box 303 Hermanus 7200 ▪ info@ bouchardfinlayson.co.za ▪ www.bouchardfinlayson.co.za ▪ S 34° 22′ 54.0″ E 019° 14′ 30.9″ ▪ F +27 (0)28-312-2317 ▪ **T +27 (0)28-312-3515**

Boucheron Wines

Based in Gauteng, Boucheron has grown from a boutique-wine merchant founded by Fredy Pummer in 1996 to a full-fledged producer of close to 5,000 cases of fine own-label wines, overseen since 2011 by cellarmaster Nicholas Ridley. New are an interactive website with, among others, ideas on food-and-wine pairing; a monthly ezine aiming to demystify the world of wine; an unwooded Chardonnay and #ZenMaster red blend; and a harvest festival, with plans for many more.

#ZenMaster ⓝ **★★★** Eclectic blend of alicante bouschet & 6 other red grapes, **13** has depth & body, thick tannins needing time to soften. WO W Cape. **White Merlot ★★** Among handful in this category, pale blush **13** preview from unwooded Helderberg fruit is unfruity & austere, perfect for sushi. **Chardonnay** ⓝ **★★★** Unwooded **13** off Helderberg vines, light, leesy, interesting. — GdB

Location: Randburg/Kya Sand ▪ WO: Stellenbosch/Western Cape ▪ Est 1996 ▪ 1stB 2012 ▪ Closed to public ▪ Owner(s) Fredy Pummer ▪ Cellarmaster(s) Nicholas Ridley (Sep 2011) ▪ 4,932cs ▪ PO Box 870 Strathavon 2031 ▪ info@ boucheron.co.za ▪ www.boucheron.co.za ▪ F +27 (0)11-708-3615 ▪ **T +27 (0)11-708-3444**

Boutinot South Africa ⓠ ⓝ

Having done business in South Africa for 22 years, this UK-based company of grape growers, winemakers, importers and agents for over 150 top producers worldwide has officially established Boutinot South Africa. Currently responsible for vinifying 60 to 80 tons of grapes from long-term con-tracted growers in rented cellar space at Zorgvliet, dedicated manager/winemaker Marinda Kruger-van Eck reveals plans to establish a boutique winery in Stellenbosch to produce her 'wines with prov-enance, purity, expression and finesse'.

Mon Vieux range

★★★★ **Hell's Height Sauvignon Blanc** 'Wet pebble' minerality, sage, oaking a subtle infusion from natural ferment/ageing 9 months in older French wood, emphatic, individual **13** shows restraint but heaps of class. Banghoek WO.

★★★★ **Acquifer Semillon** Has depth, breadth, gravitas, **13** stonefruit, raw almonds, threaded through with piquant limy acidity. Swartland grapes, naturally fermented in older oak.

For more information, visit wineonaplatter.com

Sheer Syrah-Tannat ★★★★ Deep pruney fruit, attractive oak spicing, a hint of scrub; mainly shiraz **11** from Devon Valley, polished & streamlined, supple tannins giving great palate appeal.

Tiger Horse range

Shiraz-Mourvèdre ★★★ With a dash viognier. Dark fruit & salty liquorice, white pepper, unwooded **13** has an easy-drinking juiciness, a gentle grip from grape tannin. WO W Cape for these. **Chenin Blanc-Pinot Grigio** ★★★ Summer fruits, light texture (12.5% alcohol) & eminently quaffable, **14** freshly dry.

Growers Ark range

Shiraz-Cabernet Franc-Pinotage ★★☆ Cab franc's scrubby, herbaceous tone dominates the bouquet, the other varieties play their role in the flavours. Unwooded **13** light textured, undemanding. WO W Cape, like next. **Chenin Blanc-Pinot Grigio-Viognier** ★★★ Floral note to **13**'s stonefruit flavours, elegantly refreshing. — CR, CvZ

Location/map: Stellenbosch ▪ WO: Western Cape/Stellenbosch/Banghoek/Swartland ▪ Est/1stB 2011 ▪ Tasting, sales & cellar tours by appt ▪ Closed all pub hols ▪ Owner(s) Dennis Whitely & Michael Moriaty ▪ Cellarmaster(s)/winemaker(s) Marinda Kruger-Van Eck (May 2010) ▪ 80t/7,000cs own label 35% red 63% white 2% rosé + 7m L bulk ▪ Brands for clients: Percheron, Hoophuis, Cape Heights ▪ marindak@boutinot.com ▪ www.boutinot.com ▪ S 33° 54' 41.7" E 018° 56' 32.0" ▪ F +27 (0)86-293-4577 ▪ **T +27 (0)82-357-2697**

☐ **Boutique Baratok** *see* Baratok Wines
☐ **Bovlei** *see* Wellington Wines
☐ **Bradgate** *see* Jordan Wine Estate
☐ **Brahms** *see* Domaine Brahms Wineries

Bramon Wines

Siblings Bram and Manon Thorpe gave their names to pioneering family winery Bramon, this year entering the second decade of winemaking in Plettenberg Bay. An occasion for celebration and, fittingly, a festival joined by all the younger wine-producing farms in the area at press time was set to take place at the iconic Beacon Isle Hotel, whose ocean-braving prow reminds that this is a cool, maritime and still pristine winegrowing area, with concomitant opportunities and challenges.

Bramon Wines range

★★★★☆ **Sauvignon Blanc MCC** Grape variety now identified in name of bubbly with hallmark mineral complexity, seabreeze tang & effortless elegance. **10** (★★★★) showing honey, icing sugar, green apple complexity. Sweeter impression, less focus than **08**. **09** sold out untasted.

Chardonnay MCC (NEW) ⊕ ★★★★ Invigorating & persistent **12** sparkler with intense baked apple character, satisfying breadth & weight from smidgen older-oak-aged portion. One to watch.

The Crags range

★★★★ **Anton's Barrel** (NEW) Three Italians & a Frenchman (barbera, sangiovese, nebbiolo & cab) in savoury & bright **12**, interesting glassful from Fairview grapes, for now or few years.

★★★★ **Rosé** (NEW) Tank sample **14** intensely fruity, racy mix pinot noir (67%), shiraz. Emphatically dry but packed with flavour, lower 11% alcohol a bonus. For food & fans of a more serious style of pink.

★★★★ **Sauvignon Blanc** ⊘ Revisited **13** (★★★★★) shows cool-climate origin in 'wet pebble' minerality & green fig aromas, slight creaminess & tempered acidity courtesy year in bottle. Restrained & understated. Like **12**, needed time to unfurl its charms.

Anton's Selection (NEW) ★★★★ Individual 5-way blend led by muscat de Frontignan, roussanne. **13** highly perfumed, gently sweet, nice pithy grip to finish. Enjoy well chilled. WO Coastal. — CvZ

Location: Plettenberg Bay ▪ Map: Klein Karoo & Garden Route ▪ WO: Plettenberg Bay/Coastal ▪ Est 2000 ▪ 1stB 2004 ▪ Tasting & sales daily 9-5.30 ▪ Fee R5/tasting glass, waived on wine purchase ▪ Closed Dec 25 ▪ Cellar tours by appt ▪ Restaurant ▪ Facilities for children ▪ Southern Crags Conservancy ▪ Owner(s) Private company ▪ Cellarmaster(s)/winemaker(s) Anton Smal (Feb 2010) ▪ Viticulturist(s) Peter Thorpe (2000) ▪ 10ha/6ha (chard, sauv) ▪ 50t/6,400cs own label 100% white ▪ PO Box 1606 Plettenberg Bay 6602 ▪ accounts@bramonwines.co.za ▪ www.bramonwines. co.za ▪ S 33° 57' 20.30" E 023° 28' 45.02" ▪ F +27 (0)86-589-6816 ▪ **T +27 (0)44-534-8007**

Brampton

Starting life in the Rustenberg cellars, and named for a champion Jersey bull, this DGB brand attracts the creative and 'green' to the Brampton Wine Studio, its brand home in Stellenbosch town centre. Here winemaker Bertho van der Westhuizen's creations can be sampled with snacks or a light lunch.

★★★★ OVR ⊘ Cab-led blend with shiraz, merlot **12** (★★★★), ex tank, vanilla-infused plum & prune nose, note of savoury spices; just enough grip for food. Greater refinement came from **10**. **Pinotage** (NEW) ★★★ Restrained on the nose (though showing variety's slightly lifted aromas), **13** still delivers a juicy punch on palate, with fresh tannic grip. **Unoaked Chardonnay** ★★★ Interesting peanut nuance to white peach on **14**, carrying through to palate; fruit-sweet & rounded for easy enjoyment. WO W Cape. Also tasted: **Cabernet Sauvignon 12 ★★★ Shiraz 12 ★★★ Rosé 14 ★★★ Sauvignon Blanc 14 ★★★☆** — CvZ

Location/map: Stellenbosch ▪ WO: Coastal/Western Cape/Stellenbosch ▪ Est/1stB 1996 ▪ Tasting & sales Mon-Sat 10-7.30 ▪ Fee R25/3 wines R50/6 ▪ Closed Good Fri, Dec 25/26 & Jan 1 ▪ Light lunches 11.30-7; snacks & refreshments all day ▪ Owner(s) DGB (Pty) Ltd ▪ Winemaker(s) Bertho van der Westhuizen (Nov 2012) ▪ Viticulturist(s) Stephan Joubert (Nov 2006) ▪ 500t/80,000cs own label 40% red 55% white 5% rosé ▪ WIETA ▪ Private Bag X3 Groot Drakenstein 7680 ▪ brampton@dgb.co.za ▪ www.brampton.co.za ▪ S 33° 56' 17.42" E 018° 51' 38.08" ▪ **T +27 (0)21-883-9097**

Brandvlei Cellar

The grower-owned winery in the shadow of Jonaskop peak turns 60 this year, having started out on premises beside Brandvlei Dam and moving to the current location between Worcester and Villiersdorp when the dam was enlarged in 1974. 'Quality wines that everyone can enjoy and afford' is their aim, and the small fraction of output that appears under the BC label certainly hits that target.

BC Wines range

Ruby Cabernet-Merlot ⊘ ★★★ Light oaking on **13** adds hint of spice to bright juicy fruit. Nicely rounded, dry & quaffable. **Chenin Blanc** ⊘ ★★★ Delicious tropical fruit salad nose, luscious flavours on zippily dry **14**. **Bacchanté** ⊘ ★★★ Fruitily dry blend chenin, colombard with subtle drop viognier. **14** well made & enjoyable. Also tasted: **Cabernet Sauvignon** ⊘ **13 ★★☆ Chardonnay** ⊘ **14 ★★★ Sauvignon Blanc 14 ★★ Hanepoot Jerepigo 13 ★★** Not retasted: **Shiraz 12 ★★ Shiraz Rosé 13 ★★** — AL

Location/map/WO: Worcester ▪ Est 1955 ▪ Tasting & sales Mon-Thu 8–5 Fri 8–4.30 Sat 9-1 ▪ Closed all pub hols ▪ Cellar tours by appt only ▪ Conferences ▪ Owner(s) 19 members ▪ Cellarmaster(s) Jean le Roux (Aug 1995) ▪ Winemaker(s) Willie Biggs (Sep 2009) & Daneel Jacobs (Sep 2007) ▪ Viticulturist(s) Danie Conradie (Sep 2004) ▪ 1,630ha (cab, ptage, chard, chenin, cbard, sauv) ▪ 28,500t 20% red 80% white ▪ PO Box 595 Worcester 6849 ▪ sales@bcwines.co.za ▪ www.bcwines. co.za ▪ S 33° 48' 19.5" E 019° 28' 8.1" ▪ F +27 (0)23-340-4332 ▪ **T +27 (0)23-340-4215**

☐ **Bredell's** see JP Bredell Wines

Breëland Winery

When farmer Kosie Marais bought this large Slanghoek Valley spread in 2006, he and wife Lizelle set about creating a wine tourism destination. Now visiting triathletes, archery enthusiasts, hikers and mountain bikers have the added bonus of enjoying a small selection of Breëland's own wines from largely replanted vineyards made in a modernised cellar.

Sauvignon Blanc ★★★ Guava fermentation character on previewed **14** not a detraction; intensely flavoured, lively & very sippable. Also tasted: **Pinotage 13 ★★** Not retasted: **Chenin Blanc 13 ★★★** Not tasted: **Cabernet Sauvignon**. — CvZ

Location: Rawsonville ▪ Map: Breedekloof ▪ WO: Slanghoek ▪ Est 1825 ▪ 1stB 2010 ▪ Tasting, sales & cellar tours Mon-Sat by appt ▪ Fee R10pp tour & tasting ▪ Closed Ash Wed, Easter Fri-Mon, Ascension day, Dec 25 & Jan 1 ▪ Pre-booked lunches

For more information, visit wineonaplatter.com

(5 days prior notice) ▪ BYO picnic ▪ Walks/hikes ▪ Mountain biking & 4x4 trails ▪ Conservation area ▪ Guest accommodation (mountain hut/farm house/camping) ▪ Owner(s) Kosie & Lizelle Marais ▪ Cellarmaster(s) Wickus Erasmus (Dec 2008) ▪ Winemaker(s) Wickus Erasmus (Dec 2008), with Jefry Fry (Jan 2009) ▪ Viticulturist(s) Wickus Erasmus, Kosie Marais ▪ 1,000ha/100ha (cab, cinsaut, ptage, shiraz, chenin, cbard, hanepoot, sauv, sem) ▪ 2,500t/500cs own label 20% red 80% white + 500cs for clients ▪ Brands for clients: Kaap Agri ▪ PO Box 26 Rawsonville 6845 ▪ wickus@breede.co.za ▪ www. buchukloof.co.za ▪ S 33° 39' 2.87" E 019° 13' 40.08" ▪ F +27 (0)86-562-6056 ▪ **T +27 (0)23-344-3129**

Brenaissance

Under owners Tom and Hayley Breytenbach, this Devon Valley property has undergone a (b)renais-sance from an anonymous Stellenbosch grape-growing farm into a wine and lifestyle destination. While fruit is vinified off-site by specialists in each variety or style, the Breytenbachs have established a Boran cattle stud as part of a 'diversification and sustainable' agriculture approach, and, keen locavores, serve Devon Valley food at their Café Blanc de Noir. Development phase complete, they're confident of a busy year ahead, including the opening of a wine deck offering tastings, a pop-up food station and sundowners.

★★★★ King of Clubs Cabernet Sauvignon Ⓥ Focused **09** shows complexity: mint, cedar, cassis, black olive, tobacco, cigarbox; ripe & supple tannins for youthful enjoyment or cellaring.

Full House Bordeaux Style Blend Ⓥ **★★★** Herbaceous cab-led **10** leaner, more elegant than single-variety reds in range; ready now. Not retasted: **Queen of Hearts Merlot 10 ★★★ Jack of Diamonds Shiraz 09 ★★★★** Not tasted: **Lord T Secret Blend, Knight of White Chardonnay, Lady H Sauvignon Blanc.** — AL

Location/map/WO: Stellenbosch ▪ 1stB 2010 ▪ Tasting & sales Wed-Sun 11-5 ▪ Pizza & wine pairing ▪ Café Blanc de Noir ▪ Wine Deck (Oct-Mar): tastings, pup-up food station & sundowners ▪ Child friendly ▪ Conferences/functions ▪ Wedding venue & chapel ▪ B&B ▪ Boran cattle stud ▪ Owner(s) Tom & Hayley Breytenbach ▪ Winemaker(s) various ▪ 58.23ha/31.65ha (cabs s/f, malbec, merlot, p verdot, shiraz, chard) ▪ 5,058cs own label 70% red 30% white ▪ Suite 3, Private Bag X4, Die Boord, Stellenbosch 7613 ▪ info@brenaissance.co.za ▪ www.brenaissance.co.za ▪ S 33° 55' 4.31" E 018° 49' 7.82" ▪ **T +27 (0)21-200-2537**

☐ **Brendel Collection** *see* Le Manoir de Brendel

Brenthurst Winery

Having long made the boutique Brenthurst wines himself, Paarl-based advocate and keen axeman José Jordaan now has himself on rhythm, winemaker Martin Fourie on lead guitar and vastly experienced viticulturist Johan Wiese – adviser here for almost 25 years – laying down the bass.

Location: Paarl ▪ Est 1993 ▪ 1stB 1994 ▪ Open to public only by special appt ▪ Owner(s) José Jordaan ▪ Winemaker(s) Martin Fourie, assisted by José Jordaan ▪ Viticulturist(s) Johan Wiese (1991, consultant) ▪ 5ha (cabs s/f, merlot, p verdot) ▪ 15t ▪ PO Box 6091 Paarl 7622 ▪ martin@amatawines.co.za ▪ F +27 (0)21-424-5666 ▪ **T +27 (0)21-863-1154/1375, +27 (0)83-418-4110**

Bridge Wines

Rosemary Mosia's 'virtual' wine company does not have its own vineyards or production facilities. Instead, she buys in fruit and outsources winemaking in order to focus on supplying high-level res-taurants, well-known taverns and retailers. 'Within the next three years we are planning to have a tasting place in Rondebosch [Cape Town] to cater for tourists,' Rosemary notes. 'Tourism is crucial because it creates awareness for our products and our country.'

Reserve Shiraz ★★★ Lovely cinnamon, nutmeg & vanilla spice on **10** adds interest to the plummy fruit. Tannins are sinewy, need a bit more time to meld. In the meantime, serve with rich, creamy dishes. **Chardonnay ★★★★** Oak is a full partner in **13**, but in a good way: buttered toast, preserved citrus peel, crushed hazel nuts, melon. Finish is long & savoury, very food friendly. Partial barrel fer-ment. Also tasted: **Merlot Reserve 08 ★★** — CR, CvZ

Location: Cape Town ▪ WO: Wellington ▪ Est 2005 ▪ 1stB 2010 ▪ Tasting & sales Mon–Fri by appt ▪ Closed all pub hols ▪ Owner(s) Rosemary P Mosia ▪ Winemaker(s) Hennie Huskisson, with JG Auret (both consultants) ▪ Viticulturist(s) Vlok Hanekom ▪ 70% red 30% white ▪ 66 Loch Road, Rondebosch 7700 ▪ rmosia@yahoo.com, rosemary@ thebridgewines.co.za ▪ www.thebridgewines.co.za ▪ F +27 (0)86-594-1501 ▪ **T +27 (0)21-686-2294**

☐ **Brink Family** *see* Pulpit Rock Winery
☐ **Broken Rock** *see* Riebeek Cellars
☐ **Broken Stone** *see* Slaley

Brothers Wines

Capetonian Greg Castle is an advocate of exposing more South Africans to the less snobbish side of wine and breaking down any intimidating perceptions. His focus is thus on domestic sales rather than exports, and his brand, named for sons Dylan and Alex, aims to please those simply wanting good value and quality.

★★★★ **Legacy** Substantial, darkly spiced shiraz with 20% cab. **11** rich yet not overly heavy; savoury concentration complemented by resonant rumbling tannins. Tasty winter tipple. Improvement on last **08** (★★★☆).

Shiraz ★★★☆ Generously spiced **12** in similar hearty style as **11** but much more supple, softer tannins for current enjoyment. Swartland grapes, as all. **Chardonnay** ★★★☆ Interesting lime, lees aromatic interplay on naturally fermented **13**. Lively, subtly oaked, few grams sugar give sweetish impression. Not tasted: **Sauvignon Blanc**. — AL

Location: Cape Town ▪ WO: Western Cape ▪ Est/1stB 2005 ▪ Closed to public ▪ Owner(s) Greg Castle ▪ Cellarmaster(s)/ winemaker(s) Greg Castle (2005) ▪ 10t/1,666cs own label 55% red 45% white ▪ PO Box 21681 Kloof Street Cape Town 8008 ▪ info@brotherswines.co.za ▪ www.brotherswines.com ▪ F +27 (0)86-528-6081 ▪ **T +27 (0)82-600-2555**

Brunia Wines

Named for the silver-bloomed *Brunia laevis* – appropriately, for a home-farm blessed with 300 ha of unspoilt fynbos - Willie and Annetia du Preez's wine brand turns ten years this year, and to celebrate there are three new wines. Fruit from their Cold Mountain Vineyards property near Stanford is now vinified under contract by specialist winemakers. The visitor venue is as welcoming as ever, with many and varied amenities on offer.

★★★★ **Pinot Noir** (NEW) Delicately spiced red cherries lead the way in harmonious **13** - bright & pure, showing lovely freshness throughout. Good balance, finesse & savoury finish.

★★★★ **Shiraz** (⚥) Peppery **10** (★★★) generously proportioned but short somewhat on finish & complexity compared with elegant & suave **09**.

★★★★ **Sauvignon Blanc** Lime-scented **13** has fine mineral fruit core, smooth acidity, chalky finish & a steely dryness. Complex, made for fresh oysters. No **12**.

Chardonnay (NEW) ★★★☆ Soft, with a touch of sweetness & flavours of ripe nectarine, **13** is easy rather than concentrated or serious. **Semillon** (NEW) ★★★☆ Smooth, fragrant **13**, some hay aromas & lean, lightish, unlingering body. — WB

Location: Stanford ▪ Map: Southern Cape ▪ WO: Walker Bay ▪ Est 2005 ▪ 1stB 2009 ▪ Tasting & sales by appt Tue–Sun 10-4 & daily during holidays ▪ Closed Dec 25/26 ▪ Light lunches, picnics & tractor rides ▪ Self-guided hiking trails ▪ Mountain biking ▪ Conservation area ▪ Owner(s) W P du Preez ▪ Winemaker(s) various ▪ Viticulturist(s) Andrew Teubes (consultant) ▪ 417ha/17ha (pinot, shiraz, chard, sauv, sem) ▪ 75t/5,600cs own label 16% red 84% white ▪ PO Box 368 Stanford 7210 ▪ info@bruniawines.co.za ▪ www.bruniawines.co.za ▪ S 34° 28' 9.25" E 019° 39' 42.60" ▪ F +27 (0)86-669-6064 ▪ **T +27 (0)28-341-0432**

Bryan MacRobert Wines

Young Bryan MacRobert calls himself a private viticulture and oenology contractor to cellars, which have included fellow Swartland Independent members Sadie Family and Hughes Family (home of

Nativo). In a short but promising career, he has earned his stripes - and wide acclaim - with his own select but growing range of Tobias and latterly Abbotsdale wines. These are small parcels, mostly old-vine chenin and cinsaut. Increased production comes with an eye to establishing exports.

Tobias range

★★★★ **Red (Shiraz-Cinsault-Mourvèdre)** Was 'Red Blend'. These equal partners on **13**. Balance, light elegance, pure fruit, spice & herbs add to modest 12.5% alcohol for drinkability. Old oak; nothing added except sulphur.

★★★★ **White (Chenin Blanc)** Maiden **12** (★★★★) was 'Steen'. Oxidatively made **13** has breadth from old oak maturation, modest alcohol like all these, balanced light richness, & savoury succulence supporting fine fruit.

Abbotsdale range (NEW)

Red ★★★★ Very tasty, nicely dry **13** blend, same varieties as Tobias but less ambitious - for easy early drinking. **Rosé** ★★ Pale coppery **13** from mourvèdre, wooded. Light, dry & rather dilute. **Chenin Blanc** ★★★ Part barrel-fermented **13** has quiet, pleasant aromas & slightly dulled, unlingering flavours. — TJ

Location: Velddrif ▪ Map/WO: Swartland ▪ Est/1stB 2010 ▪ Tasting by appt only ▪ Closed all pub hols ▪ Owner(s) Bryan MacRobert & Jean-Paul Stuyck ▪ Cellarmaster(s) Bryan MacRobert (Jan 2010) & Jean-Paul Stuyck (Jan 2014) ▪ Winemaker(s)/viticulturist(s) Bryan MacRobert (Jan 2010) ▪ (cinsaut, mourv, shiraz, chenin) ▪ 10t/1,500cs own label 45% red 45% white 10% rosé + 3,000cs for clients ▪ IPW ▪ tobiaswines@gmail.com, jpstuyck@mweb.co.za ▪ S 33° 29' 12.64" E 018° 38' 50.53" ▪ **T +27 (0)71-223-3129/+27 (0)71-610-1284**

☐ **Buchu Berg** *see* Oude Compagnies Post Private Cellar
☐ **Buckleberry** *see* Louis
☐ **Buddy** *see* Overhex Wines International

Buffalo Creek Wines

Ten years ago, father and son growers Leroy and Mark Tolmay embarked on winemaking with little knowledge or experience, simply to benefit their farm workers - all profits are distributed amongst them. Friends in the wine industry and McGregor Valley neighbours have shared their expertise, and limited output and personal attention produce easily drinkable wines at friendly prices.

Location: McGregor ▪ Map: Robertson ▪ Est/1stB 2005 ▪ Tasting, sales & cellar tours Mon-Fri 9-6 Sat 9-12.30 Sun by appt only ▪ Closed Easter Sun, Dec 25 & Jan 1 ▪ Owner(s) Leroy & Mark Tolmay ▪ Cellarmaster(s)/winemaker(s) Mark Tolmay (Jun 2005) ▪ 1,328ha/30ha (p verdot, ptage, pinot, merlot, chard, chenin, cbard, sauv) ▪ ±350-380t/500-600cs own label 65% red 25% white 10% rosé ▪ PO Box 124 McGregor 6708 ▪ info@buffalocreek.co.za ▪ S 34° 0' 2.97" E 019° 53' 11.94" ▪ F +27 (0)23-625-1727 ▪ **T +27 (0)23-625-1727**

Buitenverwachting

Buitenverwachting's revival under new ownership in the early 1980s (no wine had been made at the historic estate for 30 years) was vital to re-establishing Constantia's fine-wine claims. The family-owned property is now a bastion of continuity and quality, with the rare benefit of the long leadership in the cellar of the accomplished Herman Kirschbaum, for over two decades now - he shares winemaking responsibility with young Brad Paton. But the untiring work of Lars Maack, representing the family, is also crucial to the success of Buitenverwachting (or Bayten, the more easily pronounceable primary name on export labels). Change in the interests of quality is not precluded, however, as testified by occasional new wines, replanted vineyards, and an increased focus on sustainability and social responsibility.

★★★★ **Cabernet Sauvignon** ⊘ Richly ripe, velvet-textured **12** (★★★★★) an extraordinarily well-balanced, seamless step up from **09**. Broachable now, but dense fruit, outlined by firm supple tannins, needs time to reveal the full charms of this fine vintage. **10, 11** sold out untasted.

★★★★ **Cabernet Franc** ⚗ **09** (★★★★★) last time showed rich spicy concentration, stern but fine tannins - all soaking up the mostly new French oak. Great young; better with time. **08** perhaps less complex.

★★★★ **Merlot** Deep-fruited **10** reflects vineyard management in perfectly ripened fruit, classically styled in dry, savoury fashion to yield an accomplished version of this tricky variety.

★★★★☆ **Christine** Expressively perfumed, pure-fruited cab franc- & merlot-led **10** Bordeaux blend (with cab & petit verdot) justifies long-established reputation. Fine-grained tannins seamlessly integrate with layers of plushly textured red fruit in gracious, classic & complete wine.

★★★★☆ **Chardonnay** Wonderfully graceful balance of richly layered fruit & gentle oaking in **13** reflects stalwart winemaker's easy confidence. Deeply delicious creaminess & concentration add to appeal.

★★★★ **Maximus** ⚗ Softer, more accessible than imposing name suggests. Seriously oaked **11** sauvignon has pretty floral appeal, more depth than maiden **09** (★★★☆), which had some semillon. Ripeness supported by finely judged oak spice. No **10**.

★★★★☆ **Husseys Vlei Sauvignon Blanc** ⊘ Classy, exceptionally well-made **13** (★★★★★) from same single site as **12**, packed with intense fruit flavours, without overpowering. Tingling, savoury acidity carries fine-textured, mineral mouthful to decisive finish.

★★★★☆ **Sauvignon Blanc** Vibrant, pure **13** similar to Husseys Vlei, though more overtly crisp & succulently fruity. Lipsmacking grapefruit acidity gives appealing touch to flavour-driven finish.

★★★★☆ **3rd Time Lucky** Charmingly floral **13** a softly tasty & textured viognier (gladly lacking variety's alcohol glow). Abundant stonefruit flavours given breadth & structure by well-judged oaking offering a firm, spicy & engaging conclusion.

★★★★ **Méthode Cap Classique Brut** Finely beaded bubbles & complex brioche character in freshly flavoured **NV** chardonnay-pinot noir sparkler.

★★★★☆ **1769** Exceptional Noble Late Harvest from muscat de Frontignan. Unctuously sweet, marmalade-infused **13** a masterpiece, as is lighter-footed **12** (also tasted), both rendered delightfully dry at end by seamless acidity. Former's all-new-oak superbly absorbed, latter saw older barrels.

Blanc de Noir ★★★ **13** cab-merlot led blush wine, dry, vivaciously fresh & fruity. Also tasted: **Meifort 10** ★★★★ **Buiten Blanc 13** ★★★★ Discontinued: **Batavia**. — IM

Location: Constantia ▪ Map: Cape Peninsula ▪ WO: Constantia/Western Cape ▪ Est 1796 ▪ 1stB 1985 ▪ Tasting & sales Mon-Fri 9–5 Sat 10–5 ▪ Closed all pub hols ▪ Cellar tours by appt ▪ Buitenverwachting Restaurant ▪ Deli & coffee shop ▪ Picnic area ▪ Conferences ▪ Owner(s) Richard & Sieglinde (Christine) Mueller, Lars Maack ▪ Cellarmaster(s) Hermann Kirschbaum (Jan 1993) ▪ Winemaker(s) Brad Paton (Jan 2005) ▪ Viticulturist(s) Peter Reynolds (Jan 2001) ▪ 147ha/105ha (cab, chard, sauv) ▪ 800t/320,000cs own label 20% red 80% white ▪ PO Box 281 Constantia 7848 ▪ info@buitenverwachting.com ▪ www.buitenverwachting.com ▪ S 34° 2' 30.4" E 018° 25' 1.5" ▪ F +27 (0)21-794-1351 ▪ **T +27 (0)21-794-5190/1**

BurCon Wines

Nerina Guest Farm's BurCon house wines aren't taken too seriously, co-owner Amanda Conradie reports, except perhaps by the bank manager, who, she says, feels ill every time he thinks about them. The unusual brand name commemorates the marriage of a Burger into the Conradie family.

Oompie se Oeps ⚗ ★★ Unwooded **NV** pinotage & shiraz (co-planted in error - oops!) plummy fruit & spice. Not tasted: **Miskien Christien**. — JP, CvZ

Location/map: Robertson ▪ 1stB 2004 ▪ Tasting by appt only Tue-Fri 9-4 Sat/Sun 10-2 ▪ Restaurant ▪ Conferences ▪ Farm produce ▪ Facilities for children & tour groups ▪ Walks/hikes ▪ Mountain biking & guided horseback trails ▪ Owner(s) Frans & Amanda Conradie, Renée Burger ▪ Winemaker(s) Christie Steytler (Feb 2004, Roodezandt) ▪ 234ha/25ha (ptage, shiraz, muscadel) ▪ 16t/2,500cs own label ▪ PO Box 86 Robertson 6705 ▪ info@nerinaguestfarm.com ▪ www.nerinaguestfarm.com ▪ S 33° 50' 5.2" E 019° 45' 55.3" ▪ F +27 (0)23-626-2012 ▪ **T +27 (0)23-626-2012/+27 (0)82-823-4231**

Burgershof

This fourth-generation wine farm has successfully made the transition from traditional Cape special-
ities (fortified desserts) to modern, market-ready varietal wines. These are mainly for Dutch supermarket chain Jumbo, but also available at local area outlets La Verne Wine Boutique in Robertson and
Ashton Wine Boutique.

Merlot ★★ Warm, ripe plums with meaty nuance, previewed **13** offers smooth & round drinkability.
WO W Cape. **Sauvignon Blanc ★★★** Peardrops, suitably light textured for amiable quaffing, **14**
tank sample nice tangy fruity freshness. Also tasted: **Cabernet Sauvignon-Shiraz 14 ★★★ Chardonnay 14 ★★** Not tasted: **Pinotage**. — CR

Location: Robertson ▪ WO: Robertson/Western Cape ▪ Est 1864 ▪ 1stB 2000 ▪ Closed to public ▪ Sales at La Verne Wine
Boutique & Ashton Wine Boutique ▪ Owner(s) HJ Reynecke ▪ Cellarmaster(s)/winemaker(s)/viticulturist(s) Hennie
Reynecke (Jan 1979) ▪ 68ha (cab, merlot, muscadel r/w, ptage, ruby cab, shiraz, chard, chenin, cbard, sauv) ▪ IPW ▪ PO
Box 72 Klaasvoogds River 6707 ▪ burgershof@barvallei.co.za ▪ www.burgershof.com ▪ F +27 (0)23-626-5433 ▪
T +27 (0)23-626-5433

☐ **Bush Camp** see Landskroon Wines
☐ **Bushman's Creek** see Wines of Cape Town

Bushmanspad Estate

Having made his money in the hospitality industry, Hollander Menno Schaafsma followed a dream 15
years ago by acquiring this property near Bonnievale, named for the old traders' footpath over the
mighty Langeberg Mountains. The wines are vinified in a refurbished 18th-century cellar by
winemaker/viticulturist Arthur Basson. The luxury cottages boast some of the best views in the Cape.

Bushmanspad range

★★★★ The Menno ⊘ Shiraz-led mix, only in best years. Berry-rich **12** has a supple texture, its
savoury adding complexity, flavour, definition, & promising a future. No **10**, **11**.

Malbec ⊘ **★★★** Smoky dark-toned **12** has salty liquorice spicing, attractive succulent smoothness.
Drinks easily & well. Not retasted: **Cabernet Sauvignon 12 ★★★ Cabernet Franc 12 ★★★** Not
tasted: **Rosé**, **Sauvignon Blanc**.

Red Gold range

Shiraz ⊘ **★★★** After impressing with its ripeness & black cherry fruit density, **12** follows through
with a smooth, round texture. Not tasted: **Blend**. — CR

Location: Bonnievale ▪ Map/WO: Robertson ▪ Est 2000 ▪ 1stB 2006 ▪ Tasting & sales Mon-Fri 8.30–5 ▪ Fee R15/6
wines ▪ BYO picnic ▪ Walks/hikes ▪ B&B/self-catering cottages ▪ Owner(s) Menno Schaafsma ▪ Cellarmaster(s)/
winemaker(s)/viticulturist(s) Arthur Basson (Feb 2011) ▪ 52ha (cabs s/f, malbec, merlot, mourv, shiraz, sauv) ▪ 400t
own label 80% red 15% white 5% rosé ▪ PO Box 227 Bonnievale 6730 ▪ info@bushmanspad.co.za ▪ www.
bushmanspad.co.za ▪ S 33° 53' 55.0" E 020° 11' 46.7" ▪ F +27 (0)86-268-3756 ▪ **T +27 (0)23-616-2961**

Butcher Shop & Grill

Alan Pick, proprietor of Butcher Shop & Grill in Sandton and Cape Town, has long been a prolific,
high-profile Cape Winemakers Guild customer, and has built good relationships with its members.
Some (as well as other producers) provide exclusive bottlings for his various ranges.

Limited Editions

★★★★ Hartenberg The Snuffbox Merlot ⊘ Single-vineyard bottling, **07** fruit-filled mouthful:
cassis, black plums, rum-soaked raisins embraced by sturdy tannins, enlivened by brisk acidity. 18
months oak, 80% new.

★★★★☆ Morgenster ⊘ Herb, cassis & eucalyptus toned **03** dominated by cabs (sauvignon, franc
70%). When last tasted mid-2005, fruit, tannins & alcohol (14.3%) already well-aligned but needed
time to integrate fully; should be ready now. Followed merlot-driven **01**. No **02**.

★★★★ Vergelegen The Dani ⓥ Labelled for the restaurant, **04** a fully mature, meaty & firm, ready to drink Bordeaux-styled red blend from this famous Stellenbosch estate.

★★★★☆ Niels Verburg Cabernet Sauvignon-Shiraz-Mourvèdre Fragrantly spicy **11** (★★★★), seamlessly constructed blend of Luddite's own grapes. 15% alcohol fits snugly, as does predominantly new oak which frames succulent, savoury red & black fruits. Not quite as handsome as standout **09**, with shiraz leading cab.

★★★★ Vergelegen The Carine ⓥ Ingratiatingly fruity **11** sauvignon is softer, less steely & bracing than the property's usual style.

Pick's Pick Gold Label range ⓝ

★★★★ Reserve Pinot Noir Expressive **11** from Winery of Good Hope. Elgin fruit gives fresh acidity, earthiness, while Stellenbosch provides body, structure, in elegant & harmonious blend.

Blend Twelve ★★★☆ Light, savourily spicy lunchtime red from Hartenberg. **12** a supple shiraz-led blend with cab & 5 others.

Pick's Pick range

★★★★ Merlot ⓥ Taking a step up from last-tasted **09** (★★★☆), carefully made (80% new oak) **11** from Jordan offers ageing potential coupled with current enjoyment. Cassis & dark chocolate, its sleekly curvaceous body ends dry & food friendly.

★★★★ Shiraz ⓥ Stepping up on **07** (★★★), **09** from Zevenwacht is full bodied, with ample savoury & spicy fruit clothed in dry amenable tannins. Splashes mourvèdre & grenache add interest. No **08**.

★★★★ Sauvignon Blanc ⓥ Lovely fruit purity on Jordan's **13**, gooseberries & lime, with a core minerality showing on the flavours & finish, taut & focused. No **12**.

★★★★ Cape White Blend ⓥ Last-tasted **09** mix of chenin, viognier & chardonnay by Teddy Hall had intriguing perfume, flavours. Portion oaked. More delicious than **06** (★★★☆).

Shiraz-Cabernet Sauvignon ⓝ **★★★☆** Juicy, ripe **12** blend from the Ernie Els stable in supple, balanced & savoury form. WO W Cape. Not retasted: **Cabernet Sauvignon 11 ★★★☆ Protea Merlot 12 ★★☆ Shiraz 12 ★★★☆ Classic French Blend 12 ★★★☆ Rosé 11 ★★★ Chardonnay 11 ★★★ Protea Sauvignon Blanc 13 ★★★ Bubbly NV ★★★☆** — IM

Location: Cape Town/Sandton ▪ WO: Stellenbosch/Western Cape/Elgin ▪ Owner(s) Alan Pick ▪ Beach Road Mouille Point (opposite lighthouse) Cape Town 8005; Shop 30 Nelson Mandela Square Sandton 2196 ▪ thebutchershop@mweb.co.za ▪ F +27 (0)11-784-8674 ▪ **T +27 (0)11-784-8676/7**

☐ **By Norwegians** see Nordic Wines
☐ **Cabrière** see Haute Cabrière
☐ **Café Culture** see KWV

Calais Wine Estate

Founded in 1692 by French Huguenot Jean Manje, who named the estate in Paarl's Daljosafat area after his home town, Calais today is run by 'proactive young management', and the grapes vinified in a boutique cellar by Helene van der Westhuizen with an eye on the two intended styles: New-World fruitiness for the Calais range, Old-World elegance for the Klein Valley flagships.

Klein Valley range

St Katerina Barrel Fermented Viognier ⓥ **★★★** Attractive, peachy **13** has some richness & texture, sufficient acidity to refresh the creamy finish.

Calais range

Bel Canto ⓥ **★★ 10** very ripe & savoury cab-led 4-way blend with firm tannins. **Chardonnay** ⓥ **★★** Unoaked **13** straightforward easy-drinker with tropical pineapple flavour. Wellington WO.

Not retasted: **Sauvignon Blanc 13 ★★** Not tasted: **Merlot, Petit Verdot, Pinotage, Shiraz, Applause, Cape Riesling, Chenin Blanc.** — IM

Location: Paarl ▪ Map: Paarl & Wellington ▪ WO: Paarl/Wellington ▪ Est/1stB 2000 ▪ Tasting by appt ▪ Sales daily 8–4 ▪ Guest accommodation ▪ Owner(s) Calais Wine Estate shareholders ▪ Winemaker(s)/viticulturist(s) Helene van der Westhuizen ▪ 23ha (cab, merlot, p verdot, ptage, ruby cab, shiraz, chard, chenin, sauv) ▪ 150t/3,000cs own label 70% red 30% white ▪ PO Box 9006 Klein Drakenstein 7628 ▪ info@calais.co.za ▪ www.calais.co.za ▪ S 33° 42' 32.1" E 019° 1' 24.6" ▪ F +27 (0)21-868-1400 ▪ **T +27 (0)21-868-3888**

☐ **Calico** *see* Osbloed Wines

Calitzdorp Cellar

Alwyn Burger this edition adds a fourth - unofficial - job title to GM, Cellarmaster and Winemaker of this welcoming grower-owned winery in the heart of Calitzdorp. With 25 crushes here, he's truly Part of the Furniture. A glance at the ratings and notes below confirms he still does the traditional sweet fortifieds very well but the new Tinto shows he's also trendy, vinifying Portuguese 'port' blends as unfortified table wines along with the best of the local privately owned producers.

★★★★ Red Muscadel Fortified dessert **14** improves on previous **NV** (★★★★) with vivid raisins & tropical scents, but sweet palate is main attraction, raisined toffee flavours, rich, mouthcoating.

★★★★ White Muscadel Liquid sultanas with a freshening spicy, pineapple seam in fortified dessert **14** (★★★★★). The beauty is that the richness, sweetness, is tempered by the other nuances, giving remarkable balance, appeal. Enjoy chilled. Even better than **12**. **13** untasted.

Tinto (NEW) **★★★** A classic Portuguese 'port' blend, but **12** is made as a red wine. Fruitcake flavours, rich & spicy, bolstered by a nice firm grip from new & 2nd fill French and American oak. Accessible now, drink until 2019. **Limited Edition Muscat Delight** (NEW) **★★★** The expected grapiness, floral notes from **NV** equal parts white muscadel & viognier. A bit of spritz livens the sweetness. Serve well chilled, perfect summertime patio wine. Also tasted: **Touriga Nacional 13 ★★★ Sauvignon Blanc 14 ★★★ Cape Ruby NV ★★★** Not retasted: **Shiraz 12 ★★ Rosé NV ★★ Cape Vintage 11 ★★★☆** Not tasted: **Cabernet Sauvignon, Merlot, Pinotage, Chardonnay, Hanepoot, Hanepoot-Muskadel Reserve, Golden Jerepigo.** — CR

Location/WO: Calitzdorp ▪ Map: Klein Karoo & Garden Route ▪ Est 1928 ▪ 1stB 1976 ▪ Tasting & sales Mon–Fri 8–5 Sat 8–1 ▪ Closed Good Fri & Dec 25 ▪ Cellar tours by appt ▪ Tour groups ▪ Farm produce ▪ Picnics/meals by appt; or BYO picnic ▪ Conferences ▪ Succulent garden ▪ Owner(s) 39 members ▪ Cellarmaster(s) Alwyn Burger (1990) ▪ Winemaker(s) Alwyn Burger (1990), with Abraham Pretorius ▪ Viticulturist(s) Johannes Mellet (2005, consultant) ▪ 286ha (13 varieties, r/w) ▪ 5,000t/7,000cs own label 12% red 88% white ▪ IPW ▪ PO Box 193 Calitzdorp 6660 ▪ manager@calitzdorpwine.co.za ▪ www.calitzdorpwine.co.za ▪ S 33° 32' 18.9" E 021° 41' 10.6" ▪ F +27 (0)44-213-3328 ▪ **T +27 (0)44-213-3301**

Callender Peak

This boutique wine business, which defied adversity from fauna and the elements in vineyards on the higher reaches of Ceres' Winterhoek Mountains, is being wound down, but the Chardonnay was still available at Bluejay Farmstall in Stellenbosch at press time.

★★★★ Chardonnay (②) Heavily oaked & oxidatively styled, with beeswax & marzipan at finish, **11** (★★★★) is taut & restrained, with underlying citrus, after more forceful **10**. — GdB

Location: Ceres ▪ WO: Western Cape ▪ Est/1stB 2007 ▪ Closed to public ▪ Owner(s) MacDonald & Jeffrey families ▪ Cellarmaster(s)/winemaker(s) Johan Kruger (whites, consultant) & Clive Torr (reds, consultant) ▪ Viticulturist(s) Willem Mouton (2010) ▪ 2ha (cab, merlot, pinot, chard) ▪ 2t/400cs own label 50% red 50% white ▪ clivetorrwines@mweb.co.za ▪ **T +27 (0)82-557-0826**

Camberley Wines

What started as a hobby for energetic quantity surveyor John Nel and his caterer wife Gaël on their Helshoogte Pass property evolved into a full-fledged wine business. Focusing mainly on big reds, they

happily supply overseas as well as local Stellenbosch student markets. Combining their many talents, including his love of sport and art and hers of gardening, the couple welcomes visitors to their stylish B&B, cosy pub/winebar and boule court.

Camberley Wines range

★★★★ **Cabernet Franc** Ⓖ **10** has trademark alcoholic kick, but with attractive leafy blackcurrant, layers of tobacco & dark berry leading to plush, powerful end. Decanting or time needed.

★★★★ **Philosophers' Stone** Ⓖ **10** cab franc-based Bordeaux blend, with usual big, bold, extracted richness, kept fresh with poised bright red berry fruit, good dry tannins, integrated oak.

★★★★ **Cabernet Sauvignon-Merlot** Ⓖ **10** in bold house style with ripeness in complex layers of dark & red fruit. Bright freshness on the nose & palate harmonises oak, acid & very big alcohol.

Not retasted: **Pinotage 12** ★★★★ Not tasted: **Cabernet Sauvignon Reserve**, **Elm Tree Merlot**, **Shiraz**, **Charisma**, **Sparkling Shiraz**, **Elixir Fortified Red**.

Prohibition range

Red Ⓖ ★★★ **NV** blend like a light port, with big alcohol, dryish end. Not tasted: **White**. — HJ

Location/map/WO: Stellenbosch ▪ Est 1990 ▪ 1stB 1996 ▪ Tasting & sales Mon-Sat & pub hols 9–5 Sun 9-3 ▪ Fee R40 max (depending on wine choice), waived on purchase ▪ Closed Dec 25 & Jan 1 ▪ Cellar tours by appt ▪ Lunch/refreshments by appt; or BYO picnic ▪ Boule court for hire ▪ B&B guest cottage ▪ Owner(s) John & Gaël Nel ▪ Winemaker(s) John Nel ▪ Viticulturist(s) Bennie Booysen ▪ 7ha (cabs s/f, merlot, p verdot, ptage, shiraz, touriga) ▪ ±35t/6,400cs own label 100% red ▪ PO Box 6120 Uniedal 7612 ▪ john@camberley.co.za ▪ www.camberley.co.za ▪ S 33° 55' 8.9" E 018° 55' 58.3" ▪ F +27 (0)21-885-1822 ▪ **T +27 (0)21-885-1176**

Cameradi Wines

One of the quieter (and smaller) parts of the garagiste winemaker scene... but we hope for more to emerge from the cellar behind co-owner/winemaker Casper Lategan's Wellington house.

Location: Wellington ▪ Est 1999 ▪ 1stB 2000 ▪ Closed to public ▪ Owner(s) Stelvest cc (Nic Swingler, Hendrik du Preez & Casper Lategan) ▪ Winemaker(s) Casper Lategan (Jan 1999) ▪ 2t/260cs own label 100% red ▪ 48 Bain Str Wellington 7655 ▪ cas@lategans.co.za ▪ F +27 (0)21-873-4910 ▪ **T +27 (0)21-873-1225**

☐ **Camino Africana** see Edgebaston

Capaia Wine Estate Ⓖ Ⓜ Ⓐ

Under ambitious German ownership, Capaia was established with no expense spared, on a Philadelphia hillside where only wheat had grown before. Vineyards were planted with every care, and a splendid cellar built, with one of the world's largest arrays of oak fermenters. Baroness Ingrid von Essen remains as the devoted owner. A restaurant now takes advantage of the view across to the mountains and rolling wheatfields of the Swartland, and a new blend shares its name, Mariella's.

★★★★ **Merlot-Cabernet Sauvignon** Ⓖ Intense & plush **10**, demure dark fruit & beautifully managed tannins, some spice, showy yet restrained. Firmer, better, than softly ripe **09** (★★★★).

★★★★ **ONE** Ⓖ Flagship from petit verdot & cab with merlot, cab franc & 11% shiraz. Intense black fruit with restrained herbal & tomato notes on **10** (★★★★), savoury, but chunkier, less fresh than **09**.

★★★★ **Mariella's** Ⓝ Graphite frames plush blue & black fruit of **11** cab, merlot, cab franc & petit verdot with splash (8%) shiraz. Spicy oak adds body & length to lithe, rewarding & supple mouthful.

★★★★ **Sauvignon Blanc 14** (★★★★) crisp lemon/passionfruit nose & palate, flinty undertone. Fresh vibrancy, good body & focus though bit short on finish so a step down on **13**. — FM

Location/WO: Philadelphia ▪ Map: Durbanville, Philadelphia & Darling ▪ Est 1997 ▪ 1stB 2003 ▪ Tasting, sales & cellar tours Mon-Fri 8-5; Sat/Sun tasting & sales at Mariella's ▪ Tour groups ▪ Mariella's restaurant T +27 (0)21-972-1103/+27 (0)72-770-9695, mariella@capaia.co.za ▪ Facilities for children ▪ Owner(s) Ingrid Baronin von Essen ▪ Cellarmaster(s) Bernabé Strydom (Oct 2006), assisted by Stephan von Neipperg (consultant) ▪ Winemaker(s) Adriaan Burger (Oct 2010) ▪ Viticulturist(s) Schalk du Toit (2009, consultant) ▪ 140ha/60ha (cabs s/f, merlot, p verdot, shiraz, sauv) ▪ 260t/26,000cs own label 85% red 15% white ▪ IPW ▪ PO Box 25 Philadelphia 7304 ▪ info@capaia.co.za ▪ www.capaia.co.za, www.capaia.com ▪ S 33° 42' 45.9" E 018° 34' 6.9" ▪ F +27 (0)21-972-1894 ▪ **T +27 (0)21-972-1081**

☐ **Cap du Vin** *see* Bellevue Estate Stellenbosch
☐ **Cape Elephant** *see* Lutzville Cape Diamond Vineyards
☐ **Cape Auction** *see* Vinopoly Wines
☐ **Cape Avocet** *see* Rooiberg Winery

Cape Chamonix Wine Farm

Chamonix was originally part of La Cotte, the first farm granted to Huguenot refugees in what is now called the Franschhoek Valley. This section has belonged to German businessman Chris Hellinger since 1991. The mostly unirrigated vines are on mountain slopes – the altitude one reason for the quality of fruit vinified in Gottfried Mocke's cellar. But Gottfried's tenure since 2001 proves that hard and intelligent work in vineyard and winery are also vital - his uniquely, thoughtfully vinified pinotage is one example of an approach that has seen Chamonix rising to the highest levels in Cape wine. New plantings on promising sites on the farm are coming into production. In the cellar, Gottfried says, 'it's a matter of paying more and more attention to detail'.

Reserve range

★★★★☆ **Pinot Noir** Serious & complex **13** shows aromas of pomegranate, cherries & raspberry. The refreshing palate is intense but with a sense of weightlessness & lift, the oak well integrated. Spontaneous ferment; 10% whole bunches included. Approachable but will gain in complexity.

★★★★☆ **Troika** **12** has 50% cab franc - **11** (★★★★★) had 85% - with cab & petit verdot. Rich dark fruit, fennel & hints of oak. Palate offers depth & complexity, with finely structured ripe tannin. Needs 5+ years to open up & show its best - will reward the patient even longer.

★★★★★ **Chardonnay** Powerful yet restrained **13** (★★★★☆) has complex play of fruit & mineral elements, with a great sense of presence. Steely mineral core wrapped round with subtle fruit; integrated oak & long, peacock tail finish. Natural ferment mostly in oak (70% new), 20% in concrete 'egg'. Will age well, like **12**.

★★★★☆ **White** 55% sauvignon in **13** (a little more than in **12**), with semillon. Fine blend shows intriguing aromas of cape gooseberry, fresh mint, honeysuckle & beeswax. Fresh palate is seamless, with well integrated oak (50% new) & long, mineral finish.

Cape Chamonix range

★★★★☆ **Cabernet Franc** (NEW) Debut displays cassis, aniseed & tobacco notes. **12** ripe & intense yet fresh, but needs time to polish the tannin & develop more complexity. Matured in large vats; 30% new oak. Good lingering conclusion.

★★★★ **Feldspar Pinot Noir** (NEW) More obviously fruit-driven than Reserve version, & with less new oak (well-integrated 20%), barrel sample **13** shows vibrant berry notes & hints of pine needles. Still youthfully tight.

★★★★☆ **Greywacke Pinotage** **12** with 7% pinot is the usual complex mix of early & late picked grapes (including some desiccated grapes). Intense spicy, dark fruit aromas, all finely woven. Fruit on the bone-dry & well-structured palate supported by sensitive oaking (30% new). Long-lingering finish.

★★★★☆ **Chardonnay** Less new oak than Reserve (50%), also spontaneous fermentation, all in barrel. **13**'s aromas of ripe melon, honeysuckle & yellow apple lead to open palate which adds a stony note & hints at the integrated wood. Properly dry, like all Chamonix wines (mostly ±2 grams/litre residual sugar).

★★★★ **Unoaked Chardonnay** Vibrant, juicy **14** tank sample more complex than **13** (★★★★), with green apple, melon & crushed stone. 5 months on lees; includes 5% oaked portion. Dry & zesty; long finish.

★★★★ **Sauvignon Blanc** Nettle, cut grass & unripe tropical fruits on **14** tank sample. Tight, fresh & lingering, the balance & intensity pointing to good development potential.

Also tasted: **Rouge** ⊘ 12 ★★★★ Not tasted: **MCC Blanc de Blancs**. Discontinued: **Cabernet Sauvignon**. — JPf

Location/map/WO: Franschhoek ▪ Est 1991 ▪ 1stB 1992 ▪ Tasting & sales Mon-Sun 8.30–5 ▪ Fee R60 ▪ Closed Dec 25 & Jan 1 ▪ Cellar tours by appt ▪ Restaurant T +27 (0)21-876-2393 ▪ Conservation area ▪ Marco Polo Lodge, Waterfall Lodge, Forest Suites & fully equipped self-catering cottages ▪ Owner(s) Chris Hellinger ▪ Cellarmaster(s)/winemaker(s)/viticulturist(s) Gottfried Mocke (Sep 2001) ▪ 300ha/50ha (cabs s/f, malbec, merlot, p verdot, ptage, pinot, chard, chenin, sauv, sem) ▪ 220-250t/40,000cs own label 60% red 40% white ▪ IPW ▪ PO Box 28 Franschhoek 7690 ▪ marketing@chamonix.co.za ▪ www.chamonix.co.za ▪ S 33° 53' 60.0" E 019° 7' 34.0" ▪ F +27 (0)21-876-3237 ▪ T +27 (0)21-876-8400

Cape Classics

This large-scale export business in Somerset West concentrates on the United States, and markets its own affordably priced Indaba and Jam Jar ranges, among other prominent brands, in 49 states. Long involved in empowerment education, funded by sales of Indaba wines, it is now shifting emphasis from tertiary to early childhood education, specifically farmworker children via the WELL (Winelands Early Living & Learning) Project. Full-service Cape Classics Travel, inter alia offering custom luxury winelands excursions, has opened. And watch for a new wine, Braai, coming to a Weber near you...

Indaba range

Merlot ★★★ Soft & plummy, easygoing **13** shows good weight & balance. **Chenin Blanc** ★★★ Bright, ripe stone & tropical fruit, **13** hint of tinned pineapple, fresh, fullish & soft. Also tasted: **Mosaic 13** ★★★ **Chardonnay 13** ★★★ Not retasted: **Sauvignon Blanc 13** ★★★

Jam Jar range

Sweet White ★★ **14** medium sweet & light (10% alcohol), with muscat spice & perfume. Not retasted: **Sweet Shiraz 13** ★★ — GdB

Location: Somerset West ▪ Map: Helderberg ▪ WO: Western Cape ▪ Est 1991 ▪ 1stB 1996 ▪ Tasting by appt only ▪ Owner(s) André Shearer ▪ Winemaker(s) Bruwer Raats (May 2010) ▪ 270,000cs own label 35% red 65% white ▪ PO Box 1695 Somerset West 7129 ▪ info@capeclassics.com ▪ www.capeclassics.com, www.indabawines.com, www.jamjarwines.com ▪ S 34° 4' 5.9" E 018° 53' 38.2" ▪ F +27 (0)21-847-2414 ▪ T +27 (0)21-847-2400

☐ **Cape Colony** see Malanot Wines
☐ **Cape Diamond** see Lutzville Cape Diamond Vineyards
☐ **Cape Discovery** see Waterstone Wines
☐ **Cape Diversity** see Withington

Cape Dreams

Bunty Khan, owner of export venture Croft Sales, created Cape Dreams to market quality wines at competitive prices. The brand name refers partly to Bunty's desire to nurture untapped young talent in rural winelands communities and produce 'leaders and stars of the future'. Accordingly, part of profits go towards upliftment and youth development.

Cape Dreams range

Chardonnay ★★★ Unwooded **14** with lemon cream biscuit aroma, crisp lime flavour, elegant citrus finish. Appealing & fresh. **Colombar** (NEW) ★★★ Typical guava scent, soft sweetish fruit salad flavour on **14** easy quaffer. Also tasted: **Chenin Blanc 14** ★★ **Sauvignon Blanc 14** ★★ Not retasted: **Cabernet Sauvignon 12** ★★★ **Merlot 11** ★★ **Pinotage 12** ★★★ **Shiraz 12** ★★★ Not tasted: **Pinotage Rosé**.

Reserve range

Not retasted: **Cabernet Sauvignon 11** ★★★ **Pinotage 11** ★★★☆ **Shiraz 11** ★★★☆ — DB

Location/map/WO: Robertson ▪ Est/1stB 2009 ▪ Tasting & cellar tours by appt ▪ Owner(s) Bunty Khan ▪ Cellar-master(s) André van Dyk ▪ 600ha (cab, merlot, ptage, shiraz, chard, chenin, sauv) ▪ 60% red 40% white ▪ ISO 9001, HACCP, BEE, BWI ▪ croftsales@telkomsa.net, info@croftsales.co.za ▪ www.croftsales.co.za ▪ S 33° 46' 35.3" E 019° 45' 42.9" ▪ **T +27 (0)21-531-2016/+27 (0)83-792-7638/+27 (0)71-898-7923**

☐ **Cape Elements** *see* Nico van der Merwe Wines
☐ **Cape Grace** *see* African Pride Wines
☐ **Cape Heights** *see* Boutinot South Africa
☐ **Cape Hill** *see* Stellenrust

Cape Hutton

Founded by oral and maxillofacial surgeon Gerrit Wyma and wife Lesley, and named for the dominant vineyard soil type, Blaauwklippen Valley's Cape Hutton leverages its scenic location and proximity to Stellenbosch town to offer weddings and corporate functions in a dedicated venue, as well as cellardoor amenities. Vinification is by specialist contracted winemakers.

★★★★ **Cabernet Sauvignon** ⓧ Smooth, ripe & concentrated **09** reflects good vintage. Elegantly oaked, with subtle spices filling out healthy fruit profile.

★★★★ **Sauvignon Blanc** ⓧ **11** intense, complex aromatic profile & steely lees minerality. Fine expression of cool West Coast fruit. Step up from **09** (★★★).

Not tasted: **Veri Beri**. — GdB

Location/map: Stellenbosch ▪ WO: Stellenbosch/Western Cape ▪ Est 2003 ▪ 1stB 2004 ▪ Tasting, sales & cellar tours by appt 8-4.30 ▪ Weddings/functions ▪ Owner(s)/viticulturist(s) Gerrit & Lesley Wyma ▪ Winemaker(s) Piet Smal (cab), Wynand Hamman (sauv) & Hilko Hegewisch (merlot) ▪ 2ha (merlot) ▪ PO Box 2200 Somerset West 7129 ▪ lesley@capehutton.com ▪ www.capehutton.com ▪ S 33° 58' 27.6" E 018° 51' 10.3" ▪ F +27 (0)21-880-0666 ▪ **T +27 (0)21-880-0527**

Capelands Estate

Johann Innerhofer, with some 30 years in the international wine trade, and partner Laura Mauri own boutique Somerset West estate Capelands, featuring accommodation, a restaurant with stellar winelist - and a walled vineyard, from which consultant Louis Nel vinifies the top red, now supple-mented by a 'second label'. The new white wine comes from further afield.

★★★★ **Redstone** With the 2012 vintage moved to a second label, **13** drops the malbec & is straight cab from a small, mature Hederberg vineyard. More restrained in fruitiness than the Klein version, but still forthrightly ripe & generous; firmly structured & judiciously oaked.

★★★★ **Whitestone Chardonnay** (ℕ) Interesting tropical, peachy ripeness on the aromas of **13**, while the finish shows citrus freshness. Crisp & flavoursome, with elegantly integrated acidity & modest oaking. WO W Cape.

Klein Redstone (ℕ) ★★★★ **12** has malbec added to the cab as previously in Redstone - just 10%, but giving vibrant sweet loganberry fruitiness. Cab's structure comes through, without diminishing the tasty intensity. — TJ

Location: Somerset West ▪ WO: Stellenbosch/Western Cape ▪ Est 2004 ▪ 1stB 2010 ▪ Closed to public ▪ Tasting at Capelands Restaurant available to patrons ▪ Guest house ▪ Owner(s) Capelands Estate (Pty) Ltd ▪ Cellarmaster(s) Louis Nel (Feb 2010, consultant) ▪ Viticulturist(s) Francois Hanekom (Feb 2009, consultant) ▪ 12.5ha/2.8ha (cab) ▪ 6t/1,333cs own label 100% red ▪ 3 Old Sir Lowry's Pass Road Somerset West 7130 ▪ restaurant@capelands.com ▪ www.capelands.com ▪ F +27 (0)86-299-3905 ▪ **T +27 (0)21-858-1477**

Capenheimer

South Africa's original perlé wine, launched 1962. By Distell. 750ml & 1.5L bottles.

Capenheimer ★★ Lightish, off-dry **NV** white blend with gentle sparkle, quite a fresh finish. — DB

☐ **Cape of Good Hope** *see* Anthonij Rupert Wyne

Cape Point Vineyards

Perched high and proud above the charming oceanside village of Noordhoek, Cape Point Vineyards has been breaking new ground, literally and figuratively, for well over a decade under talented cellarmaster and Cape Winemakers Guild member, Duncan Savage. Vineyards have been established in extreme locations and on treacherous slopes, producing unique terroir-specific wines. The cellar is a converted subterranean mine bunker on the home farm, clad in local rock and offering sweeping views from its decks. This pioneer has elevated the now officially declared Cape Peninsula district's status for fine sauvignon-based wines and firmly established itself amongst the elite of the industry. The estate is closely involved with the community on many levels, including performing arts, community markets, feeding schemes and conservation of the indigenous Western Leopard Toad.

Cape Point Vineyards range

★★★★ **Cabernet Sauvignon** (NEW) Convincing blackcurrant fruit on **12** takes centre stage. Juicy & plush, with sweet cassis notes. Dashes petit verdot, malbec; Stellenbosch & Napier fruit. Only ex farm.

★★★★☆ **Chardonnay** Classic Burgundian styling shows in barrel-fermented **13**. Noble & firmly structured, with restrained but persistent citrus fruit easily coping with 10 months in oak. Integrated, but promising more.

★★★★ **Sauvignon Blanc** Seductively subtle, with spicy perfume & wild nettle notes, borne on creamy lees texture, partly wooded **13** shows real class. Will make any seafood meal special.

★★★★☆ **CWG Auction Reserve White** Spicy oak aromas weave elegantly with heady lavender scents on **13** oak-fermented 50/50 sauvignon-semillon blend. Delightful lime marmalade mingles with riper tropical fruit in seamless, lingering harmony.

★★★★☆ **Isliedh** Beguiling, aromatic blend sauvignon (82%) & semillon maintains enviable track record in ripe & layered **13**. Oak fermentation at its subtle best, offering spicy nuances, rich body & lingering finish. Like **12** (★★★★★) will improve for several years.

Not tasted: **Sauvignon Blanc Reserve, Noble Late Harvest**.

Splattered Toad range

Syrah ⊘ ⊛ ★★★★ Was 'Shiraz'. Fuller than previous, gushing red fruit with spicy, herbaceous notes, silky tannins. **13** punches above its weight. WO W Cape, like Sauvignon. Also tasted: **Sauvignon Blanc 14** ★★★ — GdB

Location: Noordhoek ▪ Map: Cape Peninsula ▪ WO: Cape Point/Western Cape ▪ Est 1996 ▪ 1stB 2000 ▪ Tasting & sales Mon-Sun 10-6 ▪ Fee R10-R60 ▪ Cheese/antipasti platters available during tasting hours ▪ Restaurant with chef Clayton Bell, booking essential ▪ Weddings & events ▪ Picnics & sundowners ▪ Nature trails & vineyard walks ▪ Facilities for children ▪ Weekly community market Thu evenings in summer ▪ Conservation area ▪ Owner(s) Sybrand van der Spuy ▪ Winemaker(s) Duncan Savage (Dec 2002) ▪ Viticulturist(s) Duncan Savage (Dec 2002), with Hendri Burger (Sep 2010) ▪ 22ha (chard, sauv, sem) ▪ 16,000cs own label 100% white; Splattered Toad, Stonehaven, The Point: ±50,000cs; ±3,000cs for clients ▪ Brands for clients: Woolworths ▪ BWI, IPW, Farming for the Future ▪ PO Box 100 Noordhoek 7985 ▪ info@cape-point.com ▪ www.capepointvineyards.co.za, www.splatteredtoad.co.za ▪ S 34° 5' 41. 82" E 018° 22' 17.28" ▪ F +27 (0)21-789-0614 ▪ **T +27 (0)21-789-0900**

☐ **Cape Promise** *see* uniWines Vineyards

Cape Rock Wines

Father-and-son team Willie and Gavin Brand are emerging as leaders of the Olifants River Valley's nascent fine-wine making movement, their increasingly Rhône-influenced varietal bottlings and blends improving by the vintage - and packaged to charm and impress. Winemaker Gavin was working on a low-alcohol Rhône red at press time, and intending to 'focus on what we've been doing the past year or so and making it better'.

★★★★ **SMV** Well-composed flagship, co-fermented shiraz, mourvèdre & viognier in **12** (★★★★☆) goes up a level with restrained tannin & fruit, balanced savouriness despite 15% alcohol. Similar herby berry complexity to elegant **09**, also a step up. No **11**, **10** sold out untasted.

★★★★ **Rosé** **13** from 4 Rhône grapes, lightish & bone-dry with food-friendly earthy cherry aromas, chalky tannins & savoury touch.

★★★★ **GRV** Sophisticated near-equal blend grenache blanc, roussanne & viognier seasoned with smidgen chenin & older oak. **12** leesy, rich & savoury, with fair vivacity; also-tasted **13** (★★★★☆) a notch up. Harmonious juxtaposition of floral, nutty & fruity elements, distinctly dry.

Not tasted: **Cabernet Sauvignon**, **Shiraz**, **SGMV**, **Capa Roca**. — HJ, CvZ

Location: Vredendal ▪ Map/WO: Olifants River ▪ Est 2001 ▪ 1stB 2002 ▪ Tasting, sales & cellar tours by appt ▪ Closed Good Fri, Dec 25 & Jan 1 ▪ BYO picnic ▪ Owner(s) Willie Brand ▪ Cellarmaster(s) Willie Brand (Jan 2001) ▪ Winemaker(s) Willie Brand (Jan 2001) & Gavin Brand ▪ Viticulturist(s) Jeff Joubert (Jan 2001, consultant) ▪ 62ha/32ha (cab, grenache, merlot, mourv, ptage, roobernet, ruby cab, shiraz, chard, chenin, cbard, rouss, sauv, viog) ▪ 480t/1,200cs own label 50% red 40% white 10% rosé + 32,000L bulk ▪ PO Box 261 Vredendal 8160 ▪ caperockwines@gmail.com ▪ www.caperockwines.co.za ▪ S 31° 37′ 24.0″ E 018° 24′ 52.9″ ▪ F +27 (0)27-213-5567 ▪ **T +27 (0)27-213-2567**

☐ **Cape Royale** see Waterstone Wines
☐ **Cape Sparrow** see TCB Wines

Cape to Cairo Wines

Each case of this Syrah (sibling to the separately listed Emineo wines) comes with a large map detailing the route from Cape to Cairo, with information on legendary sites inviting winelovers to dream of Africa as they smell and taste.

Syrah ★★★ Accessible **07**'s ripe fruit wrapped in sweet oak, pleasing lingering savouriness when tasted some years ago. — KM, CvZ

Location: Cape Town ▪ Map: Cape Peninsula ▪ WO: Breede River Valley ▪ Est 2007 ▪ 1stB 2008 ▪ Tasting by appt ▪ Owner(s) Trans-Scripto (Pty) Ltd ▪ Winemaker(s) Nico van der Merwe (consultant) & Jolene Calitz-Le Roux ▪ 7,000cs 100% red ▪ PO Box 8 Cape Town 8000 ▪ info@capetocairo.net ▪ www.capetocairowines.com ▪ S 33° 56′ 29.06″ E 018° 23′ 47.76″

☐ **Cape to Cape** see Nordic Wines
☐ **Cape Tranquility** see Pulpit Rock Winery
☐ **Cape View** see Kaapzicht Wine Estate
☐ **Cappupinoccinotage** see Boland Kelder
☐ **Cap Vino** see Winkelshoek Wine Cellar

Carisbrooke Wines

The brand from lawyer-winegrower Willem Pretorius' Stellenboschkloof farm takes its name from the little train station of Carisbrooke, made famous by Alan Paton's masterpiece Cry, the Beloved Country.

Alan Paton Cabernet Sauvignon ★★★★ Seriously styled & elegant **10** savoury, spicy, with fine acid backbone & judicious oaking (75% new). — IM

Location/map/WO: Stellenbosch ▪ Est 1989 ▪ 1stB 1996 ▪ Tasting & sales Mon-Fri 10-2 ▪ Closed all pub hols ▪ Owner(s) Willem Pretorius ▪ Cellarmaster(s)/winemaker(s) Kowie du Toit (1997), Willem Pretorius ▪ Viticulturist(s) Kowie du Toit (1997) ▪ 19ha/6ha (cab, sem) ▪ 50t/800cs own label 100% red ▪ PO Box 25 Vlottenburg 7604 ▪ willem@carisbrooke.co.za ▪ F +27 (0)21-881-3796/+27 (0)86-518-8767 ▪ **T +27 (0)21-881-3798**

Carmel Wines (NEW)

Elgin is a long way from the North Sea, but that 'wild ocean' is present in the name of the boutique wine brand from apple, pear and vine farm Carmel, owned the past six years by Gauteng businessman Recht 'Tak' Hiemstra and wife Ceceilia, whose family are from Friesland in the Netherlands. Their young pinot noir and riesling blocks are overseen by Elsenburg-trained Andrew Semple, advised by viticulturist neighbour Paul Wallace, and vinified in Bot River by Luddite's Niels Verburg.

Wilde Haf range

Pinot Noir ★★☆ Forest floor, white pepper, piquant raspberries resting on savoury tannins; **13** youthful but supple. **Riesling** ★★★ Gently aromatic, some floral notes, fresh pineapple, even ginger but off-dry **14**'s racy acidity dominates the fruit, needs time to soften. — CR, CvZ

Location/WO: Elgin ▪ Map: Elgin, Walker Bay & Bot River ▪ Est/1stB 2013 ▪ Tasting & sales by appt only ▪ Owner(s) Recht (Tak) & Ceceilia Hiemstra ▪ Cellarmaster(s)/winemaker(s) Niels Verburg (Luddite Wines) ▪ Viticulturist(s) Paul Wallace (Jul 2010, consultant) ▪ 19ha/1.3ha (pinot, riesling) ▪ 7t/531cs own label 30% red 70% white ▪ PO Box 2 Elgin 7180 ▪ voyabiz@hotmail.co.za ▪ S 34° 12' 44.03" E 019° 3' 8.67" ▪ F +27 (0)21-859-3031 ▪ **T +27 (0)79-359-5583**

☐ **Carnival** see Orange River Wine Cellars
☐ **Carpe Diem** see Diemersfontein Wines

Carrol Boyes Collection

South African designer Carrol Boyes partners with her brother, farmer and financier John Boyes, in this range of limited-edition wines, featuring Carrol's bold and striking designs on the labels. See Barnardt Boyes Wines for contact details.

Shiraz ★★★ **12** black plums & cherries, smoky spice, lots of vanilla, with the appeal continuing on the silky smooth palate. A peppery finish. Stellenbosch grapes, as next. **Cape Blend** ★★★ Cab with pinotage & merlot. A cocoa note adds interest to **12**'s dark-fruited flavours, 18 months French/American oak providing a firm foundation for further maturation, although already drinks well. — CR

Casa Mori

After 'a gap year' in which no wine was bottled, the Mori family's boutique winery in Devon Valley is back in production, and serendipitously a celebratory sparkling is in gestation there under the watchful eye of new winemaker/GM, John Kotze, with Tokara and Marklew Family Wines experience.

Bruno ⊘ ★★★★ Unfiltered **NV** combo sangiovese/cab (78/22) elegant & dry, attractive polished leather nuance, firm food-pairing tannins. — TJ

Location/map/WO: Stellenbosch ▪ Est 1995 ▪ 1stB 2009 ▪ Tasting, sales & tours by appt ▪ Farm produce ▪ Conferences/functions ▪ Artichoke festival ▪ B&B facilities (3 rooms) ▪ Owner(s) Eugene Mori ▪ Winemaker(s)/viticulturist(s) John Kotze (2014) & Bruno Julian Mori (1997, consultant) ▪ 4.4ha/2.3ha (cab, malbec, sangio, shiraz, viog) ▪ 15t/2,000cs own label 97% red 1% white 2% rosé ▪ Other export label: Mori ▪ PO Box 71 Koelenhof 7605 ▪ casamoricucina@gmail.com ▪ www.casamori.co.za ▪ S 33° 53' 15.28" E 018° 48' 27.64" ▪ F +27 (0)21-865-2312 ▪ **T +27 (0)21-865-2312/+27 (0)83-620-0016 (Eugene)/+27 (0)60-381-3381 (John)**

Catch Of The Day

This Cape Town negociant house for the restaurant trade, with DeMorgenzon-seasoned Warwick Denman skippering the cellar, is always looking out for their next 'catch' – interesting, good-value wines for the table. Latest vintages untasted.

Location: Cape Town ▪ Closed to public ▪ Owner(s) Cunicsar Vintners cc ▪ Winemaker(s) Warwick Denman ▪ PO Box 26500 Hout Bay 7872 ▪ catchotd@mweb.co.za ▪ www.rainbownationwines.com ▪ F +27 (0)86-624-4780 ▪ **T +27 (0)21-671-6024/+27 (0)82-577-1608**

☐ **Cathedral Cellar** see KWV

Catherine Marshall Wines

A small-scale venture helmed by equally diminutive but dynamic Catherine Marshall. Ever self-effacing, Cathy has been an ardent protagonist of pinot noir for many years, honing her skills with this fickle variety to a fine art. Chenin and merlot have not escaped her attentions either, and she now proudly sources all her grapes from Elgin Valley. Upgrades at her Valley Green base in Elgin were still in progress at press time ('took longer than expected because we wanted to make sure everything was perfect'), and promotional trips in conjunction with overseas importers were planned.

Catherine Marshall range

★★★★ **Pinot Noir 12** fruit from four Elgin sites (Cape South Coast WO), clean, focused & flavoursome. Showcases Marshall's hallmark 'feminine' styling, achieving intensity with silky elegance. Fittingly selected for the Blue Train.

★★★★ **Barrel Reserve Pinot Noir** Was '9 Barrels'. **12** iron-rich clay soils impart savoury, darker fruit nuances & 'masculine', muscular tone. Retains polished texture, elegance & balance. Selected for British Airways first class.

★★★★ **Sauvignon Blanc** Super-racy **12** shows bright greengage & gooseberry fruit in exuberantly tangy & vivacious style. Also-tasted **13** vineyard blend of 3 clones with more oaked semillon (12%). Rich & succulent, threaded with clean minerality & a long finish. Both fine food partners.

Not retasted: **Myriad 08** ★★★ Occasional release: **Peter's Vision Merlot Reserve**.

Amatra range

★★★★ **Merlot** ⊘ Opulent step up in **13** (★★★★★) on **12**. Exudes berry & prune flavours from French clone & meticulous viticulture. Achieves elegance & structure without sacrificing ripeness. Seamlessly balanced, intense & polished, already tempting but with pedigree for 6-8 years.

★★★★ **Chenin Blanc Jono's Wave 13** from Elgin's only 2 ha of chenin. Pure & piquant, crunchy apple freshness with a subtle brush oak. Balanced succulence & clean lines attracted top Chicago restaurant Moto. — MW

Location: Elgin ▪ Map: Elgin, Walker Bay & Bot River ▪ WO: Elgin/Cape South Coast ▪ Est/1stB 1997 ▪ Tasting, sales & cellar tours by appt ▪ Closed Easter Fri-Sun, Dec 25 & Jan 1 ▪ Meals/refreshments by appt ▪ Owner(s) Cathy Marshall, Greg Mitchell, Jonathan Oxenham & Jeff Jolly ▪ Cellarmaster(s) Catherine Marshall (Oct 1996) ▪ Winemaker(s) Shawn Fortuin (Jan 2010) ▪ Viticulturist(s) Various ▪ 40-50t/8,000cs own label 60% red 37% white 3% fortified ▪ IPW ▪ PO Box 30913 Tokai 7966 ▪ cathy@cmwines.co.za ▪ www.cmwines.co.za ▪ S 34° 12' 12.07" E 019° 02' 35.10" ▪ F +27 (0)86-523-7479 ▪ **T +27 (0)83-258-1307**

Cavalli Wine & Stud Farm

A passion for horses, wine and food has impelled the Smith family to create the remarkable Cavalli estate in the shadow of the Helderberg. It's a showpiece in every sense, from the manicured paddocks and landscaped indigenous gardens to the extensive, multifaceted visitor amenities. An equine theme is pervasive, including the name of the estate and fine-dining restaurant Equus. Equally ubiquitous is a concern for sustainability. The 25 ha of new virus-free vine material is planted with vermicompost for maximum root development, and all practices are aimed to be as environmentally friendly as possible. Currently vinification is off-site.

Flagship range

Cremello ★★★★ Top-tier white blend with attractive gold-foiled horse label design befitting its status. **13** chenin with chardonnay, verdelho. Coconut & fresh summer fruits, limy acidity; enough personality to handle game fish or shellfish, age 3+ years.

Passions range

Black Beauty ★★★ Smoky, hedgerow/brambleberry fruit, salty liquorice, **12** a good rendition of shiraz, juicy & smooth. WO W Cape. **Pink Pony** ★★ Dry rosé from grenache. **13** redcurrants with a slightly earthy note, flavourful & food friendly. **White Knight** ★★★ Light, fresh & very easy to like, **13** chenin designed for food or solo sipping while admiring the view on a sunny day. — CR, CvZ

Location: Stellenbosch ▪ Map: Helderberg ▪ WO: Stellenbosch/Western Cape ▪ Est/1stB 2008 ▪ Tasting & sales Wed-Sat 10-7 Sun 10-3 ▪ Fee R30 ▪ Closed Dec 26 & Jan 1 ▪ Equus Restaurant Wed-Sun bistro lunch & fine dining dinner ▪ Gift shop ▪ Conferences ▪ Banqueting facility (350 seater) ▪ Conservation area ▪ Art gallery ▪ Boutique ▪ Equestrian centre tours on Sat ▪ Owner(s) Smith family ▪ 80ha/28ha (cab, malbec, p verdot, shiraz, tempranillo, chard, chenin, verdelho, viog) ▪ 100t/6,500cs own label 45% red 40% white 15% rosé ▪ BWI, IPW, WIETA ▪ PO Box 102 Somerset West 7129 ▪ info@cavalliestate.com ▪ www.cavalliestate.com ▪ S 34° 0' 35.91" E 018° 48' 47.06" ▪ F +27 (0)86-766-6556 ▪ **T +27 (0)21-855-3218**

Cecilia Wines

Cerina van Niekerk, Klawer winemaker and concert pianist, named her own brand after the patron saint of music. Cerina interweaves wine, music and philanthropy, the latter through donating proceeds from her Pinotage ('seven years in the dreaming' before debut) to the local community.

★★★★☆ **Pinotage** Gently & naturally crafted fruit from 50 year old Citrusdal Mountain vines yields subtle yet intense, scented red berry & wet heath flavours. **13**'s sleek but serious profile an elegant nod to pinotage's parent, pinot noir. Enjoy now & over next 4 years.

In abeyance: **Shiraz-Mourvèdre**. — MW

Location: Klawer ▪ Map: Olifants River ▪ WO: Citrusdal Mountain ▪ Est 2010 ▪ 1stB 2007 ▪ Tasting by appt ▪ Owner(s) Cerina van Niekerk ▪ Cellarmaster(s)/winemaker(s) Cerina van Niekerk (2007) ▪ 2t/100cs own label 100% red ▪ PO Box 23 Trawal 8147 ▪ cecilia@mylan.co.za ▪ www.ceciliawines.co.za ▪ S 31° 51' 32.16" E 018° 36' 13.37" ▪ F +27 (0)86-617-0101 ▪ **T +27 (0)82-334-9422**

☐ **Cecil John** *see* Boschendal Wines

Cederberg Private Cellar

At around 1,000m above sea level, the vineyards of Cederberg Private Cellar are among the highest in the Western Cape. David Nieuwoudt took over as winemaker in 1997 and in so doing, became the 5th generation to farm this remote land, his great-great-grandfather having originally settled here in 1893. Vines were first planted in 1973, when David's grandfather decided to dabble in winemaking, and in 1977 the first vintage was made. Another - maritime - site, in play since David presciently bought land near Cape Agulhas in 2008, is coming into its own under the acclaimed Ghost Corner label. Vinification, with estimable lieutenants Alex Nel and Tammy Turck-Nel, on the home farm is in the newly refurbished cellar, complete with tasting centre. Focus now is on 'vineyard renewal, planting everything on the perfect terroir'.

Five Generations range

★★★★☆ **Cabernet Sauvignon 12** is complex & layered, with ripe blackcurrant fruit, whiff of cherry tobacco & tealeaf. Delicate & elegant yet lush. Fruit concentration & plenty of ripe tannin give body, grip & longevity. Like **11** (★★★★★), selection of 12 barrels (all new).

★★★★☆ **Chenin Blanc** Mostly barrel-fermented **12** is seductive, with concentrated flavours of vanilla & cinnamon-dusted baked apples. Dollop viognier adds to complexity with delicate floral lift, while 6% unoaked chenin refreshes. Opulence & richness, tangy dry finish.

David Nieuwoudt Ghost Corner range

★★★★ **Pinot Noir 13** (★★★★☆) ups the ante on **12** with sweet, concentrated red-fruit purity, pristine balance. Rich yet refined, with inspired oaking (20% new French) supporting the delicate fruit flavours & making them shine. Chalky minerality on the unflagging finish. Elim fruit, as all.

★★★★★ **Wild Ferment Sauvignon Blanc** As elegant, dry & uncompromising as **12**, wild yeast barrel-fermented **13** (★★★★★) shows tightly wound citrus, dusty minerality & subtle creamy vanilla oak. Serious structure with clear & energetic finish, good persistence.

★★★★ **Sauvignon Blanc 13** (★★★★★) trumps **12** with steely & flinty tone, & gravelly wet stone character - dusty & complex; mouthfilling racy grapefruit, lime & tangy granadilla flavours. Lush & rounded from weekly lees-stirring, great depth on the finish.

For more information, visit wineonaplatter.com

★★★★☆ **Semillon** 12 offers crushed stone, dusty green capsicum, grass with a hint of smoke & seabreeze. Well-judged oak (3 months older French), extended lees contact & weekly stirring broaden the palate. Elegant & harmonious now, but age for future enjoyment.

★★★★☆ **CWG Auction Reserve Semillon** ⓃⒺⓌ Flint, nettles, powdered wet stone, intense citrus aromas announce superlative 50% barrel-fermented 13. Great cool-climate expression, with a silky texture from extended lees contact & regular stirring. Complex mineral, smoky finish.

★★★★★ **The Bowline** Gorgeous combo of sauvignon & barrel-fermented semillon with jump-out-the-glass aromas of pear, zesty citrus, nettles, candied ginger & a whiff of salty sea air on 13 (★★★★☆). Intense, with elegance, luscious texture & same long finish as 12.

Cederberg Private Cellar range

★★★★ **Cabernet Sauvignon** 12 shows succulent ripe fruit, tealeaf, black olive & vanilla oak (60% new). Supple, with a firm, ripe tannin grip & same build as big brother, a little more approachable in youth.

★★★★★ **CWG Auction Reserve Teen die Hoog Shiraz** ⊘ 12 (★★★★☆) offers ripe, tight concentrated fruit flavours, chewy structure in harmony with rich vanilla oak (all new, 15 months). Full bodied but well balanced, with outstanding complexity. Like 11, will reward the patient.

★★★★ **Shiraz** What a joy! 12 is harmonious & juicy, for lovers of a serious fruit-driven style. Rounded, not weighty, spicy vanilla oak (French & American) & tobacco smoke balancing pristine fruit.

★★★★ **Chenin Blanc** 14 is lighter bodied than sibling but still serious, showing intense tropical & citrus flavours. Unoaked, bright & focused, lees-ageing adding breadth. Good varietal expression.

★★★★ **Sauvignon Blanc** Tangy lime & bright orchard fruit flavours on enthralling 14. Fruitier than Elim partners. Generously textured & elegant, palate-saturating citrus curd finish.

★★★★☆ **Blanc de Blancs Brut** 09 méthode cap classique sparkling from chardonnay (part barrel fermented) in extra-dry style. Creamy vanilla biscuit notes from 52 months on lees marry with intense fresh citrus & roasted nut flavours; textured, with great depth & length.

Also tasted: **Merlot-Shiraz** 12 ★★★★ **Sustainable Rosé** 14 ★★★★ **Bukettraube** 14 ★★★ — WB

Location: Citrusdal ▪ Map: Olifants River ▪ WO: Cederberg/Elim ▪ Est 1973 ▪ 1stB 1977 ▪ Tasting Mon-Sat 9–12; 2–4.30 pub hols 9–11.30; 4-5.30 ▪ Fee R20 ▪ Closed Easter Fri/Sun, Dec 25 & Jan 1 ▪ Sales Mon-Sat 8-12.30; 2-5 Sun/pub hols 9-12; 4-6 ▪ BYO picnic ▪ Sanddrif Holiday Resort self-catering cottages; camping ▪ Walks/hikes ▪ Mountain biking ▪ Conservation area ▪ Rock climbing ▪ Sport climbing ▪ Observatory ▪ Owner(s) Nieuwoudt family ▪ Cellarmaster(s) David Nieuwoudt (Jan 1997) ▪ Winemaker(s) David Nieuwoudt (Jan 1997), with Alex Nel & Tammy Turck-Nel (Aug 2011) ▪ Viticulturist(s) Ernst Nieuwoudt (Jan 1960) ▪ 5,500ha/60ha (cab, shiraz, bukettraube, chenin, sauv) ▪ 600t/64,000cs own label 40% red 60% white ▪ PO Box 84 Clanwilliam 8135 ▪ info@cederbergwine.com ▪ www.cederbergwine.com ▪ S 32° 30' 12.8" E 019° 15' 27.7" ▪ F +27 (0)86-531-0491 ▪ **T +27 (0)27-482-2827**

Celestina

Over three decades, Caroline Rillema has built up a classy Cape Town wine merchant business but only more recently realised her dream of owning a vineyard small enough to be managed over weekends. She and partner Ray Kilian's sauvignon blanc and semillon, on a slice of land at Baardskeerdersbos near Gansbaai, is vinified by Dirk Human (Black Oystercatcher) and reflects the area's cool elegance.

★★★★ **Sauvignon Blanc-Semillon** ⊘ Flint & zest zing to 12 60/40 blend. Lightish yet concentrated with no trace of wood despite ferment in older oak. White pepper lift on long clean tail. — FM

Location: Gansbaai ▪ WO: Cape Agulhas ▪ Est 2004 ▪ 1stB 2009 ▪ Closed to public ▪ Owner(s) Caroline Rillema ▪ Winemaker(s) Dirk Human (Black Oystercatcher) ▪ Viticulturist(s) Caroline Rillema & Ray Kilian ▪ 3.4ha/1.85ha (sauv, sem) ▪ 6t/600cs own label 100% white ▪ c/o Caroline's Fine Wine Cellar, Shop 44 Matador Centre, 62 Strand Street, Cape Town 8001 ▪ carowine2@mweb.co.za ▪ F +27 (0)21-419-8985 ▪ **T +27 (0)21-419-8984**

Cellar Cask

South Africa's first bag-in-box, launched in 1979, styled by Distell to meet rising demand for Natural Sweet wines with lower alcohol levels.

Select Johannisberger Rosé ★☆ Simple & sweet coral pink **NV** for easy quaffing. 750 ml bottles, 2L & 5L packs, as all. **Select Johannisberger White ★☆** Unashamedly sweet raisin notes but with a flick of acidity. **NV**. Serve well chilled. Also tasted: **Select Johannisberger Red NV ★** — DB

- ☐ **Cellar Door** see Namaqua Wines
- ☐ **Cellar Foot** see Lammershoek Winery
- ☐ **Cellar Road** see Darling Cellars

Chabivin Champagne & MCC House   ⓠ

Chabivin is a collaboration between local bubbly specialist Hendrik Snyman and the Charbaut family, third-generation producers of fine champagne near Epernay. Their boutique vineyard, cellar and visitor venue outside Stellenbosch offers tastings of Charbaut champagnes and Chabivin méthode cap classiques, most of the latter still on the lees at press time and unavailable for review.

Signature Series
Zero Dosage ⓠ ★★★☆ 10 sparkler mainly pinot noir, with 26% chardonnay. Assertively dry, refreshingly brisk bubble showing off bold leesy, bruised apple features. Not tasted: **Brut Rosé**.

Diary Series
Not tasted: **Mademoiselle Mégane**, **Aclémée**, **Cuvée Jean-Michel**. — AL

Location/map/WO: Stellenbosch ▪ Est 2008 ▪ Tasting & sales Tue-Fri 9-5 Sat/Sun 10-4; in winter by appt only ▪ Fee R30/3 MCC, R100/4 champagnes ▪ Winemaker(s)/viticulturist(s) Hendrik Snyman ▪ 3ha/0.4ha (pinot, chard) ▪ ±8t/1,500cs own label 100% MCC ▪ PO Box 12456 Die Boord Stellenbosch 7613 ▪ info@chabivin.co.za ▪ www.chabivin.co.za ▪ S 33° 58' 24.27" E 018° 51' 8.17" ▪ F +27 (0)86-540-6237 ▪ **T +27 (0)21-880-1643**

- ☐ **Chameleon** see Jordan Wine Estate
- ☐ **Chamonix** see Cape Chamonix Wine Farm
- ☐ **Chandos** see Malanot Wines
- ☐ **Chapel** see Robertson Winery
- ☐ **Chapel Cellar** see Zanddrift Vineyards - Chapel Cellar
- ☐ **Charles Borro** see Govert Wines

Charles Fox Cap Classique Wines   ⓠ ⓐ

Charles and Zelda Fox, in search of 'a better lifestyle for us and our children', replaced big city life in Johannesburg for an old fruit farm in Elgin in 2005. Guided by 'the soils and climate' (and adviser Kevin Watt) to plant classic champagne varieties, they are looking to gradually expand the range.

★★★★☆ Brut Rosé Méthode Cap Classique Very fine-flavoured **11** sparkling from mainly pinot noir with chardonnay & pinot meunier. Flavours of raspberry Pavlova with subtle, balanced, savoury edge, freshening acidity & persistent, fine mousse. Enough depth of flavour to stand up to food.

★★★★ Brut Méthode Cap Classique Pinot noir-led **11** sparkler with almost equal amounts chardonnay/pinot meunier shows savoury notes with citrus on the nose before creamy palate of lemons, almonds, salty oysters, all backed with good length & acidity. 30 months on lees, like Rosé. — CM

Location/WO: Elgin ▪ Map: Elgin, Walker Bay & Bot River ▪ Est 2007 ▪ 1stB 2010 ▪ Tasting, sales & cellar tours Mon-Fri 11-4 Sat/Sun 10-4 ▪ Fee applicable ▪ Closed Easter Sun, Dec 25/26 & Jan 1 ▪ Play area for children ▪ Owner(s) Charles & Zelda Fox ▪ Cellarmaster(s) Charles Fox (2010) ▪ Winemaker(s) Nicolas Follet (2010, consultant) ▪ Viticulturist(s) Kevin Watt (2008, consultant) ▪ 33.4ha/6.3ha (pinot meunier, pinot, chard) ▪ 960cs (2010)/3,360cs (2011) own label 100% MCC ▪ PO Box 105 Elgin 7180 ▪ charlesfoxmcc@gmail.com ▪ www.charlesfox.co.za ▪ S 34° 14' 14.38" E 019° 04' 41.99" ▪ F +27 (0)86-536-2924 ▪ **T +27 (0)21-300-1065/+27 (0)82-569-2965/+27 (0)82-471-3444**

☐ **Charmé** *see* Vin du Cap International
☐ **Chateau Beau Belle** *see* Beau Belle

Chateau Libertas

The grandfather of South African reds, available since 1932 and still a paragon of value and drinkability. By Distell.

Chateau Libertas ★★★ In usual consistent form, **13** plentiful well-sustained soft black berry fruit in a gentle rounded frame. Bordeaux varieties with shiraz & ruby cab. WO W Cape. — AL

Chateau Naudé Wine Creation

Ebullient Francois Naudé snr is an instantly likeable man with a wonderful sense of humour. Being irrepressible by nature, retirement from his regular winemaking job simply meant redeploying his creative oenological talents to start his own family venture - boutique in size, but internationally renowned (exported to eight different countries). Part of the output is sold at a family-staged black-tie auction in mid-March. Flamboyant as this may sound, Francois is self-effacing ('Wingnut' a reference to the shape of his ears!), driven by an ardent belief in the potential of pinotage, the only variety in his masterly multi-cellar blend, Le Vin de François, this year sourced chiefly from Stellenbosch.

Chateau Naudé Wine Creation range

★★★★☆ **Le Vin de François 12** pinotage from 7, mostly Stellenbosch, vineyards. Alluring, complex infusion of dark choc & spicy cherry in fine-grained but firm tannin structure. Silky textured, iron fist in velvet glove, with same François magic as in stylish **11** (★★★★★).

Wingnut range

★★★★ **Cabernet Sauvignon** ⓥ **10** a shade off stellar **09** (★★★★★), but still shows classical elegance & restraint, underpinned by deft oaking. WO Stellenbosch, as most of these.

★★★★ **Méthode Cap Classique Brut Rosé** ⓥ Refined & flavoursome **10**, from chardonnay (70%) & pinotage, savoury freshness & fine creamy mousse. Perfect with ceviche or for any occasion.

Pinotage ⓥ ★★★ Swaggeringly ripe **11** dark liquorice tone, sweet new oak & alcohol add power. A tad brawny & unbalanced last edition, needed time & robust fare. **Chenin Blanc Barrel Fermented** ⓥ **12** tank sample off Wellington vines too youthful to rate. Not retasted: **Chardonnay 10** ★★★★ **White Port 10** ★★★

Nuts About range

Shiraz ⓥ ★★★ **11** shows tart & tangy acidity offset by a smoky, savoury nuance. Lightish & juicy, for al fresco fare. From Wellington, as next. Not retasted: **Chenin Blanc 11** ★★★★ — MW

Location: Stellenbosch ▪ WO: Wellington/Stellenbosch ▪ Est 2006 ▪ 1stB 2007 ▪ Closed to public ▪ Owner(s) Francois Naudé snr, Magda Naudé, Francois Naudé jnr, Melissa Naudé ▪ Cellarmaster(s) Francois Naudé (Jul 2007) ▪ 1,000cs own label 65% red 35% white ▪ 11 Weidenhof Street Stellenbosch 7600 ▪ naude@levindefrancois.co.za ▪ www.levindefrancois.com ▪ F +27 (0)86-651-3192 ▪ **T +27 (0)21-883-8469**

Chateau VO Extra Fine

After being handled by Distell subsidiary Henry Tayler & Ries for a number of years (as were Limosin and Olof Bergh), Chateau brandy has returned to owner Distell. A stalwart of the Cape blended brandy scene, Chateau VO has been bottled as such since 1921, having previously been sold wholesale by 19th-century Cape liquor trading company Sedgwick's.

Chateau VO Extra Fine ⓥ ★★★ Decent, straightforward blended brandy designed for mixers. Not short of fruit & floral notes, rich enough, firm & smooth. — WB, TJ

☐ **Chatta Box** *see* Distell

Chennells Wines

In 2003 Jeremy and Colleen Chennells resolved to replace orchards with vines on their smallholding on the Helderberg. Preparing the land, planting and nurturing vines, and making wines (with the eminent Chris Keet advising) in the cellar of nearby Romond has been 'truly fulfilling'.

The Journey (NEW) ★★★ Equal cab/shiraz blend in **12**. Very ripe, mere hint of spice, bone-dry & firmly tannic. **A Handful of Summers** ★★★ Was 'Viognier'. Oak-enriched **13** shows ripe apricot compote features; fresher flavours, dry rather grippy conclusion. Not retasted: **Cabernet Sauvignon 10** ★★★★ **Shiraz 10** ★★★ — AL

Location: Somerset West ▪ Map: Helderberg ▪ WO: Stellenbosch/Western Cape ▪ Est 2004 ▪ 1stB 2008 ▪ Tasting, sales & cellar tours Mon-Sun 9-5 by appt ▪ Closed all pub hols ▪ Owner(s) Jeremy & Colleen Chennells ▪ Cellarmaster(s)/winemaker(s) Jeremy Chennells & Chris Keet (Jul 2009, consultant) ▪ Viticulturist(s) Colleen Chennells & Chris Keet (Jul 2009, consultant) ▪ 5ha/3.2ha (cab, shiraz, viog) ▪ 26t/330cs own label 85% red 15% white ▪ Romond Vineyards, Klein Helderberg Road, Somerset West 7130 ▪ chennell@iafrica.com ▪ S 34° 1' 52.61" E 018° 49' 59.67" ▪ F +27 (0)21-683-6280 ▪ **T +27 (0)21-855-3905**

☐ **Chip Off The Old Block** *see* Ormonde Private Cellar
☐ **Chris Keet** *see* Keet Wines
☐ **Christina Van Loveren** *see* Van Loveren Family Vineyards
☐ **Christine-Marié** *see* Niel Joubert Estate
☐ **Cilliers Cellars** *see* Stellendrift - SHZ Cilliers/Kuün Wyne
☐ **Circle of Life** *see* Waterkloof
☐ **Circumstance** *see* Waterkloof

Cirrus Wines

A transcontinental venture between the owners of California's Silver Oaks Cellars, Ray Duncan and sons David and Tim, and Jean Engelbrecht of Rust en Vrede, aimed at 'capturing the very essence of shiraz influenced by both Stellenbosch and Napa'.

★★★★☆ **Cirrus Syrah** Smoothly muscular **12** keeps up form of **11**. Dense & powerful, the oak (combo French & American) is a tad prominent but will knit with ripe plum & black berry fruit given time. Concentrated, deep & focused, its long conclusion leaves a happy memory. — FM

Location/map/WO: Stellenbosch ▪ Est/1stB 2003 ▪ Tasting & sales at Guardian Peak (see entry) ▪ Owner(s) Jean Engelbrecht & Ray Duncan ▪ Cellarmaster(s)/winemaker(s) Coenie Snyman (Jun 2010) ▪ Viticulturist(s) Dirkie Mouton (Jun 2010) ▪ 30t/3,626cs own label 100% red ▪ IPW ▪ PO Box 473 Stellenbosch 7599 ▪ info@cirruswines.com ▪ www.cirruswines.com ▪ S 34° 0' 44.31" E 018° 50' 33.22" ▪ F +27 (0)21-881-3388 ▪ **T +27 (0)21-881-3899**

Citrusdal Wines

Citrusdal Wines' Six Hats Fairtrade label is named for the principles (partnership, change, potential, equity, dignity and sustainability) which guide the collaboration between the winery, Fairtrade grape farmers and Fairview's Charles Back to bring ethically traded wines to winelovers locally and overseas.

Location: Citrusdal ▪ Est/1stB 2007 ▪ Closed to public ▪ Owner(s) Charles Back, Mike Paul & other grape farm owners ▪ Cellarmaster(s) Jaco Brand (Nov 2009) ▪ Winemaker(s) Welma Visser (Nov 2013) & Andries de Klerk (Nov 2009) ▪ Viticulturist(s) Charl du Plessis (Nov 2009) ▪ 550ha (cab, cinsaut, grenache n/b, merlot, mourv, ptage, ruby cab, shiraz, tannat, chard, chenin, hanepoot, pinot grigio, sauv, viog) ▪ 9,000t/50,000cs own label 45% red 50% white 5% rosé + 200,000cs for clients ▪ Brands for clients: Co-op, Fairtrade Original, M&S, Sainsbury's ▪ Fairtrade, HACCP 2004, IPW, WIETA ▪ PO Box 41 Citrusdal 7340 ▪ info@citrusdalwines.co.za ▪ www.citrusdalwines.co.za ▪ F +27 (0)22-921-3937 ▪ **T +27 (0)22-921-2233**

CK Wines

Bushveld-born Christian Kuun was bitten by the wine bug (specifically cabernet sauvignon) while studying stock farming at Elsenburg in Stellenbosch. Happily employed as a full-time winemaker, he took it one step further when his son's birth in 2009 inspired investment in his eponymous after-hours label CK, to date featuring select bottlings of Bordeaux varieties.

★★★★ **Sincera** ⓥ Appealing rich cocoa & oodles of succulent black fruit on pre-bottling debut **11**, 100% cab franc. Yielding & plush textured; harmonious oaking with long star anise & liquorice finish.

★★★★ **Integra** ⓥ Switches from varietal cab to 60/40 blend cab & cab franc in **10**, goes up notch on **09** (★★★★). Rich & ripe yet gently soft, heaps of cassis flavour, lovely mouthfeel & balance. Structured & elegantly long. — FM

Location/WO: Stellenbosch ▪ Est 2009 ▪ 1stB 2010 ▪ Tasting by appt ▪ Fee R50 ▪ Owner(s)/cellarmaster(s)/winemaker(s) Christian Kuun ▪ 400cs own label 100% red ▪ winemaker@ckwines.co.za, sales@ckwines.co.za ▪ F +27 (0)86-504-6209 ▪ **T +27 (0)82-615-8105**

Claime d'Or   ⓥ

Gold is referenced in the name of the boutique winery of husband and wife team Bernardo Rapoport and Magriet de Wet, sourcing from 10 ha of vines in the Goudmyn ('Gold Mine') area between Robertson and Bonnievale, and in the Solidus range, named for a Roman empire gold coin and now featuring a fine and smartly packaged sur lie-style chardonnay.

Claime d'Or range

★★★★ **Cabernet Franc** Now bottled, **10** (★★★☆) ultra-ripe aromas; meaty, rich, slightly grainy palate is generous, but lacks definition of supple **09**. Acidity balances the few extra grams sugar.

★★★★ **Cabernet Sauvignon-Cabernet Franc** Rich **10** (★★★☆), now bottled, prunes & some raisins; lacks precision, but concentrated & long-finishing. Few grams of sugar balanced by highish acid. **09** less savoury.

Cabernet Sauvignon Rosé ★★☆ Fragrant **12**, with floral & red fruit notes, just-dry & straightforward, with modest 12% alcohol. Also tasted: **Sauvignon Blanc 13** ★★★☆ Not retasted: **Pinot Noir 11** ★★★☆ **Shiraz 11** ★★★ **Chardonnay 12** ★★★

Solidus range

Unwooded Chardonnay (NEW) ★★★☆ Subtle aromas of apple & orange blossom, **13** dry, & with some richness from extended lees-ageing. Not retasted: **Cabernet Sauvignon 12** ★★★☆ — JPf

Location: Robertson ▪ WO: Robertson/Western Cape ▪ Est/1stB 2008 ▪ Tasting & sales at Rietvallei Wine Estate (see entry) ▪ Owner(s) Magriet de Wet & Bernardo Rapoport ▪ Cellarmaster(s)/winemaker(s) Kobus Burger (2002, Rietvallei) ▪ Viticulturist(s) Wilhelm Treurnicht (2007, Rietvallei) ▪ 10ha (cabs s/f, sauv) ▪ 30% red 60% white 10% rosé ▪ PO Box 2040 Parklands 2121 ▪ info@claimedorwines.co.za ▪ www.claimedorwines.co.za ▪ F +27 (0)86-691-7497/+27 (0)11-788-7346 ▪ **T +27 (0)11-447-8776**

Clairvaux Private Cellar

Amid booming bulk-wine sales, Clairvaux has built a new cellar to expand capacity. Cellarmaster Jaco van der Merwe bottles just enough of the 3+ million litre production under the own label to supply the tasting venue – just off Robertson's main road - and keep the De Wet family owners in wine.

Cabernet Sauvignon ★★★ Early-drinking **11**'s smoky aromas, cassis taste & dry tannic finish satisfy. **Good Night Irene** ★★★ Fortified hanepoot dessert for those who prefer zest to sweetness. **14** floral & grapey, lifted by bright citrus acidity. **Madonna's Kisses Golden Muscadel** ★★★★ Improved **14** fortified dessert successfully walks tightrope between hedonistic honey & raisin sweetness, tangy lime acidity. Also tasted: **Shiraz 11** ★★ **Sandberg Purple 13** ★★ **Sauvignon Blanc 14** ★★★ **Cape Vintage 12** ★★★ Not retasted: **Red Muscadel 12** ★★★★ — CvZ

Location/map/WO: Robertson ▪ Est/1stB 2000 ▪ Tasting & sales Mon-Fri 8-5 ▪ Closed all pub hols ▪ Cellar tours by appt ▪ BYO picnic ▪ Sales (at cellar price) also from La Verne Wine Boutique T +27 (0)23-626-4314 Mon-Fri 9-5.30 Sat 9-5 ▪ Owner(s) Wouter J de Wet snr & jnr ▪ Cellarmaster(s) Jaco van der Merwe (Oct 2011) ▪ Winemaker(s) Jaco van der Merwe (Oct 2011), with Coenraad Groenewald (Jan 2010) ▪ 200ha (cab, merlot, ptage, shiraz, chard, chenin,

cbard, muscadel, sauv) ▪ 4,000t/3.2m L bulk ▪ PO Box 179 Robertson 6705 ▪ info@clairvauxcellar.co.za ▪ www.
clairvauxcellar.co.za ▪ S 33° 48′ 13.8″ E 019° 52′ 21.1″ ▪ F +27 (0)23-626-1925 ▪ **T +27 (0)23-626-3842**

Clayton Wines

'My aim is to make honest, natural wines that my family and I will enjoy drinking for many years to
come,' says owner/winemaker Roger Clayton, a security expert (with some winemaking experience in
his youth) who moved to SA from Scotland and soon found himself 'captured by the spirit' of the
Swartland Independent Producers. After three years of garagiste winemaking at DeanDavid, he's now
producing his own small batches at Antebellum near Riebeek-Kasteel.

★★★★☆ **Jolly Roger Chardonnay** Thrilling expression of bushvine chardonnay! Despite stonefruit
& tropical opulence, plushness, subtle oaking, **13** more site- than fruit-driven, the palate laced with dry
minerality & crystalline purity. — HJ

Location: Riebeek-Kasteel ▪ WO: Swartland ▪ Est/1stB 2013 ▪ Closed to public ▪ Owner(s) Roger & Natasha Clayton ▪
Winemaker(s) Roger Clayton (Jan 2013) ▪ 4t/300cs own label 50% red 50% white ▪ PO Box 56 Green Point Cape Town
8051 ▪ roger@rmafrica.com ▪ **T +27 (0)76-826-8500**

☐ **Clearsprings** *see* Trizanne Signature Wines

Clive Torr Wines

A chance meeting with the late Robert Mondavi in Napa Valley inspired Clive Torr, then studying
pomology, a branch of horticulture focused on fruit, to switch to winegrowing. Now a Cape Wine
Master, wine educator and garagiste mentor, his eponymous venture involves limited-edition handmade wines from parcels in Elgin and the western slopes of the Cape Peninsula.

Clive Torr range (NEW)
Pinot Noir NW ★★★☆ Riper, fuller of the 2 Elgin pinots, from warmer north-west slope. **13** concentrated, with inky finish, mostly redcurrant & plum fruit, some cherry notes too. **Pinot Noir SE** ★★★
From a cooler, south-east Elgin site, **13** prominent sour cherry, cranberry & Chinese spice, lively acidity, subtle oaking. Some farmyard funkiness, dry tealeaf finish. Drink soon. **Shiraz** ★★★ From Elgin
fruit, **13** rustic leather & spice, black pepper & smoke with firm tannins for winter stews & rich meaty
dishes. **Sauvignon Blanc** ★★★☆ Atypical of variety & origin (Cape Peninsula), **13** oily texture &
warm finish, could use more zip & zing. **Viognier** ★★★ Peach pip & fynbos interest in medium-bodied **13**; fleshy, with slightly astringent/pithy conclusion. Elgin fruit.

Scarborough Affair range (NEW)
Cabernet Sauvignon ★★ Red fruit & cassis perfume on **13** belies austere, acidic palate, with drying tannins needing food. **Shiraz** ★★★☆ Wild blackberries & spice lead to a heady palate with red &
black fruit, hiding 16% alcohol; **13** finishes with flamboyant vanilla swish. — HJ, AL

Location: Somerset West ▪ Map: Helderberg ▪ WO: Elgin/Cape Peninsula ▪ Tasting by appt ▪ Owner(s)/winemaker(s)
Clive Torr ▪ 26 Topaz Street Heldervue Somerset West 7130 ▪ clivetorrwines@mweb.co.za ▪ www.clivetorrwines.co.za
▪ S 34° 3′ 19.09″ E 018° 49′ 1.51″ ▪ F +27 (0)86-513-4034 ▪ **T +27 (0)82-557-0836**

Cloof Wine Estate

In the heart of maritime-influenced Darling, this large former wheat farm (with vines dating back to
the 1960s) was replanted to classic varieties in the late 1990s. Foreign owned since 2003, its vineyard
holdings more than doubled with the acquisition of neighbour Burghers Post, feeding its tiered, red-
led ranges. Sustainability is key to the eco-award-winning and conservation-conscious team (including a member of the area's noted Duckitt family), as is community development. Cloof's visitor attractions include the annual Rocking the Daisies indie music festival.

Premium range

★★★★ **Cloof Shiraz** As sexy as its Signature stablemate, dense yet remarkably fresh **12** oozes ripe raspberry while hints of black pepper, smoked meat & sweet spice from year oak add intrigue.

★★★★ **Cloof Lynchpin** ② **10** (★★★★) first since **06**. Austere cab franc (70%) & merlot mix proffers brooding plum, with a tannic frame requiring decanting.

Not retasted: **Merlot 11** ★★★★ Occasional release: **Crucible Shiraz**.

Signature range

★★★★ **The Very Sexy Shiraz** ⊘ From vineyards described as 'shiraz heaven', **12** seduces with spicy perfume, ripe black berry flavours & a voluptuous body, more smooth & supple than **11** (★★★★).

★★★★ **Duckitt Cabernet Sauvignon-Merlot-Cabernet Franc** ⊘ Showing potential, **12** is big & bold yet balanced, with plum pudding & Ribena blackcurrant notes. Velvety **11**, also tasted, seriously over-delivers: rich & concentrated, with lovely definition.

Duckitt Chardonnay-Pinot Noir ⑩ ⊘ ★★★★ Merest hint of copper on **13**, floral nose leading to silky mouthful of apricot & tangy red berries, nicely balanced. **Summertime Sauvignon Blanc** ★★★ Green apple & lime on fresh & zippy **14**. **The Very Vivacious Viognier** ★★★★ Pale pink-gold **14** bursts with peach, ripe apricot, melon & honey, exuberant flavours toned down by smooth oak (three months 100% new French) giving lovely viscosity. Also tasted: **Cab Cult Cabernet Sauvignon 12** ★★★ **Inkspot Vin Noir 11** ★★★ Not retasted: **Cloof Pinotage 11** ★★★ **The Dark Side Cabernet Sauvignon-Shiraz 11** ★★★ Discontinued: **The Very Posh Pinotage**, **Cellar Blend**, **40 Days Natural Sweet**.

Darling range

Ruby Darling ⊘ ★★★ Easy to drink, unwooded **13** combines sweet ripe berry fruit of mostly pinotage (86%) with dash of shiraz spice. **Daisy Sweet Darling** ⑩ ★★★ From chenin, **14** lives up to its name: sweet but nicely balanced, so not too cloying, lowish 11.5% alcohol. Also tasted: **Daisy Darling Chardonnay Unwooded 14** ★★★ **Daisy Darling 14** ★★★ Not retasted: **Rosy Darling 13** ★★ **Happy Dragon Chenin 13** ★★★ — JG

Location/WO: Darling ▪ Map: Durbanville, Philadelphia & Darling ▪ Est/1stB 1998 ▪ Tasting & sales Mon-Sat 10–4 ▪ Closed Easter Fri/Sun, Dec 25 & Jan 1 ▪ Cellar tours by appt ▪ Meals/refreshments Tue-Sat 10-3 ▪ Farm produce ▪ Conservation area ▪ Game & eco drives by appt ▪ Child friendly ▪ Owner(s) Cloof Wine Estate (Pty) Ltd ▪ Winemaker(s) Christopher van Dieren (Jan 2002) & Jody Johannes (Jan 2012) ▪ Viticulturist(s) Peter Duckitt (May 2004) ▪ 1,300ha/166ha (cabs s/f, merlot, ptage, shiraz, chard, chenin, viog) ▪ 600t/100,000cs own label 88% red 12% white ▪ BWI champion ▪ PO Box 269 Darling 7345 ▪ info@cloof.co.za ▪ www.cloof.co.za ▪ S 33° 28' 58.1" E 018° 31' 23.4" ▪ F +27 (0)22-492-3261 ▪ **T +27 (0)22-492-2839**

Clos Malverne ⑨ ⑪ ⑥ ⑥

Seymour and Sophia Pritchard have seen their Devon Valley estate — once Stellenbosch's smallest — grow like Topsy. Now the scenically located winery offers conferences, a restaurant that's packed at weekends and a day spa for indulgent treatments — and still uses a basket press for its signature pinotage and pinotage blends. Winemaking is in the competent hands of Suzanne Coetzee, who has shepherded into bottle a rare rosé MCC bubbly from shiraz.

★★★★ **Pinotage Reserve** Traditionally crafted, brambleberry & spice scented **12**, very firmly structured palate with good freshness & developing complexity. Pity not to give it more time - there's plenty of potential, less so in lighter **11** (★★★★).

★★★★ **Auret** ② Cape Blend of cab (60%), pinotage & merlot in **11**. Now bottled, aromas of dark & red fruit with truffle & wet earth notes. Firm, fine prominent tannin & good freshness, well-judged 30% new oak.

For more information, visit wineonaplatter.com

★★★★ **Spirit of Malverne Limited Release** Retasted, **11** Cape Blend blend of pinotage (50%), cab, shiraz is concentrated & bold, with oak & acidity better integrated - very young still. Modern, ambitious styling, needs more time.

★★★★ **Ellie MCC** (ⁿᵉʷ) Unusual pink sparkling from shiraz, with 15% oaked component. **11** frivolous but well made & very appealing, ripe red berries & a little spice, fine if somewhat languid bubbles.

Chardonnay ★★★☆ Sparingly wooded **13**, juicy ripe melon & pear broadening on palate into succulent fruit flavours with better-tuned oak than previous. WO W Cape. **Sauvignon Blanc** ★★★☆ Only Devon Valley grapes for this label, showing juicy tropical fruit & green undertones in **13**. Friendly, succulent, not-too-complex palate with evident lees-ageing. Also tasted: **Cabernet Sauvignon-Merlot 12** ★★★☆ **Cabernet Sauvignon-Shiraz 12** ★★★ **Sauvignon Blanc Brut Reserve NV** ★★★ Not retasted: **Merlot 11** ★★★☆ **Le Café Pinotage 12** ★★★☆ Not tasted: **Auret Limited Release**. — JPf

Location/map: Stellenbosch ▪ WO: Stellenbosch/Western Cape/Devon Valley ▪ Est/1stB 1986 ▪ Tasting & sales Mon-Sat 10–5 Sun 10-4.30 ▪ Fee R25/4 wines ▪ Closed Good Fri, Dec 25 & Jan 1 ▪ Cellar tours Mon-Fri ▪ The Restaurant @ Clos Malverne ▪ Tour groups ▪ Gifts ▪ Conferences ▪ Weddings/functions ▪ Walks/hikes ▪ Wellness Day Spa ▪ Owner(s) Seymour & Sophia Pritchard ▪ Cellarmaster(s)/viticulturist(s) Suzanne Coetzee (Oct 2010) ▪ Winemaker(s) Suzanne Coetzee (Oct 2010), with Mynardt Hitchcock (1999) ▪ 18ha (cab, ptage, sauv) ▪ ±200t/80,000cs own label 50% red 50% white ▪ PO Box 187 Stellenbosch 7599 ▪ info@closmalverne.co.za ▪ www.closmalverne.co.za, www.capeblend.co.za ▪ S 33° 54' 38.0" E 018° 48' 49.2" ▪ F +27 (0)21-865-2518 ▪ **T +27 (0)21-865-2022**

Clouds Wine Estate

International owners Paul Burema and Jolanda van Haperen have given consultant winemaker Donovan Rall carte blanche to produce top quality from the vineyard on their boutique estate, which also has luxury accommodation, conferencing and a wedding venue atop Stellenbosch's Helshoogte Pass, boasting spectacular vistas of the Simonsberg and Drakenstein mountains.

★★★★ **Pinot Noir** Now bottled, **13** realises the promise it showed last time. Lacy delicacy hides tensile strength & bright cherry, berry vibrancy from Walker Bay fruit. Long, concentrated & focused. — FM

Location/map: Stellenbosch ▪ WO: Western Cape ▪ Est/1stB 1993 ▪ Tasting & sales Mon-Sat 10-5 ▪ Breakfast ▪ Guest house & self-catering villas ▪ Conferences ▪ Weddings & functions ▪ Owner(s) Paul Burema & Jolanda van Haperen ▪ Cellarmaster(s) Donovan Rall (Jan 2014, Vuurberg) ▪ Winemaker(s) Donovan Rall (Jan 2014, Vuurberg), with Paul Burema (Jan 2012) ▪ Viticulturist(s) Wynand Pienaar (Aug 2009, consultant) ▪ 4.5ha/2.7ha (cab, pinot, chard, sauv) ▪ 24t/2,500cs own label 40% red 60% white ▪ PO Box 540 Stellenbosch 7599 ▪ info@cloudsestate.co.za ▪ www.cloudsestate.co.za ▪ S 33° 55' 23.9" E 018° 55' 29.7" ▪ F +27 (0)21-885-2829 ▪ **T +27 (0)21-885-1819**

Clovelly Wines

From a base in Stellenbosch's Devon Valley, vintner Jacques Fourie focuses on a small-volume, high-quality production, a limited-release varietal malbec under a special label in the offing. Jacques has expanded the viticulture and winemaking consulting side of his business and now advises four clients, all in Stellenbosch.

Cabernet Sauvignon ★★★☆ Cedar notes, rum & raisin ripeness on **09**; supportive & well-controlled tannin structure plumped by plush fruit for good drinking now, cellaring few years. **Three Sides Vineyard Blend** ★★★☆ Characterful & appealing mix cab, merlot, pinotage; **09** slight farmyard, earth & spice tones plus vibrant red fruit & enlivening acidity, tannic grip. Elegant dinner companion. Not tasted: **Patina Shiraz**, **Chardonnay**. — WB, CvZ

Location/map/WO: Stellenbosch ▪ Est/1stB 2000 ▪ Tasting, sales & tours strictly by appt ▪ Owner(s) York Partnership t/a Clovelly Wines ▪ Winemaker(s)/viticulturist(s) Jacques Fourie ▪ 4ha/3ha (cab) ▪ 90% red 10% white ▪ Postnet Suite 215 Private Bag X5061 Stellenbosch 7599 ▪ info@clovellywines.com ▪ www.clovellywines.com ▪ S 33° 53' 54.1" E 018° 47' 52.3" ▪ F +27 (0)21-865-2511 ▪ **T +27 (0)82-853-7190**

Cloverfield Private Cellar

Family history has an honoured place - in the winery branding and name of the Shamrock Red - for the much-loved Irish lass who bore Cloverfield patriarch Pietie Marais three sons and brought hope, love as well as luck to the Robertson farm.

Sauvignon Blanc ⊘ ★★★ Forward-flavoured **14**, vaguely pleasant & fresh; modest 12% alcohol aids quaffability. Also tasted: **Chardonnay Wooded 14** ★★ **Chenin Blanc 14** ★★ **Shamrock Red NV** ★★ Not retasted: **Chardonnay Unwooded 13** ★★★ Not tasted: **Shiraz**. — TJ

Location/map/WO: Robertson ▪ Est 1945 ▪ 1stB 2002 ▪ Tasting & sales Mon-Fri 9-5 ▪ Closed Easter Fri-Mon, Dec 25 & Jan 1 ▪ Owner(s)/viticulturist(s) Pieter Marais ▪ Cellarmaster(s) Cobus Marais (2002) ▪ Winemaker(s) Cobus Marais (2002), with Gerald Smith (Jun 2009) ▪ ±200ha total (shiraz, chard, chenin, sauv) ▪ 40% red 60% white ▪ PO Box 429 Robertson 6705 ▪ info@cloverfield.co.za ▪ www.cloverfield.co.za ▪ S 33° 49' 57.3" E 019° 55' 34.1" ▪ F +27 (0)23-626-3203 ▪ **T +27 (0)23-626-4118**

☐ **Coast** *see* PicardiRebel
☐ **Cocoa Hill** *see* Dornier Wines
☐ **Cogmanskloof** *see* Zandvliet Wine Estate & Thoroughbred Stud

Cold Duck (5th Avenue)

Long-established sweet, low-alcohol carbonated sparkling rosé by Distell.

5th Avenue Cold Duck ★★★ Fragrant pink party fizz, **NV**, simple but balanced, uncloying. — DB

☐ **Cold Mountain** *see* Brunia Wines
☐ **Collection** *see* Mooiplaas Estate & Private Nature Reserve

Collison's

Recalling brothers John and Francis Collison, English general dealers who distributed and distilled brandy in the Cape Colony, this Distell brandy intends to be funky and fun, and appeal to a young, trendy and inclusively female market.

White Gold ⊗ ★★★★ Near colourless (useful in cocktails). Light tropical fruity nose, hints of vanilla & roasted nuts. Elegant, youthful with lingering slightly sweet aftertaste. Blended; from chenin & colombard. — WB, TJ

Colmant Cap Classique & Champagne

It's more than a decade since Jean-Philippe and Isabelle Colmant 'landed in unknown territories from our native Belgium, with luggage, five children and a passion for bubbly...' Now, drawing on grapes from their tiny Franschhoek vineyard and from elsewhere, they have one of the Cape's few wineries devoted to sparkling wine classically made from classic varieties. The wines are mostly kept for unusually long periods on their lees before disgorging, which adds to their finesse and subtle richness of flavour. On which subject JP notes: 'Although demand has been exceeding our capacity, we are not planning to increase production or shorten time on the lees, but instead to work further on quality.'

★★★★ **Brut Rosé** Floral-scented quince, fresh apples & red berry fruit on **NV** combine with sherbert grip for extreme refreshment. 10 g/l sugar tempers crisp acid. 73% pinot with chardonnay.

★★★★☆ **Brut Reserve** Harmoniously refined bubbly from near-equal parts pinot noir & chardonnay, latest **NV** release follows previous formula precisely. Wisps of citrus rind, toasted brioche & nutty yeast entwine with finely judged acidity & creamy mousse.

★★★★☆ **Brut Chardonnay** Toasty biscuit aromas woven with delightful citrus rind & baked apple on seductive **NV** sparkler. Lingering hazelnut & nougat on richly textured finish. Elegantly poised yet expressive. 20% oak fermented, 45 months on lees, 10% reserve portion.

★★★★ Sec Reserve NV made on same lines as Brut Reserve but retaining 20 g/l sugar. Sweetness is detectable but appealing, softening the acidity & raising the fruit profile. — GdB

Location/map: Franschhoek ▪ WO: Western Cape ▪ Est 2005 ▪ 1stB 2006 ▪ Tasting Mon-Fri 11-1; or by appt ▪ Fee R15 per ½ glass MCC ▪ Owner(s) Jean-Philippe Colmant ▪ Cellarmaster(s) Jean-Philippe Colmant ▪ Wine consultants Nicolas Follet & Pieter Ferreira ▪ Viticulturist(s) Paul Wallace (consultant) ▪ 5ha/3ha (pinot, chard) ▪ 7,400cs own label 100% MCC ▪ PO Box 602 Franschhoek 7690 ▪ info@colmant.co.za ▪ www.colmant.co.za ▪ S 33° 55' 22.4" E 019° 7' 37.3" ▪ F +27 (0)21-876-3732 ▪ **T +27 (0)21-876-4348/+27 (0)72-368-4942**

☐ **Compagnies Wijn** *see* Oude Compagnies Post Private Cellar
☐ **Condé** *see* Stark-Condé Wines
☐ **Confluence** *see* Douglas Wine Cellar

Conradie Family Vineyards

Cellarmaster CP Conradie's family has been growing grapes in the Nuy Valley since 1871. Ronwan Griffiths, who also grew up on the farm, works alongside him in the cellar, which speaks for continuity. They're proud of having to increase cellar capacity because of demand, but also pleased to note that 400 ha of the farm is dedicated to protecting indigenous fauna and flora.

Single Vineyard Barrel Selection Reserve range

★★★★ Pinotage ⊘ **12** moves to this range (tasted last year). Juxtaposition of sweet vanilla & chocolate with savoury bacon & spice in juicy **12**.

Shiraz (NEW) **★★★** Powerful **13** is house's first shiraz, offering black pepper, olive & dark fruit, together with obvious vanilla, espresso & chocolate oak notes from 50% new wood. Also tasted: **Cabernet Sauvignon 13 ★★★**

Conradie Family Vineyards range

Sauvignon Blanc ★★★ 14 has usual green aromas; just off-dry, uncomplicated & well behaved as usual. Includes Darling grapes. **Rooi Muskadel** (NEW) **★★★** Luscious & exuberant floral, grapey character on **09** (5 years in old oak). More cloyingly sweet than complex, but with lingering intensity. Also tasted: **Cabernet Sauvignon-Pinotage 13 ★★★ Sweet Rosaline Perlé Rosé NV ★★** — JPf

Location/map: Worcester ▪ WO: Nuy/Western Cape ▪ Est/1stB 2004 ▪ Tasting, sales & cellar tours Mon-Fri 8.30–4.30 Sat 9-3 Sun 11-2; after-hours by appt ▪ Closed Good Fri, Ascension Day, Dec 25 & Jan 1 ▪ Nuy Vallei Restaurant & Guest House: meals daily 8-5, or by appt ▪ Facilities for children ▪ Tour groups ▪ Farm produce ▪ BYO picnic ▪ Conferences ▪ Walks/hikes ▪ Mountain biking & 4x4 trails ▪ Conservation area ▪ Annual Nuy Valley Feast (May) ▪ Owner(s) Conradie family ▪ Cellarmaster(s) CP Conradie (Jan 2004) ▪ Winemaker(s) CP Conradie (Jan 2004), with Ronwan Griffiths (Sep 2009) ▪ Viticulturist(s) Riaan Lambrechts (Aug 2011) ▪ 4,500ha/83ha (cab, ptage, pontac, chenin, cbard, crouchen, muscadel w, pinot gris, sauv) ▪ 1,840t total 70t/5,400cs own label 50% red 25% white 25% rosé ▪ BWI ▪ PO Box 5298 Worcester 6851 ▪ wine@conradievineyards.co.za ▪ www.conradie-vineyards.co.za ▪ S 33° 39' 28. 0" E 019° 37' 59.6" ▪ F +27 (0)86-509-4911 ▪ **T +27 (0)23-342-7025**

Conspirare

Boutique vintner Henry Dowling hasn't vinified his blended red Conspirare in several years, but the 02 is still available from his Helderberg farm.

Location: Stellenbosch ▪ Map: Helderberg ▪ Est/1stB 2002 ▪ Tasting by appt ▪ Owner(s) HB Dowling/LRD Trust ▪ Winemaker(s) Henry Dowling ▪ 24ha (cabs s/f, merlot, shiraz, chenin) ▪ 250t/850cs own label 100% red ▪ PO Box 1210 Stellenbosch 7599 ▪ dowls@mweb.co.za ▪ S 34° 1' 18.4" E 018° 50' 54.6" ▪ F +27 (0)86-516-3086 ▪ **T +27 (0)21-855-0708**

Constantia de Tulbagh

Constantia de Tulbagh, sibling to Montpellier, is owned by Johannesburg advocate Lucas van Tonder. The revitalised vineyards are overseen, and their fruit vinified by recently appointed Flip Smith and Harold Versfeld.

Location/map: Tulbagh ▪ Est 1965 ▪ 1stB 2000 ▪ Tasting, sales & tours by appt ▪ Owner(s) Lucas J van Tonder ▪ Cellar-master(s)/winemaker(s)/viticulturist(s) Flip Smith (Oct 2013) & Harold Versfeld (Sep 2014) ▪ 330ha/35ha (cab, mer-lot, pinot, chenin, riesling, sauv) ▪ 6–10,000cs own label 20% red 80% white ▪ PO Box 79 Tulbagh 6820 ▪ montpellier@montpellier.co.za ▪ www.montpellier.co.za ▪ S 33° 17' 21.3" E 019° 6' 30.7" ▪ F +27 (0)23-230-1574 ▪ **T +27 (0)23-230-0656**

Constantia Glen

Originally part of Simon van der Stel's Constantia farm, the portion now called Constantia Glen was covered by forest or grazed by cattle before the Waibel family joined it to the valley's great tradition of winegrowing in 2000. Thanks to the longer sunlight hours at this northern end of the valley, their favoured Bordeaux grapes, both white and red, flourish. The tasting and sales venue on the estate has been upgraded, and the already superb wines are set to go up a notch too, as winemaker Justin van Wyk and team tweak production methods and experiment with vineyard practices 'to build even more on the quality of our wines so that we maintain the good market presence we have captured'.

★★★★☆ **Constantia Glen Five** Elegant flagship blend of all five Bordeaux red varieties, hence the name, with 26% cab & 22% petit verdot harmonising with merlot, cab franc & malbec in stately **10**. Savoury tobacco & allspice add complexity to concentrated black fruit.

★★★★☆ **Constantia Glen Three** Improving on **10** (★★★★), **11** is 45% merlot, 37% cab franc, 18% cab. Red berry & violet perfume leads to juicy dark fruit on palate with hint of mocha. Plush & velvety yet vibrant thanks to high natural acidity after cool season.

★★★★☆ **Sauvignon Blanc 14** has 4% semillon, adding rich texture to crisp acidity as well as hints of orange & greengage to intense lime, kiwi & cling peach flavours. Beautifully balanced, multi-layered, with elderflower entry & white pepper finish. A keeper.

★★★★ **Constantia Glen Two** Previous vintage's recipe of 71% sauvignon & 29% semillon, with six months of lees-maturation, works even better in **13**. Rich texture is perfectly balanced by freshness; ripe tangerine, pineapple & papaya flavours on mineral backbone. — JG

Location/WO: Constantia ▪ Map: Cape Peninsula ▪ Est 2000 ▪ 1stB 2005 ▪ Tasting & sales Mon-Sun 10-5 ▪ Fee R50, waived according to purchase ▪ Closed Good Fri, Dec 25 & Jan 1 ▪ Cheese & charcuterie platters; various soups during winter ▪ Owner(s) Tumado Investments (Pty) Ltd ▪ Winemaker(s) Justin van Wyk (Dec 2011) ▪ Viticulturist(s) Etienne Southey (Sep 2012, farm manager) & Andrew Teubes (consultant) ▪ 60ha/28.5ha (cabs s/f, malbec, merlot, p verdot, sauv, sem) ▪ 160t/20,000cs own label 70% red 30% white ▪ PO Box 780 Constantia 7848 ▪ wine@constantiaglen.com ▪ www.constantiaglen.com ▪ S 34° 0' 39.6" E 018° 24' 30.6" ▪ F +27 (0)21-795-6101 ▪ **T +27 (0)21-795-6100**

Constantia Mist

Work pressure has obliged owner John Schooling to pause production from his tiny Constantia prop-erty, planted only with sauvignon blanc, the valley's trademark white grape, but the 2010 vintage is still available from the farm.

★★★★☆ **Sauvignon Blanc** ⓦ Riper tropical profile on **10** (★★★★). Bone-dry & bracing, with some toasty lees extras, but it lacks the intensity & length of **09**. — AL

Location/WO: Constantia ▪ Map: Cape Peninsula ▪ Est 2004 ▪ 1stB 2009 ▪ Tasting by appt only ▪ Fee R30 ▪ Sales daily 10-5 ▪ Closed Good Fri & Dec 25 ▪ BYO picnic ▪ 4-star guest house (self-catering) ▪ Owner(s) Eagles Nest Property Investments (Pty) Ltd ▪ Cellarmaster(s) John Schooling (2009) ▪ Winemaker(s) Karl Lambour (2009 & 2010 vin-tages), with Justin van Wyk ▪ Viticulturist(s) Alan Cockroft (2009) ▪ 6.6ha/2.8ha (sauv) ▪ 6t/ha 1,120cs own label 100% white ▪ Postnet Suite 96, Private Bag X16, Constantia 7848 ▪ johns@stagprop.com ▪ www.constantiamist.co.za ▪ S 34° 1' 0.48" E 018° 24' 58.32" ▪ F +27 (0)21-794-4123 ▪ **T +27 (0)21-794-0904**

Constantia Uitsig

Exciting plans and lofty ambitions at these auspiciously sited Constantiaberg vineyards, meticulously tended the past 18 years by André Rousseau, and yielding consistently excellent, elegant wines. Under new ownership, design and planning have started on a new tasting and sales venue, with a cellar as part of phase two. The tourist facility will incorporate design, construction and operational green building practices that are energy efficient, resource efficient and environmentally responsible (application will be made for an official Green Star rating). 'The proposed state-of-the art winery and tourist facility,' the team promises, 'will be unique in South Africa and establish Constantia Uitsig as a world leader in the wine industry.'

★★★★ **Constantia Red** Elegant, seamlessly integrated **12**, merlot-led blend with both cabs, flaunts abundant plum & red fruit, underpinned by well-structured tannins from predominantly new barrels.

★★★★☆ **Chardonnay Reserve** Luxuriously buttery, toasty, creamy textured barrel-fermented **13** is classy, confident & plush. Fine line pithy acidity threads richly layered peach & citrus fruit to effect superbly precise balance.

★★★★ **Sauvignon Blanc** Confident ultra-fresh & vibrant **14** exhibits clarity in generous fruitiness with underlying minerality. Time on lees creates extra breadth & gratifying weight.

★★★★☆ **Semillon** Flinty, austere **13** reinforces this property's reputation for fine semillon. Elegant layers of lime & grapefruit tightly wound around pithy core, held by firm acidity, minerality. Needs time to unfold, as did serious **12** (★★★★★).

★★★★☆ **Constantia White** Crystalline, classic semillon-sauvignon **13** (★★★★★) blend smart, polished & harmonious. Standout balance of tight core lemon fruit & pithy acidity, barrel-fermented semillon adds weight to concentrated, structured finish. Same lovely balance as **12**.

★★★★ **Méthode Cap Classique** All-chardonnay, barrel-fermented **11** on upward curve. Rich breadth & toastiness from third new oak & few years on lees. Creamy, persistent mousse.

★★★★ **Red Muscat d'Alexandrie** ⓥ Previewed **NV** dessert-style fortified shows overt grape aromas. Lacks wow-factor of previous, though moreish, sweet impression rendered dry by good spicy tannins.

Also tasted: **Chardonnay Unwooded 14** ★★★★ — IM

Location/WO: Constantia ▪ Map: Cape Peninsula ▪ Est 1980 ▪ 1stB 1988 ▪ Tasting Mon-Fri 9–5 Sat/Sun & pub hols 10–5 ▪ Fee R25 ▪ Closed Good Fri, Dec 25/26 & Jan 1 ▪ Wine Shop: cheese platters, deli items, gifts ▪ Hanepoot grapes sold annually ▪ Tour groups ▪ Conferences ▪ Owner(s) Constantia Uitsig Wine Estate (Pty) Limited ▪ Cellarmaster(s) JD Pretorius ▪ Winemaker(s) André Rousseau (2003) & JD Pretorius ▪ Viticulturist(s) André Rousseau (1997) ▪ 60ha/ 32ha (cabs s/f, merlot, chard, Muscat d'A, sauv, sem) ▪ 120t/20,000cs own label 10% red 90% white ▪ WIETA ▪ PO Box 32 Constantia 7848 ▪ andre@uitsig.co.za ▪ www.constantia-uitsig.com ▪ S 34° 2' 51.9" E 018° 25' 27.5" ▪ F +27 (0)21-794-7605 ▪ **T +27 (0)21-794-6500**

☐ **Constitution Road** see Robertson Winery
☐ **Contours Collection** see Swartland Winery

Conviction

Intended 'to be consumed, not collected', Conviction boutique wines are vinified naturally by winemaker Clive Torr at Romond in the Helderberg. The grapes, Clive says, are from Elgin's best site for ripening cab - ripe enough to translate into higher alcohol, in fact. 'It is what it is,' he shrugs.

★★★★ **Cabernet Sauvignon** **13** (★★★★) similar to ultra-ripe **12**, with soft styling, easy drinkability. Alcohol (shade off 16%) more obvious latest vintage, gives slight spirit lift on nose, sweetness on palate. — CvZ

Location: Somerset West ▪ WO: Elgin ▪ Est/1stB 2009 ▪ Closed to public ▪ Winemaker(s) Clive Torr & David Brown, with Anne Howell ▪ 10ha ▪ 100cs ▪ 26 Topaz Street Heldervue 7130 ▪ clivetorr@bigfoot.com ▪ **T +27 (0)82-557-0826**

☐ **Cool Bay** see Boplaas Family Vineyards
☐ **Cooperative** see Bosman Family Vineyards
☐ **Coral Reef** see Wineways Marketing
☐ **Coral Tree** see FirstCape Vineyards

Corder Family Wines

Boutique growers Ian and Anette Corder, he an advertising/marketing man, she a former wine tourism practitioner, with vine/wine gurus Kevin Watt and Joris van Almenkerk follow the principle of 'more time on the vine in search of great fruit expression but with Elgin elegance'. New additions include the US to their growing export market and a pinot noir (not ready for tasting for this edition).

Corder Family Wines range

★★★★ **Cool Climate Chardonnay** Sweet flourish of **13** not classic but will have many fans; welcoming peanut brittle richness offset by citrus tang. 9 months old oak.

★★★★☆ **Cool Climate Sauvignon Blanc** Gentle **13** (★★★★) with peach, pear & some white pepper is nicely textured, but a yard off richer **12**. Bone-dry, with percent higher alcohol at 13.5%.

★★★★☆ **Corder Barrel Crafted Viognier** Peach & hint of spice, **10** (★★★) preview is creamy but lacks intensity & freshness of last **08**.

Not tasted: **Corder Special Reserve Shiraz**.

Lorry range

Red Lorry Easy Shiraz ★★☆ 'Don't say it, drink it!' the slogan for this pair; **12** was 'Red' & **NV** previously. Easy, yes, & soft as a baby's bottom. Also tasted: **Yellow Lorry Sauvignon Blanc 13** ★★ — DS

Location: Elgin ▪ Map: Elgin, Walker Bay & Bot River ▪ WO: Elgin/Coastal ▪ Est 2003 ▪ 1stB 2007 ▪ Tasting & sales Mon-Fri 9-2 Sat/Sun by appt ▪ Closed all pub hols ▪ Owner(s) Ian & Anette Corder ▪ Cellarmaster(s)/winemaker(s) Joris van Almenkerk (Mar 2010) ▪ Viticulturist(s) Kevin Watt (2004) ▪ 40ha/14ha (pinot, shiraz, chard, sauv) ▪ 90t ▪ own label 20% red 80% white ▪ PO Box 169 Elgin 7180 ▪ ian@corderwines.co.za ▪ www.corderwines.co.za ▪ S 34° 12' 8.10" E 019° 0' 47.46" ▪ F +27 (0)21-846-8460 ▪ **T +27 (0)21-846-8083**

☐ **Country Cellars** see Orange River Wine Cellars
☐ **Couple's Wine** see Bergheim
☐ **Coutelier** see Domaine Coutelier
☐ **Craighall** see African Wines & Spirits

Cranefields Wine

Focused on the export market (Hamburg-based merchant Siegfried Greve is co-owner), Cranefields wines are named for South Africa's national bird, the Blue Crane, and sales of the brand help raise funds for birdlife conservation.

Cabernet Sauvignon ★★ True to variety, **07** blackberry fruit, juicy acidity, straightforward flavours. Not retasted: **Merlot 07** ★★ **Shiraz 07** ★★ **Red Bishop 07** ★★ — CvZ

Location/map: Villiersdorp ▪ WO: Overberg ▪ Est/1st B 1995 ▪ Tasting by appt only ▪ Owner(s) SJ Greve & CJ Roux ▪ Winemaker(s) Riaan Wassüng (Jan 2005, Stellenbosch University Welgevallen Cellar) & Christo Versfeld (Villiersdorp Cellar) ▪ Viticulturist(s) Charl Roux (Feb 1998) ▪ 35ha (cab, merlot, shiraz) ▪ 220t/6,000cs own label 100% red ▪ PO Box 417 Villiersdorp 6846 ▪ info@cranefields.com ▪ www.cranefields.com ▪ S 34° 2' 45.99" E 019° 13' 59.64" ▪ F +27 (0)28-840-0440 ▪ **T +27 (0)28-840-2565**

Craven Wines

'Bondi Boys' might be a caricature, but the mini-influx of young, sharp and empathetic Aussie wine people buoying local fine-wine making is most welcome, and includes Mick Craven, currently winegrower at Mulderbosch. He and SA-born wife Jeanine, winemaker at Dornier, are widely experienced, and both agree Stellenbosch their terroir of choice worldwide. The aim with their own brand is to create 'wines of pure site and varietal expression, adding nothing except a little sulphur'.

★★★★ **Pinot Noir** Whole-bunch, natural yeast fermentation, year French oak maturation, bottled unfined/filtered. Lot of care taken in **13**; shows in elegance & length, classic composition: a template for pinot. Slight forest floor nuance creeping into the aromas, flavours. — CR, CvZ

Location/WO: Stellenbosch ▪ Est 2013 ▪ 1stB 2014 ▪ Tasting & sales by appt only ▪ Owner(s) Jeanine & Mick Craven ▪ Winemaker(s) Jeanine & Mick Craven (Jan 2013) ▪ 7t/700cs own label 60% red 40% white ▪ PO Box 972 Somerset Mall 7137 ▪ mick@cravenwines.com ▪ www.cravenwines.com ▪ **T +27 (0)72-701-2723**

Creation Wines

It's said the kitchen is the heart of the home, and at innovative Hemel-en-Aarde property Creation, established on virgin soil below Babylons Peak just over a decade ago, Swiss-born JC Martin, wife Carolyn and investor Jonathan Drake have expanded upon that notion, extending their signature food-and-wine pairing. Unsurprising, given it's key to attracting nearly 30,000 visitors annually – though the cellardoor is a meandering 18 km off the beaten track. Defying local conventional 'pinot noir and chardonnay' wisdom, the Martins also planted Bordeaux varieties and have raked in accolades since their first bottling in 2006. Investment in training of service staff (here and in the hospitality sector generally) includes online tutorials and a training academy.

Premium range

★★★★ **Merlot** Wonderful aromas of violets & fynbos on **12** showing chalky texture & cocoa-rich flavour. Depth, concentration & body on well-judged oak platform (35% new).

★★★★ **Pinot Noir** Smoky notes to **13**'s deep & powerful dark cherry, cranberry palate. Silky layers on an integrated oak foundation (year, 25% new), long finish beautifully balanced.

★★★★☆ **Reserve Pinot Noir** Vineyard selection showing forest fruit & loamy notes, **13** (★★★★★) is lithe, supple yet firmly structured, unfruity. Set apart from **12** & sibling by fine texture, depth & concentration of flavour & intensity in long finish. Polished oak, just 25% new.

★★★★ **Syrah** Vibrant fruit melange - dark cherry, blueberry & plum - seamed with spice. Structure is restrained, 14.5% alcohol well contained in supple & rewarding **12**.

★★★★ **Merlot-Cabernet Sauvignon-Petit Verdot** **12** a tight, dense, tannic mouthful in youth, but concentration of flavour & body, as well as lengthy dry tail, bode well for few years in cellar.

★★★★☆ **Syrah-Grenache** Ⓥ Blackcurrant opulence contrasts with cocoa grip in spicy **12** 80/20 blend, muscular yet silky, refined. Firm yet yielding oak (14 months oak, 25% new) will support the wine good few years.

★★★★☆ **Chardonnay** Splendid **13** generous but not blowsy, loaded with lemon curd & vanilla cream but restrained, New World juiciness in Old World style. Like long & rich **12**, oodles of pure fruit perfectly complemented by oak, only 25% new.

★★★★ **Viognier** Typical peach vivacity on very fruity, unwooded **14**, tempered by dry chalky texture & mineral tang. Rich but not overblown despite 14% alcohol.

Also tasted: **Sauvignon Blanc 14** ★★★★ **Sauvignon Blanc-Semillon 13** ★★★★ — DS

Location: Hermanus ▪ Map: Elgin, Walker Bay & Bot River ▪ WO: Walker Bay ▪ Est 2002 ▪ 1stB 2006 ▪ Tasting, sales & cellar tours daily 10-5 ▪ Closed Dec 25 & Jan 1 ▪ Lunch; wine & canapés; secret food & wine pairing; wine & chocolate pairing; tea pairing ▪ Kiddies' beverages & snack pairing, menu & designated play area ▪ Tour groups ▪ Wine accessories, books & souvenirs on sale ▪ Walking/hiking trails ▪ Predator-friendly farm ▪ Conservation area ▪ Art exhibition (paintings & sculptures) ▪ Events: blend your own bottle; barrel/true terroir tasting; vineyard safari on foot; regular musical performances & themed cultural events ▪ Owner(s) Jean-Claude & Carolyn Martin, Jonathan Drake ▪ Cellarmaster(s) Jean-Claude Martin (Jan 2006) ▪ Winemaker(s) Jean-Claude Martin (Jan 2006), with Werner du Plessis (Jan 2012) ▪ Viticulturist(s) Jean-Claude Martin & Peter Davison (consultant), advised by Johan Pienaar (all 2002) ▪ 35ha (cab, grenache, merlot, p verdot, pinot, shiraz, chard, sauv, sem, viog) ▪ 300t/50,000cs own label 65% red 35% white ▪ BWI, EnviroWines accredited, IPW ▪ PO Box 1772 Hermanus 7200 ▪ info@creationwines.com ▪ www.creationwines.com ▪ S 34° 19' 51.90" E 019° 19' 35.53" ▪ F +27 (0)28-212-1127 ▪ **T +27 (0)28-212-1107**

☐ **Creative Block** see Spier

Credo

A Stellenbosch Vineyards premium brand, vinified by Bernard Claassen with selected growers, some 3rd generation, to 'express the best that each vintage offers'.

★★★★ **Chenin Blanc** Ⓔ Extensive oaking (2 years, 50% new) noticeable on awarded **10** but smartly handled, integrated. Complex, concentrated Granny Smith/Golden Delicious aromas & flavours.

Shiraz-Merlot-Viognier Ⓔ ★★★★ **10** savoury, with black olive & hint of mint. Not as tannic as red sibling (despite same oaking) but would also benefit from hearty meat dishes or further ageing. Stellenbosch WO, as for all. Not retasted: **Shiraz 10** ★★★★ **Chardonnay 12** ★★★ — CvZ

Crios Bríde

Named for the braided straw girdle belonging to the Celtic fertility goddess Brighid, the range of handcrafted wines from this boutique Stellenbosch family winery awaits the addition of their new MCCs, due to be released soon after extended time spent on lees.

★★★★ **Syrah-Carignan** Ⓔ Powerful **07** concentrated molten dark fruit, good structure & ageability.

Méthode Cap Classique Ⓔ ★★★☆ **07** sparkling from chardonnay & pinot noir, made extra-dry & perfect with oysters. Not retasted: **Chenin Blanc 07** ★★★★ **Sauvignon Blanc 08** ★★★★ — MW

Location: Stellenbosch ▪ WO: Darling ▪ Est/1stB 2007 ▪ Closed to public ▪ Owner(s) Yorke-Smith family ▪ Winemaker(s) Carla Pauw (Jan 2007, consultant) ▪ 2,500cs own label 15% red 25% white 60% MCC ▪ PO Box 2290 Dennesig Stellenbosch 7601 ▪ carlapauw@gmail.com ▪ F +27 (0)88-021-883-9568 ▪ **T +27 (0)21-883-9568**

Crows Nest

Marcel and Deidre de Reuck's winery on the western slopes of Paarl Mountain may be small, but the wines are big. Very big. To be expected from a vintner who spent eight years diving off Scotland's oil rigs, and believes 'wine should have a presence, shake you up a bit!' We presume at least some of the occasions at the new on-site wedding and function venue will follow the house style.

Marcel de Reuck range

★★★★ **Cabernet Sauvignon-Syrah** Ⓝᴱ Blockbuster **09** shows vibrant ripe dark fruit mingling with supple tannins, vanilla oak flavours & super-fresh acid backbone. Hides 15.5% alcohol well.

Syrah ★★★★ **09** big, with 5 years in barrel & 15.5% alcohol. Integrated tannins, harmonious melange of dark berries, oak & savoury meaty flavours. Not tasted: **Cabernet Sauvignon**, **Cabernet Sauvignon–Merlot**, **Chardonnay**.

Torres Claude range

Not tasted: **Crow's Nest**. — WB

Location: Paarl ▪ Map: Paarl & Wellington ▪ WO: Coastal ▪ Est/1stB 2002 ▪ Tasting, sales & cellar tours Mon-Fri 10–5 Sat/Sun & pub hols by appt ▪ Fee R25, waived on purchase ▪ Meals by appt; or BYO picnic ▪ Facilities for children ▪ Farm produce ▪ Weddings/functions ▪ Conservation area ▪ Owner(s) Marcel & Deidre de Reuck ▪ Winemaker(s) Marcel de Reuck ▪ 33.6ha/11.5ha (cab, shiraz) ▪ 60t/10,000cs own label 90% red 5% white 5% port ▪ PO Box 2571 Paarl 7620 ▪ dereuck@mweb.co.za ▪ www.dereuckwines.co.za ▪ S 33° 40' 33.0" E 018° 54' 25.4" ▪ F +27 (0)21-869-8714 ▪ **T +27 (0)21-869-8712**

Croydon Vineyard Residential Estate

The names of the wines made at this Helderberg residential estate reflect the character and story of the place. Portion 20 refers to the original farm, where the winery is, while the Title Deed range confirms that the house-owners are also co-owners of the vineyards and cellar. Some, in fact, get involved even before wines reach the bottle - including the occasional bit of grape-crushing by foot.

Title Deed range

★★★★ **Cape Blend** ⊘ Back to form after **11** (★★★★) dip, **12** substantial pinotage-led blend with cab, merlot, shiraz & malbec, delivers plenty of punch. Intense & ripe, with solid tannin backbone.

Also tasted: **Rosé** ⊘ **14** ★★★★ **Chenin Blanc 14** ★★★

Croydon range

★★★★ **Covenant Pinotage 12** (★★★☆), first since **09**, has variety's high-toned aromas; bold, with wild-berry fruit, dense tannin.

Not retasted: **Portion 20 09** ★★★★ — GdB

Location: Somerset West ▪ Map: Helderberg ▪ WO: Stellenbosch ▪ Est/1stB 2004 ▪ Tasting & sales Mon-Fri 10-5 Sat 9-1 ▪ Closed all religious holidays ▪ Cellar tours by appt ▪ Facilities for children ▪ Tour groups ▪ Conferences ▪ Events ▪ Owner(s) Croydon Vineyard Estate ▪ Cellarmaster(s) Beyers Truter (2004) ▪ Winemaker(s) Stephan du Toit (consultant) ▪ 8ha (cabs s/f, malbec, merlot, ptage, shiraz, chenin) ▪ 65t/4,000cs own label 95% red 5% white ▪ Unit 1 Croydon Vineyard Estate Somerset West 7130 ▪ wineco@croydon-estate.co.za ▪ www.croydon-estate.co.za ▪ S 34° 2' 23.3" E 018° 45' 5.5" ▪ F +27 (0)21-843-3609 ▪ **T +27 (0)21-843-3610**

Crystallum

Behind this small but dynamic winery are two brothers, third generation of Cape winemaking Finlaysons: Andrew, an architect, and Peter-Allan, who left his studies in philosophy and economics to be the winemaker here. Although this adventure began in 2007 with sauvignon blanc, the focus is now solely on the two great Burgundy varieties, chardonnay and pinot noir. And the range is expanding, as they look to explore different sites (currently nine, including two promising new Overberg parcels) through these grapes. Vinification is now at Gabriëlskloof (Peter-Allan also makes their wine), maturation at the original home, Crystal Kloof, in Hemel-en-Aarde Ridge.

★★★★★ **Cuvée Cinéma Pinot Noir** Marvellous lithe perfumed grace on **13** (★★★★★) from H-en-A Ridge, the finest of the range, as was **12**. Fresh, brave acidity enlivens sweet dark fruit to the lingering dry finish. Pure fruit & silky texture give early charm; structure should retain, deepen it. These all natural ferment.

★★★★☆ **Peter Max Pinot Noir** The most easily accessible of these, sensuously compelling in youth & the least 'serious'. **13** expressive & outgoing, yet poised, with balanced structure of gentle acid & tannin. Now blend includes high inland vineyard, so WO W Cape. Like all pinots except Mabalel, with portion whole-cluster fruit.

★★★★☆ **Bona Fide Pinot Noir 13** (★★★★) the boldest, ripest of these, as was **12**, though current vintage less harmonious. Appealing, yet less pure fruit, more earthy suggestion of forest floor; less finesse, more tannic grip, sweeter fruit on finish. Ex H-en-A Valley. All these pinots modestly, subtly oaked.

★★★★☆ **Mabalel Pinot Noir** (NEW) From a high-lying young inland (Overberg) vineyard, **13** from all destemmed grapes. High-toned, bright red fruit, with floral aromas even hinting at herbaceousness. Lighter in texture than the others, a touch less ripely substantial, but with a pure loveliness.

★★★★☆ **Clay Shales Chardonnay** Citrus, stone, oatmeal & ripe pear - with toasty hint - on early complexity of **13**. More classic than Agnes, but not entirely so. Fairly rich & creamy, with succulent acidity carrying it to very long finish. From just outside the H-en-A area, so WO Overberg.

★★★★ **The Agnes Chardonnay** Blended from three vineyards in H-en-Aarde & Overberg. Full-flavoured & exuberant without losing elegance, **13** (★★★★★) particularly characterful. Silky palate with vibrant acid. Like Clay Shales, naturally fermented & sensitively oaked. Long limy finish reminiscent of that on **12**. — TJ

Location: Hermanus ▪ WO: Western Cape/Overberg/Hemel-en-Aarde Ridge/Hemel-en-Aarde Valley ▪ Est 2006 ▪ 1stB 2007 ▪ Closed to public ▪ Owner(s) Crystallum Coastal Vineyards (Pty) Ltd ▪ Winemaker(s) Peter-Allan Finlayson

(2006) ▪ 50t/6,100cs own label 60% red 40% white ▪ PO Box 857 Hermanus 7200 ▪ info@crystallumwines.com ▪ www.crystallumwines.com

☐ **Cubana** *see* Leeuwenjacht

☐ **Culemborg** *see* DGB

☐ **Culinaria Collection** *see* Leopard's Leap Family Vineyards

☐ **Cutters Cove** *see* Robert Stanford Estate

☐ **Da Capo Vineyards** *see* Idiom Collection

Dagbreek

'Pleasure Through Quality' is the motto of third-generation Breede River winegrower Peet Smith, and his boutique-scale portfolio does in fact deliver pleasure and - increasingly - quality, but also interest, derived from the diverse varieties he vinifies: Italy's nebbiolo, Portugal's touriga and France's chenin.

★★★★ **Nebbiolo** Garnet-hued, cherry-toned, grippy & zesty - as expected from this variety. **11** more interesting, better balanced than also-tasted **10** (★★★), longer-oaked version of the one we reviewed last edition. Both wines express serious intent.

★★★★ **Chenin Blanc Barrel Selection** From 30+ year bushvines. Almond & thatch intro to **13**, brisk acidity, peachy freshness rounded by few grams sugar & vanilla oak. Ultra-long & harmonious. Improves on seriously styled **10** (★★★★).

Also tasted: **Touriga Nacional 11** ★★★ — CvZ

Location: Rawsonville ▪ Map/WO: Breedekloof ▪ Est/1stB 2009 ▪ Tasting, sales & cellar tours Mon-Sat by appt ▪ Closed all pub hols ▪ BYO picnic ▪ Walking/hiking trails ▪ Owner(s) Peet Smith ▪ Cellarmaster(s)/winemaker(s) Peet Smith (2009) ▪ Viticulturist(s) Leon Dippenaar (2009, consultant) ▪ 108ha/48ha under vine ▪ 7t/1,000cs own label 70% red 30% white ▪ WIETA ▪ PO Box 237 Rawsonville 6845 ▪ dagbreek@compnet.co.za ▪ www.dagbreek.co.za ▪ S 33° 39′ 56. 20″ E 019° 18′ 26.99″ ▪ F +27 (0)86-529-2865 ▪ **T +27 (0)82-820-2256**

Dalla Cia Wine & Spirit Company

Giorgio Dalla Cia arrived from Italy's Friuli region to take up the post of winemaker at hallowed Stellenbosch property Meerlust in 1978. Twenty-six years later, he set out to develop - alongside son George - the family's wine and husk spirit business. Operations are based at Bosman's Crossing in Stellenbosch, a wine and food bar called Pane E Vino ('Bread & Wine") situated next to the winery and distillery. Fruit for the wines is bought in, the wines styled to be unflashy and food friendly as has always been the Dalla Cia way. The reds show particular balance and finesse, the most recent addition being Teano, inspired by the Supertuscans of Italy and among SA's most expensive wines.

Dalla Cia Wine range

★★★★☆ **Classico Cabernet Sauvignon** After classic, ageworthy **11**, distinctly light-bodied **12** (★★★★) has generous but atypical plummy fruit, spiced by serious oak (70% new). Chalky tannins dominate rather brief finish.

★★★★☆ **Giorgio** Cab-led Bordeaux-style blend with merlot and petit verdot, **11** first since standout **07** (★★★★★), finds stature in restraint. Finely integrated, showing black fruit, tobacco & liquorice.

★★★★★ **Teano** ⓃⒺⓌ Maiden release of flagship blend (third sangiovese, rest undisclosed French varieties), **11** shows brooding power & subtle spiciness in laudable 'Supertuscan' manner. Attention-grabbing intensity, rich texture, lingering farewell. WO W Cape.

★★★★ **Chardonnay** Bigger, riper **13** shows more classic sur lie style, with generous citrus fruit. Tiny brush of oak fills out body. Big improvement on **12** (★★★).

Also tasted: **Sauvignon Blanc 14** ★★★★ Not tasted: **Pinot Noir**.

For more information, visit wineonaplatter.com

Dalla Cia Husk Spirit range

★★★★☆ **Limited Edition Pinot Noir** The most transparent, water-white of the range, & the closest in delicacy & purity to fine modern Italian examples. Ethereal, subtly complex aromas of fruit, flowers & nuts lead on to energetic, slippery textured & lingering palate.

★★★★ **Pinot-Chardonnay** Fresh aromas of fruit & nuts; some delicacy, focus & refinement evident on a delightfully textured, smooth & balanced palate.

★★★★ **Cabernet Sauvignon-Merlot Premium Selection** Slight straw tinge to this more refined, less aggressive Premium (lightly oak-barrelled) version of the standard Husk Spirit from these varieties. Supple, gently unctuous palate, lingering finish.

★★★★ **Single Cultivar Organic Merlot** Colourless; high-toned note gives magnificent lift to the red berry & floral aromas; sweet spice & some citrus buoy the spirity finish. Smooth & elegant. 43% alcohol. Only 100 bottles.

★★★★☆ **10 Year Old Cabernet Sauvignon-Merlot** Glinting amber, with most inviting floral nose on preview celebrating winery's 10th anniversary. Delicate hints of spicy plum, tobacco & tealeaves. Rich, with a velvet texture, delightfully mellow. Flavours of prune & dried hay add to complexity. Long-lasting sipper to be savoured. Only 500 bottles.

Cabernet Sauvignon-Merlot ★★★★ Robust, forward aromas & flavours - 'husky', quiet berry hint. Smooth enough, but with some old-style rusticity. — WB, GdB, TJ

Location/map: Stellenbosch ▪ WO: Stellenbosch/Western Cape ▪ Est 2004 ▪ Tasting, sales & traditional Italian meals at Pane E Vino Food & Wine Bar, Mon-Fri 10-6 Sat 10-5 ▪ Owner(s)/winemaker(s) Giorgio Dalla Cia ▪ 18,000cs ▪ 7A Lower Dorp Street Bosman's Crossing Stellenbosch ▪ info@dallacia.com ▪ www.dallacia.com ▪ S 33° 56' 25.8" E018° 50' 50.1" ▪ F +27 (0)21-887-2621 ▪ **T +27 (0)21-888-4120**

Damarakloof

A small but diversified agri-holding (grapes, olives, figs, roses, horses) that has been in Agnes de Vos' family for over a century, Damarakloof near Paarl boasts a 60+ year-old vineyard that was originally a racetrack — then deemed too gravelly for vines — vinified in tiny volumes when crops allow.

Racetrack range

★★★★ **Regale** When last tasted, **08** Bordeaux red returned to classic form after **06** (★★★☆). Fragrant, refreshingly demure & altogether delightful to drink. No **07**.

Chenin Blanc ★★★ First tasted since **07**, ripe & plump **12** from old vines on nearby Joostenberg, stewed apple & spice enveloped in warm & waxy texture, courtesy natural ferment & 9 months in older oak. — MW

Location/WO: Paarl ▪ Map: Paarl & Wellington ▪ Est/1stB 2006 ▪ Function venue by appt ▪ Owner(s) Agnes de Vos ▪ Winemaker(s) Carla Pauw (Jan 2006) ▪ 19ha (cabs s/f, merlot, chenin) ▪ 10t/1,300cs own label 50% red 50% white ▪ PO Box 38 Elsenburg 7607 ▪ agnesdev@telkomsa.net ▪ S 33° 48' 41.79" E 018° 47' 21.19" ▪ F +27 (0)21-884-4304 ▪ **T +27 (0)21-884-4304**

☐ **Danie de Wet** *see* De Wetshof Estate
☐ **Daniel Collection** *see* La Petite Vigne

D'Aria Winery

Musical themes permeate this Durbanville winery, as Rudi von Waltsleben is both musician and cellarmaster. His father, Johan, has tended the vines on the slopes of the Tygerberg Hills since 1998. That was when two old farms were bought and amalgamated by a property investment and development company — committed to both its shareholders and its Durbanville Workers' Association partners.

Reserve range

★★★★☆ **The Soprano Shiraz** Powerful but balanced **12** has sweet ripe blackberry & dark cherry fruit, fresher than last-tasted **09** (★★★★) thanks to fresh acidity. Dense yet supple, with powdery tannins. No **10**, **11** sold out untasted.

★★★★ **The Songbird Sauvignon Blanc** Ripe, full-bodied styling, with creamy texture from 5% aged in barrel, **13** is elegant nonetheless with tropical fruit packed around steely core & zesty grapefruit finish. Step up from **12** (★★★☆).

Not tasted: **The Following White Blend**.

Terra range

★★★★ **Lullaby Noble Late Harvest** (NEW) Whiffs of wild honey invite slow savouring of smooth, sweet **13**, from botrytised semillon, unwooded, tropical litchi & papaya flavours balanced by enough acidity.

Cabernet Sauvignon-Merlot ★★★★ Lovely purity of black berry fruit on luscious **12**, oak adding to its dark chocolate/mocha nuances, better structure & balance than previous. Also tasted: **Merlot 12** ★★★ **SV Shiraz 11** ★★★ **Blush 14** ★★ **Sauvignon Blanc 14** ★★★☆

Music range

Shiraz-Cabernet Sauvignon-Merlot ★★★ **13** a more serious & delicious proposition than previous, with spicy shiraz nose leading to plush merlot fruitcake richness while cab provides tannic backbone. Also tasted: **Pinotage-Shiraz** (NEW) **13** ★★★ **Sauvignon Blanc 14** ★★

Brandy range

The Piccolo 5 Year Potstill Brandy (Ⓧ) ★★★ Earthy ripe apricots, green herbal notes & a sherry cask edge. Uncomplicated, youthfully rough & fiery. 100% potstill from colombard. — WB, JG, TJ

Location/WO: Durbanville ▪ Map: Durbanville, Philadelphia & Darling ▪ Est/1stB 2007 ▪ Tasting & sales Mon 12-6 Tue-Fri 10-6 (summer)/Mon 11-5 Tue-Fri 9-5 (winter) Sat 10-5 Sun 10-4 ▪ Fee R15 ▪ Closed Dec 25 & Jan 1 ▪ Cheese platters & deli platters served in tasting room ▪ Poplars Restaurant ▪ Conferences/functions ▪ Hiking & mountain biking trails ▪ 4-star guest cottages ▪ Music concerts in summer ▪ Owner(s) Barinor Holdings ▪ Brandy master Rudi von Waltsleben (2008) ▪ Winemaker(s) Rudi von Waltsleben (Nov 2007), with Nicola Viljoen (Apr 2010) ▪ Viticulturist(s) Johan von Waltsleben (1998) ▪ 80ha/63ha (cab, merlot, shiraz, sauv) ▪ 400t/160,000cs own label 67% red 30% white 3% rosé + 400cs for clients & ±1,000btls x 500ml brandy ▪ M13 Racecourse Road Durbanville 7550 ▪ tasting@daria.co.za ▪ www.dariawinery. co.za ▪ S 33° 50' 28.6" E 018° 36' 36.2" ▪ F +27 (0)86-539-4519 ▪ **T +27 (0)21-801-6772**

Darling Cellars   (Ⓨ) (Ⓐ) (Ⓖ)

Wheatfields are punctuated by swathes of gnarled bushvine - a signature sight of the Darling region and a combination that allows for a balanced agricultural harmony that reduces disease. The pay-off line 'True to nature' was obvious to the team at this large grower-owned cellar. Bushvines, they believe, can produce particularly intense flavours and, in combination with cooling West Coast breezes, produce refined wines with a modern, fruity touch. Now they add that they're 'trying to simplify the winemaking process to better allow Darling's elegance and fruit purity to shine through'.

Limited Releases

★★★★☆ **Sir Charles Henry Darling** (Ⓧ) Cab franc leads cab, merlot & petit verdot in fine flagship. **11** has contained dark berry fruit, whiffs of cedary oak leading to cool entry with good savoury foil to dark berry ripeness. Still young, needing time for tannins to settle.

★★★★ **Cellarmaster's Signature Selection No. 7** (NEW) (✓) Part of series of once-off selections; **12** a Bordeaux quintet in elegant, retiring 'needs time' style. Classic, if a little austere.

★★★★ **Cellarmaster's Signature Selection No.8** (NEW) (✓) Veritable United Nations of wine; barbera, mourvèdre, shiraz & pinotage on one side, tannat, cab & grenache the other. **12** as boisterous as the ensuing debate!

★★★★☆ **Lime Kilns** A melange of opulent chenin, creamy chardonnay & spicy viognier melded in oak (five months). Unabashed **13** (★★★★) shade less poised than **11**. No **12**.

★★★★ **Blanc de Blancs Brut** ⊘ Vibrant **13** méthode cap classique sparkler from chardonnay has oystershell & lemon zest to cut plush brioche complexity; alluring finesse to bone-dry farewell. **12** sold out untasted.

Premium range

★★★★☆ **Cabernet Sauvignon** ② **10** has leafy tobacco top notes typical of cool region, supported by a core of cassis with poised ripe promise. Back on track after lesser previewed **09** (★★★★).

★★★★ **Shiraz** ② **10** (★★★★) lacks the intensity & length of **09**. Lighter, with red fruits, bright spice & dry medium finish.

★★★★ **Sauvignon Blanc** Sabre-like steeliness & grassy grip contain generous tropical fruit of **13**, better defined, more focused & likeable than bouncy **11**. No **12**.

Riesling (NEW) ★★★☆ Rare wood-aged riesling, in oak for an emphatic two years! Highly individual **12** carries grape's trademark stonefruit focus, lowish alcohol & dry finish well... filled out with oak. Not retasted: **Pinotage 11** ★★★ **Kroon 10** ★★★★ Not tasted: **Noble Late Harvest**.

Reserve range

Six Tonner Merlot ⊘ ★★★★ Ripe, soft **13** brims with red berry & choc-coffee characters, with enough grip to accompany food. **Black Granite Shiraz** ⊘ ★★★★ Powerfully aromatic black pepper spicing to berry fruits on savoury **13**, very satisfying & vibrant red-fruited finish. **Arum Fields Chenin Blanc** ⊘ ★★★ Blossoms & ripe peach/pear features of **14** guarantee fruity quaffing & a soft landing. **Bush Vine Sauvignon Blanc** ★★★ Floral-toned **14** offers fruity interest & gentle acidity. Also tasted: **Terra Hutton Cabernet Sauvignon 13** ★★★ **Old Blocks Pinotage 13** ★★★ Not retasted: **Shiraz-Mourvèdre 12** ★★★ **Quercus Gold Chardonnay 13** ★★★

Growers Signature Selection

The Chairman ② ★★★ Shiraz leads the way in vibrant **12** blend with mourvèdre, cinsaut. Some spice, red fruits, baked stone, fresh & savoury. Not retasted: **Cinsaut-Cabernet Sauvignon 12** ★★☆ **Chenin Blanc 13** ★★★ **Mariette 13** ★★★

Classic range

Merlot Rosé ★★ Rosy **13** charms with just-dry strawberry fruit. Also tasted: **Cabernet Sauvignon-Merlot** ⊘ **13** ★★☆ **Chenin Blanc-Sauvignon Blanc** ⊘ **14** ★★☆

Chocoholic range

Pinotage ② ★★★ Generous, opulent, decadent; it's all in the range name of off-dry **13**, retasted.

Sweet Darling

Red ② ★★ Fudge & cherry pop on **NV** sweet sipper. Not retasted: **Rosé NV** ★☆ **White NV** ★★ — DS

Location/WO: Darling ▪ Map: Durbanville, Philadelphia & Darling ▪ Est 1948 ▪ 1stB 1996 ▪ Tasting & sales Mon-Thu 9—5 Fri 9-2 Sat 10—2 ▪ Closed Good Fri, Dec 25 & Jan 1 ▪ Cellar tours by appt ▪ Wine & food pairing/sampling, no meals ▪ Facilities for children ▪ Owner(s) 20 shareholders ▪ Winemaker(s) Carel Hugo (Jun 2009), with Anthony Meduna (Oct 2011) & Maggie Venter (Jun 2014) ▪ 1,300ha (barbera, cab, carignan, cinsaut, grenache, malbec, merlot, mourv, ptage, shiraz, chard, chenin, riesling, sauv, sem) ▪ 7,500—8,500t/700,000cs own label 70% red 28% white 2% rosé ▪ Other export brands: Alta Casa, Black Granite, Cellar Road, Fountain Crossing, Mamre Road, Victoria Bay ▪ PO Box 114 Darling 7345 ▪ info@darlingcellars.co.za ▪ www.darlingcellars.co.za ▪ S 33° 26' 25.7" E 018° 31' 25.1" ▪ **T +27 (0)22-492-2276**

☐ **Darlington** see Withington

☐ **Daschbosch** see uniWines Vineyards

☐ **Dassie's Reserve** see Botha Wine Cellar

David & Nadia Sadie

Young couple David and Nadia Sadie are among the new generation making inspired wines from old vines; using older and bigger oak; relying largely on wild yeasts and less sulphur; seeking 'natural freshness and acidity'. These are also tenets of the Swartland Independent Producers organisation, of which David and Nadia are more recent members. He's the winemaker with experience gained at top-flight Saronsberg and Waterford, inspired by stints in the Rhône familiarising himself with Mediterranean varieties, and having helped resurrect Lemberg. She's the qualified viticulturist/soil scientist, working with vineyard blocks around the Perdeberg on their home turf (David's a born-and-bred Swartlander, though unrelated to its other famous Sadie). As their top-rated wine portfolio expands, they hope to become independent of rented cellar space.

★★★★☆ **Grenache** Fashionable red grape, here sourced from 3 Swartland blocks (2 organic), 40% bunch pressed. Classy **13** understated, delicate even, ultra-fine grape tannins cradle lovely limpid fruit. Sadly only 225 cases.

★★★★☆ **Elpidios** Quietly impressive Rhône blend, mostly shiraz (52%), with grenache & drops carignan, cinsaut, from 6 Swartland sites. **12** effusively fruity, concentrated yet vibrant, pure & fresh; superb now, will keep. Natural vinification - native yeasts, no additives, long lees-ageing, lower sulphur, no fining/filtration - sets tone for all.

★★★★☆ **Chenin Blanc** White & yellow stonefruit, Karoo scrub, almond nuances on oxidatively styled, emphatically dry **13** from venerable Perdeberg vines (oldest planted 1960s). Like **12**, delicious now, with focused, enlivening acidity & fruit depth for several years ageing.

★★★★★ **Aristargos** Vintage changes rung for this authoritative white blend yet always delivers. Sleek, sultry **13** from 7 dryland bushvine blocks, some 50+ years. Chenin (39%), viognier, clairette & roussanne combo more generous than **12** (with chardonnay, no roussanne). — CvZ

Location: Malmesbury ▪ Map/WO: Swartland ▪ Est/1stB 2010 ▪ Tasting by appt ▪ Owner(s)/winemaker(s)/viticulturist(s) David & Nadia Sadie ▪ (carignan, cinsaut, grenache, shiraz, chenin, clairette, rouss, viog) ▪ 28t/3,100cs own label 50% red 50% white ▪ Swartland Independent Producers (2011) ▪ wine@davidsadie.co.za ▪ www.davidsadie.co.za ▪ F +27 (0)86-512-4903 ▪ **T +27 (0)72-375-4336**

David Frost Signature Series

Champion golfer David Frost gives his name to the Signature Series (untasted this edition), made by separately listed Perdeberg Winery. The wines are available in SA retail exclusively through Pick n Pay stores, and exported to China, Germany and Ireland.

David Frost Wines

Champion golfer David Frost maintains his long association with wine (he financed his earliest golfing efforts picking grapes on his father's farm) with this own-brand, latterly focused on accessible and well-priced reds and a white, now offered for tasting in Paarl.

Pinotage 🆕 ★★★ Pleasantly old-Cape notes of tar, leather & cherries, **13** dry, food friendly, with sound tannins. **Sauvignon Blanc** ★★★ Fresh & fruity **14** gives plenty of yellow citrus with some sherbet & candyfloss confection. Barely dry & very friendly. Also tasted: **Cabernet Sauvignon 13** ★★★ **Shiraz 13** ★★★ — CM

Location: Paarl ▪ Map: Paarl & Wellington ▪ WO: Western Cape ▪ Est 1994 ▪ Tasting & sales at 191 Main Rd Paarl Mon-Sat 9.30-6.30 ▪ Owner(s) David Frost ▪ Winemaker(s) Erlank Erasmus ▪ 10,000cs 60% red 40% white ▪ PO Box 68 Main Road Paarl 7620 ▪ info@frostwines.com ▪ www.frostwine.com ▪ S 33° 44' 36.9" E 018° 57' 46.1" ▪ **T +27 (0)21-871-1850**

☐ **David Nieuwoudt** see Cederberg Private Cellar

DeanDavid Wines

Of the eponymous pair, Dean Thompson is the part-time winemaking son, David his father with a farm outside Riebeek-Kasteel, from which some of the label's Swartland grapes are sourced. Roger Clayton more recently joined Dean in the cellar (rented space at nearby Antebellum) and the range is expanding excitingly.

★★★★ **2 Mile Square Swartland Syrah** ⓐ **11** ripely soft, with melting but still-guiding tannin; delicious aromas & flavours.

★★★★ **1 Square Chenin Blanc** ⓝ Single-vineyard, limited-release unfiltered **13** has tangy green apple, fynbos & apricot kernel interest. Bone-dry palate more savoury than fruity, with firm, salty-mineral core; slight oiliness & phenolic grip.

½ Square Pinotage ⓝ ★★★★ Youthful **13** an exotic expression of pinotage, with blueberry, juniper, musk & cassis in the perfumes; slightly more one-dimensional palate, straightforwardly berry-driven but seriously easy to drink. — HJ

Location: Riebeek-Kasteel ▪ WO: Swartland ▪ Est/1stB 2003 ▪ Closed to public ▪ Wines available from Wine Kollective, Riebeek-Kasteel & Vino Pronto, Cape Town ▪ Owner(s) Dean Thompson, Roger Clayton, Peter Alexander & John Fulford ▪ Cellarmaster(s)/winemaker(s) Dean Thompson & Roger Clayton ▪ 10t/1,000cs own label 80% red 20% white ▪ PO Box 56 Green Point 8851 ▪ dean@unwined.co.za, roger@unwined.co.za ▪ www.unwined.co.za ▪ **T +27 (0)71-233-8261 (Dean)/+27 (0)76-826-8500 (Roger)**

De Bos Handpicked Vineyards

These premium Fairtrade wines, available from leading restaurants and retailers nationwide, are sourced from farms in Upper Hemel-en-Aarde Valley, Wellington and Hermon owned and managed by Bosman Family Vineyards (see entry).

★★★★ **Chenin Blanc** Easy-drinking **13** (★★★) shows quiet apple blossom aromas, gently padded mouthfeel from time on lees. **12** was more complex.

Cabernet Sauvignon ★★★ Satisfying if straightforward dark berry fruit, balanced freshness & rounded tannins provide ready-to-drink style in **12**. **Chardonnay** ★★★ Unoaked **13** has a plump, bouncy mouthfeel, complemented by creamy flavours, citrus zest. Also tasted: **Merlot 13** ★★ **Pinot Noir 13** ★★★★ **Sauvignon Blanc 13** ★★ — AL

De Breede Organic Vineyards

Boutique-scale winegrower Tim Alcock seeks to express the uniqueness of his Worcester site through organic farming in the vineyards (though this means extra-hard work, especially struggling against the weeds), and minimal intervention in the cellar. New cab franc vines in time will 'add a little difference in character to our blends'.

★★★★ **Syrah** ⓐ ⓖ Appealing freshness on bright-fruited **11** - a bit lighter, suppler, less extracted than the others, but still powerful & just as characterful.

1st XI Merlot ⓖ ★★★★ Violets, fruit pastilles & crème de cassis in abundance on **10**. Like Cab, touch jammy but more structure-giving tannins & finesse here; good juicy acidity, too. Enjoy soon. **The Rooster Reserve** ⓝ ⓖ ★★★ Savoury notes to ripe black fruit on smoky **10** Bordeaux red. Firm tannin profile gives drying effect to otherwise well-expressed, mature fruit flavours. Also tasted: **Cabernet Sauvignon** ⓖ **12** ★★ **Little Red Rooster** ⓖ **13** ★★ **The Rooster** ⓖ **12** ★★★ — HJ

Location: Worcester ▪ Map/WO: Breedekloof ▪ Est 2006 ▪ 1stB 2009 ▪ Tasting by appt ▪ Owner(s) Tim & Debbie Alcock ▪ Cellarmaster(s)/viticulturist(s) Tim Alcock (2006) ▪ Winemaker(s) Tim Alcock (2006), with Isaac Mabeta (2009) ▪ 26ha/2.5ha (cabs s/f, malbec, merlot, p verdot) ▪ ±20t/2,000cs own label 99% red 1% rosé ▪ Certified organic by BCS ▪ PO Box 511 Worcester 6849 ▪ debreedevineyards@burchells.co.za ▪ www.debreedevineyards.co.za ▪ S 33° 37' 10.69" E 019° 22' 44.79" ▪ F +27 (0)86-684-7778 ▪ **T +27 (0)23-342-5388**

☐ **Debutant** *see* De Kleine Wijn Koöp

De Doorns Wynkelder (Koöp) Bpk

Taking convenience to a new level, an Engen service station is opening at the same premises as De Doorns Wynkelder's tasting centre in De Doorns village, so you can fill up while you stock up. And, because the wine venue shares with the Tourism Centre, you can plan your Hex River Valley visit while sampling the range, which includes sweet and medium-dry 'sherry' (untasted this edition).

Sauvignon Blanc (NEW) ★★★ Satisfying lunchtime companion, **14** is grassy, with white peach aromas & tastes, moderate alcohol. **Demi-Sec Sparkling** (NEW) ★★ **14** from sauvignon, gently sweet & frothy. Also tasted: **Roodehof 12** ★★ Not tasted: **Cabernet Sauvignon**. — CvZ

Location: De Doorns ▪ Map/WO: Worcester ▪ Est 1968 ▪ Tasting & sales Mon-Fri 8–5 Sat 8–12 ▪ Cellarmaster(s) Danie Koen ▪ Winemaker(s) Danie Koen, with Peter James Thomson ▪ PO Box 129 De Doorns 6875 ▪ ddwk@hexvallei.co.za ▪ www.dedoornscellar.co.za ▪ S 33° 29' 10.3" E 019° 39' 43.2" ▪ F +27 (0)86-579-1310 ▪ **T +27 (0)23-356-2100**

Definitum Wines

Fritz van der Merwe and De Wet Schreiber first decided to produce wine, later coming to the idea of using less well known varieties. They buy the wine and bottle it themselves, aiming to be 'the definitive – hence the brand name - producer of whatever variety or blend we make'.

Cape Blend (NEW) ★★ Porty plum pudding notes on **12** from pinotage with malbec, shiraz, merlot & petit verdot. Bold build, alcohol kick in gruff tail. Not retasted: **Petit Verdot 11** ★★★ — AL

Location: Strand ▪ WO: Stellenbosch ▪ Est/1stB 2009 ▪ Closed to public ▪ Owner(s) Fritz van der Merwe & De Wet Schreiber ▪ 520cs own label 100% red ▪ PO Box 917 Strand 7139 ▪ info@definitum.co.za ▪ www.definitum.co.za

De Grendel Wines

De Grendel is a sprawling 800 ha of Durbanville land owned by Sir David Graaff, son of the late Sir De Villiers Graaff, leader of the opposition party during the mid-20th century. Mixed farming is practised here, including Holstein stud cattle, sheep, grain and, last but not least, wine grapes. Plantings of vineyard amount to 110 ha and winemaking is overseen by industry stalwart Charles Hopkins - he chairs the South African National Wine Show Association, the body responsible for the Young Wine Show and Veritas, and is a member of the august Cape Winemakers Guild. The tasting room offers a magnificent view across the bay to Table Mountain, while chef Ian Bergh heads up the deluxe restaurant on the property.

★★★★ **Op Die Berg Pinot Noir** Fine **12** sultry dark cherry fruit & wisps of oak spice, lovely satin texture brightened by crisp acidity. Ceres grapes, 13 months in oak, 20% new. Ups ante on **11** (★★★★).

★★★★☆ **Shiraz** Excellent recent form continues in **12**; savoury earthy patina to dense red & black berry fruit, good line of acidity, wonderfully dry on the finish. 20% new oak, portion American. 95% Paarl grapes.

★★★★ **Op Die Berg Chardonnay** (NEW) Scintillating **13** has poise & balance in restrained house style. 60% fruit from Graaff family Ceres vines fermented in oak (half new), 8 months on lees adds richness. Ends dry, 13.5% alcohol in harmony.

★★★★ **Sauvignon Blanc** Immensely appealing **14**, well-defined lime fruit with a herbal edge smoothed by 100 days on the lees; zippy acidity ensures fleshier 11% semillon portion remains in balance.

★★★★☆ **Koetshuis Sauvignon Blanc** Complex & complete **14** preview is arresting: piercing green pea aromas with fabulous intensity of riverstone & gunflint give flavour without weight in the mouth. Bone-dry, gently salty finish. 80% Darling fruit.

★★★★ **Méthode Cap Classique Brut** Dry **12** a classy bubble; understated assembly of 74% chardonnay & pinot noir, subtle yeast character (18 months on lees), bright acidity & fine mousse.

Rosé ★★★ Dry **14** is 58% cab with pinotage. Salmon hue, red berry fruit & bright acidity are ready for a picnic. **Pinot Gris ★★★★** Tank sample **14** offers delicate apple & pear notes, & touch of spice; 15% barrel-fermented portion adds gravitas. Also tasted: **Merlot 12 ★★★ Rubáiyát 12 ★★★★ Viognier 14 ★★★★** Not retasted: **Sauvignon Blanc Noble Late Harvest 12 ★★★** Discontinued: **Winifred.** — DS

Location: Durbanville ▪ Map: Durbanville, Philadelphia & Darling ▪ WO: Durbanville/Coastal/Ceres Plateau ▪ Est 1720 ▪ 1stB 2004 ▪ Tasting & sales Mon-Sat 9–7 Sun 10–4 ▪ Closed Dec 25 ▪ Cellar tours by appt ▪ Conferences ▪ De Grendel Restaurant ▪ Owner(s) Sir David Graaff ▪ Cellarmaster(s) Charles Hopkins (Oct 2005) ▪ Winemaker(s) Elzette du Preez (Jan 2006) ▪ Viticulturist(s) Kudzai Mwerenga (2009) ▪ 800ha/110ha (cabs s/f, merlot, mourv, p verdot, ptage, pinot noir/gris, shiraz, chard, sauv, sem, viog) ▪ 600t/35,000cs own label 35% red 50% white 15% rosé ▪ 112 Plattekloof Road Panorama 7505 ▪ info@degrendel.co.za ▪ www.degrendel.co.za ▪ S 33° 51' 2.5" E 018° 34' 18.4" ▪ F +27 (0)21-558-7083 ▪ **T +27 (0)21-558-6280**

☐ **Dekker's Valley** *see* Mellasat Vineyards
☐ **De Kleine Leeuwen** *see* Leeuwenberg

De Kleine Wijn Koöp

De Kleine Wijn Koöp is a collective of sommeliers and graphic artists, including Rohan Etsebeth and Jan Solms of Stellenbosch design studio Fanakalo. Wine being part of their day job, when they come across small and unusual bottlings, they buy these in and dress them in a more 'flip-flops and boardshorts' than 'power suit' fashion.

Location: Stellenbosch ▪ Est/1stB 2011 ▪ Closed to public ▪ Sales via email ▪ Owner(s) Rohan Etsebeth & Jan Solms ▪ 100% red ▪ Brands: Debutant, Steenbok, Duidelijk, De Kreatuur ▪ kantoor@dekleinewijnkoop.co.za ▪ www.dekleinewijnkoop.co.za

De Krans

Capitalising on its location in the usually hot, dry Succulent Karoo Biome, De Krans became one of the family-owned wineries which established Calitzdorp's reputation as South Africa's 'port capital'. But unfortified varietal bottlings of traditional 'port' grapes have been a feature almost since inception, the original Tinta Barocca (launched 1979) since joined by Touriga Nacional (an SA first in 2000), Tempranillo (now labelled 'Tinta Roriz') and most recently a best-years-only 'Calitzdorp Blend', Tritonia. The signature fortifieds, in recently revamped packaging, as all the wines, meanwhile continue to rake in awards, and Louis van der Riet, winemaker since 2013, settled in nicely, winning Klein Karoo Champion Red in his debut vintage. See also Garden Route Wines.

★★★★ Touriga Nacional ⊘ Powerful **13** barrel sample has a warm nutty character, with spicy dark berry, fig & dark chocolate flavours on a well-managed tannin foundation. Very youthful, deserves time to show best.

★★★★ Tritonia ⊗ Deftly made Calitzdorp Blend from touriga (70%), dollops tinta & tempranillo. Appealing Xmas cake notes on **11**, integrated, dense black fruit boding well for the future.

★★★★☆ White Muscadel Jerepigo ⊗ Following delicious **12** (★★★★), **13** after-dinner delight reaches for the stars with complex aromas, seamless & well-judged fortification.

★★★★ Original Espresso NV fortified from tinta & touriga is Xmas pudding in a glass! Rich raisins, dates & nuts - even suggestion of brandy butter. Delightful fireside warmer.

★★★★★ Cape Vintage Reserve Cape port-style with brilliant track record. **12** with rich & spicy dark plum & cherry notes, tangy orange zest & nutmeg spice. From touriga, tintas barocca & roriz. 19% alcohol perfectly synced. Irresistible now & for decade-plus.

★★★★☆ Cape Vintage ⊘ Invariably excellent port-style, generous & juicy, accessible on release yet cellarworthy. Previewed **13** moist plum pudding character, nutty & spicy with gentle dusty tannin underpin. From touriga, tintas barocca & roriz, souzão.

★★★★ **Cape Ruby** True-to-style **NV** 'port' with redcurrant richness, clove & hint of dark chocolate, lovely silky texture. Two vintages blended for consistency. From tintas amarela, roriz & barocca, touriga.

★★★★☆ **Cape Tawny Limited Release** (NEW) Outstanding tawny port-style, **NV**, 1,160 cases of gorgeousness from tinta & touriga. Very subtle dusty aroma, delicate tobacco pouch character & peppery undertone. Refined, low-key, shows elegant concentration. WO W Cape.

Tinta Roriz ★★★ Was 'Tempranillo'. Unfortified **13** barrel sample with nutty aroma, brisk acidity buoying black cherry flavours. **Tinta Barocca** ⊘ ★★★☆ **12** slightly dusty aroma laced with mocha & spice, sour cherry flavour ends dry. **Tinta Barocca Rosé** ⊘ ★★★ Charming **14** dry pink with floral notes, light & fresh, delicate & balanced. Also tasted: **Cabernet Sauvignon 13** ★★☆ **Chardonnay 14** ★★☆ **Chenin Blanc 14** ★★☆ **Moscato Perlé 14** ★★ **Original Cape Pink NV** ★★☆ Discontinued: **Tinta Mocha, Relishing Red, Reserve Muscat, Cape Tawny, Cape White.** — DB

Location: Calitzdorp • Map: Klein Karoo & Garden Route • WO: Calitzdorp/Western Cape • Est 1964 • 1stB 1977 • Tasting & sales Mon-Fri 8–5 Sat 10–4 • Tasting fee R25pp • Closed Easter Fri/Sun & Dec 25 • Pick your own apricots (last week Nov, 1st week Dec) & hanepoot grapes (±10 Feb–10 Mar) • 'Braaivleis' by Vygieshof Home for the Aged available on Wed & Sat during picking season • Facilities for children school hols • BYO picnic • Walking trail • Owner(s) De Krans Wines (MD Boets Nel & directors Stroebel Nel & René Oosthuizen) • Winemaker(s) Louis van der Riet (Aug 2012) • Viticulturist(s) Stroebel Nel (Jan 1988) • 78ha/45ha (cab, tempranillo, tinta barocca, touriga nacional, chard, chenin & muscats) • 500t/ 40–50,000cs own label 50% red 10% white 3% rosé 37% fortifieds • IPW, BWI • PO Box 28 Calitzdorp 6660 • dekrans@ mweb.co.za • www.dekrans.co.za • S 33° 32' 6.3" E 021° 41' 9.0" • F +27 (0)44-213-3562 • **T +27 (0)44-213-3314**

☐ **De Kreatuur** see De Kleine Wijn Koöp

Delaire Graff Estate

In the 30-odd years since it was founded by John and Erica Platter, there have been various owners and numerous winemakers at this high-flying, high-lying estate on Helshoogte Pass just outside Stellenbosch town (it literally looks down on some very classy neighbours!). But there seems now to be some brilliant stability, since it was bought by jeweller Laurence Graff a decade back and transformed into an art-studded restaurant and accommodation showpiece with a winery at its core. Morné Vrey has been in charge of the cellar since 2009, with increasingly deft confidence transforming the grapes from the home vineyards (mostly the Bordeaux black grapes and chardonnay) and from elsewhere into wines of elegance and finesse — with just a hint of diamantine glitter.

★★★★☆ **Cabernet Sauvignon Reserve** Master-crafted **12** shows all the detail & nuances of this great variety. Incredibly deep & dark yet expressively scented & almost 'feminine'. Beautifully textured, dense & concentrated, threaded through with sweet black fruit.

★★★★★ **Laurence Graff Reserve** 11 (★★★★★) has the makings of an icon: complex, layered & individual, yet classic in form & structure. Barrel selection from Cab Reserve, with dashes malbec, petit verdot; only produced in best vintages. Worthy successor to stellar **09**. No **10**.

★★★★ **Merlot** Satisfyingly mellow **12** exudes ripeness & freshness after 15 months in barrel. Plummy fruit, slightly chalky tannins, pleasant floral farewell. **11** sold out untasted. WO W Cape.

★★★★ **Shiraz** Toned-down **13** (★★★★☆) from Helderberg vines shows more Rhône-like restraint than big & juicy **12**. Appealingly fresh & spicy, though flavours don't linger.

★★★★★ **Botmaskop** ⊘ Massive & intense, with brooding black fruit on noble liquorice-toned structure, Bordeaux-shiraz blend **12** follows spectacular form of **11**. Very youthful, but showing finesse & potential suppleness though unsettled tannins & somewhat wild vinosity.

★★★★ **Chardonnay** Buttery citrus with salty-mineral undertones on **13** indicate new directions after less harmonious **12**. Oak spices integrate seamlessly, as fruit returns to the fore.

★★★★ **Chenin Blanc** Chalky, lees-driven texture, tingling acidity & high-toned apricots on **13** combine in uneasy union. Super-ripe fruit, spiced with oak, lends heavy preserved-fruit character. **12** (★★★★★) was subtler. Both ex Swartland.

★★★★☆ **Coastal Cuvée Sauvignon Blanc** ⊘ Great focus & intensity in **14** preview, from 3 Coastal areas, showing attention to detail in layered fruit & aromas. Fine balance between mineral & vibrant gooseberry flavour. Subtle touch of lees & drop wooded Franschhoek semillon add weight & texture.

★★★★ **Sauvignon Blanc** Widely sourced (50% from Olifants River), previewed **14** (★★★☆) khaki bush whiff, nervous acidity & vibrant aromas on a lightish body, shorter finish compared to **13**.

★★★★☆ **White Reserve** Barrel-fermented **12** semillon-sauvignon blend with attitude. Classic Bordeaux styling yet uniquely nuanced, showing solid mineral core overlaid by oaky spices & wild herbaceous aromas in seamless, silky package. Coastal WO.

★★★★ **Cape Vintage** Alluring brandied Christmas pudding notes on inky, dense, concentrated **12** from touriga & tinta. Restrained (79 g/l) sugar emphasises ripe berry-fruit profile.

Old Bush Vine Chenin Blanc (NEW) ★★★☆ Traces of pineapple & peach, vibrant acidity on unwooded, fresh & fruity **14**, part natural ferment of grapes from Agter Paarl. Also tasted: **Cabernet Franc Rosé 14** ★★★ Not tasted: **Reserve Noble Late Harvest**. — GdB

Location/map: Stellenbosch ▪ WO: Stellenbosch/Coastal/Western Cape/Swartland ▪ Est 1983 ▪ 1stB 1984 ▪ Tasting & sales Mon-Sat 10-5 Sun 9.30-4 ▪ Fee R50/3 wines, R70/5 wines, R150/wine & food elements tasting ▪ Cellar tours by appt (no tours during harvest) ▪ Gifts ▪ Farm produce ▪ Walks/hikes ▪ Art collection ▪ Delaire Graff & Indochine Restaurants ▪ 5-star Lodges & Spa ▪ Owner(s) Laurence Graff ▪ Winemaker(s) Morné Vrey (Jul 2009) ▪ Viticulturist(s) Kallie Fernhout (Jun 2010) ▪ 42ha/20ha (cabs s/f, malbec, merlot, p verdot, chard, sauv) ▪ 280t/34,000cs own label 40% red 55% white 5% rosé ▪ WIETA ▪ PO Box 3058 Stellenbosch 7602 ▪ info@delaire.co.za ▪ www.delaire.co.za ▪ S 33° 55′ 17.70″ E 018° 55′ 22.08″ ▪ F +27 (0)86-775-1720 ▪ **T +27 (0)21-885-8160**

Delavia Estate (NEW)

Pretoria-schooled entrepreneur Merwe Viljoen's young boutique winery is situated at the foot of the Helderberg in Stellenbosch's 'Golden Triangle' – world-class red-wine terroir. With consultant Rocco de Villiers, he's aiming to produce 'extremely high-quality wine, expressing the unique style of the Helderberg'. Officially closed to the public, tastings are available by special appointment.

Adagio ★★★★ Cab, merlot lead 5-way Bordeaux blend. **11** scented with subtle herbaceous notes & savoury Marmite; some forest floor nuances & coconut partner the sweet berry fruit on the palate. Not yet melded, tannins need 2+ years more. Only one barrel made. — CR, CvZ

Location/WO: Stellenbosch ▪ Est 2009 ▪ 1stB 2010 ▪ Closed to public ▪ Owner(s) Merwe Viljoen ▪ Winemaker(s) Rocco de Villiers (Jan 2014, consultant) ▪ Viticulturist(s) Francois Hanekom (Jan 2013, consultant) ▪ 25ha/18.5ha (cabs s/f, merlot, shiraz, chard) ▪ 115t/225cs own label 100% red ▪ IPW ▪ PO Box 12275 Die Boord Stellenbosch 7613 ▪ rocco@capecrush.co.za, merwe@delavia.co.za ▪ **T +27 (0)82-821-4625**

Delheim Wines

It was Hans and Deli Hoheisen who reintroduced vines to the historic Driesprongh farm on the lower slopes of Stellenbosch's Simonsberg, and in 1949 Delheim ('Deli's home') was born. But it was ebullient Spatz Sperling – who arrived from Germany in 1951 to help out – and his family who built Delheim into today's extensive winery and popular destination: 'worth the journey', as the labels announce with double application. The Vera Cruz farm, some three kilometres away, was later added to the estate. Patriarch Spatz is delighted with the reinvention of his Spatzendreck sweet wine, and its rise in status as part of the Heritage range - though the famous (notorious?) 'pooping sparrow' label remains. It speaks to the mix of tradition and change which characterises Delheim today.

Estate range

★★★★ **Vera Cruz Pinotage** (NEW) Spicy oak dominates ripely sweet fruit on **12**, but it deserves 3+ years before broaching. This will also serve the gentle but very firm tannins. Properly dry, but sweet sense on finish.

★★★★☆ **Vera Cruz Shiraz** Powerful, ripe **12** first made since **09** (★★★★★) from same low-yielding vineyard. Fine, complex fruit & tobacco aromas lead to supple, concentrated, savoury, firmly built palate. Still youthful - needs 3 years at least to harmonise, & will last many more.

★★★★☆ **Grand Reserve** ② All-new oak dominates flagship **09** - as usual mostly cab, with merlot. But some elegance & good dark-fruited flavour lurks, shown in a long finish, & this rating reflects hope for harmony with 5 or so more years in bottle.

★★★★ **Chardonnay Sur Lie** Naturally fermented **13** has more depth than **12** (★★★☆) & than unoaked version. Bold rather than subtle, it's balanced, reasonably concentrated, lightly creamy; well oaked. Stellenbosch WO. Note: range was 'Vera Cruz Estate'.

★★★★★ **Edelspatz Noble Late Harvest** **13** another triumphantly lovely botrytis dessert from riesling. Small oaked portion & like previous, with modest alcohol - more German than French in style. Has power from concentration, & delicacy from fine, elegant balance of sweetness & acidity.

Family range

★★★★ **Cabernet Sauvignon** **12** serious but very drinkable (should develop well a good few years). Some notes from oak mingle with already rather complex fruit intensity; integrated tannin & bright acid.

★★★★ **Shiraz** ② **12** full of juicy berried flavour, but balanced with modest oaking & good grip. Even rather elegantly fresh, despite some power. WO Simonsberg–Stellenbosch, rest Stellenbosch.

★★★★ **Chenin Blanc** (NEW) Natural ferment & light oaking on quietly forthcoming, subtly intense **13**. Citrus, dried peach notes among the pleasures on offer, controlled by a good structural grip.

Unwooded Chardonnay ★★★☆ Most appealing pure fruit aromas & flavours on **13**, now bottled, with balanced acidity; satisfyingly succulent lemon-lime finish. Also tasted: **Merlot 12** ★★★ Not retasted: **Pinotage 12** ★★★☆ Note: range was 'Delheim'.

Heritage range

Spatzendreck ★★★☆ Grapey, sweetly pretty notes on **13** Natural Sweet version of this famous brand (not discontinued after all). Now from barrel-fermented muscat de Frontignan, riesling & chenin, previously just chenin. Charming but rather simple. Also tasted: **Gewürztraminer 13** ★★★

Lifestyle range

Pinotage Rosé ★★★ Crisp, near-dry **14** has a little muscat to add fragrant note. Easy, lightly fruity, with a nice bite. Stellenbosch WO, like Sauvignon. Also tasted: **Cabernet Sauvignon-Shiraz 12** ★★★ **Sauvignon Blanc Heerenwijn 14** ★★★ Not tasted: **Chenin Blanc**. — TJ

Location/map: Stellenbosch ▪ WO: Stellenbosch/Simonsberg–Stellenbosch/Coastal ▪ Est 1971 ▪ 1stB 1961 ▪ Tasting & sales daily 9-5 ▪ Fee R25 tasting/R35 tasting & cellar tour ▪ Cupcake & wine pairing R75pp, pre-booking essential ▪ Closed Easter Fri/Sun, Dec 25 & Jan 1 ▪ Cellar tours daily at 10.30 & 2.30 ▪ Delheim Restaurant ▪ Facilities for children ▪ Tour groups ▪ Gifts ▪ Farm produce ▪ Conferences ▪ Conservation area ▪ Oakleaf Lodge B&B at Delvera ▪ Events: see website for schedule ▪ Owner(s) Sperling family ▪ Winemaker(s) Reg Holder (Jan 2012) ▪ Viticulturist(s) Etienne Terblanche (Aug 2012) ▪ 375ha/148ha (cab, ptage, shiraz, chard, chenin, riesling, sauv) ▪ 980t/120,000cs own label 50% red 30% white 20% rosé ▪ Brands for clients: Woolworths ▪ BWI champion, Level 1 B-BBEE, WIETA ▪ PO Box 210 Stellenbosch 7599 ▪ delheim@delheim.com ▪ www.delheim.com ▪ S 33° 52' 10.1" E 018° 53' 9.8" ▪ F +27 (0)21-888-4601 ▪ T +27 (0)21-888-4600

☐ **De Liefde** see Mountain Ridge Wines

De Meye Wines

De Meye owners Jan and Philip Myburgh (the latter is the MD, and particularly involved in the vineyards) are the 5th and 6th generations of their family to farm in the Stellenbosch area. Until 1998, the first vintage with wine under their own label, the grape crop was sold off – some of it still is, but there's a regular flow of rather elegant, restrained De Meye wine from the cellar where Marcus Milner has reigned from nearly the start.

De Meye range

★★★★ **Cabernet Sauvignon** Engaging blackcurrant aromas with graphite edge in **11**. Oaky finish perhaps a little too rugged for elegant red berry flavours in otherwise integrated wine.

★★★★ **Trutina** Harmonious flagship red, blend of both cabs, dashes merlot & shiraz. **11**, now bottled, shows solid savoury fruit with herbal edge.

Shiraz Rosé ★★★ Charming **14**, fruity but attractively dry, crisp & full flavoured. **Chenin Blanc** ★★★ Light, appetising lunchtime style. **14** balanced, beautifully fresh & crisp. Also tasted: **Merlot 12** ★★★ **Shiraz 12** ★★★★ **Chardonnay Unwooded 14** ★★★

Little River range

Cabernet Sauvignon ★★★ Decent grip to savoury, nicely integrated, smooth & elegant **12**. Also tasted: **Shiraz 13** ★★★ — IM

Location/map/WO: Stellenbosch ▪ Est/1stB 1998 ▪ Tasting & sales Mon-Thu by appt Fri 12-5 Sat/Sun & pub hols 11-4 ▪ Fee R15/5 wines ▪ Closed Good Fri, Dec 25/26 & Jan 1 ▪ Cellar tours Mon-Fri by appt ▪ 'The Table at De Meye' open for lunch Sat-Sun, booking essential T +27 (0)72-696-0530, www.thetablerestaurant.co.za ▪ Farm produce ▪ Owner(s) Jan Myburgh Family Trust ▪ Winemaker(s) Marcus Milner (Sep 1999) & Lofty Ellis (consultant), with Aby Bodlani (Sep 2000) ▪ Viticulturist(s) Philip Myburgh & Johan Pienaar (Jan 2006, consultant) ▪ 100ha/65ha (cabs s/f, merlot, shiraz, chard, chenin) ▪ 300t/36,000cs own label 65% red 25% white 10% rosé ▪ IPW ▪ PO Box 20 Elsenburg 7607 ▪ info@demeye.co.za ▪ www.demeye.co.za ▪ S 33° 49' 0.7" E 018° 49' 48.8" ▪ F +27 (0)21-884-4154 ▪ **T +27 (0)21-884-4131**

☐ **De Mikke Patron** *see* Almenkerk Wine Estate

DeMorgenzon

This expansive property in the Stellenboschkloof was purchased by Hylton and Wendy Appelbaum in 2003. Since then, the previously Johannesburg-based couple have devoted just some of their impressive energies (both are still involved in business and philanthropic institutions) to having vines replanted across the slopes stretching from 200 to 400 metres above sea level. 'Chenin and shiraz/syrah are doing well at higher levels, chardonnay lower down,' says cellarmaster Carl van der Merwe, who believes the best blocks of these three varieties can produce wines of greatest expression of the farm's terroir. Believing that biodiversity makes for better grapes, the Appelbaums introduced indigenous flora throughout their 'garden vineyards'. Baroque music continuously piped to the vines is an unusual concept, but something which they feel positively influences ripening.

Maestro range

★★★★ **Red** ⓧ Merlot/cab-headed Bordeaux-style blend. **11** modern, ripe-fruited, supported by fresh juicy acids, fine tannin trim. French oak polish (30% new) complements approachability.

★★★★☆ **Red ('Rhône Blend')** ⓝ Placeholder name for elegantly expressive, floral **11**, a syrah/shiraz-led blend with grenache, mourvèdre & dash zinfandel - all seamlessly integrated with spicy oak & savoury acidity. Distinguishable from Bordeaux-style 'Maestro Red' by its purple label.

★★★★★ **White 12** was our 2014 White Wine of the Year. Voluptuously rounded **13** a worthy succesor: barrel-fermented blend chenin, chardonnay, roussanne & viognier. Complex layers of rich, vibrant fruit find balance on tightrope of pithy acidity. Needs time.

DeMorgenzon Reserve range

★★★★☆ **Syrah** ⓝ Convincing rendition of variety's Rhône origins in deep-coloured, complex **12**. Vivid red fruit, white pepper spice in superb balance with supple oak (some new) & uplifting savoury acidity.

★★★★★ **Chardonnay** ⓝ Our prestigious White Wine of the Year for 2015 makes a fine case for this variety on its Stellenboschkloof site. Sleekly rich **13**'s mineral core gathered by perfectly poised line of acidity & deft oaking (66% new). Clarity of flavour broadened by year on lees for complete, thrillingly delicious mouthful.

★★★★☆ **Chenin Blanc** Seriously styled, barrel-fermented **13** boasts bright ripe fruit & tight mineral core, boosted by gram sugar, broadened by lees-ageing & well judged oak. Like **12** (★★★★★), ex old bushvines.

DeMorgenzon range

★★★★ **DMZ Syrah** Vibrant fruit core & roasted spices in brightly youthful **12** interwoven with fine, supple tannins to produce authentic, boldly expressive syrah.

★★★★ **DMZ Concerto** ⓧ Last was **08**. Re-introduced with shiraz-based **12** (★★★) & all exported to Sweden. Suppleness & gentle grip give full rein to rich spiciness. Satisfying & approachable.

★★★★ **DMZ Chardonnay** Harmonious blend cleverly crafted from cool & warmer region vineyards in **13**, rounded by small barrel-fermented portion, sufficiently subtle to please even style's detractors.

★★★★ **DMZ Sauvignon Blanc** Dusty Durbanville, elegant Elgin fruit combo quite delightful in ultra-crisp but not harsh **13** (★★★☆) multi-region blend. Follows finer **12**, also with tiny oaked portion to balance overall fresh & lively profile.

DMZ MCC Chenin Blanc ⓝⒺⓦ ★★★★ Altogether unusual **NV** bubbly, the base wine cleverly & boldly oaked giving savoury, structured rather than pretty effect. Bone-dry, though some air-dried chenin added as dosage. Also tasted: **DMZ Chenin Blanc 13** ★★★☆

Garden Vineyards range

Rosé ★★★ Appetising, dry, salmon-pink **13**, blend of flavourful syrah/shiraz, grenache, mourvèdre. — IM

Location/map: Stellenbosch ▪ WO: Stellenbosch/Western Cape ▪ Est 2003 ▪ 1stB 2005 ▪ Tasting & sales daily 10-5 ▪ Fee R25-R34 ▪ Closed Good Fri, Dec 25/26 & Jan 1 ▪ Cellar tours on request ▪ Conservation area ▪ Owner(s) Wendy & Hylton Appelbaum ▪ Cellarmaster(s) / GM Carl van der Merwe (Jul 2010) ▪ Winemaker(s) Carl van der Merwe (Jul 2010), with Craig Barnard (Dec 2012) ▪ Viticulturist(s) Louis Buys (Sep 2012) & Kevin Watt (consultant) ▪ 91ha/52ha (cab, grenache, merlot, mourv, shiraz, chard, chenin, rouss, sauv, viog) ▪ 252t/30,000cs own label 56% red 33% white 8% rosé 3% other ▪ BWI, IPW ▪ PO Box 1388 Stellenbosch 7599 ▪ info@demorgenzon.co.za ▪ www. demorgenzon.co.za ▪ S 33° 56' 22.99" E 018° 45' 0.17" ▪ F +27 (0)21-881-3773 ▪ **T +27 (0)21-881-3030**

☐ **Den** *see* Painted Wolf Wines
☐ **Denneboom** *see* Oude Denneboom
☐ **De Oude Opstal** *see* Stellendrift - SHZ Cilliers/Kuün Wyne

De Redley   ⓧ

Already established in Germany, the Dutch market now beckons for the brand co-owned by Stellenbosch-based cellarmaster Nicholas Ridley and Fredy Pummer (also proprietor of Boucheron Wines), and production is being scaled accordingly. Tastings of the rare-in-Cape blanc de noir merlot are available locally at selected slowfood markets.

White Merlot ★☆ Unusual style, previewed **14** a really pale rose colour, austere, with just a hint of fruit. Needs a seafood partner. — GdB

Location/WO: Stellenbosch ▪ Est/1stB 2012 ▪ Tasting available at slowfood markets ▪ Owner(s) Nicholas Ridley & Fredy Pummer ▪ Cellarmaster(s) Nicholas Ridley (Sep 2011) ▪ Winemaker(s) Piet Bredell ▪ 7t/766cs own label 100% white ▪ info@deredley.co.za ▪ www.deredley.co.za ▪ F +27 (0)11-708-3615 ▪ **T +27 (0)11-708-3444**

Desert Rose Wines   ⓧ

Herman Nel and Alan van Niekerk's boutique winery at Vredendal celebrates the Sting song as well as the flower-like gypsum crystals found on the surrounding plains, each 'rose' as unique as the wines the longtime Namaqua Wines supplier and the nurseryman strive to make, and name after their adored daughters.

Jada's Rose ★★★★ 09 happy 60/40 mix cab & shiraz, former's taut grip softened by shiraz's raspberry fruit. **Nicola's Rose** ★★★☆ Succulent mulberry, savoury nuances on silky **10** dry rosé from cab, merlot & shiraz. Not retasted: **Cabernet Sauvignon 10** ★★★ **Winemaker's Choice Cabernet Sauvignon 11** ★★★ **Winemaker's Choice Merlot 10** ★★☆ **Shiraz 09** ★★★ — DB, CvZ

Location: Vredendal ▪ Map: Olifants River ▪ WO: Western Cape ▪ Tasting by appt ▪ Owner(s) Alan van Niekerk & Herman Nel ▪ Winemaker(s) Herman Nel ▪ desertrose@nashuaisp.co.za ▪ S 31° 41′ 33.1″ E 018° 30′ 5.9″ ▪ F +27 (0)27-213-2858 ▪ **T +27 (0)82-809-2040/+27 (0)82-800-2270**

De Toren Private Cellar

This little piece of heaven on Stellenbosch's Polkadraai Hills was bought by business world émigrés Emil and Sonette den Dulk as a country retreat in 1991. Becoming aware of the property's viticultural potential, the couple consulted experts, evaluated the market and decided to focus on the five classic Bordeaux red varieties, planting 13 clones on seven different soil types at their sea-facing site. Attention to detail and social conscience drive everything here, from planting the carbon-sequestering spekboom to enrolling all staff in cellar assistant training courses. Since the Fusion V debut (vintage 1999), the wines have garnered ever more enthusiastic local and international acclaim, realising what we described in the 2001 edition as 'genuinely unusual promise'.

★★★★☆ **Fusion V** Cab-led (56%) 5-way Bordeaux blend; part natural ferment. **12** concentrated, with rich, fragrant fruit & tightly coiled tannins. Bold, mouthfilling & firmly structured. Half-new oak will support long & fruitful maturation. Decant if impatient.

★★★★ **Z** Second, earlier-ready 5-way blend, merlot-led. More complex **12** (★★★★★) trumps **11** with intense berry flavours in harmony with oak & supple tannin structure. Lighter-bodied than sibling, with delightful freshness & composure. Also ageworthy.

La Jeunesse Délicate ★★★☆ Cab-led, lightly oaked **NV** 4-way blend is made in a light style for early enjoyment. Soft & moreish; serve slightly chilled. — WB

Location/map/WO: Stellenbosch ▪ Est 1994 ▪ 1stB 1999 ▪ Tasting, sales & cellar tours by appt ▪ Fee R180, waived on purchase ▪ Donkey walk ▪ Owner(s) Edenhall Trust ▪ Cellarmaster(s) Albie Koch (Oct 1998) ▪ Winemaker(s) Charles Williams (Dec 2008) ▪ Viticulturist(s) Ernest Manuel (Mar 2003, consultant) ▪ 25ha/±21ha (cabs s/f, malbec, merlot, p verdot) ▪ 150t/16,000cs own label 100% red ▪ PO Box 48 Vlottenburg 7604 ▪ info@de-toren.com ▪ www.de-toren. com ▪ S 33° 57′ 34.5″ E 018° 45′ 7.5″ ▪ F +27 (0)21-881-3335 ▪ **T +27 (0)21-881-3119**

De Trafford Wines

First plantings at the Trafford family farm, Mont Fleur, high on the Helderberg slopes between Stellenbosch and Somerset West were experimental. That was over three decades ago, and softly spoken David Trafford has long since established himself as one of the Cape's foremost winemakers for his hands-off, natural approach to winemaking – something the thoughtful, articulate architect has espoused since day one. Paying more than lip service to terroir and site selection, De Trafford's reputation for shiraz, cabernet (franc and sauvignon) and chenin is richly deserved, as each wine is hand-crafted, invariably naturally fermented and frequently bottled without fining or filtration. The same philosophy underpins the separately listed Sijnn label, now vinified on site near Malgas.

★★★★ **Merlot** Succulent yet polished **10**, savoury tobacco & ripe plum, tannins still perky but elegant, approachable, already drinks well. Naturally fermented, as all De Trafford wines.

★★★★ **CWG Auction Reserve Merlot** ⓃⒺⓌ Single (new) barrel selected from special Mont Fleur vineyard for **09**. Deep, sexy blueberry spice notes. Tightly leashed yet already seductively appealing, concludes with light tannic squeeze. Bristles with potential.

★★★★ **Blueprint Syrah** Our prestigious Red Wine of the Year for 2015, powerfully poised & yet restrained **12** (★★★★★) is lithe, concentrated & textured. Ups the ante on **11** through superb harmony of naturally fermented fruit & older oak, inky depths to be plumbed & enjoyed for years. Grapes largely ex neighbour Keermont.

★★★★☆ **Syrah 393** Unfined & unfiltered, as with all the reds, **12** is deep & broad, as was **11** but somewhat softer & rounder, with intense black fruit & pepper notes. Oak (22 months, 50% new French) not apparent. Restrained & elegant.

★★★★☆ **CWG Auction Reserve Perspective** Triumvirate of cab franc, cab & merlot in **12** barrel selection for **14** Auction. Exotic perfumed nose with lipsmacking succulence to ripe, inky black berries. Twist of cocoa on long, defined finish. Tautly focused & elegant, it needs time.

★★★★☆ **Elevation 393** Merlot leads on **10** flagship blend named for home-vineyard altitude, cab & shiraz offer near-equal support. Light smoke & dried thyme nuance to blue/black fruit. Yielding & generous, rich, yet tautly muscular too, deserves time.

★★★★ **Chenin Blanc** Ripe pineapple & passionfruit bounty to wild ferment on **13** from 5 Stellenbosch blocks. As with **12**, broad, leesy & long, but with vibrant fresh acidity to cleanse.

★★★★ **Straw Wine** Unctuous **11** (★★★★) from air-dried, naturally fermented & oak-aged chenin (20 months) doesn't reach heights of **10** or previous.

Not tasted: **Cabernet Sauvignon**. — FM

Location/map/WO: Stellenbosch ▪ Est/1stB 1992 ▪ Tasting, sales & tours Fri & Sat 10–1, or otherwise by appt ▪ Fee R50, waived on purchase ▪ Closed all pub hols ▪ Owner(s) David & Rita Trafford ▪ Winemaker(s) David Trafford ▪ Viticulturist(s) Schalk du Toit (consultant) ▪ 200ha/5ha (cabs s/f, merlot, shiraz) ▪ 71t/7,000cs own label 70% red 30% white ▪ PO Box 495 Stellenbosch 7599 ▪ info@detrafford.co.za ▪ www.detrafford.co.za ▪ S 34° 0' 45.1" E 018° 53' 57. 8" ▪ F +27 (0)86-542-3959 ▪ **T +27 (0)21-880-1611**

Deux Frères Wines

The two brothers in the artisanal boutique winery's name are Stellenbosch-based Stephan and Retief du Toit, who vinify their young-vine crop in the Croydon cellar. Stephan learnt his trade at L'Avenir, where the dream of owning a small piece of land and making wine from it was born. Said land is being planted with a small block of malbec, to join a portfolio launched to some acclaim in 2013.

★★★★ **Fraternitè** American oak for shiraz, French for mourvèdre in 70/30 blend. **12** enticing smoky bacon notes & black plum fruit, supple tannins for enjoyment now or keeping few years.

Liberté ★★★★ Was 'Cabernet Sauvignon-Petit Verdot', **12** adds dashes shiraz & mourvèdre, shows some underlying seriousness in cocoa-dusted ripe fruit within supple, food-friendly structure. **Blanc de Noir** ★★ From mourvèdre, **14** changes style from fruity/floral to savoury; smoked meat aroma, very tart & tangy palate; bone-dry, needs a food partner. — MW

Location/map/WO: Stellenbosch ▪ Est 2008 ▪ 1stB 2012 ▪ Tasting & sales by appt Mon-Fri 10-5 Sat 10-1 ▪ Fee R20 ▪ Closed Easter Fri-Mon, Dec 25 & Jan 1 ▪ BYO picnic ▪ Owner(s) M Wiehe, H Wiehe, S du Toit, R du Toit ▪ Cellarmaster(s)/viticulturist(s) Stephan du Toit (Jan 2008) ▪ 4.2ha/2.1ha (cab, mourv, p verdot, shiraz) ▪ 1,700cs own label 80% red 20% rosé ▪ PO Box 209 Koelenhof 7605 ▪ stephan@dfwines.co.za ▪ www.dfwines.co.za ▪ S 33° 52' 51.16" E 18° 50' 44.93" ▪ F +27 (0)86-621-2425 ▪ **T +27 (0)21-889-9865**

De Villiers Wines

Cellarmaster on the eponymous Paarl family farm, Villiers de Villiers makes wine under an own label (maintaining a strong presence in leading local supermarkets), and for export brands, under contract to overseas buyers ranging from the Netherlands to the Indian Ocean islands to China.

Location: Paarl ▪ Map: Paarl & Wellington ▪ Est/1stB 1996 ▪ Tasting & sales by appt ▪ Owner(s) De Villiers Family Trust ▪ Cellarmaster(s)/winemaker(s)/viticulturist(s) Villiers de Villiers (1996) ▪ 50,000cs own label 80% red 20% white ▪ Other export brand: Heeren van Oranje Nassau ▪ Brands for clients: Huangtai Wines ▪ PO Box 659 Suider-Paarl 7624 ▪ vadev@mweb.co.za ▪ www.devillierswines.com ▪ S 33° 45' 43.3" E 018° 57' 40.8" ▪ F +27 (0)86-653-8988 ▪ **T +27 (0)21-863-2175**

Devonair

Leon and Rina de Wit, owners since 2003 of this Devon Valley boutique winery, specialise in cabernet. Assisted by veteran wine man Ernst Gouws and viticulturist Pierre de Wet, they await the results of the tiny vineyard's renewal with anticipation. Active community supporters, they own Khayamandi's talent showcase AmaZink Live.

The Cab ★★★☆ Medium-bodied **07** shows plush ripe blackberry fruit backed by a fine tannin structure & firm acid balance. Not tasted: **The Cab Family Reserve**. — WB

Location/map/WO: Stellenbosch ▪ Est 1994 ▪ 1stB 2000 ▪ Tasting & sales by appt ▪ Closed all pub hols ▪ 2 self-catering cottages ▪ Owner(s) Leon & Rina de Wit ▪ Winemaker(s) Ernst Gouws (Mar 2006) ▪ Viticulturist(s) Pierre de Wet (2012) ▪ 2.2ha (cab) ▪ 10t/920cs own label 100% red ▪ PO Box 1274 Stellenbosch 7599 ▪ info@devonair.co.za ▪ www. devonair.co.za ▪ S 33° 53' 44.45" E 018° 48' 27.46" ▪ F +27 (0)21-865-2327 ▪ **T +27 (0)21-865-2190**

Devon Hill

There's no more stock in South Africa of this mainly for export label originating from Stellenbosch's Devon Valley and typically including fruit from there. Owner Geir Tellefsen and his team have also halted production while they plot a new course for the brand.

Location: Stellenbosch ▪ Est 1994 ▪ 1stB 1996 ▪ Closed to public ▪ Owner(s) Geir Tellefsen ▪ Cellarmaster(s)/winemaker(s)/viticulturist(s) Therese de Beer (Jan 2011, consultant) ▪ 20,000cs own label 80% red 15% white 5% rosé ▪ geir@rosendalwinery.com ▪ F +27 (0)21-424-1571 ▪ **T +27 (0)21-424-4498**

Devon Rocks

No new wines from Jürgen and Brita Heinrich's small vineyard in Devon Valley, but their Pinotage 05, 07 and 08, and Shiraz Rosé 09 are still available.

Location/map/WO: Stellenbosch ▪ Est 1998 ▪ 1stB 2003 ▪ Tasting, sales & tours by appt ▪ B&B accommodation ▪ Owner(s) Jürgen & Brita Heinrich ▪ Winemaker(s) Simon Smith (Louisvale) ▪ Viticulturist(s) Gawie du Bois & Paul Wallace (advisers) ▪ 4ha/3.5ha (ptage, shiraz) ▪ 4,400cs 57% red 18% white 25% rosé ▪ PO Box 12483 Die Boord 7613 ▪ info@devonrocks.co.za ▪ www.devonrocks.co.za ▪ S 33° 53' 19.9" E 018° 48' 30.1" ▪ F +27 (0)21-865-2621 ▪ **T +27 (0)21-865-2536**

Devonvale Golf & Wine Estate

Residents of this upmarket Stellenbosch lifestyle estate at harvest time invite family and friends to help bring in the crop from vines fringing some of the fairways, for vinification and bottling at Bellevue. The branding honours Devonvale founder and round-the-world yachtsman JJ Provoyeur.

Provoyeur range

★★★★ **Cabernet Sauvignon** **07** modern styling with rich cassis & mint. Sweet & spicy oak nuance integrated, giving sleek polished texture, ready to enjoy. **06** (★★★) was charry, chunkier.

Shiraz ★★ Brawny **11** with smoky cooked fruit aromas, soft sweet-ripe fruit & putt-impairing 15% alcohol. **Special Reserve Shiraz** ★★★★ **10** shows a supple structure, smooth, rich & elegant without being intense or complex; to drink now & for couple of years. — MW

Location/map/WO: Stellenbosch ▪ Est 1997 ▪ 1stB 2004 ▪ Tasting by appt ▪ Fee R25pp ▪ Sales Mon-Sat 11–6 ▪ Chez Shiraz restaurant ▪ Tour groups ▪ Golf ▪ Pro shop ▪ Conferences ▪ Devonvale Golf Lodge ▪ Owner(s) Devonmust (Pty) Ltd ▪ Winemaker(s) Wilhelm Kritzinger (2004, Bellevue Estate) ▪ Viticulturist(s) Anja Hart (2014) ▪ 117ha/1.5ha (shiraz) ▪ 14t/±2,000cs own label 100% red ▪ PO Box 77 Koelenhof 7605 ▪ info@devonvale.co.za ▪ www.devonvale.co.za ▪ S 33° 52' 59.6" E 018° 48' 15.0" ▪ F +27 (0)21-865-2601 ▪ **T +27 (0)21-865-2080**

DeWaal Wines

There's a lot of history here. The De Waal family has been involved in Cape winegrowing for nine generations and the lovely home-farm, Uiterwyk, in Stellenboschkloof dates back to 1682. Pieter de Waal owns the brand, brothers Chris and Daniël make the wines. Pinotage remains a great tradition:

forbear CT de Waal was the first to successfully vinify the grape (at Stellenbosch's Welgevallen), and tribute to his pioneering work is given in the name of one of the three versions made.

DeWaal range

★★★★ **Cabernet Sauvignon** Richly ripe **11** back on form after lesser **08** (★★★★), offering succulent dark fruit & spice, underpinned by finely textured tannins from half new oak.

★★★★ **Merlot** Some classic styling in well-structured **10**, less resolutely dry than last. Supple tannins support juicy black plum flavours to ensure harmonious conclusion.

★★★★ **CT de Waal Pinotage** Stellar example of variety in elegant form. **11** (★★★★★) pitched closer to top end of trio in range than **09**. (No 2010.) Expressive, compact fruit, smartly oaked, from 50 year old vineyard, yields freshness & vibrancy.

★★★★★ **Top of the Hill Pinotage** Kingpin of estate's pinotage trio gets grand treatment: tiny yields from 60 year old bushvines judiciously seasoned in all-new oak, yielding a magisterial example of this local variety. Although **11** still youthful, has building blocks of compact fruit & fine acidity for promising future.

★★★★ **Signal Rock** Cab-driven **08** Bordeaux-style blend was big & angular when tasted a few years back; tealeaf & forest floor layers over rich blackcurrant fruit.

Also tasted: **Pinotage 12** ★★★ Discontinued: **Viognier**.

Young Vines range

Shiraz ★★★ Spicy, confident **13** has appealing lively berry fruit; balanced, youthful. **Sauvignon Blanc** ★★★ Both **13** & **14** show vibrantly crisp, fresh flavours. Latter has lighter alcohol with no loss of zesty flavour. Also tasted: **Merlot 12** ★★★ **Chenin Blanc 14** ★★ — IM

Location/map/WO: Stellenbosch ▪ Est 1682 ▪ 1stB 1972 ▪ Tasting & sales Mon-Fri 10—12.30 & 2—4.30 Sat 10—4.30 (Sep-May only) ▪ Fee R20 ▪ Closed Easter Fri-Mon, Jun 16, Dec 25/26 & Jan 1 ▪ Owner(s) Pieter de Waal ▪ Winemaker(s)/viticulturist(s) Chris de Waal & Daniël de Waal (whites/reds, consultants) ▪ 800t ▪ 50% red 50% white ▪ IPW ▪ PO Box 15 Vlottenburg 7604 ▪ admin@dewaal.co.za ▪ www.dewaal.co.za ▪ S 33° 56' 29.3" E 018° 45' 59.9" ▪ F +27 (0)21-881-3776 ▪ **T +27 (0)21-881-3711**

Dewaldt Heyns Family Wines

Celebrated Saronsberg winemaker and Cape Winemakers Guild member Dewaldt Heyns' own boutique-scale vinifications are about capturing 'the elegance and understated complexity that older vineyards offer'. The wines, joined this edition by a pinotage, are intended as a tribute to Dewaldt's father and the Swartland, where he grew up. 'You don't get a venture more personal than this.'

Weathered Hands range

★★★★ **Chenin Blanc** From ±40 year old bushvines on weathered granite, **11** (★★★★★) like previously tasted **10** is elegant, perfumed, pure; the younger wine slightly richer, with bigger structure but similarly quickened by minerality.

Pinotage (NEW) ★★★★ **12** from old bushvines. Oak (55% new barrels) dominates the aromas, but ripe berry fruit emerges more on the palate. Juicy & well balanced, if not harmonious yet, with dry tannins & sweet-fruited finish. Not tasted: **Shiraz**. — TJ

Location: Tulbagh/Swartland ▪ WO: Swartland ▪ Est/1stB 2006 ▪ Tasting by appt at Saronsberg ▪ Owner(s) Dewaldt Heyns Family Wines ▪ Cellarmaster(s)/winemaker(s)/viticulturist(s) Dewaldt Heyns ▪ (ptage, shiraz, chenin) ▪ 15t/ 1,100cs own label 60% red 40% white ▪ dewaldtheyns@mweb.co.za ▪ **T +27 (0)82-441-4117**

De Wet Cellar

As a stakeholder in FirstCape, Worcester's oldest winery is focused on supplying millions of litres to one of SA's great export successes, but a not insubstantial 30,000 cases of fun and good-value still, sparkling and fortified wines are bottled under the owner-growers' own label, and conveniently available from the cellardoor just off the main artery into the winelands.

★★★★ **Cravate** Among first méthode cap classique sparklings from the region. 100% chardonnay, vibrant **10** raises bar on **09** (★★★★): lemon meringue taste, creamy mousse, clean citrus ending.

★★★★ **White Muscadel** ② **11** fortified sweetie has sunripe sultanas, dried peaches & apples, uncloying tangerine finish.

★★★★ **Cape Ruby** ⊘ Latest **NV** port-style adds 10% touriga to tinta & pontac, goes up a notch. Chocolate wafts, tobacco, prunes & dark berry compote make for a rich & warming after-dinner charmer.

★★★★ **Cape Vintage** ② **08** port-style is firm & luscious, with complex curry spice, Xmas cake & smoky aromas. From now-uprooted, ultra-rare pontac.

Cabernet Sauvignon ⊘ ⊕ ★★★ Toasty oak, blackberry & savoury notes & easy tannin. **13** a charming drink & great value. **Merlot-Cabernet Sauvignon** ⊕ ⊘ ⊕ ★★★ Chocolate & dark berry flavours with nut & black pepper overlay. **13** easy-drinking braai wine with attitude. Also tasted: **Shiraz 13** ★★★ **Rosé 13** ★★ **Chardonnay** ⊘ **13** ★★★★ **Chenin Blanc 14** ★★★ **Petillant Fronté NV** ★★ **Sauvignon Blanc 14** ★★★ **Hanepoot** ⊘ **13** ★★★★ Not retasted: **Red Muscadel 12** ★★★★ Discontinued: **Pinotage, Dry Red**. — DB

Location/map/WO: Worcester • Est 1946 • 1stB 1964 • Tasting & sales Mon-Fri 9–5 Sat 9–12 • Fee R1/wine • Closed all pub hols • Cellar tours by appt • BYO picnic • Owner(s) 60 members • Cellarmaster(s) Piet le Roux (Jan 2000) • Winemaker(s) Tertius Jonck (Sep 2007) & Phillip Vercuiel (Dec 2007) • Viticulturist(s) Hennie Visser (Jul 2008, Vinpro) • 1,000ha (cab, shiraz, chard, chenin, sauv) • 15,500t/30,000cs own label 29% red 36% white 5% rosé 30% fortified + 10m L bulk • ISO 22000, SGS • PO Box 16 De Wet 6853 • admin@dewetcellar.co.za • www.dewetcellar.co.za • S 33° 36' 24.2" E 019° 30' 36.5" • F +27 (0)23-341-2762 • **T +27 (0)23-341-2710**

De Wetshof Estate   ⓠ ⓞ ⓖ

Brothers Peter and Johann de Wet were always going to have to fill impressively large shoes: respectively, those of father Danie, winemaker and titan of the industry, and mother Lesca, whose massive marketing and sales contribution saw the Robertson family estate winning the President's Export Achievement Award five times. But the younger generation clearly is equally dynamic, among others initiating a study of regional terroir expressions of Robertson's signature grape, chardonnay, and phasing in mixed farming to enhance soil (and hence grape) quality. A year of critical acclaim (especially for tiny but outstanding vintage 2013), slew of airline listings (American, Emirates, SAA) and socio-economic milestones culminated in the hosting of the biannual Celebration of Chardonnay, underlining De Wetshof's long synonymy with the grape.

De Wetshof Estate range

★★★★ **Naissance Cabernet Sauvignon** ② Classically styled & elegant **11** has lead pencil whiffs, taut structure. On song after slightly leafy, austere **10** (★★★★).

★★★★ **Thibault** Impressive Bordeaux-style red, one of handful made over the years. **10** merlot (88%) & cab; plush, harmonious plum & vanilla. Elegant, with a supple tannin structure. Age or decant now to appreciate fully.

★★★★ **Nature In Concert Pinot Noir** ② **10**'s ebullient spice, earth & peppery cherry notes coupled with malleable tannins take it up a notch on choc-mocha **09** (★★★★). Enjoy solo or with food. Was in Danie de Wet range.

★★★★★ **Bateleur Chardonnay** From 28 year old vineyard & named for majestic African eagle, **12** brims with citrus & vanilla (90% new oak), showing class, poise & complexity. Succulent, bright mouthfeel, harmony & unflagging finish. Deserves time to reveal full charm.

★★★★ **Finesse Chardonnay 13** from 4 different vineyards delivers plenty of flavour, richness from extended lees-ageing; complex butterscotch & toffee notes, crisp citrus acidity. Only 20% new barrels used.

★★★★☆ **The Site Chardonnay** Estate's oldest single Block 17B is origin of fine new-barrel-fermented **13**. Vibrant concentrated lemon peel, apple blossom & pear flavours underpinned by creamy vanilla, hint of roasted nuts, silky mouthfeel. Ageworthy.

★★★★ **Bon Vallon Chardonnay** Going up a notch on **13** (★★★☆), unoaked **14** oozes tropical fruit, lime zest & granadilla, mouthfillingly rich from weekly lees stirring. Perfect for roast duck.

★★★★ **Riesling** ⓧ **12** (★★★☆), first since steely **09**, slightly more alcohol & richness, still poised & delicately sweet thanks to lively acidity.

★★★★ **Sauvignon Blanc** After **13** (★★★☆), back-to-form **14** offers signature fresh lime fruit profile, depth & focus, with lemon blossom floral note, mouthfilling marzipan (from lees-ageing) & lemony finish.

★★★★ **Méthode Cap Classique Pinot Noir Brut** New disgorgement of sophisticated **08** sparkling owes its elegant brioche character to 60 months on fine lees, no dosage after disgorgement. A fine, stately celebratory sparkler.

★★★★☆ **Méthode Cap Classique Brut** Champagne-method bubbly from chardonnay (60%) & pinot noir. **08** (previous was **NV**) has benefited from 63 months on the lees, showing fine almond brioche notes, creamy mousse, balanced acidity & persistent savoury conclusion.

★★★★☆ **Edeloes** Exceptional botrytised riesling dessert wine, occasional release. **06** is voluptuous, complex & rich, with bright pineapple & apricot flavours complemented by pristine acid backbone for a clean lifted finish. Terrific length. 500 ml.

Limestone Hill Chardonnay ★★★☆ Limy fruit curd character, fruit-sweetness on unoaked, lees-aged **14**.

Danie de Wet range

★★★★ **Chardonnay Sur Lie** ⓧ Unwooded, lees-aged version. **14** shines with warm ginger & citrus whiffs, silky mouthfeel & focused lemon-lime finish. Great value - stock up!

★★★★ **Cape Muscadel** ⓧ Sweetly simple **07** (★★★), missed complexity of **06** & previous.
Also tasted: **Sauvignon Blanc 13** ★★★

Limelight range

Pinot Noir ⓃⒺⓌ ★★★ Ripe, bright strawberry fruit on unwooded **12**, savoury edge, for fun in the late afternoon. **Chardonnay** ⓃⒺⓌ ★★★ **13** pops with citrus flavours, uncomplicated, unoaked, balanced - zesty, with aftertaste of grapefruit. Also tasted: **Chardonnay-Pinot Noir 14** ★★★ — WB

Location/map/WO: Robertson ▪ Est 1949 ▪ 1stB 1972 ▪ Tasting & sales Mon-Fri 8.30–4.30 Sat 9.30–12.30 ▪ Closed Easter Fri/Sun/Mon, May 1, Dec 25/26 & Jan 1 ▪ Cellar tours by appt Mon-Fri 8.30-4.30 ▪ Conservation area ▪ Owner(s) Danie, Peter & Johann de Wet ▪ Cellarmaster(s) Danie de Wet (Jan 1973) ▪ Winemaker(s) Danie de Wet (Jan 1973), Mervyn Williams (2001) & Peter de Wet (2007) ▪ Viticulturist(s) Rudolf Kriel (2012), advised by Phil Freese & Francois Viljoen (both 1997) ▪ 600ha/180ha (cab, merlot, pinot, chard, riesling, sauv) ▪ 1,800t 8% red 90% white 1% rosé 1% MCC ▪ ISO 9001:2008, ISO 22000:2005, BBBEE Grade 2, BWI, Enviro Scientific, Integrity & Sustainability, IPW ▪ PO Box 31 Robertson 6705 ▪ info@dewetshof.com ▪ www.dewetshof.com ▪ S 33° 52' 38.0" E 020° 0' 35.1" ▪ F +27 (0)23-615-1915 ▪ **T +27 (0)23-615-1853**

☐ **De Wilde Haf** *see* Carmel Wines
☐ **De Wit Family** *see* Signal Gun Wines

De Zoete Inval Estate

The Frater family have been at home on this historic Paarl wine farm — originally granted as such in 1688 — for over 130 years. Fifth-generation John Robert and wife Eulalia continue the legacy of non-interventionist winemaking and grape growing (Rhône varieties among the most recently planted).

★★★★ **Pinotage Reserve** ⓧ Spicy oak dominates **08**, with well-layered plummy fruit, meaty savoury notes. Supple body & texture. From Simonsberg vines.

Sweet Surrender Shiraz ⓐ ★★★ Fortified campfire warmer, **06** pastille-like blackcurrant flavour & solid spirit grip. Not retasted: **Cabernet Sauvignon-Shiraz 09** ★★★ **Chardonnay 10** ★★ **Chenin Blanc-Viognier-Semillon 11** ★★★ Not tasted: **Pinotage**. — DB

Location: Paarl ▪ Map: Paarl & Wellington ▪ WO: Paarl/Stellenbosch ▪ Est 1878 ▪ 1stB 1976 ▪ Tastings & sales by appt ▪ Owner(s) DZI Agricultural Investments cc (John Robert & Eulalia Frater) ▪ Cellarmaster(s)/winemaker(s) John Robert Frater (1999) ▪ Viticulturist(s) Dirk Blom (2007) ▪ 80ha/20ha (cab, grenache, malbec, mourv, p verdot, shiraz, chard) ▪ 200t/16,000cs own label 50% red 50% white ▪ Other export brands: Eskdale, Safari ▪ PO Box 591 Suider-Paarl 7624 ▪ info@dezoeteinval.co.za ▪ www.dezoeteinval.co.za ▪ S 33° 46' 35.9" E 018° 57' 50.9" ▪ F +27 (0)21-863-2158 ▪ **T +27 (0)21-863-1535/+27 (0)82-731-3898**

☐ **De Zuydpunt** see Group CDV

DGB

Well-established merchant house with strong portfolio of premium and own-brand wines and port- and sherry-styles, including Beach House, Bellingham, Boschendal, Brampton, Culemborg, Douglas Green, Franschhoek Cellar, Legacy, Millstream, Oude Kaap, Tall Horse, The Bernard Series and The Saints, most listed separately.

Wellington ▪ Est 1942 ▪ Closed to public ▪ Owner(s) DGB management, Brait Capital Partners & Kangra ▪ Winemaker(s)/viticulturist(s) see Bellingham, Boschendal & Franschhoek Cellars ▪ PO Box 246 Wellington 7654 ▪ exports@dgb.co.za ▪ www.dgb.co.za ▪ F +27 (0)21-864-1287 ▪ **T +27 (0)21-864-5300**

☐ **D'Hero's** see Govert Wines
☐ **Diamant & Son** see Baratok Wines
☐ **Diamond Collection** see Lutzville Cape Diamond Vineyards
☐ **Diamond Creek** see Wines of Cape Town
☐ **Dido** see Township Winery

Die Bergkelder Wine Centre   ⓠ ⓞ ⓖ

Literally 'Mountain Cellar', after the maturation facilities deep within Stellenbosch's Papegaaiberg, Die Bergkelder is the home of Fleur du Cap, listed separately. FdC wines can be tasted during a cellar tour and monthly salt pairing dinners, while other premium and super-premium wines in the Distell portfolio can be tasted and purchased at Die Bergkelder Wine Centre. The Vinotèque, now in its 31st year, markets fine wines with the option of having purchases stored in perfect cellar conditions. T +27 (0)21-809-8281 ▪ info@vinoteque.co.za ▪ www.vinoteque.co.za.

Location/map: Stellenbosch ▪ All day tasting & sales Mon-Fri 8–5 Sat 9–2 ▪ Tour fee R25 ▪ Open non-religious pub hols ▪ Tours Mon-Fri 10, 11, 2 & 3; Sat 10, 11 & 12; incl AV presentation; bookings: info@bergkelder.co.za ▪ Tel +27 (0)21-809-8025 ▪ Special group tours, private tastings by appt ▪ Owner(s) Distell ▪ Cellarmaster(s) Andrea Freeborough ▪ Winemaker(s) Pieter Badenhorst (whites) & Wim Truter (reds), with John November ▪ Viticulturist(s) Bennie Liebenberg ▪ 2,500t/428,000cs 45% red 55% white ▪ PO Box 184 Stellenbosch 7599 ▪ info@bergkelder.co.za ▪ www.bergkelder.co.za ▪ S 33° 56' 8.8" E 018° 50' 54.7" ▪ F +27 (0)21-883-9533 ▪ **T +27 (0)21-809-8025**

☐ **Die Laan** see Stellenbosch University Welgevallen Cellar

Die Mas van Kakamas   ⓠ ⓟ ⓐ ⓗ ⓞ ⓢ

Ex-teachers Vlok and Welna Hanekom's 1,400 ha of wine and table grapes stretch out on the Orange River banks near Kakamas in the Northern Cape's Green Kalahari. Here winemaker/viticulturist Danie van der Westhuizen makes predominantly sweet dessert styles but also an ever-improving range of unfortified table wines and, debuting this edition, potstill brandies, their names referencing an exotic desert fungus and a traditional paean to the region's 'endless plains'.

Rooi Kalahari range

Cabernet Sauvignon ★★★ Savoury blackberry notes with slight saltiness, **12** earthy & soft on palate with the ripeness of prunes. **Pinotage** ★★★★ Goes up a notch up in **14**, warm, toasty character with prunes & figs partnering savoury & earthy notes. Not retasted: **Droë Rooi Versnit NV** ★★★ **Rooi Muskadel 11** ★★★ **Rooi Jerepigo 12** ★★ **Cape Ruby 08** ★★★

Groen Kalahari range

Sauvignon Blanc ★★★ Lots of aromatic interest in **14**, grassy, wild herbal notes & lemon zest served up with the tang of pomelo. Not retasted: **Chardonnay 12** ★★★

Goue Kalahari range

Wit Muskadel ⊘ ★★★ Jasmine & peach syrup appeal to richly sweet, ambrosial **10**. Despite 240 grams sugar, it finishes dry & clean. Not retasted: **Hanepoot 10** ★★★ **Wit Jerepigo 08** ★★★

Die Mas range

Shiraz ⊘ ★★★ Savoury salami notes add interest to **11**'s blue & black fruity mouthful. Backbone supports gentle texture. Long finish. Not tasted: **Merlot**.

Brandy range (NEW)

Die Kalahari Truffel ★★★★ 100% potstill from chenin delights with soft, genteel flavours of sundried fruit, hints of vanilla oak with dark chocolate & roasted almonds on the finish. **Vêr In Die Ou Kalahari** ★★★ Blended brandy from chenin is robust, fresh & vibrant, brims with ripeness & sweet fruit. Has fiery Kalahari sunsets deeply embedded in it. — DB

Location: Kakamas ▪ Map: Northern Cape, Free State & North West ▪ WO: Northern Cape ▪ Est/1stB 2005 ▪ Tasting & sales Mon-Fri 8-5 Sat/Sun by appt ▪ Closed Easter Fri-Mon & Dec 25 ▪ 3-hr full farm tour on tractor-pulled wagon during tasting hours ▪ Meals/refreshments by appt; or BYO picnic ▪ Facilities for children ▪ Tour groups ▪ Gift shop ▪ Farm produce ▪ Conferences ▪ Walks/hikes ▪ Mountain biking trail ▪ Conservation area ▪ Camping facilities, 3 self-catering chalets & large lapa/bush pub ▪ Owner(s) Die Mas Boerdery (Pty) Ltd ▪ Cellarmaster(s)/winemaker(s)/viticulturist(s) Danie van der Westhuizen (May 2010) ▪ 1,400ha/80ha (cab, merlot, muscadel r/w, p verdot, pinot, ptage, sangio, shiraz, souzão, tinta, touriga, chard, chenin, cbard, sauv, viog) ▪ 350t/14,000cs own label 30% red 20% white 50% brandy ▪ PO Box 193 Kakamas 8870 ▪ winemaker@diemasvankakamas.co.za ▪ www.diemasvankakamas.co.za ▪ S 28° 45' 48.59" E 020° 38' 26.45" ▪ F +27 (0)86-531-9243 ▪ **T +27 (0)54-431-0245/+27 (0)82-931-5902**

Diemersdal Estate

Last year, 6th-generation winemaker at this family-owned Durbanville estate, Thys Louw, received almost as many accolades for his flagship white as the number of sauvignons he vinifies. There's the more serious siblings MM Louw (awarded locally and abroad), Reserve and 8 Rows, youngsters Diemersdal and Matys, plus the techie in the clan, Sauvignon.com, the West Coast cousin, Sir Lambert, and finally sundry nearer-by relatives and friends such as Maastricht. But the grape currently gripping Thys' attention is grüner veltliner, the classy white from Austria which debuts here.

MM Louw range

★★★★★ **Estate Red** Classic & restrained blend of mostly cab & the four other red Bordeaux grapes; **12** typical aromas of green walnut, tobacco, cassis & toasty oak. The well-integrated & balanced palate is finely structured, with firm yet fine tannin, while the finish is tight & needs cellaring to open up.

★★★★★ **Sauvignon Blanc** This version of Diemersdal's speciality variety is aged 9 months in 500-litre, 50% new barrels. **13** is opulent & powerful, with great class & complexity; the oaking is detectable but well integrated, supporting flavours of orange zest & passionfruit.

Reserve range

★★★★ **Grenache** Fragrant & fresh cherry & red berry aromas. **13** vibrant, older oak not obscuring the fruit. Still tight, should start opening up around 2015. Previously was **11** (★★★★).

★★★★ **Pinotage** Rich & generous **13** shows plenty of plum, spice & toasty oak. Well balanced, fresh, & with intense fruit & tannin. Shows promising complexity but needs time to integrate the oak.

★★★★ **Private Collection** Cassis, redcurrant & dusty capsicum show on **12** (★★★☆) cab-led 5-way Bordeaux blend. Subtle, structured, sensitively oaked, but slightly lean - as was **11**. Needs time.

★★★★ **Chardonnay** Lemon curd & honeysuckle emerge on **13** (★★★★), well supported by 30% new oak, with classic flavours of vanilla, ripe melon & yellow apple. **12** showed toasty oak.

★★★★☆ **Sauvignon Blanc** ⊘ Rather closed & restrained 6 months post harvest, but good under-lying fruit & structure. Unwooded **14** aromatic hints of subtle capsicum, blackcurrant & green tropical fruit. Saline quality on palate, with a crystalline purity & good finish.

★★★★☆ **8 Rows Sauvignon Blanc** Finely chiselled & concentrated **14** had 5 months on lees in stainless steel for extra depth & texture. Lifted palate with great vigour & presence, notes of crushed stone, blackcurrant & even mint.

Diemersdal Estate range

★★★★ **Pinotage** Star of this range. Spiced plum, red fruit & subtle smoke characters. **13** altogether well managed, fine tannin & open fruit allowing early consumption with keepability.

★★★★ **Shiraz** Promising & typical smoky, peppery, meaty aromas on **13** (★★★★). Soft & approach-able, flavourful though a bit lacklustre, less concentrated than **12**. Big alcohol, like other reds.

★★★★ **Sauvignon Blanc** ⊘ **14** loaded with zesty lime & passionfruit - raises the bar on **13** (★★★). Thirst-quenching palate not all that complex but fresh tropical flavours & crisp finish.

★★★★ **Grüner Veltliner** (NEW) Altogether welcome example of rare (here) Austrian variety. **13** spicy, floral & tropical fruit aromas. Vibrant, fresh, unoaked palate interwoven with white pepper.

Also tasted: **Merlot 13** ★★★☆ **Sauvignon Rosé 14** ★★☆ **Chardonnay Unwooded 14** ★★★☆

Matys range

Cabernet Sauvignon-Merlot ★★★ Light-hearted & delicious **13**, uncomplicated fresh berry fruit & tobacco notes. WO W Cape, like Sauvignon. Also tasted: **Sauvignon Blanc 14** ★★★ — JPf

Location: Durbanville ▪ Map: Durbanville, Philadelphia & Darling ▪ WO: Durbanville/Western Cape ▪ Est 1698 ▪ 1stB 1976 ▪ Tasting & sales Mon-Sat/pub hols 9–5 Sun 10–3 ▪ Closed Easter Fri, Dec 25 & Jan 1 ▪ Cellar tours by appt ▪ Diemersdal farm eatery ▪ Owner(s) Tienie Louw ▪ Winemaker(s) Thys Louw & Mari Branders ▪ Viticulturist(s) Div van Niekerk (1980) ▪ 210ha (cab, grenache, malbec, merlot, mourv, p verdot, ptage, shiraz, chard, grüner veltliner, sauv) ▪ 2,100t 70% red 30% white ▪ BWI, BRC, HACCIP ▪ PO Box 27 Durbanville 7551 ▪ thys@diemersdal.co.za ▪ www.diemersdal.co.za ▪ S 33° 48' 6.3" E 018° 38' 25.1" ▪ **T +27 (0)21-976-3361**

Diemersfontein Wines

The 18th-century Wellington fruit farm that had been in the family since the early 40s was sending grapes to the local cooperative when owners David and Susan Sonnenberg returned home from the UK in 2000. Seizing the day, the couple set about developing the estate, its staff and the local community, and now Diemersfontein is endowed with a full-scale hospitality offering, employee empowerment wine business Thokozani, and burgeoning reputation as a top-end producer. Pinotage is a particular focus and success, with many accolades including Drinks International's World's Best Wine Event 2014 for the Pinotage-on-Tap festival, dedicated to the coffee-toned Diemersfontein Pinotage.

Carpe Diem Reserve range

★★★★ **Malbec** Ⓑ Blueberry, roasted coffee & nutmeg profile of **11** finds counterpoint & balance in its lithe tannin structure; a beautifully elegant finish.

★★★★☆ **Pinotage** Deep, rich & powerful, a serious expression of the variety. Super **12** packed with lavish dark fruit, heady oak vanilla & warm 14% alcohol, but layered in an oh-so-sleek composition. Like **11**, 70% new oak (French & American) does not detract.

★★★★☆ **Chenin Blanc** Bold & beautiful in New World style, partly barrel-fermented & oozing tropical fruit in creamy texture. Now bottled, **12** (★★★★) not quite dry, shade off impressive **11**.

★★★★ **Viognier** ⓥ Bang for your buck. Peach & apricot flavours glide over fragrant oak (30% barrel fermented, 30% new) in upfront **12**; luscious, now semi-dry.

Diemersfontein range

Pinotage ★★★★ The original 'coffee pinotage', going strong at 40,000 cases. Sweet plummy generosity in **13**, with choc-mocha sheen from lots of oak. Needs a plump steak to please. **Shiraz** ★★★★ Juicy mulberry fruit & white pepper/allspice of **13** in harmony with supple tannins. More integrated than previous. **For The Birds White** ★★★ Previewed last time, **13** is nicely rounded now. Chenin & sauvignon with 10% viognier. Sales benefit BirdLife South Africa, as for red partner. Also tasted: **Cabernet Sauvignon 12** ★★★ **For The Birds Red 12** ★★★ **Summer's Lease 12** ★★★☆ Not retasted: **Maiden's Prayer Red 12** ★★☆ **Chenin Blanc 13** ★★★☆ **Maiden's Prayer White 13** ★★★ — DS

Location/WO: Wellington • Map: Paarl & Wellington • Est 2000 • 1stB 2001 • Tasting & sales daily 10–5 • Closed Dec 25 • Cellar tours by appt • Seasons Restaurant • Tour groups • Conferences • Weddings • Walks/hikes • 3-star Diemersfontein Country House • Owner(s) David & Susan Sonnenberg • Winemaker(s) Francois Roode (Sep 2003), with Lauren Hulsman (Nov 2011) • Viticulturist(s) Waldo Kellerman (Aug 2007) • 180ha/60ha (cabs s/f, grenache, malbec, mourv, p verdot, ptage, roobernet, shiraz, chenin, viog) • 600t/80,000cs own label 90% red 10% white • BWI, HACCP • PO Box 41 Wellington 7654 • wine@diemersfontein.co.za • www.diemersfontein.co.za • S 33° 39' 41.1" E 019° 0' 31.1" • F +27 (0)21-864-2095 • **T +27 (0)21-864-5050**

☐ **Die Tweede Droom** *see* Groot Parys Estate

Dieu Donné Vineyards

This French-Mauritian-owned mountainside winery produces consistently awarded reds, whites and méthode cap classique sparkling made by longtime winemaker (and Cape Wine Master) Stephan du Toit. Other visitor-friendly attractions, including a restaurant and an onsite micro brewery, have made it a popular stop on the Franschhoek Wine Tram route.

Location/map: Franschhoek • Est 1984 • 1stB 1986 • Tasting & sales Mon-Fri 9–4 Sat/Sun 10.30–4 • Fee R15 • Closed Dec 25 & Jan 1 • Cellar tours Mon-Fri by appt • Cheese platters • Gifts • Micro beer brewery • Roca Restaurant • Owner(s) Robert Maingard • Cellarmaster(s)/winemaker(s) Stephan du Toit (May 1996) • Viticulturist(s) Hennie du Toit (Apr 1988) • 40ha (cab, merlot, shiraz, chard, sauv, viog) • ±280t/33,000cs own label 60% red 32% white 3% rosé 5% MCC • PO Box 94 Franschhoek 7690 • info@dieudonnevineyards.com • www.dieudonnevineyards.com • S 33° 53' 46.9" E 019° 7' 45.0" • F +27 (0)21-876-2102 • **T +27 (0)21-876-2493**

Diners Club Bartho Eksteen Academy

Cape Winemakers Guild member Bartho Eksteen and wife Suné started this wine academy at Bartho's Paarl alma mater, Boland Agricultural High School, with Diners Club sponsorship after Bartho had won Diners Club Winemaker of the Year in 2010. The wines produced from the 3-year winemaking course are sold to help fund the project, which has now extended to wine service, tasting and international wine industry knowledge. Note: Platter's Guide is a wholly owned subsidiary of Diners Club.

★★★★ **Wijnskool Shiraz** Going up a notch on **11** (★★★★), **12** inviting bright ruby glow, with brooding aromas of blackberry, chocolate, violets & pepper. Lush, with terrific acid spine giving a lifted goodbye.

★★★★☆ **CWG Auction Reserve Sluitsteen Shiraz** ⓝⒺⓦ **12** is kaleidoscopic, with astonishingly perfumed nose of violet essence, dark berries & cured meat. Polished tannins, terrific depth of fruit & oak spice (50% new) in harmony. Finishes very long with a vibrant blackberry lift.

★★★★ **Wijnskool Sauvignon Blanc** Fragrant, with piquant aromas of capsicum, grapefruit & fresh pineapple, **13** rich & expansive, with a generous texture & steely backbone. Noteworthy energy from Upper Hemel-en-Aarde vines.

★★★★★ **CWG Auction Reserve Vloekskoot Sauvignon Blanc** ⓃⒺⓌ Bunch-pressed, naturally (older) oak-fermented **13** starts with scents of a spring meadow, then tangy citrus & granadilla to fresh thyme & salty minerals. Spicy, sharply focused & complex; great depth & clarity. Hemel-en-Aarde fruit. Also tasted: **Wijnskool Veraison Méthode Cap Classique NV** ★★★☆ Discontinued: **Wijnskool Chenin Blanc**. — WB

Location: Paarl/Hermanus ▪ Map: Paarl & Wellington ▪ WO: Paarl/Upper Hemel-en-Aarde Valley/Western Cape/ Hemel-en-Aarde Valley ▪ Est/1stB 2011 ▪ Tasting, sales & cellar tours by appt ▪ Walks/hikes ▪ Nature reserve ▪ Owner(s) Bartho & Suné Eksteen ▪ Cellarmaster(s) Bartho Eksteen (Feb 2011) ▪ Winemaker(s) Bartho Eksteen (Feb 2011), with Pieter Willem Eksteen (Jan 2012) & learners at Hoër Landbouskool Boland ▪ Viticulturist(s) Willie van der Linde (Hoër Landbouskool Boland); Pieter Carstens (De Bos Estate, Hermanus); bought in grapes ▪ 11t/1,500cs own label 43% red 42% white 15% MCC ▪ PO Box 1999 Hermanus 7200 ▪ bartho@hermanus.co.za, sune@hermanus.co.za ▪ www.wijnskool.co.za ▪ S 33° 39' 11.45" E 018° 52' 59.77" ▪ F +27 (0)86-554-0896 ▪ **T +27 (0)28-312-4612**

Dispore Kamma Boutique Winery 💡

Philip Mostert and Hannes Coetzee have written themselves a leave of absence note from their after-hours-only 'job' of vinifying and marketing a highly regarded shiraz. But the Caledon-based medicos have back vintages to sell, and a Michelangelo Best Garagiste Wine trophy to inspire them to make 'quality part of our dream' as soon as circumstances allow.

Location: Caledon ▪ Map: Elgin, Walker Bay & Bot River ▪ Est/1stB 2002 ▪ Tasting, sales & cellar tours by appt ▪ Owner(s) Philip Mostert & Hannes Coetzee ▪ Winemaker(s) Philip Mostert (Jan 2002), with Hannes Coetzee (Jun 2002) ▪ 150cs own label 100% red ▪ PO Box 272 Caledon 7230 ▪ disporekamma@overnet.co.za ▪ S 34° 13' 40.2" E 019° 25' 10.5" ▪ F +27 (0)28-214-1077 ▪ **T +27 (0)28-212-1096**

Distell

Helmed by MD Richard Rushton, Distell is Africa's largest producer of wines, spirits, ciders and RTDs, and the SA leader with 21% value share of the total local liquor market. From its Stellenbosch headquaters, Distell vinifies some of South Africa's most successful and enduring brands. They include: 4th Street, Cold Duck (5th Avenue), Autumn Harvest Crackling, Capenheimer, Cellar Cask, Chateau Libertas, Chatta Box, Drostdy-Hof, Fleur du Cap, Graça, Grand Mousseux, Grünberger, Ixia, Kellerprinz, Kupferberger Auslese, Libertas, Monis and its sherry-style wines, Obikwa, Oom Tas, Overmeer, Place in the Sun, Pongrácz, RED ESCape, Sedgwick's sherry-style, Ship, Tassenberg, Taverna Rouge, Two Oceans, Virginia and Zonnebloem. Distell also owns the House of JC le Roux, a dedicated sparkling-wine cellar in Devon Valley. Then there are the stand-alone 'estate' labels: Nederburg, Plaisir de Merle and Lomond. Distell is also the co-owner, together with Lusan Holdings, of top Stellenbosch properties Alto, Le Bonheur, Neethlingshof, Stellenzicht/Hill & Dale, Uitkyk/Flat Roof Manor, and, with several local growers, of Durbanville Hills. Distell also has agreements with independently owned cellars Allesverloren, Jacobsdal and Theuniskraal to provide a range of services. Finally, there's the black empowerment venture on Papkuilsfontein farm near Darling, source of Earthbound wines. Brandy labels include Chateau VO Extra Fine, Collison's, Commando, Klipdrift, Flight of the Fish Eagle, Limosin, Mellow-Wood, Olof Bergh Solera, Oude Meester, Richelieu, Van Ryn and Viceroy. See Die Bergkelder for details about the Vinoteque Wine Bank, and separate entries for most of the above.

Stellenbosch ▪ PO Box 184 Stellenbosch 7599 ▪ info@distell.co.za ▪ www.distell.co.za ▪ **T +27 (0)21-809-7000**

☐ **Dixon's Peak** *see* Waverley Hills Organic Wines & Olives
☐ **Dolphin Bay** *see* Wines of Cape Town
☐ **Dolphin Sands** *see* Wines of Cape Town

Domaine Brahms Wineries 💡 📷

Gesie and Johan van Deventer's Paarl Mountain foothills property is farmed as sustainably as possible, counting carbon emissions and offsetting them by extensive tree planting. A wedding and conference venue is set among the vines, from which Gesie produces a small quantity of mostly red wine, though this edition it's the long-untasted white that really shines.

★★★★ **Shiraz 10** improves on **08** (★★★☆) with lots of concentrated dark-berried fruit & hints of sweaty leather. Silky tannins, lower alcohol make for thoroughly enjoyable wine. **09** untasted.

★★★★ **Chenin Blanc** ⊘ Truly lovely **13**, first tasted since **06** (★★★★), floats softly & delicately into play with plenty of lively pineapples & cream touched by the gentlest of oak (15% new). Lots of tropical notes throughout & a refreshing finish.

Quartet ★★★★ **12** now a merlot-dominated Bordeaux blend. Brightly-fruited, soft & enticing.

Unwooded Chenin Blanc ★★★ Fruity notes of pineappple, candyfloss, bubblegum on appealing **14**. Zesty & bright for summer sipping. Also tasted: **Cabernet Sauvignon 10** ★★★ **Sonato 11** ★★ Not tasted: **Merlot, Pinotage.** — CM

Location/WO: Paarl • Map: Paarl & Wellington • Est 1998 • 1stB 1999 • Tasting & tours (vyd/cellar/wine) by appt • Fee R5/wine • Chapel & wedding/function venue • Owner(s) Johan & Gesie van Deventer • Winemaker(s)/viticulturist(s) Gesie van Deventer (1998) • 12ha (cab, merlot, ptage, shiraz, chenin) • 30,000L 90% red 10% white • PO Box 2136 Windmeul 7630 • brahms@iafrica.com • www.domainebrahms.co.za • S 33° 40' 27.28" E 18° 53' 29.24" • F +27 (0)86-614-9445 • **T +27 (0)21-869-8555**

Domaine Coutelier

Inspiration for the wines made (with advisers) by UK-born businessman Quint Cutler comes from Bordeaux, among others, hence the 1,400 new carmenère vines, among the first in South Africa, at the Devon Valley domaine. The tasting venue is now fully operational, and an on-site boutique cellar is planned. Quint's aim is to cater for all consumers and budgets, and to this end an undisclosed new range was due around press time, with a Reserve du Vigneron label debuting early this year.

Feast range

★★★★ **Chardonnay 13** from Durbanville in showy style, with plenty of aroma & flavour (lemon, nut, oatmeal), supported by fairly discreet oak & a powerful acidity. Good long lemony finish.

Cabernet Sauvignon (NEW) ★★★☆ **12** in house's massive, chunky, powerful style, but less strident than the Merlot. Strong tannin structure partly from 85% new oak, but the savoury fruit just survives. A few years might bring more harmony. **Merlot** (NEW) ★★★ Plenty of very ripe berry fruit mixed with tarry tobacco (ex 60% new oak) on big, powerful, solid **12**. Like Cab, from Stellenbosch. **Méthode Cap Classique** (NEW) ★★★ Some oxidative mustiness & rather brief flavours on mid-gold **12** sparkling from chardonnay & pinot. — TJ

Location/map: Stellenbosch • WO: Coastal/Stellenbosch • Est/1stB 2012 • Tasting, sales & cellar tours by appt • Closed all pub hols • Owner(s) Quint Cutler • Winemaker(s) Quint Cutler (March 2013), with consultants • Viticulturist(s) Kevin Watt (May 2013, consultant) • 4ha/3.5ha (cab, carmenère, merlot) • ±21t/2,300cs own label 70% red 10% white 10% rosé 10% MCC • PO Box 346 Stellenbosch 7599 • quint.cutler@gmail.com • www.domainecoutelier. com • S 33° 54'2.80"E 018° 47'58.46" • **T +27 (0)79-498-0772**

Domaine des Dieux

The Parnell family vineyards, poetically named 'Home of the Gods', in the Babylonstoren foothills benefit from their elevation and proximity to the ocean. Since buying the farm in the Hemel-en-Aarde Ridge ward in 2002, the owners have planted an assortment of varieties, using early-bearing clones to ensure ripeness in the cool conditions. The wines, by contracted specialists, have expanded from a debut MCC sparkling to non-bubbly varietals and a blend. An on-site cellar is a year or two away.

★★★★ **Syrah-Mourvèdre 12** (★★★) tightly buttoned & lean, nothing like intense **11**. Piquant red fruit veined by really fresh acidity, may settle & bloom given time.

★★★★ **Sauvignon Blanc** After flinty & herbaceous **11**, **12** (★★★) is tropical & lighter toned, tangy acidity underpinning a summer-styled easy-drinker with clean dry limy farewell.

★★★★★ **Rose of Sharon MCC Brut Rosé** Sweeter, more gregarious bubbles in 09 (★★★) than 08, pale sunset orange with fresh berry/cherry tone, frothy & with no great depth but perfect for summer get-togethers & celebrations.

★★★★ **Claudia Brut MCC** 09 sparkling from undisclosed varieties. Lovely fresh apple, toasted nut & brioche flavours, mouthfilling, with creamy lees undertone. Shows refined balance, ready to enjoy with potential to age few years.

Also tasted: **Josephine Pinot Noir 12** ★★★ Not retasted: **Chardonnay 11** ★★★☆ — MW

Location: Hermanus ▪ Map: Elgin, Walker Bay & Bot River ▪ WO: Hemel-en-Aarde Ridge/Walker Bay/Walker Bay/Elgin ▪ Est 2002 ▪ 1stB 2006 ▪ Tasting & sales at the vineyards Tue-Sun 11-4.30 ▪ Closed Easter Fri/Sun, Dec 25 & Jan 1 ▪ Owner(s) Domaine des Dieux (Pty) Ltd ▪ Winemaker(s) Specialists ▪ Vineyard manager Petrus Bothma ▪ Viticulturist(s) Johan Pienaar ▪ 28ha/20ha (pinot, shiraz & other red varieties, chard, sauv) ▪ 15,000cs own label 25% red 25% white 50% MCC ▪ PO Box 2082 Hermanus 7200 ▪ info@domainedesdieux.co.za ▪ www.domainedesdieux.co.za ▪ S 34° 19' 35.81" E 019° 19' 50.71" ▪ F +27 (0)87-230-6286 ▪ **T +27 (0)28-313-2126/+27 (0)83-536-5916**

Dombeya Wines

Named after a scented indigenous tree, Dombeya has been in the hands of American Preston Haskell since 2002, and operating from a purpose-built cellar under the aegis of Rianie Strydom since 2005. (Sibling brand Haskell Vineyards also vinified there.) Well worth a visit, the family-friendly estate's amenities include the convivial Long Table Restaurant and luxury self-catering accommodation.

★★★★ **Merlot** Velvety 12 is restrained yet generous, as was last-tasted 09. Sleek, fine tannins & harmonious balance of fruit & oak (30% new). 10 & 11 sold out untasted.

★★★★ **Boulder Road Shiraz** 11 follows tone of 09, full of inky cherry & plum delight. Sinewy, with Rhôneish twist of pepper. Layered, with brooding power lurking deep. 10 sold out untasted.

★★★★ **Fenix** Was 'Altus '. 09 retains cab in Bordeaux-style mix with merlot & malbec support. Pared down, elegant & restrained, with squeeze of dry tannin & herb, cocoa notes. Deep, rich & long aftertaste, like rewarding 08.

★★★★ **Chardonnay** 13 mirrors restraint & focus of 12. Lovely citrus vibrancy within focused oak frame. Fresh & succulent, with broad, structured palate.

Also tasted: **Sauvignon Blanc 14** ★★★☆ Discontinued: **Cabernet Sauvignon**. — FM

Location/map: Stellenbosch ▪ WO: Stellenbosch/Western Cape ▪ Est 2005 ▪ 1stB 2006 ▪ Tasting & sales Tue-Fri 9-5 Sat/Sun 10-5 ▪ Fee R40 ▪ Closed Mon, Easter Fri-Mon & Dec 25 ▪ Cellar tours on special request only ▪ The Long Table Restaurant & Café: Tue-Sun 9-5; dinner Fri (Sep-Mar) - booking essential ▪ Facilities for children ▪ Self-catering accommodation in The Residence and Cottage ▪ Owner(s) Preston Haskell ▪ Cellarmaster(s) Rianie Strydom (Jan 2005) ▪ Viticulturist(s) Wikus Pretorius (Dec 2005) ▪ 25ha/13.5ha (cabs s/f, merlot, shiraz, chard) ▪ ±80t/15,000cs own label 80% red 20% white ▪ PO Box 12766 Die Boord 7613 ▪ info@dombeyawines.com ▪ www.dombeyawines. com ▪ S 34° 0' 13.9" E 018° 51' 38.4" ▪ F +27 (0)21-881-3986 ▪ **T +27 (0)21-881-3895**

Domein Doornkraal

Urbane septuagenarian Swepie le Roux and daughter Celia le Roux Mostert respectively shape the wines and vines at the family's multi-enterprise farm near De Rust. Their upgraded roadside emporium showcases not only the Doornkraal range but all the labels of both Klein and Groot Karoo. 'We introduce visitors to wines they've never heard of,' Celia says. 'So much more interesting than beer ;-)'

★★★★ **Kaptein** Multi-vintage amber-hued oaked muscadel NV dessert has sherry's 'tealeaf' aromas, saline finish, tawny port's dried fruit flavours. Ends unusually but nicely dry.

Pinta ★★★ Fortified 4-variety sweet red wine with a fruitcake character, rich & full bodied, pruney & syrupy. Latest NV needs friends around a campfire. **Tanige Port** ★★★☆ Unusual dated tawny portstyle from tinta & touriga, 8 years in barrel. 92 (!) prunes & wild honey aromas, savoury/toasty tastes. Very sweet, full bodied with long almost malty finish. No finesse but gets your attention. Also tasted: **Majoor NV** ★★★ **Luitenant NV** ★★★ **Jerepigo NV** ★★★ — CR, CvZ

Location: De Rust ▪ Map: Klein Karoo & Garden Route ▪ WO: Klein Karoo ▪ Est 1880 ▪ 1stB 1973 ▪ Tasting & sales Mon-Fri 9-5 Sat 9-3 ▪ Closed Easter Fri/Sun & Dec 25 ▪ Light refreshments ▪ Farm produce ▪ Gifts ▪ Conference facility on farm ▪ Self-catering farm cottages & lodge ▪ Owner(s) Swepie, Piet & Celia le Roux ▪ Cellarmaster(s) Swepie le Roux (Apr 2011) ▪ Winemaker(s) Swepie le Roux ▪ Viticulturist(s) Celia le Roux Mostert ▪ 2,000ha/10ha (cab, merlot, muscadel, ptage, chard, chenin, cbard) ▪ 105t/4,000cs own label 15% red 15% white 70% fortified ▪ PO Box 14 De Rust 6650 ▪ wyn@doornkraal.co.za ▪ www.doornkraal.co.za ▪ S 33° 32' 43.5" E 022° 26' 42.6" ▪ F +27 (0)86-528-5633 ▪ **T +27 (0)44-251-6715**

☐ **Donatus** *see* Dornier Wines

Donkiesbaai

Rust en Vrede owner Jean Engelbrecht adroitly combines a number of elements and trends - a family heritage backstory, 'proudly Afrikaans' product naming, inspired packaging and, by no means least, outstanding winemaking - in this boutique brand, honouring the West Coast reserve (Donkin - 'Donkey' - Bay) where four generations of Engelbrechts have vacationed, glass of cold chenin in hand.

★★★★ **Pinot Noir** (NEW) Stellar debut for **13** with bright cherry vibrancy tempered by cracked pepper spicing. Powerful yet delicate & steely - the pinot paradox expressed via Ceres Plateau fruit, ably framed by year older French oak. Great palate length.

★★★★☆ **Steen 13** tones down ripeness on **12**, not at the expense of fruit expression from venerable 1979 Piekenierskloof chenin. Rich, ripe & creamy yet freshly elegant. Honeyed peach notes but dry, rounded & full from partial ferment in older oak. Focused & lively throughout.

★★★★☆ **Hooiwijn** Nectar of the (chenin) gods, **13** (★★★★) rich & tad sweeter than debut **12** yet still vivacious. Piekenierskloof fruit (same block as Steen) air-dried on straw ('hooi' in Afrikaans). Lighter in alcohol (10.5%) & acid, though sun-dried pineapple & apricot beauty lingers. — FM

Location/map: Stellenbosch ▪ WO: Piekenierskloof/Ceres Plateau ▪ Est/1stB 2011 ▪ Tasting & sales at Guardian Peak (see entry) ▪ Owner(s) Jean Engelbrecht ▪ Winemaker(s) Coenie Snyman & Philip van Staden (both Jan 2011) ▪ Viticulturist(s) Dirkie Mouton (Jan 2011) ▪ 15t/1,200cs own label 50% red 50% white ▪ PO Box 473 Stellenbosch 7599 ▪ info@donkiesbaai.com ▪ www.donkiesbaai.com ▪ S 34° 0' 40.19" E 018° 50' 31.99" ▪ F +27 (0)21-881-3000 ▪ **T +27 (0)21-881-3881**

☐ **Don Morris** *see* Govert Wines

Doolhof Wine Estate

Named 'Labyrinth' after its many hills and vales, this venerable (1707) Wellington estate was acquired by the Kerrison family in 2003 and transformed into a showcase, with a new modern cellar, refurbished tasting venue and numerous amenities such as the 5-star Grand Dédale Country House. New in the extensive wine portfolio is an excellent red blend honouring Doolhof's first winemaker.

Legends of the Labyrinth range

★★★★ **The Minotaur** (🔍) Back on track after **08** (★★★☆), showy **09** has curves to spare. Spicy dark fruit & thanks to pinotage, merlot, shiraz & malbec which comprise most of the blend, it is rich, power packed.

★★★★ **1712 Jacques Potier** (NEW) Merlot-led, with 4 other Bordeaux varieties plus pinotage. **09** deeply rich, dark plums, vanilla, creamy coffee, the body smoothly juicy. Good grip from 2 years French barrels.

Theseus (NEW) ★★★★ Classic 5-variety Bordeaux blend, merlot-led. Black plums & cherries, Marmite, vanilla perfume is opulent, rich. **09**'s juicy fruit counterbalances the savoury firm tannins; there's enough grip for a further 6+ years ageing. Also tasted: **Lady in Red 09** ★★★ **Dark Lady 12** ★★★
Not retasted: **Lady in White 10** ★★★

Signatures of Doolhof range

★★★★ **Cabernet Franc** ⓐ **09** has attractive cedary oak, tart red berry, floral perfume & earthy complexity. Juicy, but balanced by vinosity & fine tannin grip. Stays fresh though big alcohol & few grams sugar.

Malbec ★★★★ Perfumed black plums, almost pruney richness dusted with cocoa, but **11**'s palate is livelier, berry-fresh, has attractive drinkability without being a pushover, the tannin support shows on the finish. **Merlot** ★★★★ Hedonistic creamy fruitcake perfume, becoming more savoury on the palate, just what meat dishes need. **11** has enough tannin grip for 4+ years ageing. **Sauvignon Blanc** ★★★★ Trademark flintiness with green edges positions **13** as an ideal shellfish wine, yet sufficient body for solo drinking. Also tasted: **Cabernet Sauvignon 11** ★★★ **Chardonnay Unwooded 12** ★★★ Not retasted: **Petit Verdot 09** ★★★★ **Shiraz 08** ★★★★ **Renaissance Cabernet Sauvignon-Merlot 07** ★★★★ **Chardonnay Wooded 09** ★★★★ Not tasted: **Pinotage**.

Cape range

Loerie Rosé ⑭ ★★ Dry **13** mainly grenache, shiraz, giving strawberry tones, rounded, fruity drinkability. WO W Cape, like next. **Crane Chenin Blanc** ⑭ ★★★ Pear drops & passionfruit, rounded mouthfeel, **13** finishing sufficiently light & dry for casual quaffing or food matching. Not retasted: **Boar 12** ★★★ **Eagle 10** ★★★ Discontinued: **Roan, Robin, Loerie**. — CR

Location: Wellington ▪ Map: Paarl & Wellington ▪ WO: Wellington/Western Cape ▪ Est 1995 ▪ 1stB 2003 ▪ Tasting & sales Mon-Sat 10–5 Sun 10-4 ▪ Fee R20/5 wines ▪ Closed Good Fri, Dec 25/26 & Jan 1 ▪ Cellar tours by appt ▪ Light lunches Tue-Sun 11-3; picnics by appt; wine & canapé pairings by pre-booking ▪ Conferences ▪ Walks/hikes ▪ Mountain biking & 4x4 trails ▪ 5-star Grand Dédale Country House ▪ Owner(s) Dennis Kerrison ▪ Cellarmaster(s) Gielie Beukes (Aug 2014) ▪ Winemaker(s) Gielie Beukes (Aug 2014) & Rianie Strydom (consultant) ▪ Viticulturist(s) Hendrik Laubscher (Aug 1996) ▪ 380ha/38ha (cabs s/f, malbec, merlot, p verdot, ptage, shiraz, chard, sauv) ▪ 300t/24,000cs own label 73% red 26% white 1% rosé ▪ BWI, IPW, WIETA ▪ PO Box 157 Wellington 7654 ▪ wine@doolhof.com ▪ www.doolhof.com ▪ S 33° 37' 35.6" E 019° 4' 58.7" ▪ F +27 (0)21-864-2321 ▪ **T +27 (0)21-873-6911**

Doran Vineyards

After selling his UK travel business, Irishman Edwin Doran bought the Voor Paardeberg farm Far Horizons and the Horse Mountain brand that went with it in 2010. He asked his old friend André Badenhorst, who had a hand in setting up the top Constantia wineries Buitenverwachting and Constantia Uitsig, to come on board and the renaissance of the property continues apace.

Doran Vineyards range

★★★★ **Chenin Blanc** ⓐ **12** peach (& its kernel), some nice yeasty character. Good richness, tangy acidity, savoury finish. Understated but not middle of the road. Swartland WO.

Pinotage ⓐ ★★★ **12** comes in an uncomplicated, fruit-driven style. Red & black cherry, vaguest hint of vanilla, fresh acidity. Not retasted: **Shiraz 12** ★★★ **The Romy D 12** ★★★ **Rosie D** **Pinotage Rosé 13** ★★

Horse Mountain range

Not tasted: **Pinotage, Shiraz, Michele, Chenin Blanc-Viognier**. — CvZ

Location: Paarl ▪ Map: Paarl & Wellington ▪ WO: Voor Paardeberg/Swartland ▪ Est 2010 ▪ 1stB 2012 ▪ Tasting Mon-Fri by appt Sat/Sun & pub hols 10-4 ▪ Closed Good Fri, Dec 25/26 & Jan 1 ▪ Owner(s) Edwin Doran & André Badenhorst ▪ Winemaker(s) Martin Lamprecht ▪ Viticulturist(s) Basson Potgieter ▪ 170ha/50ha (cabs s/f, merlot, ptage, shiraz) ▪ 450t/30,000cs own label ▪ PO Box 2143 Windmeul 7630 ▪ andrebad@iafrica.com ▪ www.doranvineyards.co.za ▪ S 33° 34' 56.12" E018° 51' 59.15" ▪ F +27 (0)21-869-8329 ▪ **T +27 (0)21-869-8328**

☐ **Doreen** *see* Teddy Hall Wines

Dormershire Estate

Frost family boutique winery Dormershire is an oasis of vines in suburban Kuils River. With the departure of the full-time winemaker, the old team of co-owner Sunette Frost and adviser Kowie du Toit have returned to winemaking duty. Another reminder of the early years at this mainly red-wine estate is the Stoep Shiraz, so named because when grapes were first harvested, the cellar wasn't ready and the barrelled wine ended up maturing on the Frosts' veranda.

Stoep Shiraz ⓥ ★★★ Wood here a toasty backdrop, **07** earthy & savoury blackberry fruit, pepper seasoning. **Cabernet Sauvignon-Shiraz** ⓥ ★★★★ **07** has this estate's Old World character: peppery/dusty notes, cherry flavours & firm tannins. Not retasted: **Cabernet Sauvignon 07 ★★★★ Reserve Cabernet Sauvignon 07 ★★★★ Shiraz 07 ★★★ Sweet Red NV ★★★★** Not tasted: **Rosé, Sauvignon Blanc**. — DB

Location: Kuils River ▪ Map/WO: Stellenbosch ▪ Est 1996 ▪ 1stB 2001 ▪ Tasting, sales & tours by appt only ▪ Closed all pub hols ▪ Owner(s) SPF Family Trust ▪ Winemaker(s) Sunette Frost & Kowie du Toit ▪ Viticulturist(s) Johan Pienaar (consultant) ▪ 8ha/6ha (cab, shiraz, sauv) ▪ ±50t/8,000cs own label 85% red 10% white 5% rosé ▪ PO Box 491 Bellville 7535 ▪ wine@dormershire.co.za ▪ www.dormershire.com ▪ S 33° 56' 27.0" E 018° 42' 54.7" ▪ F +27 (0)21-945-1174 ▪ **T +27 (0)21-801-4677/4991**

Dornier Wines

The focus on classic varieties is no accident at this visually stunning Stellenbosch winery, because the owners are Swiss - the Dornier family, with the cellar design the work of late founder and artist Christoph Dornier. Extensive and ongoing research and experimentation has gone into finding the right soil, climate and clone match for each variety — the farm includes mountain slopes and has terroir diversity - and the results are reflected in the wines. The exceptions being pinotage and rare-planted tempranillo - both are in the line-up because terroir compatibility was found.

Founders range

★★★★★ **CMD** Elegant flagship with malbec (80%) leading cab franc & petit verdot, 50% new oak in **12**. Spiced plums, cherry & fresh herbs; plushness reined in by firm, dry tannic finish. Like concentrated **11**, will reward cellaring up to a decade.

Donatus range

★★★★★ **Red 11** (★★★★) 4-way Bordeaux blend with cab (43%) main component; 30% new oak noticeable in toasted vanilla notes to brooding dark fruit & sweet spice. Serious structure from 30% petit verdot, attractive graphite focus & grip, as in more elegant **10**.

★★★★ **White** Unusual blend chenin (75%) & semillon. **13** (★★★★★) intricate bouquet of apricot, marmalade, green fruit, white flowers & hints of well-judged oak (25% new), equally arresting palate. Step up on **11**, serious & elegant, commendably savoury & long. Some Swartland fruit.

Dornier range

★★★★ **Cabernet Sauvignon** ⓥ Complex **07**'s dark plum centre shows dried herb, allspice, fynbos nuances. Tannins are supple with a backbone for good few more years.

★★★★ **Malbec** Ripe black fruit with savoury dryness & mouthcoating tannins in **12** (★★★★). Spicy, firm acidity, dry finish; but shade less polished than **11**.

★★★★ **Pinotage 12**'s (★★★) varietally-true bramble, smoke & banana combine neatly with ripe mulberries, slight meaty, savoury edges. Similar serious tannic grip as **11** but not the same depth or ageing potential.

Also tasted: **Tempranillo 12 ★★★ Cabernet Sauvignon-Merlot 12 ★★★★ Chenin Blanc Bush Vine 13 ★★★★** Not retasted: **Merlot 07 ★★★★** Not tasted: **Semillon, Froschkoenig Natural Sweet**.

Cocoa Hill range

Rosé ⊕ ★★★ Attractive light, salmon-coloured **14** from merlot has vibrant freshness, delicious red berry purity & dry drinkability. Best buy in this range. **Sauvignon Blanc** ★★★ Brisk, light & dry **14**, steely, with mouthwatering green apple freshness, flavours. Also tasted: **Red 12** ★★★ **Chenin Blanc 14** ★★★ — HJ

Location/map: Stellenbosch • WO: Stellenbosch/Western Cape/Swartland • Est 1995 • 1stB 2002 • Tasting & sales daily 10-5 • Cellar tours by appt • Dornier Bodega Restaurant: lunch daily 12-5 dinner (Oct-Apr) Thu-Sat • Facilities for children • Gift shop • Conference venue • Conservation area • Homestead with 6 bedrooms & large entertainment areas offered • Owner(s) Dornier family • Winemaker(s) Jeanine Craven (Mar 2012) • Viticulturist(s) Theunis Bell (Sep 2009) • 180ha/55ha (cabs s/f, malbec, merlot, p verdot, ptage, shiraz, tempranillo, chenin, sauv, sem) • 350t 65% red 28% white 7% rosé • PO Box 7518 Stellenbosch 7599 • info@dornier.co.za • www.dornier.co.za • S 33° 59' 31.00" E 018° 52' 19.00" • F +27 (0)21-880-1499 • **T +27 (0)21-880-0557**

Dorrance Wines ⊕ ⑪

Christophe Durand arrived from France in 1995 to import barrels, but soon started buying in grapes – they now come from diverse terroirs across the Cape - and latterly vinifying them in a fully equipped cellar, with production and maturation facilities plus a tasting room and wine shop, in Cape Town city centre. Classically oriented, with a stylish je ne sais quoi, his wines salute his daughters Ameena and Anaïs, with Kama ('sensual pleasure' in Sanskrit) for his wife Sabrina, of South African Indian origin. Note: entry previously listed as 'Vins d'Orrance'.

Dorrance range

★★★★☆ **Syrah Cuvée Ameena** ⓐ Polished blend of Elgin's elegant florality & pepper with Perdeberg's deep, dark, spicy fruit, integrated with judicious oaking. Complex **11** flaunts mineral vibrancy & fine acidity.

★★★★☆ **Chardonnay Cuvée Anaïs** Again from Franschhoek & Elgin fruit, naturally fermented **13** is sophisticated & stylish. Delicate hazelnut, lemon peel & spiced apple aromas lead on to a full & energetic palate with a grippy, tactile sensation. Seamless oak integration (30% new).

★★★★☆ **Chenin Blanc Kama** Restrained **13**, from 38 year old Voor Paardeberg bushvines, shows subtle notes of apple, melon & spice. Intriguing spicy palate with a round, soft texture & enticing mineral undertones - & just the slightest hint of oak. Very burgundian, in a way.

Simply Wines range

Simply White ⓐ ★★★ Pleasingly straightforward chenin-viognier **12** for easy, chilled summery enjoyment. Not retasted: **Simply Red 10** ★★★ — JPf

Location: Cape Town • Map: Cape Peninsula • WO: Western Cape • Est/1stB 2000 • Tastings & sales Mon-Fri 9-5 • French deli • Owner(s) Christophe & Sabrina Durand • Cellarmaster(s)/winemaker(s) Christophe Durand • 11ha • 30t/ 4,666cs own label • 95 Hout Street Cape Town 8001 • christophe@vinsdorrance.co.za • www.vinsdorrance.co.za • S 33° 55' 12.26" E 018° 25' 6.42" • F +27 (0)86-588-2989 • **T +27 (0)21-683-7479**

Douglas Green

Douglas Green started trading from the Stukvat Bottlestore in Main Street, Paarl, in 1938. By 1942 he was making his own wine, negociant style, from grapes sourced around winelands. His approach – good wine, at a good price, that people enjoy – remains the foundation of the DGB-owned brand that today bears his name. Recently substantial investments in new bottling technology have been made, and the Sunkissed Natural Sweet wines repackaged and expanded by an untasted Red.

Vineyard Creations

Merlot ★★☆ Ripe, approachable **13**; juicy, with grip, personality & freshness. Good solo, or match with pizza, tomato-based pastas. **Shiraz** ★★☆ Swartland & Robertson grapes in slightly tarry **13**, supple tannins make for super-juicy easy sipper. Also tasted: **Cabernet Sauvignon 13** ★★☆ Not retasted: **Pinotage 13** ★★★ Not tasted: **Chardonnay, Chenin Blanc, Sauvignon Blanc**.

Diversity range

Merlot-Malbec ★★ Melange of red berries, subtle grip on sweetish **13** quaffer. **Chenin Blanc-Sauvignon Blanc** ⊘ **★★★ 14** sauvignon's grassiness, chenin's florals in fresh & fruity mouthful. Ideal summer white. Also tasted: **Cabernet Sauvignon-Merlot 13 ★★** Not retasted: **Sunkissed Natural Sweet Rosé NV ★★ Sunkissed Natural Sweet White NV ★★**

Douglas Green Signature Brands

Ribshack Red ★★ Fetchingly packaged, friendly 60/40 pinotage & shiraz combo, **13** with few grams sugar smoothing the tannins, upping gulpability. **St Augustine ★★★** Enduring label. Fruit-packed **13** from shiraz, pinotage & cab offers smooth, succulent drinkability plus affinity with food. Also tasted: **Beach House Rosé 14 ★★ Beach House Sauvignon Blanc 14 ★★★** Not retasted: **Cape Ruby Port NV ★★★☆**

Douglas Green Sherry-Styles

Dry Fino No. 1 ⓠ **★★★☆** Pale gold colour, very dry & aromatic, with green olive, savoury & salty nut flavours. Good balancing acidity, with a refreshing lift, spirity grip. Palamino & chenin from Worcester & Robertson, made in a solera, as rest of the range. **Medium Cream No. 2** ⓠ **★★★☆** Pale amber delicately sweet, with layers of dried & candied fruit, nuts & spice. Smooth & silky, slips down easily, but has a refreshing orange zest finish. **Full Cream No. 3** ⓠ **★★★☆** Smooth winter warmer: rich, with raisin, spiced nut & honey flavours, aromas; full bodied & mouthfilling, but not cloying. — CR, CvZ

Location: Wellington ▪ WO: Western Cape/Wellington/Worcester ▪ Est 1942 ▪ Closed to public ▪ Owner(s) DGB (Pty) Ltd ▪ Blending manager Dico du Toit (2012) ▪ Oenologist Jaco Potgieter (2000) ▪ Viticulturist(s) Stephan Joubert (2006) ▪ 50% red 49% white 1% rosé ▪ ISO 9001:2000, Fairtrade, HACCP, IPW, WIETA ▪ PO Box 246 Wellington 7654 ▪ douglasgreen@dgb.co.za ▪ www.douglasgreenwines.com ▪ F +27 (0)21-864-1287 ▪ **T +27 (0)21-864-5300**

Douglas Wine Cellar

Located in the Northern Cape town of Douglas, near the confluence of South Africa's greatest rivers, the Orange and Vaal, Douglas Cellar is owned by agribusiness GWK (as is sibling Landzicht, listed separately, whose wines are made here). Wine ranges include Confluence and Barney Barnato (a legend of nearish-by Kimberley's diamond trade), and are described by viticulturist Hein Janse van Rensburg as 'easily accessible wines that don't intimidate with too much "posh".

Location: Douglas ▪ Map: Northern Cape, Free State & North West ▪ Est 1968 ▪ 1stB 1977 ▪ Tasting & sales Mon-Fri 8–5 ▪ Closed all pub hols ▪ Cellar tours by appt ▪ BYO picnic ▪ Gifts ▪ Owner(s) GWK Ltd ▪ Cellarmaster(s)/winemaker(s) Ian Sieg ▪ Viticulturist(s) Hein Janse van Rensburg ▪ Douglas + Landzicht GWK: 350ha (cab, ruby cab, shiraz, chard, chenin, cbard, muscadels r/w) ▪ 40,000cs own label 20% red 40% white 5% rosé 35% fortified ▪ PO Box 47 Douglas 8730 ▪ wynkelder@gwk.co.za ▪ www.landzicht.co.za ▪ S 29° 3' 57.0" E 023° 46' 7.8" ▪ F +27 (0)53-298-1845 ▪ **T +27 (0)53-298-8314/5**

☐ **Down to Earth** *see* Villiera Wines

Dragonridge

Fynbos Estate on Perdeberg is an established eco-tourism getaway, with most of the farm formally recognised as a nature reserve. In this idyll, winemaker Johan Simons produces his dryland wines with gentle hands, recycling, repairing, reusing; taking the natural options whenever possible.

Sangiovese ★★★☆ Grape variety is classic Italian, but off-dry styling & jammy fruit certainly isn't. Yet **13** has its own appeal, persistent flavourful finish. Wild yeast ferment, as all these. **Cosmos ★★☆** Pleasantly full, dry rosé from pinotage, **14** cinders on nose, sour tang on palate. Also tasted: **Jack's Red 13 ★★★** Not tasted: **Chenin Blanc, Galaxy.** — GdB

Location: Malmesbury ▪ Map/WO: Swartland ▪ Est 2004 ▪ 1stB 2006 ▪ Tasting, sales & cellar tours by appt ▪ Fee R30, waived on purchase ▪ Closed Easter Fri, Dec 25/26 & Jan 1 ▪ Country meals by arrangement for groups of 8+ ▪ Facilities for children ▪ Farm produce ▪ BYO picnic ▪ Weddings/functions ▪ Conferences ▪ Walks/hikes ▪ Mountain biking trail ▪ Nature reserve ▪ Guest house ▪ Owner(s) Fynbos Estate (3 partners) ▪ Cellarmaster(s)/winemaker(s) Johan Simons (Jan 2004) ▪ Viticulturist(s) Johan Simons (Jun 1997) ▪ 320ha/13ha (cab, mourv, ptage, sangio, shiraz, chard, chenin, viog) ▪ 35t/1,400cs own label 40% red 40% white 20% rosé ▪ P O Box 526 Malmesbury 7299 ▪ info@fynbosestate.co. za, info@dragonridge.co.za ▪ www.dragonridge.co.za ▪ S 33° 33' 28.9" E 018° 47' 5.6" ▪ F +27 (0)86-611-5125 ▪ **T +27 (0)22-487-1153**

☐ **Dragon's Back** see Kumala
☐ **Driefontein** see Jasper Raats Signature Wines

Driehoek Wines

Driehoek is the oldest farm in the Cederberg Mountains - the Du Toit family have been here for five generations. The vineyards (amongst the Cape's highest) are newcomers, however, at less than a decade old. Their grapes are vinified by neighbour David Nieuwoudt at Cederberg Private Cellar.

★★★★ **Pinot Noir** 'Feminine' **13** trumps debut **12** (★★★★) with a subtle perfume, violet, wisp of vanilla & cranberry flavours dancing on the palate. Smooth, savoury & textured.

★★★★ **Shiraz** Inky black, dark-fruited **12** shows intense berry, savoury spice & cedar flavours layered with sprinkling of white pepper & lavender. Balanced oaking, with a lipsmacking fresh finish.

★★★★ **Sauvignon Blanc** Loads of concentrated lemon, lime & tropical fruit are finely etched on **14**, with a zest mineral bite at the end. Refreshing & precise, admirable balance. — WB

Location: Citrusdal ▪ Map: Olifants River ▪ WO: Cederberg ▪ Est/1stB 2009 ▪ Sales Mon-Sat ▪ Closed Good Fri & Dec 25 ▪ Facilities for children ▪ Gift shop ▪ BYO picnic ▪ Walking/hiking & mountain biking trails ▪ Horse riding ▪ Bird watching ▪ Fishing ▪ Bushman paintings ▪ Conservation area ▪ Self-catering cottages & camping ▪ Beauty treatments ▪ Owner(s) Du Toit family ▪ Cellarmaster(s)/winemaker(s) David Nieuwoudt (Jan 2008, Cederberg) ▪ Viticulturist(s) Dawie Burger & Hennie Spamer (both Jun 2006), advised by David Nieuwoudt ▪ 375ha/5ha (pinot, shiraz, sauv) ▪ 3,500cs own label 40% red 60% white ▪ PO Box 89 Clanwilliam 8135 ▪ driehoekcederberg@gmail.com ▪ www.cederberg-accommodation.co.za ▪ S 32° 26' 34.40" E 019° 11' 24.32" ▪ F +27 (0)86-720-2474 ▪ **T +27 (0)27-482-2828**

Drift Farm

The family farm near Napier is where Bruce Jack (Flagstone winemaker) likes to play — with varieties, styles and names. Take Year of the Rooster Rosé, so named because it's his and wife Penny's Chinese birth year (the colourful graphic on the bottle is her design). Made from touriga franca, it's one of several unusual varieties planted here, most not yet bottled. But with consultants Duncan Savage (Cape Point) and Chris Keet (Keet Wines) on the team there obviously are plans afoot.

★★★★ **Bowwood Cabernet Sauvignon-Merlot** ⓧ Classic Bordeaux style, **05** sumptuous blackcurrant & leafy tobacco; well developed, drinking very well now. Agter Paarl grapes.

★★★★ **Riesling** ⓧ Off cool Swartberg vines, **08** shows some development though still lively, fruity & a good expression of the variety. Lightish alcohol (±11%) perfect for lunchtime.

Year of the Rooster Rosé ⓧ ★★★★ From Douro/port grape touriga franca, dry, sleek **12** is gently perfumed but the brambleberries power up in the flavours & finish. WO Overberg. — CR

Location: Napier ▪ WO: Western Cape/Overberg ▪ 1stB 2005 ▪ Wine sales Mon-Fri 8.30-4 ▪ Owner(s) Jack family ▪ Winemaker(s) Duncan Savage ▪ Viticulturist(s) Chris Keet (consultant) ▪ 204ha/12ha (barbera, malbec, pinot, shiraz, tannat, tinta barocca, touriga franca, touriga nacional, chard) ▪ WIETA ▪ PO Box 55 Napier 7270 ▪ info@thedrift.co.za ▪ www.thedrift.co.za ▪ F +27 (0)86-563-9533 ▪ **T +27 (0)86-150-2025**

Drostdy-Hof Wines

The name of this Distell-owned brand comes from the gabled Oude Drostdy in Tulbagh, designed by the renowned Louis-Michel Thibault as a magistrate's court, and now a national monument, museum and characterful winetasting venue. Value and a convenient range of pack sizes are attributes of the wines, now repackaged, re-stratified and marketed under the tagline 'Pure Country', alluding to the kinder and gentler rural lifestyle.

Core range

Merlot ★★☆ Not a moment too soon to crack open **14**, packed with tangily fresh, ripe plummy fruit. 3L box. **Reserve Shiraz** (NEW) ★★★☆ Oak-aged portion adds extra dimension to dark-fruited & zestily spiced **12**. Well built for current enjoyment, further year/2. 3L pack. Stellenbosch WO. **Shiraz-Pinotage** ★★★ Generously spiced **14**, lush berry fruits on smooth, harmonious palate. 3L box. **Rosé** ★★ Glinting ruby lights on **14** from cab. Refreshing wild strawberry flavours, crisply dry. **Chenin Blanc/Steen** ★★★ Fynbos & guava in quaffable **14**; crisp with well-sustained juicy fruit. **Late Harvest** (NEW) ★★ Gently sweet **NV**, clean & fresh. Comfortable sundowner sipping. 2L box. Also tasted: **Cabernet Sauvignon 14** ★★★ **Pinotage 14** ★★★ **Claret Select NV** ★★ **Shiraz-Merlot 13** ★★☆ **Chardonnay 14** ★★☆ **Sauvignon Blanc 14** ★★ **Premier Grand Cru NV** ★★ **Stein Select NV** ★ **Adelpracht 14** ★★★☆ Not retasted: **Chardonnay-Viognier 13** ★★★ Discontinued: **Shiraz**, **Chardonnay-Semillon**. Note: range was 'Winemaker's Collection'.

Light range

Extra Light ☆ Plain **NV** bone-dry white. 9% alcohol.

Natural Sweet range

Rosé ★★ Candyfloss pink & flavours on fun low-alcohol **NV** party wine. Also tasted: **Red NV** ★☆ **White NV** ★★ Note: range was 'Natural Sweet Light'. — AL

Location/map: Tulbagh ▪ WO: Western Cape/Stellenbosch ▪ Est 1804 ▪ Tasting & sales at De Oude Drostdy Mon-Fri 9–5 (last tasting 4.30) Sat 10–2 (last tasting 1.30) ▪ Fee R20pp ▪ Closed Good Fri, Dec 25 & Jan 1 ▪ Private functions by arrangement ▪ Owner(s) Distell ▪ Cellarmaster(s) Andrea Freeborough ▪ Winemaker(s) Wim Truter (reds) & Pieter Badenhorst (whites) ▪ Viticulturist(s) Bennie Liebenberg ▪ PO Box 213 Tulbagh 6820 ▪ info@drostdywines.co.za ▪ www.drostdyhof.com ▪ S 33° 15' 23.3" E 019° 8' 57.5" ▪ F +27 (0)23-230-0211 ▪ **T +27 (0)23-230-0203**

Druk My Niet Wine Estate

The Kirchner and Stein families' 17th century estate in Paarl Valley has been lovingly restored and refurbished, and now includes an 80-ton boutique cellar and three self-catering cottages. Similar close attention has been paid to the floral kingdom biosphere setting. Winemaking emphasis is firmly on high-end reds and chenin, including a superb straw wine from a block planted in 1968.

Flagship range

★★★★☆ **Invictus** Merlot-led **11** flagship blend (with cabs sauvignon & franc, splash malbec) in classic, plush Bordeaux style; seamless & understated with pristine dark fruit wrapped around a core of ripe, firm tannins; serious & balanced. A keeper.

★★★★☆ **T3** Intriguing red fruit & leafy aromas on creative & one-of-a-kind **11** tempranillo (45%), tannat & tinta amarela blend. Fruit clarity shines in restrained, elegant style. Lipsmacking acidity & rounded tannins. Handsome packaging a feature of this range. WO Western Cape.

★★★★☆ **C68 Puella** (NEW) **13** from air-dried chenin naturally fermented in new oak, offers pure aromas of orange peel, apricot, honey, sweet vanilla & exotic spices. Unctuous & super-sweet, with seamless texture & bold acid backbone. Terrific grip & clarity.

Also tasted: **C68 Chenin Blanc 14** ★★★ Not retasted: **T3 Reserve 13** ★★★

Druk My Niet Collection

★★★★ **Cabernet Sauvignon** Boldly fruited **11** exhibits generous dark-toned flavours & firm yet elegant structure. Balanced vanilla oak adds complexity & velvet mouthfeel.

★★★★ **Cabernet Franc 11** (★★★☆) misses complexity of **10** (which showed dust, leaf, mint - you name it). Green, with quite hard tannin, herbal notes.

★★★★ **Malbec 11** offers loads of bright cranberry fruit, wild herbs & earthy tones. Good balance & supple structure with ageing potential. — WB

Location: Paarl ▪ Map: Paarl & Wellington ▪ WO: Paarl/Western Cape ▪ Est 2003 ▪ 1stB 2009 ▪ Tasting, sales & cellar tours by appt ▪ Fee R50pp ▪ Closed all pub hols ▪ Meals/refreshments on request ▪ BYO picnic ▪ Tour groups ▪ Walks/hikes ▪ Mountain biking trail ▪ Conservation area ▪ 3 self-catering cottages ▪ Owner(s) Georg & Dorothee Kirchner, Jens-Peter Stein ▪ Winemaker(s)/viticulturist(s) Lukas van Loggerenberg (Nov 2013) ▪ 24.5ha/9ha (cabs s/f, malbec, merlot, shiraz, tannat, tempranillo, tinta amarela, chenin, viog) ▪ 60t/3,500cs own label 80% red 20% white ▪ BWI, IPW ▪ PO Box 7383 Paarl 7620 ▪ georg.kirchner@dmnwines.co.za ▪ www.dmnwines.co.za ▪ S 33° 41' 23.26" E 019° 1' 40.23" ▪ F +27 (0)21-868-2392 ▪ **T +27 (0)21-868-2393**

☐ **Duel** *see* Ameera
☐ **Duidelijk** *see* De Kleine Wijn Koöp

Dunstone Winery

Dunstone is the name of the UK village where Lee Wallis bought his first house; he and wife Abbi gave the name to their first home. But the Cape proved a strong drawcard and they bought this Wellington property in 2003. Now the onsite luxury lodgings have been renamed (to 'Dunstone Country House') and extended, and the plan is to replace 1 ha of guavas with bushvines 'to make a BIG Rhône red blend'.

Dunstone range
★★★★ **Shiraz** ⓥ **12** lighter in texture, fresher fruited than **09**. Hint of American oak (but mostly French) lifts bright spicy scents & flavours, adds character. Drinks well now, good for 5+ years.
Also tasted: **Merlot 12** ★★★ **Shiraz Rosé 14** ★★★ Not tasted: **Sauvignon Blanc**.

Stones in the Sun range
Syrah ⓥ ★★☆ Fresh, with tasty spice & red fruit lending ready appeal to **11**. WO W Cape. — CR

Location: Wellington ▪ Map: Paarl & Wellington ▪ WO: Wellington/Western Cape ▪ Est/1stB 2006 ▪ Tasting, sales & cellar tours Wed-Sun 10-4, Mon-Tue by appt ▪ Fee R15pp, waived on purchase ▪ Closed Dec 25 & Jan 1 ▪ The Stone Kitchen ▪ Facilities for children ▪ Conferences ▪ Dunstone Country House luxury B&B guest house & self-catering cottage ▪ Owner(s) Abbi & Lee Wallis ▪ Winemaker(s) Lee Wallis & Robert Frith, with Neil Marais (Jun 2011) ▪ Viticulturist(s) Johan Viljoen (Icon Vines & Wines) ▪ 2ha/2.5ha (merlot, shiraz) ▪ 20t/3,300cs own label 65% red 25% white 10% rosé ▪ PO Box 901 Wellington 7654 ▪ wine@dunstone.co.za ▪ www.dunstone.co.za ▪ S 33° 38' 5.3" E 019° 3' 36.8" ▪ F +27 (0)21-873-6770 ▪ **T +27 (0)21-873-6770**

☐ **Du Plevaux** *see* Imbuko Wines

Du Preez Estate

Successive generations of the Du Preez family have grown wine on this Breedekloof farm since 1926. Vinifying about 6,000 tons, the cellar has supplied a substantially growing export market in recent years. While the reds regularly find favour, the small range of whites is being extended with a chenin.

Du Preez Private Cellar range
Cabernet Sauvignon ★★★ Toasty **11** has black fruit, cedar & spice aromas, fair balance within a medium body. **Sauvignon Blanc** ★★★ Clean, crisp, with appealing tropical fruit nuances, **14** lightish (12% alcohol) sipper. Also tasted: **Merlot 12** ★★★ **Shiraz 11** ★★★ Not retasted: **Polla's Red 11** ★★★ **Hanepoot 11** ★★★★ Not tasted: **Chardonnay**, **Maranda Rosé Méthode Cap Classique**.

Rockfield range
Cabernet Sauvignon ★★☆ **12** firm fleshed, with brisk acidity, BBQ companion. Also tasted: **Shiraz 12** ★★ Not retasted: **Merlot 12** ★★★ Not tasted: **Sauvignon Blanc**.

Hendrik Lodewyk range

Not tasted: **Petit Verdot, Méthode Cap Classique**. — HJ

Location: Rawsonville ▪ Map: Breedekloof ▪ WO: Western Cape/Breedekloof ▪ Est 1916 ▪ 1stB 1998 ▪ Tasting & sales Mon-Fri 8–5 Sat 10–1 ▪ Closed all pub hols ▪ Cellar tours by appt, 2-day prior notice required ▪ BYO picnic ▪ Tour groups (20 pax) ▪ Owner(s) Du Preez family ▪ Cellarmaster(s)/winemaker(s) Lolly Louwrens (Jan 2013) ▪ Viticulturist(s) Jean du Preez ▪ 350ha (merlot, p verdot, ptage, shiraz, chard, chenin, cbard, nouvelle, sauv) ▪ 6,000t ▪ Other export brand: Martinique ▪ IPW ▪ PO Box 12 Route 101 Rawsonville 6845 ▪ info@dupreezestate.co.za ▪ www.dupreezestate.co.za ▪ S 33° 41' 37.1" E 019° 16' 59.6" ▪ F +27 (0)23-349-1923 ▪ **T +27 (0)23-349-1995**

Durbanville Hills

Though large in size and scope, hi-tech Durbanville Hills' output reflects the quality of the Durbanville vineyards from which it mainly draws its fruit, courtesy of a collaboration between industry giant Distell and local growers. That cellarmaster Martin Moore has been here from its 1998 beginnings helps ensure consistency year after year. Though exports are a prime focus, locals aren't neglected. Visitors to the stylish tasting room, restaurant, lounge and picnic area enjoy panoramas of Table Mountain and Cape Town across Table Bay. The Durbanville Hills Share Purchase Trust invests farming revenues in children's education and adult lifeskills programmes. A new wine club provides subscribers with twice-yearly or quarterly selections by Martin, plus special members-only benefits.

Vineyard Selection

★★★★ **Biesjes Craal Sauvignon Blanc** A sauvignon for every palate from this cellar. Sample **14** for those who like it more lively; steely, with a stony minerality, cool-climate green pea notes, & an invigorating acidity.

Not tasted: **Luipaardsberg Merlot**.

Rhinofields range

★★★★ **Chardonnay** Spicy oak (30% new) jostles with juicy fruit of **13**, but ample, ripe tropical/pineapple flavours are most satisfying. **12** (★★★★) not quite as balanced.

★★★★☆ **Noble Late Harvest** This cellar loves sauvignon! Scintillating **13** coated with textbook honeyed botrytis, but it's carefully judged not to swamp untamed 'sauvage' varietal edge; great sugar/acid balance emphasises fruit sweetness rather than sugar. Light 10% alcohol is cherry on top.

Also tasted: **Sauvignon Blanc 14 ★★★★** Not tasted: **Merlot**. Discontinued: **Cabernet Sauvignon, Cape Blend**.

Durbanville Hills range

Shiraz ★★★ Versatile & reliable label. **12** offers smoked bacon aromatic interest & broad mulberry flavours. **Chardonnay ★★★** Easy to drink (& find, given ±40,000 case production). Tropical, sweet-fruited **13** brushed with oak, finishes nicely dry. **Sauvignon Blanc ★★★** A trusted winelist stalwart. Juicy **14** satisfies with an easygoing vivacity. Also tasted: **Cabernet Sauvignon 12 ★★★ Merlot 12 ★★★ Pinotage 12 ★★★ Merlot Rosé 14 ★★☆** Discontinued: **Bastion**. — DS

Location/WO: Durbanville ▪ Map: Durbanville, Philadelphia & Darling ▪ Est 1998 ▪ 1stB 1999 ▪ Tasting & sales Mon-Thu 9–4.30 Fri 9-6 Sat 10–3 Sun 11–3 ▪ Fee R45/8 wines incl glass ▪ Closed Good Fri, Dec 25 & Jan 1 ▪ Chocolate/biltong & wine pairing ▪ Tasting room menu available Tue-Sun ▪ Cellar tours Mon-Fri 11 & 3; groups of 10+ to book ahead ▪ Restaurant Tue-Sun 8.30-3; dinner 6-10 Wed-Sat (summer) & Fri (winter) ▪ Picnics (Oct-Apr) ▪ Facilities for children & cyclists ▪ Conferences ▪ Weddings/functions ▪ Owner(s) Distell, 9 farmers & workers trust ▪ Cellarmaster(s) Martin Moore (Nov 1998) ▪ Winemaker(s) Wilhelm Coetzee (reds, Sep 2008) & Günther Kellerman (whites, Jul 2003) ▪ Viticulturist(s) Henk van Graan (consultant) ▪ 770ha (merlot, sauv) ▪ 6,000t/300,000cs own label 40% red 58% white 2% rosé ▪ ISO 9000-1, ISO 14000-1, BWI, BRC, HACCP, IPW, WIETA ▪ PO Box 3276 Durbanville 7551 ▪ info@durbanvillehills.co.za ▪ www.durbanvillehills.co.za ▪ S 33° 49' 29.9" E 018° 33' 56.7" ▪ **T +27 (0)21-558-1300**

Dusty Heath Vineyard

Though based in the summer-rainfall Midlands of KwaZulu-Natal, Mark and Paula Haldane always fancied making wine. When some of their neighbours started doing it successfully, they thought why not? The resulting 'happy sexy wine' will be available for tasting onsite, and a functions venue open, once the Haldanes get the necessary licences - 'which should happen soon'.

Dusty Heath range

Cabernet Sauvignon ★★☆ Only 2nd fill barrels for **13**, naturally fermented, as all. Attractive blackcurrants, liquorice & scrub nose; light & dry, more gamay in character but very sippable. **Barrel No. 2 Red Blend** ★★ 13 equal cabernets sauvignon & franc with bright red-berry focus, some tobacco nuances, balanced tannins. Modest alcohol (11%), as for all, due to lower late-summer temperatures. **Good Luck Blend** ★★★ Four-part Bordeaux blend in **13** delivers sappy red berries, some herbaceous notes. Partial oaking (both cabs) gives smoothness, no tannin intrusion. Not for ageing.
— CR, CvZ

Location: Hilton ▪ WO: KwaZulu-Natal ▪ Est 2009 ▪ Closed to public ▪ Owner(s) Mark & Paula Haldane ▪ Cellarmaster(s)/viticulturist(s) Paula Haldane (Aug 2009) ▪ Winemaker(s) Paula Haldane (Aug 2009), with Maqua Madlala (Aug 2009) ▪ 20ha/2ha (cabs s/f, merlot, p verdot) ▪ 100% red ▪ dhvineyard@sai.co.za ▪ F +27 (0)86-542-8704 ▪ **T +27 (0)33-383-2001/+27 (0)82-901-4304**

☐ **Dusty Rhino** *see* United Nations of Wine

Du'SwaRoo

Former analytical chemist Tony Bailey, from Durban, and wife Nita, born in SWA (South West Africa/Namibia) moved to the Klein Karoo to grow olives and fruit. Making wine 'was supposed to be a hobby but the bug bit' and now their Calitzdorp boutique winery is in the vanguard of the local trend to use Portuguese varieties for unfortified wines as well as traditional port-styles.

Shiloh Winemakers Blend ★★ **13** uncertified blend of touriga, tinta & shiraz with friendly berry cordial vivacity. **Sirocco Bin 3** ★★★ Softly rounded cherry spice generosity on **NV** blend of **12** & **13**, touriga, tinta & shiraz - uncertified. Also tasted: **Shiraz 11** ★★★ **Cape Vintage 10** ★★★★ Not tasted: **Mistral**. Discontinued: **Shiraz Winemakers Reserve, Shiloh, Sirocco Bin 2, Quintette Rouge, Cape Ruby**. — FM

Location/WO: Calitzdorp ▪ Map: Klein Karoo & Garden Route ▪ Est/1stB 2008 ▪ Tasting & sales by appt Mon-Fri 9-5 Sat 9-1 ▪ Closed all pub hols ▪ Wines also available at Withoek Cellar ▪ Farm produce ▪ Owner(s) Tony Bailey ▪ Cellarmaster(s)/winemaker(s)/viticulturist(s) Tony Bailey (2008) ▪ 0.6ha (shiraz, tinta, touriga) ▪ 200cs own label 80% red 20% port ▪ 1.5ha/20t hanepoot also grown but delivered to Calitzdorp Cellar ▪ PO Box 279 Calitzdorp 6660 ▪ duswaroo@telkomsa.net ▪ www.kleinkaroowines.co.za/cellars/duswaroo.asp ▪ S 33° 30' 58.7" E 021° 41' 39.5" ▪ F +27 (0)44-213-3137 ▪ **T +27 (0)44-213-3137/+27 (0)83-378-8101**

Du Toitskloof Winery

Established as a co-operative more than half a century ago, this stalwart Breedekloof winery and its member-growers keep up with the times. On the right as one emerges from the Du Toitskloof Pass tunnel through spectacular mountain scenery, it's a must-stop for consistent value-for-money wines (and some pretty impressive new flagships). There's something for everyone, from the regular to the exotic, covering the gamut of red, white, dry and sweet desserts, all of solid character. It helps when guidance comes from a long-serving cellarmaster like Shawn Thomson, crushing his 16th vintage here this year.

Quest range

★★★★☆ **Heroes Journey 2 Bordeaux Blend** Cab-led (76%) **11** with equal merlot, petit verdot, is powerful, supple, complex & generous, with deeply scented aromas of cassis, tobacco & spicecake. Liqueur-like intensity is tempered by polished tannins with terrific grip. A keeper.

For more information, visit wineonaplatter.com

★★★★ **Heroes Journey 1 Rhône Blend** Gorgeous blend of shiraz & 19% mourvèdre, **11** offers a melange of earthy, savoury, dark berry flavours & cherry preserve, mingling with firm but supple tannins. Attractive & classy.

Reserve Collection

★★★★ **Chardonnay-Viognier** ⊘ Intense floral & peach melba notes, vanilla wafts from barrel ferment. **13** seduces with fine structure & balance. Excellent value! No **12**.

Dimension Red ★★★ Near-equal cab, merlot, shiraz with pinotage. **12** bright, savoury berry fruit with a smooth core. Not retasted: **Nebbiolo 10** ★★★☆

Du Toitskloof range

Pinotage-Merlot-Ruby Cabernet ⊘ ★★★ Soft, succulent plum fruit on charming **13**, just-dry with a moreish savoury conclusion. **Cabernet Sauvignon-Shiraz** ⊘ ★★★ Medley of rich dark berries, smoke & spice on **13**, fruit-sweet & easy. Supple structure & lingering finish makes this a good everyday quaffer. **Chardonnay** ★★★ Improved depth on softly dry **13**'s 50% unwooded portion lets the citrus fruit shine while the oaked fraction creates a delicious creaminess in the wine. **Sauvignon Blanc** ★★★ Ever-dependable **14** oozes tropical fruit & the few grains of sugar makes it extra drinkable. Will thrill its many fans. **Vin Doux Red Sparkling Wine** (NEW) ★★☆ Unusual style; sweet & frothy, with dusty grip from pinotage, **NV** with low ±8% alcohol. Also tasted: **Cabernet Sauvignon 12** ★★★ **Merlot 13** ★★☆ **Shiraz 10** ★★★ **Chenin Blanc** ⊘ **14** ★★★ **Beaukett 13** ★★☆ **Sparkling Brut NV** ★★★ Not retasted: **Pinotage 11** ★★★

Tunnel range (NEW)

Red ⊘ ★★☆ Semi-sweet cab, soft & well balanced, with nice gentle grip, fun, **NV**. **Sweet Rosé** ★★ Easy rosepetal & plum fruit. Engaging summer fun, **NV** from pinotage. **Moscato** ⊘ ★★☆ Sunshiney **NV** semi-sweet muscat d'Alexandrie with lovely grip & zip for clean, uncloying sipping. **White** ⊘ ★★☆ **NV** from mostly chenin, fruity, just-dry & effortless. Serve chilled. **Sweet Red** ★★ **NV** from pinotage, with the variety's generous fruitiness.

Dessert Wines

Not retasted: **Hanepoot Jerepigo 13** ★★★ **Red Muscadel 13** ★★★☆ **Cape Ruby 10** ★★★ Not tasted: **Noble Late Harvest**.

Discontinued: **Perlé Wines**. — WB

Location: Rawsonville ▪ Map: Breedekloof ▪ WO: Western Cape ▪ Est 1962 ▪ Tasting & sales Mon-Fri 8–5 Sat 9–3.30 ▪ Closed Good Fri, Dec 25 & Jan 1 ▪ Cellar tours by appt ▪ Deli: light meals ▪ Cheese platters ▪ BYO picnic ▪ Owner(s) 22 members ▪ Cellarmaster(s) Shawn Thomson (Oct 1999) ▪ Winemaker(s) Chris Geldenhuys (Mar 2005) & Willie Stofberg (Feb 2011), with Derrick Cupido (Jan 1993) & Jaco le Roux ▪ Viticulturist(s) Leon Dippenaar (Jan 2005, consultant) ▪ 900ha (cab, merlot, ptage, shiraz, chard, chenin, cbard, sauv) ▪ 14,000t/±700,000cs own label 40% red 60% white ▪ Fairtrade ▪ PO Box 55 Rawsonville 6845 ▪ info@dutoitskloof.co.za ▪ www.dutoitskloof.com ▪ S 33° 42' 9.2" E 019° 16' 8.9" ▪ F +27 (0)23-349-1581 ▪ **T +27 (0)23-349-1601**

DuVon Private Cellar

When not growing grapes for bigger brands, Armand du Toit vinifies soupçons under a label reflecting the collaboration with his uncle, Alex von Klopmann, in this Robertson micro-winery. US market growth has encouraged attempts at progress in Europe and 'extra effort' in establishing locally.

Location/map: Robertson ▪ Est/1stB 2003 ▪ Tasting, sales & cellar tours by appt ▪ Conferences ▪ Weddings ▪ Guest house ▪ Owner(s) Armand du Toit & Alex von Klopmann ▪ Cellarmaster(s)/winemaker(s)/viticulturist(s) Armand du Toit ▪ 29.5ha/27ha (cab, ruby cab, shiraz, chenin, cbard, sauv) ▪ 400t/1,200cs own label 70% red 30% white ▪ PO Box 348 Robertson 6705 ▪ info@duvon.co.za ▪ www.duvon.co.za ▪ S 33° 48' 46.8" E 019° 47' 4.1" ▪ F +27 (0)86-626-1490 ▪ **T +27 (0)72-514-4204**

☐ **D'Vine** see Swartland Winery
☐ **Dwyka Hills** see Eagle's Cliff Wines-New Cape Wines

□ **Dyasonsklip** *see* Bezalel-Dyasonsklip Wine Cellar

Eagle's Cliff Wines-New Cape Wines ⓘ ⓘ ⓘ ⓘ ⓘ

These are the entry-level brands of Diners Club Winemaker of the Year 2013 Christiaan Groenewald, whose vineyards in the mountains between Worcester and Villiersdorp are planted on ancient Dwyka tillite soils. Under his separately listed Arendskloof top label, Christiaan explores varieties and styles uncommon in the Breede River Valley (and indeed the Cape) such as tannat, which he blends to great effect with shiraz/syrah. Local pioneer of pinot noir, new exponent of MCC sparkling, busy exporter through New Cape Wines, Christiaan is enjoying the growing involvement of his two young sons.

Eagle's Cliff range

Pinotage ⊘ ★★★ Appealing fireside warmer, **12** supple, juicy & subtly spiced; slips down easily.
Chenin Blanc ⊘ ★★★ Zesty pineapple/mango aromas & flavours, tangy dryness make **14** an ideal summer salad partner. Also tasted: **Shiraz Rosé 14** ★★ **Sauvignon Blanc 14** ★★★ Not retasted: **Cabernet Sauvignon-Merlot 11** ★★★ **Shiraz-Pinotage 11** ★★★

Dwyka Hills range

Not tasted: **Shiraz**.

Hoeksrivier range

Not retasted: **Cabernet Sauvignon 11** ★★☆ **Chenin Blanc 13** ★★★ **Sauvignon Blanc 13** ★★ — CvZ

Location/map: Worcester ▪ WO: Breede River Valley ▪ Est 2000 ▪ Tasting & sales Mon-Fri 8-4.30 ▪ Closed all pub hols ▪ Cheese & meat platters Mon-Fri 10-2 ▪ Facilities for children ▪ Tour groups ▪ Owner(s)/winemaker(s) Christiaan Groenewald ▪ 600ha/80ha ▪ 40% red 60% white ▪ PO Box 898 Worcester 6849 ▪ christiaan@ncw.co.za ▪ www.eaglescliff.co.za ▪ S 33° 50' 25.4" E 019° 25' 7.4" ▪ F +27 (0)23-340-4132 ▪ **T +27 (0)23-340-4112**

Eagles' Nest ⓘ ⓘ ⓘ

Like a phoenix (or eagle) rising from the ashes, this acclaimed wine label (which supports a local raptor research programme) was born of a potentially devastating fire in 2000. A decimated pine forest left unstable, erosion-prone ground on the steep slopes of the Mylrea family's Constantia eyrie overlooking False Bay. Advised to consider terraced vineyards, they wisely called in the experts (including viticulturist Kevin Watt and red-wine maker par excellence Martin Meinert). The result has been a specialist portfolio of distinctive, cool-climate Constantia origin. Besides standout reds (the shiraz especially fine and acclaimed), there's a benchmark viognier.

★★★★☆ **Merlot** Like **09**, lush **10** revels in care taken to create it, including multiply sourced barrels. Plum & complex spice attractions, fine-grained tannins, unforced concentration & depth. Deservedly considered one of SA's consistently finest merlots.

★★★★☆ **Shiraz** Sleek & vibrant **11**, plush, with dark berry fruit spiced with black pepper & scrub, its smooth polished lines & resonating length - the property's hallmark - hard to resist, as in seductive **10** (★★★★★). French oak 16 months, half new.

★★★★☆ **Viognier 13** has variety's gorgeous peach & apricot notes, intriguing jasmine nuance. Barrel-fermentation, ageing (6 months, 10% new) add texture, satisfying weight; there's also a savoury element in the lingering farewell, aiding food compatibility.

Also tasted: **Little Eagle 12** ★★★ **Sauvignon Blanc 13** ★★★★ Discontinued: **Verreaux**. — CvZ

Location: Constantia ▪ Map: Cape Peninsula ▪ WO: Constantia/Western Cape ▪ Est 2001 ▪ 1stB 2005 ▪ Tasting & sales daily 10-4.30 ▪ Fee R40pp, waived on purchase of R300+ ▪ Closed Good Fri, Dec 25/26 & Jan 1 ▪ Light meals ▪ Owner(s) Mylrea family ▪ Winemaker(s) Stuart Botha (2007), with consultant Martin Meinert (2001) ▪ Viticulturist(s) Kobus Jordaan (2008), with consultant Kevin Watt (2001) ▪ 38ha/12ha (merlot, shiraz, viog) ▪ 90t/15,000cs own label 85% red 15% white ▪ PO Box 535 Constantia 7848 ▪ info@eaglesnestwines.com ▪ www.eaglesnestwines.com ▪ S 34° 0' 54.2" E 018° 24' 54.3" ▪ F +27 (0)21-794-7113 ▪ **T +27 (0)21-794-4095**

Eaglevlei Wine Estate

Having emerged in the 1990s as a small, exclusive wine farm newly planted to red varieties, Eaglevlei after several owners and development strategies has become a buzzing, family-friendly, tourist-attuned winelands destination. Home and bought-in grapes produce characterful wines; a restaurant, live music, a vast jungle gym and other attractions please all.

★★★★ **Kroonarend** Now 100% merlot, previous **09** a shiraz blend. **12 (★★★★)** mixed berries, ripe & forthcoming, some tobacco flavours from 18+ months in variety of barrels, still youthful, would reward cellaring 3-5 years.

★★★★ **Tiervoël** Switches from Cape Blend to varietal pinotage. **12** complex & involving, cigarbox & well-cured meat shading to deep plummy fruit, the flavours savoury yet juicy. Some intriguing scrub notes.

Dwerg Arend (NEW) ★★★ From Swartland chenin. **14** passionfruit freshened by citrus acidity, more flavour than you'd expect from such an alcohol-friendly (12%) dry white. **Visarend** (NEW) ★★ Swartland sauvignon in **14**. Intense gooseberries & chopped herbs, fragrant & inviting, but the racy acidity gives it an edginess needing creamy food. Friendly 9.6% alcohol. **Lekkerbek Sweet Sparkling** (NEW) ★★★ From Swartland chenin, **NV**. The fruit's the thing, honeydew melon & ripe fig, fitting perfectly into the sweet style. A partygoer! Also tasted: **Roofarend 12 ★★★★ Red Affair 13 ★★★☆ Berghaan 13 ★★★ Langkuif 13 ★★★★** Not retasted: **Breëkop 12 ★★★** Discontinued: **Muscat d'Alexandrie**. — CR

Location/map: Stellenbosch ▪ WO: Stellenbosch/Swartland/Hemel-en-Aarde Valley/Western Cape ▪ Est/1stB 1997 ▪ Tasting & sales Tue-Sun 10—5 ▪ Fee R30, waived on purchase ▪ Eaglevlei Restaurant Tue-Thu 8-8 Fri/Sat 8-9 Sun 8-6 ▪ Facilities for children ▪ Tour groups ▪ Conferences ▪ Functions ▪ Owner(s) Rennart van Rensburg ▪ Cellarmaster(s)/winemaker(s)/viticulturist(s) Clarise Sciocatti-Langeveldt (Jan 2012) ▪ ±8ha (cab, merlot, ptage) ▪ 75t/14,000cs own label 70% red 25% white 5% rosé ▪ PO Box 969 Stellenbosch 7599 ▪ info@eaglevlei.com ▪ www.eaglevlei.com ▪ S 33° 49' 33.5" E 018° 48' 52.2" ▪ F +27 (0)21-884-4716 ▪ **T +27 (0)21-884-4713**

Earthbound

Earthbound — established as Tukulu in 1998 - is an empowerment joint venture between wine giant Distell, entrepreneurs and a local community trust. Grapes for the wines, all certified as both organic and Fairtrade, are from unirrigated bushvines on Papkuilsfontein farm near Darling.

Chenin Blanc ⊘ ★★★ Lovely focus & fruit purity, from both the terroir & the vineyard handling; **14** quince & fresh apple, zesty & dry. **Sauvignon Blanc** ⊘ ★★★ Tropical perfumes of guava & mango, with an intriguing leafy top note, tightening into citrus flavours, **14** zingy, fresh & dry. Not retasted: **Cabernet Sauvignon 12 ★★★ Pinot Noir 12 ★★★ Pinotage 12 ★★★** — CR

Location: Darling ▪ WO: Groenekloof ▪ Est 1998 ▪ 1stB 1999 ▪ Tasting by appt at Trinity Lodge, Darling ▪ Owner(s) Distell, Leopont 98 Properties, Maluti Groenekloof Community Trust & consortium of Gauteng-based black taverniers ▪ Winemaker(s) Samuel Viljoen (Sep 2007) ▪ Viticulturist(s) Hannes van Rensburg (1998) ▪ 975ha/373.36ha (of which 172ha organically grown) ▪ 73% red 27% white ▪ BWI, Fairtrade, SGS, WIETA ▪ PO Box 184 Stellenbosch 7599 ▪ info@earthboundwines.co.za ▪ www.earthboundwines.co.za ▪ F +27 (0)21-882-9575 ▪ **T +27 (0)21-809-7000**

☐ **Eden Crest** *see* Lournsford Wine Estate
☐ **Edenhof** *see* Schalkenbosch Wines

Edgebaston

When David Finlayson purchased this Simonsberg farm outside Stellenbosch it was called Woodlands. He returned it to its original name of Edgebaston, also the area in England his mother, Jill, was born and raised in. The farm buildings are utilitarian and modern, and the doubled cellar floor-space to accommodate the smaller lots he's recently working with 'is coming into its own'. With some of his leftover energy he is a longtime member of the Cape Winemakers Guild, serving a term as chair, thus following in the steps of his father Walter, a founder member.

Camino Africana range

★★★★☆ **David Finlayson Pinot Noir Reserve** Pinot noir & Finlayson family symbiotic partners, as illustrated by very special **12**, from mature (20+ years) experimental-clone vineyard. Same evocative label design as Chenin, also 100% new oak. Needs time to give full rein to pinot complexity, suppleness. Pleasing natural vitality, dry & persistent.

★★★★☆ **David Finlayson Chenin Blanc Old Vine 13** from one of SA's oldest chenin vineyards, planted 1947, has power with effortless elegance. Dried herbs, fresh earth woven into its still taut mineral length. Underlying silkiness, assimilation of all-new oak will come. Tiny yield, natural ferment.

Edgebaston range

★★★★☆ **David Finlayson 'GS' Cabernet Sauvignon** Honours legendary George Spies cabs. **12** much bigger, richer feel than standard bottling. Abundance of very ripe yet pure cab fruit, underlying tannic harness, oak (100% new French) ensure long cellaring prospects. Needs year/2 to shed youthful gawkiness.

★★★★ **Cabernet Sauvignon 12** returns to more restrained style after fruit-forward **11**. Quiet yet attractive cab scents, dark fruit still enveloped by youthful grip. Underneath, the freshness & mineral energy hint at future complexity. Includes drops petit verdot & cab franc.

★★★★ **Pinot Noir** Had 'David Finlayson' prefix. Darker fruit spectrum provides touch more serious note in **13**; supple texture, freshness & gentle tannins ensure it remains in fruitier, approachable house style. Oak, 40% new, subtle accessory. WO W Cape.

★★★★ **Syrah** Returns to range after 4 year break. Familiar varietal spice, red fruits & florals on **13**. Full bodied though gentle tannins, creamy flesh lend approachability. Promising future too.

★★★★ **The Pepper Pot** ⃠ Aptly named, shiraz-based blend. **13** captures savoury satisfaction of **12** with weave of dark spice & gamey notes in its fleshy texture. Finishing flourish of spicy tannins prolongs pleasure. WO Coastal.

★★★★☆ **Chardonnay** ⃠ **13** more subtle, sophisticated than **12**, just as engaging. More about texture - creaminess, freshness & an intriguing grainy grip - than obvious fruit. Oak 30% new, also underplayed yet an effective enricher & blended with 10% fermented in concrete eggs.

★★★★ **DLDC Natural Sweet** ⃝ Opulent **12** pretty much dessert in itself! Sauvignon-semillon blend, new-oak fermented/18 months matured, offers lifted peach aromas & a swish silky richness with timeless persistence.

Also tasted: **The Berry Box Red 12** ★★★★ **Cast In Stone Sauvignon Blanc 14** ★★★★ **The Berry Box White 14** ★★★ — AL

Location/map: Stellenbosch ▪ WO: Stellenbosch/Western Cape/Coastal ▪ Est/1stB 2004 ▪ Tasting by appt only ▪ Owner(s)/vineyard manager(s) David Finlayson ▪ Cellarmaster(s) David Finlayson (Jan 2004) ▪ Winemaker(s) David Finlayson (Jan 2004), with Franco Lourens (Jun 2013) ▪ 30ha/24ha (cab, shiraz, chard, sauv) ▪ 300t/60,000cs own label 60% red 40% white ▪ PO Box 2033 Dennesig 7601 ▪ david@edgebaston.co.za ▪ www.edgebaston.co.za ▪ S 33° 53' 33.82" E 018° 51' 17.61" ▪ F +27 (0)21-889-9572 ▪ **T +27 (0)21-889-9572/+27 (0)83-263-4353**

Eenzaamheid

'A small wine business with an intense focus on quality and personal relationships', Eenzaamheid ('Loneliness') is the newish Briers-Louw family winery on their very old Agter Paarl farm. Harnessing the potential of their dryland vines (grapes from which go into several awarded brands), Janno Briers-Louw vinifies on a boutique scale and aims for an Old World style. Caring for the families resident on the property, some 7th generation, is a concerted and ongoing concern.

Location: Paarl ▪ Map: Paarl & Wellington ▪ Est 1693 ▪ 1stB 2010 ▪ Tasting by appt only ▪ Conferences ▪ Owner(s) Christo & Karina Briers-Louw ▪ Winemaker(s) Janno Briers-Louw (Apr 2008) ▪ Viticulturist(s) André Coetzee (Sep

2003) ▪ 1,185ha/400ha (cab, cinsaut, ptage, shiraz, chenin) ▪ ±3,000t/1,900cs own label 75% red 25% white ▪ PO Box 22 Klapmuts 7625 ▪ wine@eenzaamheid1.co.za ▪ S 33° 44' 52.67" E 018° 50' 12.06" ▪ F +27 (0)86-583-5741 ▪ **T +27 (0)82-493-9930**

Eerste Hoop Wine Cellar

Having noted Belgian restaurateur Lode Lemahieu as an owner of this boutique winery off the beaten track between Villiersdorp and Bot River has ensured that its labels are listed in his establishments, and helped distribution in Belgium and Holland, where most of the wines are sold. Now in the care of winemaker/viticulturist Werner Barkhuizen, the terracotta cellar is named for the lodge used by 17th century Cape governor Willem Adriaan van der Stel on hunting trips here in Theewaterskloof Valley.

Lodewijkx range
White Blend ★★★☆ Chardonnay-led with 31% chenin & viognier, soft & creamy **12** is redolent of cling peaches & green melon, acidity balancing rather than piercing.

Eerste Hoop range
★★★★ Cabernet Sauvignon 10 matches impressive **09** quality; dense & rich, with black fruit, dark chocolate & liquorice. Oak (20% new) is well judged, making wine accessible now but worth keeping.
Shiraz ★★★☆ Rich but nicely integrated **10** has generous dark berries with a mocha finish. Also tasted: **Blushing Bride Pinot Noir Rosé 14** ★★ Not retasted: **Viognier 11** ★★★ Not tasted: **Wooded Chardonnay**.

Witklip range
Chardonnay ★★★ Easy-drinking unwooded **12** shows tangerine & other sweet citrus, crisp & zesty, finishes rather abruptly. Not retasted: **Shiraz 11** ★★★ — JG

Location: Villiersdorp ▪ Map: Elgin, Walker Bay & Bot River ▪ WO: Western Cape ▪ 1stB 2006 ▪ Tasting, sales & cellar tours Mon-Sat by appt ▪ Owner(s) Belgium owners ▪ Winemaker(s)/viticulturist(s) Werner Barkhuizen (May 2013) ▪ 24.5ha/11ha (cab, grenache, mourv, pinot, shiraz, chard, chenin, viog) ▪ 95t/14,000cs 55% red 42% white 3% rosé ▪ Brands for clients: Oggendau, Skoon Vallei, Stilfontein ▪ IPW ▪ PO Box 89 Elgin 7180 ▪ wine@eerstehoop.co.za ▪ www. eerstehoop.co.za ▪ S 34° 5' 23.7" E 019° 11' 50.7" ▪ **T +27 (0)28-841-4190/+27 (0)82-754-4408**

Eikehof Wines

Winelovers approaching Franschhoek are encouraged to pop into the homely little cellar on the right shaded by its ancient oaks (eike). In the Malherbe family for over a century, the roadside property is now open daily for tastings (and cheese platters in season), hosted by owners Francois and wife Elize.

Semillon-Chardonnay (NEW) ★★★ Semillon shades chardonnay (60/40) on naturally co-fermented **13** blend, giving rich honeyed nuance to broad citrus palate. Also tasted: **Cabernet Sauvignon 11** ★★★ **Chardonnay 14** ★★★ Not retasted: **Merlot 11** ★★☆ **Shiraz 12** ★★ **Sauvignon Blanc 13** ★★☆ — FM

Location/map: Franschhoek ▪ WO: Franschhoek/Western Cape ▪ Est 1903 ▪ 1stB 1992 ▪ Tasting, sales & cellar tours Mon-Sat 10-5 (Aug-Apr) & 11-4 (May-Jul) ▪ Closed Good Fri, Dec 25 & Jan 1 ▪ Cheese platters ▪ Weddings & functions ▪ Owner(s)/cellarmaster(s)/winemaker(s) Francois Malherbe ▪ 29ha/24ha (cab, merlot, pinot, shiraz, chard, sem) ▪ 28t/3,000cs own label 80% red 20% white ▪ PO Box 222 Franschhoek 7690 ▪ eikehof@mweb.co.za ▪ www.eikehof. com ▪ S 33° 52' 53.3" E 019° 3' 52.0" ▪ F +27 (0)21-876-2469 ▪ **T +27 (0)21-876-2469**

Eikendal Vineyards

Some two decades back, this guide noted that Eikendal was 'one of the least-trumpeted cellars in the Cape' – but always reliable. The estate is not ancient, in Cape terms, but was formed from portions of older farms when the Swiss Saager family established it in 1981. The trumpets nowadays echo more around these Helderberg slopes, and reliability is at a high level - though there's still not much flashiness, restraint being more the style of cellarmaster Nico Grobler. Who seems content with the vineyards at his disposal: 'With the Helderberg at our backs, False Bay to the left and Table Mountain in the distance, what more do I need than Eikendal?'

Reserve range

★★★★☆ **Classique** 12 does justice to excellent red-wine vintage. Wonderfully harmonious blend mainly cab, merlot, spiced with cab franc. Sleek, elegant, with great depth of rich flavour within its current tannic fortress. Has classic ageability, as did 11 (★★★★★).

★★★★☆ **Chardonnay** Fine example of delicacy, precision & freshness achieved in warmer area. 13 so alive in its weave of citrus blossom aromas, poised creamy mouthfeel & clean, lengthy tail. Classic & ageworthy. Subtle oaking (French 500L) & just on 13% alcohol add to overall understatement.

Premium range

★★★★☆ **Cabernet Sauvignon** 12 restrained yet compelling, as is whole range. As with previous, expressive yet refined in its silkily fresh texture, ripe, pure fruit. Crafted to last; should achieve a grand maturity.

★★★★ **Merlot** ⊘ A classic merlot, commanding attention. 12 (★★★★★), step up on 11 hits sweet spot in its perfectly ripe, spicy fruit, freshness & focused structure. Needs year/two for juicy grape tannins to integrate; can improve for many more.

★★★★ **Pinotage** Ⓢ Opulently ripe & muscular, 12 struts its intense wild berry fruit with distinct swagger. Dash of cab tones down the extroverted brashness. 11 sold out untasted.

★★★★ **Charisma** Ⓢ Change in direction for 11 red blend, now shiraz-led, with dashes petit verdot & sangiovese, less oak. Stellenbosch vines. Also-assessed 12, from Swartland & Paarl, follows suit: rich, with fruity appeal, but retaining noble bearing.

★★★★ **Sauvignon Blanc** Ⓢ Ex-tank 13 from Elgin, Franschhoek & Lutzville, has some barrel ferment, lees-ageing & dash semillon, showing in rich, lingering mouthfeel. Finely tuned mix of spicy aromas & ripe figs.

Not retasted: **Janina Unwooded Chardonnay 13** ★★★☆ — AL

Location: Stellenbosch ▪ Map: Helderberg ▪ WO: Stellenbosch/Stellenbosch/Elgin/Western Cape ▪ Est 1981 ▪ 1stB 1984 ▪ Tasting & sales Mon-Sat 9.30-4.30 (Sep-May)/10-4 (Jun-Aug) Sun 10-4 ▪ Fee R20/4 wines ▪ Closed Good Fri, Dec 25/26 & Jan 1 ▪ Cellar tours Mon-Fri 10 & 2.30 ▪ Restaurant @ Eikendal T +27 (0)21-855-5033: lunch Tue-Sun & dinner Wed ▪ Facilities for children ▪ Tour groups ▪ Conferences ▪ Walks/hikes ▪ MTB trail ▪ Flywaters fly fishing ▪ Cheetah Outreach ▪ Eikendal Lodge ▪ Owner(s) Substantia AG ▪ Winemaker(s)/viticulturist(s) Nico Grobler (2007), with Christo Hanse & Willem van Kerwel (both 2012) ▪ 78ha/±50ha (cabs s/f, malbec, merlot, p verdot, chard) ▪ 250t/70-80,000cs own label 70% red 30% white ▪ IPW ▪ PO Box 2261 Stellenbosch 7601 ▪ info@eikendal.co.za ▪ www.eikendal.com ▪ S 34° 0' 46.7" E 018° 49' 24.5" ▪ F +27 (0)21-855-1027 ▪ **T +27 (0)21-855-1422**

☐ **Eksteens' Family Vineyards** *see* Stone Ridge Wines

Elana Wine

⚲ Ⓝⓔⓦ

Perhaps best known as a host on breakfast show Expresso, bubbly media personality Elana Afrika-Bredenkamp has launched her own wine, crafted in Durbanville's D'Aria cellar with winemaker Rudi von Waltsleben. Hands-on from pressing to packaging, she knew nothing about winemaking when she started. 'But it's a joy working with her,' says Rudi, 'and I believe you can taste it in the wine.'

Shiraz ★★★★ Stylish 12 rich & slightly smoky, intensely vanilla-sweet, particularly the finish, from 18 months 50% new oak. Plush & rounded, only the gentlest tannic grip. Red wine for the dessert course. — WB, CR

Location/WO: Durbanville ▪ Est 2012 ▪ 1stB 2013 ▪ Tasting by appt only ▪ Cellarmaster(s)/viticulturist(s) Elana Afrika-Bredenkamp (2012) ▪ Winemaker(s) Elana Afrika-Bredenkamp (2012), with Rudi von Waltsleben (D'Aria, 2012) ▪ 6ha ▪ 7t/200cs own label 100% red ▪ M13 Racecourse Road Durbanville 7550 ▪ elana.afrika@gmail.com ▪ F +27 (0)21-439-1480 ▪ **T +27 (0)83-593-6329**

For more information, visit wineonaplatter.com

□ **Elandsberg** *see* Viljoensdrift Wines & Cruises

Elemental Bob

Spookfontein winemaker Craig Sheard, nicknamed Farmer Bob by his brother, has his own boutique winery based in the Hemel-en-Aarde area, where he makes wine eschewing modern convention. Natural ferments and 'interesting experiments' with less-favoured grapes are what exercises his creative mind.

Crystal Series (NEW)

★★★★ **White Blend** Idiosyncratic yet exciting mix of pinot blanc, semillon, roussanne & chenin. **13** tank sample full-bodied, rich, creaminess underpinning vibrant fresh citrus & stonefruit. Bold debut.

Pinot Noir ★★★☆ Mix of **12** & **13** fruit on **NV**, all natural from start to end - as others. Smoky red fruit, vibrant, powerful yet ethereally delicate. Long powdery tail. **Shiraz-Pinot Noir** ★★★☆ Unusual blend confidently contrasts ripe succulence & dark power of shiraz with lacy delicacy of pinot in **12**. Dry but soft tannic squeeze from oak. Assured & long. — FM

Location: Hermanus ▪ WO: Upper Hemel-en-Aarde Valley ▪ Est/1stB 2004 ▪ Closed to public ▪ Owner(s)/winemaker(s) Craig Sheard ▪ 200-300cs own label 65% red 30% white 5% port ▪ elementalbob@gmail.com ▪ **T +27 (0)82-265-1071**

□ **Elements** *see* Hartswater Wine Cellar

Elgin Heights

When the Joubert family from Stellenbosch bought Elgin's Smarag ('Emerald') farm in the mid-1960s, they grew deciduous fruit. Some 30 years later, fifth-generation winefarmer DD Joubert saw how well his neighbours were doing with wine and developed his own extensive vineyards. For the brand, the Jouberts adopted the original farm name, Elgin Heights.

★★★★ **Sauvignon Blanc** ⓐ **11** juicy gooseberry, fig flavours, balanced vitality. Easy, characterful. Not retasted: **Shiraz 10** ★★★★ **Chardonnay 11** ★★★ Not tasted: **Emerald Méthode Cap Classique Chardonnay**. — JG

Location/map: Stellenbosch ▪ WO: Elgin ▪ 1stB 2007 ▪ Tasting & sales by appt ▪ Conference facilities ▪ Owner(s) Ryk Joubert ▪ Winemaker(s) Andries Burger, Kobie Viljoen & Corné Marais (sauv/shiraz/MCC, consultants) ▪ Viticulturist(s) DD Joubert ▪ 111ha/70ha (cab, merlot, shiraz, chard, sauv, viog) ▪ PO Box 52 Vlottenburg 7604 ▪ mwddj@mweb.co.za ▪ www.elginheights.co.za ▪ S 33° 57' 2.60'' E 018° 45' 28.91'' ▪ F +27 (0)86-648-1704 ▪ **T +27 (0)84-517-9300**

Elgin Ridge

Brian and Marion Smith exchanged their London IT company for an Elgin apple farm in 2007. Assisted by top viticulturist Kevin Watt and Luddite's Niels Verburg, they replanted orchards to vines focusing on cool-climate varieties for their specialist - very meticulous - production. Marion tends the vineyards, Brian mans the custom-built boutique cellar, certified organic.

★★★★ **282 Sauvignon Blanc** ⓥ Delicate green peach & lemongrass aromas, good palate weight from long lees-ageing & natural ferment, all ensuring food compatibility for **13**. Greater presence than very good **12** (★★★☆).

282 Pinot Noir (NEW) ⓥ ★★★★ Uncomplicated earthy tones with bruised strawberry & blackberry on own-yeast-fermented **12**, pleasant, well-padded palate, bonus of moderate 13% alcohol. Thought to be SA's only certified organic pinot noir. — JPf

Location/WO: Elgin ▪ Map: Elgin, Walker Bay & Bot River ▪ Est 2007 ▪ 1stB 2009 ▪ Tasting, sales & tours by appt Mon-Fri 10-4 Sat/Sun/pub hols by appt only ▪ Food & wine pairing during Elgin Open Gardens weekends 10-4 ▪ Farm produce ▪ BYO picnic ▪ Owner(s) Brian & Marion Smith ▪ Winemaker(s) Brian Smith ▪ Viticulturist(s) Kevin Watt (Apr 2007, consultant), with Marion Smith ▪ 10.2ha/4.5ha (pinot, chard, sauv, sem) ▪ 25t/4,000cs own label 20% red

80% white ▪ Organic certification ▪ PO Box 143 Elgin 7180 ▪ info@elginridge.com ▪ www.elginridge.com ▪ S 34° 12' 10.68" E 019° 0' 14.34" ▪ F +27 (0)21-846-8060 ▪ **T +27 (0)21-846-8060**

☐ **Elgin Valley Vineyards** *see* Corder Family Wines

Elgin Vintners

There is definitely strength in unity, as this partnership of six Elgin Valley growers has shown. Not just ordinary farmers, but 'otherwise apple farmers going (gr)ape', they devised a successful concept of appointing a specialist winemaker for each of their chosen varieties, sourcing all grapes from the valley. The opening of a brand home on Elgin Orchards farm means wines now can be tasted at set hours (previously by appointment) and many amenities enjoyed, such as mountain biking along the pristine Palmiet River, fynbos walks, and weekend getaways in the renovated Ridgelands homestead.

★★★★ **Shiraz** ② **09** big, but with sense of delicacy. Lots of dark spice, smoked meat appeal, gentle tannins & judicious oaking; delicious drinking now, with potential. Step up on **08** (★★★★).

★★★★ **Agama** Savoury blend of cab, merlot & malbec (74/14/12) from 4 farms. **09** starting to reveal charm after 26 months in oak (25% new). Classically styled, with dense fruit core & supple tannins. Ageworthy, whereas **08** (★★★★) wasn't for keeping.

★★★★ **Chardonnay 12** less overt fruit richness than **11** (★★★★★) & tad oaky mid-2014. Still has lovely core of tangy dried peach & lime. Shows cooler provenance & elegant styling, just needs time.

★★★★ **Viognier** ② Flamboyant **11** (★★★★★) captures more of the essence of viognier's aromatic allure & rich fruit than **10** (★★★★) or **09**. Succulent, svelte & stylish.

★★★★ **The Century** Unoaked **12** (★★★★) sauvignon-led blend with semillon (32%). A textural, food-pairing wine with broader, creamy nuance, less tangy than **11**. Honours Elgin's visionary centenarian, Douglas Moodie.

Pinot Noir ★★★★ From 3 sites & 2 clones, **12** appealing earthy red berry flavours in tightly knit, but piquantly fresh balance. Less new oak (22%) in supportive tannic framework. Shows potential to develop. Also tasted: **Merlot 10** ★★★★ **Merlot Rosé 14** ★★★ **Sauvignon Blanc 13** ★★★★ Not retasted: **Cabernet Sauvignon 08** ★★★ — MW

Location/WO: Elgin ▪ Map: Elgin, Walker Bay & Bot River ▪ Est 2003 ▪ 1stB 2004 ▪ Tasting & sales Wed-Sun 10-4 ▪ Function facility ▪ Mountain biking route ▪ Fynbos walks ▪ Fishing ▪ Birding ▪ Vineyard tours ▪ Home to rent for getaway weekends ▪ Owner(s) Derek Corder, Max Hahn, Alastair Moodie, James Rawbone-Viljoen, Rob Semple & Paul Wallace ▪ Cellarmaster(s)/winemaker(s) Various (Kevin Grant, Gavin Patterson, Nico Grobler, Martin Meinert, Niels Verburg, Joris van Almenkerk) ▪ Viticulturist(s) Paul Wallace ▪ ±75ha (cab, malbec, merlot, pinot, shiraz, chard, riesling, sauv, sem, viog) ▪ 750t/14,500cs own label ▪ BWI, IPW ▪ PO Box 121 Elgin 7180 ▪ info@elginvintners.co.za ▪ www.elginvintners.co.za ▪ S 34°10'52.18" E 019° 0'42.54" ▪ F +27 (0)86-646-3693 ▪ **T +27 (0)21-848-9587**

Elsenburg Agricultural Training Institute

This 17th-century Stellenbosch wine farm became a government agricultural school in 1898. In 1917 it gave birth to the Stellenbosch University faculty and its later Viticulture & Oenology degree. This and Elsenburg's Cellar Technology major, introduced in 1976, have produced most of SA's modern-era winemakers. A recent R11-million cellar revamp saw world-class equipment installed and training provided. Bottling of selected final year students' creations for tasting and sale (licence pending) has been re-introduced, hence the fine collection of table wines, 'port' and brandy below.

Elsenburg range

★★★★ **Muscat d'Frontignan** Bright, golden, unfortified **13** oozing grape, orange marmalade & cinnamon aromas. Smooth, light-footed & bright, with deep intense flavour & vibrant citrus lift to end. Harmonious & delicious.

Cinsaut ★★★★ Unoaked **13** shows earthy black fruit on the nose, soft & easy flavours. **Sauvignon Blanc** ★★★★ **13** tropical fruit flavours, fine perfume & balance. Good varietal expression, with zippy, pleasantly grippy finish. **Viognier ★★★☆** Fragrant peach melba & lavender aromas on **13**, hint of clove & exotic spice. Light & cheerful. **Cape Vintage ★★★★** Bright ruby colour on **11** port-style, tobacco & spicecake flavours, understated & vibrant, with lingering alcohol grip on the finish.

Brandy range

★★★★☆ Potstill 13 Years What a debut! From colombard, fragrant apricot, cashew & warm spice on the nose. Rich & smooth, with bright fruit flavours, hints of fresh apple & a long mellow taste in the mouth - harmonious, with great finesse. Attractive modern packaging. 500 ml. — WB

Location/WO: Stellenbosch ▪ Est 1976 ▪ Closed to public ▪ Owner(s) Western Cape Government, Department of Agriculture ▪ Winemaker(s) Lorraine Geldenhuys, with Sandile Mkhwanazi (both Jan 2013) ▪ Viticulturist(s) Anton Nel (Feb 2013) ▪ 40ha (cinsaut, tinta barocca, cbard, muscadel, sauv, viog) ▪ 178t/1,363cs own label 65% red 35% white ▪ IPW ▪ Private Bag X1 Elsenburg, Muldersvlei 7607 ▪ lorraineg@elsenburg.com ▪ www.elsenburg.com ▪ F +27 (0)21-808-5484 ▪ **T +27 (0)21-808-7034**

☐ **Embrace** *see* Stellenrust

Emineo Wines

This legally themed brand, with sibling Cape to Cairo, is produced on an occasional basis for Cape Town patent attorney Otto Gerntholtz by Nico van der Merwe (Saxenburg, Nico van der Merwe Wines) and Thys Louw (Diemersdal).

★★★★ Liber II JLS Poised **07** cab (65%) with merlot & pinotage. When last tasted, minty chocolate aromas, lively cassis underpinned by acidity & tannin.

★★★★ Liber III RG **07** big, ebullient shiraz with splash mourvèdre ex Durbanville & Swartland. Seriously styled, with polished oak when tasted some time ago.

Not retasted: **Liber I OCG 06 ★★★★** — KM, CvZ

Location: Cape Town ▪ Map: Cape Peninsula ▪ WO: Durbanville/Coastal ▪ Est 2004 ▪ 1stB 2006 ▪ Tasting by appt ▪ Owner(s) Trans-Scripto (Pty) Ltd ▪ Winemaker(s) Nico van der Merwe & Thys Louw ▪ 1,500cs own label 100% red ▪ PO Box 8 Cape Town 8000 ▪ info@emineo.com ▪ www.emineo.com ▪ S 33° 56' 29.06" E 018° 23' 47.76"

☐ **Enigma** *see* Zorgvliet Wines
☐ **Enon** *see* Zandvliet Wine Estate & Thoroughbred Stud
☐ **Enoteca Bottega** *see* Idiom Collection

Entre Nous

New to the guide, Entre Nous ('Between Us') perfectly sums up this group of friends (three lawyers, a quantity surveyor and barrel expert) making wine together in Stellenbosch's Banhoek Valley from bought-in grapes. 'All winemaking decisions are made by consensus, which is very time consuming but generally we make good decisions that way.' Mostly, however, it's about having fun: 'We love the exciting mix of art, science, magic, and never being quite sure what the end result will be.'

★★★★ Cabernet Sauvignon **10** (**★★★★**) from Stellenbosch, shade off **09**. Refreshing on palate, packed with pure blackcurrant & oak flavours. Soft textured & harmonious, but a swift farewell. Previously listed under AntHill.

8:2:3 ★★★ Cabernets sauvignon & franc, with merlot, working well together in **11**'s plush plums, mocha chocolate flavours. Brisk acidity livens everything up. **Chardonnay ★★★★ 12** quite savoury from 24 months barrel ferment/maturation but in a nice way. Toasted brioche, prosciutto, kumquat presence throughout, satisfying fresh tail. — CR, CvZ

Location/map: Stellenbosch ▪ WO: Western Cape ▪ Est/1stB 2000 ▪ Tasting, sales & cellar tours by appt ▪ BYO picnic ▪ Owner(s) Geoff Brooker, Mark Howell, Steve Kirk-Cohen, Andre Smalberger & Terry Winstanley ▪ Cellarmaster(s)/winemaker(s) Steve Kirk-Cohen, Andre Smalberger & Terry Winstanley (2000), Mark Howell & Geoff Brooker (2005) ▪ ±1,176cs own label 85% red 15% white ▪ c/o Terry Winstanley PO Box 695 Cape Town 8000 ▪ terry.winstanley@dlacdh.com ▪ S 33° 55' 25.96" E 018° 57' 03.12" ▪ F +27 (0)21-481-9516 ▪ **T +27 (0)21-481-6332**

Epicurean Wines

The ancient Greek philosopher Epicurs understood pleasure as the measure of what is good. The idea appeals to the four socially powerful winelovers - Mutle Mogase, Mbhazima Shilowa, Moss Ngoasheng and Ron Gault - behind this venture. 'All the luxury boxes have been ticked' by the Rupert & Rothschild team in Franschhoek, who source the grapes and make the wine.

★★★★ **Epicurean 10** (★★★★★) expertly blends merlot with cab, cab franc & a dab petit verdot. Firmly built, but eschews power in favour of gently rich, bright-fruited elegance & suavity. Easily absorbs all-new oak. Modern, but not too fruity, with savoury vinosity. Will develop. **08** lighter; no **09**. — TJ

WO: Western Cape ▪ Est 2001 ▪ 1stB 2003 ▪ Closed to public ▪ Owner(s) Global Pact Trading 125 (Pty) Ltd ▪ Cellarmaster(s) Mutle Mogase, Mbhazima Shilowa, Moss Ngoasheng, Ron Gault (Nov 2002) ▪ Winemaker(s) Schalk Willem Joubert (consultant) ▪ 1,000cs own label 100% red ▪ WIETA ▪ PO Box 280 Parklands Johannesburg 2121 ▪ info@epicureanwine.co.za ▪ www.epicureanwine.co.za ▪ F +27 (0)11-530-9101 ▪ **T +27 (0)11-530-9100**

Equitania

Equitania, in the shadow of the Helderberg, is the dream home of Esme de Beer, with garden designed by a feng shui master and small vineyard. The resulting harvest has been vinified at Stellenbosch Hills since maiden 2008. Stock is moving nicely, thanks to referrals, prompting farm manager Danita Rogers to remark: 'Word of mouth advertisement is truly on the palate.'

★★★★ **Flag** ⊘ Classic Bordeaux-style aromas of berries & lead pencil on pleasingly restrained **12** (★★★★) sample. Like **10**, from cab, cab franc. Unexceptional savoury palate, dry & balanced; modestly oaked. **11** not made.

Not tasted: **Fluke**. — TJ

Location: Somerset West ▪ Map: Helderberg ▪ WO: Stellenbosch ▪ Est 2000 ▪ 1stB 2008 ▪ Tasting & sales by appt ▪ Fee R10 ▪ Closed all pub hols ▪ BYO picnic ▪ Walking/hiking trails ▪ Owner(s) Esme Kruger de Beer ▪ Winemaker(s) PG Slabbert (Stellenbosch Hills) ▪ Viticulturist(s) Gavin Dun (May 2007) ▪ 4.65ha/1.38ha (cabs s/f) ▪ 10.54t/12,000cs own label 100% red ▪ PO Box 5308 Helderberg 7135 ▪ esme14@mweb.co.za ▪ www.equitania.co.za ▪ S 34° 2' 26.15" E 018° 49' 5.51" ▪ F +27 (0)21-300-1092 ▪ **T +27 (0)21-300-1140/1**

Ernie Els Wines

One of the world's top professional golfers, Ernie Els' career wins include four major championships. Nicknamed 'The Big Easy' due to his fluid, seemingly effortless golf swing, Ernie established an eponymous winery in Stellenbosch in 1999, Louis Strydom head winemaker since inception. Originally, there was just one Bordeaux-style red blend made in a modern, full-bodied style and carrying an ultra-premium price tag, but the range has grown and now includes a number of more modestly conceived, medium-priced wines. The intention is to focus increasingly on cabernet sauvignon: a planting programme underway will result in 10 different clones of the variety on the property.

Ernie Els Wines range

★★★★ **Cabernet Sauvignon** Earthy, tight **12** (★★★★★) merges deep, dark blackcurrants with mineral-iodine, cloaked with chalky ripe tannins. Bold & statuesque, blending flamboyant New-World strut with classic structure. Stellenbosch WO, like next. Back to best after lighter **11**.

★★★★★ **Proprietor's Cabernet Sauvignon** Massive, show-style **12** (★★★★★) impregnably tight & dense but promises great things given time. Pure & concentrated, with chalky tannins & endless finish. Crafted & deftly handled, showing in classic profile. A statement wine, like **11**.

★★★★ **Proprietor's Syrah** **12** is taut, ripe & full, offering massive substance & dense black fruit, power over finesse. Still dominated by oaky vanilla, should smooth out with time.

★★★★☆ **Ernie Els Signature** Sumptuous, dense **11** cab-led Bordeaux blend returns to form after less convincing **10** (★★★★). Powerful but elegantly poised, with herbaceous aromas, deep, dark liquorice & iodine, overlaid by intense blackcurrant essence. Stellenbosch WO.

★★★★ Proprietor's Blend Big, overtly ripe & forceful, yet still showing delicate leafy herbaceous notes, **12** blend of 5 Bordeaux red grapes plus shiraz (all Stellenbosch) has dense chalky tannins & rich currant fruit though lacks a bit on finish.

★★★★☆ CWG Auction Reserve Impressive **12** (**★★★★★**) blends Stellenbosch cab, shiraz & merlot (as did **11**) in a tour de force. Dark & tarry, with massive tannins, but showing underlying subtlety of fruit, spices & aromas. Needs & deserves several years to emerge & soften.

Also tasted: **Merlot 12 ★★★★ Sauvignon Blanc 14 ★★★☆**

Big Easy range

★★★★ Red Juicy, fruit-packed, Rhône-style 6-way blend with cab, **12** offers charming fynbos & peppery notes. **13**, also tasted, hass family resemblance but plumper, riper fruit on still-rigid tannins.

Rosé **★★★** From shiraz. **14** typical strawberry cordial character, biggish body, good fruity just-dry finish. Also tasted: **White 14 ★★★☆** — GdB

Location/map: Stellenbosch ▪ WO: Western Cape/Stellenbosch ▪ Est 1999 ▪ 1stB 2000 ▪ Tasting, sales & cellar tours Mon-Sat 9–5 ▪ Fee Player's tasting R40/Major's tasting R60 (4 wines each) ▪ Closed Easter Fri/Sun, Dec 25 & Jan 1 ▪ Light lunches & cheese platters Tue-Sat ▪ Tour groups ▪ Gift shop ▪ Corporate events & functions ▪ Small conference facilities ▪ Mountain biking trail ▪ Ernie Els' Trophy Room ▪ The Big Easy Restaurant at 95 Dorp Str ▪ Owner(s) Ernie Els ▪ Cellarmaster(s) Louis Strydom (Dec 1999) ▪ Winemaker(s) Louis Strydom (Dec 1999), with Danie van Tonder (2013) ▪ Viticulturist(s) Charl van Reenen (2008) ▪ 72ha/45ha (cab, merlot, shiraz) ▪ 250t/18,000cs own label 90% red 10% white + 1,500cs for clients ▪ Brands for clients: SA Rugby ▪ PO Box 7595 Stellenbosch 7599 ▪ info@ernieelswines.com ▪ www.ernieelswines.com ▪ S 34° 0' 52.8" E 018° 50' 53.5" ▪ F +27 (0)21-881-3688 ▪ **T +27 (0)21-881-3588**

Ernst Gouws & Co Wines

Members of the Gouws family have been active in the Stellenbosch wine business for more than 150 years. Today, Koelenhof-based Ernst and wife Gwenda are the driving force, and following in the footsteps of their father are Ezanne and Ernst jnr, both graduate winemakers from Stellenbosch University.

★★★★ Chardonnay 13 (**★★★★**) has aromas of green melon, peach & lemon curd. Rich but fresh, if straightforward despite the subtle hint of oak & spice. **12** notably good. WO Wellington.

★★★★★ Nineteenfiftytwo Stunning debut few years back as 'Depth'. **11** Bordeaux-style white, 65% sauvignon & new-oaked semillon, from Elgin. Mouthfilling yet harmonious & elegant.

Merlot ★★★☆ Mulberry, tobacco & plum notes on **12** lead to a palate with some depth & complexity, seamless oak integration. **Pinotage ★★★☆** Juicy **13**, aromas of plum, banana & allspice; youthful, vibrant & fruity, with very fine tannin & a thirst quenching quality. WO Coastal. Also tasted: **Pinot Noir 12 ★★★ Shiraz 12 ★★★☆ Sauvignon Blanc 14 ★★★** — JPf

Location/map: Stellenbosch ▪ WO: Stellenbosch/Coastal/Bot River/Wellington/Elgin ▪ Est/1stB 2003 ▪ Tasting & sales at Koelenhof Winery Mon-Thu 9-5 Fri 9-4 Sat 10-2 ▪ Fee R15pp ▪ Closed Easter Fri/Sun, Ascension day, Dec 25/ 26 & Jan 1 ▪ Facilities for children ▪ Owner(s) Ernst & Gwenda Gouws ▪ Cellarmaster(s) Ernst Gouws ▪ Winemaker(s) Ernst Gouws snr ▪ 60,000cs own label 40% red 60% white ▪ Other export brand: New Gate ▪ IPW ▪ PO Box 7450 Stellenbosch 7599 ▪ ernst@ernstgouws.co.za ▪ www.ernstgouws.co.za ▪ S 33° 50' 3.4" E 018° 47' 52.7" ▪ F +27 (0)21-865-2894 ▪ **T +27 (0)21-865-2895**

Esau Wines

Ex-chemical engineer Wim Hugo describes his Paarl venture as a 'micro-winery' - small but not garagiste (in fact, he plans to double production in the medium term). Focus is on red blends - cabernet-, pinotage-, shiraz- and mourvèdre-based — though 'once in a while we bottle exceptional cultivar wines'. He's toying with a light-style grenache, and now offers private tastings on request.

Non Pareille **★★★** Cab & shiraz blend from dryland bushvines high on Paarl Mountain, showing modest extraction yet big alcohol in **12**. Perhaps time will bring harmony. **Moerwetter** **★★★** Deep, big & solid mourvèdre ('moerwetter', get it?), drop grenache in **12**, equally forceful tannins, & medicinal note from oak spice. Also tasted: **Holy Cow** ⊘ **12 ★★★★ Château Esau 12 ★★★★** Occasional release: **Cabernet Sauvignon Reserve, Grenache Reserve**. — GdB

Location/WO: Paarl ▪ Map: Paarl & Wellington ▪ Est/1stB 2010 ▪ Private tastings on request ▪ Owner(s) Wim Hugo ▪ Cellarmaster(s) Wim Hugo (2009) ▪ Winemaker(s) Wim Hugo & Jorrie Jordaan (both 2009) ▪ 3t/2,500L 100% red ▪ PO Box 3175 Paarl 7620 ▪ whugo@mbv.co.za ▪ http://urlmin.com/esau ▪ **T +27 (0)79-875-4646**

Escapades Winery

The Greek friends behind this venture (which as yet concentrates primarily on exporting) is serious and experienced: two, Evangelos Gerovassiliou and Vassilis Tsaktsarlis, are leading winemakers, while Takis Soldatos built Sweden's top wine distribution company. All are fully involved, while Kiwi winemaker Chris Kelly is the local lynch-pin. Grapes are sourced widely and flexibly, says Chris – 'new vineyards can be included in our top ranges, while others may fall away if they don't meet our strict criteria'.

★★★★ Pinotage Improving label. Plush dark fruit, spice dusted, mocha chocolate threaded through, the **13** bouquet draws you in to firm but ripe tannins, showing the wine's serious side. Good food match. No **12**.

★★★★ Semillon New French oak gives an almond tone to **14**'s waxy lemon/lime flavours, fits the character. Quiet, youthful, needs time. With refinement, finesse, improves on **13** (★★★★).

★★★★ Semillon-Sauvignon Blanc Oaked semillon is 65% of **14**'s blend, dictates the style. Lemon/lime & tropical fruit, subtle oatmeal seam adds a savoury touch. Harmonious, seamless, sauvignon's role a hidden support. WO W Cape.

Also tasted: **Cabernet Sauvignon-Shiraz-Malbec 13 ★★★★ Pinotage Rosé 14 ★★★ Sauvignon Blanc 14 ★★★★** Discontinued: **Cabernet Sauvignon, Merlot, Shiraz**. — CR

Location/map: Stellenbosch ▪ WO: Coastal/Western Cape ▪ Est/1stB 2006 ▪ Tasting by appt ▪ Owner(s) Evangelos Gerovassiliou, Vassilis Tsaktsarlis & Takis Soldatos ▪ Cellarmaster(s) Vassilis Tsaktsarlis & Evangelos Gerovassiliou (both 2006) ▪ Winemaker(s) Chris Kelly (Oct 2010, consultant) ▪ (cab, malbec, merlot, ptage, shiraz, sauv, sem) ▪ 100t/10,000cs own label 40% red 50% white 10% rosé ▪ PO Box 99 Somerset Mall 7129 ▪ info@escapadewinery.com ▪ www.escapadewinery.com ▪ S 33° 54' 47.7" E 018° 44' 7.7" ▪ F +27 (0)86-585-6549 ▪ **T +27 (0)82-569-3371**

☐ **Eskdale** *see* De Zoete Inval Estate

Esona Boutique Wine

Family-owned Esona ('The Very One'), on a scenic stretch of the Breede River near Robertson, specialises in limited-release single-vineyard wines, available for tasting and sale in the original cellar. A deli has opened there, serving light meals indoors or on the deck overlooking the river and vineyards.

Location/map: Robertson ▪ Est 2002 ▪ 1stB 2010 ▪ Tasting, sales & cellar tours Mon-Fri 9-5 Sat/pub hols 10-4 ▪ Closed Dec 25 & Jan 1 ▪ Deli serving light picnic meals ▪ Facilities for children ▪ Owner(s) Rowan & Caryl Beattie ▪ Winemaker(s)/viticulturist(s) Lourens van der Westhuizen (Jan 2010, Arendsig) ▪ 17ha/9.83ha (pinot, shiraz, chard, chenin, cbard, sauv) ▪ ±250t/6,000cs own label 34% red 66% white ▪ PO Box 2619 Clareinch 7400 ▪ info@esona.co.za ▪ www.esona.co.za ▪ S 33° 54' 16.14" E 020° 0' 38.66" ▪ F +27 (0)21-787-3792 ▪ **T +27 (0)76-343-5833**

☐ **Essay** *see* MAN Family Wines
☐ **Eternal** *see* Kumala

Excelsior Estate

Bearing a surname synonymous with racehorses and wines, both nurtured by Robertson's lime-rich soils, Freddie de Wet and son Peter showcase another familial characteristic: hospitality. The family (and family-friendly) estate with its century-old Cape Dutch Revival manor guest house and damside picnic spot has added a deli and new rosé to its array of wine-and-food offerings. Community support continues through a farm crèche and local school funding.

Excelsior Reserve range

★★★★ **Evanthuis Cabernet Sauvignon** Off farm's oldest vines, a homage to champion Hackney horse imported in 1913. Cassis, nice espresso note, **12** is back on track after **10** (★★★☆); tannins firm but ripe. No **11**.

San Louis Shiraz ★★★☆ Recognises never-say-die Guineas winner. **12** black plums, meaty tones, a spice array from French/America/Hungarian barrels, remains sleek & accessible. Not retasted: **Agricola Sauvignon Blanc 12** ★★★☆ Not tasted: **Gondolier Merlot**.

Excelsior Estate range

Merlot ★★★ Cassis & cedar, only partially oaked in **13** to get the best of both worlds, spicing & structure yet retaining juicy fruit. **Caitlyn Rosé** ★★★ **14** exuberantly fruity in style, touch of sugar makes it even friendlier. From cab. **Chardonnay** ★★★ Previewed **14** flavourful & plumply round from partial oaking, dab sugar. Versatile food partner or enjoy solo. **Viognier** ★★★ Peach & floral perfume on this off-dry **14** charmer, enough freshness to give a tangy effect to the flavours. Also tasted: **Cabernet Sauvignon 12** ★★★ **Paddock Shiraz 12** ★★★ **Purebred Red** ⊘ **13** ★★★ **Sauvignon Blanc 14** ★★★ — CR

Location/map/WO: Robertson ▪ Est 1859 ▪ 1stB 1990 ▪ Tasting & sales Mon-Fri 10-4 Sat 10-3 ▪ Deli serving light lunches ▪ Picnics available on request, or BYO picnic ▪ Facilities for children ▪ Conferences ▪ 4-star Excelsior Manor Guest House ▪ Owner(s) Freddie & Peter de Wet ▪ Cellarmaster(s) Johan Stemmet (Aug 2003) ▪ Winemaker(s) Johan Stemmet (Aug 2003), with Kelly Gova (2005) ▪ Viticulturist(s) Freddie de Wet (1970) ▪ 320ha/220ha (cab, merlot, p verdot, shiraz, chard, sauv) ▪ 2,200t/320,000cs own label 75% red 25% white ▪ Other export brand: Stablemate ▪ BRC ▪ PO Box 17 Ashton 6715 ▪ info@excelsior.co.za ▪ www.excelsior.co.za ▪ S 33° 51' 15.1" E 020° 0' 25.6" ▪ F +27 (0)23-615-2019 ▪ **T +27 (0)23-615-1980**

Excelsior Vlakteplaas

Danie Schoeman's early 20th-century bulk wine-cellar, where he produces muscadel for bottling under his own label in even years only, stars in another type of production: SA film director Koos Roets' adaptation of playwright Pieter Fourie's 1975 local classic Faan se Trein, released in 2014.

His Master's Choice range

Red Muscadel ★★★★ Honey & blossoms on **12** raisin-sweet fortified charmer, just enough acid & tannic grip to prevent it being cloying. **White Muscadel** ★★★ Winter-warming **12** fortified dessert, succulent Golden Delicious apple & honey flavours, slightly sticky conclusion but still lovely. — DB

Location: De Rust ▪ Map: Klein Karoo & Garden Route ▪ WO: Klein Karoo ▪ Est 1934 ▪ 1stB 1998 ▪ Tasting & sales by appt only ▪ Closed Easter Fri-Mon, Ascension Day, Dec 16/25/26 & Jan 1 ▪ Owner(s)/winemaker(s) Danie Schoeman ▪ 41ha (merlot, ptage, ruby cab, chenin, muscadel r/w) ▪ 490t/2,000cs own label 50% red 50% white ▪ PO Box 112 De Rust 6650 ▪ jjschoeman@telkomsa.net ▪ S 33° 29' 16.74" E 022° 35' 25.50" ▪ F +27 (0)44-241-2569 ▪ **T +27 (0)82-821-3556**

Fable Mountain Vineyards

Bought in 2010 by Charles Banks of Californian-based wine and hospitality investment firm Terroir Capital, Fable (with Stellenbosch property Mulderbosch) forms part of the Terroir Selections portfolio of wine sites in California, Chile, Argentina, Italy and New Zealand, handpicked for viticultural uniqueness. Australian Rebecca Tanner and South African Paul Nicholls, young partners in life and wine-growing, are the dedicated duo here, working with the deep shale soils of the Witzenberg Mountain foothills between Tulbagh and Wolseley. Chenin and Rhône varieties are the focus, blending 'a top priority', belief in sustainable, biodynamic farming unshakeable. All this aimed at making great wines from small, meticulously vinified parcels of fruit to express 'our increasingly solid knowledge of the site and the elements of this beautiful wilderness area'.

For more information, visit wineonaplatter.com

★★★★★ **Syrah** Masterly **12** shows great depth & freshness in its expressive dark spice, gentle red fruit. Good in youth thanks to perfect balance & refined tannins but promises much more in long term. Natural ferment, bottled unfined/filtered, as all.

★★★★☆ **Night Sky** Rich yet unheavy **12** tank sample has sound core freshness in its shiraz (60%) with grenache (25%) & mourvèdre blend. Clean leather & spice notes cradled by fine juicy tannins make for youthful accessibility; good potential too. **11** (★★★★) more chewy. WO Coastal.

★★★★☆ **Jackal Bird** Beautifully textured **13**, with delicate mineral vitality, form-giving pithy grip. Structure in harmony with elegant whole of its pure chenin, grenache blanc, chardonnay, viognier & roussanne make-up. Bought in fruit, like **12** (★★★★★). WO W Cape. — AL

Location/map: Tulbagh ▪ WO: Tulbagh/Coastal/Western Cape ▪ Est 1989 ▪ 1stB 2009 ▪ Tasting & cellar tours by appt only ▪ Conservation area ▪ Owner(s) Terroir Selections ▪ Winegrowers Rebecca Tanner & Paul Nicholls (both Jul 2009) ▪ 185ha/30ha (grenache, mourv, syrah, viog) ▪ PO Box 12817 Die Boord 7613 ▪ rebecca@fablewines.com ▪ www.fablewines.com ▪ S 33° 21' 7.9" E 019° 12' 46.1" ▪ **T +27 (0)78-315-3861/+27 (0)73-768-1600**

☐ **Fairhills** see Origin Wine
☐ **Fairtrade Original** see uniWines Vineyards

Fairvalley Wines

One of the original employee empowerment ventures in SA, Fairvalley is wholly owned by 42 families from next-door Fairview. Their overseas markets continue to grow, notably the US, and sales are helped by Fairtrade accreditation and a sustainability programme, preserving the land for the future.

Pinotage ★★★ A raspberry bomb of a wine, **13** ex barrel has loads of varietal character, well-balanced, well-priced everyday glugger. **Sauvignon Blanc** ★★★ Pre-bottling, **13** shows ripe fruit salad notes & zippy grapefruit finish. Happy summer wine. Fairtrade certified, as all. Not retasted: **Chardonnay 13** ★★★ **Chenin Blanc 13** ★★☆ Not tasted: **Cabernet Sauvignon**. — CM

Location: Paarl ▪ WO: Western Cape ▪ Est 1997 ▪ 1stB 1998 ▪ Tasting by appt only ▪ Fee R25 ▪ Sales at Fairview 9-4.30 daily ▪ Closed Good Fri, Dec 25 & Jan 1 ▪ Owner(s) Fairvalley Farmworkers Association ▪ Cellarmaster(s) Jaco Brand (2010) ▪ Winemaker(s) Jaco Brand, with Andries de Klerk (both 2010) ▪ 30,000cs own label 50% red 50% white ▪ Fairtrade ▪ PO Box 6219 Paarl 7620 ▪ wine@fairvalley.co.za ▪ www.fairvalley.co.za ▪ F +27 (0)21-863-2591 ▪ **T +27 (0)21-863-2450**

Fairview

Nothing stands still at this Paarl powerhouse, and all areas of the bustling wine and cheese business continue to grow and improve. Crowning more than thirty years of pioneering innovation and outstanding success, Fairview owner Charles Back was a well-deserved and universally applauded recipient of the prestigious International Wine Challenge's Lifetime Achievement Award last year. The award cited his pioneering work in introducing new varieties to SA, developing new regions (such as Swartland) as well as his commitment to empowering and investing in staff on the home farm. Fairview's various labels including Goats do Roam, Leeuwenjacht, Spice Route and Land's End, listed separately, offer a range of classic and unusual varieties, cleverly packaged to suit their markets.

Fairview range

★★★★ **Cabernet Sauvignon** Good varietal expression on **12** (★★★☆) but, compared to **11**, slightly unfocused mid-palate disappoints, finish doesn't linger.

★★★★ **Barbera** Dense & chewy **13** (★★★★) with hints of mint, fruit a little raisined & over-ripe compared to **11**. No **12**. Coastal WO.

★★★★ **Mourvèdre** ⊘ Deliciously supple **13** steps up on **11** (★★★☆) with a rounded mouthful of red & black berried fruit underlined by a pleasing savoury grip. From Paarl & Malmesbury. No **12**.

★★★★ **Petite Sirah** ⊘ Was 'Durif'. **12** (★★★★☆) improves on **11** with a heady mouthful of exuberant black cherries, liquorice, menthol & polish. Lovely rustic texture & mouthfeel add interest, grippy tannins should soften & fully integrate with time.

★★★★☆ **Primo Pinotage** Powerful & poised **12** impresses with a polished mouthful of blackberries, leather & spice. Given presence by muscular tannins, American oak adds plenty of spice & smoke whilst the French wood gives elegance & charm.

★★★★☆ **Eenzaamheid Shiraz** The silky one of the three 'vineyard' shirazes, **12** delivers a sweet-fruited nose with whiffs of juniper berries & cranberries. 'Graceful elegance' are the watchwords, as black fruit & silky tannins meld delightfully into a poised finish.

★★★★☆ **The Beacon Shiraz** 'The spicy one.' Needing time to show off its charms, **12** already impresses with layers of perfumed black pepper, coriander & hints of smoke. Plushy black fruit, backed up by tight tannins, **11** oakier with plenty of sweet fruit. Now WO Swartland following regional reorganisation.

★★★★☆ **Jakkalsfontein Shiraz** 'The perfumed one.' **12** has an enticing mixture of aromatic, hedonistic perfume & spice. Savoury notes on the palate add another dimension, deliciously rounded by black plummy notes, leather & excellent lengthy finish. Swartland WO.

★★★★☆ **Cyril Back** Powerful & intense tribute to Back patriarch, **12** packs a heady punch of dense black fruit, hints of dark chocolate with brooding tannins lurking smoothly in the background. Needs, & absolutely deserves, more time. WO Coastal. **10** & **11** sold out untasted.

★★★★ **Caldera** Upfront nose of fresh juicy red berries - strawberries & currants - on **12** southern Rhône blend led by grenache. Smooth tannins swirl around punchy alcohol, both indicating time required.

★★★★ **Extraño** ⊘ Rocking Rioja-lookalike blend of tempranillo, grenache & carignan, **11** is packed with clean, fresh black & red fruit now, but hints of savoury meatiness suggest lots more to come. More interesting than **10** (★★★★). Coastal WO.

★★★★ **Oom Pagel Semillon** ⊘ Delicious **12** (★★★★★) now just starting to edge towards mature flavours of pine needles, herbal honey & baked citrus. Wonderful balance throughout of oak (none new), concentrated, elegant fruit & acidity. From Darling bushvines, like **11**.

★★★★ **Viognier** One of the Cape's earliest & leading examples, **13** is perfumed & aromatic with prominent orange citrus & fragrant gingery notes. Refreshing acidity, delicate oak make for an elegant mouthful.

★★★★★ **Nurok White Blend** Very lovely **13** (★★★★★) continues to impress after complex **12** with viognier-dominated chenin, roussanne & grenache blanc in enticing melange of spiced peaches & golden raisins, subtle oaking keeps interest right through to lengthy finish.

★★★★ **Méthode Cap Classique Brut** **12** great follow-up to debut **11** as viognier, grenaches blanc & noir combine to give mouthful of honeyed peaches & yellow citrus, with frothy mousse & crisp acidity.

★★★★☆ **La Beryl Blanc** Utterly delicious **13** blends two-thirds chenin with muscat (up from 21% in **12** in lavish & unctuous unoaked straw wine. Flavours of honey & rosepetal vie with tangy marmalade & honey plus hints of sweet spice, all freshened & lifted by acidity.

Pinotage ★★★★ Attractive, characterful **13** has grippy edge to the black fruit & a dry finish. **Tannat** ★★★★ Charry coffee nose of **12** gives way to interesting fennel & liquorice notes with black fruit & some rather plushy tannins. **Darling Chenin Blanc** ★★★★ Delicious mouthful of tinned pears on **14** with hints of grapefruit & spice. Good depth of flavour, should improve. **Roussanne** ⓃⒺⓌ ★★★★ Delightful debut **14** shows real typicity, with peachy notes & almond blossom. Gentle acidity & a positive finish make for a great food wine. Also tasted: **Merlot 12** ★★★★ **Shiraz 12** ★★★★ **Chardonnay 13** ★★★★ **Darling Riesling 14** ★★★ **Darling Sauvignon Blanc 14** ★★★ **Viognier Special Late Harvest 14** ★★☆ **Sweet Red 12** ★★☆ Not tasted: **Pegleg Carignan**. In abeyance: **La Beryl Rouge**. Discontinued: **Sangiovese**.

La Capra range

Malbec ★★★☆ **13** really interesting flavours of black cherry yoghurt & vanilla spice. **Sangiovese** ⓝ ◌ ★★★ Cheery **13** offers lots of berried fruit, pleasing dryness, good length. Coastal WO. **Pinotage Rosé** ★★★ Fruity little number **14** - strawberries & leaves - for easy dry drinking. **Viognier** ★★★ **14** terrific example for the price - all mandarin oranges, perfume & spice. Also tasted: **Merlot** ◌ **13** ★★★ **Pinotage** ◌ **13** ★★★ **Shiraz** ◌ **13** ★★★☆ **Chardonnay 14** ★★★ **Chenin Blanc 14** ★★★ **Pinot Grigio 14** ★★★ **Sauvignon Blanc 14** ★★☆ Not retasted: **Cabernet Sauvignon 12** ★★★ — CM

Location: Paarl ▪ Map: Paarl & Wellington ▪ WO: Paarl/Coastal/Darling/Stellenbosch/Swartland ▪ Est 1693 ▪ 1stB 1974 ▪ Tasting & sales Mon-Sun 9–5, last tasting 30min before closing ▪ R25/standard tasting, R60/master tasting ▪ Closed Good Fri, Dec 25 & Jan 1 ▪ The Goatshed Restaurant ▪ Tour groups by appt only ▪ Deli: artisanal cheeses & fresh farm breads ▪ Owner(s) Charles Back ▪ Winemaker(s) Anthony de Jager (Dec 1996), with Stephanie Betts (2010) & Adele Dunbar (2006) ▪ 500ha/300ha (cab, carignan, grenache, merlot, mourv, petite sirah, ptage, shiraz, tannat, tempranillo, chenin, sauv, viog) ▪ 2,100t/260cs own label 80% red 15% white 5% rosé ▪ ISO 9001:2001, BWI, BRC, Fairtrade, HACCP, IPW, WIETA ▪ PO Box 583 Suider-Paarl 7624 ▪ info@fairview.co.za ▪ www.fairview.co.za ▪ S 33° 46' 19.16" E 018° 55' 25.26" ▪ F +27 (0)21-863-2591 ▪ **T +27 (0)21-863-2450**

False Bay Vineyards

False Bay and Peacock Ridge are the pocket-friendly offerings of Paul Boutinot's Helderberg-based Waterkloof winery. Though grapes are sourced widely, they are treated with the respect shown for the home-farm's labels, even using natural fermentation in many cases.

False Bay Vineyards range

Pinotage ◌ ★★★☆ A veritable berry orchard of a wine, medium-bodied **13** is quite tangy, with dusty tannins. Calls for biltong. **Chardonnay** ★★★☆ Unwooded **13** ex Robertson & Perdeberg, pear & melon notes, soft texture caressing the palate, citrus tang adding freshness. Also tasted: **Shiraz 12** ★★★ **Rosé 13** ★★ **Chenin Blanc 13** ★★☆ **Sauvignon Blanc 14** ★★★

Peacock Ridge range

Wild Ferment Cabernet Sauvignon ★★★ Was 'Cabernet Sauvignon'. Basket-pressed, spontaneously fermented **12** cinnamon & cassis on nose, ultra-ripe dark fruit flavours leaving almost off-dry, dark chocolate impression. Stellenbosch WO. Also tasted: **Sauvignon Blanc 13** ★★★ Not retasted: **Merlot 11** ★★★☆ **Shiraz 12** ★★☆ **Chenin Blanc 12** ★★★ — JG

Location: Somerset West ▪ WO: Western Cape/Stellenbosch ▪ Est/1stB 2000 ▪ Tasting at Waterkloof (see entry) ▪ Owner(s) Paul Boutinot ▪ Cellarmaster(s) Nadia Barnard (Jan 2013) ▪ 160,000cs own label 30% red 65% white 5% rosé ▪ PO Box 2093 Somerset West 7129 ▪ info@waterkloofwines.co.za ▪ www.falsebayvineyards.co.za ▪ F +27 (0)21-858-1293 ▪ **T +27 (0)21-858-1292**

☐ **Fantail** *see* Morgenhof Wine Estate
☐ **Far & Near** *see* L'Avenir Vineyards

Faraway House Wine Estate

Extensive Faraway farm, mostly given over to indigenous flora, lives up to its name, lying high above Theewaterskloof Dam near Villiersdorp. Only a small portion is planted with vines and an even smaller quantity of grapes vinified for the estate label, the remainder sold off to high-profile wineries.

Shiraz ★★★☆ **10** very ripe olive & leather aromas; tightly gripped by assertive grape tannins; lightish, very fresh feel. Not retasted: **Quadrille 10** ★★☆ **Classic 10** ★★★☆ — AL

Location/map: Villiersdorp ▪ WO: Overberg ▪ Est 2002 ▪ 1stB 2008 ▪ Tasting by appt ▪ Closed Easter Fri-Mon, Ascension day, Pentecost & Dec 25/26 ▪ Owner(s) Faraway House Estate (Pty) Ltd ▪ Winemaker(s) Nicolas Follet & David Ciry ▪ Viticulturist(s) Willem Pelser ▪ 90ha/9ha (merlot, ptage, shiraz, chard, sauv) ▪ 30t/4,000cs own label 80% red 15% white 5% rosé ▪ PO Box 403 Villiersdorp 6848 ▪ sales@farawayhouse.co.za ▪ www.farawayhouse.co.za ▪ S 33° 56' 24.63" E 019° 19 '39.41" ▪ F +27 (0)28-840-2740 ▪ **T +27 (0)72-342-5052**

☐ **Farm Animals** *see* Osbloed Wines

Fat Bastard

What started out as an experimental chardonnay tasted in a dank cellar by two friends, UK wine brand creator Guy Anderson and French winemaker Thierry Boudinaud, who pronounced it a 'fat bastard', has become a successful range on both sides of the Atlantic. In South Africa, it's made by Robertson Winery.

Pinot Noir ⓃⒺⓌ ★★★☆ Smoky forest floor & spicy red fruit, **13** firm core to lithe, supple body, light but powerful. **Chardonnay** ★★★ Softly rounded, tropical-styled **13** shows just a brush of oak from wood chips. Creamy delight. Also tasted: **Cabernet Sauvignon 12 ★★★☆ Sauvignon Blanc 13** ★★★ Not retasted: **Pinotage 11 ★★★☆ Shiraz 12 ★★★** — FM

☐ **Feast** *see* Domaine Coutelier

Feiteiras Vineyards

Brothers Manuel and Jose de Andrade brought traditional Portuguese winemaking — including a rare pole-operated basket press — to their Bot River farm over a decade ago. They since moved operations up the road to Beaumont, where Marelise Jansen van Rensburg crafts the wine under Jose's guidance.

Troca Tintas ★★★★ Fragrant & polished **13** sample with spiced black fruits & sweet, cheery finish. From shiraz + Bordeaux varieties. Not retasted: **Cabernet Sauvignon 11 ★★★★ Casa Merlot Rosé 12 ★★★ Verdelho 13 ★★★★** Not tasted: **Vinho Forte Tinto**, **Vinho Forte Branco**. Discontinued: **Côr de Rosa**. — CM

Location/WO: Bot River ▪ Map: Elgin, Walker Bay & Bot River ▪ Est 2003 ▪ 1stB 2004 ▪ Tasting & sales by appt ▪ Owner(s) De Andrade family ▪ Cellarmaster(s)/winemaker(s) Marelise Jansen van Rensburg (Beaumont) & Jose de Andrade ▪ Viticulturist(s) Manuel de Andrade ▪ 16.2ha/4.2ha (cab, merlot, mourv, shiraz, verdelho) ▪ 1,200cs own label 60% red 30% white 10% rosé ▪ PO Box 234 Bot River 7185 ▪ feiteiraswine@icon.co.za ▪ www.feiteiraswine.co.za ▪ S 34° 14' 3.6" E 019° 12' 33.3" ▪ F +27 (0)28-284-9525 ▪ **T +27 (0)82-453-1597**

Félicité

Easygoing wines that pass through clever winemaking hands in the Newton Johnson winery, though the chardonnay and rosé are vinified at Stettyn Cellar. Rising volumes have put pressure on the limited space in the premium NJ cellar - but the pinot, cornerstone of the brand, is fully vinified there.

Dry Rosé ★★★ Carnival pink & jammed with cranberries, **14** ends bracingly dry. From shiraz, with splashes sauvignon & viognier. A party treat. WO W Cape, as all. Not retasted: **Pinot Noir 12 ★★★★** Not tasted: **No Oak Chardonnay**. — DS

☐ **Ferling Noble** *see* Rooiberg Winery

Fernskloof Wines

Fernskloof's Diederik le Grange has these observations about being a vintner in Prince Albert Valley, a Groot Karoo area traditionally associated with sheep farming: 'Our wines have more of a spicy note to them. Maybe it's a climate thing, or the fact that Fernskloof is organic. We and the other local wineries add nice diversity to the SA wine scene, not just because our wines are different but our visitor experience is different too. We're fortunate to represent a small town [Prince Albert] that's increasingly popular. Saying your wine is the best is just boring. What I do hope is that you will like our wine, and everything associated with it. Then I'm happy!'

Merlot ⓃⒺⓌ ⓋⒼ ★★★ Soft, sweet plums on **12**. Easy & succulent, with gentle tannin structure. **Shiraz-Merlot** ⓃⒺⓌ ⓋⒼ ★★★ Espresso-toned, creamy & just-dry **12**. Meaty-spicy savoury flavours, smooth & effortless, slight grip on finish. **Barrel Fermented Pinotage Rosé** ⓋⒼ ★★★ Salmon pink, off-dry **12**, creamy texture, fragrant strawberry fruit & spice aromas & flavours. Also tasted:

Cabernet Sauvignon **12** ★★★★ Not tasted: **Red**, **Pinotage-Shiraz**, **Chardonnay**. In abeyance: **Pinotage**. — WB

Location: Prince Albert ▪ Map: Klein Karoo & Garden Route ▪ WO: Prince Albert Valley ▪ Est 2009 ▪ 1stB 2010 ▪ Tasting & sales Mon-Fri 9-5 Sat 10-5 Sun by appt 10-5 ▪ Closed Good Fri, Ascension Day & Dec 25 ▪ Facilities for children ▪ BYO picnic ▪ Walks/hikes ▪ 10km mountain running trail ▪ Conservation area ▪ Angeliersbosch guest house (up to 8 guests), no pets allowed ▪ Owner(s) Le Grange family ▪ Cellarmaster(s)/winemaker(s) Diederik le Grange (2010) ▪ Viticulturist(s) Diederik le Grange (2009) ▪ 1,026ha/8ha (cab, merlot, ptage, shiraz, chard) ▪ 40t/1,900cs own label 42% red 29% white 29% rosé ▪ BWI, SGS Organic ▪ PO Box 41 Prince Albert 6930 ▪ info@fernskloof.co.za ▪ www. fernskloof.co.za ▪ S 33° 16' 23.77" E 022° 10' 55.60" ▪ F +27 (0)23-541-1702 ▪ **T +27 (0)23-541-1702**

☐ **5th Avenue Cold Duck** *see* Cold Duck (5th Avenue)
☐ **56Hundred** *see* Nederburg Wines

Fijndraai Estate

Originally part of Welmoed, a subdivision of Meerlust given to Jacobus van der Heyden for his courage in refusing to apologise for calling later-disgraced Cape governor Willem Adriaan van der Stel a crook, Fijndraai is now planted with Mediterranean blends in mind. 'Although complex, they are non-pretentious wines that can be enjoyed by novices and connoisseurs alike,' say owners Laurel van Coller and Veronique Kritzinger, who offer an 'intimate' winefarm experience.

Family Reserve range

VCR ⊕ ★★★★ Viognier-led white blend with oak fermented/aged chenin (15%) & dash roussanne in **12**, shows the expected aromatic entry: orange blossom & peach, with almost muscaty flavours. Dry & modest alcohol. Bring out the spicy dishes! — CR, CvZ

Location/WO: Stellenbosch ▪ Est 2007 ▪ 1stB 2011 ▪ Sales via website ▪ Olive oil ▪ Walks/hikes ▪ Mountain biking trail ▪ Self-catering accommodation ▪ Equestrian centre ▪ Owner(s) Laurel van Coller & Veronique Kritzinger ▪ Winemaker(s) Ken Forrester (Jan 2010, consultant) ▪ Viticulturist(s) Pieter Rossouw (Feb 2011, consultant) ▪ 93ha/12ha (durif, grenache, sangio, shiraz, pinot grigio, rouss, viog) ▪ 134t/1,094cs own label 57% red 43% white ▪ WIETA ▪ PO Box 24 Lynedoch Stellenbosch 7603 ▪ fijndraaiwine@gmail.com ▪ www.fijndraai.com ▪ **T +27 (0)82-817-6372**

☐ **Finch Mountain** *see* Rooiberg Winery
☐ **Firefly** *see* Stellar Winery

FirstCape Vineyards

Formed in 2002, this joint venture between five Breede Valley cellars and British marketer Brand Phoenix retains its position as the biggest-selling South African brand in the UK wine market overall. All bottling is now done offshore in the UK. The export-only wines are available as FirstCape (Five Cellars, Winemaker's Selection, Limited Release, Special Cuvée, Coral Tree, First Selection, Special Reserve); Discovery Series Light (5.5% alcohol); FirstCape Sparkler; and FirstCape Rosé Sparkler.

Location: Paarl ▪ Est 2002 ▪ Closed to public ▪ Owner(s) De Wet, Goudini, Aan de Doorns, Badsberg & Stettyn wineries ▪ Winemaker(s) David Smit ▪ WIETA accredited ▪ PO Box 62 Simondium 7670 ▪ david@firstcape.com ▪ www.firstcape. com ▪ F +27 (0)21-874-8344 ▪ **T +27 (0)21-874-8340**

☐ **First Sighting** *see* Strandveld Wines

Fish Hoek Wines

The good-value and accessible Fish Hoek bottlings from Accolade Wines SA continue to prove popular both at home and overseas, particularly in Asia. Belief in keeping things simple while maintaining quality is reflected in this growing success.

Shiraz ⊘ ★★★★ Over-delivering **13** shows peppered & spiced meats in a juicy mouthful, with red & black berries to the fore. **Sauvignon Blanc** ⊘ ★★★★ Step-up **14** gains depth & concentration from lees-ageing, offers delicious crunchy green apple & lemon curd flavours. Has summer embedded

For more information, visit wineonaplatter.com

in it. Also tasted: **Merlot** 13 ★★★ **Pinotage** 13 ★★★ **Pinotage Rosé** 14 ★★★ **Chenin Blanc** 14 ★★★ — CM

Location: Somerset West ▪ Map: Helderberg ▪ WO: Western Cape ▪ Tasting, sales & cellar tours at Flagstone Winery (see entry) ▪ Owner(s) Accolade Wines South Africa ▪ Winemaker(s) Karen Bruwer (Feb 2013) & Bruce Jack (1998) ▪ 50% red 50% white ▪ PO Box 769 Stellenbosch 7599 ▪ flagstone@accolade-wines.com ▪ S 34° 5' 26.38" E 018° 48' 30.04" ▪ F +27 (0)21-852-5085 ▪ **T +27 (0)21-852-5052**

☐ **Five Climates** *see* Boland Kelder
☐ **Five Generations** *see* Cederberg Private Cellar
☐ **Five's Reserve** *see* Van Loveren Family Vineyards

Flagship

A Stellenbosch Vineyards premium brand, with back label referencing Nature's fickleness and the 'magic' that happens on the rare occasions when she smiles on the viticultural team. 'The result is a wine that is, in every sense, deserving of the name "The Flagship".'

★★★★★ **Petit Verdot** Enticing black berry, dark chocolate & exotic spice aromas on flagship **10** from Groenekloof vines. Lush, with acid & tannin backbone to give shape to concentrated fruit flavours. Seamless, velvety texture & unflagging sappy finish. — WB

Flagstone Winery

'It's a tough thing for me to say, but since winemaker Gerhard Swart took over the day to day running of Flagstone, the wines have never looked better. I've lost count of the gold medals we've won!,' says Bruce Jack, founder of this quality-focused arm of international wine company, Accolade Wines. In the vineyards, consultant Chris Keet continues to offer his expert advice on the many unique terroirs in diverse regions, including some of the oldest viticultural soils in the world at Elim near Cape Agulhas. Volumes have doubled in the last two years, a fact that Bruce attributes to the consistency of the brands as well as the launch of new labels such as the (untasted) Cheetah Reserve wines, with profits going to the winery's neighbours, the Cheetah Outreach project in Somerset West.

Flagstone range

★★★★☆ **Music Room Cabernet Sauvignon** Dark-berried fruits vie with red cherries, almonds & raspberries on fruit-packed **12**. Layers of dark chocolate edged with chewy tannins, vanilla & cedar spice all suggest a wine in waiting, one almost sure to improve.

★★★★☆ **Writer's Block Pinotage** Powerful **12** (★★★★) rocks between savoury notes of baked ham & black olives, & sweet red cranberry & redcurrant fruit. Polished tannins integrate well while alcohol asserts at finish. WO Breedekloof, like **11**.

★★★★☆ **Dark Horse Shiraz** Brooding **11** a melange of different aromas - ham, berries & spices all giving way to assertive coffee, dark chocolate & black cherry palate, backed by plushy tannins.

★★★★ **Dragon Tree** Shy **12** Cape Blend perks up quickly in glass with lots of polished black fruit - currants, plums, damsons - added to leather & liquorice. Cab, shiraz & pinotage all add texture & finesse. **11** sold out untasted.

★★★★☆ **Free Run Sauvignon Blanc** Masterly cool-climate **12** benefits from 14% semillon adding richness to gently pungent green figs & dusty hay. Layers of flavours including quince, green melons, guavas, wax & perfume. A sexy Sophia Loren, proudly showing her age. Elim & Elgin vines.

★★★★ **Word of Mouth Viognier** Expressive **13** shows classic ginger spice with orange stonefruit & citrus in elegant mouthful. Restrained oak (only 40% barrel-fermented) & well-managed alcohol give a fresh feel.

★★★★★ **Treaty Tree Reserve White Blend** Multi-layered, fine textured - **13** from Elim oozes class & refinement. A third of the sauvignon/semillon (74/26) blend undergoes barrel fermentation, adding toasted almond notes & incense to the baked citrus & flowers. Unspittable.

Also tasted: **Longitude** ⊘ 13 ★★★★ **Noon Gun** ⊘ 14 ★★★★ **Last Word** 09 ★★★☆ Occasional release: **Fiona Pinot Noir**.

Time Manner Place range
★★★★☆ **Pinotage** Only made in good years, **12** (★★★★★) certainly deserves attention & respect. Massive & powerful, flavours of peppered steak, smoked meats, perfumed blossom & spiced fruit compote. Upfront but ripe tannins deserve fine food or time to meld. From Breedekloof, like **11**.

Stumble Vineyards range
Verdelho ★★★ Interesting **13** shows improvement with stonefruit, yellow plums & citrus all in balance with acidity. Also tasted: **White Pinotage 13** ★★★ Not retasted: **Malbec 12** ★★★★ **Merlot 12** ★★★ **Cape Blend 12** ★★★

Poetry range
Cabernet Sauvignon (NEW) ★★★ **13** slots into this easy-drinking, consumer-friendly range, offering sweet black fruit & juicy texture. Also tasted: **Merlot 13** ★★★ **Sauvignon Blanc 13** ★★☆

Rustler range
Pinotage ★★★☆ Tar with sweet fruit, berries & smoked meat, **13** consumer-friendly tipple for roast duck, BBQ ribs. Also tasted: **Chenin Blanc 13** ★★★ Not retasted: **Sauvignon Blanc 13**

Whispering Jack range
Chardonnay ★★★★ Buttered popcorn notes on **13** give way to caramelised grapefruit with pleasing acidity & soft finish. — CM

Location: Somerset West ▪ Map: Helderberg ▪ WO: Western Cape/Breedekloof/Cape South Coast/Elim/Overberg ▪ Est 1998 ▪ 1stB 1999 ▪ Tasting & sales Mon-Fri 10-4 Sat 10-3 ▪ Fee R20, waived on purchase ▪ Closed Dec 25/26 & Jan 1 ▪ Cellar tours by appt ▪ Owner(s) Accolade Wines South Africa ▪ Winemaker(s) Gerhard Swart (Sep 2008) & Bruce Jack (1998), with Gerald Cakijana (Jan 2000) ▪ Viticulturist(s) Chris Keet (consultant) ▪ 70% red 30% white ▪ PO Box 769 Stellenbosch 7599 ▪ flagstone@accolade-wines.com ▪ www.flagstonewines.com ▪ S 34° 5' 26.38" E 018° 48' 30.04" ▪ F +27 (0)21-852-5085 ▪ **T +27 (0)21-852-5052**

Flat Roof Manor

These are the trendy counterpoint to the more serious Uitkyk Estate offerings. The flat roof in the branding is real - it's on the elegant Georgian manor house at the Uitkyk property outside Stellenbosch.

Merlot ★★★ Dash of malbec adds rustic touch, hefty tannins & hint of earthiness to plummy fruitcake notes of **13**. **Pinot Grigio** ★★★ Well-made **14** has a floral nose with more than a hint of sweetness on the palate deftly balanced by acidity. Not retasted: **Shiraz-Mourvèdre-Viognier 11** ★★★★ **Pinot Rosé Light 13** ★★ **Sauvignon Blanc Light 13** ★★ — JG

Fledge & Co

Ebullient, impassioned 'terroirists' operating out of Calitzdorp (where she's Boplaas winemaker), Margaux Nel and Leon Coetzee, partners in wine and life, winkle grapes from Elgin to Outeniqua, Perdeberg to False Bay for their 'individual, small batches of old-school wines [combining] New World freedom with Old World sensibility'. A trip to Chile and Argentina added fuel to their fire.

Fledge & Co range
★★★★ **HoekSteen** Unoaked old bushvine chenin ex Stellenbosch. Intensity not the point in **13** (★★★★☆), like **11** (no **12**), let alone fruitiness. Both subtly there, shaped by minerally, flinty, vinous refinement. All in lovely balance, making for delicious drinkability. In youth benefits from decanting.

★★★★ **Hatchi** ⊘ Delectable vine-dried Calitzdorp white muscadel, naturally fermented. **12** honey, dried apricot & spice. Only 350 (500 ml) bottles of vivacious sweetness to pair with savoury dishes.

Also tasted: **Vagabond 13** ★★★★

Experimental Barrels range

Straw Wine ★★★★ Though sweet, **13** from air-dried viognier off 10 year old Calitzdorp vines is delicate, almost ethereal. Earthy, raisiny quality keeps it tethered. Old oak; just 10.8% alcohol. — TJ

Location: Calitzdorp/Riebeek West ▪ WO: Stellenbosch/Calitzdorp/Western Cape/Klein Karoo ▪ Est 2007 ▪ 1stB 2010 ▪ Tasting & sales by appt at Boplaas ▪ Closed all pub hols ▪ Owner(s) Margaux Nel & Leon Coetzee ▪ Winemaker(s) Margaux Nel & Leon Coetzee (both Jan 2007) ▪ Viticulturist(s) Margaux Nel (Jan 2007) ▪ 12t/250cs own label 30% red 70% white ▪ IPW ▪ winemaker@boplaas.co.za, leon.mrfoo@gmail.com ▪ www.thefledge.co.za ▪ T +27 (0)82-828-8416/+27 (0)72-385-6503

Fleur du Cap

Distell-owned Die Bergkelder ('Mountain Cellar') has been home to the prestige Fleur du Cap brand since its opening in 1968. Grapes, in significant volumes, are sourced from the far corners of the winelands, offering Andrea Freeborough and her team an enviable choice of components. Die Bergkelder Wine Centre centre in Stellenbosch (see entry), including the labyrinthine cellar burrowed into the Papegaaiberg hillside, offers visitors insights into South Africa's winemaking past. The Unfiltered Collection represents their no-holds-barred efforts to produce the best possible wines, but the real stars are in the Bergkelder Selection, including a consistently remarkable botrytis chenin.

Unfiltered Collection

★★★★☆ **Cabernet Sauvignon** Seriously conceived & stylishly executed, **11** Stellenbosch-sourced flag bearer delivers noble black fruit, with leafy notes & firm but supple tannin. Quintessential cab, showing potential for graceful ageing.

★★★★ **Merlot** Classy, liquorice-scented **11** is smooth & seamless, showing plum pudding dark fruit with rich savoury undertones. Substantial & satisfying. Stellenbosch fruit.

★★★★☆ **Chardonnay** Barrel-fermented, high-end **13** follows classic form of **12**. Understated, very elegant & complex, with silky texture, finely integrated citrus fruit, acid & oak spices (35% new). Impressive finish.

★★★★☆ **Sauvignon Blanc** Was 'Limited Release'. Bold, ripe & self-assured, **14** shrugs off fermentation aromatics to deliver an emphatic varietal statement. Fine, tingling acidity, generously ripe passionfruit, mouthcoating intensity, following form of impressive **13**.

★★★★ **Semillon** Partly older-wood-fermented **13** shows waxy minerality with toasted nuts & aromatic spices. Generous body, with silky texture, elegant background oak, winding down to sweet marzipan finish.

Discontinued: **Viognier, Sauvignon Blanc-Chardonnay-Semillon-Viognier**.

Fleur du Cap Bergkelder Selection

★★★★☆ **Laszlo** Deep, dark, with elegant violet scent woven into taut, intricate merlot-led 5-way Bordeaux blend, **09** speaks of exceptional vintage & careful handling. Like judiciously oaked **08** (★★★★★), supple & smooth textured, despite awesome body. Coastal WO.

★★★★★ **Noble Late Harvest** Perfectly formed, honeyed & rich, with delightful dried apricot fruit layer, unwooded **13** (★★★★☆) just escaped the long run of 5-star ratings (**12** was last). Intensely sweet, with piercing acidity to balance, showing fine chenin character.

Shiraz ★★★☆ **13** has big toasted oak & coffee nose, appealing peppery spiciness, ripe cherry/plum/prune fruit with tarry finish, fair length. **Chenin Blanc** ★★★★ From Stellenbosch, Darling & Elgin fruit. Pineapple-toned **14** ripe, juicy & appealing, with crisp acid. Touch of oak flavours ripe peach & pear fruit complexity. Also tasted: **Cabernet Sauvignon 12** ★★★ **Merlot 12** ★★★ **Pinotage 12** ★★☆ **Chardonnay 13** ★★★ **Sauvignon Blanc 14** ★★★ **Natural Light 14** ★★ — GdB

Location: Stellenbosch ▪ WO: Western Cape/Stellenbosch/Coastal ▪ Est 1968 ▪ 1stB 1969 ▪ Tasting, sales & tours at Die Bergkelder Wine Centre (see entry) ▪ Owner(s) Distell ▪ Cellarmaster(s) Andrea Freeborough (Aug 2005) ▪ Winemaker(s) Wim Truter (2014, reds) & Pieter Badenhorst (Dec 2006, whites), with Christoff de Wet (Sep 2010) &

Elmarie Botes (2014) ▪ Viticulturist(s) Bennie Liebenberg (Apr 2001) ▪ ±17,000t/±290,000cs own label 47% red 53% white ▪ ISO 14001, ISO 9001, BRC, HACCP, IFS ▪ info@fleurducap.co.za, info@bergkelder.co.za ▪ www.fleurducap.co.za, www.bergkelder.co.za ▪ **T +27 (0)21-809-8025**

Flight of the Fish Eagle

Named after one of Africa's best-loved raptors (for its evocative call), this Distell brandy is, says marketing manager Oupa Lehaha, 'perfect for first-time brandy drinkers'. A significant ad and events campaign pitches it at South Africa's young high flyers, particularly young professionals.

★★★★ Natural Brandy Pale gold colour belies the intense red berry fruit, orange, honey; delicate traces almond & vanilla. Refined, with a long finish. Modern style; 100% potstill from chenin & colombard. — WB, TJ

☐ **Flutterby** see Boland Kelder

Foothills Vineyards

Foothills' wines originate on Klein Welmoed Wine & Olive Estate, where Glenn Hesse and Tim Featherby have established a luxury guest house and boutique winery on a formerly run-down property along Raithby Road in the Helderberg foothills. Consultants Bennie Booysen and Bernard le Roux are assisting in unlocking potential in an area 'historically known to produce great wines'.

Sauvignon Blanc **★★★** Early picked **13**, a tank sample previously, has improved. Fresh, with good weight, presence from 6 months on lees. **The Partners ★★★★ 13** mainly sauvignon, with 17% each semillon & viognier, unwooded. Last a sample, now peachy & zesty, flavoursome & dry for chilled summer sipping. Also tasted: **Syrah 12 ★★★ Dry Rosé 13 ★★★** — CvZ

Location/WO: Stellenbosch ▪ Map: Helderberg ▪ Est 2008 ▪ 1stB 2012 ▪ Tasting & sales by appt ▪ Fee R25 ▪ Meals/refreshments by appt ▪ Olive oil ▪ Conferences ▪ Luxury guest house (B&B) ▪ Owner(s) Glenn Hesse & Tim Featherby ▪ Winemaker(s) Bernard le Roux (consultant) ▪ Viticulturist(s) Bennie Booysen (consultant) ▪ 39ha/19ha (shiraz, sauv, sem, viog) ▪ 4,000cs own label 15% red 80% white 5% rosé ▪ IPW ▪ PO Box 647 Somerset Mall 7137 ▪ steve@foothillsvineyards.co.za ▪ www.kleinwelmoed.co.za, www.foothillsvineyards.co.za ▪ S 34° 0' 58.86" E 018° 47' 43.08" ▪ **F +27 (0)21-842-2775 ▪ T +27 (0)21-842-0045**

☐ **Foot of Africa** see Kleine Zalze Wines
☐ **Footprint** see African Pride Wines
☐ **Forresters** see Ken Forrester Wines
☐ **Fortress Hill** see Fort Simon Wine Estate

Fort Simon Wine Estate

Forts are usually intended to repel or intimidate strangers but not at this Bottelary Hills cellar, modelled on the magnificently eccentric Duwisib Castle in Namibia. The Uys family added a functions and wedding venue and, most recently, a 120-seat chapel in the old cellar to attract more visitors to their late father Simon's crenellated creation.

Platinum Collection

★★★★ Viognier Vibrant & alive **12 (★★★)** has ample nectarine & peach, with light nuttiness on dry finish, but shade less impressive than **09**.

★★★★ Viognier Noble Late Harvest Older-oak-fermented **10** matches intensity of last-tasted **07**. Concentrated but still light on its feet. Long, appealing finish & peach brûlée aftertaste. 375 ml.

Fort Simon Estate range

★★★★ Shiraz Return to form for **11** after uncomplicated **09** (no **10**). Complex melange of juicy red & black fruit, pepper & spice. Deeply textured & rich, with long cocoa aftertaste. Lovely integration & harmony.

Pinotage ★★★ Cheerful & friendly ripe blueberry appeal to **12**, integrated oak adds dimension.
Barrel Select Merlot-Malbec ★★★ Campfire charm on juicy **12**, light-bodied, approachable & easy-drinking BBQ sipper. Also tasted: **Cabernet Sauvignon 10** ★★★★ **Merlot 12** ★★★★
Chardonnay 13 ★★★★ **Sauvignon Blanc 13** ★★★★ Not tasted: **Rosé, Chenin Blanc**.

Fortress Hill range
Merlot-Cabernet Sauvignon ★★★ Merlot leads 85/15 mix on **13** blend, graphite & black-currant ease with solid tannin core. Rewarding drink. Also tasted: **Merlot 13** ★★★ **Shiraz 12** ★★★
Sauvignon Blanc 14 ★★★

Michelle d'Or (NEW)
Merlot ★★★☆ Soft mulberry & pepper on light-bodied & approachable **12**. **Shiraz** ★★★ **12** offers uncomplicated friendly berry compote with crack of pepper & squeeze of tannin from oak staves.
Merlot-Cabernet Sauvignon ★★★ Dried thyme & soft juicy berries on **12** 60/40 blend, good integration & length. **Sauvignon Blanc** ★★★☆ Leafy gooseberry vibrancy to light **14**, easy-drinking, fruity & friendly. — FM

Location/map: Stellenbosch ▪ WO: Stellenbosch/Western Cape ▪ Est 1997 ▪ 1stB 1998 ▪ Tasting & sales Mon-Fri 9. 30–5 Sat 10–2 ▪ Fee R20/5wines ▪ Closed all pub hols ▪ Cellar tours by appt ▪ Cheese platters ▪ Farm produce ▪ Venue for after-hours functions/weddings & conferences (120 guests) ▪ Owner(s) Renier, Petrus & Michéle Uys ▪ Winemaker(s) Stander Maass (Sep 2006) ▪ Viticulturist(s) Renier Uys ▪ 80ha (cabs s/f, malbec, merlot, p verdot, ptage, shiraz, chard, chenin, sauv, viog) ▪ 800t/80,000cs own label 60% red 30% white 10% rosé ▪ PO Box 43 Sanlamhof 7532 ▪ accounts@fortsimon.com ▪ www.fortsimon.co.za ▪ S 33° 55' 9.5" E 018° 45' 19.4" ▪ F +27 (0)21-903-8034 ▪ **T +27 (0)21-906-0304**

☐ **Foundation Stone** see Rickety Bridge Winery

Foundry

Meerlust cellarmaster Chris Williams and Voor Paardeberg vinegrower (and local operations director of Accolade Wines) James Reid established this expanding joint venture well over a decade ago. Although Reid's farm is becoming 'home' to the label, the wines are as yet made at Meerlust - the original pair (Syrah and Viognier) and the Roussanne sourced in Stellenbosch, the fine Grenache Blanc from further inland. Chris talks of 'wines of purity, focus and distinction', which is the imprint that all in this portfolio bear, along with laudably modest pricing given the stellar quality.

★★★★☆ **Syrah** Always a class act, Stellenbosch's Faure area the source of **09**, well crafted, multi-layered & smooth, with dark fruit, generous spice & violets. 10% new oak provides support, & 30% whole berry (with stems) ferment lends structure to a rich, round, complex palate.

★★★★★ **Grenache Blanc** ⊘ Beautifully layered **13** opens with lifted aromas of apple & aniseed, then flavours of lemon curd & blackcurrant, a lipsmacking tangy finale turning mineral. 5% roussanne adds touch of je ne sais quoi to a stunning expression of Voor Paardeberg.

★★★★ **Roussanne** Standout **13** (★★★★★) expressive yet delicate nose of peach blossom with slight melon & mineral undertones; bone-dry, succulent, with refreshing pebbly flavour & a peacock finish showing more complexity than **12**. Seasoned oak & partial malo, as for Grenache Blanc.

★★★★ **Viognier** Improving on **12**, older-oak-fermented **13** (★★★★☆) from Stellenbosch is expressive but well controlled. Floral, apricot & earthy perfumes; elegant, delicious & thirst-quenching flavours of melon, lemon & under-ripe peaches. — JPf

Location/map: Stellenbosch ▪ WO: Stellenbosch/Coastal ▪ Est 2000 ▪ 1stB 2001 ▪ Tasting, sales & cellar tours by appt ▪ Closed all pub hols ▪ Owner(s) Chris Williams & James Reid ▪ Cellarmaster(s)/winemaker(s) Chris Williams (Nov 2000) ▪ Viticulturist(s) Chris Williams (Nov 2000), with growers ▪ 11ha (grenache, shiraz, rouss, viog) ▪ ±30t/4,000cs own label 40% red 60% white ▪ PO Box 12423 Die Boord 7613 ▪ thefoundry@mweb.co.za ▪ www.thefoundry.co.za ▪ S 34° 1' 1.7" E 018° 45' 24.7" ▪ F +27 (0)21-843-3274 ▪ **T +27 (0)82-577-0491**

☐ **Fountain Crossing** see Darling Cellars

☐ **Four Cousins** *see* Van Loveren Family Vineyards

Four Fields Vineyards

Rising costs have caused Chris Kühn, a retired life insurance and medical man (who once worked with SA heart transplant pioneer Chris Barnard), to close his diminutive Durbanville cellar. Vinification of bought-in grapes may continue in rented space. Meanwhile the life-long winelover, who co-founded Wellington's Napier Winery in the 1980s, still has stock of his '09 Bordeaux blend.

Cabernet Sauvignon-Cabernet Franc ② ★★★★ Improved **09** shows supple black fruit with commendable spicy complexity. Hint of earthiness & sour cherry on finish. — GdB

Location/WO: Durbanville ▪ Est/1st B 2004 ▪ Closed to public ▪ Sales mainly via Wine Concepts, Cape Town ▪ Owner(s) 8 shareholders ▪ Cellarmaster(s)/winemaker(s) Chris Kühn (Sep 2004) ▪ 5t 100% red ▪ 49 Arabella Drive Augusta Place Sunningdale 7441 ▪ dockuhn@gmail.com ▪ **T +27 (0)83-929-9199**

4G Wines

Based near Stellenbosch, and sourcing from various carefully selected sites, 4G Wines is about building a South African 'first growth', says director Philipp Axt, adding this is not about flattering shareholders' or customers' egos. 'Our ambition is rather to create delicate, delicious and inimitable wine [by] combining European winemaking expertise, craftsmanship and innovative technologies with SA's outstanding natural assets and winemaking skills.' Hence French consultants Denis Dubourdieu and Valérie Lavigne are on board, with Giorgio Dalla Cia, creator of iconic Meerlust Rubicon.

Location: Stellenbosch ▪ Est 2009 ▪ 1stB 2010 ▪ Closed to public ▪ Owner(s) Private shareholders ▪ Winemaker(s) Mia Fischer, Giorgio Dalla Cia, Denis Dubourdieu & Valérie Lavigne ▪ 20t ▪ own label 100% red ▪ Other export brands: G, The Echo of G ▪ info@4g-wines.com ▪ www.4g-wines.com

Four Paws Wines

'Authentic, small, warm and personal' is how the trio of cat lovers, with day jobs in the wine industry, describe their Four Paws joint venture. Guided by 'what we like to drink', and sourcing grapes from selected growers around the winelands, they offer variety and interest each vintage.

★★★★ **Pinotage** Brambleberry notes on full-bodied **11** from Piekenierskloof, showing vanilla tone from year 30% new oak. Drinks easily & well but underlying seriousness invites cellaring ±5 years.

★★★★ **Picatso** ② Feline theme given cubist edge. **11** naturally dried viognier 8 months in seasoned oak; voluptuous, luxurious & moreish. Pity, only 560L in 375 ml format.

Shiraz (NEW) ★★★ Spiced with 10% grenache, **12** offers red fruit dusted with clove & cinnamon, dark chocolate & some mocha character from 18 months oaking. WO W Cape. Also tasted: **Chardonnay 11** ★★★★ Not retasted: **Pablo 11** ★★★★ **Sauvignon Blanc 12** ★★★ Not tasted: **Calico**. — GM

Location/map: Franschhoek ▪ WO: Piekenierskloof/Western Cape/Franschhoek ▪ Est 2005 ▪ 1stB 2006 ▪ Tasting by appt at La Vigne, Robertsvlei Road, Franschhoek (contact Anne +27 (0)83-447-1376/Gerda +27 (0)82-375-0524) ▪ Owner(s) Rob Meihuizen, Gerda Willers & Anne Jakubiec ▪ Winemaker(s) Gerda Willers (2005) ▪ Viticulturist(s) Gerda Willers ▪ 60t/12,000cs own label 70% red 30% white ▪ PO Box 69 Simondium 7670 ▪ anne@southerntrade.co.za ▪ www.fourpawswines.com ▪ S 33° 53' 28.0" E 019° 5' 0.5" ▪ F +27 (0)21-874-2110 ▪ **T +27 (0)21-874-1033**

Four Secrets

The 'mystery' behind this Stellenbosch Vineyards brand is that the wines are blends sourced over four vintages from the same vineyards in the Helderberg.

Sparkling Shiraz ② ★★★ Among tiny handful of shiraz sparklers in SA. Characterful carbonated **NV** has firm, ever so slightly sweet lavender & blackberry bubbles. Try with smoked salmon, say winemakers. Not retasted: **Shiraz NV** ★★★ — CvZ

4th Street

'Increased demand for low-alcohol drinks and on-the-go accessibility' sees Distell adding three slightly sparkling Natural Sweet wines, in colourful 'sixpacks' of 300 ml crown-capped bottles, to the trendy 4th Street range.

Lightly Sparkled range

Natural Sweet Petillant Red ★★ NV Plum & berry flavours plus hint of tannin & raisin stalks on **NV**. Could be chilled. **Natural Sweet Petillant Rosé ★★** Cheerful, slightly fizzy **NV**, nicely balanced for uncloying fun. **Natural Sweet Petillant White ★★☆** Simple appley **NV** enlivened by slight tingle of fine bubbles.

4th Street range

Natural Sweet White ★★★ NV oozes grapey sweetness, but crisp acidity comes to the rescue. Also tasted: **Natural Sweet Red NV ★★ Natural Sweet Rosé NV ★★** — DB

Fraai Uitzicht 1798

Karl Uwe and Sandra Papesch's very old Langeberg Mountain farm, aptly named for its pretty view, may be best known for its luxury guesthouse and restaurant. But a small vineyard amidst the conserved indigenous vegetation provides grapes for Karl Uwe's now mostly Rhône-focused wines.

Syrah ★★★ 13, with dash viognier, showy, bold, ripe aromas & sweet-fruited flavours, though final alcohol only 13.6%. Very softly structured. **Viognier** (new) **★★☆** Oak influence shows more than fruit on **14** preview. Quite restrained; touch clumsy rather than big. Discontinued: **Merlot**, **Prima**. — TJ

Location/map: Robertson ▪ WO: Klaasvoogds ▪ 1stB 2000 ▪ Tasting & sales daily 10-6 ▪ Closed Easter Fri/Sun, Dec 24/25/31 & Jan 1 ▪ Restaurant ▪ 4-star guest house ▪ Owner(s) Karl Uwe Papesch ▪ Winemaker(s) Karl Uwe Papesch (2005) ▪ Viticulturist(s) Michael Marson ▪ 175ha/13ha (grenache, merlot, mourv, shiraz, viog) ▪ 3,000cs own label 90% red 10% white ▪ PO Box 97 Robertson 6705 ▪ info@fraaiuitzicht.com ▪ www.fraaiuitzicht.com ▪ S 33° 47' 43.0" E 020° 0' 18.2" ▪ F +27 (0)86-662-5265 ▪ **T +27 (0)23-626-6156**

Fram Wines

Thinus Krüger's fledgling independent wine venture invokes Norwegian wooden ship Fram, used by legendary 19th-century explorers. The former Fleur du Cap and Boschendal young gun says he's sailing uncharted territory in search of untapped vineyard potential in 'here be dragons' areas of the local wine map, to contribute to SA's quality-wine profile. Bottlings from the Swartland, Citrusdal Mountain and Robertson have already been shipped to, aptly, Norway as well as the UK.

★★★★★ Chenin Blanc Intense, evocative bouquet, kumquats & almonds, thatch, with wildness from natural ferment (in older oak). **13**'s palate also fascinating: marzipan, dried peach, then a nice pithy end, just a hint of positive bitterness. Individual, layered & flavoursome.

Pinotage ★★★☆ Dark & brooding **12**, meaty & savoury, with some plum undertones. Quite tannic, needs time to soften, meld; could show better over time & then reward handsomely. **Shiraz ★★★** Prunes & liquorice, there's full ripeness here, tamed by the savoury oak backbone, dusty dry finish. **13** perfect charcuterie match. Swartland vines. **Chardonnay ★★★ 13** unoaked, elegant & dry, with citrus & tropical fruit flavours, appealing drinkability but short finish. Robertson grapes. — CR, CvZ

Location: Stellenbosch ▪ WO: Citrusdal Mountain/Robertson/Swartland ▪ Est/1stB 2012 ▪ Tasting by appt only ▪ Owner(s)/viticulturist(s) Thinus Krüger ▪ Cellarmaster(s)/winemaker(s) Thinus Krüger (Dec 2012) ▪ 30t/2,500cs own label 45% red 55% white ▪ PO Box 2272 Dennesig Stellenbosch 7601 ▪ thinus@framwines.co.za ▪ www.framwines.co.za ▪ **T +27 (0)72-545-4959**

Francois La Garde

Stellenbosch bubbly lover Piet Matthée says he's fulfilling the dream of an ancestor (after whom this specialist label is named) to make champagne-method wine. And he's responding to his own passion too, while he also runs a specialist bottling and labelling company. Vinification is at Zorgvliet.

String of Pearls range

★★★★ **Brut Méthode Cap Classique** Marked dryness noted on **08** sparkling taken to new level in zero-dosage **09** (★★★), equal pinot noir & chardonnay. Alluring brioche & toasted nut aromas cut short by steely gunflint nuance on austere, food-demanding palate.

Not tasted: **Reinette Rosé MCC, Blanc de Blancs**. — MW

Location/map: Stellenbosch ▪ WO: Franschhoek ▪ Est 2004 ▪ Tasting by appt ▪ Owner(s) PL Matthée ▪ Cellarmaster(s)/winemaker(s) Piet Matthée (Jan 2009) ▪ 15t/2,000cs own label 100% white ▪ PO Box 12366 Die Boord 7613 ▪ admin@technofill.co.za ▪ F +27 (0)21-887-5274 ▪ **T +27 (0)21-887-3674**

Franki's Vineyards

Among Swartland's smaller and lower-profile cellars, Franki's is also home to a collection of classic cars, upmarket accommodation and, under construction, giant solar energy array. Winemaker since inception Erica Joubert's guiding principles are 'old school meets new techniques' and 'natural ferments with an open mind'.

Barn Find range

Grenache ★★☆ Understated fruit on **13**, unlike most SA examples; firm, even hard structure.
Joubert Red Blend ★★★ **13** mourvèdre (75%) with grenache fuller-fruited than Grenache, but dry, little in the way of charm. These both a year in old oak. — TJ

Location: Malmesbury ▪ Map: Swartland ▪ WO: Swartland/Western Cape ▪ Est 2004 ▪ 1stB 2007 ▪ Tasting, sales & cellar tours Mon-Fri 8-5 by appt ▪ Closed all pub hols ▪ Meals by arrangement ▪ Tour groups ▪ BYO picnic ▪ Conferences ▪ Walks/hikes ▪ Conservation area ▪ Classic car museum ▪ Franki's Guest Lodge (10 rooms) & Solitude @ Franki's B&B (4 rooms) ▪ Owner(s) Franco Afrique Technologies (Pty) Ltd ▪ Winemaker(s) Erica Joubert (Jan 2004), with Nicci Hanekom (Jan 2004) ▪ 700ha/22ha (grenache, mourv, viog) ▪ ±160t/450cs own label 100% red ▪ PO Box 972 Malmesbury 7299 ▪ erica.joubert@cropspec.com ▪ www.frankisvineyards.co.za ▪ S 33° 20' 59.5" E 018° 32' 12.4" ▪ F +27 (0)86-660-3677 ▪ **T +27 (0)22-482-2837/+27 (0)82-888-3702**

Franschhoek Cellar

Major renovations at this DGB-owned winery, conveniently situated at the gateway to Franschhoek village, see the cellardoor, function venue and outdoor areas remodelled and upgraded. The revamp coincides with a milestone for winemaker Richard Duckitt, who joined exactly ten years ago and since accumulated an impressive cabinet of competition hardware, here and abroad.

Franschhoek Vineyards range

★★★★ **Shiraz 12**'s rich yet pure fruit cossetted by 25% new oak, accented by pleasant pepperiness. Drinks well now but should improve for 3+ years. WO Franschhoek. **10** (★★★★) was more introverted. No **11**.

★★★★ **Semillon** Part natural ferment in 25% new oak for **13**, toasty, with lemongrass, lemon thyme whiffs, vibrant conclusion. Like **11**, step up on less sumptuous **12** (★★★). Franschhoek grapes.

Village Walk range

Stone Bridge Pinotage ⊛ ★★★★ Old-oak-aged **13** ticks all the (good) pinotage boxes: clean strawberry fruit, refreshing acidity & lengthy balanced tail, all subtly oak enhanced. **Our Town Hall Chardonnay** ⊛ ★★★★ Unwooded **14** restrained & elegant, with faint lemon tones, pleasing weight & measured acidity. **Statue de Femme Sauvignon Blanc** ★★★★ Lively **14** bursts with green apple & grass, ends long & full. Also tasted: **The Churchyard Cabernet Sauvignon 12**

★★☆ Old Museum Merlot 13 ★★★ Baker Station Shiraz 12 ★★★ Clubhouse Rosé 14 ★★ La Cotte Mill Chenin Blanc 14 ★★★ — CvZ

Location/map: Franschhoek ▪ WO: Western Cape/Franschhoek ▪ Est 1945 ▪ Tasting & sales Mon–Fri 10–5 (Apr–Sep) & 10-6 (Oct–Mar) Sat 10-5 Sun 11–5 ▪ Wine tasting, 6 wines with 6 cheeses, 6 wines with assorted chocolates ▪ Closed Good Fri, May 1, Jun 16 & Dec 25 ▪ Cheese lunch daily during tasting hours ▪ BYO picnic ▪ Farm produce ▪ Events venue (seat 300 pax) ▪ Owner(s) DGB (Pty) Ltd ▪ Winemaker(s) Richard Duckitt (Dec 2005) ▪ Viticulturist(s) Stephan Joubert (Nov 2006) ▪ 300ha (cab, merlot, shiraz, chard, chenin, sauv, sem) ▪ 30,000t 49% red 50% white 1% rosé ▪ ISO 9001:2001, IPW ▪ PO Box 52 Franschhoek 7690 ▪ fhcellardoor@dgb.co.za ▪ www.franschhoek-cellar.co.za ▪ S 33° 54' 16.4" E 019° 6' 40.7" ▪ F +27 (0)21-876-4107 ▪ **T +27 (0)21-876-2086**

☐ **Frans K Smit** *see* Spier

Freedom Hill Wines

Breaking free from being synonymous as the southern Paarl winery overlooking Victor Verster prison from whence Nelson Mandela took his first steps to freedom is the goal of energetic CEO and industrial engineer Chanine Klomp, daughter of owner and civil engineer Francois Klomp. Having re-engineered the dining and functions aspect, labels and wine are next. 'Small steps…' she says.

Freedom Hill range

Shiraz Cellar Selection ⊛ **★★★★ 10** is nicely chunky with oodles of spice. Medium bodied, lightly tannic from 20% new oak. **Chardonnay** ⊛ **★★★☆** Toasty, buttery peaches & cream on oaked **10** from Stellenbosch grapes, poised & rounded. Not tasted: **Pinotage Cellar Selection, Cape Blend, Shiraz-Cabernet Sauvignon, Chenin Blanc, Sauvignon Blanc**.

Freedom Walk 1335/88 range

Shiraz ⊛ **★★★** Liquorice & cocoa depth to juicy black fruit, **10** straightforward but ripe & approachable. Not tasted: **Pinotage, Cape Blend**. — FM

Location: Paarl ▪ Map: Franschhoek ▪ WO: Paarl/Stellenbosch ▪ Est 1997 ▪ 1stB 2000 ▪ Tasting Mon-Fri 10-5 Sat 12-4 Sun/pub hols by appt ▪ Closed Easter Fri/Sun & Dec 25 ▪ Wedding & function venue ▪ Owner(s) Francois Klomp ▪ Cellarmaster(s)/winemaker(s) Kowie du Toit (Feb 2007) ▪ Viticulturist(s) Paul Wallace & Bruce Mcreadie ▪ 82ha/19ha (cab, ptage, shiraz) ▪ ±70t/12,000cs own label 100% red ▪ PO Box 6126 Paarl 7620 ▪ info@freedomhill.co.za, chanine@freedomhill.co.za ▪ www.freedomhill.co.za ▪ S 33° 49' 48.33" E 019° 0' 35.90" ▪ F +27 (0)86-244-9748 ▪ **T +27 (0)21-867-0085**

☐ **Freedom Walk** *see* Freedom Hill Wines
☐ **Frid hem Gaard** *see* Migliarina Wines
☐ **Frieda's Vine** *see* Savanha
☐ **Friesland** *see* Kaapzicht Wine Estate
☐ **Frisky Zebras** *see* United Nations of Wine
☐ **Frog Hill** *see* Anura Vineyards
☐ **Frogner** *see* Nordic Wines
☐ **Frost Vineyards** *see* David Frost Wines

Fryer's Cove Vineyards

The dream of exploring the cool-climate maritime potential of vineyards on the near-deserted Atlantic shoreline resulted in this collaboration between West Coast grower Jan 'Ponk' van Zyl and Stellenbosch-based winemaker and brother-in-law Wynand Hamman. Six hectares of vines only 600 m from the sea contribute to an evolving range of acclaimed sauvignons and rare pinot noir. The harbour at Doring Bay is home to the cellar (an old fish factory), convivial tasting room and rustic seafood eatery extending onto the reclaimed wooden jetty and run in tandem with the local community.

★★★★ **Doringbaai Sauvignon Blanc** Delightful retro 'sardine can' label invites you to Unlock the Taste. **14** classic cool-climate green nettle & gooseberry aromas, juicy & refreshingly zesty, twist of lime on the finish. Includes fruit from other West Coast vines.

Pinot Noir ★★★☆ Subtle aromas of strawberry & a little floral note. **13** juicy, soft, uncomplicated palate shows good lift & generosity. Inc Koekenaap grapes. Not tasted: **Bamboes Bay Sauvignon Blanc**, **The Jetty Sauvignon Blanc**. Discontinued: **Bay To Bay Sauvignon Blanc**. — JPf

Location: Doring Bay ▪ Map: Olifants River ▪ WO: Western Cape ▪ Est 1999 ▪ 1stB 2002 ▪ Tasting, sales & cellar tours Mon-Fri 8-5 Sat 10-5 ▪ Fee R5 ▪ Closed Christian hols ▪ Pre-booked cheese platters & picnics; or BYO picnic ▪ Restaurant ▪ Farm produce ▪ West Coast walking trail ▪ Owner(s) Jan Ponk Trust, JH Laubscher Family Trust & Wynand Hamman ▪ Cellarmaster(s) Wynand Hamman (Apr 1999) ▪ Viticulturist(s) Jan van Zyl (Apr 1999) ▪ 10ha/6ha (pinot, sauv) ▪ 50t/6,000cs own label 25% red 75% white ▪ PO Box 93 Vredendal 8160 ▪ admin@fryerscove.co.za, cellar@fryerscove.co.za ▪ www.fryerscove.co.za ▪ S 31° 45' 53.1" E 018° 13' 55.8" ▪ F +27 (0)27-213-2212 ▪ **T +27 (0)27-213-2312 (office)/+27 (0)27-215-1092 (tasting)**

☐ **Fugue** see Anatu Wines

Gabriëlskloof

Seldom does one have an opportunity to start a winefarm from scratch, but that is what co-owner Bernhard Heyns and partners had with a neglected Bot River wheat and sheep farm bought in 2002. A detailed soil analysis showed it was best suited to Bordeaux and Rhône varieties, which are now the main focus of the wines. The Mediterranean climate has also led to a companion product, olives, a thriving part of the business. Keeping it in the family, Crystallum co-owner/winemaker Peter-Allan Finlayson (married to Bernhard's daughter Nicolene) has joined the team.

Reserve range

★★★★☆ **Five Arches** Blend of 5 Bordeaux varieties. Burly, heavyish **11** (★★★★) offers berry fruit & spice/tobacco notes from dominating new oak. Rich & savoury; ripe smooth tannins. Like **10**, should develop.

★★★★ **Viognier** A quieter style of often exuberantly showy variety. Supportively oaked (like **12**), dry **13** (★★★☆) has dried peach, almond & spice. Slightly lean & sour, with pleasant fruit but no real intensity.

★★★★ **Magdalena** 55% semillon on **13**, harmoniously adding breadth & notes of honey, citrus & wax to the flavours & penetrating zing of sauvignon. Charming, elegantly balanced & fresh. Subtly oaked.

Also tasted: **Swartriver Shiraz 11** ★★★☆

Special Collection

★★★★ **Noble Late Harvest** Very pretty unoaked **13** dessert from semillon with aromatic viognier (partly ex Elgin). Sweetly delicate, fresh & really charming - no great complexity or depth but poised & delightful.

Premium range

Sauvignon Blanc ★★★★ Forthcoming, flavoursome **14** nicely blends riper tropical & greener characters. Deft, precise & clean; crisp but not aggressively fresh. Also tasted: **Rosebud 14** ★★☆ Not retasted: **Shiraz 11** ★★★★ **The Blend 11** ★★★★ — TJ

Location: Bot River ▪ Map: Elgin, Walker Bay & Bot River ▪ WO: Bot River/Cape South Coast ▪ Est 2002 ▪ 1stB 2007 ▪ Tasting & sales Mon-Fri 9–5 Sat 11-3 ▪ Fee R15/4 wines or R30/8 wines, waived on purchase ▪ Closed Dec 24/25 ▪ Cellar tours by appt ▪ Restaurant ▪ Deli ▪ Child-friendly; dogs welcome ▪ Weddings (very limited availability) ▪ Annual market (Dec 12-13) ▪ Owner(s) Bernhard Heyns & shareholders Johan Heyns, Barry Anderson & Wally Clarke ▪ Winemaker(s) Peter-Allan Finlayson (Jul 2014), with Christiaan van der Merwe (Jan 2011) ▪ Viticulturist(s) Barry Anderson (2001) ▪ 150ha/68ha (cabs s/f, malbec, merlot, mourv, p verdot, pinot, shiraz, sauv, sem, viog) ▪ BWI, IPW,

WIETA ▪ PO Box 499 Kleinmond 7195 ▪ info@gabrielskloof.co.za ▪ www.gabrielskloof.co.za ▪ S 34° 14' 19.89" E 019° 14' 58.68" ▪ F +27 (0)28-284-9864 ▪ **T +27 (0)28-284-9865**

Galleon Wines

When founder-winemaker of this Durbanville boutique label, retired cardiologist Andries Brink, passed away in 2012, his family entrusted the brand to friends Jansen and Mari Branders. While subsequent vintages were made by Mari and Diemersdal's Thys Louw, plans for 2015 and beyond were still on the drawing board at press time.

Isaac Pinotage ★★★ Appealing mix of modern 'mocha' oak styling & traditional plum fruit; **11** delicious in & with hearty lamb or oxtail stews. Not retasted: **Cabernet Sauvignon 09 ★★★** Not tasted: **Shiraz, Chardonnay, Sauvignon Blanc.** — CvZ

Location/WO: Durbanville ▪ Est 2003 ▪ 1stB 2004 ▪ Tasting by appt ▪ Owner(s)/winemaker(s) Jansen & Mari Branders ▪ 1,700cs own label 50% red 50% white ▪ PO Box 1155 Durbanville 7551 ▪ info@galleonwines.co.za ▪ www. galleonwines.co.za ▪ F +27 (0)86-549-9331 ▪ **T +27 (0)79-692-4891/+27 (0)84-954-0814**

☐ **Game Reserve** *see* Graham Beck Wines
☐ **Gander** *see* Goose Wines

Gantouw Farm (NEW)

Wetherlys furniture and decor business founder James Smith and wife Linky are the owners of this Hottentots-Holland mountain property, named for the eland (gantouw) once hunted here. The Smiths are combining daughter Julia's equestrian training skills, their own garlic-growing expertise and award-winning olive oil production with niche winefarming, primarily sauvignon blanc and petit verdot. Collaboration with nearby Onderkloof sees crops shared and wines made by Yves Musfeld.

Sauvignon Blanc ★★★ Gooseberries & passionfruit with a zinging fresh acidity that would be a good seafood match, **13** unmistakably sauvignon & for summer. — CR, CvZ

Location: Sir Lowry's Pass ▪ WO: Stellenbosch ▪ Est 2006 ▪ 1stB 2012 ▪ Closed to public ▪ Sales (wine, olives/olive oil, garlic) via website & social media ▪ Owner(s) James Alexander Smith ▪ Winemaker(s) Yves Musfeld (Jan 2012, Onderkloof) ▪ 25ha/3.3ha under vine ▪ 10t/1,600cs own label 100% white ▪ PO Box 2649 Somerset West 7129 ▪ james@gantouwfarm.co.za ▪ www.gantouwfarm.co.za ▪ F +27 (0)86-518-0518 ▪ **T +27 (0)83-794-6070**

Garden Route Wines

De Krans' champion port-style maker Boets Nel revels in working with grapes from a small Outeniqua mountain vineyard (600m altitude) on the coastal Garden Route. The cool climate slow-ripens the grapes – the 2014 sauvignon was picked only in late March and shiraz end April! The resulting wines are or will be available at home base in Calitzdorp and Outeniqua Wine Emporium on the N12.

★★★★ Sauvignon Blanc ⊘ **14** offers clean minerality & greenpepper tang with soft, controlled acidity.

Not retasted: **Shiraz 12 ★★★★** — DB

Location: Calitzdorp ▪ Map: Klein Karoo & Garden Route ▪ WO: Outeniqua ▪ Est/1stB 2008 ▪ Tasting & sales at De Krans (see entry) ▪ Wines also available at Outeniqua Wine Emporium, Waboomskraal on N12 between George & Oudtshoorn ▪ Owner(s) Boets Nel ▪ Cellarmaster(s)/viticulturist(s) Boets Nel (2008) ▪ 9ha (shiraz, chard, sauv) ▪ 80t/ ±3,000cs own label 50% red 50% white ▪ PO Box 28 Calitzdorp 6660 ▪ dekrans@mweb.co.za ▪ S 33° 32' 6.3" E 021° 41' 9.0" ▪ F +27 (0)44-213-3562/+27 (0)23-541-1702 ▪ **T +27 (0)44-213-3314/+27 (0)23-541-1702**

☐ **Garden Vineyards** *see* DeMorgenzon
☐ **Gecko Ridge** *see* Long Mountain Wine Company
☐ **Genade Water** *see* Nuweland Wynkelder

Genevieve Méthode Cap Classique

Melissa Genevieve Nelsen's bubbly inspiration comes from her grandmother who was inclined to broach a bottle no matter how minor the occasion. Melissa's grapes come from near Bot River and are vinified in Paarl.

★★★★ **Genevieve** **10** sparkling from chardonnay is fruit driven, as expected from blanc de blancs, the small oak-fermented portion almost invisible among crisp, bright appley bubbles. — MW

Location: Bot River ▪ WO: Overberg ▪ Est 2009 ▪ 1stB 2008 ▪ Tasting by appt ▪ Owner(s) Melissa Nelsen ▪ Viticulturist(s) Leon Engelke (2008) ▪ 16t/1,650cs own label 100% MCC ▪ PO Box 122 Elgin 7180 ▪ melissa@genevievemcc.co.za ▪ www.genevievemcc.co.za ▪ **T +27 (0)83-302-6562**

Gentleman Spirits (NEW)

After travelling the world for 25 years to find exceptional fruit for his award-winning spirits, German distiller Hubertus Vallendar has teamed up with Blaauwklippen MD/winemaker Rolf Zeitvogel and Swiss partner Urs Gmuer to create 'superlative distilled beverages that will lift the spirit and sooth the soul'. Offering a hands-on distillery experience at Blaauwklippen, they intend introducing South Africans to the 'totally new world' of clear spirits.

Husk Spirit range

★★★★ **Malbec Noble Late Harvest** Rich, elegant & oh-so-smooth, with honeysuckle & jasmine perfumes. Lively flow & silky texture, full flavours, integrated spirit – a party in your mouth!

★★★★ **Shiraz** Colourless, as all these. Scented with notes of violet & lavender, black berries & exotic spice. Smooth, elegant, with a lovely depth & balance.

★★★★ **Merlot** Fresh, pure & enticing floral & spicy red berry nose; focused & fresh with soft, sweet berry flavours; concludes with a raspberry lift. 500 ml, as all.

★★★★ **Zinfandel** Wild flowers, dried herbs & warm spice introduce the silky palate & delicate fire. Clean, bright, with subtle nut & red berry perfume. Balanced, with spirit well integrated.

Zinfandel Noble Late Harvest ★★★ Floral fragrances, but cloying musk essence on the palate gives sensation of viscosity rather than lightness.

Eau de Vie range

★★★★ **Lemon** Upfront lemon blossom & rind jump out of the glass; zesty, creamy & fresh – fun with dessert or on the deck after lunch.

★★★★ **Orange** Richly layered marmalade, orange rind & sweet-spiced orange flavours take over the palate. Depth, with elegance & a fresh, lifted finish. Delicious! — WB

Location/map: Stellenbosch ▪ Est/1stB 2012 ▪ Tasting & sales Mon-Fri 10-6 (summer)/10-5 (winter) Sat 10-5 Sun 10-4 ▪ Closed Dec 25 & Jan 1 ▪ Distillery tours by appt only ▪ Amenities: see Blaauwklippen entry ▪ Owner(s) Hubertus Vallendar, Urs Gmuer, Rolf Zeitvogel ▪ Brandy master(s) Hubertus Vallendar (Feb 2012) ▪ 1,000cs ▪ rz@gentleman-spirits.com ▪ www.gentleman-spirits.co.za ▪ S 33° 58' 23.3" E 018° 50' 51.0" ▪ F +27 (0)21-880-0136 ▪ **T +27 (0)82-907-9787**

☐ **Ghost Corner** *see* Cederberg Private Cellar

Giant Periwinkle

Lawyer Pierre Rabie clearly felt the genetic tug to become a winemaker, hence this garagiste venture in Bredasdorp where a barn (with useful vineyard attached, to complement what he buys in) is being turned into a cellar (early vintages were made in rented space). He deals with his cool-climate grapes with minimal intervention – no additives, no fining or filtration, only older oak. Add in some passion, and characterful, pure wines are the result.

For more information, visit wineonaplatter.com

★★★★☆ **Blanc Fumé** Subtle influence of older oak adds to complexity of intriguing **13** - with tropical fruit, citrus, blackcurrant, & a note of petrol too. Fresh & mineral; balanced & harmonious; altogether convincing. Should develop interestingly a good few years.

Sea Witch Pinot Noir ★★★★☆ Modest, lightish (±12% alcohol) **13**, mixing berry fruit with savoury element. Fresh acidity & a light tannic tug. One to watch as vineyards mature. Also tasted: **21 Degrees Sauvignon Blanc 13** ★★★★ Not retasted: **Kelp Forest Syrah 12** ★★★ Discontinued: **Sea Money Malbec.** — TJ

Location: Bredasdorp ▪ Map: Southern Cape ▪ WO: Elim ▪ Est 2009 ▪ 1stB 2012 ▪ Tasting by appt only ▪ Owner(s)/winemaker(s) Pierre Jacques Rabie jnr ▪ 0.06ha (sauv, pinot) ▪ ±300cs own label 50% red 50% white ▪ PO Box 415 Bredasdorp 7280 ▪ pjrabie@capebar.co.za ▪ F +27 (0)21-422-2142 ▪ **T +27 (0)21-426-2653**

☐ **Giant's Peak** *see* Wine-of-the-Month Club

Gilga Wines

Cellarmaster Stefan Gerber is now also co-owner with John Rowan of Stellenboschkloof's Gilga boutique winery, whose untasted line-up includes varietal Syrah and blends Amurabi and Zagros. A spacious self-catering guest house on the property can be booked via the website.

Location/map: Stellenbosch ▪ Est/1stB 2002 ▪ Tasting & sales by appt ▪ Guest house ▪ Owner(s) John Rowan & Stefan Gerber ▪ Cellarmaster(s) Stefan Gerber (Jun 2010), with assistant winemaker Roelof du Toit (Jan 2014, consultant) ▪ Viticulturist(s) Stefan Gerber (Jun 2010) ▪ 4ha/3.5ha (grenache, mourv, shiraz, tempranillo) ▪ 10t/1,100cs own label 100% red ▪ PO Box 871 Stellenbosch 7599 ▪ info@gilga.co.za ▪ www.gilga.co.za ▪ S 33° 56′ 46.1″ E 018° 47′ 20.6″ ▪ F +27 (0)86-531-7137 ▪ **T +27 (0)84-515-6677**

☐ **Gilysipao** *see* Orange River Wine Cellars
☐ **Girlfriends Wine** *see* Val du Charron
☐ **Glass Collection** *see* Glenelly Estate

Glen Carlou

Since Donald Hess' Hess Family Estates Ltd bought out the Finlaysons, founders of this Paarl farm, it has become a destination venue; apart from the wine, there's the Hess Art Museum, a restaurant, tapas bar and a speciality shop, where wine paraphernalia and wines from the other Hess Estates may be purchased. In their commitment to the environment, the team established a fynbos garden, set among giant boulders and filled with endemic indigenous plants, through which visitors are encouraged to wander. Grape varieties too are chosen for their suitability to the farm's warmer climate. Cellarmaster Arco Laarman particularly likes petit verdot and his unusual blend with tannat 'shows how these tannic varieties can partner well in the correct climate with no new oak.'

Prestige range

★★★★☆ **Gravel Quarry Cabernet Sauvignon** Ⓩ Handsome & powerful, farm's top cab in purefruited bramble form in **09**. Classy blackcurrant flavours are melded with the pliable tannin frame, giving great grip.

★★★★☆ **Quartz Stone Chardonnay 13** shows benefit of fruit from this single, old vineyard; most powerful, concentrated - also this year - best of cellar's trio of chardonnays. Beautifully proportioned, with refinement in its creamy breadth, mineral thread. Vinified in oak (90% new French) & concrete 'eggs'. Deserves cellaring.

★★★★ **The Welder** Ⓩ Concentrated, silky chenin Natural Sweet a mouthful of light-bodied refreshment. **12** returns to sizzling form after lesser **11** (★★★★), with pinpoint sugar/acid balance, low 10.5% alcohol.

The Curator's Collection

★★★★ **Pinot Noir Reserve** Ⓩ Serious package; dense **11** has forest floor & farmyard richness, firm tannins. 11 months all-new casks. Needs 2-5 years to develop.

★★★★ Chenin Blanc **13** has sunny hue & disposition of its Swartland origin with digestible 12.5% alcohol. Barrel ferment in older French oak adds breadth, texture to bright melon, pineapple juicy flavours. Smoothly dry & lingering.

Malbec **★★★☆** Soft tannins, a tangy freshness & succulent mulberry flavours provide ready enjoyment in **11**. Can go a few years too, but pity to lose the fruity charm. Not retasted: **Tannat 10 ★★★☆**

Limited Releases

★★★★ Méthode Cap Classique MCC from chardonnay & pinot; exclusive bottling by Robertson's Bon Courage under Glen Carlou label. **07** (**★★★☆**) shade off **06**; creamy, soft with bright but quickly departing bubble. 4 years on lees.

Classic range

★★★★ Cabernet Sauvignon Usual touch mint lifts riper, dark fruits on modern **12**. Unaggressively firm & well fleshed, though perhaps lacks depth to gain greater complexity in long term. Harmonised in older oak.

★★★★ Grand Classique Much appeal in **11** cab-led Bordeaux quintet. Depth of ripe, generous fruit, supported by freshness & fine tannin, all seamlessly knit with poise & elegance. Oak, 40% new French adds finishing polish.

★★★★ Petit Verdot-Tannat Was 'Petit Verdot Blend'. Unusual but successful pairing. **11** rich in flavour & confidently built, though both its natural fresh feel & fine-grained tannins temper its full body.

★★★★ Chardonnay Familiar pickled lime, toast combo on New World style **13**. A touch less intense than **12** but good fresh core, well-balanced oaking (30% new) ensures good drinking now, few years more.

★★★★ Unwooded Chardonnay 13 (**★★★★**) has good presence if not quite the textured layers of **12**. Medium-bodied mouthful of lees-enhanced juicy citrus flavours; roundly dry & food friendly.

Also tasted: **Merlot 12 ★★★** Not retasted: **Pinot Noir 12 ★★★** **Syrah 10 ★★★★** **Zinfandel 09 ★★★★** **Sauvignon Blanc 13 ★★★**

Contemporary range

Not retasted: **Tortoise Hill Red 12 ★★★** **Tortoise Hill White 13 ★★★** — AL

Location: Paarl ▪ Map: Paarl & Wellington ▪ WO: Paarl/Coastal/Robertson/Durbanville/Swartland ▪ Est 1985 ▪ 1stB 1988 ▪ Tasting & sales Mon-Fri 8.30–5 Sat/Sun 10–4 ▪ Fee R25-R50 ▪ Closed Good Fri, Dec 25 & Jan 1 ▪ Cellar tours by appt ▪ Restaurant ▪ Facilities for children ▪ Tour groups ▪ Gifts ▪ Honey ▪ Conferences ▪ Conservation area ▪ Hess Art Collection Museum ▪ Owner(s) Hess Family Wine Estates Ltd (Switzerland) ▪ Cellarmaster(s)/winemaker(s) Arco Laarman (Jan 2000) ▪ Viticulturist(s) Marius Cloete (2000) ▪ 145ha/68ha (cabs s/f, malbec, mourv, p verdot, pinot, shiraz, chard) ▪ ±700t/100,000cs own label ▪ PO Box 23 Klapmuts 7625 ▪ welcome@glencarlou.co.za ▪ www.glencarlou.co.za ▪ S 33° 48' 44.85" E 018° 54' 12.88" ▪ **F** +27 (0)21-875-5314 ▪ **T +27 (0)21-875-5528**

Glenelly Estate

Repeated South African success in winning the Pichon Lalande Trophy at the International Wine & Spirit Competition was an initial attraction for Madame May-Eliane de Lencquesaing, then owner of that Bordeaux classed growth, to invest in the Cape. After she bought Glenelly on Stellenbosch's Simonsberg, a redevelopment of the old fruit farm to vineyards was undertaken and a cellar built. All her projects have been carried out along environmentally friendly lines, and the local community and social development, particularly of Glenelly's employees, have been ongoing focuses.

Lady May range

★★★★☆ Lady May Classic cab, naturally fermented **11** still youthfully taut, with subtle lead pencil, dark fruit aromas; complementary oaking (100% new). Full bodied, but fine acid backbone & properly dry finish lends overall refinement. Includes a little petit verdot, merlot.

For more information, visit wineonaplatter.com

Grand Vin de Glenelly range

★★★★☆ **Red** Was 'Grand Vin de Glenelly'. Elegant & accessible shiraz/Bordeaux blend, earlier drinking than Lady May. **09** with polished dark berry fruit laced with spice & supple tannins. **08** (★★★★) was lighter.

★★★★ **Chardonnay** Delicate yet convincing **13**. Natural ferment in 500L oak with only partial malolactic fermentation provide polish, harmony & freshness to the lively citrus fruit, oatmeal, lees underpin. A charmer!

Glass Collection

★★★★ **Cabernet Sauvignon** ⊘ This & Merlot benefit from strength of **12** red-wine vintage. Leavens ripeness of dark berry fruit & dense yet integrated tannins with freshness. 25% new French oak further enhancement. Already approachable, will benefit from further few years. **11** (★★★☆).

★★★★ **Merlot** ⊘ **12** has more focus & precision than **11** (★★★★). The perfectly ripe dark plum, chocolate flavours are concentrated & well sustained on the firm yet unharsh finish.

Also tasted: Syrah 11 ★★★☆ **Chardonnay Unwooded 13** ★★★☆ — AL

Location/map/WO: Stellenbosch ▪ Est/1stB 2003 ▪ Tasting & sales Mon-Fri 10-4.30 Sat 10-4 ▪ Closed Easter Fri/Sun, Dec 25/26 & Jan 1 ▪ Cellar tours by appt ▪ Gift shop ▪ Glass museum ▪ Owner(s) May-Eliane de Lencquesaing ▪ Cellarmaster(s) Luke O'Cuinneagain (Jan 2008) ▪ Winemaker(s) Luke O'Cuinneagain (Jan 2008), with Jerome Likwa (Jan 2008) ▪ Viticulturist(s) Heinrich Louw (2003) ▪ 125ha/60ha (cabs s/f, merlot, p verdot, shiraz, chard) ▪ 500t/55,334cs own label 90% red 10% white ▪ PO Box 1079 Stellenbosch 7599 ▪ wine@glenelly.co.za ▪ www.glenellyestate.com ▪ S 33° 55' 6.1" E 018° 52' 45.1" ▪ F +27 (0)21-809-6448 ▪ **T +27 (0)21-809-6440**

Glen Erskine Estate

Replanting their Elgin apple farm in 2005, Reine and Annalien Dalton decided to turn over a tiny portion to vines. Their approach to marketing is also to keep things small and personal, build relationships with visitors and sell as much wine as possible from the cellardoor. It is in the cellar that visitors are introduced to the wines.

Reserve Sauvignon Blanc-Semillon ★★★☆ **12** gentle yet compelling blend; the 33% semillon portion oaked, adding breadth & texture to the cool-climate elegance. Not retasted: **Sauvignon Blanc 12** ★★★★ **Reserve Viognier 12** ★★★★ — AL

Location/WO: Elgin ▪ Map: Elgin, Walker Bay & Bot River ▪ Est 2005 ▪ 1stB 2009 ▪ Tasting, sales & cellar tours by appt ▪ Closed Easter Fri/Sun, Dec 25 & Jan 1 ▪ BYO picnic ▪ Owner(s) Reine & Annalien Dalton ▪ Cellarmaster(s)/ winemaker(s) Annalien Dalton ▪ Viticulturist(s) Reine Dalton ▪ 14.6ha/3.04ha (sauv, sem, viog) ▪ 21t/840cs own label 100% white + 250cs for clients ▪ Ranges for customers: Kievits Kroon ▪ PO Box 111 Elgin 7180 ▪ annalien.dalton@gmail.com, reinedalton@gmail.com ▪ S 34° 10' 34.94" E 019° 2' 12.75" ▪ F +27 (0)86-547-4473 ▪ **T +27 (0)21-848-9632**

Glen Heatlie

One of Solms-Delta's young winemakers, Joan-Marie Heatlie continues to explore the potential of her family's Worcester vines in her spare time. High-lying shiraz planted in ancient Dwyka soils from the Klein Karoo supergroup engages this Rhône lover, a national indoor hockey player whose Scottish great-grandfather distilled brandy here.

Location: Worcester ▪ Est 2006 ▪ Tasting by appt only ▪ Owner(s) Orange Grove Trust ▪ Winemaker(s) Joan-Marie Heatlie ▪ Viticulturist(s) Charlie Heatlie ▪ 3,100ha/45ha (cab, merlot, shiraz, chenin, chard, cbard, sauv, sem) ▪ Orange Grove PO Box 18 De Wet 6853 ▪ joan@glenheatlie.co.za ▪ F +27 (0)23-341-2708 ▪ **T +27 (0)82-364-4702**

Glenview Wines

Vintner and surfer Robin Marks continues to do steady on-line business, locally and abroad, by sourcing wines from coastal vineyards for his own label (the brand name a reference to Glen Beach near Robin's Camps Bay home). His selling point is easy-drinking, affordable quality.

Merlot ★★ Partially oaked **13** from Stellenbosch vines has ripe red fruit flavours, smooth tannins & gentle herb lift for anytime easy drinking. **Sauvignon Blanc** ★★★ Wellington grapes in fresh **14**, bone-dry weight watcher's friend, with limy tang in tail. Discontinued: **Chenin Blanc**. — GM

Location: Cape Town ▪ WO: Coastal ▪ Est/1stB 1998 ▪ Closed to public ▪ Owner(s) Robin Marks ▪ Winemaker(s) Frank Meaker (Nov 2010, consultant) ▪ 14,000cs own label 50% red 50% white ▪ PO Box 32234 Camps Bay 8040 ▪ bayexport@kingsley.co.za ▪ F +27 (0)21-511-2545 ▪ **T +27 (0)21-438-1080**

GlenWood

Owner Alastair Wood left a career in business consulting to set up his picturesque estate at Robertsvlei in Franschhoek Valley, with its characterful boutique winery and 'fine-dining French bistro' Le Bon Vivant. Under seasoned winemaker, DP Burger, they have built a reputation for standout chardonnay and consistent quality throughout the range. A botrytis dessert from the 2013 vintage joins the impressive Grand Duc flagship range this year.

Grand Duc range

★★★★☆ **Syrah** This range only in exceptional vintages; bunch pressing, wild yeast ferments & 100% new oak, 2 years. From Wellington fruit, **12** a beautifully crafted, balanced & complex wine showing concentrated plum, white pepper, blueberry aromas & flavours. Like richly textured **11**, good for up to a decade.

★★★★☆ **Chardonnay** Range credo 'Simple, Natural, Quality' evident in **12**, vinified as for Syrah. Pure & precise flavours of yellow stonefruit, dried mango, nuts & vanilla in a crisp, elegant structure & long, succulent finish. 2 years new oak effortlessly absorbed & integrated.

GlenWood range

★★★★ **Merlot** Intricate **12** shows lots of ripe berry, plum & nutmeg. Juicy enough for solo sipping, yet enough grip for food & cellaring a few years.

★★★★ **Shiraz** Judicious oaking (30% new, 18 months) evident in **12**'s smoky profile, firm grip. Bountiful fruit, spice & pepper attractions also serve to balance high 14.8% alcohol. Last-tasted **08** (★★★★★) was exceptional.

★★★★☆ **Chardonnay Vigneron's Selection** Barrel-fermented **13** has a lot going on: stonefruit, vanilla, citrus & roasted nuts plus subtle oak flavours that integrate well with peach & honey, linger. As sumptuous & multi-dimensional as **12**, potentially as long lived.

★★★★ **Unwooded Chardonnay 13** 8 months lees-maturation for weight & depth; white peach, pear, Golden Delicious apple complexity, creamy texture. Has credentials for ageing few years.

★★★★ **Semillon Vigneron's Selection** Bunch-pressed, wild-yeast-fermented **13** billows honey, peach, apple pie & oats; bold & lipsmacking, deserves keeping, as did toasty, silky **12**.

Also tasted: **Merlot-Shiraz 12** ★★★☆ **Sauvignon Blanc 14** ★★★★ Discontinued: **Syrah Vigneron's Selection**. — GM

Location/map: Franschhoek ▪ WO: Franschhoek/Coastal ▪ Est/1stB 2002 ▪ Tasting & sales Mon-Fri 11–4 Sat/Sun (Aug-May only) 11-3 ▪ Closed Easter Fri/Sun, Dec 25 & Jan 1 ▪ Tasting R50/cellar tour R150 ▪ Tours daily at 11; cellar tour with owner/winemaker available by prior arrangement, min 2 persons ▪ Le Bon Vivant@GlenWood open for lunch Thu-Tue ▪ Hikes ▪ Owner(s) Alastair G Wood ▪ Cellarmaster(s)/winemaker(s)/viticulturist(s) DP Burger (Apr 1991) ▪ 49ha/30ha (merlot, shiraz, chard, sauv, sem) ▪ 150t/16,000cs own label 50% red 50% white ▪ BWI, IPW ▪ PO Box 204 Franschhoek 7690 ▪ info@glenwoodvineyards.co.za ▪ www.glenwoodvineyards.co.za ▪ S 33° 54' 56.7" E 019° 4' 57.0" ▪ F +27 (0)21-876-3338 ▪ **T +27 (0)21-876-2044**

Goats do Roam Wine Company

A kid - of Franco-South African parentage - is born this edition to the herd of well-established, well-made blends which play on the synergy between the goats, grapes and cheese (much of it from goats' milk) at Charles Back's busy Fairview property in Paarl. The wines, interesting and modestly priced, now are all Fairtrade accredited.

★★★★ **Goat Roti** Refined & elegant **12** from shiraz co-fermented with 2% viognier. 2 years in oak makes for soft flavours of baked plums & dark cherries, & silky tannins.

Goats in Villages Red (NEW) ★★★ Unusual **12** a Cape Blend of shiraz (76%) & pinotage makes for a soft, smooth drink with plenty of minty herbaceousness to freshen. **Goats do Roam White** ⊘ ★★★☆ Tank sample **14** shows plenty of fresh peaches & pineapples on this unwooded Rhône blend of viognier, roussanne & grenache blanc, all backed up by fresh acidity & good length. Also tasted: **Goats do Roam Red** ⊘ 13 ★★★☆ **The Goatfather** 13 ★★★☆ **Goats do Roam Rosé** 14 ★★★☆ — CM

Location: Paarl ▪ WO: Coastal/Western Cape/Paarl ▪ Est/1stB 1998 ▪ Tasting & sales at Fairview (see entry) ▪ Owner(s) Charles Back ▪ Winemaker(s) Anthony de Jager, with Stephanie Betts ▪ PO Box 583 Suider-Paarl 7624 ▪ info@goatsdoroam.com ▪ www.fairview.co.za ▪ F +27 (0)21-863-2591 ▪ **T +27 (0)21-863-2450**

Goede Hoop Estate

This venerable family estate spreads its vineyards on a horseshoe of slopes in Stellenbosch's Bottelary Hills. Consultant Albert Ahrens brings new-Swartland experience - giving some wines an unpretentious elegance, balance and eminent drinkability (though power now creeps in too). The Heritage label is a joint venture between Albert and Goede Hoop's owner Pieter Bestbier (3rd generation here).

Heritage Wines
★★★★ **Estate Wine** ⊘ **11** blends merlot, pinotage, cab, shiraz, malbec & cinsaut to express the estate. More power than **10** (needs time), but some elegance, & depth of fruit too. Lovely use of larger oak barrels.

★★★★ **Estate Straw Wine** (½) **10** from chenin; hugely sweet & concentrated, ripe fruit flavours.

Goede Hoop Estate range
Merlot ★★★ **12** notch up on Domaine version, with a little more structure; friendly & easy enough, but not trivial. **Chardonnay** ★★★ Expressive aromas & flavours on **13**, with a little spice from oak. Fresh, unshowy & easy. Also tasted: **Cabernet Sauvignon 10** ★★★ **Sauvignon Blanc 13** ★★☆ Not retasted: **Pinotage 10** ★★★☆ **Shiraz 09** ★★★☆ Not tasted: **Shiraz LBV Port**.

Domaine range
Merlot (NEW) ★★★☆ Lightish, modest & rather charming **13**, but not dumbed down; has gentle tannic bite. Unwooded. **Chenin Blanc** (NEW) ★★★ Just-dry **13** offers tasty, nicely balanced & gentle quaffing. **Sauvignon Blanc** (NEW) ★★ Sprightly green-tropical aromas on **13**; tangy & rather tart. — TJ

Location/map: Stellenbosch ▪ WO: Bottelary ▪ Est 1928 ▪ 1stB 1974 ▪ Tasting, sales & cellar tours Mon-Fri 9–4 Sat 10–1 ▪ Closed Easter Fri-Sun, Dec 24/25/26/31 & Jan 1 ▪ Pieter's private cellar: monthly 4-course gourmet meal with wine R325pp, booking essential (12 seats only) ▪ BYO picnic ▪ Mountain biking trail ▪ Owner(s) Pieter Bestbier ▪ Winemaker(s) Albert Ahrens (Jun 2009, consultant), with Janette Hartshorne (Jan 2012) ▪ 122ha/71ha (cab, cinsaut, malbec, merlot, ptage, shiraz, chard, chenin, sauv) ▪ ±600t/10,000cs own label 80% red 20% white & ±200,000L bulk ▪ PO Box 25 Kuils River 7579 ▪ goede@adept.co.za ▪ www.goedehoop.co.za ▪ S 33° 54' 32.0" E 018° 45' 14.0" ▪ F +27 (0)21-906-1553 ▪ **T +27 (0)21-903-6286**

Goedvertrouw Estate

If you think cellardoors are becoming too homogenised, program your GPS for Elreda Pillmann's farm, a few kilometres from Bot River on the Van der Stel Pass. The delightful tannie Elreda is a force of nature, making wine, fund-raising for Tommy Prins Foundation, featuring in Elgin Open Gardens Week and Bot River Pink Weekend, running a B&B, and cooking 'boeremeals' for visitors!

Pinot Noir (½) ★★ Earthy strawberry notes & hint of vanilla on light-hearted **09**. Not retasted: **Cabernet Sauvignon 05 Chardonnay 06** ★★★ **Sauvignon Blanc 08** ★★☆ — DS

Location: Bot River ▪ Map: Elgin, Walker Bay & Bot River ▪ WO: Overberg ▪ Est 1990 ▪ 1stB 1991 ▪ Tasting & sales by appt ▪ Home-cooked meals & accommodation by appt ▪ Play area for children ▪ Walks ▪ Farm produce ▪ Small conferences ▪ Conservation area ▪ Small art gallery ▪ Owner(s)/winemaker(s)/viticulturist(s) Elreda Pillmann ▪ 8ha (cab, pinot, chard, sauv) ▪ 70% red 30% white ▪ PO Box 37 Bot River 7185 ▪ goedvertrouwwineestate@telkomsa.net ▪ S 34° 9' 56.7" E 019° 13' 24.1" ▪ F +27 (0)28-284-9769 ▪ **T +27 (0)28-284-9769**

Goedverwacht Wine Estate

Steady growth and development continues on the Du Toit family farm near Bonnievale. The 5th generation, university-educated son Gawie, has joined the team. Besides annual vineyard renewal, virgin land acquisition has allowed for new plantings (durif/petite sirah, nouvelle, chardonnay and sauvignon). Warehousing, more storage tanks, tasting room extensions… business is good.

Maxim range

★★★★ **Cabernet Sauvignon** ② Polished & modern. **11** similar leafy notes to elegant **10** (★★★★) but greater presence, complexity (chocolate, coffee, liquorice) from 100% new French oak.

Chardonnay ★★★☆ Judicious wooding (40% new) & 9 months lees-ageing add pleasing spicy breadth to **13**'s fresh citrus attraction. Ideal partner for galjoen (SA's national fish) & butter chicken.

Private Cellar range

Shiraz Rosé ⑨ ★★☆ Pale **14** delicate but generously fruited everyday dry pink sipper. Wallet-friendly alternative to the big brands. **The Good Earth Sauvignon Blanc** ★★★ Bright & perky **14** ideal poolside companion: good length, packed with grassy sauvignon character. Also tasted: **Great Expectations Chardonnay 14** ★★☆ **Crane White Colombar 14** ★★☆ **Crane Rosé Brut Sparkling 13** ★★★ Not retasted: **Crane Red Merlot 13** ★★ **An Acre of Stone Shiraz 12** ★★★ **Triangle 11** ★★★ Note: range was 'Goedverwacht'. — CvZ

Location: Bonnievale ▪ Map/WO: Robertson ▪ Est 1960's ▪ 1stB 1994 ▪ Tasting, sales & cellar tours Mon-Fri 8.30-4.30 Sat 10-1 ▪ Closed Easter Fri/Sun, Dec 25/26 & Jan 1 ▪ Mediterranean or quiche & salad platter; picnic basket for 2 (incl sparkling wine) - 2 days prior booking essential ▪ BYO picnic ▪ Tour groups ▪ Conservation area ▪ Owner(s) Jan du Toit & Sons (Pty) Ltd ▪ Winemaker(s) Henry Conradie (Aug 2005) ▪ Viticulturist(s) Jan du Toit, advised by Francois Viljoen ▪ 220ha/130ha (cab, merlot, shiraz, chard, cbard, sauv) ▪ 1,600t/1m L 43% red 50% white 7% rosé ▪ Other export brands: Ama Ulibo, Misty Kloof's, Mzanzi's, Soek die Geluk ▪ Brands for clients: Vinimark Trading ▪ BEE, BWI, IPW ▪ PO Box 128 Bonnievale 6730 ▪ goedwachtestate@lando.co.za, winemaker@goedverwacht.co.za ▪ www. goedverwacht.co.za ▪ S 33° 55' 11.3" E 020° 0' 19.1" ▪ F +27 (0)23-616-2073 ▪ **T +27 (0)23-616-3430**

☐ **Gôiya** *see* Namaqua Wines
☐ **Goldcoast** *see* Val du Charron
☐ **Golden Chalice** *see* Southern Sky Wines
☐ **Golden Triangle** *see* Stellenzicht Vineyards

Goose Wines

High in the Outeniqua Mountains near George is the cool-climate farm Ganzekraal ('Goose Kraal') co-owned, appropriately enough, by renowned professional golfer Retief 'The Goose' Goosen. The wines, now also exported to the US, this edition are all listed under 'Goose' (some previously under the 'Gander' label). All are still made off-site.

Goose range

★★★★ **Expression** ② Plush ripe-styled **09** from cab & shiraz. Dark plummy fruit has vibrant acid support, soft supple tannins. 30% new French oak. WO W Cape.

★★★★ **T-Box Sauvignon Blanc** ② Weightiest of the sauvignons, **11** 9 months new oak. Citrus peel, spice & pure fruit in fine balance with wood, acid & alcohol.

Cabernet Sauvignon ★★★☆ Cassis & cherries, **12** leaps from the glass, succulent & fresh with just enough tannin grip for few years ageing. **Sauvignon Blanc** ★★★ Pre-bottled **14** shows herbaceous whiffs, appley flavours; softly rounded & easy. Not retasted: **Shiraz 11** ★★★ — CR

STEENBERG

www.steenbergfarm.com

Minutes from Cape Town, Miles from the World

Hotel reservations: +27 21 713 2222
email: info@steenberghotel.com

Catharina's Restaurant reservations: +27 21 713 7178
email: reservations@catharinasrestaurant.co.za

Bistro Sixteen82 reservations: +27 713 2211
email: reservations@bistro1682.co.za

Not for Sale to Persons Under the Age of 18.

www.jfhillebrand.com

100% GLOBAL 100% LOCAL

No matter where you are in the world of wine, beer and spirits, you will find JF Hillebrand is there. While the reach of our 2000 professionals in 47 offices is 100% global, our touch remains 100% local.

Peu importe où vous êtes dans le monde du vin, de la bière et des spiritueux, vous verrez JF Hillebrand est là. Bien que la portée de nos professionnels 2000 dans 47 bureaux est de 100% global, notre touche reste 100% locale.

100% BEVERAGE. 100% LOGISTICS.

JF Hillebrand South Africa
T +27 21 809 2000
capetown@hillebrandgroup.com

JFHillebrand
global beverage logistics

PRACTICE THE ART
of FINE FOOD.

Live in Italian

FOUNDED   ANNO 1694

HAUTE CABRIÈRE

Cellar Restaurant & Terrace

FRANSCHHOEK

"I'm newly inspired every day. By the view from the restaurant of the valley beyond. By the restaurant itself, with its vaulted ceilings and crystal chandeliers. By the window in the restaurant that gives you a glimpse of the underground cellar and which reminds me of what I'm here to do: To pair amazing food with spectacular wines. So, when I'm wandering through the kitchen garden, Pinot Noir and Chardonnay are never far from my mind. The wines of Haute Cabrière are my muses. They define every culinary decision; they inspire every new idea. The quest is deceptively simple: to make sure that every bite of food you take is made magical by a sip of matching wine." – Ryan Shell, Head Chef.

Experience the true marriage of food and wine.

Address
Pass Road (R45), Franschhoek
Cape Winelands.

Reservations & Enquiries
+27 (0)21 876 3688
restaurant@cabriere.co.za

GPS Co-ordinates
33°54'51.63"S : 19° 8'7.90"E

For more information visit
www.cabriere.co.za

also follow us on

The **Glass**
is always **greener** on *our* side...

ngwenya glass   handmade • eco friendly • recycled
locally produced in Swaziland

V&A Waterfront, Watershed, Cape Town | Tel. +27 21 418 0654
ngwenya@ngwenyaglass.co.sz | www.ngwenyaglass.co.sz
Tel/Fax. +268 – 244 24053 | 244 24142 | 244 24151 | 244 24588
Fax from SA only.   086 5305 452

Riedel recognises that the bouquet, taste, balance and finish of a wine is affected by the shape of the glass from which it is drunk. Over forty years ago Claus Riedel began his pioneering work to create stemware that would match and complement different wines and spirits.

"The Finest glasses for both technical and hedonistic purposes are those made by Riedel. The effect of these glasses on fine wine is profound.

I cannot emphasize enough what a difference they make."

Robert M Parker Jr - The Wine Advocate.

RIEDEL
THE WINE GLASS COMPANY

GRAPE ⬤⬤⬤ VARIETAL SPECIFIC®

Cheers!

to the good stuff

www.westfaliafruit.com

Dreams also get better with time.

Introducing the new Mercedes-Benz SL 400 in the Dream Cars range.

With the addition of the exceptionally desirable new SL 400 cabriolet, Mercedes-Benz Dream Cars offer a range of cabriolets designed for the driver with an acquired taste. Aesthetically pleasing and exhilarating on the road, they're the cars you've always aspired to drive and now you can. For more information visit www.mercedes-benz.co.za/dreamcars

Vehicle specifications may vary for the South African market.

DINERS CLUB IS A REGISTERED CREDIT PROVIDER (NCRCP983).
WWW.DINERSCLUB.CO.ZA
28.00771

OliverMcIntyre 17/11

-26.191125

Diners Club
INTERNATIONAL®

BELONG

DINERS CLUB TRAVEL GUIDE

FOR THOSE WHO ARE ALWAYS EXPLORING, NOW THERE'S AN
APP. AT THE PUSH OF A BUTTON YOU CAN QUICKLY DISCOVER
RESTAURANTS, ENTERTAINMENT AND PLACES OF INTEREST
NEARBY. IT'S LIKE HAVING YOUR OWN PERSONAL TOUR GUIDE.
DOWNLOAD THE DINERS CLUB TRAVEL GUIDE AT YOUR APP
STORE OR VISIT DINERSCLUB.CO.ZA WHERE YOU BELONG.

 Diners Club SA   @DinersClubSA   Diners Club South Africa

Capped with service

Superior service is about refinement, perfection, innovation, ability to adapt and style. Most importantly, it is about meeting these high standards with no fuss.

As South Africa's largest metal and plastic closures manufacturer, Nampak Closures has a well established and proven track record of delivering professional service. We are supported by Nampak R&D, widely regarded as one of the most advanced packaging science and technology facilities in the southern hemisphere and have access to cross divisional packaging technology, expertise, market trends and knowledge.

Our range of proudly South African screw caps, backed up by our superior personal service, are designed to give your wine a perfect sense of style that appeals to even the most sophisticated connoisseur.

Contact us on +27 21 507 8411

Nampak
Closures
packaging excellence

www.nampak.com

MURATIE
s t e l l e n b o s c h

A S T O R Y T O T E L L

Tucked into the exquisite Knorhoek Valley north of Stellenbosch, Muratie Wine Estate, under the stewardship of Rijk Melck and his family, has been at the heart of a lot of passionate debate. This debate is centred largely around the desire to protect a century's old wine experience that is a magnet for wine lovers around the world.

The farm itself dates back to 1685 when it was granted by Governor Simon van der Stel who was Governor of the Cape of Good Hope at the time. This makes Muratie one of the oldest estates in South Africa and along with that age come many characters and truly fascinating stories.

Muratie's rich history is captured in every nook and cranny. Wherever you are on the estate you cannot help being moved by a sense of the many generations that have lived and worked here. The buildings, the artifacts and even the shrubs and trees exude an aura of the colourful past reaching towards an even more fruitful future.

Then once you have experienced this absorbing atmosphere, you will literally taste it in the Tasting Room where our wines can be savored every day of the week. And Wednesday to Sunday you can relish authentic farm platters and other traditional cooking in our Farm Kitchen.

We also offer accommodation, mountain bike and running trails as well as an art gallery. So do take time out to explore our world. We look forward to hosting you.

TASTING HOURS
Monday to Sunday: 10h00 to 17h00

FARM KITCHEN HOURS (Lunch)
Wednesday to Sunday: 12h00 to 15h00

MURATIE WINE ESTATE
Knorhoek Road/R44, Koelenhof, Stellenbosch
Tel: 021 865 2330
Fax: 021 865 2790
Email: info@muratie.co.za
Website: www.muratie.co.za

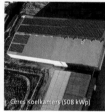

EAT GOOD
FEEL GREAT

The Grill Jichana is a modern and stylish Grill House
that offers from prime beef cuts and Karoo lamb
to free-range chicken, fish and
vegetarian dishes.

THE GRILL JICHANA – GROUND
FLOOR AT THE ELANGENI TOWER.

Southern Sun Elangeni & Maharani
63 Snell Parade, Durban 4001
t: 27 31 362 1300 I e: garika.ramdarie@tsogosun.com

THE
GRILL
JICHANA

Powerful antioxidant as found in red grapes and red wine. **Resveratrol**, a polyphenol, was first isolated in grape skins. It also occurs in peanuts, red wine, and some herbs such as Polygonum cuspidatum. Polyphenols possess powerful antioxidant activity that helps fight cell-damaging free radicals in the body. Free radicals can lead to the premature aging of cells. Antioxidants work in the body by neutralizing and eliminating these free radicals. They may also boost the body's ability to repair, regenerate and protect itself from further damage.

SOLGAR | It's Your Choice.

SOLGAR *Vitamins* INNOVATION AND QUALITY *Since 1947*

Available from Independent Health Stores and Healthcare Practitioners
For more information e-mail infosa@solgar.com www.solgarsa.co.za Tel 011 462 1652

CAREFULLY MANUFACTURED in the USA BY SOLGAR LABORATORIES

EAT STAY LOVE

Serving the finest steaks complimented by an impressive wine selection with international appeal. The Meat Co is a 'must visit' destination when in town.

TheMeatCo

www.themeatco.com

The Meat Co Melrose Arch
Contact: +27 11 684 1787/8

The Meat Co Montecasino
Contact: +27 11 511 0235

Location: George ▪ Map: Klein Karoo & Garden Route ▪ WO: Upper Langkloof/Western Cape ▪ Est 2005 ▪ Tasting by appt ▪ Meals/refreshments by appt ▪ Owner(s) Retief Goosen & Werner Roux ▪ Winemaker(s) Alwyn Liebenberg (Jan 2007, consultant) ▪ Viticulturist(s) Bennie Botha (Jan 2009) ▪ 500ha/21ha (cab, shiraz, sauv) ▪ 120t/18,666cs own label 66% red 34% white + 140cs for clients ▪ Brands for clients: Reuben's (Franschhoek & Robertson) ▪ HACCP ▪ PO Box 2053 George 6530 ▪ michele@thegoosewines.com ▪ www.thegoosewines.com ▪ S 33° 47' 25.72" E 022° 41' 45.36" ▪ F +27 (0)86-543-1808 ▪ **T +27 (0)82-610-2276**

Goudini Wines

'No real news,' says Hendrik Myburgh, winemaker/viticulturist for grower-owned Breedekloof winery Goudini Wines, 'just constant tweaking and trialling to ensure we produce the best possible product'. The names of certain wines are related to long-lived desert plant Welwitchia mirabili, some thought to be over 1,500 years old. The wines themselves, however, are mostly for drinking young.

Reserve range

★★★★☆ **Gevonden Hendrik de Wet Cape Hanepoot** ⓧ Marvellous fortified dessert wine from single-vineyard believed planted ca 1880. Unoaked **13** luxurious, smooth & very sweet but balanced by pinpoint acidity. Cellarworthy; 375 ml.

Not retasted: **Mirabilis Primus-Capio 11 ★★★☆ Mirabilis Regis-Filia 11 ★★★☆**

Goudini range

Merlot ★★☆ Lightly oaked **13** has slight herbaceous, leafy tones, juicy enough core for solo sipping. **Chenin Blanc ★★★ 14** has thatch & grass whiffs, melon wafts; brisk acidity to balance 8.5 g/l sweetness. **Brut Sparkling ★★** Sleek black packaging for lightish **NV** bubbly from sauvignon, with 'wet pebble' aroma, seabreeze freshness. Stylish party date. **Natural Sweet Red** ⓝⓔⓦ **★★★** Easy-sipping **NV** from undisclosed varieties, packed with juicy berries, with enlivening tannic tug; modest 12% alcohol. Also tasted: **Cabernet Sauvignon 12 ★★★ Shiraz 13 ★★★ Unwooded Chardonnay** ⊘ **13 ★★★★ Sauvignon Blanc 14 ★★ Natural Sweet NV ★★** Not retasted: **Pinotage 11 ★★★ Rosé 13 ★★ Hanepoot 10 ★★★☆** Not tasted: **Ruby Cabernet-Merlot**. — CvZ

Location: Rawsonville ▪ Map: Breedekloof ▪ WO: Goudini/Western Cape ▪ Est 1948 ▪ Tasting & sales Mon-Fri 9—5 Sat 9—2 ▪ Closed Good Fri, Dec 25/26 & Jan 1 ▪ Cellar tours by appt ▪ Bistro: light meals during tasting hours ▪ Fully licensed bar ▪ Conferences ▪ Owner(s) 40 members ▪ Cellarmaster(s) Hennie Hugo (Dec 1984) ▪ Winemaker(s) Hendrik Myburgh (Nov 2001), with Tinus le Roux (Jan 2010) & Marius Prins (Jul 2013) ▪ Viticulturist(s) Hendrik Myburgh (Nov 2001) ▪ 1,000ha (merlot, ruby cab, shiraz, chard, chenin, sauv) ▪ 22,000t/66,000cs own label 45% red 45% white 10% rosé ▪ PO Box 132 Rawsonville 6845 ▪ info@goudiniwine.co.za ▪ www.goudiniwine.co.za ▪ S 33° 41' 37.8" E 019° 19' 9.5" ▪ F +27 (0)23-349-1988 ▪ **T +27 (0)23-349-1090**

☐ **Goue Kalahari** see Die Mas van Kakamas
☐ **Gouverneurs** see Groot Constantia Estate

Govert Wines

The Stellenbosch-based Keuzenkamp family source export wines from around the Cape winelands for clients and their own labels Charles Borro, D'Heros, Don Morris, Loyal Brothers and Ruby Ridge.

Location: Stellenbosch ▪ Est 2002 ▪ 1stB 2007 ▪ Closed to public ▪ Owner(s) Teuns Keuzenkamp ▪ 180,000cs own label 80% red 5% white 15% rosé ▪ PO Box 1977 Somerset West 7129 ▪ info@govertwines.com ▪ www.govertwines.com ▪ F +27 (0)86-224-9348 ▪ **T +27 (0)21-887-5812**

☐ **Gower Family Wines** see Ross Gower Wines

Graça

Inspired by Portugal's vinho verde wines, these popular easy-drinkers are made by Distell from widely sourced vineyards.

Rosé ★★ Lots of flavour on sweetish **NV** from mostly white grapes. Modest alcohol. **Graça ★★** Fruity, moderate-alcohol, off-dry **NV** blend - tasty enough, but pretty dilute. — TJ

Graceland Vineyards

The McNaughton family's small but ambitious estate in Stellenbosch's viticultural 'Golden Triangle' since inception more than 15 years ago has focused on handcrafted (by winemaker Susan), sumptuous reds, beautifully packaged. Current sales growth is being driven by their red blends, while investment in building strong brand identity is creating exciting new export opportunities.

★★★★ **Cabernet Sauvignon** Intensity of ripe blackberries maximised in **12** by careful oaking (25% new), as in all these reds. Well assembled; drier finish than others.

★★★★ **Merlot** ⓘ Rich plummy nose with fine gravelly edge evolves to dark berry & ripe plums. **11** shows better balance & rounder palate than **09** (★★★★). Good grippy end bodes well for cellaring.

★★★★ **Strawberry Fields** Forceful, modern shiraz, cab blend with drop merlot. Lashings ripe berries & spice on densely textured **12**. Noticeable 14.5% alcohol.

★★★★ **Three Graces** **12** reflects big, bold house style. Half cab provides firm structure, shiraz & merlot sweet, spicy plum flesh. Warming tail.

Also tasted: **Shiraz 12** ★★★ **Colour Field 12** ★★★ — AL

Location/map/WO: Stellenbosch ▪ Est/1stB 1998 ▪ Tasting & sales Mon-Fri by appt ▪ Fee R50 ▪ Closed all pub hols ▪ Owner(s) Paul & Susan McNaughton ▪ Cellarmaster(s)/winemaker(s)/viticulturist(s) Susan McNaughton (2001) ▪ 18ha/10ha (cab, merlot, shiraz) ▪ 55t/8,333cs own label 100% red ▪ Suite 144 Private Bag X4 Die Boord 7613 ▪ graceland@iafrica.com ▪ www.gracelandvineyards.com ▪ S 33° 59' 37.5" E 018° 50' 3.1" ▪ F +27 (0)86-556-4600 ▪ **T +27 (0)21-881-3121**

Graham Beck Wines

When the late Graham Beck (who'd made a fortune in coal mining) in 1983 bought a stretch of Robertson scrubland upon which to develop an ambitious winery, he almost immediately set aside a large portion as a nature reserve. Today, his company continually fine-tunes its Conservation Management Plan: 'Protecting our precious indigenous fauna and flora has now become an integral part of our day to day operations', they say. Social concerns are also important, with the Graham & Rhona Beck Skills Centre in Robertson only part of the evidence. As for the wine, although today sourcing grapes widely for their large range (prominently featuring the bubblies so beloved of celebrated cellarmaster Pieter Ferreira), the original Madeba wine and thoroughbred estate remains the Graham Beck nerve centre.

Ad Honorem range

★★★★☆ **Coffeestone Cabernet Sauvignon** Regal Stellenbosch cab **12** quite reticent mid-2014, but decent grip & satisfying fruit intensity suggest it will evolve in similar manner to elegant **11**.

★★★★☆ **The Ridge Syrah** Barrel selection from Robertson single-vineyard; spice & violet-perfumed **12** exudes confidence, is plush & polished, with better integrated tannins than **11** (★★★★).

★★★★☆ **The Joshua** ⓘ Co-fermented shiraz, 5% viognier seriously wooded (90% new oak, some American) in **11** (★★★). Aromatic & dense, with big 14.7% alcohol. Misses the generous fruit & muscular structure that underpinned **09**. No **10**. WO Coastal.

★★★★★ **Ad Honorem** ⓘ Oak-spicy **09** (★★★★★) *grand vin* is opulent & tarry, with impressive dark fruit, weight & length. More shiraz than noble **07** cab-shiraz blend (72:28). WO Coastal.

★★★★ **Bowed Head Chenin Blanc** ⓘ Orange blossom & baked apple on extroverted **12**. Expansive oak, slippery palate, with great fruit concentration from Agter Paarl dryland vines.

★★★★☆ **Pheasants' Run Sauvignon Blanc** As attention-grabbing as **12**, & showing greater vivacity than **13**, **14** is finely crafted, with precise acid balance, intense cool khaki bush & blackcurrant aromas, ripe fig flavours. Enough grip & structure for few years cellaring.

★★★★ **Rhona Muscadel** Fragrant & luxurious fortified dessert from Montagu, rounded in oak, 10% new. **13** preview back on track after slightly spirituous **12** (★★★★). Grapey sunshine, floral scents & satiny conclusion.

Méthode Cap Classique Sparkling range

★★★★ **Brut Rosé** Stellenbosch & Robertson pinot noir (82%) & chardonnay, co-fermented ('a first for South Africa'). New disgorgement after 54 months forthright & bold, **09** finishes emphatically dry.

★★★★ **Brut Rosé** Engaging strawberry shortcake smells & tastes, tempered acidity in latest **NV** celebratory tipple; more pinot than chardonnay, tad weightier than previous bottling.

★★★★☆ **Cuvée Clive** Flag-bearer of the accomplished MCC sparklings. **09** profoundly mineral, with elegant lemon persistence & freshness, creamy texture courtesy lengthy lees-ageing. Chardonnay (80%, small portion barrel-fermented) & pinot noir, 60 months on lees. No **08**.

★★★★☆ **Blanc de Blancs Brut** From Robertson chardonnay. Small oaked portion adds breadth & depth to new bottling of **09** (★★★★★) - look for a March 2014 disgorgement date on the label. Lively lemon & brioche scents, endless creamy mouthful enlivened by 'oystershell' minerality. 54 months lees contact; improves on **09** version tasted last year.

★★★★ **Brut Zero** New disgorgement (after 66 months) step up on **06** (★★★★), **08** dances across the palate: ultra-dry but with depth, breadth (courtesy lees-ageing, wooded portion, 20% pinot noir). Coiled, flinty, precise.

Also tasted: **Brut NV** ★★★★ **Bliss Demi Sec NV** ★★★

The Game Reserve range

★★★★ **Cabernet Sauvignon 12** classy mouthful with cassis aromas, firm tannins & long focused conclusion, leafiness managed with aplomb. Ex Stellenbosch, Groenekloof & Robertson.

Shiraz ★★★☆ Appealing scrub & red berries, vanilla & cardamom oak spice (year, 10% American; 20% new) on **12**; smooth fruit encased by firm tannins. WO Stellenbosch. **Chardonnay** ★★★☆ Partially fermented/aged in 20% new oak, **13** ex Robertson has vanilla, lemon butter & dried apricot flavours; improves on previous with lipsmacking dryness. **Chenin Blanc** ★★★ Tank sample **14** spice & thatch, fresh & bright for laid-back summer enjoyment. Lightly oaked; WO Coastal. Also tasted: **Merlot 12** ★★★ **Sauvignon Blanc 14** ★★★ Not retasted: **Pinotage 12** ★★★☆ **Viognier 13** ★★★

Everyday Favourites range

Gorgeous (NEW) ★★☆ Previewed **14** bone-dry rosé from pinot noir & chardonnay offers tantalising strawberry & lime for any time enjoyment. WO Robertson. Also tasted: **Railroad Red 12** ★★★ **Waterside Unoaked Chardonnay 14** ★★☆ Not retasted: **Pinno 12** ★★★ — CvZ

Location/map: Robertson ▪ WO: Western Cape/Robertson/Coastal/Stellenbosch/Paarl ▪ Est 1983 ▪ 1stB 1991 ▪ Tasting & sales Mon-Fri 9–5 Sat/Sun 10–4 ▪ Tasting fees: classic is complimentary; deluxe R50, waived on purchase of R200+; MCC R75 ▪ Closed Good Fri & Dec 25 ▪ Owner(s) Graham Beck Enterprises ▪ Cellarmaster(s) Pieter Ferreira (Aug 1990) & Erika Obermeyer (Jan 2005) ▪ Winemaker(s) Pierre de Klerk (Oct 2010) ▪ Viticulturist(s) Dérick Hamman & Pieter Fouché ▪ 226ha (cabs s/f, grenache, merlot, p verdot, pinot, shiraz, chard, chenin, sauv); Robertson 150ha/Stellenbosch 76ha ▪ 2,800t/540,000cs own label ▪ ISO 14001, BWI champion, IPW, SABS 1841, WIETA ▪ PO Box 724 Robertson 6705 ▪ cellar@grahambeckwines.co.za, market@grahambeckwines.co.za ▪ www.grahambeckwines.com ▪ S 33° 48' 14.95" E 019° 48' 1.41" ▪ F +27 (0)23-626-5164/+27 (0)21-874-1712 (marketing) ▪ **T +27 (0)23-626-1214/+27 (0)21-874-1258 (marketing)**

☐ **Grand Beach Café** *see* Stellekaya Winery
☐ **Grand Duc** *see* GlenWood

Grande Provence Heritage Wine Estate (Q) (M) (A) (O) (A) (&)

The estate dates back to a land grant to a French Huguenot in 1694 (the grand manor house is from the following century). After many vicissitudes, 310 years later Grande Provence was acquired by a Dutch-Belgian consortium, who confirmed it as a place offering more than wine — luxurious accommodation, fine dining and an art gallery, among others. The Angels Tears range returns to this entry from a separate listing, and a grandly named new range also arrives.

For more information, visit wineonaplatter.com

Premier range

★★★★ The Grande Provence In typical blockbuster house style, Bordeaux blend **10** from cab & merlot has aromas of crème de cassis, toasty oak & ripe cherries. **11**, also tasted, with more merlot in the blend, same big, warm structure & richness, though alcohol a little lower at 14.5%, & showing oak rather more (3 years new French).

★★★★ Chardonnay 12 & **13** both tasted; they share classic aromas of vanilla, ripe melon & pear, with good fruit & oak influence on the balanced palate. Satisfying, lingering flavours, but not a great deal of complexity.

★★★★ The Grande Provence White ⓝ **13** blend of chenin blanc & viognier shows an intense but not very complex palate mirroring the aromas of pear skin, apricot blossom & vanilla-infused apple.

★★★★ Chenin Blanc-Viognier 13 is 66% chenin. Return to elegance after more alcoholic **12** (★★★★). 30 year old vines give notes of mandarin, peach & orange blossom, & a clean, precise, concentrated palate.

Rosé ⓝ **★★★ 14** dry blend of cab & merlot shows frivolous red berry fruit & a rich round palate. Also tasted: **Pinot Noir 13 ★★★☆ Shiraz 10 ★★★☆ Sauvignon Blanc 14 ★★★☆** Not retasted: **Cabernet Sauvignon 10 ★★★ Muscat d'Alexandrie 12 ★★☆**

Vignerons Reserve 4 Barrel Selection ⓝ

★★★★ Chenin Blanc Inviting aromas of green & tropical fruit. **13**'s dry palate shows vigour & an appealing complexity, but with a slightly warming finish.

★★★★ Viognier Varietal hallmark perfumes & flavours of white flowers & apricot, & the usual element of viscosity. **13** finish touch more unusual, with an interesting slightly saline note.

Zinfandel ★★★☆ From Wellington, **13** commendably modest alcohol (13%). Berry, cherry & floral tones; soft & very accessible.

Angels Tears range

Muscat d'Alexandrie-Chenin Blanc ★★☆ Aromatic semi-sweet **13** from equal hanepoot & chenin. Lush, floral palate delivers easygoing pleasure. Also tasted: **Rosé 13 ★★ Sauvignon Blanc 14 ★★** Not retasted: **Merlot-Cabernet Sauvignon-Shiraz-Petit Verdot 12 ★★** — JPf

Location/map: Franschhoek ▪ WO: Franschhoek/Western Cape/Durbanville/Wellington ▪ Est 1694 ▪ 1stB 2004 ▪ Tasting & sales Mon-Sun 10–6 ▪ Fee R40/4 wines, R50/7 wines, R100/food & wine pairing ▪ Group tastings in cathedral extension of art gallery (seat up to 80 pax) ▪ Cellar & gallery tours Mon-Fri 11 & 3 Sat/Sun by appt ▪ Wine blending sessions by appt ▪ Kiddies grape juice tastings ▪ Picnics ▪ The Restaurant at Grande Provence ▪ Tour groups ▪ Gift shop ▪ Conferences ▪ Art gallery ▪ Harvest festival ▪ The Owner's Cottage & La Provençale at Grande Provence ▪ Owner(s) Dutch & Belgium consortium ▪ Cellarmaster(s)/winemaker(s)/viticulturist(s) Karl Lambour (May 2012) ▪ 32ha/22ha (cab, merlot, chard, sauv) ▪ Grande Provence: 120t/10,000cs own label 60% red 40% white; Angels Tears: 600t/60,000cs own label 30% red 60% white 10% rosé ▪ PO Box 102 Franschhoek 7690 ▪ reservations@grandeprovence.co.za ▪ www.grandeprovence.co.za ▪ S 33° 53′ 57.6″ E 19° 06′ 10.5″ ▪ F +27 (0)21-876-8601 ▪ **T +27 (0)21-876-8600**

Grand Mousseux

Enduring (launched 1929) budget-priced carbonated sparkling brand by Distell.

Vin Doux ⓧ **★★** Bubbly that's launched a million brides, **NV** explosively fizzy, sweet, serve well chilled. — DB

Grangehurst ⓠ ⓐ

Jeremy Walker's maiden wines were from the 1992 vintage, but he speaks of his wine activities then as a 'commercial hobby' – which grew into a 'fully-fledged small winery' when his own production cellar was constructed (out of a squash court!) on the small Helderberg family farm. With a partner, he bought another farm near Stellenbosch town in 2000, whose now-mature 6 ha supply cab for the cellar, supplemented by bought-in fruit from the Helderberg. Grangehurst specialises in classically styled reds, widely respected for their elegant longevity, and with the advantage for the serious winelover of generally being released only when they've lost the rawness of youth and are settling into themselves. See Wavescape Wines for details on Jeremy's new joint venture in wine production.

★★★★ **Cabernet Sauvignon Reserve** Ⓥ After charming **05**, classic **06** (★★★★☆) showed bold ripe tannins, delicate blackcurrant fruit with extended finish. Tasted some years back.

★★★★ **Mourvèdre** ⑰ **08**, with 14% shiraz, is rich, fresh, spicy & dark fruited. Very 'masculine' wine - with burly 14.4% alcohol, but the palate is vibrant, with well-melded oak & lingering flavours.

★★★★☆ **Pinotage** Ⓥ Mature **05** full of fresh charm. Refined though exotic perfume - more in pinot noir vein, as is light-textured, smooth-tannined, lively palate. Inc 14% cab. Tasted few years back.

★★★★ **CWG Auction Reserve** **09** (★★★★☆) true to the classic, unhurried Grangehurst philosophy. Cab-led, with petit verdot & merlot, as was previous **07**. Fruit concentration, but with restraint; tightly knit with ripe yet firm tannin. Needs 5+ years to open up & reach its full potential.

★★★★ **Cabernet Sauvignon-Merlot** Ⓥ Despite maturity, **06** last year displayed youthful cedary, cassis fragrance. Tannins also finely & firmly in control on this elegant, focused cab-dominated blend.

★★★★☆ **Grangehurst** The flagship. Cab-led **07** (★★★★) with merlot, petit verdot, as was **06**. House's restraint shows earthy, dark fruit, & hints of smoked redpepper. Accessible, but vibrant acid & firm tannin give ageability.

★★★★ **Nikela** Ⓥ Just a whisper of pinotage's raspberry & tannin bite on elegantly rich & savoury **06**, cab a dominant presence. Also shiraz & a little merlot. Fresh & firm with good further potential.

★★★★☆ **CWG Auction Cape Reserve Blend** ⑰ Virile **09** from half cab, with pinotage, shiraz & a dollop mourvèdre. Generous dark fruit complicated by Asian spice & attractive toasty oak. Rich, but with great definition & impeccable length. Despite 14.8% alcohol, there's a fine lift & freshness.

★★★★☆ **Shiraz-Cabernet Sauvignon Reserve** Ⓥ Complex cassis, redpepper, spice, leather & earthy notes on **05** (★★★★) after finer **03**. Tasted some years back.

★★★★ **Cape Rosé Blend** Easygoing but intriguing **13** (★★★★) multi-variety blend shows a medley of red fruit & a little spice, with a food-friendly modest alcohol. Like **11**, 'a rosé for red-wine drinkers'. No **12**. — JPf

Location/WO: Stellenbosch ▪ Map: Helderberg ▪ Est/1stB 1992 ▪ Tasting & sales Mon-Fri 9–4 Sat/Sun 10-3 (plse phone to confirm) ▪ Fee for group tastings depends on wines being presented ▪ Closed Easter Fri-Mon, Dec 25/26 & Jan 1 ▪ Self-catering guest cottages ▪ Owner(s) Grangehurst Winery (Pty) Ltd ▪ Cellarmaster(s) Jeremy Walker (Jan 1992) ▪ Winemaker(s) Jeremy Walker (Jan 1992), with Gladys Brown (Jan 2002) ▪ ±13ha/6ha own (cab) + 8ha bought in grapes (merlot, p verdot, ptage, shiraz) ▪ 80t/10,000cs own label 90% red 10% rosé + 2,000cs for clients ▪ Brands for clients: Woolworths ▪ PO Box 206 Stellenbosch 7599 ▪ winery@grangehurst.co.za ▪ www.grangehurst.co.za ▪ S 34° 01' 02.9" E 018° 49' 50.5" ▪ F +27 (0)86-710-6070 ▪ **T +27 (0)21-855-3625**

☐ **Granny Smith** see Boland Kelder

Grape Grinder

Oliver Kirsten and Johan du Toit founded their Paarl-based wine business to showcase SA wines, with all their creativity and energy, to an international audience. Market focused, most of their wines have mass appeal - 'like catnip for wine consumers', said a UK-based wine blogger of the Pinotage. The new unoaked Grinder Chenin is from low-yielding Swartland bushvines.

The Grinder range

Pinotage ★★★ 'Coffee pinotage' has pronounced - but not entirely unexpected! - coffee, smoke & charred notes on **13**. WO W Cape. **Shiraz** ★★★ Soft, smooth, juicy **12** makes for uncomplicated everyday drinking. **Chenin Blanc** ⑰ ★★★ Marzipan & honey on nose of **13**, ripe baked apple flavours, clean finish.

Milkwood range

Not retasted: **Shiraz-Viognier 12** ★★★★

For more information, visit wineonaplatter.com

Wild Olive range

Not retasted: **Old Vines Chenin Blanc 13** ★★★ — CM

Location: Paarl • WO: Coastal/Western Cape • Est/1stB 2010 • Closed to public • Owner(s) Oliver Kirsten & Johan du Toit • Cellarmaster(s)/winemaker(s) Pieter Carstens (Dec 2010, consultant) • 68,000cs own label 80% red 20% white • ISO 2009, BRC, WIETA • PO Box 606 Paarl 7624 • oliver@grapegrinder.com • www.grapegrinder.com • F +27 (0)86-588-4338 • **T +27 (0)21-863-3943**

☐ **Greendale** *see* Withington
☐ **Green House** *see* Bon Cap Organic Winery
☐ **Green Shebeen** *see* Org de Rac
☐ **Griffin** *see* Stettyn Cellar
☐ **Grimont** *see* Tulbagh Winery
☐ **Groblershoop** *see* Orange River Wine Cellars
☐ **Groen Kalahari** *see* Die Mas van Kakamas

Groenland

The Steenkamp family's farm on Stellenbosch's Bottelary Road is a cheerful place to be, with good old-fashioned hospitality from the affable Kosie and his son, fellow winemaker Piet. They like people, wine and good humour, and shun pretension. Only a small selection is bottled under their own label.

Premium range

★★★★ **Cabernet Sauvignon 09** reflects fine vintage, shows appealing blackcurrant & liquorice gently cosseted in smooth tannins. Youthful but integrated; would benefit from further ageing.

★★★★ **Merlot 11** regains ripeness & opulence after leaner **10** (★★★☆). Focused red berries on soft, supple structure. 100% new oak barrels, as for all Premium range.

★★★★ **Shiraz 10** a step up on previous, new oak lending structure to dense ripe fruit. Elegant herbaceous & peppery notes on satisfying finish. Follows generously ripe **09** (★★★☆).

★★★★ **Antoinette Marié 10** follows previous form: equal parts cab, merlot & shiraz produce elegant, finely structured blend. Style tends towards leafy blackcurrant of Bordeaux varietal bottlings.

Classic range

Cabernet Sauvignon ★★★☆ Impressive 2nd-tier **08** still fresh & vibrant, pure & dense. Excellent value. Also tasted: **Shiraz** ⊘ **09** ★★★☆ **Antoinette Marié 09** ★★★ **Sauvignon Blanc** ⊘ **14** ★★★★

Landskap range

Chenin Blanc ★★★ Nice balance, good fruit intensity, light & crisp **14**. Not retasted: **Shiraz-Merlot 12** ★★☆ — GdB

Location/map/WO: Stellenbosch • Est 1932 • 1stB 1997 • Tasting & sales Mon-Fri 10–4 Sat 10–1 • Fee R15pp for groups of 6+, waived on purchase • Closed Easter Fri/Sun & Dec 25 • Cellar tours by appt • Gift shop • BYO picnic by appt • Conference/function venue (20-60 pax) • Kids parties • Owner(s) Kosie Steenkamp • Winemaker(s) Kosie Steenkamp (Feb 1975), with Piet Steenkamp (Jan 2001) • Viticulturist(s) Piet Steenkamp (Jan 2001) • 192ha/154ha (cab, merlot, ptage, shiraz, chard, chenin, sauv) • 1,500t/±13,000cs own label 75% red 25% white • BEE level 3, BWI, IPW • PO Box 4 Kuils River 7579 • steenkamp@groenland.co.za • www.groenland.co.za • S 33° 53' 48.9" E 018° 44' 5.3" • F +27 (0)21-903-0250/+27 (0)86-571-4969 • **T +27 (0)21-903-8203**

Groot Constantia Estate

Laden with historical, cultural and viticultural significance by lying at the heart, in all respects, of the vaunted cool-climate Constantia wine ward, this Cape Town 'big six' tourist destination occupies the challenging position of having to be managed as both national treasure and model wine farm. Owners have ranged from founder Simon van der Stel (late 17th century Cape Dutch colonial governor and knowledgeable wine man) to the Cloete family (who further burnished the property's

For more information, visit wineonaplatter.com

architectural and oenological reputation during the late 18th to early 19th centuries) to various government bureaucracies. Successfully run as a commercially viable entity by a trust since 1993, the grand old lady has seen modern cellar upgrades, sound vineyard replanting and a quality-driven range produced by long-serving and dedicated winemaker Boela Gerber.

Gouverneurs range

★★★★☆ **Reserve Red** Cab franc-led Bordeaux blend with merlot & cab (36/10) in **11** (★★★★). Perfumed red fruit restrained by oak (76% new, 13 months) & dry chalky tannins. Both powerful & more subdued than **10**.

★★★★☆ **Reserve White 12** (★★★★) generously oaked semillon-led blend with 25% sauvignon. A shade off **11**, with lime & nectarine an understudy to opulent oaky tone in youth, lovely creamy texture & length. Needs time for harmony.

Groot Constantia range

★★★★ **Cabernet Sauvignon** ⊘ Fine **12** (★★★★★) perfumed cassis & cedar with some leafy freshness. Lovely fruit purity, bright & sappy, supported by dry fine-grained tannins. Complex, elegant step up on **11**, with good length & excellent ageing potential.

★★★★ **Pinotage 12** with dash shiraz, still tightly buttoned in more concentrated vintage. Brooding, dense kernel of smoky cherry fruit in chalky tannin framework. Will reward ageing.

★★★★ **Shiraz** ⊘ Hints of smoked bacon on **11**, less focused than **10** (★★★★★), but still showing muscle tempered with subtle liquorice, white pepper & violet aromas.

★★★★☆ **Chardonnay** Sumptuously styled with generous fruit in harmony with 40% new oak, adding richness & polish. **13** lovely varietal expression, intensity & length with a pervasive lime freshness. Showy, but has class.

★★★★☆ **Sauvignon Blanc** Feisty **13** back on form after hot-off-the-press **12** (★★★★). Intense nettle & oystershell flavours, with some creamy breadth & clean tangy freshness. Intensity & length, perfect for food pairing.

★★★★☆ **Grand Constance** Concentrated elixir to be savoured by the viscous spoonful. Partly oaked **11** (★★★★) Natural Sweet from red & white muscat de Frontignan, smartly packaged. Tad less elegantly balanced than **10**, intense citrus rind tang & slight burnt-sugar bitterness in sweet/sour tussle.

Also tasted: **Blanc de Noir 14** ★★★ **Semillon-Sauvignon Blanc 13** ★★★ Not retasted: **Constantia Rood 11** ★★★ Not tasted: **Merlot, Méthode Cap Classique, Cape Ruby**. — MW

Location/WO: Constantia ▪ Map: Cape Peninsula ▪ Est 1685 ▪ 1stB 1688 ▪ Tasting & sales daily 9–6 ▪ Fee R40 incl glass, R50 tasting & tour ▪ Closed Good Fri & Dec 25 ▪ Cellar tours 10-4 on the hour, every hour ▪ Simon's at Groot Constantia Restaurant; Jonkershuis Constantia Restaurant ▪ Facilities for children ▪ Tour groups ▪ Gifts ▪ Conferences ▪ Walks/hikes ▪ Conservation area ▪ Iziko Museum, manor house, historic buildings & orientation centre ▪ Owner(s) Groot Constantia Trust NPC RF ▪ Estate manager Floricius Beukes ▪ Winemaker(s) Boela Gerber (Jan 2001), with Daniel Keulder (Sep 2009) ▪ Viticulturist(s) Andrew Teubes (2009) ▪ 170ha/±90ha (cab, merlot, ptage, shiraz, chard, muscat, sauv, sem) ▪ 483t/68,000cs ▪ Private Bag X1 Constantia 7848 ▪ enquiries@grootconstantia.co.za ▪ www.grootconstantia.co.za ▪ S 34° 1' 36.5" E 018° 25' 27.3" ▪ F +27 (0)21-794-1999 ▪ **T +27 (0)21-794-5128**

☐ **Grootdrink** *see* Orange River Wine Cellars
☐ **Groot Eiland** *see* uniWines Vineyards

Groote Post Vineyards   ⓨ ⑪ ⓘ ⓐ ⓑ

At 3,000 hectares, the Pentz family farm is one of the largest in the winelands. Once home to a famous dairy herd, earning for co-owner and patriarch Peter Pentz the SA Farmer of the Year title in 1998, it has now become a destination in itself with game drives, bird viewing, eco-hikes and of course wine. Darling is justifiably renowned for cool-climate sauvignon blanc, and Groote Post has capitalised on the conducive climate for its other wines too, in particular the shiraz, from a vineyard showing the benefits of maturity. 'As people,' seasoned viticulturist Jannie de Clerk notes, 'we age to get balance in our lives, and this seems to be what happened with this block.'

Kapokberg range

★★★★ **Pinot Noir** Raspberries, forest floor & slight floral perfume with spicy hint ex deft oaking (5% new); **13** smooth but noticeable tannins for food, cellaring few years.

★★★★ **Chardonnay** **13** smartly oaked (mostly older) to allow yellow stonefruit to shine, almonds, honeycomb & oatmeal add aromatic dimension. Full & delicious, tangy-fresh nectarine farewell.

★★★★☆ **Sauvignon Blanc** A selection of top blocks, **13** continues upward path of thrilling **12**. Green-spectrum perfumes of capsicum, lime, peas & fig; 5 months lees-ageing gives impressive palate presence at moderate 13.5% alcohol. Delicious now & for good few years.

Varietal range

★★★★☆ **Shiraz** From a gravelly west slope, **13** is textbook shiraz. Ripe & silky, showing savoury complexity in white pepper & salami nuances to plum & prune fruit; full bodied, flavoursome, with graceful supportive tannins. Needs few years to drink at best, but so tempting now.

★★★★ **Unwooded Chardonnay** 3 months on lees add weight & depth to **13**'s citrus, pear appeal. Multi-layered & mineral, super seam of enlivening acidity. Stands proud without oak.

★★★★ **Riesling** Lingering ripe citrus fruit, gingery tail on **14** (★★★★) provisionally rated tank sample. Tangerine, kumquat aromas, good sugar/acid balance; lacking **13**'s purity & focus but could show better once bottled.

★★★★ **Sauvignon Blanc** Previewed **14** (★★★★☆) seems riper & shade less vibrant than lipsmacking, tangy **13**, though tropical-toned granadilla & gooseberry fruit well & clearly expressed.

Also tasted: **Merlot 12** ★★★ **Chenin Blanc 14** ★★★★

The Old Man's Blend range

★★★★ **The Old Man's Blend White** Cut-above-everyday white, unwooded, mostly sauvignon. **14** (★★★★) greengage & citrus scents, zingy Granny Smith apple palate, shade less piquant than **13**. WO Coastal, like Red.

Also tasted: **The Old Man's Blend Red 13** ★★★

Méthode Cap Classique range

Brut Rosé ★★★ Chardonnay with pinot (30%), **NV** bubbly shows maraschino cherry & strawberry bouquet, citrus flavours; fresh, fine mousse makes quite a refined sip. — GM

Location: Darling ▪ Map: Durbanville, Philadelphia & Darling ▪ WO: Darling/Coastal ▪ 1stB 1999 ▪ Tasting, sales & cellar tours Mon-Fri 9–5 Sat/Sun & pub hols 10–4 ▪ Fee R25 for groups of 10+ ▪ Closed Good Fri, Dec 25 & Jan 1 ▪ Hilda's Kitchen open for lunch Wed-Sun, booking essential ▪ Facilities for children ▪ Conferences ▪ Walks/hikes ▪ Farm drive to be pre-booked ▪ Conservation area & bird hide ▪ Owner(s) Peter & Nicholas Pentz ▪ Winemaker(s) Lukas Wentzel (Nov 2000) ▪ Viticulturist(s) Jannie de Clerk (1999), advised by Johan Pienaar ▪ 3,000ha/100ha (cabs s/f, merlot, pinot, shiraz, chard, chenin, riesling, sauv, sem) ▪ 580t/64,000cs own label ▪ Brands for clients: Woolworths ▪ PO Box 103 Darling 7345 ▪ wine@grootepost.co.za ▪ www.grootepost.com ▪ S 33° 29' 0.5" E 018° 24' 35.0" ▪ F +27 (0)22-492-2693 ▪ **T +27 (0)22-492-2825**

Groot Parys Estate ⓛ

Dutch-born Paarl winegrowers Mariëtte Ras and Eric Verhaak (with partner Peter Ras) are passionate about chenin, organic cultivation and pushing boundaries, and the combination makes their portfolio – not to mention their CV – among SA's more compelling. This edition sees an experiment with amphora fermentation, a joint-venture Pinotage-Chenin with Willie and Tania de Waal of Scali and, mid-2014, the dawn of commercial winegrowing in Lesotho through the maiden Sani Chenin, made with the Thamae family at Ha-Ntsi, southeast of the capital, Maseru. Grootparys.blogspot.com (in Dutch) is the way to keep up with all the happenings.

Die Tweede Droom range

★★★★ **Chenin Blanc Wellustig Vatgegis** ⊘ Flagship chenin gets 'Voluptuous' added to name, which **13** is: rich & mouthfilling, with myriad aromas/flavours, but also exuberantly fresh. From single block, mix new & older oak. Enjoy now or keep few years.

★★★★ **Chenin Blanc Dopkontak** ⊘ Extended skin/lees-ageing & natural yeast ferment give **13** a fino sherry nuttiness but there's also thatch & wet clay complexity. Emphatically dry, pleasantly firm; an individual.

Pinotage ⊘ ★★★ Taking 'boutique' to a new level, only 9 cases (x 6 bottles) made of old-oak-fermented, nouveau-style **14**, infused with delicate, savoury cherries & strawberries. Enjoy lightly chilled. **Chenin Blanc Extra Matured** (NEW) ⊘ ★★★☆ Even after 16 months in older oak, at bottling time promising **12** 'needed extra time' before release to show best. Mellow honey & floral notes, zestier acidity, endless flavoursome finish. **Chenin Blanc Amfora Gegis** (NEW) ⊘ ★★★ 2 amphoras, one with juice from early picked grapes & this one, which made it to bottle. Unfined/filtered. **14** attractive honeycomb notes, chenin's trenchant acidity on bone-dry palate. Promising experiment; doe zo voort! Also tasted: **Rosé Vatgegis** ⊘ ⊘ 13 ★★★ **Chardonnay Vatgegis** ⊘ 13 ★★★ **Chenin Blanc Spontane Gisting** ⊘ 13 ★★★ **Chenin Blanc Sparkling** ⊘ ⊘ 13 ★★★☆ Not tasted: **Straw Wine**. Discontinued: **Chenin Blanc Iced**.

Special Projects (NEW)

Pinotage-Chenin Blanc ⊛ ⊘ ★★★ With Voor Paardeberg's Scali. Lovely light, cherry-scented red, the grapes co-fermented. **14** bone-dry, packed with flavour. Enjoy young.
Discontinued: **Groot Parys range**. — CvZ

Location/WO: Paarl ▪ Map: Paarl & Wellington ▪ Est 1699 ▪ 1stB 1709 ▪ Tasting & sales by appt ▪ Owner(s) Eric Verhaak, Mariëtte Ras & Peter Ras ▪ Viticulturist(s) Gawie Kriel (consultant) ▪ 81ha/45ha (ptage, ruby cab, chard, chenin, cbard) ▪ 105t 90% white 10% rosé ▪ CERES internationally certified organic ▪ PO Box 82 Huguenot 7645 ▪ grootparys@wam. co.za ▪ www.grootparys.co.za ▪ S 33° 44' 48.0" E 018° 58' 41.6" ▪ **T +27 (0)76-567-8082**

Group CDV

Selling well over 1m cases, mainly to supermarkets in Europe, Group CDV (Cape Dutch Vignerons) is owned by Groupe LFE of the Netherlands. Primarily a negociant, it also offers services to buyers of value-for-money South African wines. The ever-changing portfolio now includes slightly higher-priced (over 5 euros) ranges like De Zuydpunt, and bottling for all labels is approached pragmatically: entry-level wines mostly done overseas, 'tricky' ones (eg sparkling, sweet and low-alcohol) in SA.

Vry Burger (NEW)

Bourgeois Rouge ★★ Very ripe, earthy shiraz-led blend with mourvèdre & grenache. **13** previewed. **Bourgeois Blanc** ★★★ Viognier's apricot/peach features to fore on tank sample **13**, with chenin (60%), grenache blanc (20%) partners. Full bodied, crisp & dry. WO W Cape, as for Rouge.

Groupe LFE South Africa range

Grâce Blanche Natural Sweet ⊘ ★★ Delicate **13** balanced sweetness, low alcohol for all-day quaffing. WO W Cape.

Klein Kasteelberg Private Bin range

Merlot ⊘ ★★★ Greater depth of aroma & flavour in this export-only line-up than sibling KK range. **12** exudes plums, mulberries, firmer tannins need food. Not retasted: **Pinotage** 12 ★★ **Chardonnay** 13 ★★ **Secco NV** ★★★ Discontinued: **Shiraz Rosé**.

Klein Kasteelberg range

Merlot ⊘ ★★ **12** uncomplicated dry red to enjoy with friends at the braai. Not retasted: **Pinotage** 12 ★★ **Chardonnay** 13 ★★ Discontinued: **Shiraz Rosé**, **Chenin Blanc**.

Nuwe Wynplaas range
Cabernet Sauvignon ⓧ ★★☆ Juicy **12** has cranberry flavours, firm tannins to pair with steak.
Not retasted: **Merlot 12** ★★★ **Chardonnay 13** ★☆

Klein Centennial range
Not tasted: **Pinotage**, **Shiraz Rosé**, **Chenin Blanc-Viognier**.
Discontinued: **Elephantasy range**, **Centennial 5 Barrel Reserve range**. — AL

Location: Somerset West ▪ WO: Swartland/Western Cape ▪ Est/1stB 2006 ▪ Closed to public ▪ Owner(s) Groupe LFE BV Netherlands ▪ Cellarmaster(s) Nicky Versfeld (consultant) ▪ 1,200,000cs own label 60% red 35% white 5% rosé ▪ Fairtrade ▪ PO Box 88 Somerset Mall 7137 ▪ rob@groupcdv.co.za ▪ www.groupcdv.co.za ▪ F +27 (0)21-851-3578 ▪ **T +27 (0)21-850-0160**

☐ **Growers Ark** *see* Boutinot South Africa

Grünberger

Introduced more than 60 years ago, the flattish, rounded 'bocksbeutel' flagon, first of its kind in South Africa, remains a feature of this lower-alcohol, mostly Natural Sweet range by Distell.

Freudenlese ★★☆ Very ripe **14** combo sauvignon, muscadel & gewürztraminer. Light, honeyed - good partner to light curries. WO W Cape, as all these. Also tasted: **Spritziger 14** ★★★ **Spritziger Rosé 14** ★★ **Rosenlese 14** ★★ — DB

Grundheim Wines

Stalwarts of the Klein Karoo's history of grape growing, winemaking and brandy distilling, the Grundling family is delighted with 6th-generation winemaker Dys' foray into table wine, introduced with a shiraz (untasted this edition). It joins an array of fortified wines, colourfully named renditions of SA's traditional eau de vie, witblits, and brandies.

Grundheim Wines range
★★★★ **Rosyntjiewyn** ⓧ Jerepiko-style dessert, **11** (★★★) is 100% touriga & very sweet; though checked by firm tannin, misses crispness & alcohol punch of previous **NV**, which included pinotage.
★★★★ **Late Bottled Vintage** ⓧ Commendable & complex port-style from touriga & tinta. **09** (★★★☆), first since **05** (only touriga), is richly fruity & textured. WO W Cape, as Rosyntjiewyn.
Red Muscadel ★★★ **12** full-sweet fortified, powerfully raisiny fireside warmer. Also tasted: **White Muscadel 13** ★★ Not retasted: **Cape Ruby Port NV** ★★★ **White Port 10** ★★★ Not tasted: **Cape Vintage Port**. Discontinued: **Rooi Jerepiko**.

Brandy range
Potstill ⓧ ★★★ 100% potstill from colombard & chenin. Firm & powerful, floral & dried fruit notes, hint of smoke & caramel. Leanish style, quite fiery for 9 year old. **Kuipers** ⓝⓔⓦ ★★★ 5 year old blended brandy (43% alcohol) from colombard & chenin. Nuts, fynbos & dried apricot flavours; sweet, fragrant & spicy finish. **Boegoe** ⓝⓔⓦ ⓧ ★★★ Blended 9 year old potstill with natural buchu, giving a minty, herbal character, dusty palate. For medicinal purposes or with a mixer for a refreshing drink. 375 ml. **Gemmer** ⓝⓔⓦ ⓧ ★★★★ Blended 9 year old potstill, natural fresh ginger for a delightful balanced drink with spicy kick. Enjoy on its own or with ginger ale for a cocktail. — WB, CR, TJ

Location: Oudtshoorn ▪ Map: Klein Karoo & Garden Route ▪ WO: Klein Karoo/Western Cape ▪ Est/1stB 1995 ▪ Tasting & sales Mon-Fri 9-5 Sat 9-1 ▪ Fee R20 for groups of 10+ ▪ Closed Easter Fri/Sun, Dec 25 & Jan 1 ▪ Owner(s) Danie Grundling ▪ Winemaker(s) Dys Grundling (1997) ▪ 25ha (cinsaut, muscadel r/w, ruby cab, tinta, touriga, cbard, hanepoot, palomino) ▪ 360t/10,000L own label 100% fortified ▪ PO Box 400 Oudtshoorn 6620 ▪ grundheim@ absamail.co.za ▪ S 33° 37' 40.1" E 022° 3' 54.6" ▪ F +27 (0)86-616-6311 ▪ **T +27 (0)44-272-6927**

☐ **G Spot** *see* United Nations of Wine

Guardian Peak Wines

Guardian Peak takes its name from the highest point on Stellenbosch Mountain, visible in the splendid view from winery and restaurant. It has no vineyards of its own, but has long-term contracts with grape-growers in Stellenbosch and beyond – which not only ensures consistency of supply, says owner Jean Engelbrecht, but also allows cellarmaster Philip van Staden to express a continuing sense of place in the wines. Unlike Engelbrecht's Rust en Vrede estate (nearby on the Helderberg), this winery does not eschew white wines: not quite, there's a modest sauvignon blanc lurking among the big and powerful – but ever-friendly - reds.

★★★★☆ Lapa Cabernet Sauvignon 12 maintains stellar quality of **11**: dense, ripe, dark, brooding fruit & herbal edge. Balanced, elegant & beautifully textured, oak (40% new) is integrated & tannins dry. Seamless & silky yet still powerfully muscular. WO Stellenbosch.

★★★★ Frontier ⊘ 100% cab, showing lively blackcurrant & hint of fynbos on **13**. Chewy & dense but refined, with good depth & length. Spice from judicious use of 10% American oak adds interest. Soft textured throughout.

★★★★ Summit Name changes from 'SMG' but varieties remain (unoaked) grenache mingling well with syrah/shiraz & mourvèdre in **12**, which retains form of previous blends. Focused, ripe & powerful but with peppery highlights providing vibrancy. WO Stellenbosch.

★★★★ Tannat-Malbec ⊘ Cheery blueberry anise appeal to **10** (**★★★☆**). Friendly, ripe & juicy, it's light bodied, ending on a gentle note. **09** more firm. Dual Wellington/Stellenbosch WO.

Sauvignon Blanc ★★★ Flint & gravel nuances vie with grapefruit generosity on broad, textured **14**. Also tasted: **Merlot 13 ★★★★ Shiraz 13 ★★★** — FM

Location/map: Stellenbosch ▪ WO: Western Cape/Stellenbosch/Wellington-Stellenbosch ▪ Est 1998 ▪ 1stB 2000 ▪ Tasting & sales Mon-Sun 9–5 ▪ Closed Easter Fri/Sun & Dec 25 ▪ Guardian Peak Winery & Grill ▪ Owner(s) Jean Engelbrecht ▪ Winemaker(s) Philip van Staden (Jan 2009), with Pieter van der Merwe (Jan 2013) ▪ Viticulturist(s) Dirkie Mouton (Jun 2010) ▪ 50,000cs own label 100% red ▪ Brands for clients: Pick's Pick ▪ IPW ▪ PO Box 473 Stellenbosch 7599 ▪ info@guardianpeak.com ▪ www.guardianpeak.com ▪ S 34° 0' 40.19" E 018° 50' 31.99" ▪ F +27 (0)21-881-3388 ▪ T +27 (0)21-881-3899

☐ **Guinea Fowl** *see* Saxenburg Wine Farm
☐ **Guru** *see* Hoopenburg Wines
☐ **Gwendolyn** *see* Saxenburg Wine Farm
☐ **Hagelsberg** *see* Middelvlei Estate

Halala Afrika Wines

These are export wines of highly rated Stellenbosch producer Rudera, intended for early and easy drinking. The name means 'Celebrate Africa'.

Pinotage 🆕 Dark-fruit aromas on **12**, with sweet light fruit. A trifle bony & awkward, with strong dry tannins. WO W Cape, like all. **Red** 🆕 **★★★** Pleasantly fruity Bordeaux blend, mostly cab; **12** easygoing & flavoursome, held together on a gentle structure. Unoaked, like Pinotage. Not retasted: **Merlot 12 ★★** Not tasted: **Shiraz, Chenin Blanc.** — TJ

Hamilton Russell Vineyards

Hemel-en-Aarde Valley pioneer and 2nd generation family estate, Hamilton Russell Vineyards specialises in classically styled pinot noir and chardonnay. Enjoying an enviable, enduring international reputation for quality, HRV's recent accolades include SA's first appearance in the top 20 of Wine Spectator's Top 100 Wines of the Year (with the '12 Chardonnay). Steps being taken to retain the lofty status include an extensive overhaul of fermentation facilities – on owner Anthony Hamilton Russell's to-do list for the past 24 years! – and green lighting the progressive adoption of biodynamic farming practices. In the vineyards an 'estate' pinot noir clone is under trial, courtesy of an unusual mutation in one of the oldest blocks on the property. The first crop in 2016 is eagerly awaited.

★★★★ **Pinot Noir** Pure, sweet strawberry, cherry fragrance with less common minty note matched by similar delicate flavours on **13**. Usual silky charm presently overshadowed by slightly angular structure. May settle, harmonise with few years' cellaring. **12** (★★★★☆) riper, generous.

★★★★★ **Chardonnay** Long-established, consistently ageworthy SA classic, notable for taut structure, minerality, subtle lime & oatmeal complexity. Supremely elegant **13** (★★★★☆) tantalises with all these, even in youth. As on **12** & previous, age will deliver even more complexity, satisfaction. — AL

Location: Hermanus ▪ Map: Elgin, Walker Bay & Bot River ▪ WO: Hemel-en-Aarde Valley ▪ Est 1975 ▪ 1stB 1981 ▪ Tasting & sales Mon-Fri 9—5 Sat 9—1 ▪ Closed Easter Fri/Mon, Dec 26 & Jan 1 ▪ Tours by appt ▪ Fynbos reserve & 2 wetlands ▪ Owner(s) Anthony Hamilton Russell ▪ Winemaker(s) Hannes Storm (2004) ▪ Viticulturist(s) Johan Montgomery (2005) ▪ 170ha/52ha (pinot, chard) ▪ 18,704cs own label 50% red 50% white ▪ BWI Champion ▪ PO Box 158 Hermanus 7200 ▪ hrv@hermanus.co.za ▪ www.hamiltonrussellvineyards.com ▪ S 34° 23' 23.0" E 019° 14' 30.6" ▪ F +27 (0)28-312-1797 ▪ **T +27 (0)28-312-3595**

Hannay Wines

Owner Malcom Dicey's shift from growing table grapes in the Hex River Valley to producing fine wine in the heart of the Elgin region is based on 'vines planted in the correct terroir' – with a smart collection of consultants in vineyard and cellar advising him and winemaker Kosie van der Merwe. The winery is being expanded, allowing for a larger custom crush as well Hannay's own range.

Sauvignon Blanc ★★★☆ Striking 'wild' aromas, **13** with 5% wooded semillon borders on quirky but appeals in its way. Not tasted: **Cabernet Franc**. — GdB

Location/WO: Elgin ▪ Map: Elgin, Walker Bay & Bot River ▪ Est/1stB 2011 ▪ Tasting, sales & cellar tours by appt ▪ Fee R30 for groups of 10+ ▪ BYO picnic ▪ Light/buffet lunches by appt only ▪ Owner(s) Malcolm J Dicey ▪ Winemaker(s) Kosie van der Merwe, assisted by Richard Kershaw (Jan 2014, consultant) & Catherine Marshall (Jan 2011, consultant) ▪ Viticulturist(s) Kevin Watt (2012, consultant) ▪ 72ha/10ha ▪ 180t majority custom crush ▪ 50% red 50% white ▪ IPW, WIETA ▪ PO Box 36 Elgin 7680 ▪ winemaker@hannaywines.co.za, info@valleygreen.co.za ▪ S 34° 12' 12.07" E 19° 02' 35.10" ▪ F +27 (0)86-718-2203 ▪ **T +27 (0)21-848-9770**

☐ **Harmonie Wine Cellar** *see* Snowfield Boutique Winery
☐ **Harmony Tree** *see* United Nations of Wine

Harrison Hope

American owners, missionaries Ronnie and Janet Vehorn, arrived in the Eastern Cape in 1988, the first wine producers there. No wines tasted this edition, though a shiraz has joined the range of merlot, pinotage and chardonnay, and sauvignon is in the pipeline. With funding from the Eastern Cape Development Fund, they have hired assistant winemaker Vumile Makapela, ex Asara, and will double their cellar size in time for this harvest, to accommodate increased production.

Location: Queenstown ▪ Est 2000 ▪ 1stB 2009 ▪ Tasting & tours by appt ▪ Accommodation ▪ Owner(s) Ronnie & Janet Vehorn ▪ Cellarmaster(s)/viticulturist(s) Ronnie Vehorn ▪ Winemaker(s) Ronnie Vehorn, with Vumile Makapela (Aug 2014) ▪ 2ha (merlot, ptage, shiraz, chard, sauv) ▪ 2,000cs own label ▪ PO Box 1394 Queenstown 5320 ▪ rvehorn@ gmail.com ▪ www.harrisonhope.com ▪ S 32° 10' 01.11" E 026° 50' 28.28" ▪ F +27 (0)40-842-9200 ▪ **T +27 (0)40-842-9444/+27 (0)82-808-5284**

Hartenberg Estate

Under the quiet, calm leadership of veteran cellarmaster Carl Schultz, this renowned Bottelary Hills estate's offering has become shiraz focused, with five distinct and classy varietal iterations, plus a blend and CWG Auction bottling in the line-up. Yet there's enough novelty to maintain winelovers' attention - see the riesling below - and, with the annual Riesling Rocks and Shiraz & Charcuterie festivals, enough pizazz and warm country welcome to keep visitors returning to the cellardoor. The food offerings – now including picnics and à la carte menu – through an upliftment initiative give previously disadvantaged budding chefs valuable practical experience.

Ultra Premium range

★★★★☆ **Gravel Hill Shiraz** Fruit purity of **10** ably framed by subtle violet, spice & pepper nuances. Layered, textured, elegant & refined, it speaks of its gravelly vineyard. Superbly smooth, with wonderful integration of all-new oak & fruit. Lithe yet restrained, one for the long haul.

Super Premium range

★★★★☆ **The Stork Shiraz** Vibrant immediacy to **11**, from clay-rich soils, echoes bold **10**. Deeper cocoa notes than Gravel Hill (though similar oaking: new, 20 months). Supple, silky & succulently stylish but with ample breadth, concentration & focus on multi-tiered palate. Long tail.

★★★★☆ **The Mackenzie** Cab leads, as always, on **11** (★★★★★) Bordeaux quartet with merlot, petit verdot & dab malbec. Fynbos edge to deep, rich, dark spicy fruit. Firm backbone & refinement from 19 months new French oak. Effortlessly elegant & polished, with long rounded end, like **10**.

★★★★☆ **The Eleanor Chardonnay** Graceful, broad & stylishly poised **11** displays harmonious balance of lime cordial, marmalade fruit & nutty oak from ferment & 10 months ageing in 70% new French barrels. Replicates smart **10**.

CWG Auction Reserves

★★★★☆ **Shiraz** Blend of the best Stork & Gravel Hill for CWG auction, **11** is superb in its sophistication. Powerful, pure, ripe, dark, pepper & cocoa smoothness yet reined in & taut from 18 months oak, 70% new. Rewardingly long but will improve with age, like svelte **10**.

Premium range

★★★★ **Cabernet Sauvignon** Light fynbos brush to blackcurrant earthiness of **11**, with droplets 3 other Bordeaux reds. Succulent & rich yet subtle, with classy wood maturation - 16 months, just 60% new - adding a gentle tannic squeeze.

★★★★ **Merlot** **11** retains form of **10** in bright bramble & cocoa notes on plush, approachable yet defined & structured palate. Broad, deep & concentrated. Small dabs cab & petit verdot.

★★★★ **Shiraz** Steady as she goes for **11** from farm's signature grape. Supple & lithe, it displays spicy blue fruit & medium body with rewarding aftertaste.

★★★★ **Chardonnay** Fresh crispness of barrel-fermented **12** (★★★★) more pronounced than **11**. Mimics citrus cream & broad, textured palate though.

★★★★ **Riesling** **13** replicates typicity & 10% botrytis portion of **12**. Defined lime zest, apple & character-building slight wax/terpene nuance on dry palate. Opens in the glass & lingers.

★★★★ **Sauvignon Blanc** Lovely concentration, breadth & length on **13** raises the bar on **12** (★★★★). Fresh, lively lemon/lime cordial but with full mid-palate & long, taut tail.

Doorkeeper Shiraz ★★★☆ Juicy & friendly **12** maintains tone of **11**. Tangy black berry fruit & pepper vibrancy with gentle concentration. With splash mourvèdre. Also tasted: **Cabernet Sauvignon-Shiraz 12** ★★★★ Occasional release: **Occasional Riesling**, **Riesling Noble Late Harvest**. — FM

Location/map/WO: Stellenbosch ▪ Est/1stB 1978 ▪ Tasting & sales Mon-Fri 9–5 Sat 9–4 Sun (Nov-Apr only) 10-4 ▪ Closed Good Fri, Dec 25 & Jan 1 ▪ Tasting fee refunded with purchase ▪ Cellar tours by appt ▪ Picnics & lunches 12-3.30 ▪ Light snacks, charcuterie and cheese platters served throughout the day ▪ Specialised food & wine pairings by appt only ▪ Facilities for children ▪ Walking/hiking trail ▪ Bird watching ▪ Bottelary Renosterveld Conservancy ▪ Function venue: outdoor & underground cellar ▪ Owner(s) Hartenberg Holdings ▪ Cellarmaster(s) Carl Schultz (Nov 1993) ▪ Winemaker(s) Patrick Ngamane (Jan 2001), with Oscar Robyn (Nov 2003) ▪ Viticulturist(s) Wilhelm Joubert (May 2006) ▪ 187ha/85ha (cab, merlot, shiraz, chard, riesling, sauv) ▪ 550t/60,000cs own label 80% red 20% white ▪ BWI, IPW ▪ PO Box 12756 Die Boord 7613 ▪ info@hartenbergestate.com ▪ www.hartenbergestate.com ▪ S 33° 53' 52.5" E 018° 47' 30.4" ▪ F +27 (0)21-865-2153 ▪ **T +27 (0)21-865-2541**

Hartswater Wine Cellar

Owned by Orange River Wine Cellars, this far-flung winery in the Hartswater irrigation region of the Northern Cape produces uncomplicated, mostly sweet easy-drinkers with whimsical elemental names for its own brand.

Elements range

Earth ⊕ ★★ Juicy, fruity, light-bodied & near-dry **NV** red from ruby cab. Not retasted: **Fire NV** ★★ **Wind NV** ★★ **Rain NV** ★★ **Thunder NV** ★★

Overvaal range

Red Jerepico ⊕ ★★★ Extremely sweet **NV** ruby cab fortified dessert is rescued by firm spirit grip. Not retasted: **White Jerepico NV** ★★ — DB

Location: Hartswater ▪ Map: Northern Cape, Free State & North West ▪ WO: Northern Cape ▪ Tasting & sales Mon-Fri 8. 30-1, 2-5 ▪ Sales also from outlet in Hartswater; orders delivered to liquor stores in Northern Cape (350km radius), Free State & North West ▪ Cellar tours by appt ▪ Owner(s) Orange River Wine Cellars ▪ Winemaker(s) Deon Truter ▪ 800t ▪ PO Box 2335 Hartswater 8570 ▪ deon@wynkelder.co.za ▪ S 27° 55' 2.2" E 024° 49' 38.2" ▪ F +27 (0)53-474- 0975 ▪ **T +27 (0)53-474-0700**

Haskell Vineyards

'Location, location, location' is the estate agent's mantra — and it's what international real estate magnate, American-born Preston Haskell IV, achieved when buying this prime Stellenbosch property over a decade ago. A variety of soils, aspects and elevations can be found on the 25 ha property, located in the sought-after 'Golden Triangle' on the slopes of the Helderberg. The challenge for Australian CEO Grant Dodd and cellarmaster Rianie Strydom is to shepherd the best possible product into bottle. Preston invested wisely, and patiently waited seven years for the first release, seeing the guide's ultimate 5 star rating at the first attempt.

★★★★☆ **Pillars Syrah 10** a hard act to follow, but **11** succeeds. Voluptuous & plush but with restrained black-fruit ripeness & a smoky sheen from 30% new French oak. Silky, serious, textured palate. Swarthy & intense but with deftness of touch evident.

★★★★☆ **Aeon Syrah** Suave, sleek **11** back to form after **10** (★★★★). Black cherry spice & liquorice, with spicy note from dab mourvèdre evident. Oak in perfect harmony with ripe fruit. Lovely lingering aftertaste.

★★★★☆ **Haskell II** Graceful & sexy blend of shiraz (62%), cab & mourvèdre in **10**. Leashed power evident in restrained pepper, dark fruit & chocolate notes which merge seamlessly with precise oaking (40% new for 16 months). Textured, with lingering, rich tail.

★★★★☆ **Haskell IV** Brambly fruitcake abundance on **09** blend of cab & merlot with seasoning of petit verdot & shiraz. Succulent & lithe yet concentrated & deep. Focused & structured, with firm core that needs time to yield a little.

★★★★☆ **Anvil Chardonnay** ⊕ Seamlessly svelte & elegant **12** offers lime & lemon curd vibrancy as it glissades on polished oak stage. Refined & silky, with a light zesty twist in the long, full finish. — FM

Location/map/WO: Stellenbosch ▪ Est 2002 ▪ 1stB 2008 ▪ Tasting & sales Tue-Fri 9—5 Sat/Sun 10-5 ▪ Fee R40 ▪ Closed Mon, Easter Fri-Mon & Dec 25 ▪ Cellar tours on special request only ▪ The Long Table Restaurant & Café Tue-Sun 9-5; dinner Fri (Sep-Mar) - booking essential ▪ Facilities for children ▪ Self-catering accommodation in The Residence and Cottage ▪ Owner(s) Preston Haskell ▪ Cellarmaster(s) Rianie Strydom (Jan 2005) ▪ Viticulturist(s) Wikus Pretorius (Dec 2005) ▪ 25ha/13.5ha (cabs s/f, merlot, shiraz, chard) ▪ ±80t/3,600cs own label 80% red 20% white ▪ PO Box 12766 Die Boord 7613 ▪ info@haskellvineyards.com ▪ www.haskellvineyards.com ▪ S 34° 0' 13.9" E 018° 51' 38.4" ▪ F +27 (0)21-881-3986 ▪ **T +27 (0)21-881-3895**

Hathersage

Originally part of Willem Adriaan van der Stel's Vergelegen estate, Hathersage is almost in the centre of today's Somerset West, with soil and climate remarkably similar to Bordeaux's Médoc. The 1920s homestead is now a tasting, conference and wedding venue, and the wines, by consultant Michael Liedtke, are increasingly exported and locally promoted by a new enthusiastic freelancer.

Special Edition Red Reserve ★★★☆ Promising cab-led **12** blend with merlot, cab franc. Fragrant tobacco, dark berries subtly oak spiced. Balanced tannins framing supple flesh. Tasted pre-bottling, ratings provisional, as all these. **Sauvignon Blanc ★★★** Forthcoming tropical tones on **14**; sweet, juicy fruit styled for easy drinking. Also tasted: **Cabernet Sauvignon 12 ★★★ Merlot 12 ★★★ Mouille Grange 12 ★★★ Chardonnay 14 ★★ Special Edition White Reserve 14 ★★** Not retasted: **Semillon 12 ★★★☆** — AL

Location: Somerset West ▪ Map: Helderberg ▪ WO: Stellenbosch ▪ 1stB 2007 ▪ Tasting & sales by appt Mon-Fri 9-4 ▪ Closed all pub hols ▪ Tour groups ▪ Conference & wedding/function venue with catering (10-150 pax) ▪ Conservation area ▪ Owner(s) Stephan Holdings cc & Stephan Brothers (Pty) Ltd ▪ Winemaker(s) Michael Liedtke (Jan 2010, consultant) ▪ 40ha/12ha (cabs s/f, merlot, p verdot, shiraz, chard, sauv, sem) ▪ 52t/3,036cs own label 43% red 57% white ▪ PO Box 2517 Somerset West 7129 ▪ info@hathersage.co.za ▪ www.hathersage.co.za ▪ S 34° 4' 54.42" E 018° 51' 55.32" ▪ F +27 (0)21-851-8382 ▪ **T +27 (0)21-851-1644/+27 (0)21-851-5076**

Haute Cabrière

Family-owned Haute Cabrière has made the transition to the 2nd generation, Takuan von Arnim taking over from winegrowing father and founder Achim, and Takuan's wife Christiane stepping up from marketer to MD. (Achim keeps a seasoned eye on operations as chairman.) The 2014 vintage marked the 20th anniversary of both the Chardonnay-Pinot Noir blend and the opening of the underground cellar on Franschhoek Pass, its vaulted halls designed to allow diversification into still wines (the bubblies continue to be made in the original cellar on Clos Cabrière estate). Vineyards are being replanted, and ever-popular Haute Cabrière Restaurant's new 'delicious little things' menu lets guests enjoy a few small bites with a glass of wine and a memorable panorama of Franschhoek Valley.

Haute Cabrière range
Chardonnay-Pinot Noir ★★★☆ Boasting fresh citrus flavours for pairing with white meat, intense berries to match with red, versatile sweet-sour **14** vintage is 20th since pioneering debut. Also tasted: **Pinot Noir 11 ★★★★ Unwooded Pinot Noir 14 ★★★**

Pierre Jourdan range
Cuvée Belle Rose ★★★ Blushing prettily, with bright red cherry notes, latest **NV** food-friendly pink MCC bubbly less herbal than previous, with lovely fruit purity & fine brioche mousse. Also tasted: **Tranquille NV ★★★★ Brut NV ★★★ Ratafia NV ★★★★** Discontinued: **Blanc de Blancs, Brut Sauvage, Cuvée Reserve.** — JG

Location/map: Franschhoek ▪ WO: Western Cape/Franschhoek ▪ Est 1982 ▪ 1stB 1984 ▪ Tasting & sales Mon-Fri 9–5 Sat/pub hols 10–4 Sun 11-4 ▪ Public cellar tour/tasting Mon-Fri at 11; cellarmaster's tour/tasting Sat at 11; private tasting/tour (pre-booked) ▪ Closed Good Fri, Dec 25/26 & Jan 1 ▪ Haute Cabrière Restaurant ▪ Tour groups ▪ Owner(s) Clos Cabrière (Pty) Ltd ▪ Cellarmaster(s) Takuan von Arnim (2005) ▪ Viticulturist(s) Nikey van Zyl (Aug 2011) ▪ 30ha (pinot, chard) ▪ 40% red 60% white ▪ PO Box 245 Franschhoek 7690 ▪ marketing@cabriere.co.za ▪ www.cabriere.co.za ▪ S 33° 54' 51.8" E 019° 8' 8.2" ▪ F +27 (0)21-876-8501 ▪ **T +27 (0)21-876-8500**

Haut Espoir

Biodynamic farming is a big focus for the coming years, says Rob Armstrong, co-owner of the eco-conscious family farm high on Franschhoek's Scherpenheuwel, as is custom-crushing of grapes for other smaller-scale producers and thus boosting utilisation of Haut Espoir's facilities, now overseen by Simon Thompson, ex Oldenburg winemaker.

★★★★ **Chardonnay** Hint of spicy oak shows along with sweet lemon on **10**. Full flavoured & substantial, with a pleasing texture & a reasonably lingering effect. Ready for drinking. **09** untasted.

★★★★ **Semillon** Drops 'Reserve' on **09**. Less shy than last-tasted **07** (★★★), with appealing mix of lemon, wax & dried herbs. Graceful, but not intense; dry, savoury palate; supportive light oaking.

Cabernet Franc ⓃⒺⓌ ★★★ **08** ex Helderberg, bottled only in magnums. Notable herbaceous element along with ripe sweet fruit notes. Gentle structure, but altogether rather insubstantial, short finishing. Also tasted: **Cabernet Sauvignon 06** ★★★★ **Shiraz 07** ★★★ **Gentle Giant 09** ★★★★ Discontinued: **Petit Verdot**, **Shiraz Rosé**. — TJ

Location/map: Franschhoek ▪ WO: Franschhoek/Stellenbosch ▪ Est 1999 ▪ 1stB 2004 ▪ Tastings, sales & cellar tours by appt ▪ Closed all pub hols ▪ Fynbos walks ▪ Conservation area ▪ Owner(s) Armstrong family ▪ Cellarmaster(s)/winemaker(s) Rob Armstrong & Simon Thompson ▪ Viticulturist(s) Rob Armstrong ▪ ±23ha/12ha (cab, merlot, p verdot, shiraz) ▪ 70t/10,000cs own label 70% red 30% white ▪ BWI ▪ PO Box 681 Franschhoek 7690 ▪ wine@hautespoir.com ▪ www.hautespoir.com ▪ S 33° 56' 23.6" E 019° 6' 20.9" ▪ F +27 (0)21-876-4038 ▪ **T +27 (0)21-876-4000**

Havana Hills

At the turn of the millennium, Cape businessman Kobus du Plessis discovered almost 300 ha of wheatlands between Melkbosstrand and Philadelphia which he thought would be ideal for high-quality wine production. Today, there are some 60 ha under vineyard and Mike Dobrovic, who previously enjoyed a successful career at Mulderbosch, is consultant. The farm is only 10km from the Atlantic Ocean so there's a strong maritime influence on the vines.

Kobus range

★★★★☆ **Red** Ⓥ Bordeaux-style **08** (★★★★) 59% cab, rest merlot, cab franc, already seems quite mature. Sweet fruit, moderate acidity & soft tannins. Coastal WO. Lacks majesty of last **05**.

★★★★ **Chardonnay** Ⓥ **12** very youthful on preview. Lime, burnt matchstick, prominent oak (100% new, 8 months). Pleasantly lean with bright acidity & pithy finish. No **11**.

Havana Hills range

★★★★ **Sauvignon Blanc** Ⓥ Dramatic **13** massive intensity of flavour, thick texture but also racy acidity, lowish alcohol. Even more over the top than **12** (★★★★).

Cabernet Sauvignon ★★★ Sprightly blackcurrant aromas on **10**. Pleasant palate not without freshness to accompany the soft, gentle tannins & some sugar. **Sangiovese** ⓃⒺⓌ ★★★ Red fruit & a little smoke entice on **12**. Easygoing & gentle, with an ingratiating touch of sweetness. Not retasted: **Merlot 08** ★★★ **Shiraz 10** ★★★ **Cabernet Sauvignon-Barbera 09** ★★★★ **Chardonnay-Pinot Noir 12** ★★★ Not tasted: **Petit Verdot**, **Du Plessis Reserve**.

Lime Road range

Cabernet Sauvignon-Merlot-Cabernet Franc ★★ Herbal as well as fruity notes on rounded, soft, unstructured & sweetish **11**. WO W Cape, as all these. Also tasted: **Cabernet Sauvignon Rosé 14** ★★ **Sauvignon Blanc 14** ★★ Not retasted: **Shiraz 10** ★★★ — TJ

Location: Philadelphia ▪ WO: Philadelphia/Coastal/Western Cape ▪ Est 1999 ▪ 1stB 2000 ▪ Closed to public ▪ Owner(s) Kobus du Plessis ▪ Winemaker(s) Piet Kleinhans (Sep 2008), Joseph Gertse (Jan 2000) & Mike Dobrovic (consultant) ▪ Viticulturist(s) Rudi Benn (Jan 2001) ▪ 260ha/60ha (barbera, cabs s/f, merlot, mourv, sangio, shiraz, sauv) ▪ 70,000cs own label 50% red 20% white 30% rosé ▪ Fairtrade, IPW, WIETA ▪ PO Box 451 Melkbosstrand 7437 ▪ sales@havanahills.co.za ▪ www.havanahills.co.za ▪ F +27 (0)21-972-1105 ▪ **T +27 (0)21-972-1110**

☐ **Haven Point** *see* Overhex Wines International
☐ **Hawk's Head** *see* Southern Sky Wines

Hawksmoor at Matjieskuil

Grape farming started in the 18th century at Matjieskuil, but the Hawksmoor branding is much more recent, the maiden wine bottled exactly ten years ago. Buildings have been returned to their former glory and serve as a luxury guest house. The two wines tasted this edition have interesting names: serliana is a design element favoured by famous Baroque architect Nicholas Hawksmoor; triginta is Latin for 30, the number of months aged in barrel.

Limited Releases

Triginta Shiraz ★★★★ **11** full bodied & ripe, easily able to accommodate oaking & 15% alcohol. Prunes & fruitcake flavours, appealing plushness. Not retasted: **Shiraz 09** ★★★★ **Cape Blend 09** ★★★☆ **French Blend With A Cape Twist 09** ★★★★ **Magdalen 12** ★★★ Not tasted: **Mourvèdre**, **Pinotage**, **Vanbrugh**, **Barrel 69**, **Saint Alfege's**, **Algernon Stitch**, **Rosé**, **Edward Goodge**, **Paradox**.

Classic range

Serliana ★★★ From 30+ year old vines, **14** shows quince & melon throughout, softly rounded, light & dry. Not tasted: **Hawksmoor Pinotage**. — CR

Location/WO: Paarl • Map: Paarl & Wellington • Est 1692 • 1stB 2005 • Tasting by appt 10-4 daily • Fee R30 • Sales by appt Mon-Sat • Specialise in group tastings (10-20 pax), with option of lunch in the Cape Dutch manor house - prior arrangement essential • Closed Easter Fri-Sun, Dec 25/31 & Jan 1 • Luxury guest house • Owner(s) Brameld Haigh • Winemaker(s) various • Viticulturist(s) Paul Wallace (2004) • Farm manager Jan Lategan • ±23ha (cab f, mourv, ptage, shiraz, chenin) • ±130t/1,000cs own label 65% red 25% white 10% rosé • PO Box 9 Elsenburg 7607 • wines@hawksmoor.co.za • www. hawksmoor.co.za • S 33° 48' 47.4" E 018° 46' 14.1" • F +27 (0)86-605-9008 • **T +27 (0)21-884-4587**

Hazendal

Tourist-friendly Hazendal in Stellenbosch's Bottelary Hills dates from 1699, making it one of SA's oldest wine estates. Russian-born entrepreneur and current co-owner Mark Voloshin came to Cape Town for business and fell in love with the beauty of the winelands. He purchased Hazendal 20 years ago and set out to restore it to its former glory. Hazendal now houses a restaurant, conference and function facilities, farmstall and deli, mountain biking trails and a Russian museum of arts and culture.

Location/map: Stellenbosch • Est 1699 • 1stB 1950 • Tasting, sales & Hermitage Restaurant Tue-Sun 9–4.30 • Fee R10/5 wines • Closed Good Fri & Jan 1 • Cellar tours Tue-Fri 11-3 • Facilities for children • Tour groups • Gifts • Cheese platters • Conferences • Mountain biking trail • Russian Arts & Culture Museum • Owner(s) Voloshin & Schumacher families • Winemaker(s) Ronell Wiid (Jan 1998) • 140ha/40ha (cab, merlot, pinot, shiraz, chenin, sauv) • 200t/ 30,000cs own label 50% red 50% white • PO Box 111 Soneike 7583 • info@hazendal.co.za • www.hazendal.co.za • S 33° 54' 2.7" E 018° 43' 9.1" • F +27 (0)21-903-0057 • **T +27 (0)21-903-5034/5**

☐ **HB Vineyards** see Hout Bay Vineyards
☐ **Head butt** see Rooiberg Winery
☐ **Heaven on Earth** see Stellar Winery
☐ **Heeren van Oranje Nassau** see De Villiers Wines
☐ **Heinrich Kulsen** see Kulsen Wines

Helderberg Wijnmakerij

Owned by Boekenhoutskloof, this cellar and brand, taking its name from a famous Stellenbosch sub-region (and mountain!), offers just a pair of varietal wines, imaginatively packaged and well made.

Cabernet Sauvignon ★★★★ **13** ups the ante but retains typicity of tobacco & cassis. Powerful, rich & juicy with dry tannin grip. **Sauvignon Blanc** ★★★ Vibrant lime zest zip on succulent & typical **14**. Refreshing quaffer. — FM

Location/WO: Stellenbosch • Est 2010 • 1stB 2009 • Closed to public • Owner(s) Boekenhoutskloof Winery (Pty) Ltd • Winemaker(s) Heinrich Hugo (Sep 2010) • 75% red 25% white • BRC, HACCP • PO Box 1037 Stellenbosch 7130 • info@ helderbergwijnmakerij.com • www.helderbergwijnmakerij.com • F +27 (0)21-842-2373 • **T +27 (0)21-842-2371**

☐ **Hendrik Lodewyk** see Du Preez Estate
☐ **Hercules Paragon** see Simonsvlei International

☐ **Heritage Heroes** *see* Nederburg Wines

Hermanuspietersfontein Wynkelder

This 'proudly local' winery, located at the entrance to Hemel-en-Aarde Valley, takes its long Afrikaans name from the coastal resort town Hermanus, founded in 1855 as Hermanuspietersfontein. With grapes grown on the Pretorius family co-owners' cool-climate Sunday's Glen Biodiversity & Wine Initiative Champion farm, Hermanuspietersfontein focuses on Bordeaux and Rhône-style blends, and especially on sauvignon blanc – dry, sweet, wooded and unoaked. Its only single-varietal red – a cabernet franc – is the appropriately named Swartskaap ('Black Sheep'). Testimony of their support for the local community is the charitable Sondagskool 20/20 Love to Learn project.

Flagship Wines

★★★★☆ **Die Arnoldus** Cab-led Bordeaux quintet **10** has presence with purity & freshness. Ripe, refined, soft yet intense blackberry & juniper notes with a clean seam of redcurrant acidity. Already showing great complexity, with cedar, spice & smoky tobacco. Will age gracefully. New French oak, 26 months, seamlessly absorbed.

★★★★ **Die Martha** Full-bodied **11** (★★★★☆) Rhône-style blend of shiraz, mourvèdre, grenache, viognier ups the ante on **10**. Shows elegance & presence, with spiced meat perfume, mocha, pepper & wild herb flavours. Supple texture, fresh & rich. A keeper. WO W Cape.

★★★★☆ **Die Bartho** ⓖ Mix oak-fermented sauvignon (65%) & semillon, with splash nouvelle, all then a year in large oak. **12** more sombre toned than **11**. Bracing acid tension cloaks textural richness which time should expose.

Classic Wines

★★★★ **Swartskaap** Understated **11** (★★★★★) overshadows **10** (★★★★) & **09** with bright, vibrant black & red berry fruit steeped in fragrant green herbs. Subtle oak spice adds to liquid silk texture. Superb expression of variety.

★★★★ **Kleinboet** Younger brother of Arnoldus is back to form in **11** after **10** (★★★★). Offers generous spicy berries & fruitcake, with good restraint. Lighter in build, but wine with personality.

★★★★ **Sauvignon Blanc No 5** Distinctive oaked sauvignon. Improved **13** (★★★★★) offers expressive tropical & fresh greenpepper aromas. Mouthfilling, with powdery texture, enhanced by regular lees stirring, hints of allspice on the lengthy goodbye, as in **12**.

★★★★ **Sauvignon Blanc No 3 Bergblokke** ⓖ Only in best years. Tasted mid-2012 just post-bottling, current release **12** should reveal more with time. Usual succulence, perkily dry finish. **13** though tasted last edition, not released.

★★★★ **Sauvignon Blanc No 7** Unoaked, intense & fresh, lees-enriched **14** lives up to expectation with bouncy tropical flavours, impressive concentration & focus, lemon zest twist to finish. Tasted just after bottling.

★★★★☆ **Sauvignon Blanc No 2** Delectable Noble Late Harvest sauvignon, unwooded **13** shows great balance of noble rot & varietal character. Full of long-lingering flavour, invigorating fruity acid tension; low 10.5% alcohol. Sunday's Glen sunshine in 375 ml bottles.

Also tasted: **Bloos 14** ★★★★☆ Not retasted: **Skoonma 12** ★★★

Lifestyle Wines

1855 Posmeester ★★★ Veritable fruit basket of 8 varieties, mainly cab, merlot, mourvèdre in rounded, richly flavoured **13** pizza wine. WO W Cape. — WB

Location: Hermanus ▪ Map: Elgin, Walker Bay & Bot River ▪ WO: Sunday's Glen/Western Cape/Walker Bay ▪ Est 2005 ▪ 1stB 2006 ▪ Tasting & sales Mon-Fri 9–5 Sat 9–4 Sun (15 Dec-15 Jan) 10.30-3 ▪ Fee R20/4 wines, waived on purchase ▪ Closed Easter Fri/Sun, Dec 25/26 & Jan 1 ▪ Cellar tours on request ▪ Food & wine market Sat 9–1 ▪ Self-catering cottages ▪ Owner(s) The Pretorius Family Trust, Gerrie Heyneke ▪ Winemaker(s) Bartho Eksteen (2005-2014), with Kim McFarlane (Feb 2006) ▪ Viticulturist(s) Lochner Bester (Nov 2012) ▪ 320ha/±62.2ha (cabs s/f, grenache, malbec, merlot, mourv, p verdot, shiraz, nouvelle, sauv, sem, viog) ▪ 265t/20,000cs own label 50% red 40% white 10% rosé ▪ BWI champion ▪ Hemel en Aarde Village, Suite 47, Private Bag X15, Hermanus 7200 ▪ kelder@hpf1855.co.za ▪ www.hpf1855.co.za ▪ S 34° 24′ 38.7″ E 019° 11′ 51.7″ ▪ F +27 (0)28-316-1293 ▪ **T +27 (0)28-316-1875**

Hermit on the Hill Wines

'The hermit largely withdrew to his cave,' confesses boutique winemaker and registered tour guide Pieter de Waal, explaining 2014's temporary hiatus in production. (The winery and wine names reflect Pieter's fascination with the Crusades and Arthurian legend.) In fact, energies were being directed at establishing a partnership with longtime friend Krige Visser in Swartland-based Mount Abora. But the hermit is re-emerging, fired up by 'freaky, geeky' varieties.

★★★★ **Paarl Syrah** Expressive **12** without any new oak to obstruct its fruit-driven aromas. The palate shows lavender, cassis & Asian spice, & is fresh, easygoing & lingering. **09** (★★★★) last tasted.

★★★★☆ **Stellenbosch Syrah 10** (★★★★) perhaps less complex than **09**. Black pepper & ripe berry aromas; gently structured palate is fresh but needs time to flesh out a bit; good length. Year in older oak.

★★★★ **The Second Crusade** ⓥ Shiraz, the Hermit's signature red grape, combo with third each grenache, mourvèdre. **08** shows red fruit, floral fragrance; fresh, with fine tannins. Natural ferment, like all these.

★★★★☆ **The Round Table Roussanne** (NEW) ⊘ Unoaked **13** a full bodied, vibrant wine with subtle aromas of pear, white flowers & acacia. The palate is intense, with rounded texture & admirable viscosity from gentle lees stirring but shows impeccable lift & freshness. WO Paarl.

★★★★ **The Infidel** ⓥ Unconventional **12** (★★★★☆) from Stellenbosch sauvignon (as was **10**), naturally fermented/9 months older oak. Subtle leesy character, herbal bite. Rich, full, smooth. No **11**.

The Starry Knight (NEW) ★★★★ **13** bottle-fermented bubbly from Paarl grenache blanc, offers a soft texture & a mouthfilling, creamy mousse. Palate is bone-dry, with a slight pithiness on its finish. Also tasted: **Knights in Tights 13** ★★★★ **The Souvenir Viognier 13** ★★★★ Not retasted: **Wellington Grenache 09** ★★☆ **The Red Knight 10** ★★★ Not tasted: **Aurora Grenache**, **Aurora Syrah**, **Aurora Chardonnay**, **Aurora Blanc**, **The White Knight**. — JPf

Location: Durbanville ▪ WO: Paarl/Stellenbosch/Wellington/Swartland/Coastal/Durbanville ▪ Est/1stB 2000 ▪ Tasting & sales by appt ▪ Owner(s)/cellarmaster(s) Pieter de Waal ▪ Winemaker(s) Pieter & Lohra de Waal ▪ bastardo, cinsaut, gamay, grenache n/b, malbec, mourv, shiraz, chard, rouss, sauv, viog ▪ 15t/1,600cs own label 60% red 40% white ▪ PO Box 995 Bellville 7535 ▪ pieter@dw.co.za ▪ www.hermitonthehill.co.za ▪ F +27 (0)21-948-6666 ▪ **T +27 (0)83-357-3864**

Herold Wines

Clinging to Cradock Peak 450-600 m up the Outeniqua Mountain, these vineyards helped launch the cool-climate Outeniqua wine ward in the late 1990s. Current hands-on owners Nico and Maureen Fourie face the challenge of 'extreme' winegrowing on a site visited by floods, fungus, feathered and furry creatures, summer hail and frost. And love it!

Pinot Noir 'Screwcap' ★★★★ Shy **13** opens up with redcurrant tang to mushroomy flavours. Brushed with seasoned oak, genteel alcohol for lunch partnering. **Skaam Skaap** ★★★ **14** cheerful dry rosé from mostly pinot, old oak fermented. Spicy edge to green apple crunch, very dry farewell. **Sauvignon Blanc** ★★★ Initially reticent **13** comes alive with zesty gooseberry & lemon continuing to bone-dry tail. Not tasted: **Cabernet Sauvignon**, **Merlot**, **Pinot Noir**, **Red Men**. — DS

Location: George ▪ Map: Klein Karoo & Garden Route ▪ WO: Outeniqua ▪ Est 1999 ▪ 1stB 2003 ▪ Tasting, sales & cellar tours Mon-Sat 10-4 ▪ Fee R15, waived on purchase ▪ Closed Easter Sun, Dec 25 & Jan 1 ▪ Light refreshments/cheese platters during opening hours ▪ Picnic baskets/farm lunches with 2 days prior notice ▪ Facilities for children ▪ Tour groups ▪ Gifts ▪ Farm produce ▪ Walks/hikes ▪ Mountain biking ▪ Conservation area ▪ Self-catering cottages ▪ Owner(s) Nico & Maureen Fourie ▪ Winemaker(s)/viticulturist(s) Nico Fourie (Jul 2011) ▪ 324ha/6ha (cab, merlot, pinot, shiraz, chard, sauv) ▪ 35t/3,400cs own label 55% red 25% white 20% rosé ▪ PO Box 10 Herold 6615 ▪ info@heroldwines.co. za ▪ www.heroldwines.co.za ▪ S 33° 51' 49.4" E 022° 28' 9.9" ▪ F +27 (0)86-698-6607 ▪ **T +27 (0)72-833-8223**

Heron Ridge

Co-owner Jane Orpen reports 'rearrangement' of family involvement in this tiny biodynamically farmed red specialist winery. Qualified, experienced winemaker son Harry returns home, taking over from sister Pippa (who filled her late father's shoes for several years before becoming a nature conservation field guide). Mum hopes he taps into brother Tom's sales/marketing expertise.

Family Reserve range

Shiraz ⓘ ★★★★ **06** is full bodied, slightly rough around the edges but not without charm. Red & black fruit, vanilla, hint of spice. Contains 13% cab.

Heron Ridge range

★★★★ **Shiraz** ⓘ **07** raised the bar on **06** (★★★★), showed attractive rusticity & real liveliness, interest when last tasted. 30% oak well integrated.

Not retasted: **The Flight 06** ★★★★ — CE

Location: Somerset West ▪ Map: Helderberg ▪ WO: Stellenbosch ▪ Est 1997 ▪ 1stB 2001 ▪ Tasting, sales & cellar tours by appt ▪ Fee R20 ▪ Closed all pub hols ▪ Cheese lunches on Saturdays by appt ▪ Owner(s) Orpen family ▪ Cellarmaster(s)/ winemaker(s) Harry Orpen (Jun 2014) ▪ Viticulturist(s) Paul Wallace (Sep 1999, consultant) ▪ 4.29ha/4ha (cab, shiraz) ▪ 20t/300cs own label 100% red ▪ PO Box 5181 Helderberg 7135 ▪ orps@xsinet.co.za ▪ www.heronridge.co.za ▪ S 34° 2' 45.6" E 018° 47' 58.1" ▪ F +27 (0)86-613-6960 ▪ **T +27 (0)21-842-2501**

Het Vlock Casteel

The Vlok family, wine and table grape farmers near Riebeek-Kasteel since 1958, named their boutique brand after the Castle of Good Hope. Vinified to spec by Riebeek Cellars, the wines are just one of a cornucopia of products and amenities on offer at their castle-like visitor venue, newly upgraded.

Shiraz ★★★ Light, rather earthy tones, brisk freshness & determined grip suggest **10** needs early drinking with red meat. Also tasted: **Cabernet Sauvignon 10** ★★ **Merlot 10** ★★★ Not tasted: **Sauvignon Blanc**. — AL

Location: Riebeek-Kasteel ▪ Map/WO: Swartland ▪ Est/1stB 2005 ▪ Tasting & sales Mon-Fri 9-5 Sat 9-2 ▪ Closed Good Fri & Dec 25 ▪ Tour groups ▪ Gift shop ▪ Farm produce: olives, olive oil, jams, chutneys etc - sampling available ▪ Conferences ▪ Café Merlot functions: by appt only ▪ Owner(s) Johan Louw Vlok ▪ Winemaker(s) Alecia Boshoff ▪ Viticulturist(s) Johan Vlok snr & Johan Vlok jnr ▪ 100ha (cab, merlot, ptage, shiraz, chard) ▪ 1,300t/14,000cs own label 100% red ▪ PO Box 8 Riebeek-Kasteel 7307 ▪ info@hetvlockcasteel.co.za ▪ www.hetvlockcasteel.co.za ▪ S 33° 23' 22.74" E 018° 53' 40.75" ▪ F +27 (0)86-720-6281 ▪ **T +27 (0)82-567-9132**

☐ **Hex River Crossing Private Cellar** see Auction Crossing Private Cellar
☐ **Heyden's Courage** see Stellenbosch Vineyards

Hidden Valley Wines

Dave Hidden's showpiece winery, also home to celebrated Overture Restaurant, gazes out over the breathtaking surrounds from its eyrie on the northern slopes of the Helderberg. It's a good few kilometres south, though, near the Hidden vineyards at Elim on the shipwreck-strewn Cape Agulhas coast, where this edition's main news originated: a barrel of shiraz submerged in the icy Atlantic and allowed to undergo a 'marine maturation process' for more than a year. The resulting 300 bottles are extremely fine, collectible and, somehow, redolent of stormy seas.

Shipwreck Collection ⓝⓔⓦ

★★★★☆ **Shiraz** 'Marine matured' (see intro) **09** from Elim commands attention with complex & captivating layers of dark berry, spicecake, pepper, tobacco & smoke. Intense, lush & creamy, with a fine tannin balance - & suggestion of ocean tang. Only 300 bottles made.

For more information, visit wineonaplatter.com

Hidden Valley Wines range

★★★★ **Pinotage** Lighter-style **13** (★★★★) has less gravitas than **11**. Layers of spices, ripe fruit; clean & perhaps too soft, not enough grip on finish. **12** sold out untasted.

★★★★☆ **Hidden Gems** Bold New-World style **12** from Bordeaux varieties (cab, petit verdot & merlot) is rich, with blackcurrant fragrance. Gorgeous core of acidity to support intense fruit & satin oak flavours. Depth & breadth for ageing.

★★★★ **Hidden Secret** Shiraz & tannat blend ups the ante on **11** in **12** (★★★★). Understated yet intense velvet mouthfeel, rich berry flavours multiplying on base of rounded tannins & fresh acidity. For the long haul.

★★★★ **Sauvignon Blanc** Ever-dependable label. Full-bodied **14** seduces with ripe honeysuckle perfume, steely lemon & lime flavours reflecting different picking times. Smooth acidity & mouthwatering citrus goodbye. — WB

Location/map: Stellenbosch ▪ WO: Stellenbosch/Elim ▪ Est/1stB 1995 ▪ Tasting & sales: summer Mon-Thu 9-6 Fri 9-8 (sundowners on the deck) Sat/Sun 9-6; winter Mon-Fri 9-4 Sat/Sun 9-5 ▪ Fee R45pp ▪ Open pub hols, but closed Dec 25/26 & Jan 1 ▪ Cellar tours by appt ▪ Overture Restaurant ▪ Cheese/winter/chocolate platters ▪ Picnics, to be pre-booked ▪ Table olives & olive oil ▪ Tour groups by appt ▪ Conferences ▪ Weddings/functions ▪ Walks/hikes ▪ Conservation area ▪ Owner(s) David Hidden ▪ Winemaker(s) Emma Moffat (May 2010) ▪ Viticulturist(s) Johan 'Grobbie' Grobbelaar (Feb 1999) ▪ 28ha/15ha (cab, merlot, p verdot, shiraz, tannat, sauv, viog) ▪ 200t/10,000cs own label 60% red 40% white ▪ BWI ▪ PO Box 12577 Die Boord 7613 ▪ info@hiddenvalleywines.com ▪ www.hiddenvalleywines.com ▪ S 34° 1′ 15.3″ E 018° 51′ 13.9″ ▪ F +27 (0)21-880-2645 ▪ **T +27 (0)21-880-2646**

Highberry Wines

Grapes for this new label are from vinegrower Andre Parker's farm Highberry on Schapenberg Hill near Sir Lowry's Pass, partnering with Thabani Wines' Jabulani Ntshangase (sometime taster for this guide) and featuring the winemaking talents of ex-Waterkloof Werner Engelbrecht. Just two of the nine varieties planted - sauvignon blanc and cabernet sauvignon — have been chosen for the maiden release, mostly for the US market where SA-born Jabulani earned his spurs and currently resides.

Location: Sir Lowry's Pass ▪ Map: Helderberg ▪ 1stB 2014 ▪ Tasting by appt only ▪ Owner(s) Andre Parker & Jabulani Ntshangase ▪ Winemaker(s) Werner Engelbrecht (Jan 2014) ▪ Viticulturist(s) Edward Etson (Jul 2003) ▪ 65ha/49ha (cabs s/f, malbec, merlot, p verdot, shiraz, chard, sauv, sem) ▪ 350t/1,600cs own label 50% red 50% white ▪ werner@highberry.co.za ▪ www.highberry.co.za ▪ **T +27 90)21-852-3754**

High Constantia Wine Cellar

High Constantia was once an aristocrat of the Cape's wine culture. Under owner/winegrower Sebastiaan van Renen, the property competed with its illustrious neighbour Groot Constantia for the favour of Europe's mid-19th century royal courts. Present owner David van Niekerk is reviving the glory days with new plantings and wines vinified in a cellar 'reminiscent of High Constantia's original home for wine' and sold under the High Constantia and Silverhurst labels.

Location: Constantia ▪ Map: Cape Peninsula ▪ Est 1693 ▪ 1stB 2000 ▪ Tasting, sales & cellar tours Mon-Fri 8–5 Sat 10-1 ▪ Fee R50 ▪ Closed Easter Sun, Dec 25 & Jan 1 ▪ BYO picnic ▪ Meals pre-arranged with private chef, Marc Wassung ▪ Owner(s) David van Niekerk ▪ Cellarmaster(s)/viticulturist(s) David van Niekerk (Jan 1999) ▪ Winemaker(s) David van Niekerk (Jan 1999) & Roger Arendse (Jan 2001) ▪ 14.5ha (cabs s/f, malbec, merlot, pinot, chard, sauv) ▪ 70t/11,000cs own label 52% red 15% white 3% rosé 30% MCC + 3,800cs for clients ▪ Brands for clients: Terra Madre ▪ Groot Constantia Rd Constantia 7800 ▪ david@highconstantia.co.za, info@highconstantia.co.za ▪ www.highconstantia.co.za ▪ S 34° 1′ 31.3″ E 018° 25′ 36.1″ ▪ F +27 (0)21-794-7999 ▪ **T +27 (0)21-794-7171/+27 (0)83-300-2064**

Highgate Wine Estate

Among a handful of vintners bringing wine culture to KZN-Natal province are Rudi and Cindy Kassier, wine-passionate fresh produce growers who planted vines in a 2005 trial. Releases, under the label Lions River, have been sporadic but the appointment of a farm manager/winemaker, Reghardt Dunn, and relocation of the cellar to larger premises hopefully presage continuity. Tasting and sales are by appointment; sales also at Meander Fine Wines in Piggly Wiggly Village on the Midlands Meander.

Location: Howick ▪ Map: KwaZulu-Natal ▪ Est/1stB 2010 ▪ Tasting, sales & cellar tours by appt ▪ Closed Dec 25 ▪ Facilities for children ▪ Coffee shop (see www.pigglywiggly.co.za) ▪ Country shops catering for all ages ▪ Owner(s) Rudi & Cindy Kassier ▪ Winemaker(s)/viticulturist(s) Reghardt Dunn ▪ 57ha/3ha (cab, merlot, ptage, shiraz, chard) ▪ 2.5t/ 840cs own label 50% red 50% white ▪ PO Box 1025 Howick 3290 ▪ rudi@pigglywiggly.co.za, manager@ highgatewineestate.co.za ▪ www.highgatewineestate.co.za ▪ S 29° 27' 29.92" E 030° 8' 8.66" ▪ F +27 (0)86-535-3187 ▪ T +27 (0)82-895-1667/+27 (0)33-234-2911

Highlands Road Estate

New in time for the 2014 harvest was the appointment of Jacques Maree as winemaker. With crushes at top wineries locally, in Australia and the US, Jacques brings welcome experience to this Elgin family farm. Older is what owner Michael White would like to see Elgin sauvignons on release: 'Sell them too young and they don't have a chance to reach their potential.'

Pinot Noir ★★★ Elegant & vibrant, with red fruit, firm tannins & savoury acidity. At just 13%, **12** more balanced & satisfying than alcohol-laden previous. **Sine Cera ★★★★** Partially oaked (10%) semillon adds weight, breadth to equal partner sauvignon in **14** preview. Takes step up with green apple, citrus, lemongrass & greengage complexity, lively acidity. Also tasted: **Rosé 13 ★★★ Sauvignon Blanc 14 ★★★** Not retasted: **Ruadh 11 ★★★ Slainte MCC Bubbly 08 ★★★ Tinta Amarela 11 ★★** Not tasted: **Sauvignon Blanc Sweet.** — GM

Location/WO: Elgin ▪ Map: Elgin, Walker Bay & Bot River ▪ Est 2005 ▪ 1stB 2007 ▪ Tasting, sales & cellar tours Mon-Sun 10–4 ▪ Light lunches & picnics ▪ Facilities for children ▪ Fly fishing ▪ Boule court ▪ Owner(s) Michael White ▪ Winemaker(s) Jacques Maree ▪ Viticulturist(s) Paul Wallace ▪ 28ha/10ha (pinot, shiraz, chard, sauv, sem) ▪ 30t/ 4,500cs own label 35% red 65% white ▪ PO Box 94 Elgin 7180 ▪ info@highlandsroadestate.co.za ▪ www. highlandsroadestate.co.za ▪ S 34° 14' 4.4" E 019° 4' 14.3" ▪ T +27 (0)71-271-0161

High Road

One-time high-fliers from the world of insurance, Les Sweidan and Mike Church, turned to wine-growing and named their venture for 'the peaceful transition achieved when our country took the high road in 1994'. Specialists in small-volume Bordeaux blends, vinified close to Stellenbosch town centre, they've created a wine club, hosted media events and plan to show their wines at functions in the major centres, so potential customers can 'try before they buy'.

★★★★ Director's Reserve Rich, expressive Bordeaux blend led by cab (69%), with expected crème de cassis fruit laced with dark chocolate & toasty oak in **10**. Rounded, well-polished palate reflects all-new oak & good ripeness. 4% petit verdot adds interest; ends slightly warmer than elegant **09** (★★★★★).

Classique ★★★★ The junior but still very good Bordeaux red. Friendly **10** is cab-led, with merlot & cab franc, showing dark fruit & dark chocolate note. Firm, with sufficient length. — JPf

Location/map/WO: Stellenbosch ▪ Est/1stB 2003 ▪ Tasting by appt only ▪ Closed all pub hols ▪ Boardroom facilities ▪ Owner(s) Les Sweidan & Mike Church ▪ Winemaker(s) Mark Carmichael-Green (2004, consultant) ▪ Viticulturist(s) Paul Wallace (2004, consultant) ▪ 26t/2,000cs own label 100% red ▪ PO Box 4721 Cape Town 8000 ▪ wine@ thehighroad.co.za ▪ www.thehighroad.co.za ▪ S 33° 56' 27.1" E 018° 50' 49.1" ▪ F +27 (0)21-886-4288 ▪ T +27 (0)76-044-5020

Hildenbrand Wine, Olive & Art Estate

International olive and olive oil judge Reni Hildenbrand's small Wellington farm is a haven for the large number of animals she has rescued over the years, many of which are commemorated as wine labels. She hopes to crack the Canadian market this year while maintaining her loyal local following.

★★★★ Shiraz ⓧ Big wine though not bold, more understated in last **07**. Cracked pepper, black cherry & warm spice meld in ripe palate.

★★★★ Wild Style Méthode Cap Classique (NEW) Named for a racehorse, maiden **12** sparkling from chardonnay & malbec presents a polished debut. 24 months on lees has given a salty tang to the creamy citrus fruit. Balanced acidity, fresh finish.

Malbec ★★★★ Shows delightful varietal typicity with blackcurrants & liquorice backed up by lovely vanilla & smooth tannins in **12**. Crop thinned by Florina the potbelly pig! **Chardonnay Barrique ★★★** Big mouthful of orange citrus fruit, white blossoms & creamy vanilla. **13** carries oak nicely, alcohol not so much. **Coconut & Angel** (NEW) **★★★☆** Quirky **13** blends 70% chardonnay with 30% malbec into surprisingly enjoyable drink. Rich & creamy, with baked apples & stewed guavas. Also tasted: **Shiraz Rosé 12 ★ Chardonnay Unwooded 12 ★★ Chenin Blanc 13 ★★ Semillon 13 ★★★** Not retasted: **Cabernet Sauvignon Barrique 07 ★★★★ Emma & Asa 09 ★★★ Sleepless Nights Semillon Noble Late Harvest 07 ★★★** Discontinued: **Cabernet Sauvignon Unwooded**. — CM

Location/WO: Wellington ▪ Map: Paarl & Wellington ▪ Est 1991 ▪ 1stB 1999 ▪ Tasting & sales Mon-Sat 10-4 Sun 9-12 by appt ▪ Wine tasting R50pp; olive & oil tasting R20pp ▪ Closed Easter Sat/Sun, Dec 24/25 & Jan 1 ▪ Klein Rhebokskloof Country & Guest House ▪ Owner(s)/cellarmaster(s)/winemaker(s) Reni Hildenbrand ▪ ±4,500cs ▪ PO Box 270 Wellington 7654 ▪ info@wine-estate-hildenbrand.co.za ▪ www.wine-estate-hildenbrand.co.za ▪ S 33° 39' 33.3" E 019° 1' 46.3" ▪ T +27 (0)82-656-6007

Hill & Dale

Easy-drinking wines vinified from grapes off selected Stellenbosch vineyards at Stellenzicht (see that entry for tasting/sales information).

Cabernet Sauvignon-Shiraz ⊘ **★★★★** Sound marriage of these two noble red varieties in fruit-filled **12**. Light spice & dusty tannins; elegant & complete. **Dry Rosé Merlot ★★☆** Baked red apples on creamy, easy-drinking **14**. Dry, as promised, balanced, ready for poolside enjoyment. **Sauvignon Blanc ★★★** Youthful vibrancy on straightforward, crisp-fruited **14**. Made for summer fun. Also tasted: **Merlot 12 ★★ Pinotage** ⊘ **13 ★★★ Shiraz 12 ★★★ Chardonnay 13 Pinot Grigio 14 ★★★** — HJ

Hillcrest Estate

The vineyards, their soils and management are paramount to Graeme Read, the self-taught, talented winemaker here. He revels in the cool climate and special terroir, which, together with his fine-tuning, make the wines of this small-scale Durbanville winery so distinctively elegant. The Metamorphic Collection's name alludes to the farm's interesting and ancient geology. Much younger, and 'vibrantly active', is the functions venue which, Graeme says, has put Hillcrest on the entertainment map and caused wine sales to boom.

Metamorphic Collection

★★★★ Quarry Elegant, polished **12** from merlot in classic style. Cool Atlantic breezes ensure ripeness at lower alcohol & lovely acid thread throughout; subtly structured by predominantly new oak.

★★★★☆ Hornfels Named for vineyard's baked shale soils which contribute to distinctive minerality in **12** equal blend both cabs & petit verdot, with merlot, malbec. Mostly new oak outlines fine compact red fruit in classically elegant style.

★★★★☆ Atlantic Slopes Was 'Relief', **14** from sauvignon in same poised, seriously steely, mineral style as **12**. Tightly wound, concentrated pithy lime fruit, balanced by thrilling acidity, needs time to emerge from austere shell. Dash semillon adds weight to focused finish. Blend of distinctive ocean-facing vineyards. No **13**.

Hillcrest Estate range

★★★★ Cabernet Franc Gorgeously perfumed **13** exhibits earthy edge to core pure red fruit, elegantly framed by supple tannins. Unfined/filtered. Like Malbec & Petit Verdot only available from cellar.

★★★★ Malbec Opaque, youthful **13** in solidly structured, well-grounded style. Compact, ripe dark fruit shines in carefully balanced display of fruit, tannin & acidity.

★★★★☆ Sauvignon Blanc ⊘ Thrillingly vibrant, passionfruit-laden **13** impeccably poised & focused. Layered flavours gathered by savoury acidity & persistent minerality. Dollop semillon adds to dimension. Less steely, more accessible than Atlantic Slopes label.

Cabernet Sauvignon Rosé ★★★ Light, dry, ultra-crisp **14** in zesty strawberry style for summer picnics. Also tasted: **Petit Verdot 13 ★★★★ Robbenzicht 13 ★★★☆** — IM

Location: Durbanville ▪ Map: Durbanville, Philadelphia & Darling ▪ WO: Durbanville/Western Cape ▪ Est/1stB 2002 ▪ Tasting & sales daily 9–5 ▪ Fee R10, waived on purchase ▪ Closed Good Fri, Dec 25 & Jan 1 ▪ Cellar tours by appt ▪ Restaurant T +27 (0)21-975-2346 open daily for breakfast & lunch ▪ Wedding/function venue ▪ Farm produce ▪ Walking/hiking & mountain biking trails ▪ Conservation area ▪ Owner(s) PD Inglis, R Haw & G du Toit ▪ Winemaker(s) Graeme Read (Jan 2003) & Arno Smith (Jan 2014) ▪ Viticulturist(s) G du Toit ▪ 25ha (cabs s/f, malbec, merlot, p verdot, sauv) ▪ 60t/±6,000cs own label 45% red 55% white ▪ Private Bag X3 Durbanville 7551 ▪ cellardoor@hillcrestfarm.co.za ▪ www.hillcrestfarm.co.za ▪ S 33° 49′ 38.2″ E 018° 35′ 25.9″ ▪ F +27 (0)21-975-2195 ▪ **T +27 (0)21-970-5800**

Hillock Wines

Expect a warm welcome at retired surgeon and keen aviator Andy Hillock and wife Penny's boutique winery on their Mymering Guest Farm outside Ladismith. Andy is fulfilling a lifelong dream with this venture and, following the departure of the full-time winemaker, must be doubly delighted to have the cellar controls too.

Mile High ⊘ **★★★** Easy-drinking **NV** blend pinotage & cab plus cab franc (ex Stellenbosch) & shiraz. Every pilot's wine range has to have one! Not tasted: **Shiraz, Big Harry, Blanc de Noir, Black Poodle Reserve Chardonnay, Chenin Blanc, Sauvignon Blanc, Black Poodle Reserve Sauvignon Blanc, Barrel Roll.** — CR

Location: Ladismith ▪ Map: Klein Karoo & Garden Route ▪ WO: Western Cape ▪ Est 2010 ▪ 1stB 2011 ▪ Tasting, sales & cellar tours daily 10-5 ▪ Closed Dec 25 ▪ Light lunches & refreshments 10-5 daily ▪ Tour groups ▪ Gifts ▪ Farm produce ▪ Guided hikes & vineyard tours ▪ Mountain biking ▪ 4-star guest house (sleeps 20), Mymering Estate www.mymering.com ▪ Owner(s) Andy & Penny Hillock ▪ Winemaker(s) Andy Hillock ▪ Viticulturist(s) Riaan Steyn ▪ 400ha/50ha (shiraz, chard, chenin) ▪ 24t/3,600cs own label 50% red 50% white ▪ PO Box 278 Ladismith 6655 ▪ penny@mymering.com ▪ www.hillockwines.com ▪ S 33° 29′ 55.24″ E 021° 10′ 18.65″ ▪ F +27 (0)28-551-1313 ▪ **T +27 (0)28-551-1548**

Hills

Chimanimani is a smallholding in Stellenbosch's prime Devon Valley where Vic Hills, whose family has owned the property since 1964, oversees 5ha of noble reds (including a new pinot noir vineyard) and a block of venerable chenin. The harvest is mostly sold but since 2006 a soupçon is made for the own label by celebrated neighbour Martin Meinert.

Ensemble ★★★ Repeating 60/40 cab/shiraz formula for 3rd-vintage **10**. Engaging blackcurrant, oak spice, slight menthol character; full-bodied but friendly glassful. Also tasted: **Cabernet Sauvignon 10 ★★★ Shiraz 10 ★★★ Chenin Blanc 14 ★★** Not tasted: **Pinot Noir.** — GM

Location/map: Stellenbosch ▪ WO: Devon Valley ▪ Est/1stB 2006 ▪ Tasting & sales by appt ▪ Owner(s) The Victor Hills Family Trust ▪ Winemaker(s) Martin Meinert (Feb 2006, consultant) ▪ Viticulturist(s) Vic Hills (Jan 1998) ▪ 6ha/5ha (cab, pinot, shiraz, chenin) ▪ 40t/600cs own label 80% red 20% white ▪ PO Box 12012 Die Boord Stellenbosch 7613 ▪ vwhills@iafrica.com ▪ S 33° 55′ 04.1″ E 018° 48′ 47.1″ ▪ **T +27 (0)21-865-2939**

Hilton Vineyards

Boutique winemaker and tour company owner Richard Hilton continues his love affair with Rhône grape varieties using fruit sourced from Helderberg and Elgin for his own-label wines. After his first five star wine last year, he's been concentrating on his single-variety viognier, promising a new selection process in the vineyard, a different approach to the winemaking and new regalia. And: 'My wife's pregnant with our second and life is grand!!'

★★★★ **Ironstone** Name change from 'Blazing Hill Syrah' but that (syrah/shiraz) still the only grape in **11**. Mixes black-berried fruit & cream with nice leathery hints & a touch of freshening salinity, possibly from 10% portion of 2012. Poised & refined, satisfying drink.

★★★★★ **The Dalmatian Syrah** Beguiling aromas of baked plums, pepper & aniseed on **11** (★★★★☆) give way to silky tannin-wrapped blackberries & damson jam. Shade less impressive than stellar **10** but nevertheless a wine of class & elegance, sure to reward cellaring for up to 10 years.

Occasional release: **Rockwater Fountain Viognier**. — CM

Location/WO: Stellenbosch ▪ Est 2003 ▪ Closed to public ▪ Owner(s) Richard Hilton ▪ Cellarmaster(s)/winemaker(s) Richard Hilton (2003) & Riaan Wassüng (2005) ▪ Viticulturist(s) Tjuks Roos & Richard Rose ▪ (shiraz, viog) ▪ 21t/2,600cs own label 35% red 65% white ▪ richard@hiltonvineyards.co.za ▪ www.hiltonvineyards.co.za ▪ F +27 (0)86-618-4089 ▪ T +27 (0)21-855-5244

☐ **Hippo Creek** *see* PicardiRebel
☐ **His Master's Choice** *see* Excelsior Vlakteplaas
☐ **Hoeksrivier** *see* Eagle's Cliff Wines-New Cape Wines

Hofstraat Kelder

Naming your winery for a street in Malmesbury does not necessarily summon up the bucolic glories of the Swartland vineyards where some of your grapes come from — but if that's where your cellar is, why not? A small concern it may be, but for friends Wim Smit, Jack de Clercq and Jerry Finley it's a sideline in which passion rules.

Renosterbos range

★★★★ **Barbera** 13 version of rare varietal bottling will please its fans more than **12** (★★★★☆). Cherries & slight balsamic whiffs, varietally correct high acidity that will easily stand up to rich food.

Chenin Blanc (NEW) ★★★ Oak fermented/aged **13** from Darling has fresh stonefruit & peach aromas, interesting slippery texture, easy & fruit driven. **Die Solder** (NEW) ★★★★ Interesting, quirky experiment with hanepoot, intricately & naturally vinified 'in the Tokaji manner'. Complex, rich on nose, powerfully sweet palate lacks freshness despite 10 g/l acid. Uncertified **NV** more condiment than wine! Also tasted: **Cabernet Sauvignon 13** ★★☆ **Pinotage 13** ★★★☆ **Shiraz 13** ★★★ **Cape Vintage 09** ★★☆ Not tasted: **Merlot**. — HJ

Location: Malmesbury ▪ Map: Swartland ▪ WO: Swartland/Darling ▪ Est 2002 ▪ 1stB 2003 ▪ Tasting, sales & tours by appt ▪ Owner(s)/cellarmaster(s)/winemaker(s) Wim Smit, Jack de Clercq & Jerry Finley ▪ 4t/505cs own label 100% red ▪ PO Box 1172 Malmesbury 7299 ▪ renosterbos@cornergate.com ▪ S 33° 26' 56.1" E 018° 44' 1.8" ▪ F +27 (0)22-487-3202 ▪ T +27 (0)83-270-2352

Holden Manz Wine Estate

Named after owners Gerard Holden and Migo Manz, this Franschhoek property was originally developed into a wine farm in 1999. Today it is also a lifestyle destination, boasting five-star guest house and spa, restaurant, riverside picnics and an art collection housed in the town. New since last time are a Reserve range, promising Bordeaux-shiraz blend, and head of marketing and sales, the dynamic Krige Visser. Watch this space.

Reserve range

★★★★ **Syrah** Serious intent in **12**: natural ferment on 50% of fruit. Layered palate with good concentration of plum, spice & liquorice depth. Gentle oaking, just 20% new.

Cabernet Franc ★★★★ Fynbos sheen to rich earthy black berry fruit of maiden **12**. Ripe & rewarding but perhaps a little light bodied for Reserve status.

Avant Garde range

★★★★ **Big G** Though somewhat reticent, **11** Bordeaux blend steps up on **10** (★★★☆) with petit verdot & malbec joining cab & cab franc. Rich plum & berry boldness with cocoa sheen. WO Coastal.

Visionaire ★★★☆ Spicy entry with juicy Christmas pudding notes on **12** 5-way Bordeaux-blend mostly cab & merlot plus drop shiraz. Rounded texture, unforced lightweight palate. WO W Cape. Also tasted: **Chardonnay 13** ★★★ Not retasted: **Good Sport Cape Vintage 10** ★★★

Modern range

Vernissage ★★★☆ Merlot joins cab/shiraz blend in chunky yet appealingly ripe improved **13**. Body & grip, with good definition & memorably long aftertaste. Also tasted: **Rosé 14** ★★☆

Contemporary range

Shiraz ★★★ **11** mimics Merlot stablemate in ripeness & lightness of body. Uncomplicated & approachable. Also tasted: **Cabernet Sauvignon 11** ★★★ **Merlot 11** ★★★ — FM

Location/map: Franschhoek ▪ WO: Franschhoek/Coastal/Elgin/Western Cape ▪ Est 2010 ▪ 1stB 2005 ▪ Tasting, sales & cellar tours daily 10-5 ▪ Fee R30 ▪ Franschhoek Kitchen ▪ Spa ▪ Picnic area ▪ Holden Manz Country House ▪ Owner(s) Gerard Holden & Migo Manz ▪ Winemaker(s) Schalk Opperman (Sep 2011) ▪ Viticulturist(s) Tertius Oosthuizen (Sep 2010) ▪ 20ha/16ha (cabs s/f, shiraz) ▪ 110t/13,332cs own label 85% red 3.85% white 6.65% rosé 4.5% port ▪ IPW ▪ PO Box 620 Franschhoek 7690 ▪ info@holdenmanz.com ▪ www.holdenmanz.com ▪ S 33° 56' 6.3" E 019° 7' 8.3" ▪ F +27 (0)21-876-4624 ▪ **T +27 (0)21-876-2738**

Hoopenburg Wines

The Schmitz family's estate on the northern fringe of Stellenbosch has appointed a new cellarmaster, Helanie Olivier, freeing GM Anton Beukes to focus on non-wine duties, notably vineyard renewal, portfolio expansion and marketing. One of Helanie's first wines here is a méthode cap classique, with a pinot noir component joining the current chardonnay. Sexier packaging is envisaged for the sparkler to reflect the new house style - 'elegant, feminine but not thin'.

Integer range

★★★★ **Cabernet Sauvignon** Compact blackcurrant fruit appeals in solid **11**. 30 months in barrel ensures dry tannic grip & spicy savouriness.

★★★★ **Syrah** ⊘ Statement **10** exuberant & bold. Richly heady, spicy pepper & layered dark fruit flavours, plenty of oak but not let down by heavy-handedness of **09** (★★★★).

★★★★ **Syrah-Mourvèdre-Carignan** Aromatic **11** almost equal blend of trio from Wellington & Swartland. Violets, clove spice & darkly rich fruit deliver textured mouthfeel.

★★★★ **Chardonnay** Sweet marzipan **13** (★★★) spicily oaked. Less stern than **12** but regrettably let down by excessively ripe tangerine fruit aromas & flavours.

★★★★ **Méthode Cap Classique Brut** ⊘ Candied fruits & fine, persistent mousse herald rich, full-bodied **NV** chardonnay sparkling, mostly from fine 2012 vintage, given breadth & freshness by 18 months on lees. Good value; improves on last release.

Hoopenburg Bush Vine range

Cabernet Sauvignon ★★★ Firm-footed **12** exhibits cab fruit character, judicious oaking provides grip & spiciness. **Pinot Noir** ★★★ Acidity structures light, simple, vibrant, smoky, well-oaked **11** from Elgin. **Rosé** From cab, candyfloss pink **14** light, dry & crisp, pleasantly fruity. **Chardonnay** ★★★ Unoaked **13** uncomplicated, fresh appeal from green apple flavours. Also tasted: **Merlot 11**

★★★ **Pinotage** 12 ★★☆ **Shiraz** 11 ★★★ **Chenin Blanc** 14 ★★☆ **Sauvignon Blanc** 14 ★★★
In abeyance: **Shiraz-Cabernet Sauvignon**. Discontinued: **Shiraz Rosé**.

Guru range
Sauvignon Blanc ★★☆ Fresh, easy **14** offers uncomplicated summer quaffing. Also tasted: **Merlot**
11 ★★ In abeyance: **Cabernet Sauvignon-Merlot**. — IM

Location/map: Stellenbosch ▪ WO: Stellenbosch/Coastal/Western Cape/Paarl ▪ Est/1stB 1992 ▪ Tasting, sales & cellar
tours Mon-Fri 8.30-4 ▪ Fee R20/6-8 wines ▪ Closed all pub hols ▪ BYO picnic ▪ Conferences ▪ Guest house T +27 (0)21-
884-4534 ▪ Owner(s) Gregor Schmitz ▪ GM Anton Beukes (Aug 2009) ▪ Cellarmaster(s) Helanie Olivier ▪ Viticultur-
ist(s) Gert Snyders ▪ 70ha/30ha (cab, merlot, shiraz, chard) ▪ 180t/40,000cs own label 80% red 18% white 2% MCC ▪
PO Box 1233 Stellenbosch 7599 ▪ info@hoopenburg.com ▪ www.hoopenburgwines.co.za ▪ S 33° 49' 33.4" E 018° 49'
9.3" ▪ F +27 (0)21-884-4904 ▪ **T +27 (0)21-884-4221**

☐ **Hoophuis** *see* Boutinot South Africa
☐ **Hope** *see* Almenkerk Wine Estate

Hornbill Garagiste Winery

Architect John Dry seamlessly combines his love of art, food and wine at the Hermanus family home.
Sourcing grapes from the premium Hemel-en-Aarde Valley, he handcrafts soupçons of wine garagiste
style (literally in the garage), supported by family and friends. The adjacent ceramics studio, art gallery and eatery provide similarly creative outlets.

★★★★ **Pinotage** Succulent, ripe juicy fruit in **11** (★★★☆), with some oaky notes & a high-toned
note on the otherwise soft & fruit-driven palate. Maiden **10** was full, rounded & complex.

★★★★ **Cape Blend** Equal pinotage & merlot on **11** (★★★★) - **10** was cab franc, pinotage, shiraz.
Dusty chocolate & brambleberry notes; acidity balanced by a little sugar. Modest 12.5% alcohol. — JPf

Location: Hermanus ▪ Map: Elgin, Walker Bay & Bot River ▪ WO: Upper Hemel-en-Aarde Valley ▪ Est 2004 ▪ 1stB 2005 ▪
Tasting, sales & tours Mon-Fri 9-5 Sat 9-2 ▪ Closed Easter Fri/Sun, Dec 25 & Jan 1 ▪ Gifts ▪ Art gallery & ceramic studio ▪
Self-catering accommodation ▪ Restaurant ▪ Owner(s) John Dry ▪ Winemaker(s) John Dry (2004) ▪ 6t/800cs own
label 100% red ▪ PO Box 4 Hermanus 7200 ▪ hornbill@intekom.co.za ▪ www.hornbillhouse.co.za ▪ S 34° 24' 46.3" E
019° 11' 54.4" ▪ F +27 (0)28-316-3794 ▪ **T +27 (0)28-316-2696**

☐ **Horse Mountain** *see* Doran Vineyards
☐ **Horses of the Apocalypse** *see* Osbloed Wines
☐ **Houdamond** *see* Bellevue Estate Stellenbosch

House of GM&AHRENS

This tiny méthode cap classique house in Franschhoek is a dedicated, single-minded partnership
between Albert Ahrens (Goede Hoop winemaker) and lawyer Gerrit Maritz - with the input of bubbly
expert Pieter Ferreira gratefully received. In its striking and unorthodox packaging (cases contain 5
bottles, not the ubiquitous 6), the sparkler is launched each year on Spring Day. Also untraditional is
their serving suggestion: 'Poured in a Burgundy wine glass, the mousse and the wine behind the
bubble come into balance and hence the food compatibility increases dramatically. Try this!'

★★★★☆ **Vintage Cuvée** Classy, understated **10** MCC sparkling in multi-regional (8 sites) blend
chardonnay, pinot, spent year in barrel gaining breadth & richness before bottling & 35 months lees
maturation. Glamorous packaging in keeping with seamless elegance & luxuriously textured style.
— IM

Location/map: Franschhoek ▪ WO: Western Cape ▪ Est 2007 ▪ 1stB 2008 ▪ Tasting, sales & cellar tours by appt ▪ Closed
all pub hols ▪ Meals/refreshments by appt ▪ Owner(s) Albert Ahrens & Gerrit Maritz ▪ Cellarmaster(s)/viticulturist(s)
Albert Ahrens (Jan 2007) ▪ 10t/400 x 5-btl cs own label 100% MCC ▪ P O Box 5619 Helderberg 7135 ▪ info@
gmahrens.com ▪ www.gmahrens.co.za ▪ S 33° 54' 14" E 019° 07' 08" ▪ **T +27 (0)79-196-6887 (Albert)/+27
(0)83-348-1230 (Gerrit)**

House of JC le Roux

Named after French Huguenot Jean le Roux, Distell's high-profile, dedicated sparkling-wine house operates from a 'lifestyle' cellar in Stellenbosch's Devon Valley. The range covers all levels, from stand-out méthode cap classique to carbonated sweet reds. Fruit is sourced from an extensive portfolio of suppliers and contracted growers as well as own vineyards. The venue has lots to offer visitors, like the new pairing of non-alcoholic fizzes with fudge, coconut ice and other sweets - ideal for non-drinkers and designated drivers.

Méthode Cap Classique range

★★★★ **Pinot Noir** ⊘ Appealing strawberry & shortbread on **09**, with crisply precise acidity. Rounder, more generous than **08** (★★★★), the perfect summertime aperitif.

★★★★ **Scintilla** Jump to **08** vintage, first since **03** shows change to leaner, more focused sparkling style. Creamy mousse with soft acid. Chardonnay/pinot noir 70/30 is complex & integrated.

Also tasted: **Pinot Noir Rosé 09** ★★★★ **La Vallée Rosé** ⊘ **NV** ★★★ **Brut** ⊘ **NV** ★★★★ **La Vallée NV** ★★☆

Sparkling range

La Chanson ★★ Sweet red bubbles from mostly pinotage. Potent plum fruit in latest **NV**, with low alcohol (7.5%), as for all except Sauvignon. **Sauvignon Blanc** ★★★ Perennially dependable bubbly. **14** off-dry, frothy & pleasantly fruity. With 10% colombard. Also tasted: **La Fleurette NV** ★☆ **Le Domaine NV** ★★ — GdB

Location/map: Stellenbosch ▪ WO: Western Cape ▪ 1stB 1983 ▪ Tasting & sales Mon-Fri 9–4 Sat/pub hols 10–3 Sun 10–2 ▪ Fee R40-R85 ▪ Self tour available during opening hrs ▪ Closed Good Fri, Dec 25 & Jan 1 ▪ Tour groups ▪ Gifts ▪ Le Venue restaurant ▪ Owner(s) Distell ▪ Cellarmaster(s) Elunda Basson ▪ Winemaker(s) Elunda Basson (2007), with Hentie Germishuys (Oct 2002) ▪ Farm manager Willem Laubscher ▪ Viticulturist(s) Bennie Liebenberg (Jan 2000) ▪ 27ha own vyds ▪ 20% red 80% white ▪ ISO 9200 ▪ PO Box 184 Stellenbosch 7599 ▪ info@jcleroux.co.za ▪ www. jcleroux.co.za ▪ S 33° 54' 16.6" E 018° 48' 37.4" ▪ **T +27 (0)21-865-8200**

☐ **House of Krone** *see* Twee Jonge Gezellen Estate-House of Krone

House of Mandela

The negociant wine business owned by Makaziwe and Tukwini Mandela, children of South Africa's celebrated past president and Nobel laureate, the late Nelson Mandela, shows its respect for ancestry in the brand names chosen. The ranges, including Fairtrade-accredited Thembu, have been created with the help of consultant (and former Fairview winemaker) Erlank Erasmus.

Royal Reserve range

★★★★☆ **Cabernet Sauvignon 12** first since **08**, now from Paarl & Stellenbosch grapes - with dollops of shiraz (adding floral notes to the aromas) & mourvèdre. Serious-minded wine; firmly, even powerfully structured; generous new oak - but all this in balance. Needs a few years to show its best.

★★★★ **Shiraz** Big, burly **11**, like previous **07** from Paarl. Ripe, dark fruit flavours held in check by obvious, tobacco-ish oak, which should integrate in a few years. Finishes rather sweet, with some alcohol glow.

★★★★ **Chardonnay 13** (★★★★) from Paarl follows **09** from Elgin. In lightish, elegant style, with balanced oaking, & a good vein of acidity enlivening the lemony, peachy flavours.

Vusani Series

Pinotage ★★★ Juicy, fresh fruit on **13**, with a core of dry tannin keeping all under control. Good light oaking. Also tasted: **Shiraz 12** ★★★ Not retasted: **Cabernet Sauvignon 11** ★★★ **Merlot 11** ★★★

Thembu Collection

Merlot ★★★☆ Ripe berry flavours & a hint of milk choc on softly ingratiating, balanced **13**. **Chardonnay** ★★★ Lightly oaked **13** has authentic varietal character. Tasty & light, pretty dry & fresh, with a nice buzz of citrus fruit. Also tasted: **Cabernet Sauvignon 13** ★★★ **Pinotage 13** ★★★ **Shiraz 13** ★★★ **Sauvignon Blanc 14** ★★★ Not retasted: **Chenin Blanc 13** ★★

Méthode Cap Classique range 🆕

★★★★ **Brut** Xhosa beads on the label, while fine gas beads enliven this chardonnay-based MCC (with pinot noir & a little pinotage). Lightly rich & crisply dry; fresh, balanced & flavourful. **NV**, ex Stellenbosch. — TJ

WO: Western Cape ▪ Est 2009 ▪ Closed to public ▪ Owner(s) Makaziwe Mandela & Tukwini Mandela ▪ Winemaker(s) Erlank Erasmus ▪ Viticulturist(s) Various ▪ 60% red 40% white ▪ info@houseofmandela.com ▪ www. houseofmandela.com ▪ **T +27 (0)21-872-9214**

Hout Bay Vineyards ⓠ ⓐ

Cathy and Peter Roeloffze learned the hard way about viticulture and winemaking – from the initial backbreaking (and pioneering) work of planting vines (each one tied to its own pole) on steep rocky slopes not far from picturesque Hout Bay. Birds and wind didn't help. The family vineyards being limited, grapes are also brought in - mostly from the area, but from further afield too.

★★★★ **Petrus** Roundly ripe, plush-textured shiraz-led blend, with equal mourvèdre, grenache & carignan. **11**, now bottled, appealing, succulent fruit informed by well-judged oaking to finish sweet & spicy. WO W Cape.

★★★★ **Klasiek by Catherine** Elegant, austere **10** pale gold MCC sparkling with finely beaded bubbles. Bone-dry, almost equal blend own pinot, chardonnay. Few years on lees provide yeast complexity & lovely freshness.

Also tasted: **Merlot 12** ★★★★ **Shiraz 12** ★★★★ Not retasted: **Sauvignon Blanc 13** ★★★★ Not tasted: **Cabernet Sauvignon**, **Blush**. — IM

Location: Hout Bay ▪ Map: Cape Peninsula ▪ WO: Hout Bay/Western Cape ▪ Est 2001 ▪ 1stB 2004 ▪ Tasting, sales & cellar tours by appt ▪ Fee R30 ▪ Facilities for children ▪ Owner(s) Peter & Catharine Roeloffze ▪ Cellarmaster(s)/ winemaker(s)/viticulturist(s) Peter & Catharine Roeloffze (both Jan 2004) ▪ 1.5ha/1.1ha (pinots meunier/noir, merlot, shiraz, chard, sauv, viog) ▪ 15t/4,200cs own label 44% red 24% white 14% rosé 18% MCC ▪ Other brand: HB Vineyards ▪ PO Box 26659 Hout Bay 7872 ▪ cathy@4mb.co.za ▪ www.houtbayvineyards.co.za ▪ S 34° 1' 31.0" E 018° 22' 31.0" ▪ F +27 (0)86-514-9861 ▪ **T +27 (0)83-790-2372**

Howard Booysen Boutique Wines

The first Protégé of the Cape Winemakers Guild, with mentorships at prestigious Guild member estates, Howard Booysen launched his own brand with an impressive German-inspired semi-sweet Riesling 2010. It has since been joined by an Australian-style steelier version, under a Pegasus sublabel, and a cinsaut.

Pegasus range

Riesling ⓠ ★★★★ Pineapple & spice, limy tang on near-dry **11**, satisfying flavour, intensity & length; enjoy well chilled. From Stellenbosch grapes. Not tasted: **Cinsault**.

Howard Booysen range

Not tasted: **Riesling**. — CvZ

Location/WO: Stellenbosch ▪ Est 2009 ▪ 1stB 2010 ▪ Sales by appt ▪ Owner(s) Howard Booysen ▪ Cellarmaster(s)/ winemaker(s)/viticulturist(s) Howard Booysen (Nov 2009) ▪ (cinsaut, riesling) ▪ 3,500cs own label 33.3% red 66.7% white ▪ howard@howardbooysenwines.com ▪ www.howardbooysenwines.com ▪ **T +27 (0)72-414-5458**

☐ **Huangtai Wines** *see* De Villiers Wines

Hughes Family Wines

Argentina-born, Swartland-based Billy Hughes and wife Penny talk of their 'trilogy approach to growing wine': mineral soils, organic cultivation (certified since 2012) and, now, biodynamic practices, including 'beautiful compost windrows inoculated with biodynamic preparations using old copper backpacks from the 1950s'. If all goes to plan, recently appointed consulting winemaker Bryan MacRobert will vinify the 2015 vintage in a new naturally ventilated underground cellar built from old shipping containers.

Nativo range

★★★★ **Red Blend** Rich in flavour (cinnamon spice, iron, red soil) yet light of foot, **11** is the essence of Swartland. Good potential. Mainly shiraz with equal parts mourvèdre, grenache, pinotage, tempranillo.

★★★★ **White Blend** ⊘ Purity & precision in **13** (★★★★☆) blend of viognier (58%) & chenin, with grenache blanc & roussanne adding intrigue. Notes of hay & fragrant flowers in its creamy yet mineral-laced delicacy. Intricate & ageworthy. Worthy successor to unshowy, satisfying **12**. — AL

Location: Malmesbury ▪ Map/WO: Swartland ▪ Est 2000 ▪ 1stB 2004 ▪ Tasting by appt ▪ Owner(s) Billy & Penny Hughes ▪ Cellarmaster(s) Billy Hughes ▪ Winemaker(s) Bryan MacRobert ▪ Viticulturist(s) Kevin Watt (Jul 2005, consultant) ▪ 52ha/27ha (grenache n/b, mourv, ptage, tempranillo, shiraz, chenin, rouss, viog) ▪ 180t total 25t/3,600cs own label 70% red 30% white ▪ Organic ▪ 6 Riverstone Road Tierboskloof Hout Bay 7806 ▪ billy@nativo.co.za ▪ www. nativo.co.za ▪ S 33° 20' 37.71" E 018° 43' 45.09" ▪ F +27 (0)86-549-1080 ▪ **T +27 (0)21-790-4824**

☐ **Hugh Masekela** *see* Veenwouden Private Cellar

Huguenot Wine Farmers

Privately owned wholesalers in Wellington, blending, marketing and distributing a range of liqueurs; spirits such as Huguenac Brandy and Buchu Brandy; wine brands including Huguenot (Cabernet, Smooth Red, Nagmaalwyn, Jeripico, Hanepoot) and Zellerhof Vats; and Huguenot Fortified Sherry.

Wellington ▪ Closed to public ▪ Owner(s) JC Botha (Pty) Ltd ▪ Cellarmaster(s) Bill Matthee (1984) ▪ Trade enquiries Gert Brynard ▪ PO Box 275 Wellington 7654 ▪ gmbrynard@jcbotha.co.za ▪ F +27 (0)21-873-2075 ▪ **T +27 (0)21-864-1277**

Huis van Chevallerie

Making winzersekt, Germany's 'winegrower's bubbly', and travels in Italy's and France's sparkling wine regions ignited Christa von La Chevallerie's passion for the style. Since last edition she's left her day job to focus on making her chenin-based Filia ('Daughter') bubbly and managing the vineyards on Swartland family farm Nuwedam. A distributor appointed, she's working on a 'fresh, fizzy, sassy' rosé and mentoring new small-scale producers.

Filia ★★★☆ Food-styled, zero dosage bubbly from Swartland chenin. **12** fine energetic bead, bone-dry Granny Smith apple flavours, delightful clean flinty freshness throughout. In both 750ml & 1.5L magnum — winemaker believes (& we agree) smaller format takes longer to unfurl; both show potential to develop nicely though. — MW

Location: Malmesbury ▪ Map/WO: Swartland ▪ Est 2005 ▪ 1stB 2011 ▪ Tasting by appt only ▪ Closed most pub hols ▪ Owner(s) Chevallerie Family Trust ▪ Cellarmaster(s)/winemaker(s)/viticulturist(s) Christa von La Chevallerie ▪ 110ha/20ha (ptage, chenin) ▪ 100% sparkling wine ▪ PO Box 185 Malmesbury 7299 ▪ info@chevallerie.co.za ▪ www. chevallerie.co.za ▪ **T +27 (0)72-237-1166**

Hunneyball Wines

IT businessman Jim Hunneyball and wife Marie swapped Sweden for Stellenbosch in 2007, eventually expressing their growing love of wine in becoming part-time garagistes. After experimenting with cabernet and shiraz, they have taken time to learn, travel and plan, 'giving us a clearer picture of what we want to focus on'.

For more information, visit wineonaplatter.com

Cabernet Sauvignon ★★★ Unfettered by new oak, **11**'s walnutty blackcurrant powers through. Textbook cab, forthright, will have you reaching for braai tongs. Swartland vines. — HJ, JP

Location: Stellenbosch ▪ WO: Western Cape ▪ Est 2012 ▪ 1stB 2011 ▪ Closed to public ▪ Winemaker(s) Jim & Marie Hunneyball ▪ 3.75t ▪ 100% red ▪ PO Box 795 Stellenbosch 7599 ▪ jim.hunneyball@gmail.com ▪ **T +27 (0)76-284-6951**

☐ **Hunterspeak** *see* Niel Joubert Estate
☐ **Hunting Family** *see* Slaley
☐ **Idelia** *see* Swartland Winery
☐ **Ideology** *see* Spier

Idiom Collection

Even without knowing that the Helderberg home of Idiom was called Da Capo Vineyards, a casual glance at the range of wines would reveal that this winery speaks with an Italian accent: nebbiolo recalling Piedmont, for example, sangiovese the hills of Tuscany. But when the Rosso was introduced, someone asked: 'Rosso di Montalcino'? 'No', said Roberto Bottega, of the owning family, firmly – 'Rosso di Stellenbosch!'

Idiom range

★★★★ **Nebbiolo** **10** robust but restrained, with good structure, built to last. For food & Nabucco at full volume. Improves on last-tasted **08** (★★★☆), listed as '900 Series Nebbiolo'.

★★★★ **Zinfandel** Wild strawberry, spice & dried herbs on varietally expressive **11** (★★★★), showing higher alcohol (15.5%) than elegant **10**.

★★★★ **Cabernet Sauvignon-Merlot-Petit Verdot** Bordeaux red loses cab franc component in fragrant, medium-bodied **10**, tasted out of vintage sequence. Packed with dark fruit & firm structure; lifting acidity & hint of dark chocolate on the finish. Notch above **08** (★★★).

★★★★ **Cabernet Sauvignon-Pinotage-Merlot-Petit Verdot** Pinotage is 30% of **10** Cape Blend, with wide array of aroma & flavour: plums, red cherry, fynbos & toasty oak. Rich & full, good intensity before savoury finish.

★★★★ **Viognier** Full-bodied yet elegant **12**, with rich floral perfume, voluptuous peach melba flavour & subtle vanilla complexity on the finish.

Also tasted: **Shiraz-Mourvèdre-Viognier** 10 ★★★☆ Not retasted: **900 Series Mourvèdre 08** ★★ **900 Series Sangiovese 10** ★★★☆ **Sauvignon Blanc-Semillon 12** ★★★★ Not tasted: **900 Series Cabernet Franc**, **900 Series Barbera**.

Enoteca Bottega range

Bianco di Stellenbosch ★★★ Soft fruited, understated **13** from pinot grigio/gris, light styled for summer. Not retasted: **Rosso 10** ★★★ Not tasted: **Super Rosso**. — WB

Location: Sir Lowry's Pass ▪ Map: Helderberg ▪ WO: Stellenbosch ▪ Est 1999/1stB 2003 ▪ Tasting & sales: see website - new visitor centre opens in 2015 with Idiom wines, deli, fynbos perfumery & imported Italian wine library; see also Whalehaven entry ▪ Vineyard tours by appt (Sir Lowry's Pass) ▪ Owner(s) Bottega family ▪ Winemaker(s) Reino Thiart ▪ 35ha (barbera, cabs s/f, merlot, mourv, nebbiolo, p verdot, ptage, sangio, shiraz, zin, sauv, sem, viog) ▪ 85% red 15% white ▪ PO Box 3802 Somerset West 7129 ▪ wine@idiom.co.za ▪ www.idiom.co.za, www.bottegafamilywine.co.za ▪ S 34° 6' 14.1" E 018° 56' 12.4" ▪ F +27 (0)21-858-1089 (vyds)/+27 (0)21-851-5891 (sales)/+27 (0)28-316-1640 (winery) ▪ **T +27 (0)21-858-1088 (vyds)/+27 (0)21-852-3590 (sales)/+27 (0)28-316-1633 (tasting: Whalehaven)**

☐ **Imagine** *see* Southern Sky Wines

Imbuko Wines

The road to Wellington's Uitkyk farm, home of Imbuko Wines, has been tarred, making it a smoother drive for visitors stocking up on wine, jams and relishes from wine grapes, olives and olive oils. A

softer ride, too, for the 120,000 cases leaving the recently enlarged and upgraded premises bound for over 30 markets worldwide, increasingly in Africa.

Du Plevaux Private Collection

Shiraz ★★★ Sturdy **12** from Wellington fruit, brief but nicely flavoured with red plums & liquorice.
Sauvignon Blanc ⓦ ★★★★ Step-up **14** ebulliently aromatic & flavourful; grass, dust, khaki bush, lipsmacking acidity - the full sauvignon package! Also tasted: **Pinotage 12** ★★★ **Chenin Blanc-Viognier 14** ★★★

Imbuko range

Chenin Blanc (NEW) ★★ Newcomer **14** has guava & musk appeal, gentle sweetness for easy sipping. Also tasted: **Sauvignon Blanc 14** ★★ Not retasted: **Cabernet Sauvignon 12** ★★ Not tasted: **Iswithi Pinotage, Chardonnay**.

Pomüla

Moscato Spumante ⓦ ★★★ Exuberant grapey flavours laced with minuscule bubbles, low-alcohol **NV** perlé from muscadel to be served well chilled.

Shortwood range

Rosé ⓦ ★★ Spice & boiled sweets on leafy **12** pink sipper. Not retasted: **Red NV** ★★ Not tasted: **White**. — CvZ

Location: Wellington ▪ Map: Paarl & Wellington ▪ WO: Western Cape/Wellington/Coastal ▪ Est/1stB 2004 ▪ Tasting Mon-Fri 9-4 Sat by appt ▪ Fee R15/5 wines ▪ Closed all pub hols; Dec 25-Jan 1 ▪ Sales 8-5 ▪ Meals/refreshments by appt (48hr notice) ▪ Olives, olive oil, pinotage/merlot/shiraz jams, pinotage relish ▪ Owner(s) Imbuko Wines (Pty) Ltd ▪ Cellarmaster(s) Theunis van Zyl (2004) ▪ Viticulturist(s) Jan-Louw du Plessis ▪ 60ha (cab, cinsaut, merlot, ptage, shiraz, chenin, sauv, viog) ▪ 570t/120,000cs own label 60% red 40% white ▪ Other export brands: Makulu, Releaf Organic & Rebourne Fairtrade, Van Zijls Family Vintners ▪ Fairtrade, IPW, ISO, Organic ▪ PO Box 810 Wellington 7654 ▪ crm@imbuko.co.za ▪ www.imbuko.co.za ▪ S 33° 40' 30.84" E 019° 01' 18.87" ▪ F +27 (0)21-873-7351 ▪ **T +27 (0)21-873-7350**

☐ **Imoya** *see* KWV
☐ **Indaba** *see* Cape Classics
☐ **Ingenuity** *see* Nederburg Wines
☐ **Inglewood** *see* Neil Ellis Wines
☐ **Inkará** *see* Bon Courage Estate
☐ **Innings** *see* Rietvallei Wine Estate
☐ **Insignia Series** *see* Bellingham
☐ **Integer** *see* Hoopenburg Wines

Intellego Wines

Intellego ('Understand') brand owner Jurgen Gouws hopes consumers 'get' his handcrafted bottlings. Assistant at Lammershoek, where he makes his small runs, Jurgen's committed to the natural wine ideals of Swartland Independent, handcrafting 'real' wines true to their origins - and full of life.

★★★★☆ **Elementis Skin Contact** (NEW) From chenin, fermented 3 weeks on skins, 10 months old oak. Sauvignon-like dryness & acidity, lower alcohol (12.5%), but oh, **13**'s perfume & flavour! Peach & mango to start, evolving into a nutty, earthy, savoury beauty, svelte & pure. The name says it all.

★★★★ **Chenin Blanc** Melon, quince & lavender biscotti, **12** is wonderfully aromatic, different, the fruit & older oak combo well judged, allows both to shine. Round & ripe, finishes ultra-long. Could age 4+ years for those who can resist drinking it now. Takes perfumed **11** (★★★★) up a level.

Kolbroek (NEW) ★★★★ Shiraz, bunch-fermented, 15 months oak. **12** Morello cherries, sweet spice, nutmeg & cinnamon, elegant verging on austere (12.5% alcohol), with a firm tannin backbone. Serve with rich casseroles, creamy pastas. **Syrah** (NEW) ★★★★ Violets, cranberries & hedgerow fruit on a bed of grainy tannins, will meld, keep **13** in perfect conditions for ±5 years. — CR, CvZ

Location: Malmesbury • WO: Swartland • Est/1stB 2009 • Closed to public • Owner(s)/winemaker(s) Jurgen Gouws • 1,000cs own label 40% red 60% white • jurgen@intellegowines.co.za • **T +27 (0)82-392-3258**

Iona Vineyards

Co-owners of this high-lying Elgin family farm, Andrew and Rozy Gunn, are always on the lookout for varieties that might produce wine with a sense of place. A walking and tasting tour through Italy's Piedmont enthused them for nebbiolo; this to possibly replace a small block of under-performing shiraz, which will continue to be the main component of the One Man Band. At the other end of the business, the Gunns intend to upgrade their labels with improved paper and print colour; update the website with new images and information; and welcome smaller groups for a more personal experience at the Open Gardens weekends and special wine events.

Iona Vineyards range

★★★★☆ **Pinot Noir Limited Release 12** (★★★★) slightly riper, heavier feel than delicate, fresh **11**. Still agreeably silky, the gentle tannins framing flavoursome sweet dark cherries.

★★★★☆ **One Man Band 09** (★★★★) unusual mix shiraz, cab with petit verdot, merlot, mourvèdre & viognier. Aromatic generosity matched by fruit richness, grip. May gain greater interest with few more years. **08** seamless, polished.

★★★★☆ **Chardonnay** Elegance, composure & an intrigue of flavours mark **13** (★★★★★). Soft fleshed, with cool lemon blossom tones & citrus freshness all cushioned by enriching lees, this infant Elgin classic should give greater complexity by 2018-20. Superb successor to focused, intense **12**.

★★★★☆ **Sauvignon Blanc 13** follows **12**'s fruitier profile but here showing intense wild scrub, herbs, gooseberry aromas. Drop wooded semillon & time should alleviate more angular feel. Bone-dry.

Husk Spirit range 🆕

Corretto ★★★ From cab & merlot; light amber hue, playful label, fragrant black-fruit perfume; alcohol quite prominent - perhaps better to 'correct' your shot with an espresso. — WB, AL

Location/WO: Elgin • Map: Elgin, Walker Bay & Bot River • Est 1997 • 1stB 2001 • Tasting, sales & tours Mon-Fri 8–5 Sat by appt • Closed all pub hols • Walks/hikes • Mountain biking • Conservation area • Owner(s) Andrew & Rozanne Gunn, Workers Trust • Winemaker(s) Werner Muller (May 2011), with Thapelo Hlasa (Jun 1997) • Vineyard manager Joseph Sebulawa • 100ha/40ha (cab, merlot, mourv, p verdot, pinot, shiraz, chard, sauv) • 250t/24,000cs own label 25% red 75% white • BWI • PO Box 527 Grabouw 7160 • orders@iona.co.za • www.iona.co.za • S 34° 16' 42.2" E 019° 4' 58.2" • F +27 (0)28-284-9078 • **T +27 (0)28-284-9678**

☐ **Isis** *see* Schalkenbosch Wines
☐ **Island View** *see* Orange River Wine Cellars
☐ **iSPY** *see* Overhex Wines International
☐ **Ithemba** *see* Stellar Winery
☐ **Iwayini** *see* Maiden Wine Cellars
☐ **Ixia** *see* Distell

Izak van der Vyver Wines

Living among Elgin's cool vineyards, general practitioner Izak van der Vyver couldn't resist having a go at producing his own wine. In the cellar of his friend Paul Cluver, he has vinified two rows of sauvignon from a local farm since 2002. The new vintage not ready for tasting this edition.

Location: Elgin • 1stB 2002 • Closed to public • Owner(s) Izak van der Vyver • Cellarmaster(s) Andries Burger (Paul Cluver Wines) • Winemaker(s) Izak van der Vyver (Jan 2002) • 1.4t/±166cs own label • PO Box 42 Grabouw 7160 • drs@telkomsa.net • F +27 (0)21-859-3607 • **T +27 (0)21-859-2508**

☐ **Jabari** *see* Vin du Cap International

Jacaranda Wine & Guest Farm

Boutique guesthouse owners René and Birgit Reiser continue with the regeneration of their organically farmed vineyards and cellar, and expect the first crop from new plantings next year. Visitors to the Wellington farm can expect a personalised experience as the Reisers share their passion and love for good wine.

Cuvée Rouge ⊘ ★★★ Friendly red quaffer from Bordeaux varieties, **11** offers juicy black cherries & dark chocolate. Not retasted: **Pinotage Rosé 12** ★★★ Not tasted: **SMV, Chenin Blanc**. — CM

Location/WO: Wellington ▪ Map: Paarl & Wellington ▪ Est/1stB 2009 ▪ Tasting & sales Mon-Sat 10-5 ▪ Fee R20/4 wines, served with olives & bread ▪ Closed Easter Fri/Sun, Dec 25 & Jan 1 ▪ Mediterranean/cheese platters & picnic baskets by appt ▪ B&B: 2 cottage units ▪ Owner(s) René & Birgit Reiser ▪ Cellarmaster(s)/viticulturist(s) René Reiser (Jun 2009) ▪ Winemaker(s) René Reiser (Jun 2009) & Jean-Paul Schmitt (2013) ▪ 4.5ha/4ha (cab, merlot, shiraz, chenin, viog) ▪ 9t/1,500cs own label 50% red 40% white 10% rosé ▪ PO Box 121 Wellington 7654 ▪ jacarandawines@gmail.com ▪ www.jacarandawines.co.za ▪ S 33° 36' 49.2" E 019° 0' 16.1" ▪ **T +27 (0)21-864-1235**

☐ **Jacksons** *see* Stanford Hills Winery

Jacobsdal

Tradition is… the Dumas family's Stellenbosch wine estate. Fourth-generation Hannes is the winemaker with father Cornelis, incumbent since 1966. Their signature pinotage (introduced in 1974) and cabernet (2001) are from dryland bushvines vinified in tried-and-true open concrete tanks using only wild yeasts. Marketing is through Distell, a longstanding collaborator.

Cabernet Sauvignon ★★★ Naturally fermented **11** has subtle red fruit spiced with cedar from 40% new oak. **Pinotage** ⊘ ★★★ Savoury tone to the chocolaty red/dark fruit of **11**, tannins are well integrated & there's an interesting chicory note in the conclusion. — GM

Location/map/WO: Stellenbosch ▪ Est 1916 ▪ 1stB 1974 ▪ Tasting on the farm by appt only ▪ Tasting & sales also at Die Bergkelder (see entry) ▪ Owner(s) Dumas Ondernemings (Pty) Ltd ▪ Cellarmaster(s) Cornelis Dumas ▪ Winemaker(s)/viticulturist(s) Cornelis Dumas, with Hannes Dumas ▪ 100ha (cab, ptage, chenin, sauv) ▪ 600t/26,000cs own label 100% red ▪ PO Box 11 Kuils River 7579 ▪ info@jacobsdal.co.za ▪ www.jacobsdal.co.za ▪ S 33° 58' 4.9" E 018° 43' 34.6" ▪ F +27 (0)21-881-3337 ▪ **T +27 (0)21-881-3336**

☐ **Jacoline Haasbroek Wines** *see* My Wyn

Jacques Germanier

Previously 'African Terroir', the export-focused wine business based on Sonop farm near Paarl now has the name of its Swiss owner, Jacques Germanier. With the name change, and new leadership (daughter Sophie comes in as executive director), the business model has also been updated and now no bottled stock is held onsite – filling is done only on order and for export, and the only local wine sales are at cellardoor, open strictly by appointment. Unchanged is a commitment to sustainable farming and community upliftment.

Location: Paarl ▪ Map: Paarl & Wellington ▪ Est/1stB 1991 ▪ Tasting, sales & cellar tours Mon-Fri 8.30-4 strictly by appt ▪ Closed all pub hols ▪ Conferences ▪ Functions ▪ Conservation area ▪ Owner(s) Jacques Germanier ▪ Winemaker(s) Jaco Marais (Nov 2012), with Marco Swartz (Feb 2009) ▪ Viticulturist(s) Johan Barnard (Nov 2009) ▪ 75ha (cab, merlot, ptage, shiraz, chard, cbard, sauv, viog) ▪ 540t ▪ Brands for clients: Azania, Mwitu, Out of Africa, Sonop Organic, The Big 5, Tribal, Winds of Change ▪ ISO 22000, BWI, Fairtrade, FOA, HACCP, IPW, Organic ▪ PO Box 2029 Windmeul Paarl 7630 ▪ info@germanier.co.za ▪ www.african-terroir.co.za ▪ S 33° 37' 1.8" E 018° 50' 38.4" ▪ F +27 (0)21-869-8104 ▪ **T +27 (0)21-869-8103**

Jacques Smit Wines

Vine nurseryman Jacques Smit, who counts Calitzdorp 'port' champion Boets Nel among his longtime clients and former classmates (and mentors when it comes to Jacques' artisan winemaking), provides an interesting stop on the popular Wellington Wine Walk, where visitors tarry for a tasting under shady oaks in wife Marina's garden.

Limited Releases
Cape Ruby Roobernet Port ★★★★ Exuberantly fruity **07** given ageability by firm tannins. Also in 375 ml. Not retasted: **Cabernet Sauvignon 07** ★★★★ **Shiraz 05** ★★★★ **Vine Valley 06** ★★★★ Not tasted: **Chenin Blanc**. — MW

Location/WO: Wellington ▪ Map: Paarl & Wellington ▪ Est/1stB 2003 ▪ Tasting, sales & tours by appt ▪ Closed Easter Fri/Sun/Mon, Ascension Day, Dec 25/26 & Jan 1 ▪ Facilities for children ▪ Owner(s) Jacques & Marina Smit ▪ Cellarmaster(s)/winemaker(s)/viticulturist(s) Jacques Smit ▪ 60ha/32ha (cab, roobernet, shiraz, chenin, Cape riesling) ▪ 300t total 100% red ▪ Welvanpas PO Box 137 Wellington 7654 ▪ info@vines2wine.com ▪ www.vines2wine.com ▪ S 33° 39' 2.2" E 019° 1' 9.0" ▪ F +27 (0)21-873-2143 ▪ **T +27 (0)21-873-1265**

Jakkalsvlei Private Cellar

Named for the many foxes, jackal and wild cats in the mountains above the farm, Jakkalsvlei near Herbertsdale has been in Jonker family hands for decades. Making bulk wines is also well established but boutique vinification, by Jantjie Jonker, is more recent. Watch for his wines at shops on the Garden Route or 'come and explore this unique wine farm', now with a much enlarged visitor venue.

Jakkalsvlei Private Cellar range (NEW)
Pinotage Coffee Edition ★★★ Blueberry flavours, lush & ripe, the off-dry styling giving **13** friendly appeal. **Sauvignon Blanc** ★★★ Bone-dry, some leafy & fresh apple whiffs, but **14** essentially a mineral style, zesty & long. **Hanepoot** ★★★★ Sultanas & wild honey, mouthcoatingly rich & full bodied; the flavours in this **NV** go on & on. Either enjoy on its own after a meal or serve with strong cheese. Also tasted: **Cabernet Sauvignon Reserve 12** ★★★ **Mount Cuvée Pinotage-Merlot 13** ★★★ **La Perlé Rosé NV** ★★ **River Cuvée Chenin Blanc-Sauvignon Blanc 14** ★★★ **Red Muscadel NV** ★★★ — CR, CvZ

Location: Herbertsdale ▪ Map: Klein Karoo & Garden Route ▪ WO: Western Cape ▪ Est 1987 ▪ 1stB 2008 ▪ Tasting & sales Mon-Fri 9.30-5 Sat 9.30-3 ▪ Closed Sun ▪ Cheese platters ▪ Deli ▪ BYO picnic ▪ Walks/hikes ▪ Mountain biking ▪ Owner(s)/cellarmaster(s)/viticulturist(s) JG Jonker ▪ 80ha/26ha (cab, merlot, muscadel r, ptage, chenin, hanepoot, sauv) ▪ 350t/12,000cs own label 40% red 20% white 20% rosé 20% dessert + 150,000L bulk ▪ PO Box 79 Herbertsdale 6505 ▪ info@jakkalsvlei.co.za ▪ www.jakkalsvlei.co.za ▪ S 33° 59' 15.31" E 021° 43' 9.33" ▪ F +27 (0)86-593-0123 ▪ **T +27 (0)28-735-2061**

Jakob's Vineyards

André and Yvonne de Lange - he an attorney, she a scientist, then living in Johannesburg - bought this tiny farm in 2002 and now have a hectare of – unusually for Hemel-en-Aarde – cabernet. In line with a philosophy of 'simplicity and striving for excellence', they've culled their Bordeaux blend to focus on a varietal cab, vinified by new winemaker Peter-Allan Finlayson (Crystallum/Gabriëlskloof).

★★★★ **Cabernet Sauvignon** First since **06**, beautifully crafted **11** displays lively red berry aromas & earthy tone, reflecting 100% whole-berry natural ferment. Well-judged 30% new oak frames a very friendly, juicy palate with lowish acidity, giving a broad mouthfeel. — JPf

Location: Hermanus ▪ Map: Elgin, Walker Bay & Bot River ▪ WO: Hemel-en-Aarde Ridge ▪ Est 2002 ▪ 1stB 2006 ▪ Tasting by appt ▪ Owner(s) André & Yvonne de Lange ▪ Winemaker(s) Peter-Allan Finlayson (2010, consultant) ▪ Viticulturist(s) Johan Pienaar (Jun 2003, consultant) ▪ 5ha/1ha (cab) ▪ 5t/±500cs own label 100% red ▪ PO Box 15885 Vlaeberg 8018 ▪ wine@jakobsvineyards.co.za ▪ www.jakobsvineyards.co.za ▪ F +27 (0)86-589-4619 ▪ **T +27 (0)82-371-5686**

☐ **Jam Jar** see Cape Classics
☐ **Jardin** see Jordan Wine Estate

Jason's Hill Private Cellar

Internationally experienced, award-winning winemaker Ivy du Toit put her family's 19th-century farm (named after an old farmhand) on the wine map by establishing an own label in 2001. Now husband Alister Oates tends the Slanghoek Valley vineyards, and the modern visitor venue hosts various family-friendly activities and events.

Location: Rawsonville ▪ Map: Breedekloof ▪ Est/1stB 2001 ▪ Tasting & sales Mon-Fri 8–5 Sat 10-3 ▪ Closed Easter Fri-Sun, Dec 25 & Jan 1 ▪ Cellar tours by appt ▪ Bistro Mon-Sat 10–3 (also available for functions) ▪ Shop ▪ Facilities for children ▪ Spa ▪ Weddings/functions ▪ 6.5km hiking trail ▪ Owner(s) Du Toit family ▪ Cellarmaster(s) Ivy du Toit (Jan 2001) ▪ Viticulturist(s) Alister Oates (Jan 2004) ▪ 100ha ▪ 45% red 50% white 5% rosé ▪ PO Box 14 Rawsonville 6845 ▪ info@jasonshill.co.za, ivy@jasonshill.co.za ▪ www.jasonshill.com ▪ S 33° 39' 52.3" E 019° 13' 40.6" ▪ F +27 (0)86-523-6655 ▪ **T +27 (0)23-344-3256**

Jasper Raats Signature Wines

Jasper Raats, who earned a reputation for producing sauvignon blanc and pinot noir at New Zealand's Koru and Clos Henri, here vinifies a tiny sauvignon block on Driefontein in the Helderberg and pinot noir in Elgin. The wines are available at Longridge, where Jasper is cellarmaster. Note: entry last listed as 'Driefontein'.

Driefontein range

★★★★ **Sauvignon Blanc** Expressive **13**, ripe tropical fruit & crushed stone aromas, natural ferment results in full, round yet refreshing palate with moderate acidity & friendly 13% alcohol. Ex single site in Stellenbosch, like **12** (★★★★).

Cuvée range

★★★★ **Pinot Noir** Vibrant, naturally fermented **12**, ripe raspberry, cherry & spice; fine, slightly warm palate reflects creamy raspberry, floral notes & modest oak influence - only 5 months, older barrels, as for **11** (★★★★), allowing Elgin terroir to shine. — JPf

Location: Stellenbosch ▪ Map: Helderberg ▪ WO: Elgin/Stellenbosch ▪ Est 2010 ▪ 1stB 2011 ▪ Tasting & sales by appt only ▪ Closed Easter weekend & Dec 25 ▪ Owner(s) Vigneron Consulting Ltd ▪ Winemaker(s)/viticulturist(s) Jasper Raats (2010) ▪ 2ha (pinot, sauv) ▪ 10t/600cs own label 70% red 30% white ▪ jasper@longridge.co.za ▪ S 34° 0' 55.2" E 018° 49' 60.0" ▪ F +27 (0)21-855-4083 ▪ **T +27 (0)76-752-5270**

☐ **JC Kannemeyer** see Wolfkloof
☐ **JC le Roux** see House of JC le Roux
☐ **JD Initial Series** see Jean Daneel Wines

Jean Daneel Wines

Veteran winemaker Jean Daneel had award-winning stints at top cellars Buitenverwachting and Morgenhof but always wanted to do his own thing. After a few itinerant years he and food-and-deco-passionate wife René found their niche in southern Cape hamlet Napier, turning it into a must-stop restaurant and larder destination for fresh bread, a meal or even a chandelier! Their small home-vineyard is in production, and son Jean-Pierre has his hand on the winemaking tiller. He's proud that the JD Initial Series, repackaged and with new blend components, is now made entirely from Napier fruit. The Signature range sauvignon promised last edition, also from local grapes, has materialised – and what a stunner it is!

Signature Series

★★★★☆ **Red** Vividly vibrant, deeply coloured, complex **11** blend shiraz, merlot, cab. Gentle grip & spiciness, well-absorbed oak tannins from lengthy (38 months) barrel maturation. No **10**. WO W Cape, like White.

★★★★★ **Chenin Blanc** Limpid, pale gold **13** (★★★★☆) a smart, rich rendition of Jean Daneel's favourite variety. A year in oak, some new, delivers structure, breadth to layered apple, citrus fruit, while chenin's wonderful natural acidity imparts vibrantly fresh finish, as on **12**.

★★★★☆ **Sauvignon Blanc** (NEW) Thrilling maiden **13** from Napier grapes complements this classy range. Refined & complex, makes a statement with lean minerality & super-long racy finish. Winemaker remarks: 'Brand new wine, here to stay.' You betcha!

Not tasted: **Directors Signature Red**, **Directors Signature Chenin Blanc**.

JD Initial Series

Red ★★★☆ Spicy, lightly elegant shiraz-led **13** blend with merlot, dash pinot, seasoned in older oak, with marked bright acidity. **White** ★★★★ Ultra-fresh, focused, mineral **13** blend has sauvignon's zippiness & chenin's fruit weight.

Le Grand Jardin

Not tasted: **Red**, **Chenin Blanc**, **White**. — IM

Location: Napier ▪ Map: Southern Cape ▪ WO: Napier/Western Cape ▪ Est/1stB 1997 ▪ Tasting, sales & cellar tours by appt ▪ Closed Dec 25 & Jan 1 ▪ Restaurant & deli ▪ Owner(s) Jean & René Daneel ▪ Winemaker(s) Jean-Pierre Daneel ▪ 50t 40% red 60% white ▪ PO Box 200 Napier 7270 ▪ info@jdwines.co.za ▪ www.jdwines.co.za ▪ S 34° 28'38.11"E 019° 54'15.47" ▪ F +27 (0)28-423-3197 ▪ **T +27 (0)28-423-3724**

☐ **Jemma** *see* Painted Wolf Wines

Jeu

Nadia Barnard, cellarmaster at Waterkloof, decided the first wine under her own label should be a port to honour her gran, who taught her to love fortifieds. Friend Margaux Nel of Boplaas also offered inspiration, and grapes were sourced from a scion of another famous port family, Albert Bredell.

Jeu (☑) ★★★ Port-style from tinta, **10** delicious but not usual Ruby affability: chunky mouthful, lots of extracted flavours, very low sugar. Mid-2013 needed time to soften & unfurl. — WB, IM

Location/WO: Stellenbosch ▪ Est/1stB 2010 ▪ Closed to public ▪ Owner(s)/winemaker(s) Nadia Barnard ▪ jeuwines@gmail.com ▪ **T +27 (0)83-324-8466**

JH Meyer Signature Wines

Rising star Johan Meyer's day job is vinifying for others, but a love for Burgundy varieties chardonnay and pinot noir compelled him to make his own wine. Production again leapt since last edition (to all of 8 tons!), and the single-vineyard range mentioned previously is well in hand, its aim to focus on pinot noir in different Cape terroirs 'stretching as far as George on the Garden Route!'

★★★★ **Pinot Noir** **13** has a lightness to it, as did **12** (★★★★), but also a perfumed & gentle, clean, sweetly fruity plenitude. Fine acidity & modest but influential tannins. Partly whole-bunch fermented.

★★★★ **Chardonnay** Quiet, subtly complex & interesting character, with a fairly oxidative approach to winemaking evident in **13**. Harmoniously balanced, with enlivening lemony acidity. As for Pinot, no new oak used. — TJ

Location: Riebeek-Kasteel ▪ WO: Elgin ▪ Est/1stB 2011 ▪ Private tastings on request ▪ Owner(s) Johan Meyer ▪ Cellarmaster(s)/winemaker(s)/viticulturist(s) Johan Meyer (2011) ▪ 8t total ▪ own label 50% red 50% white ▪ PO Box 396 Riebeek-Kasteel 7307 ▪ jhmeyerwines@gmail.com ▪ www.jhmeyerwines.co.za ▪ **T +27 (0)79-280-0237**

☐ **JJ Handmade Wines** *see* Stellenrust
☐ **Johan de Wet Wines** *see* Lorraine Private Cellar
☐ **John B** *see* Rietvallei Wine Estate
☐ **Jonkheer** *see* Vinopoly Wines

Joostenberg Wines

The younger, 5th-generation Myburghs continue to run the Joostenberg farm between Stellenbosch and Paarl, in the family since 1877. They have expanded the enterprise beyond their small-scale winery and mainly organically grown vineyards, to include a new winetasting centre, some luxury accommodation and 'pop-up' concerts and events. They also have a longer-established and popular bistro and deli conveniently located on the nearby Klein Joostenberg property off the R304.

Premium range

★★★★ **Syrah** Sumptuously rich **12** first since **10**. (No **11**.) Densely packed, spicy dark fruit & chocolate in firm but supple tannic embrace. Bright acidity & peppery grip ensure liveliness. Powerful, will reward cellaring.

★★★★ **Fairhead** Chenin-led blend with viognier & roussanne, retains refined freshness of **10** but has less fruit depth in **11** (★★★★), with a gentle aromatic citrus tone.

★★★★ **Family Blend White** Now-bottled **13** (★★★★) understated, smooth blend of chenin & viognier showing genteel perfumed creaminess - good for fusion/spicy food partnering - but missing some of the complexity & vitality of previewed **12**.

★★★★☆ **Chenin Blanc Noble Late Harvest** **13** (★★★★) unctuously rich dessert wine from low-yield chenin vines. Concentrated glacé pineapple, marzipan & cumin infused in very viscous texture. Decadent, but shade off elegant balance of **12**.

Also tasted: **Bakermat 11** ★★★★ Not retasted: **Family Blend Red 12** ★★★★☆ **Family Blend Rosé 13** ★★★☆ Note: range was 'Joostenberg'.

Little J range

Not tasted: **Shiraz**, **Chenin Blanc**. Discontinued: **Rosé**. — MW

Location/WO: Paarl • Map: Paarl & Wellington • Est/1stB 1999 • Tasting & cellar tours by appt at the winery • Sales daily 10–5 at the Deli on Klein Joostenberg Farm • Closed Dec 25 & Jan 1 • Joostenberg Bistro • Facilities for children • Tour groups • Gifts • Farm produce • Honey shop • Conferences • Ludwigs rose nursery & Van den Berg garden centre • Guest accommodation (3 double rooms), contact anette@joostenberg.co.za • Owner(s) Philip & Tyrrel Myburgh • Cellarmaster(s)/viticulturist(s) Tyrrel Myburgh (1999) • Winemaker(s) MC Stander (2012) • 31ha (cab, merlot, mourv, shiraz, touriga nacional, chenin, rouss, viog) • 120t/16,000cs own label 35% red 50% white 15% NLH • PO Box 82 Elsenburg 7607 • winery@joostenberg.co.za • www.joostenberg.co.za • S 33° 48' 47.21" E 018° 48' 31.70 (cellar), S 33° 49' 34.8" E 018° 47' 45.5" (deli) • **T +27 (0)21-200-9903 (winery)/+27 (0)21-884-4141 (bistro/deli)**

Jordan Wine Estate

Co-owned and run by husband and wife winemaking team Gary and Kathy Jordan, this estate reflects their history, personal philosophy and business acumen (Kathy a trained economist). All the grapes grown here are used for their own wines, resulting in various blends, varieties and terroir-specific wines in the three ranges. There are branding references to the family's previous footwear business, and some wine names reflect Gary's geology training and ongoing interest. Their love affair with food led to the establishment of three restaurants, Michelin-listed High Timber in London, with an extensive SA winelist, and two on the Stellenbosch estate, of which the newest, The Bakery, offers a more casual food alternative to chef George Jardine's haute cuisine. Nor are conservation, the well-being of their workers or mentorship neglected - this entrepreneurial couple keeps a keen eye on the sustainability of their future.

Jordan Estate range

★★★★ **Cabernet Sauvignon** Enchantingly spicy take on classic blackcurrant & liquorice cornerstones give classy **11** (★★★★★) the edge over silky, 'feminine' **10**. Supple & elegant, vibrantly youthful, but promising cellar potential.

★★★★ **Merlot** Leafy notes prevail in **12** tank sample, masking sumptuous black fruit core. Unknit, with wild oak spiciness, yet still showing promise, intensity & smooth tannins.

For more information, visit wineonaplatter.com

★★★★ **The Prospector Syrah** Intensely meaty, tobacco notes laced into plum pudding fruit, **12** struts its big-bodied stuff. Upstages last **10** (★★★☆). **11** sold out untasted.

★★★★☆ **Cobblers Hill** Classically statuesque barrel-selected, cab-led Bordeaux-style blend, **11** maintains stellar standard, with dense, brooding blackcurrant fruit, liquorice & intriguing herbaceous overtones. Supple & smooth, yet robustly textured, lingering finish.

★★★★☆ **CWG Auction Reserve Sophia** Barrel-selection cab-led Bordeaux blend for CWG Auction, **11** upstages even its aristocratic siblings; bigger, bolder, yet controlled & measured, with lithe tannins & intense aromas. Already irresistible, but should be laid down to develop.

★★★★ **Chardonnay Barrel Fermented** Oak dominates nose of **13** mid-2014, with glimpses of citrus peel. Big & showy, lees richness cosseting ripe, generous fruit. Pedigree shows good ageing potential.

★★★★☆ **CWG Auction Reserve Chardonnay** Grape selection from Nine Yards vineyard, **13** shares admirable characteristics but offers even more depth & complexity. Fruit easily dominates oak, producing matchless balance & sophistication.

★★★★☆ **Nine Yards Chardonnay** Statuesque **13** flagship label takes hefty oak regime (92% new barrels) in its stride. Opulent, mellow fruit layers meld elegantly with spicy oak notes. Big but supple body offers plush mouthfeel & lingering finish.

★★★★ **Chenin Blanc Barrel Fermented** Full, rich, ripe & generous, delicately oaked **13** shows chenin's best side. Fruit driven, with creamy lees undercarriage & charming baked apple finish.

★★★★ **The Real McCoy Riesling** Aromatic tropical fruit with orange zest, spicy edges & crisp acid combine elegantly in appealing off-dry **14**. WO W Cape. Follows perfumed **12** (★★★). **13** sold out untasted.

★★★★ **The Outlier Sauvignon Blanc** Oaked portion (60%) of **13** lends breadth & texture to palate, but also mutes fruit somewhat. Well-judged blending produces Bordeaux-like minerality & body.

★★★★ **Sauvignon Blanc 14** shows generous ripeness, purity & focus, with vibrant crispness underpinning sweet passionfruit. Good intensity & length, showing varietal's most appealing characteristics.

★★★★☆ **Mellifera** Natural Sweet from raisined riesling, **13** is unctuously honeyed (named after the Cape honey bee), with delightful spiciness & floral scents. Retains best of the varietal character with commendable finesse & elegance.

Not retasted: **Unoaked Chardonnay 13** ★★★

Bradgate range

Chenin Blanc ⓃⒺⓌ ★★★ Up-front **13** is fruity-fresh, with pineapple & peach, & dash sauvignon adding spice. Crisp, uncomplicated pleasure. WO W Cape. Also tasted: **Syrah 13** ★★★☆ **Cabernet Sauvignon-Merlot 12** ★★★☆ Discontinued: **Sauvignon Blanc-Chenin Blanc**.

Chameleon range

Cabernet Sauvignon-Merlot ★★★☆ Honest blackcurrant fruit, soft tannins, lightish body. **12** appealing lower-tier red. Also tasted: **Merlot No Added Sulphur 13** ★★★ **Rosé 13** ★★★ **Sauvignon Blanc-Chardonnay 14** ★★★ — GdB

Location/map: Stellenbosch ▪ WO: Stellenbosch/Western Cape ▪ Est 1982 ▪ 1stB 1993 ▪ Tasting & sales daily 9.30–4. 30 ▪ Tasting fee R40pp, waived on purchase ▪ Cellar tours by appt Mon-Fri 9.30-4.30 ▪ Pre-booking required for: tasting & cellar tour R75pp; speciality tasting & cellar tours from R100pp; exclusive vineyard & cellar experience tours from R350pp ▪ Jordan Restaurant ▪ Jordan Bakery ▪ Conferences (60 pax) ▪ Walks/hikes ▪ Mountain biking ▪ Conservation area ▪ Visits to old prospector's mine shafts ▪ Fly fishing (catch & release) R100/adult & R50/child under 12, booking essential ▪ Owner(s) Jordan family ▪ Cellarmaster(s) Gary & Kathy Jordan (1993) ▪ Winemaker(s) Sjaak Nelson (Jan 2002) ▪ Viticulturist(s) Gary Jordan (1983) ▪ 160ha/105ha (cab, merlot, syrah, chard, chenin, riesling, sauv) ▪ 850t/100,000cs own label 45% red 54% white 1% rosé ▪ Other export brand: Jardin ▪ Brands for clients: Pick's Pick, Woolworths ▪ BWI ▪ PO Box 12592 Die Boord Stellenbosch 7613 ▪ info@jordanwines.com ▪ www.jordanwines.com ▪ S 33° 56' 33.7" E 018° 44' 41.3" ▪ F +27 (0)21-881-3426 ▪ **T +27 (0)21-881-3441**

☐ **Joseph Barry** *see* Barrydale Winery & Distillery

Joubert-Tradauw Wingerde & Kelder

It was prescient of Schalk-Willem Joubert to leave Wellington to farm in the beautiful if remote Tradouw Valley some 6 decades ago. Grandson and current co-owner, Meyer, talks of its 'incredible' Karoo shale soils and unique micro-climate, with cool evening breezes blowing up from the sea through Tradouw Pass, 'conditions which make our wines distinctive, and suit chardonnay and shiraz in particular'.

★★★★ **Syrah** ⓥ Revisited as bottled wine, smoky & savoury **11** (★★★☆) has carefully crafted tannin structure to restrain opulent fruit, fine varietal black pepper & lily aromas. Follows **08** (no **09**, **10**).

★★★★ **Chardonnay Barrel Fermented** ⓥ Elegant & balanced **12**, oak nicely integrated with green apple flavour, some almond complexity, chalky dry finish. Better managed than **11** (★★★).

R62 ★★★ Cabernet in lean, medium-bodied mode. Simple fruit, bolder dry tannins on revisited **10**. — AL

Location: Barrydale ▪ Map: Klein Karoo & Garden Route ▪ WO: Tradouw ▪ Est/1stB 1999 ▪ Tasting, sales & cellar tours Mon-Fri 9–5 Sat 10–2 ▪ Closed Easter Fri/Sun & Dec 25 ▪ R62 Deli Mon-Fri 9-3 Sat 10-1 breakfasts, lunches & Klein Karoo tapas ▪ Walks/hikes ▪ Mountain biking ▪ Conservation area ▪ Lentelus B&B (www.lentelus.co.za) ▪ Owner(s) Lentelus Family Trust ▪ Cellarmaster(s)/winemaker(s)/viticulturist(s) Meyer Joubert (1999) ▪ 1,100ha/30ha (cab, merlot, shiraz, chard) ▪ 5,000cs own label 70% red 30% white ▪ PO Box 15 Barrydale 6750 ▪ info@joubert-tradauw.co.za ▪ www.joubert-tradauw.com ▪ S 33° 55' 26.4" E 020° 35' 40.6" ▪ F +27 (0)86-555-3558 ▪ **T +27 (0)28-572-1619**

Journey's End Vineyards

Perched on prime Schapenberg overlooking False Bay, Englishman Rollo Gabb's family vineyards previously supplied the eponymous range for SA's international bestselling Kumala brand. Since 2008, Gabb family ownership of the label, and the acquisition of nearby Mount Rozier, have generated promising new varietal plantings (most recently malbec and petit verdot) to benefit both labels. The replica trebuchet (a medieval catapult) built by Rollo and a friend has arrived from the UK, to be used for 'barrel chucking' events to raise funds for the local community.

Reserve range
★★★★ **Griffin Shiraz** (NEW) **12** more elegant than powerful JE stablemate. Svelte, understated style shows perfumed red fruit & freshness with subtle oaking & structure. Good potential to develop.

★★★★☆ **Cape Doctor Cabernet Sauvignon-Merlot-Malbec-Cabernet Franc 09** Bordeaux blend returns to form after all-cab **08** (★★★★). Rich melange of dark berries, mint & cedar in svelte, streamlined structure. Deftly oaked, showcases ample fruit. New World style with development potential for 4-6 years, but already tempting.

★★★★ **Destination Chardonnay 12** richer & more flamboyant than JE counterpart. All-new oak & 80% malolactic fermentation expressed in plump, creamy texture infused with citrus. Bold, deserves cellaring.

Journey's End range
★★★★ **Cabernet Sauvignon** Elegantly poised **09** returns to form in classic vintage, after lesser **08** (★★★★). Good core of cassis, mint & cedar in firm, supple structure with long, clean & dry finish.

★★★★ **Shiraz** Step up from **08** (★★★☆) for richly textured **09**. Subtle oak underpins luscious berry fruit. Mouthfilling, savoury & juicy with good length. Enticing, but deserves 3-5 years cellaring.

★★★★ **Chardonnay 13** (★★★★☆) is restrained yet intense, with zesty lime & lemongrass tone & clean-cut acidity, all underscored by oatmeal richness. Oaking & malolactic fermentation more subtle than in Destination version, focuses fruit purity & raises bar on **12**.

Also tasted: **Merlot 11** ★★★★

Cellar range

The Huntsman Shiraz-Mourvèdre ★★★ Spicy & savoury **11** 70/30 blend. Balanced & fla-voursome, with smooth tannins. Exudes warm-hearted drinkability. **Weather Station Sauvignon Blanc** ★★★☆ **14** medley of grassy, herbaceous & riper stonefruit. Balanced racy style with good mid-palate weight, long finish. Nudges next rung up. Also tasted: **The Pastor's Blend** ⊘ **11** ★★★☆ **Haystack Chardonnay 13** ★★★☆ — MW

Location: Sir Lowry's Pass ▪ Map: Helderberg ▪ WO: Stellenbosch ▪ Est 1995 ▪ 1stB 2001 ▪ Tasting, sales & cellar tours Mon-Fri 9-5 by appt ▪ Fee R50pp (incl cellar tour) ▪ Closed Easter Fri-Mon, Dec 25 & Jan 1 ▪ Cheese platters & snacks by appt; or BYO picnic ▪ Conferences (20 pax) ▪ Walks/hikes ▪ Horse riding ▪ Mountain biking ▪ Conservation area ▪ Owner(s) Gabb family ▪ Cellarmaster(s)/winemaker(s) Leon Esterhuizen (Jun 2006) ▪ Viticulturist(s) Lodewyk Retief (Jun 2011) ▪ 50ha/30ha (cabs s/f, merlot, mourv, shiraz, chard, sauv, sem, viog) ▪ 200t/30,000cs own label 70% red 30% white ▪ BWI, HACCP, IPW, WIETA ▪ PO Box 3040 Somerset West 7129 ▪ info@journeysend.co.za ▪ www.journeysend.co.za ▪ S 34° 6' 35.11" E 018° 54' 54.06" ▪ F +27 (0)86-540-1929 ▪ **T +27 (0)21-858-1929**

JP Bredell Wines ⓠ

In the Helderberg's lower foothills, the Bredell family's once-extensive vineyards produced fruit for KWV's premium labels from the 1960s. Fifth-generation grower Anton subsequently established Bredell's as one of South Africa's acclaimed 'port' brands during the 1990s. Following the subsequent sale of the farm, releases have been sporadic yet invariably worthwhile.

Bredell's range

★★★★ **De Rigueur** ⓠ **08** cab-led blend tasted a few years back.

★★★★ **Late Bottled Vintage** ⓠ **04** port-style from tinta, souzão, touriga last was still seductive.

★★★★★ **Cape Vintage Reserve** ⓠ Last-tasted port-style **07** usual splendid blend tinta, touriga, souzão. Intriguing & complex; fiery in richly fruity-spicy & balanced style. — JP

Location: Somerset West ▪ Map: Helderberg ▪ 1stB 1991 ▪ Tasting & sales by appt ▪ Owner(s) Helderzicht Trust ▪ Cellarmaster(s)/viticulturist(s) Anton Bredell ▪ Winemaker(s) Denzil Tromp ▪ 50ha/13ha (cab, merlot, ptage, pinot) ▪ 10,000cs own label 60% red 40% port ▪ PO Box 5266 Helderberg 7135 ▪ info@bredellwines.co.za ▪ www.bredellwines.co.za ▪ S 34° 1' 29.04" E 018° 46' 18.72" ▪ **T +27 (0)82-783-4413**

☐ **JP le Hanie Wines** *see* Vredevol Private Wine Cellar

Julien Schaal ⓠ

Alsace-based Julien Schaal wanted to make wine in South Africa since his first visit as a cellarhand in 2002. His dream was realised in 2004. He now vinifies at Paul Cluver in Elgin and visits five times a year. As with his French wines, Julien aims to reflect origin: 'Altitude and cool nights are key factors in achieving full ripeness without losing acidity in my Elgin Chardonnay, while Hemel-en-Aarde's red clay soil and sea breezes off Walker Bay are major influences on my Syrah.'

Mountain Vineyards range

★★★★☆ **Syrah 13** lovely model of cool-climate shiraz, showing intensity with restraint in its pure, dominant white spice with cured meat & red fruit. Already delicious, thanks to usual gentle handling & oaking, but few years ageing will ensure greater pleasure. Flies with KLM Business Class, like Chardonnay.

★★★★☆ **Chardonnay** Forward ripe lime aromas given free rein by limiting barrelled portion to 50% in **13** (only 20% new wood). On palate, more complex oatmeal, lees- and oak-enriched flavours focused by refreshing acid. Needs time to harmonise, like most vintages. Elgin WO. — AL

Location: Elgin ▪ WO: Hemel-en-Aarde Valley/Elgin ▪ Est 2004 ▪ 1stB 2005 ▪ Sales from Paul Cluver Estate ▪ Tasting by appt only ▪ Owner(s)/winemaker(s) Julien Schaal ▪ 28t/4,000cs own label 15% red 85% white ▪ c/o PO Box 48 Grabouw 7160 ▪ julien@vins-schaal.com ▪ www.vins-schaal.com ▪ **T +33 (0)6-10-89-72-14**

☐ **Juliet Méthode Cap Classique** *see* Tanja Beutler Wine Collection

Juno Wine Company

Named for a Roman goddess, 'fun and funky' Paarl-based Juno celebrates women everywhere through its label designs by artist Tertia du Toit. Under winemaker Erlank Erasmus, the Fairtrade-accredited brand is steadily increasing its footprint in the international market.

Shiraz ★★☆ Very soft & juicy **12**, with easy, slightly boneless black berried fruit. **Sauvignon Blanc ★★★** Accessible & friendly **14** offers tropical fruit in just-dry quaffer. Not retasted: **Shiraz-Mourvèdre-Viognier 12 ★★★** Not tasted: **Cabernet Sauvignon**. — CM

Location: Paarl ▪ Map: Paarl & Wellington ▪ WO: Western Cape ▪ Est 2004 ▪ Tasting & sales at 191 Main Rd Paarl Mon-Sat 9.30–6.30 ▪ Open most pub hols ▪ Juno Bistro & Bakery ▪ Winemaker(s) Erlank Erasmus ▪ 60% red 40% white ▪ PO Box 68 Main Road Paarl 7622 ▪ winery@junowines.com ▪ www.junowines.com ▪ S 33° 44' 36.9" E 018° 57' 46.1" ▪ T +27 (0)21-872-0697

☐ **Kaap Agri** see Breëland Winery
☐ **Kaapdal** see Robertson Wide River Export Company

Kaapzicht Wine Estate

From the Bottelary Hills is the wonderful view over Cape Town and its mountain that gives Kaapzicht its name. The large estate itself (only a third of the harvest is bottled here, the rest sold off) is a real family one, and has been so since the Steytlers arrived in 1946. Brothers Danie and George own it and have overall responsibility for, respectively, the cellar and the vines. Wives Yngvild and Mandy take care of export markets and look after the entertainment and guest venues. Danie jnr has been winemaker since 2009 (and wife Carin handles national sales). The 1947 Chenin Blanc and an untasted Riesling were introduced last year to mark 30 years of bottling under the Kaapzicht label.

Steytler range

★★★★☆ Pinotage ⓐ Massive, somewhat rustic **10**, with huge 100% new French oak, 2 years dominating finely managed fruit. In youth still with arresting tannins, though spice & brooding intensity emerging. No **09**.

★★★★☆ Pentagon ⓐ Sinewy **10** cab-based blend with merlot & malbec. Restrained, despite overt oak. Cassis notes predominate, though faint tobacco whiffs hint at forthcoming complexity. Good integration of components & the sweet fruit lift it above chunkier 08 (★★★★). No **09**.

★★★★☆ Vision ⓐ Mammoth & multi-layered **10** from cab with 37% pinotage, 10% merlot. Finely honed sweet fruit seamlessly dovetailed with vanilla-toned French oak (all new, 2 years). Polish is evident despite youthful exuberance, but fruit nuance still some way off - needs time. No **09**.

★★★★☆ CWG Auction Reserve Cape Blend ⓐ Robust & unashamedly brash **10** - similar blend, vinification to Vision. Chunky oak still sitting firmly on bright plum, raspberry fruit. Less plush than **09** though promising similar harmony, vinosity & integration.

Kaapzicht range

★★★★ Cabernet Sauvignon ⓐ Treacly & dense **10** with sweet blackcurrant spice. Brooding tarry notes, a bit chunky & youthfully gawky but purer, more harmonious than last-made 08 (★★★★).

★★★★ Merlot ⓐ Savoury & herbal, with earthy mulberry & tobacco aromas dominating **10** (★★★★), slighter than 08 but bulked-up by oak & dry tannin. No **09**.

★★★★ Pinotage ⓐ Supple 10 (★★★★★) with sensitive oaking allowing restrained strawberry fruit to show. Plusher & better integrated than **09**. Surprisingly forward & accessible but not dumbed-down.

★★★★ Estate Red ⓥ Creative blend, shiraz & cab, dab petit verdot, pinotage. **11** deep pruney fruit loaded with savoury spice, succulent underpin to supple tannins. Delicious, improves on **10** (★★★★).

 For more information, visit wineonaplatter.com

★★★★★ **The 1947 Chenin Blanc** Date estate's bushvines planted, SA's 2nd oldest chenin block. **13** bunch-pressed, natural barrel ferment, matured year, 50% new. Melon & kumquat preserve, lovely crushed almond flavours, sleekly curvaceous, ultra-long finish.

★★★★ **Kaleidoscope White** ⓝ ⊘ **14** blend with equal roussanne, verdelho, chenin, chardonnay & two others. No oak allows varieties their say: melon, ginger, lavender, a livening acidity focusing, extending it all.

Also tasted: **Shiraz 11** ★★★★ **Bin-3 11** ★★★★ **Kaleidoscope 13** ★★☆ **Chenin Blanc 14** ★★★ **Sauvignon Blanc 14** ★★★☆ **Hanepoot Jerepigo 11** ★★★☆ **Cape Vintage 07** ★★★☆ Not retasted: **Ice 09** ★★☆ Discontinued: **Combination**.

Brandy range

★★★★ **10 Year Potstill** ⓥ Complex, well-aged nose of dried fruit, almond & toasty oak. Layers of flavour, richly textured, smoothly harmonious; good length. 100% potstill from colombard, chenin, crouchen. — WB, CR, TJ

Location/map: Stellenbosch ▪ WO: Stellenbosch/Wellington/Bottelary ▪ Est 1946 ▪ 1stB 1984 ▪ Tasting & sales Mon-Fri 9–4.30 Sat 9–12 ▪ Fee R20pp, waived on purchase ▪ Closed Easter Fri/Sun, Dec 25 & Jan 1 ▪ Cellar tours by appt ▪ Conference/function/wedding & braai venues ▪ Walks/hikes ▪ Mountain biking trail ▪ Conservation area ▪ 2 self-catering cottages ▪ Owner(s) Steytdal Farm (Pty) Ltd/Steytler Family Trusts ▪ Cellarmaster(s) Danie Steytler snr (Jan 1979) ▪ Winemaker(s) Danie Steytler jnr (Feb 2009) ▪ Viticulturist(s) George Steytler (Jan 1984) & Schalk du Toit (Jun 2003) ▪ 190ha/162ha (cabs s/f, cinsaut, malbec, merlot, p verdot, ptage, shiraz, chard, chenin, hanepoot, rouss, sauv, sem, verdelho) ▪ 1,100t/60,000cs own label 70% red 30% white + 20,000cs for clients ▪ Other export brands: Cape View, Friesland, Vet Rooi Olifant ▪ BWI ▪ PO Box 35 Koelenhof 7605 ▪ carin@kaapzicht.co.za ▪ www.kaapzicht.co.za ▪ S 33° 54' 47.7" E 018° 44' 7.7" ▪ F +27 (0)21-906-1622 ▪ **T +27 (0)21-906-1620/1**

☐ **Kadette** *see* Kanonkop Estate
☐ **Kakamas** *see* Orange River Wine Cellars
☐ **Kanah Winery** *see* Twelve Apostles Winery
☐ **Kango** *see* Mooiuitsig Wine Cellars

Kanonkop Estate ⓥ 🍽 🏠 📷 ♿

One of the legendary red-wine estates of South Africa, Kanonkop is currently owned by Johann and Paul Krige, their grandfather being the late Paul Sauer, a former cabinet minister, who lends his name to the highly regarded flagship Bordeaux-style blend. First bottling under own label was in 1973 and the property has since had only three winemakers: former rugby Springbok Jan 'Boland' Coetzee (now of Vriesenhof), Beyers Truter (now of Beyerskloof) and Abrie Beeslaar, incumbent since 2002. The name alludes to the antiquity of the original farm: from the hill ('kop') to the back of the estate a cannon would signal the arrival in Table Bay of Dutch East India Company ships requiring supplies.

Kanonkop Estate range

★★★★ **Cabernet Sauvignon** Invitingly fresh, pure blackberry aromas on **11** (★★★★☆); touch fruitier profile than **10** & previous but soundly anchored by authoritative tannins, concentration & length. Good prospects.

★★★★☆ **Pinotage** Each of 3 pinotages in range shows clear definition of style. This mid-tier version is sophisticated, ageworthy; **12** also shows pleasing fruit richness & structural harmony, its weight balanced by a cleansing mineral thread.

★★★★★ **Pinotage Black Label** New to guide but first was **06** (no **09**) from vineyard planted in 1953. A wine of grandeur, authority. With its exotic yet pure dusky fruits, spice, finely toned muscle & composure, **12** elevates grape to level beyond mere varietal character. All-new French oak seamlessly absorbed.

★★★★☆ Paul Sauer Sense of place in this iconic flagship; richly vinous more than fruity, with supple muscularity. **11** touch more aromatic in youth, with hint oak (new French); but firm underbelly, austere conclusion from its 70% cab portends well for future. Cab franc & merlot complete blend.

Kadette range

Pinotage ⓃⒺⓌ **★★★★** Insatiable demand for label bearing 'Kanonkop' & 'Pinotage' addressed with **12**. More substance, plummy richness than blend, but also harmonious drinking now & further few years. WO Stellenbosch, as all Kadettes. **Pinotage Dry Rosé ★★★ 14** cheery mouthful of summery red berries; smoothly dry & easy drinking. Also tasted: **Cape Blend 12 ★★★** — AL

Location/map: Stellenbosch ▪ WO: Simonsberg–Stellenbosch/Stellenbosch ▪ Est 1910 ▪ 1stB 1973 ▪ Tasting & sales Mon-Fri 9–5 Sat 9–2 pub hols 10-4 ▪ Fee R10 ▪ Closed Good Fri, Dec 25 & Jan 1 ▪ Cheese platters in summer; traditional snoek barbecues by appt (min 15 people); or BYO picnic ▪ Conservation area ▪ Art gallery ▪ Owner(s) Johann & Paul Krige ▪ Cellarmaster(s) Abrie Beeslaar (Jan 2002) ▪ Winemaker(s) Abrie Beeslaar (Jan 2002), with Jeremy Arries (2007) & Frikkie Elias (1992) ▪ Viticulturist(s) Koos du Toit (Jan 2004) ▪ 120ha/100ha (cabs s/f, merlot, ptage) ▪ 1,480t/220,000cs own label 98% red 2% rosé ▪ WIETA ▪ PO Box 19 Elsenburg 7607 ▪ wine@kanonkop.co.za ▪ www.kanonkop.co.za ▪ S 33° 51' 18.4" E 018° 51' 36.1" ▪ F +27 (0)21-884-4719 ▪ **T +27 (0)21-884-4656**

Kanu Wines

This winery started life as 'Goedgeloof' off Stellenbosch's Polkadraai Road in the late 90s. Then owned by Hydro Holdings, which had bought sister property Mulderbosch, it was rebranded 'Kanu' – a mythical African bird symbolising the promise of a bountiful harvest. A decade later Ben Truter acquired the brand and moved operations to the old Mulderbosch property. Longtime cellarmaster Johan Grimbeek and new viticulturist Mike Dobrovic (Mulderbosch winemaker for many years) are assessing the vineyards and contemplating replacing under-performing blocks with varieties 'more accustomed to a warmer climate', like assyrtico, carricante and vermentino.

Premium range

★★★★ Keystone Fast-forward to **11**, a clean-cut Bordeaux-style red with sappy choc-mint interest. Last **08 (★★★★)** alluring, but not as polished. No **09** or **10**. Stellenbosch WO.

★★★★ KCB Chenin Blanc Barrel sample **13** bursts with flavour; ripe honeysuckle buffed with wood (down to 25% new), & tangerine twist to off-dry tail. WO Stellenbosch. **12** sold out untasted.

★★★★ KCB Envy ⓃⒺⓌ More new casks (57%) for this **NV** chenin than KCB sibling, but similar bold, broad, ripe styling with semi-dry flourish.

★★★★ Viognier ⓥ **12** ups ante on **11 (★★★★)**. It's like liquid confectionery; waves of apricot & marmalade jostle with oak in luscious off-dry send-off. Not subtle, but delicious.

★★★★ Kia-Ora Noble Late Harvest ⓥ Botrytised chenin dessert; full-blooded **10** loaded with candied peel & piquant kumquat, refined in all-new oak (16 months) & balanced by vivacious acid.

Rockwood ★★★ Ripe & accessible red quaffer. **11** a shiraz-based 7-way mix of Rhône & Bordeaux varieties. **Chenin Blanc ★★★** Ripe guava fleshiness aided & abetted by plump viognier (8.5%), **13** ends not quite dry. **Giselle ★★★★** Attractive méthode cap classique bubbly led by 66% chardonnay with pinot, grapes from Stellenbosch. **NV** mixes warm biscuit character with a refreshing mousse; for fun rather than philosophy. Also tasted: **Merlot 13 ★★★ Sauvignon Blanc 13 ★★★** Not retasted: **Cabernet Sauvignon 12 ★★★ Shiraz 08 ★★★ GSM 10 ★★★★ Chardonnay-Pinot Noir 12 ★★ Chardonnay Barrel Fermented 11 ★★★★**

Black Label range

Rifle Range Red ★★★ Multi-vintage 9-way **NV** blend (even a dash chenin) hits the full-fruited jackpot; easy-drinking pleasure. **Semi-Sweet Rosé** ⓃⒺⓌ Temporarily sold out; await next vintage. **Classic Dry White ★★** Crunchy green winter melon features & fresh acidity on latest **NV** from sauvignon & chenin. Also tasted: **Merlot Rosé NV ★★** Not retasted: **Semi-Sweet White NV ★★★ Natural Sweet Shiraz 12 ★★** — DS

Location/map: Stellenbosch ▪ WO: Western Cape/Stellenbosch/Coastal ▪ Est/1stB 1998 ▪ Tasting & sales Mon-Fri 9. 30–4.30 ▪ Fee R35pp ▪ Closed all pub hols ▪ Owner(s) Ben Truter Trust ▪ Cellarmaster(s)/winemaker(s) Johan Grimbeek (Jan 2002) ▪ Viticulturist(s) Mike Dobrovic (2014, consultant) ▪ 48ha/26ha (cab, merlot, chard, sauv) ▪ 200t/60,000cs own label 50% red 45% white 5% rosé ▪ BWI, WIETA ▪ PO Box 548 Stellenbosch 7599 ▪ info@kanu.co. za ▪ www.kanu.co.za ▪ S 33° 53' 23.35" E 018° 49' 8.44" ▪ F +27 (0)21-865-2351 ▪ **T +27 (0)21-865-2488**

☐ **Kap Hase** *see* Migliarina Wines
☐ **Karoo Classique** *see* Karusa Vineyards

Karusa Vineyards   ⓠ ⓜ ⓞ ⓖ

A must-stop destination for Klein Karoo sightseers and winelovers – it's en route to the Cango Caves – this family winery offers a wide range of products, the most recent being beer from its microbrewery. Partner/cellarmaster Jacques Conradie offers an invitation: 'Relax with an ice-cold sauvignon in one hand and a complex amber ale in the other, as you look out over the Swartberg range, pausing to snack on ostrich carpaccio from the deli.'

Reserve Collection
The 5th Element Syrah-Viognier ⓐ ★★★☆ Only a soupçon viognier in step-up **11**. Herbal notes enliven smoky bacon aroma & dense black fruit; tannins, oak (30% new) & 13.5% alcohol amenable for solo sipping or dining. Not retasted: **Earth's Art Chardonnay-Viognier 12** ★★★

Terroir Specific Collection
★★★★ **One Tree Hill Pinotage** ⓐ Super expression of the variety, **12** exuberant dark fruit & spice, vanilla from American oak (60% new), reined in by zesty acidity, fine & long tannins. Several rungs above light & easy **11** (★★★).
Southern Slope Sauvignon Blanc ★★★☆ Characterful aperitif style. Early bottled **13** unfurls to gooseberry, litchi; has enlivening tangy finish. Refreshing & light alcohol (11.5%) al fresco companion. **Stonerock Viognier** ★★★ Ripe & generous **14** has pleasant spicy-peachy flavours, sherbert-like grip on tad brief finish; creamy oak-sweet palate invites spicy accompaniment. Not retasted: **The Ancients Pinot Noir 12** ★★★☆ **Double Black Petite Sirah 12** ★★★ **Terre Noire Syrah 12** ★★★☆ Not tasted: **Aloe Ridge Unwooded Chardonnay**.

Lifestyle Collection
Muscat Rosé ★★★ Muscat-toned **14** is near-dry, with juicy plum/strawberry fruit, zippy acid & modest 11.5% alcohol for picnic basket fun. **Chenin Blanc-Sauvignon Blanc** ★★★ Equal partners in lean & dry **14**; dusty gravel notes but crisply refreshing, satisfying. Also tasted: **Shiraz-Cabernet Sauvignon 13** ★★★ **Muscat Blanc 14** ★★★

Karoo Classique Collection
Chardonnay Brut ⓐ ★★★ Attractive yeasty saline notes on **NV** dry celebratory fizz from chardonnay. Lively mousse & tangy acidity - no wallflower! Not retasted: **Pinot Noir Rosé NV** ★★★

Soleil de Karusa Liqueur Collection
White Muscadel ★★★ Dessert in a glass. Fortified **14**'s dried sultanas overlain with melon; intensely sweet & slippery with gentle acidity. 375 ml, as all these. Not retasted: **Red Muscadel NV** ★★★☆ **Cape Vintage 12** ★★ **Cape White NV** ★★★

Sherry-Style wine ⓝ
Oloroso Medium Cream ★★★☆ From viognier, 3 years barrel matured. Apricot coloured & perfumed, some candied peel, the sweetness perked up by acid freshness. Oak influence a lovely, warm toasty seam, giving a barley sugar tone to the fruit. Not classic but delicious. — GdB, CR

Location: Oudtshoorn ▪ Map: Klein Karoo & Garden Route ▪ WO: Klein Karoo/Western Cape ▪ Est/1stB 2004 ▪ Tasting & sales Mon-Fri 9.30–4 Sat 10–2.30 ▪ Closed Good Fri & Dec 25 ▪ Karoo Tapas Restaurant & Deli ▪ Microbrewery ▪ Conferences (30-40 pax) ▪ Owner(s) Karusa Partnership ▪ Cellarmaster(s) Jacques Conradie (2004) ▪ 8ha (grenache,

Katbakkies Wine

It was a Rustenberg '63 cabernet that finally inspired architect Andries van der Walt to start his own winery. The name is that of his Cederberg farm, where ravenous baboons deny a viable yield off the vines. Andries turned to Stellenbosch for fruit, which he vinifies with star winemaker Teddy Hall.

★★★★ **Cabernet Sauvignon 11** first we've tasted since **05**. Classic style, built around its crunchy ripe fruit & form-giving grape tannins. Big, but well proportioned for current enjoyment & further few years.

★★★★ **Syrah Reserve** ⊘ Dense, complex **04**; firm structure, bold but balanced.

★★★★ **Chenin Blanc 10** tempting mix dried herbs, oxidative complexity with freshening edge citrus zest. A few years' age has brought more attractive savoury richness than sweetness, & delicious persistence. **09** (★★★★) more obviously off-dry.

★★★★ **Viognier** ⊘ Vestiges of varietal honeysuckle, apricot in oxidative **10** (★★★★); these yield to alcohol glow in tail. Drink up. **08** was elegant.

Not retasted: Syrah 08 ★★★★ Perpendiculum Viognier NV ★★★ — AL

Location/map/WO: Stellenbosch ▪ Est/1stB 1999 ▪ Tasting & sales Mon-Sat by appt ▪ Closed all pub hols ▪ Owner(s) Andries van der Walt ▪ Cellarmaster(s) Andries van der Walt (1999) ▪ Winemaker(s) Teddy Hall (2002, consultant) & Andries van der Walt (1999) ▪ 29ha/10ha (cab, merlot, syrah) ▪ 1,000cs own label 40% red 60% white ▪ PO Box 305 Stellenbosch 7599 ▪ info@katbakkies.co.za ▪ www.katbakkies.co.za ▪ S 33° 55' 37.4" E 018° 49' 14.6" ▪ F +27 (0)86-557-0597 ▪ **T +27 (0)82-882-9022**

☐ **KC** *see* Klein Constantia Estate

Keermont Vineyards

'Creating wines which are grown, produced and bottled here, and which reflect the natural wonders of this beautiful place' is the goal at Keermont Vineyards, the property owned by Mark Wraith and family in the saddle between the Helderberg and Stellenbosch mountains. Indigenous vegetation beautifies much of it, with fewer than 30 ha of scattered high-altitude vineyards, the oldest dating from 1971. Marsanne and roussanne are being established on small scale under the watch of winemaker/viticulturist (and surfer) Alex Starey, who understandably is keen to visit new export markets Reunion and Mauritius. Locally, new agents are helping to spread the word and doubtless they will be enthused by the superb wines joining the portfolio.

Single Vineyard Series (NEW)

★★★★☆ **Topside Syrah** From rocky soils high on Stellenbosch Mountain. **12** much darker spicy features than Steepside. Tight, with mineral core & lively grip. Great length & potential. Just one 500L used oak barrel. Style, not quality, determines preference between these single-vineyard Syrahs.

★★★★☆ **Steepside Syrah** Named after steep Helderberg slopes home to this vineyard. Appealing & expressive lilies & red fruits introduce **12**. Savoury & well-fleshed mouthfeel with chewy tannins allow for current enjoyment but concentration & build for extended ageing. 20 months 2nd fill French oak, unfiltered.

★★★★☆ **Riverside Chenin Blanc** Intensity, layers of flavour on **13** from vineyard planted 1971. An individual, from pale yellow-gold brilliance to mineral length. Seasoned oak ferment & year on lees infuse stonefruit, blanched almonds & citrus zest with seductive underlying richness. Delicious now; great potential.

Annual Release range

★★★★ **Syrah** Blend of single vineyards above plus 5% mourvèdre. Bigger, denser & lacking some of their exciting individuality. **12**'s sound dark spice, earthy tones subdued but has structure to age & evolve.

★★★★ **Keermont** Flagship red; **12** refined Bordeaux quintet with dash syrah. Cab influential in ripe profile, flesh though merlot is main player. Fine, insinuating tannins suggest ageability; should also drink well from **15**.

★★★★ **Terrasse** **13** intricate, tasty chenin backed by 17% chardonnay, 7% sauvignon with 9% viognier infusing elegant fragrance. Still tight, linear; richness of used French barrel-fermentation needs few years to emerge.

★★★★ **Fleurfontein** Vine-dried sweet wine from sauvignon. Bright sunny gold hue on **12** (★★★★☆). Fresh honey & peach flavours, energised by riveting acid, whistle-clean finish. Natural ferment in oak imparts extra dimension to this delicious wine. **10** was previous release.

Companion ⑭ ★★★ **12** nearly all merlot with splashes petit verdot, cab franc & mourvèdre. Jammy, simple & short. — AL

Location/map/WO: Stellenbosch ▪ Est 2005 ▪ 1stB 2007 ▪ Tasting, sales & cellar tours by appt ▪ Owner(s) Wraith family ▪ Winemaker(s)/viticulturist(s) Alex Starey (Jan 2005) ▪ 156ha/27ha (cab, merlot, syrah, chenin) ▪ ±90t/3,000cs own label 65% red 33% white 2% sticky white ▪ BWI, IPW ▪ PO Box 713 Stellenbosch 7599 ▪ info@keermont.co.za ▪ www.keermont.co.za ▪ S 34° 0' 27.0" E 018° 53' 39.0" ▪ F +27 (0)21-880-0566 ▪ **T +27 (0)21-880-0397**

Keet Wines ⓘ

It's rare in the Cape for a winemaker to be as focused as this, but Chris Keet continues to produce just one wine under his own name – though any number under various labels benefit from his expertise as winemaking consultant (as well as a viticultural one), showing the influence of his understated, elegant approach. Chris makes his wine, as well as his hosts', at the Van Biljon estate on the Polkadraai Hills outside Stellenbosch town.

★★★★☆ **First Verse** Fresh **11** has lovely leafy fragrance from cab franc component - there's more cab, plus merlot, petit verdot & malbec. Some robust power, yet elegant; charming yet restrained; pure fruit, but savoury too. Only a smidgen new oak. Approachable, yet years to develop; same was true of **10** (★★★★★). — TJ

Location/WO: Stellenbosch ▪ Est 2008 ▪ 1stB 2010 ▪ Tasting by appt ▪ Owner(s) Christopher Keet ▪ Cellarmaster(s)/ winemaker(s)/viticulturist(s) Christopher Keet (Oct 2008) ▪ 10t/1,000cs own label 100% red ▪ PO Box 5508 Helderberg 7135 ▪ chris@keetwines.co.za ▪ www.keetwines.co.za ▪ F +27 (0)86-544-3347 ▪ **T +27 (0)82-853-1707**

☐ **Keimoes** see Orange River Wine Cellars
☐ **Keizer's Creek** see Roodezandt Wines

Kellerprinz

Budget-priced white for the sweet toothed, in 2L bottle, by Distell.

Late Harvest ⓐ ★★ Fresh, lively semi-sweet **NV** white with pear & peach flavours. — DB

☐ **Kelvin Grove** see Simonsvlei International

Ken Forrester Wines ⓘ ⑪ ♿

In the mid-1990s, Ken Forrester left behind a successful career as a Johannesburg restaurateur to acquire the farm Scholtzenhof at the foot of the Helderberg. There's since been no doubting Ken's vast energy and commitment. Along with longtime collaborator Martin Meinert, he's taken widely planted but commercially challenged chenin blanc and made it key to his offering, the ultra-premium FMC a notable benchmark. When it comes to reds, he's a champion of Rhône varieties on account of their suitability to the Mediterranean climate which generally prevails, the top-end Gypsy and Three

Halves both worth seeking out. On coming to the Cape, Ken didn't completely forsake his hospitality background and he remains a partner in popular winelands restaurant 96 Winery Road nearby.

Icon range

★★★★☆ **The Gypsy** Lithe rather than heftily powerful **11** (49% shiraz) has seamless layers of intense red fruit from 50 year old grenache (45%) with dash mourvèdre adding hint of black olive. Medium bodied, with dark spices & pinch of pepper on finish.

★★★★★ **The FMC** Messrs Forrester & Meinert's 'challenge to the world', mostly old-vine chenin harvested fully ripe & wild-fermented in new oak. Magnificent **12** with remarkable freshness balancing rich apricot, fynbos honey, kitka bread & savoury spice notes. Stellenbosch WO.

★★★★★ **'T' Noble Late Harvest** Barrel-fermented botrytised Stellenbosch chenin named for Mrs Forrester. Rich but refreshingly acidic **11** oozes caramelised pineapples & tangy apricots, drizzled with honey & sprinkled with allspice. Better balanced than **10** (★★★★).

Occasional release: **FMC Première Sélection Moelleux**.

Cellar Exclusives range

★★★★☆ **Three Halves** Moved from Icon range. Less complex than **09** (★★★★★) but still greater than the sum of its parts, 'half' mourvèdre plus two more 'halves' of shiraz & grenache, rich **11** is earthy, even meaty, which doesn't detract from depth & purity of ripe black berry fruit. Better realised than **07** (★★★★). No **10**, **08**.

★★★★★ **Roussanne** (ⓝ) Classic Rhône white variety gets FMC treatment in sensuous **12**. Lime blossom & lemongrass on nose explode into canned pineapple & ripe citrus intensity on palate, oily-smooth & almost marzipan-like without being sweet. Stellenbosch WO.

Also tasted: **Sparklehorse 12** ★★★

Ken Forrester range

★★★★ **Renegade** **10** rendition of Rhône-style blend has shiraz in ascendancy (54%) with piercing blackcurrant & mulberry intensity, nutmeg & salty black olive on lingering finish.

★★★★ **Old Vine Reserve Chenin Blanc** From 30+ year old Stellenbosch vines, **13** has lovely fresh apricot nose, softening into cinnamon-spiced apricot crumble on palate with soft custard-cream texture, tangy ginger conclusion.

Also tasted: **Merlot Reserve 11** ★★★☆ Not tasted: **Sauvignon Blanc**.

Petit range

Pinotage ⊘ ★★★★ Cheerful **13** has lifted berry perfume with hint of smoke. Soft & juicy, balanced by brisk acidity. Persistent sweetness on finish. **Rosé** ★★★ Lowish-alcohol **14** quaffer from Stellenbosch has floral nose, relatively dry on palate with ripe apricot & raspberry zip. **Chenin Blanc** ★★★ Acidity quite reined in on pretty **14**, a summer fruit salad of apples, peaches & pears, finishing seemingly off-dry. Also tasted: **Semi-Sweet 14** ★★★ **Sauvignon Blanc 14** ★★★ Not tasted: **Cabernet Sauvignon-Merlot**. — JG

Location: Stellenbosch ▪ Map: Helderberg ▪ WO: Western Cape/Stellenbosch ▪ Est/1stB 1994 ▪ Tasting & sales on home farm, cnr R44 & Winery Rd: Mon-Fri 9-5 Sat 9.30-3.30 ▪ Fee R60/6 wines, R100/entire range ▪ Closed Good Fri, Dec 25 & Jan 1 ▪ Sundays & after hours tasting available at 96 Winery Rd Restaurant ▪ Owner(s) Ken & Teresa Forrester ▪ Cellarmaster(s) Ken Forrester (1994) ▪ Winemaker(s) Ken Forrester (1994) & Martin Meinert ▪ Viticulturist(s) Pieter Rossouw (Oct 2009) ▪ (grenache, merlot, mourv, shiraz, chenin, sauv) ▪ 1,070t/147,000cs own label 35% red 65% white ▪ Other export brand: Workhorse (Marks & Spencer) ▪ Brands for clients: Woolworths ▪ ISO 9001:2000, BWI, HACCP, SEDEX, WIETA ▪ PO Box 1253 Stellenbosch 7599 ▪ info@kenforresterwines.com ▪ www.kenforresterwines.com ▪ S 34° 1' 31.06" E 018° 49' 05.92" ▪ F +27 (0)21-855-2373 ▪ **T +27 (0)21-855-2374**

☐ **Kevin Arnold** *see* Waterford Estate
☐ **Kevin King** *see* South Hill Vineyards
☐ **KFK** *see* Waterstone Wines

☐ **Kievits Kroon** *see* Glen Erskine Estate

Kingna Distillery

Norbert Engel's long-dreamt-of brandy distillery on his Montagu farm, named after a local river, allows brandy master Ruan Hunlun to introduce blended brandy-and-cola lovers to an alternative that is 'smooth, refined but affordable'. The 2,000L still's output, oak-matured five years, goes to Europe; farm hikers, holidaymakers and wedding parties; and restored Dutch ship Oosterschelde.

Potstill Brandy Ⓖ ★★★ Smooth textured, light, 'feminine' & elegant, with fresh apricot, fynbos, clove & floral perfume; oak rather obvious. 100% potstill from colombard. — WB, TJ

Location: Montagu ▪ Map: Klein Karoo & Garden Route ▪ Est 2007 ▪ 1stB 2012 ▪ Tasting, sales & distillery tours Mon–Fri 10-5 Sat/Sun 10-3 ▪ Closed Easter Sat/Sun, Dec 25/26 & Jan 1 ▪ Tour groups ▪ BYO picnic ▪ Conferences ▪ Weddings/functions ▪ Hiking & mountain biking trails ▪ Self-catering chalets ▪ Owner(s) Norbert Engel ▪ Brandy master Ruan Hunlun (Jan 2005, consultant) ▪ 1,000ha/8ha (chenin, cbard) ▪ 140t/9,000L ▪ PO Box 395 Montagu 6720 ▪ ruan@kingna.co.za ▪ www.kingna.co.za ▪ S 33° 49' 45.87" E 20° 15' 39.10" ▪ F +27 (0)23-614-2721 ▪ **T +27 (0)23-614-2721**

Kingsriver Estate

It's a decade since engineer Ruud de Clercq turned his entrepreneurial skills in European theme park development to revitalising part of the original Koningsrivier property near McGregor and bottling the first own-brand wines (the latest vintages not ready for review this edition). In line with Ruud's aim of 'elegantly ecological wines', biodynamic farming practices have gradually been introduced.

Location: McGregor ▪ Map: Robertson ▪ Est 2003 ▪ 1stB 2005 ▪ Tasting & sales Mon–Sun 10-5 ▪ Cellar tours by appt ▪ Tour groups by appt ▪ Hiking trails ▪ Conferences ▪ 4-star Kingsriver Country House & Restaurant ▪ Owner(s) De Clercq Family Trust ▪ Cellarmaster(s) Ruud de Clercq & Patrick Julius ▪ Winemaker(s) Ruud de Clercq (2005) ▪ Viticulturist(s) Patrick Julius (2005) ▪ 348ha/38ha (cab, ptage, ruby cab, shiraz, tannat, chard, chenin, cbard) ▪ 190t/10,000cs own label 80% red 20% white ▪ Other export label: Mzansi ▪ PO Box 203 McGregor 6708 ▪ kingsriver-office@breede.co.za ▪ www.kingsriver-estate.com ▪ S 33° 55' 19.5" E 019° 49' 45.5" ▪ F +27 (0)86-577-0834 ▪ **T +27 (0)23-004-0818**

☐ **Kipepeo** *see* Baratok Wines

Kirabo Private Cellar

The Le Roux family has strong ties to the land: six generations have grown grapes on the Breedekloof farm (the name means 'Gift from God'). Most fruit is sold, but small parcels of red have been vinified in recent years for regular, mostly private clients and visitors.

Location: Rawsonville ▪ Map: Breedekloof ▪ Est 2002 ▪ 1stB 2003 ▪ Tasting, sales & cellar/vineyard tours Mon–Fri 8.30-5 Sat by appt ▪ Closed all pub hols ▪ Meals by appt only ▪ Facilities for children ▪ Tour groups ▪ Farm produce ▪ BYO picnic ▪ Walking/hiking/4x4 trails ▪ Weddings/functions ▪ Conservation area ▪ Owner(s) Pieter & Karen le Roux ▪ Cellarmaster(s) Pieter le Roux (2002) ▪ Winemaker(s) Pieter & Karen le Roux (2002) ▪ Viticulturist(s) Pieter le Roux ▪ 1,000t/10,000L total ▪ 10t own label 100% red ▪ IPW ▪ PO Box 96 Rawsonville 6845 ▪ info@kirabocellar.co.za ▪ www.kirabocellar.co.za ▪ S 33° 42' 36.68" E 019° 21' 27.55" ▪ F +27 (0)23-349-6764 ▪ **T +27 (0)23-349-6764**

Klawer Wine Cellars

Approaching its 60th anniversary, grower-owned Klawer Wine Cellars vinifies off more than 2,000 ha of vines along the West Coast. In support of a dynamic team, investments have recently been made in additional tanks for the production facilities near Klawer and Trawal; in a new GM, the very experienced Andries Blake (former Swartland Winery cellarmaster, still with roots in that region through Blake Family Wines); and in marketing, with eyes on Russia and China.

★★★★ **Hanepoot 09** fortified dessert's bouquet more savoury & tangy than sweet, actually showing kerosene note. Intensity & freshness on palate, well-handled sweetness, orange peel & apricot complexity. Cellar further for more delicious development. Rung above **08** (★★★★).

Cabernet Sauvignon ✓ ★★★★ Honest & likable reds hallmark of this cellar. New batch **11** has developed round edges, gone up a notch. Clean fruited, touch of mint & cedar to cassis & redcurrants. **Pinotage** ✓ ★★★ Crunchy red fruit on fresh bottling of **12**; clean & forthcoming, with moreish drinkability. **Chardonnay** ✓ ★★★ Caramel oak, butter & nut paste from wood fermentation, some in barrel, on marmalade-infused **13**. Wallet friendly, for early enjoyment. **Viognier** ✓ ★★★★ Always a standout here, punches above its price. Barrel-fermented **13** fine integration, complexity & weight, with variety's peach kernel woven with citrus rind & spice. **African Ruby Rooibos** ★★★☆ Unusual rooibos-infused red muscadel. Aromatic & sweet **NV** fortified has more floral spice than rooibos; surprisingly light & delicate. Versatile cocktail option. Also tasted: **Merlot 13** ★★ **Shiraz** ✓ **12** ★★★ **Shiraz-Merlot** ✓ **12** ★★☆ **Chenin Blanc 14** ★★★ **Sauvignon Blanc** ✓ **14** ★★★ **Michelle Sparkling** ✓ **13** ★★★ **Red Muscadel 13** ★★★☆ **White Muscadel 13** ★★★★ **Travino Matador NV** ★★ Discontinued: **Grenache Blanc de Noir**. — HJ

Location: Klawer ▪ Map/WO: Olifants River ▪ Est 1956 ▪ Tasting & sales Mon-Fri 8–5 Sat 9–1 ▪ Facilities for children ▪ BYO picnic ▪ Conferences (office hours only) ▪ Owner(s) 92 members ▪ Manager Andries Blake ▪ Cellarmaster(s) Pieter van Aarde (Nov 2011) ▪ Winemaker(s) Roelof van Schalkwyk, Cerina van Niekerk, Christo Beukes, Bennie Avenant & Mariska de Bruyn ▪ Viticulturist(s) MG van der Westhuizen ▪ 2,095ha (cab, merlot, ptage, ruby cab, shiraz, chard, chenin, cbard, hanepoot, muscadel, sauv, viog) ▪ 43,000t/60,000cs own label 40% red 40% white 5% rosé 15% other ▪ Other export brand: Travino ▪ ISO 22000:2009, Organic, DLG IPW ▪ PO Box 8 Klawer 8145 ▪ klawerwyn@kingsley.co.za ▪ www.klawerwine.co.za ▪ S 31° 47′ 34.9″ E 018° 37′ 36.1″ ▪ F +27 (0)27-216-1561 ▪ **T +27 (0)27-216-1530**

☐ **Klein Centennial** *see* Group CDV

Klein Constantia Estate

As part of a complete makeover of one of SA's great wine estates, venerable Klein Constantia's 18th-century manor house is being renovated to return it to its previous splendour as the 'grand old Cape Dutch lady' of the Western Cape. MD Hans Astrom, winemaker Matt Day and their team favour a natural and holistic approach to winefarming, and are focusing more on the terroir of their vineyards as opposed to winemaking techniques. Having said that, the cellar has undergone an extensive upgrade and new equipment has been installed, including a state-of-the-art destemmer and new drainage tanks - all improvements made to further minimise interference during the winemaking process and allow the terroir to speak for itself. Site expression also underlies a collaboration with the Loire's Pascal Jolivet, resulting in a 'new and inspirational' sauvignon, the Metis 2013.

Estate Wines

★★★★☆ **Estate Red Blend 12** 3-way Bordeaux red, cab (67%), with petit verdot & malbec, showing complex interplay of cassis & black plum, subtle spice & herbs; like **11**, firm, authoritative but not stern. 60% new oak, 16 months will see it through many fruitful years in the cellar. Previous had portion shiraz.

★★★★☆ **Block 382 Sauvignon Blanc** (NEW) From the high-lying, premium 382 block, natural ferment, 7 months neutral barrel maturation for stunning **12**. Similar minerality to Estate bottling but less gravelly, smoother conclusion with savoury seam. Classic Constantia.

★★★★ **Sauvignon Blanc 13** shows estate's signature delicacy & focus, more concentrated & tighter than KC sibling. Textural expression with gravelly nuance, persistent poise.

★★★★ **Metis Sauvignon Blanc** (NEW) Joint venture with France's Domaine Pascal Jolivet, involving one of estate's highest blocks & 'natural, minimalistic and unconventional approach'. Bright **13**, lovely stonefruit purity & intensity complemented by balanced rather than arresting acidity. For contemplative enjoyment.

★★★★☆ **Brut Méthode Cap Classique** Attractive brioche & crème fraîche hints at champagne but **11** definitely a New World sparkling. Cask-aged chardonnay, 20 months on lees, packed with lemon flavour & intensity, appealing weight & steely, persistent mousse. Follows very fine **10** (★★★★★).

★★★★☆ **Vin de Constance** Iconic dessert from unbotrytised muscat de Frontignan. Rich & satisfying **08** offers fragrant aromas of candied orange peel, faint scent of fynbos. Warm alcohol asserts on entry, then unctuous flavours of toffee apples & glazed pineapples. 54 months 60% new oak, French & Hungarian.

Chardonnay ⒩ ★★★★ Intense oak aromas, flavours of shortbread & vanilla, faint lemon & lime on light-footed, zesty **13**. Balanced cool-climate expression. Partial barrel ferment/ageing, 50% new. Not tasted: **Riesling**, **Perdeblokke Sauvignon Blanc**. Discontinued: **Marlbrook**, **Madame Marlbrook**.

KC range
Cabernet Sauvignon-Merlot ★★★☆ Plush berries, sweetened with cherry & choc on lightly oaked, supple & friendly **12**, superior everyday sipper. WO W Cape, as all these. Also tasted: **Rosé 13** ★★★ **Sauvignon Blanc 13** ★★★☆

Husk Spirit range
Spirit of Constance ★★★ **NV** made from Vin de Constance husks, with powerfully grapey, floral scents pointing to its muscat origin. Soft, smooth, monolithic palate; lots of flavour but little finesse or delicacy. — WB, TJ, CvZ

Location: Constantia ▪ Map: Cape Peninsula ▪ WO: Constantia/Western Cape ▪ Est 1823 ▪ 1stB 1824 ▪ Tasting & sales Mon-Fri 9–5 Sat 10-5 (summer)/10–4.30 (winter) Sun 10-4 (summer only) ▪ Fee R30 ▪ Closed some pub hols ▪ Gift shop ▪ Estate honey for sale ▪ Collection of original Constantia bottles on display ▪ Owner(s) Zdenek Bakala, Charles Harman, Bruno Prats & Hubert de Boüard ▪ Winemaker(s) Matthew Day (2009) ▪ Brandy masters Matthew Day & Giorgio Dalla Cia (Dalla Cia) ▪ Viticulturist(s) Craig Harris (Oct 2013) ▪ 146ha/82ha (cabs s/f, malbec, merlot, p verdot, shiraz, chard, muscat de F, riesling, sauv, sem) ▪ 500t/80,000cs own label 30% red 70% white ▪ BWI champion ▪ PO Box 375 Constantia 7848 ▪ info@kleinconstantia.com ▪ www.kleinconstantia.com ▪ S 34° 2' 19.0" E 018° 24' 46.5" ▪ F +27 (0)21-794-2464 ▪ **T +27 (0)21-794-5188**

☐ **Kleindal** *see* Robertson Wide River Export Company

Klein DasBosch

Label vinified at Vriesenhof by Jan Coetzee for neighbour James 'Whitey' Basson, CEO of retailing empire Shoprite/Checkers. The wines can be tasted and purchased at Mont Marie Restaurant on Blaauwklippen Road, Stellenbosch. A small selection also appears on a few other local restaurant lists and in wine shops.

Location/map: Stellenbosch ▪ Tasting & sales at Mont Marie Restaurant, Stellenbosch T +27 (0)21-880-0777 - phone ahead as tasting hours are subject to change ▪ Owner(s) James Wellwood Basson ▪ Viti/vini consultant Jan Coetzee (1997) ▪ Winemaker(s) Jan Coetzee (1994) ▪ ±25ha ▪ 90% red 10% white ▪ PO Box 12320 Stellenbosch 7613 ▪ annalette@kleindasbosch.com ▪ www.kleindasbosch.co.za, www.montmarie.co.za ▪ S 33° 58' 56.0" E 018° 51' 44.5" ▪ F +27 (0)21-880-0999 ▪ **T +27 (0)21-880-0128/+27 (0)71-859-1773**

Klein Dauphine ⌂

This boutique Franschhoek Valley label is back under new ownership after a brief hiatus. The 2013 vintage from the half-hectare of vines was made by Ossie Sauermann, 2008 Diners Club Young Winemaker of the Year, who vinifies smidgens of wine from several small valley blocks for their owners. Klein Dauphine's scenic guest cottage is the place to find the wine, now under a new-look label.

Merlot Rosé ★★★ More Provençal than New World, **13** has red berries at its core but 9 months barrel maturation gives savoury edge making it oh-so-food-friendly. Chill well & enjoy at lunch, but note 14.9% alcohol! Only 180 cases. — CR, CvZ

Location/WO: Franschhoek ▪ Est 2001 ▪ 1stB 2003 ▪ Closed to public ▪ Fully equipped self-catering cottage (sleeps 2) ▪ Winemaker(s) Ossie Sauermann ▪ 2ha/0.5ha (cab, merlot) ▪ 3t 50% red 50% rosé ▪ PO Box 69 Simondium 7670 ▪ melaniebriers@gmail.com ▪ www.kleindauphine.co.za ▪ **T +27 (0)21-876-2454**

Kleine Draken

Still the sole kosher-only winery in SA, Kleine Draken aims to make 'good-quality, value-for-money Orthodox Union-certified wines under the supervision of the Cape Town Beth Din'. Replanting at home-farm Zandwijk on Paarl Mountain continues, winemaker Jean van Rooyen says, adding that his wines are vegan friendly as no animal products are used, and some are low alcohol.

Cabernet Sauvignon ★★☆ Black berries on smoky, uncomplicated **13** quaffer, with dry tail. **Semi-Sweet Rosé** 🆕 **★★** Plain, sweet cranberry & raspberry **NV** pink. **Chardonnay ★★** Creamy oak edge to tangy citrus of lightish **13**. **Natural Sweet Red ★★** Sweet herbal notes on **NV** merlot. Low-alcohol, like all the sweets. Also tasted: **Merlot 13 ★★ Sauvignon Blanc 13 ★★ Vin Doux NV ★★ Natural Sweet White NV ★★** Not retasted: **Kiddush NV ★★ Dry Red 06 ★★** Not tasted: **Rosé.** — FM

Location/WO: Paarl ▪ Map: Paarl & Wellington ▪ Est 1983 ▪ 1stB 1988 ▪ Tasting & sales Mon-Fri 8–4 ▪ Closed all pub hols & Jewish holy days ▪ Cellar tours by appt ▪ Pre-booked kosher picnics available ▪ Owner(s) Cape Gate (Pty) Ltd ▪ Winemaker(s) Jean van Rooyen (Dec 2007) ▪ Viticulturist(s) Frank Pietersen (1984) ▪ 12.5ha/5ha under vine ▪ 55t/20,000cs own label 50% red 47% white 3% rosé ▪ IPW, OU certified ▪ PO Box 2674 Paarl 7620 ▪ zandwijk@capegate.co.za ▪ www.kosherwines.co.za ▪ S 33° 46' 33.3" E 018° 56' 50.4" ▪ F +27 (0)21-863-1884 ▪ **T +27 (0)21-863-2368**

☐ **Kleine Parys** *see* Klein Parys Vineyards
☐ **Kleine Rust** *see* Stellenrust

Kleine Zalze Wines

The first vines were planted on this farm, on the outskirts of Stellnbosch town, well over 300 years ago. There have been many changes since then – most radically, of course, in its current incarnation as a major 'destination' (and home for golf players and others on its residential estate). And as a substantial wine producer, embracing a modern, ripe-fruited, generous aesthetic and expressing it with much-awarded expertise. Six well-defined ranges are made, from fruit off home vineyards or sourced elsewhere in Stellenbosch and beyond. Arriving in late 2014 to lead the winemaking team was Alastair Rimmer, whose international experience gives good grounds for the welcoming comment of owner and MD, Kobus Basson: 'We are excited about the next chapter in Kleine Zalze's history'.

Family Reserve range

★★★★☆ Cabernet Sauvignon Cherries & cassis stand proud in **10** despite 22 months new oak; there's lush ripeness further enhanced by grape sorting, 50% whole berry ferment. Coconut & tobacco attest to the oak influence but tannins are supple. Has a long future.

★★★★ Pinotage 🍷 Bold, alluring **09** a few years back had structure to contain - just - its 15+% alcohol.

★★★★ Shiraz Flagship **10** (★★★★☆) 22 months new French oak. Morello cherries, sweet spice & scrub perfume, hint of salty liquorice, a step up on **09**. Seductively flavoured, vanilla-brushed creamy dark fruit around a firm tannin backbone.

★★★★★ Chenin Blanc 13 (★★★★★) result of multi-vineyard blending, partial wood ferment in various aged barrels, then 12 months more. Melon & stonefruit richness, some citrus peel, all brightened by acidity. Has great presence, just short of **12**.

★★★★☆ Sauvignon Blanc Multifaceted **13** shows citrus, pear, green fig & sage, intensity deepens on the palate. Racy lemon/lime acidity, as on **12** (★★★★★) focuses the wine, giving length; so fresh & tightly held will age beautifully. WO W Cape, rest of range Stellenbosch.

Vineyard Selection

★★★★ Cabernet Sauvignon Barrel Matured With opulent cassis, **11** (★★★★☆) parades its ripeness & crafting, fleshy fruit on a bed of savoury tannin. Improves on **10**, more layered, richer, but with echoes of the gravelly, tobacco notes found there.

For more information, visit wineonaplatter.com

★★★★ **Pinot Noir** ⓥ Red cherry fruit on **11** (★★★★), less refined than **10**. A little sugar, warm alcohol & unintegrated acidity detract.

★★★★ **Shiraz Barrel Matured** **11** improves on **10** (★★★★) with black cherries & plums, enhanced by cocoa, sweet spice, a peppery note. The savoury oak needs rich dishes, gives musculature for further ageing.

★★★★ **Shiraz-Mourvèdre-Viognier** Improving on **11** (★★★★), **12**'s blend gives wild fruit, scrub, a delicate floral note. Meaty, savoury in style, there's enough juicy vitality to make this a delicious experience.

★★★★ **Chardonnay Barrel Fermented** Butterscotch, dried peach & orange peel, **13** is a proudly bold chardonnay, the oak & fruit layered throughout, opulent, rich. Just-dry, but the acidity gives freshness & length. WO W Cape, as for Shiraz-Mourvèdre-Viognier.

★★★★ **Chenin Blanc Barrel Fermented** Quince & green melon, pure & focused, **14** has lovely rounded texture. Partial barrel ferment, plus oak maturation, as for also-tasted **13**. Stonefruit & pear, with oatmeal savoury tones, ending fruity-fresh & tangy.

Cellar Selection

Gamay Noir ★★★ Now bottled, unoaked **13** softly juicy with good freshness to underpin the mulberry/brambleberry fruit. One of only a handful on the market. **Cabernet Sauvignon-Merlot** ★★★ Plush berries, smooth, juicy & vibrant, the 14 months French oaking well integrated. **12** has 'drink me' written all over it. **Gamay Noir Rosé** ★★★ Red berry fragrance & flavours, with a light-textured delicacy that makes dry **14** eminently drinkable. **Chenin Blanc Bush Vines** ⓥ ★★★★ Template for well-priced, fruity-style chenin, achieved through selective regional picking. **14** tropical, litchi & mango, yet a zesty citrus freshness throughout that has you reaching for a second glass. Also tasted: **Cabernet Sauvignon 12** ★★★ **Pinotage** ⓥ **12** ★★★★ **Chardonnay 14** ★★★ **Sauvignon Blanc 14** ★★★★ Not retasted: **Merlot 12** ★★★

Méthode Cap Classique Sparkling range ⓃⒺⓌ

★★★★ **Vintage Brut** Dry bubbly that oozes flavour & personality. **09** chardonnay/pinot noir, partial barrel ferment, 3 years on the lees. Lemon zest/brioche notes, great length. Same blend but **10** is fresher, drier. Citrus & red berries melded into a biscuity, fine-beaded delight. Both Stellenbosch WO.

Zalze range

Malbec Reserve ⓃⒺⓌ ★★ Fruitcake spiced with cloves & nutmeg, the tannins still firm but **13** is a youthful wine. There's enough fruit for a few years ageing, which will be to its benefit. **Sangiovese** ⓃⒺⓌ ★★★ Typical morello cherry nose, attractive savoury spice & dried herbs from 14 months French barrels, **13** finishes with the tannin dryness Italians love to match with pasta. WO W Cape. **Chenin Blanc Reserve** ⓃⒺⓌ ★★★★ Partial oak fermentation in new & older barrels shows in **12**'s palate density, oatmeal nuance in winter melon flavours. Nicely finished by lemony acidity. **Sauvignon Blanc** ⓃⒺⓌ ★★★ Intense slatey mineral & lime character, with accompanying lowish alcohol. **14** sleek & high toned, crisply fresh. WO W Cape. Also tasted: **Shiraz-Mourvèdre-Viognier** ⓥ **13** ★★★ **Shiraz-Grenache-Viognier 12** ★★★ **Cabernet Sauvignon-Shiraz Rosé 14** ★★★ **Bush Vine Chenin Blanc** ⓥ **14** ★★★ Not retasted: **Pinotage 10** ★★★ Note: range for export only.

Foot of Africa range

Chenin Blanc ⓥ ★★★ Powerfully fruity, including pineapple, **14** nicely rounded & tangy fresh. Also tasted: **Shiraz-Viognier 13** ★★ Note: these all exported. — CR

Location/map: Stellenbosch ▪ WO: Coastal/Western Cape/Stellenbosch ▪ Est 1695 ▪ 1stB 1997 ▪ Tasting & sales Mon-Sat 9–6 Sun 11–6 ▪ Fee R25/5 wines ▪ Closed Good Fri, Dec 25 & Jan 1 ▪ Terroir Restaurant ▪ Kleine Zalze Lodge ▪ De Zalze Golf Course ▪ Conference/function venue ▪ Owner(s) Kobus Basson ▪ Cellarmaster(s) Alastair Rimmer (Sep 2014) ▪ Winemaker(s) RJ Botha (Dec 2012), with Zara Conradie (Feb 2008) ▪ Viticulturist(s) Henning Retief (May 2006) ▪ 90ha/84ha (cab, merlot, shiraz, chenin, sauv) ▪ 2,300t/400,000cs own label 40% red 50% white 10% rosé ▪

PO Box 12837 Die Boord 7613 ▪ quality@kleinezalze.co.za ▪ www.kleinezalze.co.za ▪ S 33° 58' 14.1" E 018° 50' 8.9" ▪ F +27 (0)21-880-0716 ▪ **T +27 (0)21-880-0717**

Klein Gustrouw Estate

This early 18th century Jonkershoek Valley Cape Dutch homestead underwent a major facelift after its purchase in 2007 from the McDonald family, who had established the wine label. Development as a private residence and boutique producer by the new owners included wide-ranging replanting. The young vines are 'settling in nicely', says marketer Charité Volkwyn, and the sauvignon is now made entirely from own fruit.

★★★★ **Reserve** Ⓥ **11** blend of cab, cab franc & shiraz. Fresher & better defined than **10** (★★★☆), with a dry, firm, concentrated palate - fine-grained tannins needing time.

★★★★ **Sauvignon Blanc** Zesty **13** aromas of granadilla, cut grass & cape gooseberry. Dry palate is full & quite broad but with lift & zing. Return to quality of **09** after lesser previewed **12** (★★★☆). — JPf

Location: Stellenbosch ▪ WO: Jonkershoek Valley ▪ Est 1817 ▪ 1stB 1993 ▪ Closed to public ▪ Owner(s) Klein Gustrouw (Pty) Ltd ▪ Winemaker(s) Warren Ellis (2006) ▪ Viticulturist(s) Pieter Smit (consultant) ▪ ±23ha/±14ha under vine ▪ 70% red 30% white ▪ PO Box 6168 Uniedal 7612 ▪ info@kleingustrouw.co.za ▪ F +27 (0)86-609-7229 ▪ **T +27 (0)21-882-8152/+27 (0)82-445-4074**

Kleinhoekkloof

The De Jongh family members have nurtured their 'garden' of vines near Ashton in the Langeberg's rocky mountain soils and cool, breezy climate since acquiring Kleinhoekkloof in 2004. Having had initial vintages vinified at Robertson cellars, Theunis de Jongh has made small parcels aimed at niche markets in their boutique winery since 2011.

Location: Ashton ▪ Map: Robertson ▪ Est 2004 ▪ 1stB 2006 ▪ Phone ahead for opening hours ▪ Owner(s) Raudan Trust ▪ Cellarmaster(s)/winemaker(s) Theunis de Jongh (2011) ▪ Viticulturist(s) Loure van Zyl (Mar 2004, consultant) ▪ 114ha/11.8ha (merlot, p verdot, pinot, shiraz, sauv, viog) ▪ 110t/2,400cs own label 45% red 40% white 15% rosé ▪ Other export brand: Mountain Eye ▪ PO Box 95134 Waterkloof 0145 ▪ theunis@khk.co.za ▪ www.kleinhoekkloof.co.za ▪ S 33° 46' 51.87'' E 020° 03' 17.30'' ▪ F +27 (0)86-677-5399 ▪ **T +27 (0)23-615-2121**

☐ **Klein Kasteelberg** *see* Group CDV

☐ **Kleinood** *see* Tamboerskloof Wine – Kleinood Farm

Klein Optenhorst

This tiny, nearly quarter-century-old Wellington pinot noir vineyard, lovingly tended by retired airline pilot Naas Ferreira to once produce a red, was converted to champagne-method bubbly production in 2009. Supplementation with Shannon Vineyards grapes increased quantities from 2011's 600 bottles to 2012's just over 2,000, crafted by another Ferreira, Graham Beck's sparkling supremo Pieter.

★★★★ **Pinot Noir Méthode Cap Classique** Soupçon Elgin fruit in **12** (★★★★) sparkling. Friendly strawberries & cream aromas, crisp bright palate. Perfect for now, solo or with canapés; moreish, but less fine than **11**. — HJ

Location: Wellington ▪ Map: Paarl & Wellington ▪ WO: Western Cape ▪ Est/1stB 2001 ▪ Tasting & sales by appt ▪ Owner(s) Naas Ferreira ▪ Cellarmaster(s)/winemaker(s) Pieter Ferreira (2009, consultant) ▪ Viticulturist(s) Naas Ferreira (2001) ▪ 0.25ha (pinot) ▪ ±1t from own vyds, additional fruit from Shannon Vineyards in Elgin ▪ 100% rosé ▪ PO Box 681 Wellington 7654 ▪ kleinoptenhorstwines@gmail.com ▪ www.kleinoptenhorst.com ▪ S 33° 37' 48.60" E 019° 3' 19.54" ▪ **T +27 (0)21-864-1210**

Klein Parys Vineyards

Entrepreneurial vintner Kosie Möller, having honed his skills as KWV chief winemaker before rooting here in 2002, has turned historic grape-growing Paarl farm Klein Parys into a substantial wine

For more information, visit wineonaplatter.com

production and tourism enterprise. Rejuvenated and expanded vineyards and cellar (last used in the 1960s) feed an extensive portfolio, led by the Family Selection reflecting his experimental bent.

Family Selection
Charl Sias Selection ⓩ ★★★☆ Unusual bottle-fermented sparkling from chardonnay, nouvelle, viognier & sauvignon. Full-bodied & ripe **10** is technically bone-dry but leaves sweet impression from 14.5% alcohol. Not retasted: **Beatrix Selection 07** ★★★ Not tasted: **Jacob Selection**, **Niclas Selection**.

Kleine Parys Selection
Sauvignon Blanc ⓩ ★★★ Crisply quaffable tropical **13** dry & nicely light for summer. WO W Cape. Not retasted: **Shiraz 12** ★★★ **Chardonnay 13** ★★★ Not tasted: **Cabernet Sauvignon**, **Merlot**, **Pinotage**, **Pinotage Coffee Style**, **Chenin Blanc**, **Méthode Cap Classique**, **Red Muscadel**.

Tooverberg range
Contour Merlot ⓩ ★★★ Smooth, easy **11** red with sufficient savoury grip from 15% cab. WO W Cape. Not tasted: **Pinotage**, **Cabernet Sauvignon-Shiraz**, **Chenin Blanc**, **Chenin Blanc-Chardonnay**. — IM

Location: Paarl ▪ Map: Paarl & Wellington ▪ WO: Paarl/Western Cape ▪ Est 1692 ▪ 1stB 2002 ▪ Tasting, sales & cellar tours Tue-Sun 9–5 ▪ Tasting fee R30pp for 6 wines, waived on purchase of R50+ ▪ Closed Good Fri, Dec 25 & Jan 1 ▪ Facilities for children ▪ Conferences ▪ Weddings/functions ▪ Owner(s) Kosie Möller ▪ Cellarmaster(s)/winemaker(s) Kosie Möller (2002) ▪ 56ha/45ha (cab, shiraz, chard, chenin) ▪ 1,800t/500,000cs own label 48% red 48% white 4% sparkling + 1m cs for clients ▪ Brands for clients: Millers Mile ▪ PO Box 1362 Suider-Paarl 7624 ▪ logistics@kparys.co.za ▪ www.kleinparysvineyards.co.za ▪ S 33° 45' 0.2" E 018° 58' 48.6" ▪ F +27 (0)21-872-8527 ▪ **T +27 (0)21-872-9848**

Klein Roosboom

Karin de Villiers, energetic wife of Durbanville Hills grower Jean, started this boutique winery as a self-taught winemaker in 2007 'to bottle my husband's passion for the vine'. Her portfolio, each label dedicated to a family member, is as personalised and creative as the visitor experience.

Klein Roosboom range
Janét Shiraz ★★★ If only all mothers-in-law were this soft & approachable! **13** medium bodied, with red berries & sprinkle cinnamon from year French oak, 30% new. **Marné Brut Méthode Cap Classique** ★★★☆ Epitomising daughter's joie de vivre, **12** bubbles with white blossom & lemon from 75% chardonnay, rest pinot. Creamy & biscuity, finishing beautifully clean with cream cracker aftertaste. Also tasted: **Johan Cabernet Sauvignon 12** ★★★☆ **Nicol Merlot 12** ★★★ **My Way 12** ★★★☆ **Jean Sauvignon Blanc 14** ★★★

Bandana range
Not tasted: **Blanc**. — JG

Location/WO: Durbanville ▪ Map: Durbanville, Philadelphia & Darling ▪ Est 1984 ▪ 1stB 2007 ▪ Tasting, sales & cellar tours Tue-Fri 10-5 Sat/Sun 10-4 ▪ Fee R15, waived on purchase ▪ Closed Good Fri, Dec 25/26 & Jan 1 ▪ Cheese platters Sat/Sun; soup & bread in winter ▪ Café Ruby T +27 (0)21-975-7965 open for breakfast & lunch ▪ Facilities for children ▪ Tour groups ▪ Owner(s) Jean de Villiers Trust ▪ Cellarmaster(s)/winemaker(s) Karin de Villiers (2007) ▪ Viticulturist(s) Jean de Villiers (1984) ▪ 260ha/130ha (cab, merlot, shiraz, chard, sauv) ▪ 3,000cs own label 40% red 60% white ▪ Postnet Suite #3 Private Bag X19 Durbanville 7551 ▪ cellar@kleinroosboom.co.za ▪ www.kleinroosboom.co.za ▪ S 33° 49' 6.24" E 018° 34' 25.86" ▪ F +27 (0)21-975-7417 ▪ **T +27 (0)82-784-5102**

Klipdrift

This brandy and South African cultural icon originated in 1938 as the home brew of winegrower and distiller Kosie Marais on his Robertson farm Klipdrift. Man and brand are entertainingly presented at the town's trendy Klipdrift House and showcase boutique distillery, owned by Distell. Long popular with cola as a mixer ('Klippies and Coke'), the original, best-selling Export has been joined by a premium version and the much-awarded Gold.

★★★★☆ **Gold** ⓐ Seduces with complex aromas of dried apricot, raisin, orange peel & sweet spice. Finely textured, well rounded, much greater complexity than others. Vanilla & cinnamon come into greater focus just before long, fruit-filled finish. 100% potstill brandies of between 3 & 20 years age.

Export ⓐ ★★★☆ The famous 'Klippies', a standard blended brandy (30% potstill), but one of the best of its type. Rich ripe aromas with dried apricot, prune & toasty nut. Smooth & full bodied & a satisfying finish. From chenin & colombard, as are all in this range. **Premium** ⓐ ★★★☆ Blend of 5-year-matured potstill with 70% unmatured spirit. Richer & fuller than Export, with greater maturity bringing sweet tobacco & spice from oak. Powerful, but not too harsh to sip neat. — WB, TJ

☐ **Kloof Street** *see* Mullineux & Leeu Family Wines

Kloovenburg Wine & Olives

'Family' is core to owner Pieter du Toit's Riebeek-Kasteel wine and olive estate, named 'The Place in the Ravine'. First settled in 1704, wine hadn't been made on the property for four decades until Pieter, wife Annalene (who founded the olive business) and their children foot-stomped 200 bottles of shiraz in 1997. Vineyard renewal and maiden barrels of carignan, mourvèdre and grenache (with an eye on blends) are among the past year's highlights. Tasting venue and facility upgrades are next.

★★★★ **Cabernet Sauvignon** Best of these reds. Classic styling for previewed **12**, beautifully balanced blackcurrant fruit amongst supple, yielding tannins. Lipsmacking in youth, will reward a few years' patience.

★★★★ **Shiraz** **12** leaps back to form; white pepper spicing to medium-weight, athletic body. Yard ahead of very ripe **11** (★★★★) which lacked intensity & complexity of earlier vintages.

★★★★ **Eight Feet** Recognises the 4 children who crushed farm's first vintage. Previewed **12**, mostly shiraz, plump berry profile with heady spice. Gear up on all-shiraz **11** (★★★☆).

★★★★ **Naturally Fermented Chardonnay** Less oak (5 months), lower alcohol (13%) & dry profile of elegant, textured **13** maintains standard of **12** compared to weightier previous bottlings.

★★★★ **Cape Vintage Shiraz** ⓝ Well-judged **08** port-style is welcomely lighter feeling, fruitcake & all but not dense, over-sweet or spirituous. 375 ml.

White From Red Brut ★★★ Coppery pink **NV** dry sparkler; quiet cherry fruit lifted by busy bubble. WO W Cape. Also tasted: **Merlot 12** ★★★☆ **Shiraz Rosé 14** ★★★ **Barrel Fermented Chardonnay 14** ★★★★ **Sauvignon Blanc 14** ★★★☆ Not retasted: **Unwooded Chardonnay 13** ★★★★ — DS

Location: Riebeek-Kasteel ▪ Map: Swartland ▪ WO: Swartland/Western Cape ▪ Est 1704 ▪ 1stB 1998 ▪ Tasting & sales Mon-Fri 9–4.30 Sat 9–2 Sun at Kloovenburg Pastorie Guesthouse 10.30-2 ▪ Fee R10 wine/olive tasting ▪ Closed Easter Fri-Mon, Dec 25/26 & Jan 1 ▪ Cellar tours during tasting hours ▪ Tour groups ▪ Gift shop ▪ Farm produce/olive products ▪ BYO picnic ▪ Walks/hikes ▪ Conservation area ▪ Christmas Market (Dec) ▪ Owner(s) Pieter du Toit ▪ Cellarmaster(s)/winemaker(s) Pieter du Toit (Jan 1998) ▪ Viticulturist(s) Kobus van Graan (Jan 1998, consultant) ▪ 300ha/130ha (cab, merlot, shiraz, chard, sauv) ▪ 229t/24,000cs own label 55% red 40% white 4% rosé 1% sparkling ▪ PO Box 2 Riebeek-Kasteel 7307 ▪ info@kloovenburg.com ▪ www.kloovenburg.com ▪ S 33° 23' 36.3" E 018° 53' 27.5" ▪ F +27 (0)22-448-1035 ▪ **T +27 (0)22-448-1635**

For more information, visit wineonaplatter.com

Knorhoek Wines

The successful wedding and function business on Knorhoek, along with many other amenities, have made the picturesque Simonsberg family farm a popular destination. The wines fit right in, with their spread of varieties and styles to suit the fine food, and a value range to sip around the tree-shaded lake. Also fitting right in is new winemaker Barry van Niekerk, youngest son of co-owner/viticulturist James. Barry and Nina Bougas recently married – you know where – with the groom dressed in shorts and the two farm Bouvier 'bridesmaids' fetchingly accessorised with a Greek flag for a scarf.

Pantére range

★★★★☆ **Cabernet Sauvignon** ⊘ Still far off its peak, dark fruited **11** built for the long haul. Carefully made, its firm backbone has been crafted with the aid of 24 months new oak.

★★★★ **Bordeaux Blend** Bold fruitcake styling on **11**, like **09** a cab-led Bordeaux blend. Assured & rich, with layered, integrated fruit & oak, all-new French 2 years. Structured for the long haul. No **10**.

★★★★ **Chenin Blanc** Heady honey notes vie with lively acid on confidently ripe **13**. Bright granadilla & peach supported by subtle oak. Similar to **12** (★★★★☆) though not as opulent.

Knorhoek range

★★★★ **Cabernet Franc** Fynbos coats spicy plum fruit on **12**. Light tannic grip echoes that of last-made **09** in its approachability. Good typicity to graphite & pencil shaving nuance.

Pinotage ★★★★ **12** ups the ante with lighter red-fruit juiciness; spicy, with noticeable oak from staves. **Chenin Blanc** ★★★ Light melon & pineapple tropicality to easy-drinking **13**. Also tasted: **Merlot 12** ★★★★ Not tasted: **Cabernet Sauvignon**, **Shiraz**, **Sauvignon Blanc**. In abeyance: **Konfetti Rosé Sparkling**. Discontinued: **HVN Cape Ruby**.

Two Cubs range

Red Blend ⊘ ★★★ Name change prompted by addition of pinotage to 3-way Bordeaux blend. Muted coffee edge on **12**, juicy & friendly, with light spicy succulence. Stellenbosch WO. Also tasted: **Chenin Blanc 14** ★★★ **Sauvignon Blanc 14** ★★★ Not tasted: **Rosé**. Occasional release: **Pinotage**. Discontinued: **White Blend**. — FM

Location/map: Stellenbosch ▪ WO: Simonsberg–Stellenbosch/Stellenbosch ▪ Est 1827 ▪ 1stB 1997 ▪ Tasting, sales & cellar tours daily 10–5 ▪ Fee R20/5 wines ▪ Closed Dec 25 ▪ Towerbosch Restaurant Wed-Sun 11.30-3.30 (Sat/Sun booking essential T +27 (0)21-865-2958) ▪ Facilities for children ▪ Tour groups ▪ Gift shop ▪ Weddings/conferences ▪ Hiking trail ▪ Horse riding ▪ Conservation area ▪ 3-star guesthouse & self-catering cottages ▪ Owner(s) Hansie & James van Niekerk ▪ Cellarmaster(s)/winemaker(s) Barry van Niekerk (Jan 2014) ▪ Viticulturist(s) James van Niekerk (1977) ▪ ±80ha (cabs s/f, merlot, ptage, shiraz, chenin, sauv) ▪ 640t/20,000cs own label 51% red 42% white 4.65% rosé 2.35% sparkling ▪ 184,500L bulk ▪ BWI ▪ PO Box 2 Koelenhof 7605 ▪ office@knorhoek.co.za, cellar@knorhoek. co.za, towerbosch@knorhoek.co.za ▪ www.knorhoek.co.za ▪ S 33° 52′ 44.8″ E 018° 52′ 19.1″ ▪ F +27 (0)21-865-2627 ▪ **T +27 (0)21-865-2114**

☐ **Kobus** *see* Havana Hills
☐ **Koelenbosch** *see* Koelenhof Winery

Koelenhof Winery

Stalwart Stellenbosch grower-owned winery Koelenhof's own labels offer something for everybody at affordable prices. Recent vintages have seen record-breaking crops; investment in barrel, bin and bottle storage facilities; and overseas market demand led by China. Additions to the visitor facilities include the new Ella's Bistro.

Koelenbosch range

Nineteenfortyone ★★★ Honours cellar's founding date. **12** from cab, shiraz & merlot. Fruitcake perfume, fresh & juicy, smooth palate for easy drinking. 2 years oak fully integrated. **Chenin Blanc Wooded** ★★★ Oak dominates but **13** is attractive nonetheless, savoury, a match for richly flavoured dishes. Also tasted: **Sauvignon Blanc 14 ★★ Méthode Cap Classique** ⊘ **09 ★★★** Not retasted: **Merlot 11 ★★★ Sangiovese 12 ★★ Shiraz 11 ★★☆** Not tasted: **Pinotage.** Discontinued: **Pinotage Rosé.**

Koelenhof range

Koelenhoffer ★★★ From sauvignon, **14** greenpepper & fresh peas, tangy off-dry finish from acid/ touch sugar combo. **Sauvignon Blanc Vin Sec** ⊘ **★★★ 12** gooseberry & passionfruit throughout, semi-sweet party fare. **Hanepoot** ⊘ **★★★ 13** fortified dessert, shy but attractive melon & fynbos perfume & flavours. Good acidity freshens the sweetness, gives a lovely drinkability. Also tasted: **Koelnektar 13 ★★ Pinorto 12 ★★★** Not retasted: **Koelenberg 11 ★★ Pinotage Rosé 12 ★★ Pinotage Rosé Vin Sec 12 ★☆** — CR

Location/map/WO: Stellenbosch ▪ Est 1941 ▪ 1stB 1970's ▪ Tasting & sales Mon-Thu 9–5 Fri 9–4 Sat/pub hols 10–2 ▪ Closed Easter Fri/Sun, Ascension day & Dec 25 ▪ Facilities for children ▪ BYO picnic ▪ Conference/function venue ▪ Ella's Bistro ▪ Owner(s) 67 shareholders ▪ GM Andrew de Vries (2006) ▪ Winemaker(s) Martin Stevens (Nov 2003) & Wilhelm de Vries (2002), with Erika van Zyl (Jun 2011) ▪ Viticulturist(s) Wilhelm de Vries (2010) ▪ 16,500t/22,000cs own label 45% red 45% white 8% rosé 2% fortified + 2,000cs for clients & 100,000L bulk ▪ Other export brand: Simonsbosch ▪ IPW ▪ PO Box 1 Koelenhof 7605 ▪ koelwyn@mweb.co.za ▪ www.koelenhof.co.za ▪ S 33° 50' 5.2" E 018° 47' 52.7" ▪ F +27 (0)21-865-2796 ▪ **T +27 (0)21-865-2020/1**

Koelfontein

Being a tad off the beaten track in Ceres Valley, Handri Conradie and his team are understandably excited about their new online store which, with a few clicks, bring the wines of their cool-climate estate to the homes of winelovers around the world. Vineyards account for a tiny portion of the irrigated farmland, but they're clearly lavished with much attention by viticulturist Hennie van Noordwyk and consultant winemaker Dewaldt Heyns of Saronsberg in Tulbagh.

★★★★ Shiraz Two vintages tasted: plush **10** outclasses **11 (★★★☆)** with its violets, smoky plums, dark chocolate. Supple oak tannins give ageing backbone, savoury tones. A silky delight.

★★★★☆ Chardonnay Approach is richly savoury, walnuts & hazelnuts but **12** has more than enough fruit & flesh to handle this oak influence; lime & passionfruit threaded throughout, lingering long. Will age gracefully. — CR

Location/WO: Ceres ▪ Map: Tulbagh ▪ Est 1832 ▪ 1stB 2002 ▪ Tasting & sales Mon-Fri 9-4 Sat 10-1 ▪ Closed all pub hols ▪ Farm produce ▪ BYO picnic ▪ Walks/hikes ▪ Conservation area ▪ Die Kloof self-catering historic house (sleeps 6) ▪ Die Snystoor function venue ▪ Owner(s) Handri Conradie ▪ Winemaker(s) Dewaldt Heyns (2004) ▪ Viticulturist(s) Hennie van Noordwyk ▪ 950ha/±6ha (shiraz, chard) ▪ ±24t/2,400cs own label 50% red 50% white ▪ BWI ▪ PO Box 4 Prince Alfred's Hamlet 6840 ▪ wine@koelfontein.co.za ▪ www.koelfontein.co.za ▪ S 33° 15' 54.70" E 019° 19' 29.28" ▪ F +27 (0)23-313-3137 ▪ **T +27 (0)23-313-3304/3538**

☐ **Koffieklip** see Koopmanskloof Wingerde
☐ **Kogmans Kloof** see Zandvliet Wine Estate & Thoroughbred Stud

Koopmanskloof Wingerde

With the produce of six farms — one owned, managed and run by employees — in Stellenbosch's Bottelary Hills, winemaker Stephan Smit has a lot to work with. And more's to come, with 14 ha of cabernet, shiraz and chardonnay recently planted. All activities are nature driven (100 ha set aside for conservation), and the wines certified Fairtrade.

Koopmanskloof range

Merlot ⓝⓔⓦ **★★★ 13** fine core of mulberry & plum fruit, graphite underpin. Dry but juicy, tasty cocoa-rich tail. **Shiraz** ⊘ **★★★★** Charming **13** goes up a notch with spicy plum, cherry ripeness. Shows restraint & body, length too. **Pinotage Rosé ★★★** Improved tangy, fresh dry **14** is appealing, with raspberry vivacity. Ideal summertime quaffer. **Chardonnay ★★★** Zippy citrus on fresh unwooded **14**. Attractive body with some lees adding heft. **Chenin Blanc** ⊘ **★★★** Pear & ripe stonefruit see **14** pip previous for charm & presence. Commendable breadth, structure & balance. Also tasted: **Cabernet Sauvignon** ⊘ 13 ★★★★ **Pinotage** 12 ★★★ **Sauvignon Blanc** ⊘ 14 ★★★ Not retasted: **Motherblocks Carignan** 11 ★★★ **Cabernet Sauvignon-Shiraz** 12 ★★★ **Bushvine Chenin Blanc** 12 ★★★ **Sauvignon Blanc-Semillon** 11 ★★★ Discontinued: **Shiraz Rosé**.

Koffieklip range

Pinotage ⊘ ★★★ Smoky mocha appeal to **10**, quite chunky, for hearty country fare. — FM

Location/WO: Stellenbosch ▪ Est 1801 ▪ 1stB 1970 ▪ Private Nature Reserve ▪ Owner(s) Managed by Koopmanskloof Wingerde (Pty) Ltd ▪ Winemaker(s) Stephan Smit ▪ Viticulturist(s) Louwtjie Vlok ▪ 457ha (cab, carignan, merlot, ptage, roobernet, ruby cab, shiraz, chard, chenin, sauv, sem) ▪ ±3,700t/±2.5m L 40% red 60% white ▪ Other brands: Vredehoek, One World ▪ BWI, Fairtrade, IPW, WIETA ▪ PO Box 19 Koelenhof 7605 ▪ info@koopmanskloof.co.za ▪ www. koopmanskloof.co.za ▪ F +27 (0)86-560-7145 ▪ **T +27 (0)21-865-2355**

Kranskop Wines

This high-lying Langeberg Mountain vineyard is where Robertson-raised Newald Marais (30 years in corporate winemaking; consulting here before assuming sole ownership in 2010) has always wanted to be: hands in soil making wine to share as an experience. A new production cellar affords quiet satisfaction, presaging new wines, more plantings and deeper insights for visitors.

★★★★ **Viognier** 13 (★★★★) manages to display the variety's aromas with some restraint, lovely peach notes under the floral perfume. Racy acidity gives it some longevity, but the flavours lack **12**'s balance, though could settle with time.

Cabernet Sauvignon ★★★ Mint chocolate note to **11**'s blackcurrants, smooth textured & appealing, accessible, tannins well assimilated. **Chardonnay** ★★★★ Care taken here shows in **13**'s citrus peel & buttery oak flavours, limy freshness & length. Handsorted grapes, partial barrel ferment, then further oak maturation, 50% new. Also tasted: **Pinot Noir** 11 ★★★ **Sauvignon Blanc** 14 ★★★ Not retasted: **Merlot** 10 ★★★ **Shiraz** 10 ★★★ Not tasted: **Viognier Noble Late Harvest**. — CR

Location/map: Robertson ▪ WO: Klaasvoogds ▪ Est 2001 ▪ 1stB 2003 ▪ Tasting, sales & tours Mon-Fri 10-4.30 Sat & pub hols 10-2 ▪ Closed Easter Sun & Dec 25 ▪ BYO picnic ▪ Owner(s)/viticulturist(s) Newald Marais ▪ Cellarmaster(s)/ winemaker(s) Newald Marais (2008) ▪ 43ha/30ha (cab, merlot, pinot, tannat, chard, sauv, viog) ▪ 240t/ 3,000cs own label 75% red 25% white ▪ BWI, IPW ▪ PO Box 49 Klaasvoogds 6707 ▪ newald@kranskopwines.co.za ▪ www.kranskopwines.co.za ▪ S 33° 47' 53.1" E 019° 59' 56.6" ▪ F +27 (0)23-626-3200 ▪ **T +27 (0)23-626-3200**

☐ **Krone** see Twee Jonge Gezellen Estate-House of Krone

Kronendal Boutique Winery

Trained botanist Magdaleen Kroon's plans for an indigenous nursery on her family's 2ha property dried up through lack of water, so she planted vines instead. Quite unusually for Durbanville, she chose Rhône varieties but they - unlike the intended fynbos! — have proved a great success, and the resulting blend over half a decade has remained true to its Latin name — 'To Wonder At'.

★★★★ **Mirari** Easy-drinking yet satisfying **11**, shiraz-led blend with flavoursome gamey, earthy input from mourvèdre, tempranillo, dash viognier. Well rounded, balanced. — AL

Location/WO: Durbanville ▪ Map: Durbanville, Philadelphia & Darling ▪ Est 2003 ▪ 1stB 2006 ▪ Tasting, sales & cellar tours by appt ▪ Conference facilities ▪ Art ▪ Seasonal 'langtafel' lunches ▪ Owner(s) Pieter & Magdaleen Kroon ▪ Winemaker(s) Magdaleen Kroon ▪ 2ha/0.6ha (mourv, shiraz, tempranillo, viog) ▪ 4t/520cs own label 100% red ▪ PO Box 4433 Durbanville 7551 ▪ info@kronendalwine.co.za ▪ http://kronendal.belmet.co.za ▪ S 33° 48' 30.78" E 018° 36' 50.82" ▪ F +27 (0)86-603-1170 ▪ **T +27 (0)82-499-0198**

Kulsen Wines

Being part of the Cape Winemakers Guild Protégé Programme (2012–2014), with mentorships at prestigious guild member estates, inspired Heinrich Kulsen to start his own wine business. Eco-friendly vinification of old bushvine white varieties and Mediterranean reds that truly reflect the South African terroir, and are approachable and affordable, is his aim. 'Wine is about the love you put into it, and I'm inspired by my forefathers who all have worked the land at some stage in their lives.'

★★★★ Dimples Barrel Fermented Chenin Blanc Quince, with white pepper & celery spicing on rich, 70% new-barrel-fermented **13**. Touch botrytis adds complexity, even more depth to layered form, flavours just-dry, tangy. From 30 year old Villiera bushvines. — CR, CvZ

Location/WO: Stellenbosch ▪ Est/1stB 2013 ▪ Tasting by appt only ▪ Owner(s) Heinrich Kulsen ▪ Cellarmaster(s)/winemaker(s) Heinrich Kulsen (2013) ▪ kulsenwines@gmail.com ▪ www.kulsenwines.co.za ▪ **T +27 (0)73-234-6315**

Kumala

Owned by multinational Accolade Wines, Kumala sells some 20 million litres annually in the United Kingdom, and ranks as the No 1 South African brand there. The wines are sourced from various regions across the Western Cape and available in 40 countries worldwide, including the local market. Public tasting and sales are offered at sibling label Flagstone Winery's cellardoor in Somerset West.

Zenith range

Chenin Blanc-Chardonnay ⊘ **★★★** Dried apricot & rosepetal on lightly wooded **14**. Crisp & fresh, with appealing tangy fruit. Also tasted: **Merlot-Cabernet Sauvignon-Shiraz** ⊘ 13 **★★★** **Rosé** ⊘ 14 **★★★**

Reserve range

Shiraz ★★★☆ 12's sour cherries spiced with oak, is light & fresh (despite 14% alcohol), with oodles of quaffing appeal. Also tasted: **Chenin Blanc 13 ★★★☆**

Winemakers Release (NEW)

Ruby Cabernet-Merlot-Pinotage ★★★ Tangy red fruit, hint of mint, dash of sweetness but fairly balanced **13**.

Dragon's Back (NEW)

Medium Sweet Rosé ★★ Off-dry **NV** from pinotage & muscat, very light body, pleasantly crisp. Also tasted: **Dry Red NV ★☆ Dry White NV ★☆ Medium Sweet White NV ★☆ Medium Sweet Red NV ★**

Core range

Cabernet Sauvignon-Shiraz ⊘ **★★★** 13 has fair body & substance, leafy notes & sweet black cherry attraction. **Cape Red ★★** Was 'Dry Red'. Mostly ruby cab. Light & juicy **NV** for uncomplicated anytime enjoyment. **Chardonnay** ⊘ **★★★** 14 fuller, riper than previous, with solid lime fruit, barely perceptible oak. **Colombard-Chardonnay** ⊘ **★★★** Unusual pairing has fruit & substance, hint of buttery citrus in **13**. Briefly wooded. **Chenin Blanc-Chardonnay ★★★** Pleasantly fruity, just off-dry **14** lightly wooded tank sample, for chilled refreshment. **Chenin Blanc-Viognier** ⊘ **★★★** Peach & pineapple, tangy acid; **13** shows more character than rest of range. For export only. Also tasted: **Merlot-Pinotage 13 ★★☆ Pinotage-Shiraz** ⊘ 13 **★★★ Shiraz-Mourvèdre** ⊘ 13 **★★★ Merlot-Ruby Cabernet 13 ★★ Rosé 13 ★★ Chardonnay-Semillon 13 ★★ Sauvignon Blanc-Colombard 13 ★★ Sauvignon Blanc-Semillon 13 ★★★ Cape White NV ★★ Medium Sweet White NV ★☆ Cape Medium Sweet Red NV ★★** Not retasted: **Shiraz 12 ★★**

Eternal range

Chenin Blanc-Chardonnay-Semillon ★★☆ Candy confection, fruity & ripe **14**, pleasant sipping. Also tasted: **Merlot-Cabernet Sauvignon-Shiraz 13 ★★★** — GdB

Location: Somerset West ▪ Map: Helderberg ▪ WO: Western Cape ▪ Tasting, sales & cellar tours at Flagstone Winery (see entry) ▪ Owner(s) Accolade Wines South Africa ▪ Winemaker(s) Ben Jordaan (Jul 2002), Bruce Jack (Feb 2008) & Karen Bruwer (Oct 2008) ▪ 50% red 50% white ▪ PO Box 769 Stellenbosch 7599 ▪ flagstone@accolade-wines.com ▪ www.kumala.co.za ▪ S 34° 5′ 26.38″ E 018° 48′ 30.04″ ▪ F +27 (0)21-852-5085 ▪ **T +27 (0)21-852-5052**

☐ **Kumkani** *see* Thandi Wines

Kupferberger Auslese

Liquid history, this 1952 Distell stalwart was among the first to benefit from cold and controlled fermentation of white wines.

Kupferberger Auslese ★★ Latest **NV** from widely sourced chenin is lightish, simple, but sweetness is better balanced than previous. — DB

KWV

Founded in 1918 as the Ko-operatiewe Wijnbouwers Vereniging van Zuid-Afrika, later accorded statutory control over the Cape wine industry, KWV has evolved into a producer of over 100 products represented in more than 100 markets globally, and a leader in the arena of black economic empowerment. Its long-standing international reputation for fine wines, fortifieds and brandies is matched by modern wine tourism initiatives, no more visibly than at stately La Concorde HQ in Paarl. The Sensorium, pairing a major SA artwork collection with fine-wine tastings, is a venue for collaborations with SA creatives (foodies, designers, musicians). Note: KWV's wine ranges and brands (Bonne Esperance, Café Culture, Cathedral Cellar, Classic Collection, Concordia, Laborie, Pearly Bay, Reserve Collection and Roodeberg) not tasted this edition.

KWV Brandies

★★★★ 5 Year Old Superior ⓦ Dark amber colour; notes of sweet caramel, fruit, nuts & vanilla. Excellent balance, clean & lightly fiery on sweet-tinged finish. Blended; could compete with pure potstills on their turf!

★★★★☆ 10 Year Old Vintage ⓦ Enticing nose of apricot, raisin, red berry fruit & spice on vintage style. Full bodied & well rounded, with more complexity, power & oak than 5YO, but perhaps less charm. Long-lingering, fruity, slightly sweet finish.

★★★★★ 15 Year Old Alambic ⓦ Attractive honey, soft spice & dried fruit with floral backing & some fine oak. Smooth, fine texture & good balance; great complexity from a range of citrus & rich fruitcake flavours. Mellow & mature, with everlasting finish. 100% potstill, as next.

★★★★★ 20 Year Old ⓦ Exquisite aromas - sandalwood, apricot, scented flowers, hints spice & oxidative maturity. Rich & full, yet super-refined & delicate. A touch less forceful than 15YO, but more grace. Beautifully balanced, with supreme oak support. Long, mellow, mature notes carry to slightly sweet finish. Thrilling!

★★★★★ 12 Year Old Barrel Select ⓝⒺⓌ ⊘ On its first outing this potstill grabbed the World Brandy Award at the International Wine & Spirit Competition 2014. Rich, robust with caramelised nuts, sun-dried peaches, peardrop on the nose. The palate is that & more. Layers of cashew nut flavours melt in the mouth, honey, dark chocolate & fine sprinkling of spice. A triumph.

★★★★ Imoya Fine Potstill ⓦ Modern & beautifully presented. Fresh fruity aromas & flavours. Elegant, rich balance, subtle texture with nutty, spicy oak in support, lifted with a fresh spirity finish.

3 Year Old Finest Blend ⓦ **★★★★** Less aggressive than many young blended brandies - sippable neat. Fruity apricot nose with caramel, roasted nuts, dark molasses. Sufficiently complex, balanced.

KWV Sherry-Styles

★★★★ Cape Medium Cream ⓦ Golden brown, with candied apricot, orange peel & caramelised nuts. Balanced, fresh yet savoury, gentle spirity warmth. Chenin & colombard, year in barrel, 4-6 in solera, as next.

★★★★ **Cape Full Cream** Pale amber hue. Stewed fruit, a delightful floral note. Layered nuts & rich caramel, complex, elegant. Although sweet, uncloying finish is savoury, lifted by a spirity glow. — WB, CR, TJ

Location: Paarl ▪ Map: Paarl & Wellington ▪ WO: Western Cape/Worcester ▪ KWV Wine Emporium: Kohler Street, T +27 (0)21-807-3007/8 F +27 (0)21-807-3119, friederm@kwv.co.za, www.kwvwineemporium.co.za ▪ Tasting & sales Mon-Sat 9–4.30 Sun 11-4 ▪ Several food & wine pairings available ▪ Cellar tours: Eng Mon-Sat 10, 10.30 & 2.15; Ger 10.15; Sun Eng 11 ▪ Tour groups by appt ▪ Closed Good Fri, Dec 25 & Jan 1 ▪ KWV Sensorium: 57 Main Road, T +27 (0)21-807-3094, sensorium@kwv.co.za, www.kwvsensorium.co.za ▪ Tasting, sales & art museum Mon-Fri 9-4.30 Sat 9-2 ▪ Art & wine pairing ▪ Owner(s) KWV (Pty) Ltd ▪ Chief winemaker Johann Fourie ▪ Winemaker(s) Anneke du Plessis, Izelle van Blerk, Louwritz Louw & Kobus van der Merwe ▪ Viticulturist(s) Marco Ventralla & De Wet Hugo ▪ PO Box 528 Suider-Paarl 7624 ▪ customer@kwv.co.za ▪ www.kwv.co.za ▪ S 33° 45' 46.87" E 018° 57' 59.92" (Emporium), S 33° 45' 43.26" E 018° 57' 44.06" (Sensorium) ▪ F +27 (0)21-807-3000 ▪ **T +27 (0)21-807-3911 (office)**

Kyburg Wine Estate

Only a third of the crop from Fred and Rosmarie Ruest's Devon Valley property is vinified; the balance is sold to well-known private producers. The wines undergo extended bottle-maturation at the cellar and are released only when deemed ready for drinking.

Cabernet Sauvignon ★★★☆ Bright cassis flavours, fruit richness in balance with generous tannic base on **09**. Like 08 (★★★★) had development potential. These all tasted few years back. Not retasted: **Merlot 09 ★★★★ Shiraz 09 ★★★★ 33 Latitude 09 ★★★☆** — AL

Location/map: Stellenbosch ▪ WO: Devon Valley ▪ Est 1998 ▪ 1stB 2006 ▪ Tasting & sales by appt ▪ Closed Easter Sun, Dec 25/26 & Jan 1 ▪ Self-catering guesthouse (exclusive use - rental min 2 weeks) ▪ Owner(s) Fred & Rosmarie Ruest ▪ Cellarmaster(s)/winemaker(s) Jacques Fourie (Jan 2006, consultant) & Chris Keet (2013, consultant) ▪ Viticulturist(s) Frans Snyman (Jul 2006, consultant) ▪ 28ha/18ha (cab, merlot, shiraz) ▪ 150-160t/5,000cs own label 100% red ▪ PO Box 12799 Die Boord 7613 ▪ info@kyburgwine.com ▪ www.kyburgwine.com ▪ S 33° 54' 59.3" E 018° 49' 28.4" ▪ **T +27 (0)21-865-2876**

☐ **La Bonne Vigne** *see* Wonderfontein

Laborie Wine Farm

On the edge of bustling Paarl, KWV-owned showcase Laborie is an island of tranquility. Vineyards stretch up Paarl mountain, the historic buildings have been tastefully restored and visitors are offered a wide range of experiences. The wine range is equally comprehensive and includes some specialisations, such as MCC sparkling, shiraz and the unique Pineau de Laborie, sweet pinotage fortified with pinotage brandy. Newest offering is a low-alcohol range, Lazy Days.

Location: Paarl ▪ Map: Paarl & Wellington ▪ Est 1691 ▪ Tasting & sales Mon-Sat 9-5 Sun 11-5 ▪ Fee R20/5 wines R30/ farm tour & tasting ▪ Chocolate & wine pairing R35 ▪ Olive & wine pairing R30 ▪ Closed all Christian pub hols ▪ Tours for large groups by appt ▪ Harvest Restaurant ▪ Carols by Candlelight ▪ Conferences ▪ Weddings/functions ▪ Laborie Guest House ▪ Owner(s) KWV (Pty) Ltd ▪ Winemaker(s) Johann Fourie & Kobus van der Merwe ▪ Viticulturist(s) Marco Ventrella, with De Wet Hugo ▪ Brandy master Pieter de Bod (Nov 2011) ▪ (ptage, pinots noir/meunier, shiraz, chard, chenin, sauv) ▪ BWI, IPW, WIETA ▪ PO Box 528 Suider Paarl 7624 ▪ info@laboriewines.co.za ▪ www.laboriewines.co.za ▪ S 33° 45' 55.2" E 018° 57' 27.6" ▪ F +27 (0)21-863-1955 ▪ **T +27 (0)21-807-3390**

La Bri Estate

This is, says owner Robin Hamilton with simple eloquence, 'a small, quiet, very beautiful place'. It is also the name-bearing part of the first farm allocated to the refugee Huguenots in what was to become known as the Franschhoek Valley. Three centuries on, Irene Waller is building a fine reputation, not least through many competition successes, for crafted, eminently drinkable wines.

★★★★ **Cabernet Sauvignon Limited Release** Adds descriptor to varietal name in **12**. Made only in best years - last was softer **09** (★★★☆). Interesting floral, cassis & earthy tones, with tightly wound palate whose firm, slightly grainy tannin should even out in time. Also sold in magnum.

For more information, visit wineonaplatter.com

★★★★ **Syrah** Pleasing **12** with drop of viognier shows intense aromas & an open, fresh, vibrant, lingering palate supported by well-integrated oak. Touch less alcoholic power than **11** (★★★★).

★★★★ **Affinity 12** Bordeaux blend led by merlot & cab. Plush, rich berry notes; the open, well-structured palate densely packed with inviting dark-fruit flavours & hints of toasty oak (50% new).

Viognier Limited Release ★★★★ Adds 'Limited Release' in **13**, which is more restrained & finer than previous. Perfumed, floral nose, the palate broad & intense yet with enough lift to sustain its rich fruit. Only older oak. Also tasted: **Merlot 12** ★★★★ **Chardonnay 13** ★★★★ — JPf

Location/map/WO: Franschhoek ▪ Est 1694 ▪ Tasting, sales & cellar tours Mon-Fri 10-5 Sat 10.30-4 ▪ Fee R35pp, waived on purchase ▪ Closed Easter Fri/Mon, Dec 25/26 & Jan 1 ▪ Chocolate & wine pairing; biltong & wine experience ▪ Cheese platters ▪ Bicycle friendly ▪ Old wine cellar open by appt ▪ Weddings & functions ▪ Part of Franschhoek tram route ▪ Owner(s) Robin Hamilton ▪ Winemaker(s) Irene Waller (Oct 2010), with Glen Isaacs (Jun 2009) ▪ Viticulturist(s) Gerard Olivier (Oct 2010) ▪ ±20ha/±15ha (cabs s/f, merlot, p verdot, shiraz, chard, viog) ▪ 120t/8,000cs own label 80% red 20% white ▪ PO Box 180 Franschhoek 7690 ▪ info@labri.co.za ▪ www.labri.co.za ▪ S 33° 55' 18.3" E 019° 7' 1.5" ▪ F +27 (0)86-275-9753 ▪ **T +27 (0)21-876-2593**

☐ **La Capra** *see* Fairview
☐ **La Cave** *see* Wellington Wines
☐ **Lace** *see* Almenkerk Wine Estate

La Chataigne

Old-vine chenin and semillon have pride of place for Richard Parkfelt and family at 'The Chestnut' estate near Franschhoek. Their wines are boutique styled, with handwritten labels and limited bottlings reflecting passion and dedication. Fine guest cottages against a picturesque backdrop allow visitors to linger longer.

Kastanje ★★★★ From low-yielding chenin with dash semillon, unoaked. **13** true to form: concentrated dried fruit aromas & flavours, good pithy citrus texture & dry finish. **Sauvignon Blanc** ★★★ Waxy bottle age character, property's signature grapefruit aromas & tastes on zesty **13**; less focus than previous. Also tasted: **Marron 10** ★★★ Not retasted: **Semillon 12** ★★★ Not tasted: **Rosé**. — CvZ

Location/map/WO: Franschhoek ▪ Est 1972 ▪ 1stB 2003 ▪ Tasting & sales Mon-Sun 10-4 ▪ Closed all pub hols ▪ 3 guest cottages ▪ Owner(s) Parkfelt family ▪ Winemaker(s) Gerda Willers (2003, consultant) ▪ 27ha/17ha (cab, merlot, ptage, shiraz, chenin, sauv, sem) ▪ 200t/4,000cs own label 25% red 65% white 10% rosé ▪ PO Box 301 Franschhoek 7690 ▪ office@lachat.co.za ▪ www.lachat.co.za ▪ S 33° 52' 43.8" E 019° 3' 34.1" ▪ F +27 (0)86-545-1039 ▪ **T +27 (0)21-876-3220**

La Chaumiere Estate

Oryx Steel's Michael Pawlowski and partner Kristina's brief holiday in Franschhoek blossomed into a long-term love affair, and with man-on-the-ground Wynand Pienaar they're developing their riverside boutique property in stages. Vineyard replanting, range expansion (with input from other Pawlowski vineyards) and renovations complete, they're extending the cellar.

★★★★ **Pinot Noir 13** unshowy but engaging black & red fruit, slightly earthy tones. Dry finish & enlivening acidity extend the palate to a spicy conclusion laced with well-judged oak (30% new).

Méthode Cap Classique ★★★ New disgorgement of **10** sparkler from chardonnay steps up: elegant glassful of lemon, nut & brioche, more complexity courtesy longer (30 months) lees-ageing. Export only, as all these. Also tasted: **Cabernet Sauvignon 12** ★★★ **Shiraz 12** ★★★★ **Chardonnay 13** ★★★ — GM

Location/map: Franschhoek ▪ WO: Franschhoek/Western Cape ▪ Est 2001 ▪ 1stB 2003 ▪ Tasting & cellar tours by appt ▪ Sales from local outlets ▪ Owner(s) Michael Pawlowski ▪ Winemaker(s)/viticulturist(s) Wynand Pienaar ▪ 5ha (cab, pinot, shiraz, chard) ▪ 24t/3,400cs own label ▪ PO Box 601 Franschhoek 7690 ▪ wynlpers@iafrica.com ▪ S 33° 54' 34.0" E 019° 6' 54.9" ▪ F +27 (0)21-876-2135 ▪ **T +27 (0)21-876-4830/31**

La Couronne Wines

One of Franschhoek's original French Huguenot properties, this boutique mountainside farm has had multiple owners — including the exotic but absent president Omar Bongo of Gabon — to settle into its present three-part role of offering luxury accommodation, good food and fine wine. Rejuvenation sees a new winemaker, revamped restaurant and wine packaging and, next, a wooded chardonnay.

Malbec ★★★★ Jammy blackberry & spice combine with savoury undertones of iodine, black olives & smoke in juicy **12**. Most serious in the range. **Starboard White Sauvignon Blanc ★★☆** Crisp & light, bone-dry but packed with tropical flavours, **14** will reward fans of the style. Also tasted: **Merlot 13 ★★☆ Pinotage 12 ★★★ Shiraz 12 ★★★ Portside Red 12 ★★ Merlot Rosé 14 ★★ Chardonnay Unwooded 14 ★★☆** Discontinued: **Muscadel**. — HJ

Location/map: Franschhoek ▪ WO: Franschhoek/Western Cape ▪ Chocolate & wine tasting/sales Mon-Sun 11–4 ▪ Closed Christian religious hols ▪ Restaurant ▪ Wine tram ▪ Traditional braai & picnics to be booked in advance ▪ Facilities for children ▪ Tour groups ▪ Weddings ▪ Conferences ▪ Le Chais Villa (6 en-suite rooms) ▪ Winemaker(s) Hardus van Heerden ▪ 21ha (cabs s/f, malbec, merlot, p verdot, ptage, shiraz, chard, sauv, viog) ▪ 160t/±25,000cs own label 60% red 40% white ▪ eldorette@lacouronnewines.co.za ▪ www.lacouronnewines.co.za ▪ S 33° 55' 8.9" E 019° 6' 40.9" ▪ **T +27 (0)21-876-3939/+27 (0)82-495-8579**

Ladera Artisan Wines

After taking over the running of the family fruit farm in Wolseley in 2009, having formerly completed 15 vintages as winemaker in SA (latterly Franschhoek Cellar) and abroad, Charles Ochse keeps his hand in (and his heart happy) by making smidgens of his own Ladera ('Hillside') wine after hours.

★★★★ First Born Syrah Was 'Zahir'. **11** shows restraint in ripeness & alcohol from **09**'s 15% to 13. 6%. Juicy, rich cocoa & plum abundance with long spicy tail. Lovely concentration & integrated older oak. Confident & assured.

Not tasted: **Wild Child Chardonnay**. — FM

Location: Wolseley ▪ Map: Breedekloof ▪ WO: Coastal ▪ Est/1stB 2009 ▪ Tasting, sales & cellar tours Mon-Sat by appt ▪ Picnics & longtable lunches in the fruit orchards by prior booking ▪ Owner(s) Charles Ochse ▪ Cellarmaster(s)/winemaker(s) Charles Ochse (2003) ▪ 6-8t/800cs own label 51% red 33% white 16% rosé ▪ PO Box 193 Wolseley 6830 ▪ info@ladera.co.za ▪ www.laderawines.co.za ▪ S 33° 28' 20.66" E 019° 11' 27.45" ▪ **T +27 (0)72-536-0055**

Ladismith Winery & Distillery

The consolidation of Barrydale Cellars, Oudtshoorn and Ladismith by owner-partnership Southern Cape Vineyards and Elgin's Oude Molen Distillery has resulted in Oudtshoorn being sold off, and tastings for the two Klein Karoo companies' wines and brandies now exclusively at Barrydale. At Ladismith, where major upgrading has taken place, only 3 wines are to be made annually, based on vintage performance, with the brandy remaining under the care of distiller Bertie Burger. Sales and cellar tours at Ladismith continue as before.

Southern Cape Vineyards range

Barrydale Shiraz (NEW) **★★☆ 13** soft & spicy with delightful twist of black pepper. Easy, fun, sweet fruited. **Ladismith Chardonnay** (NEW) **★★★ 14** unoaked, bright & cheerful, with creamy apple pie flavours for chilled enjoyment. **Ladismith Chenin Blanc** (NEW) **★★★** Apple fruit, touch of oak on rounded, citrus-toned **14** easy sipper. Not retasted: **Ruby Cabernet 11 ★★ Barrydale Brut Rosé NV ★★★☆**

Brandy range

★★★★ Ladismith 8 Year Potstill Brandy Clean aromas with abundant floral notes mixed with dried fruit. Lightish, elegant style, with muted fire, unobtrusive oak & a long dry finish. — WB

Location: Ladismith ▪ Map: Klein Karoo & Garden Route ▪ WO: Klein Karoo ▪ Est 1941 ▪ 1stB 1988 ▪ Sales Mon-Thu 9–5 Fri 9–1 ▪ Closed Easter Fri-Mon, Dec 25/26 & Jan 1 ▪ Book ahead for cellar tours ▪ Owner(s) Southern Cape Vineyards (SCV) &

Oude Molen Distillery ▪ Distiller Bertie Burger ▪ Winemaker(s) Jandre Human ▪ 600ha/520ha (cab, merlot, ptage, ruby cab, shiraz, chard, chenin, cbard, viog) ▪ 20% red 80% white ▪ PO Box 56 Ladismith 6655 ▪ humanj@scv.co.za ▪ www. ladismithwines.co.za ▪ S 33° 29' 49.38" E 021° 15' 59.40" ▪ F +27 (0)28-551-1930 ▪ **T +27 (0)28-551-1042**

☐ **Lady Anne Barnard** *see* African Pride Wines
☐ **Lady May** *see* Glenelly Estate
☐ **Lady Somerset** *see* Somerset Wines

La Ferme Derik

Despite its winemaking history, this Paarl property focuses on export table grapes and macadamia nuts. But having studied part-time as a winemaker, family member Eurica Scholtz couldn't resist testing her skills on a small production, from old vines and bought-in grapes, to 'add to the package of what we offer'. No new vintages received for tasting.

Location: Paarl ▪ Map: Paarl & Wellington ▪ WO: Paarl/Western Cape ▪ Est 1695 ▪ 1stB 1895 ▪ Tasting, sales & cellar tours by appt ▪ Function venue for 160 guests ▪ Owner(s) Hardus Otto ▪ Winemaker(s)/viticulturist(s) Eurica Scholtz ▪ 7ha (shiraz, grenache b/n, rouss, viog) ▪ 45ha export table grapes & macadamia nuts ▪ 35t 10% red 90% white ▪ PO Box 2008 Windmeul 7630 ▪ functions@lafermederik.com ▪ www.lafermederik.com ▪ S 33° 40' 33.348" E 18° 55' 56. 964" ▪ F +27 (0)21-869-8433 ▪ **T +27 (0)21-869-8380/+27 (0)82-953-0185**

Laibach Vineyards

Early adoption of organic winefarming was promoted by German physician and biologist Petra Laibach-Kuehner, who bought the farm in 1994 on behalf of her industrialist father Friedrich, honoured in the flagship red blend. Located in the august Simonsberg-Stellenbosch ward (Kanonkop a neighbour), the farm was originally granted in 1818 and named Good Success. Success has been nothing short of phenomenal for the Ladybird labels, honouring the colourful critters helping control unwanted vine pests here for more than a decade. Winemaker the past 15 years Francois van Zyl says the two wines will soon account for 80% of production.

★★★★ **Widow's Block Cabernet Sauvignon** Best-years-only tribute to former owner who advised planting cab (instead of shiraz). Single-vineyard **12** (★★★★★) follows **07** with fruit purity & intensity, fine tannins. Lovely polished texture, oak (50% new) in harmony. Will develop with distinction.

★★★★ **Merlot** Fresh, bright red-berry & mulberry aromas, **12** (★★★) less appealing on palate, with unyielding dry chalky tannins. Like more charming & supple **11**, features 30% Ceres fruit. Might just need time to unfurl.

★★★★☆ **Claypot Merlot** ⊘ Classically styled **12** shows fine-textured elegance, with compact dark fruit in dry but supple chalky tannin structure; complementary oak (50% new) adds spice. Serious & sophisticated, with a pedigree for ageing.

★★★★ **Pinotage** Like **12**, **13** (★★★) speaks of grape's pinot noir parentage in earthy, farmyardy notes to stewed red fruit; balanced, but somewhat more rustic than previous.

★★★★☆ **Friedrich Laibach** ⊘ Integration & harmony the watchwords for this **11** Bordeaux red blend of cab & merlot with 1% cab franc. Light oak juxtaposed with dark concentration of ripe, juicy berries. Tobacco & cedar reminiscent of equally elegant **09**. No **10**.

★★★★ **The Ladybird Red** ⊘ Bordeaux blend mostly merlot & cab, with cab franc, petit verdot & malbec in **12**. Lively, poised & flavoursome, with friendly but sound structure. Invites drinking now but will continue to charm good few years.

★★★★ **Natural Sweet** ⒩ Delightfully light & tangy **14** from Bottelary chenin, delicate (7.5% alcohol) yet focused & really fresh. 'Designed to pair with duck pâte in top Belgian restaurants.' 375 ml.

Laibach Seeger Pinot Noir ⒩ ★★★★ Named for renowned German pinot noir exponent Thomas Seeger, **12** promising maiden vintage from high-altitude Agter Witzenberg (Ceres) vines. Elegant,

perfumed, with freshness & fine tannins, potential to develop. Also tasted: **Chenin Blanc 14** ★★★
The Ladybird White **13** ★★★☆ — MW

Location/map: Stellenbosch ▪ WO: Simonsberg–Stellenbosch/Western Cape/Stellenbosch ▪ Est 1994 ▪ 1stB 1997 ▪ Tasting & sales Mon-Fri 10–5 Sat (Nov-Apr)/pub hols 10–1 ▪ Fee R10/4 wines ▪ Closed Easter Fri/Sun, Dec 25/26 & Jan 1 ▪ Cellar tours by appt ▪ Laibach Vineyards Lodge ▪ Owner(s) Petra Laibach-Kühner & Rudolf Kühner ▪ Cellarmaster(s)/winemaker(s) Francois van Zyl (Jan 2000) ▪ Viticulturist(s) / MD Michael Malherbe (Jun 1994) ▪ 50ha/37ha (cabs s/f, malbec, merlot, p verdot, ptage, chard, chenin, viog) ▪ 300t/48,000cs own label 70% red 30% white + 9,000cs for Woolworths ▪ BWI, Organic ▪ PO Box 7109 Stellenbosch 7599 ▪ info@laibachwines.com ▪ www.laibachwines.com ▪ S 33° 50' 43.3" E 018° 51' 44.2" ▪ F +27 (0)86-665-2839 ▪ **T +27 (0)21-884-4511**

La Kavayan

The latest vintages of longtime friends and vignerons Theo Beukes and Gabriël Kriel missed our tasting deadline. Their quest, abetted by winemaker PG Slabbert, is 'wines of timeless quality'. The brand name ('Jan's Cellar') recalls previous farm owner prof Jan Sadie.

Location: Stellenbosch ▪ Est 1999 ▪ 1stB 2001 ▪ Closed to public ▪ Owner(s) Gabriël Kriel & Theo Beukes ▪ Winemaker(s) PG Slabbert (2001, consultant) ▪ Viticulturist(s) Gabriël Kriel ▪ 4ha (cab, shiraz) ▪ ±10,000L own label 100% red ▪ PO Box 321 Stellenbosch 7599 ▪ diana@lakavayan.co.za, theo@minpro.co.za ▪ F +27 (0)21-881-3211 ▪ **T +27 (0)83-601-9030/+27 (0)21-881-3246/3289**

☐ **LAM** *see* Lammershoek Winery
☐ **Lamberts Bay's Finest** *see* Teubes Family Wines

Lammershoek Winery

Lots of (good) news from the Kretzel family's large, organic farm on Swartland's Perdeberg, overseen by viticulturist-winemaker Craig Hawkins: ongoing vineyard focus has seen the weed-controlling cattle herd increase, and unsuitable blocks replaced with the likes of macabeo and roussanne; on-site composting has been expanded to supply almost all parcels; production of the younger-vines LAM range has increased (while quantities of Lammershoek Chenin and Syrah have shrunk - only the best and oldest parcels are now used); new wines under the Cellar Foot label (untasted by us) are in the works, and the Lammershoek range has had a branding refresh; the tasting room has been transformed (now seats 15 instead of 4!), the cellar is being expanded and the homestead renovated; and (whew!) a new pre-school for children from the area opened on the farm.

Lammershoek range

★★★★ **Syrah 11** follows in delicate, fresh mode of **10**. Wholesome red earth, spice aromas, iron flavours energised by vibrant fine tannins, all redolent of Swartland origin. Good drinking now to around 2019.

★★★★☆ **Roulette** Fragrantly spiced **11** given lighter, more wild scrub edge via carignan, grenache partners to shiraz base. Lively & dry, balanced by persuasive savoury length.

★★★★☆ **Chenin Blanc 12** (★★★★) has similar 'old gold' tinge from large, older oak maturation as **11**; lighter, slighter build, with juicy appley flavours, a few oxidative notes.

★★★★☆ **Roulette Blanc** Enticing oxidative savoury features introduce **12**, from chardonnay, chenin backed up by clairette & viognier. Creamy texture with hint of honey, but more vinous than fruity. Bone-dry, great length. Matured in older oak, concrete tanks.

LAM range

★★★★ **Pinotage** **13** (★★★) muted after gloriously perfumed, fruity **12**. Light strawberry flavours, balanced freshness for early drinking.

★★★★ **White** Floral-scented **13** (★★★★) blends chenin, viognier & chardonnay. Bigger body than **12** (12% alcohol vs 10.5%) but full of vitality, delicate flavours. Bone-dry.

Also tasted: **Syrah Rosé** **13** ★★★ Not tasted: **Syrah**. — AL

Location: Malmesbury ▪ Map/WO: Swartland ▪ Est 1999 ▪ 1stB 2000 ▪ Tasting, sales & cellar tours by appt ▪ Light lunch platters by appt or BYO picnic ▪ Owner(s) Lammershoek Farms & Winery (Pty) Ltd ▪ Cellarmaster(s)/viticulturist(s) Craig Hawkins (Oct 2009) ▪ Winemaker(s) Craig Hawkins (Oct 2009), with Jurgen Gouws (Jan 2011) ▪ 210ha/70ha (carignan, grenache, merlot, mourv, ptage, shiraz, tinta barocca, zin, chard, chenin, hárslevelü, macabeo, rouss, sauv, viog) ▪ 195t/25,000cs own label 55% red 40% white 5% rosé ▪ PO Box 597 Malmesbury 7299 ▪ info@ lammershoek.co.za ▪ www.lammershoek.co.za ▪ S 33° 31' 30.2" E 018° 48' 21.1" ▪ F +27 (0)22-487-2702 ▪ **T +27 (0)22-482-2835**

La Motte

Purchased by the late Anton Rupert in 1970, this property dating from the early 1700s is now owned and run by his daughter, Hanneli Rupert-Koegelenberg, with her husband, Hein Koegelenberg, as CEO. The arts and culture are given as much prominence here as the wines: the restored buildings now house, among others, a museum where many Pierneef artworks may be seen, and a restaurant which focuses on recipes brought over by early settlers, while classical music concerts are held in the historic cellar. These and many other attractions have twice earned La Motte Great Wine Capitals of the World's Best of Wine Tourism awards for South Africa. Cellarmaster Edmund Terblanche crafts wines in an elegant, classic style that complement their gracious surroundings.

Pierneef Collection

★★★★☆ **Shiraz-Viognier** Consistently one of finest of genre, **12** flagship possibly one of best to date. Power with elegance evident in its gorgeous lifted spice perfume, deep velvet texture & rich flavours. Already approachable but has build to give pleasure for many years.

★★★★ **Sauvignon Blanc (Organically Grown)** Serious, intense **13** from Bot River some grassy notes, plenty mineral vigour too. More forbidding dryness alleviated by lees enrichment. Needs food to show off best. 12.8% alcohol.

Not tasted: **Shiraz-Grenache**.

Classic Collection

★★★★ **Cabernet Sauvignon** Unshowy yet satisfying **12**. Attractive dried herbs & black berry features balanced by fine-grained, firmish tannins & a properly dry finish. Cellar with confidence.

★★★★☆ **Syrah** Was 'Shiraz', & with change of name **12** shows more traditional reticence, less youthful accessibility than **11**. Nicely balanced with good savoury flesh, complementary oaking, so time is on its side. Includes drops grenache, tempranillo, durif & cinsaut.

★★★★ **Chardonnay 13** enjoyable without great complexity of **12** (★★★★★). Natural freshness of the bright pickled limes & spice flavours, careful oaking (year, 30% new) & moderate alcohol forge balanced partnership for current drinking, few more years. Franschhoek WO.

★★★★ **Méthode Cap Classique 11** as handsome as its packaging. From Franschhoek chardonnay (55) & pinot; pale straw with light creamy, brioche tones & finest of bubbles. Totally dry yet smoothed by 31 months on lees.

Not tasted: **Straw Wine**.

La Motte Collection

★★★★ **Millennium** Approachable **12** illustrating supple, sweet-fruited nature of ripe merlot (65%). Extra spice, freshness provided by cab franc, malbec & petit verdot, each rounded 14 months in old French oak.

★★★★ **Sauvignon Blanc** Impressive quantities & consistency of this multi-regional blend. **14** charms more than **13** (★★★★) with spring blossom-like fragrance, easy-drinking balance between texture, zest & fruitily dry length. — AL

Location/map: Franschhoek ▪ WO: Western Cape/Franschhoek/Walker Bay ▪ Est 1969 ▪ 1stB 1984 ▪ Tasting & sales Mon-Sat 9–5 ▪ Fee R40pp ▪ Booking essential for: group tastings 8-16 R50pp; themed tastings R200pp; food & wine pairing Fri 10 R120pp ▪ Closed Good Fri & Dec 25 ▪ Pierneef à La Motte ▪ Facilities for children ▪ Tour groups (max 16), booking essential ▪ Farm shop: lavender, vegetables, bread ▪ Booking essential for: walking trail Mon-Sat 9-2 R50pp (duration 2-3hrs, not recommended for children under 10); historic walk Wed 10-11 R50pp; sustainable walk Tue 9-10 R50pp ▪ 35ha conservation area ▪ Museum Tue-Sun 9-5: Rupert family, history of La Motte, Cape Dutch architecture, life/art of JH Pierneef & other SA artists ▪ Monthly classical music concerts ▪ Owner(s) Hanneli Rupert-Koegelenberg ▪ CEO Hein Koegelenberg ▪ Cellarmaster(s) Edmund Terblanche (Dec 2000) ▪ Winemaker(s) Michael Langenhoven (Dec 2006) ▪ Viticulturist(s) Pietie le Roux (May 1986) ▪ 170ha/75ha (merlot, pinot, shiraz, chard, sauv, sem) ▪ 1,200t/170,000cs own label 38.2% red 61.5% white 0.3% sparkling + 30,000cs for clients ▪ Brands for clients: Woolworths ▪ ISO 14001:2003, BWI champion, HACCP, IPW, WIETA, EnviroWines, Farming for the Future: Woolworths ▪ PO Box 685 Franschhoek 7690 ▪ cellar@la-motte.co.za ▪ www.la-motte.com ▪ S 33° 52′ 52.20″ E 019° 4′ 25.76″ ▪ F +27 (0)21-876-3446 ▪ **T +27 (0)21-876-8000**

Landau du Val

The prime vineyard of unirrigated, bushvine semillon on Basil and Jane Landau's Franschhoek farm was planted in 1905, making it amongst the Cape's most venerable. Other grapes also come off the farm, La Brie, but only the one wine is made for them under the proprietary label, from the old vines' minuscule yield.

★★★★☆ **Semillon Private Selection 12** (★★★★) has aromas of lanolin, beeswax & lemon marmalade. Attractive rusticity, with the palate dry yet intense & rich, & the 50% new oak integrated. Last tasted was **09**.

Late Vintage Semillon Private Selection Occasional release. — JPf

Location/map/WO: Franschhoek ▪ Tasting by appt ▪ Sales at La Cotte Wine Sales, Franschhoek ▪ Owner(s) Basil & Jane Landau ▪ Winemaker(s) Wynand Grobler ▪ Viticulturist(s) Martin du Plessis & Pietie le Roux (consultant) ▪ 15ha under vine ▪ La Brie Robertsvlei Road Franschhoek 7690 ▪ basillandau@mweb.co.za ▪ S 33° 55′ 34.3″ E 019° 6′ 34.1″ ▪ F +27 (0)21-876-3369 ▪ **T +27 (0)82-410-1130**

☐ **Land of Hope** *see* Winery of Good Hope

Land's End

As implied, these Fairview and Hidden Valley joint-venture wines come from the southern tip of Africa and its cool, windy Agulhas plain. See Fairview entry for tasting details.

★★★★ **Syrah** Fynbos & a salty seabreeze note complement bright dark berries on harmonious **12**, from vineyards 8 km from the ocean. Restrained fruit mingling with spicy oak. Will reward cellaring.

Sauvignon Blanc ★★★★ **14**'s shows tropical fruit aromas, but fruit-shy on the palate with a zesty citrus conclusion. Elim WO, as all. In abeyance: **Rosé**. — WB

Landskroon Wines

To say Landskroon is well-established is putting it mildly: the Paarl estate has been home to wine production since the 17th century. As a family concern, it involves five members of the De Villiers clan, the fifth generation at the helm. The style is never flashy or mercurial - constant and reliable, rather, with marginal tweaks now and then, such as the current 20 ha vineyard renewal programme. Occasionally, though, there's a (pleasant) surprise, like the splendid new top-end merlot.

Paul de Villiers range

★★★★ **Cabernet Sauvignon** As with confident **11**, **12** polished cedar & pencil shavings appeal. Less fruity, more refined, with sterner tannins & fresh acidity for cellaring good few years.

★★★★ **Merlot** (NEW) Quintessential Sunday roast wine, say the team, correctly. **12** plump & plummy, with just the right tension between richness, acidity & tannic grip.

★★★★ **Shiraz** Step-up **12** effusive vanilla bouquet from 75% new American oak, plush fruit centre, peppery conclusion: a hedonistic glassful. More concentrated than **11** (★★★★), should reward even more with time.

For more information, visit wineonaplatter.com

★★★★ **Reserve** (Ⓡ) Flagship blend shiraz & merlot plus dollops cab & touriga. **11** has cedar oak welcome, leading to bright fruited, medium body with balanced tannins. Needs a year or so to settle.

Landskroon range

★★★★ **Cape Vintage** Much-awarded port-style, **11** from tintas barocca & amarela, souzão & touriga; label consistently delivers balanced sweetness, approachable grip & exotic orange rind, pot-pourri wafts.

Shiraz ★★★ Only older American oak for this version. **12**'s redcurrant fruit has slight coffee & tar edge, saline conclusion. **Chenin Blanc Dry** ★★★ **14** a treat! White peach & lime aromas & tastes, crisp dry end unfettered by oak. **Sauvignon Blanc** ★★☆ **14** tropical styled, light & easygoing for chilled summer refreshment. WO W Cape. Also tasted: **Cabernet Franc-Merlot 12** ★★ **Cinsaut-Shiraz 12** ★★ **Blanc de Noir Pinotage Off-Dry 14** ★★☆ **Chardonnay 14** ★★★ **Paul Hugo White 13** ★★☆ Not retasted: **Cabernet Sauvignon 12** ★★★ **Cinsaut 12** ★★ **Pinotage 12** ★★☆ **Paul Hugo Red 12** ★★ **Bush Camp Our Daily Red 09** ★★☆ **Bush Camp Blanc de Noir 11** ★★ **Chenin Blanc Off-Dry 13** ★★★ Not tasted: **Merlot**, **Bush Camp The Sundowner**. — CvZ

Location: Paarl ▪ Map: Paarl & Wellington ▪ WO: Paarl/Western Cape ▪ Est 1874 ▪ 1stB 1974 ▪ Tasting & sales Mon-Fri 8.30–5 Sat (Oct-May) 9.30-1 ▪ Closed Good Fri, Dec 25 & Jan 1 ▪ Fee R10/5 wines, waived on purchase of 6btls ▪ Cellar tours by appt Mon-Fri 9-4 ▪ BYO picnic ▪ Play area for children ▪ Permanent display of Stone Age artefacts ▪ Self-catering cottage ▪ Owner(s) Paul & Hugo de Villiers Family Trusts ▪ Cellarmaster(s) Paul de Villiers (Jan 1980) ▪ Winemaker(s) Abraham van Heerden (Sep 2007) ▪ Viticulturist(s) Hugo de Villiers jnr (1995) ▪ 330ha/200ha (cab, cinsaut, merlot, ptage, shiraz, souzão, tinta amarela, tinta barocca, touriga nacional, chenin, chard, sauv, viog) ▪ 1,400t 80% red 15% white 5% port ▪ IPW ▪ PO Box 519 Suider-Paarl 7624 ▪ huguette@landskroonwines.com ▪ www.landskroonwines.com ▪ S 33° 45' 38.2" E 018° 55' 0.8" ▪ F +27 (0)21-863-2810 ▪ **T +27 (0)21-863-1039**

Landzicht GWK Wines

Fruit from the Landzicht vineyards around Free State town Jacobsdal are sent south across the provincial border to sibling Douglas Wine Cellar in the Northern Cape for vinification and bottling. Grapes from Douglas growers contribute to the range, offering low-alcohol table wines and sweet desserts, with more varietal reds coming into the line-up of late.

Rosenblümchen (Ⓡ) ★☆ Faint raisin appeal on shy but fresh **NV** Natural Sweet rosé. **Red Muscadel** (Ⓡ) ★★★ Honest, well-made fortified oozing strawberries & cherries. **NV** carefully balances 16.7% alcohol with slippery sweetness, slight herbal lift. **Oak Matured** (Ⓡ) ★★ Sherry-style **NV** mainly chenin, splash muscadel, fleeting sweet choc-raisin flavours. Not retasted: **Nagmaalwyn NV** ★☆ **Blümchen NV** ★ **Hanepoot NV** ★★ **Ruby Port 11** ★☆ Not tasted: **Cabernet Sauvignon**, **Cabernet Sauvignon Reserve**, **Merlot**, **Chenin Blanc**, **Blanc de Blanc**, **White Muscadel**, **Red Jerepigo**. — DB

Location: Jacobsdal ▪ Map: Northern Cape, Free State & North West ▪ WO: Northern Cape/Douglas ▪ Est 1976 ▪ 1stB ca 1980 ▪ Tasting & sales Mon-Fri 8-5 ▪ Closed all pub hols ▪ Tours - bottling plant ▪ Meals/refreshments by appt ▪ Owner(s) GWK Ltd ▪ Winemaker(s) Ian Sieg ▪ Viticulturist(s) Hein Janse van Rensburg ▪ Production: see under Douglas Wine Cellar ▪ PO Box 94 Jacobsdal 8710 ▪ landzicht@gwk.co.za ▪ www.landzicht.co.za ▪ S 29° 8' 35.5" E 024° 46' 42.8" ▪ F +27 (0)53-591-0145 ▪ **T +27 (0)53-591-0164**

☐ **Langeberg Wineries** *see* Wonderfontein
☐ **Langtafel** *see* Mooiplaas Estate & Private Nature Reserve

Langverwacht Wynkelder

Grower-owned Langverwacht's longtime cellarmaster Johan Gerber says it's imperative to keep grape suppliers on the farm and in production. They do so by striving to maintain consistency of quality in the bulk wine they sell to the trade. They're equally proud to have their small own-label bottled selection certified 'sustainable'.

Location: Bonnievale ▪ Map: Robertson ▪ Est 1954 ▪ Tasting, sales & tours Mon–Fri 8-5 ▪ Closed all pub hols ▪ Owner(s) 25 members ▪ Cellarmaster(s) Johan Gerber (Dec 1986) ▪ Winemaker(s) Theunis Botha (Dec 2005) ▪ Viticulturist(s) Hennie Visser (Jul 2008) ▪ 640ha (cab, ruby cab, shiraz, chenin, chard, cbard, sauv) ▪ 13,500t/8,000cs own label 64% red 36% white ▪ IPW ▪ PO Box 87 Bonnievale 6730 ▪ info@langverwachtwines.co.za ▪ S 33° 57' 32.8" E 020° 1' 35.3" ▪ F +27 (0)23-616-3059 ▪ **T +27 (0)23-616-2815**

Lanner Hill

The Lanner Hill brand is a partnership between seasoned winemaker and Cape Winemakers Guild member, Nicky Versfeld, and the Tullie family. It is also the name of the family farm, open for visits by appointment in Darling's cool Groenekloof hills that have become synonymous with top sauvignons.

★★★★☆ **Sauvignon Blanc** ⓠ Like **11** preview, **13** flies the Darling flag, ticking all the variety's boxes. Lovely fruit purity & racy acidity end with a clean-cut flinty farewell. **12** sold out untasted.

Merlot ⓠ ★★★★ **11** shows cool provenance. Red fruit & mint, deftly oaked. Bright & sappy, with serious underlying structure. Not tasted: **The Yair**. — MW

Location/WO: Darling ▪ Map: Durbanville, Philadelphia & Darling ▪ Est 1999 ▪ 1stB 2002 ▪ Tasting by appt ▪ Sales Mon–Fri 9-3 via email/phone; from farm by appt only ▪ Owner(s) David & Nicola Tullie ▪ Winemaker(s) Nicky Versfeld (2002) ▪ Viticulturist(s) David Tullie ▪ 91ha/51ha (cab, merlot, p verdot, shiraz, sauv, sem, viog) ▪ 450-500t/1,000cs own label ▪ PO Box 220 Darling 7345 ▪ tulliefamilyvineyards@gmail.com ▪ S 33° 23' 36.54" E 018° 22' 10.22" ▪ F +27 (0)22-492-3664 ▪ **T +27 (0)22-492-3662/+27 (0)82-882-2260 (Anton du Toit, marketing & sales)**

Lanzerac Wine Estate

The grand old lady of Stellenbosch's eastern suburbs, Lanzerac's splendidly restored Cape Dutch farmstead and *werf* are home to a luxury resort hotel offering a quintessential winelands experience at the gateway of the Jonkershoek Valley. Recently taken over by a consortium of British investors, new life has been breathed into both the visitor facilities and vineyards, and the winemaking is now concentrating on Jonkershoek as a defined area of origin. Lanzerac provided the first commercial pinotage, vintage 1959, while it was part of then SFW, and the variety is still honoured and celebrated here.

Heritage range

★★★★☆ **Pionier Pinotage** Tribute to world's first commercial pinotage release, Lanzerac 59, bottled 1961. Naturally fermented **11** is barrel selected & will reward the patient. Though dense & big, shows beautiful grace, redolent of dark berries, spice & toasty oak.

★★★★☆ **Le Général** A wine build to last, big & powerful cab-led Cape Blend with shiraz, pinotage & malbec, **11** shows redcurrant, curry leaf & tobacco over a palate rich yet firm, finely textured & enduring. Oak (combo new & 2nd fill) needs time to integrate further. No **10**.

★★★★☆ **Mrs English** Single-vineyard **12** is big, bold & very forward - restraint not the point in this limited-release barrel selection. Intense vanilla, expansive toasty oak & tropical melon power through to rich, creamy, almost viscous palate which lingers endlessly.

Premium range

★★★★ **Cabernet Sauvignon** Well-restrained **12** shows classic notes of cassis, scorched earth & bright red fruit. Rounded, but with firm tannins which provide a beautiful lift, complementing the harmonious oak.

★★★★ **Merlot** Well crafted, but **12** lacks depth & complexity of **11**, displays plum & some herbaceous notes with a friendly yet slightly green palate.

★★★★ **Pinotage** Understatement, as usual, in **12**, with earthy notes, spicy red fruit & hint of plum. Fine, open texture & sufficient structure, perhaps lacking a bit of the customary richness.

★★★★ **Chardonnay** Previewed **13**, typical honeysuckle, vanilla & lemon notes, broad & intense flavours with hints of yeast & well-judged oaking (25% new).

Also tasted: **Sauvignon Blanc 14** ★★★★

Alma Mater range

Shiraz ★★★ Was 'Red'. Unwooded **13** tank sample displays untamed juicy red fruit, black pepper & floral notes. A little sugar helps balance the acidity. Also tasted: **Rosé 14** ★★★ **Chenin Blanc 14** ★★★ — JPf

Location/map/WO: Stellenbosch ▪ Est 1692 ▪ 1stB 1957 ▪ Tasting & sales daily 9–5 ▪ Cellar tours at 11 & 3 ▪ Closed Dec 25 ▪ Deli platters; wine & chocolate tasting; picnic baskets ▪ 5-star Lanzerac Hotel, Spa & Restaurants ▪ Conferences ▪ Weddings/functions ▪ Owner(s) Lanzerac Estate Investments ▪ Cellarmaster(s) Wynand Lategan (Jan 2005) ▪ Viticulturist(s) Danie Malherbe (2008) ▪ 150ha/46ha (cab, merlot, ptage, chard) ▪ 500t/24-26,000cs own label 55% red 30% white 15% rosé ▪ BWI ▪ PO Box 6233 Uniedal 7612 ▪ winesales@lanzerac.co.za ▪ www.lanzeracwines.co.za ▪ S 33° 56' 14.7" E 018° 53' 35.5" ▪ F +27 (0)21-887-6998 ▪ **T +27 (0)21-886-5641**

La Petite Ferme Winery

The Dendy Young family's ever-popular restaurant, guest farm and boutique winery commands splendid vistas of Franschhoek town and valley. Vigneron Mark Dendy Young says guests love to take the pre-lunch tasting and cellar tour and, of course, enjoy the ever more widely exported wines with their meal. Frans Malies, with 15 years' experience here, now heads up farming activities.

La Petite Ferme range

★★★★ **Cabernet Sauvignon** Silky **13**, dense blackcurrant & dark chocolate-dipped cherry fruit, lifted by slightly herbaceous freshness & savoury hint of green olive.

★★★★ **Merlot** Fresher than **12** (★★★☆), **13** oozes black plums rather than plum pudding, its structure & firm tannins hinting at ageability, with hints of nutmeg & mocha on the finish.

★★★★ **The Verdict** Bordeaux-style flagship from 80% cab franc with equal cab & merlot. **12**, now bottled, bursts with morello cherries & mulberries; more elegant than its inky colour & coffee/liquorice notes suggest, light tannins & silky mouthfeel.

★★★★ **Barrel Fermented Chardonnay** It may have attractive orange-blossom nose & fresh, lingering marmalade finish, but citrus **13** is all about creamy texture: lemon curd in a glass.

★★★★ **Batonnage Sauvignon Blanc Reserve** ⒩ Limited-edition 'attempt to emulate Pouilly-Fumé', maiden **NV** is like lemon tart with its creamy texture, tangy fruit & butter pastry notes from 14 months 25% new French oak.

★★★★ **Viognier** Whiff of frangipani on peach-perfumed **14**, with green melon & ripe mango flavours, lovely viscous texture & clean almost savoury finish. Fresher than **13** (★★★☆).

Also tasted: **Shiraz 13** ★★★★ **Sauvignon Blanc 14** ★★★★ Not retasted: **Baboon Rock Unwooded Chardonnay Wild Yeast Fermented 13** ★★★ Discontinued: **Cabernet Franc**.

Maison range

Rouge ⊘ ★★★☆ Soft & rich blend of 61% cab & merlot, previewed latest bottling of **11** bursts with ripe black berries, juicy & accessible. Also tasted: **Rosé 14** ★★★ Not retasted: **Blanc 13** ★★★ — JG

Location/map: Franschhoek ▪ WO: Franschhoek/Western Cape ▪ Est 1972 ▪ 1stB 1996 ▪ Tasting daily from 11 by appt ▪ Fee R50pp ▪ Sales daily 8.30-5 ▪ Cellar tours from 11-12.30 ▪ Restaurant & guest suites ▪ Gift shop ▪ Walking/hiking trails ▪ Owner(s) Dendy Young family ▪ Cellarmaster(s)/winemaker(s) Mark Dendy Young (1996) ▪ Viticulturist(s) John Dendy Young & Frans Malies ▪ 16ha/14ha (cabs s/f, merlot, shiraz, chard, sauv, viog) ▪ 60-70t/12,000cs own label 40% red 50% white 10% rosé ▪ PO Box 55 Franschhoek 7690 ▪ jomark@mweb.co.za ▪ www.lapetiteferme.co.za ▪ S 33° 55' 6.43" E 019° 8' 10.32" ▪ F +27 (0)86-720-6284 ▪ **T +27 (0)21-876-3016**

La Petite Provence Wine Company

Essentially a wine club, with wines made mainly for Franschhoek's La Petite Provence Residential Estate owners from on-site cabernet and merlot, this small business also exports some of its production to satellite 'clubs' in Europe (from where many residents hail), as well as to China via an agent.

Cabernet Sauvignon ★★★☆ **11** juicy cassis & mint, with supple structure & clean, dry finish. Unoaked, as all these. **Merlot** ★★★☆ **11** succulent, smoky berry fruit in firm, dry tannin frame. **Mélange** ★★★ Balanced, red-fruited quaffer in **11**. Mainly merlot with cab. — MW

Location/WO: Franschhoek ▪ Est 2001 ▪ 1stB 2005 ▪ Tasting & sales Mon-Sat by appt ▪ Owner(s) La Petite Provence Wine Trust ▪ Winemaker(s) Johan van Rensburg (2003, La Provence) ▪ 3.5ha (cab, merlot) ▪ 30t/900cs own label 100% red ▪ 2 Cabernet Drive, La Petite Provence, Franschhoek 7690 ▪ info@lapetiteprovence.co.za ▪ www.lapetiteprovence.co.za ▪ **T +27 (0)21-876-4178/+27 (0)21-876-4554**

La Petite Vigne

Big changes for Kevin Swart at his small Franschhoek winery, as he concentrates on Black Elephant Vinters in which he is a partner. La Petite Vigne's business has mostly been sold to Black Elephant, which also rents the cellar and tasting room. Expanded tasting facilities, and perhaps a restaurant, are in the offing.

Daniel Collection (NEW)

★★★★☆ **Amazing Grace** Elegantly styled **12** Franschhoek cabernet, seasoned in half new oak, providing ample tannic grip to rich, compact fruit. Classic blackcurrant flavours & graphite hints, with underlying seam of minerality. Deserves time to soften & unfurl.

La Petite Vigne range

Deep Red Rosé ★★★ Supple, juicily fruity **13** pink from cab, aged in older oak, leaves barely-dry, smooth impression. — IM

Location/map/WO: Franschhoek ▪ 1stB 2012 ▪ Tasting & tours by appt only ▪ Owner(s) Kema Consulting (Kevin & Mandie Swart) ▪ Cellarmaster(s) Kevin Swart (Jan 2012) ▪ Winemaker(s) Kevin Swart (Jan 2012), with Gary Swart & Jospeh Ratabana (both Jan 2012) ▪ Viticulturist(s) Jacques Wentzel (Jan 2012, consultant) ▪ 3.3ha/2.5ha (cab) ▪ 3t/450cs own label 100% red ▪ PO Box 686 Franschhoek 7690 ▪ kevin@lapetitevigne.co.za ▪ S 33° 54' 9.00 E 019° 7' 14.00" ▪ **T +27 (0)21-876-2903/+27 (0)83-655-6611**

Lateganskop Winery

The Lategan family have been vinegrowing in the scenic Wolseley area for more than 100 years. Oupa Willie, who reached a remarkable 102, built a cellar in 1969, founding a legacy that continues today, most of the wine sold in bulk but a small portion bottled under the own labels.

Lateganskop range

Livia's Laughter Méthode Cap Classique (NEW) ★★★★ Bubbly named after only daughter among 11 6th generation Lategan siblings. **11** equal chardonnay & pinot noir, 36 months on the lees giving lovely toasted brioche perfume & flavours; elegance & citrus freshness a tasty conclusion. **102** (NEW) ★★★★ Solera-style **NV** fortified dessert honouring long-lived patriarch. Unspecified varieties but grapiness, sultana flavours give a clue. Nice biscuit tone from oak maturation. Sweet, rich & full bodied, enjoy post dinner. WO W Cape. Also tasted: **The Zahir 12** ★★★★

Twin's Peak range

Sauvignon Blanc ★★ Freshness abounds in **14**, pear & apple flavours. Not retasted: **Pinotage 10** ★★★ — CR

Location: Wolseley ▪ Map: Breedekloof ▪ WO: Breedekloof/Western Cape ▪ Est 1969 ▪ 1stB 2004 ▪ Tasting & sales Mon-Fri 8–12 & 1–5 ▪ Closed Easter Fri-Mon, Dec 25/26 & Jan 1 ▪ Cellar tours by appt ▪ Owner(s) 5 members ▪ Cellarmaster(s) Heinrich Lategan (Oct 2008) ▪ Winemaker(s) Heinrich Lategan, with Kean Oosthuizen (May 2011) ▪ 238ha (cab, ptage, chard, chenin, sauv, sem) ▪ 2,900t/600cs own label 70% red 30% white & ±2m L bulk ▪ PO Box 44 Breërivier 6858 ▪ lateganskop@breede.co.za ▪ www.lateganskop.co.za ▪ S 33° 30' 57.27" E 019° 11' 13.65" ▪ F +27 (0)86-637-6603 ▪ **T +27 (0)23-355-1719**

La Terre La Mer

Guided by winemaker Peter Turck, and empowered by a Stellenbosch University garagiste course, four wine enthusiasts are vinifying from a facility overlooking East London's Quinera Lagoon. All concerned were delighted when a case of their Shiraz sold for R6,000 at a recent charity auction.

Shiraz ★★★ 11, now bottled, ripe, slightly high-toned mulberry fruit elbowed towards finish by persistent acidity. — IM

Location: East London ▪ WO: Swartland ▪ Est/1stB 2008 ▪ Closed to public ▪ Owner(s) Deon le Roux, Mark Wiehahn, Charles Benn & Adrian Toma ▪ Winemaker(s) Deon le Roux, Mark Wiehahn, Charles Benn, Adrian Toma & consultant Pieter Turck ▪ Viticulturist(s) Grapes ex Mountain View, Swartland ▪ 2.5t shiraz ▪ 6 Princess Drive, Bonza Bay 5241 ▪ dleroux@iafrica.com ▪ **T +27 (0)43-748-5808/+27 (0)82-373-6488**

Lathithá Wines

Lathitha Wines is an empowerment project spearheaded by Sheila Hlanjwa, introduced to wine through a wine marketing course at Stellenbosch University. The name is derived from a Xhosa expression meaning 'sunrise', and the venture is intended to introduce local communities to wine.

Red **★** Dense tannin overrode shy chocolate notes on **09** last edition. **Rosé** **★★** Last was **09**, with fruitily sweet wild strawberry flavours. — CR

Location: Cape Town ▪ WO: Western Cape ▪ Tasting by appt only ▪ Owner(s) Sheila Hlanjwa ▪ Winemaker(s) Rolf Zeitvogel & Albert Basson (both Blaauwklippen) ▪ Viticulturist(s) Christo Hamman (Blaauwklippen) ▪ 100ha (cabs s/f, malbec, merlot, shiraz, zin, viog) ▪ Washington Shopping Centre Langa 7455 ▪ info@lathithawines.co.za ▪ www.lathithawines.co.za ▪ F +27 (0)21-695-1953 ▪ **T +27 (0)21-556-6029**

L'Auberge du Paysan

The country inn is long closed but the vines on the small property at the edge of Raithby mission village, off Winery Road, are still producing and the grapes vinified for brand owner Michael Kovensky by neighbouring farmer Tjuks Roos.

Pinotage **★★★** Aromatic, steely wild berries on **10** are appealingly ripe & generous, let down by astringent twist at finish. Not tasted: **Merlot**. — GdB

Location: Stellenbosch ▪ Closed to public ▪ Owner(s) Michael Kovensky ▪ PO Box 36825 Chempet 7442 ▪ kovensky@aroma.co.za ▪ F +27 (0)21-555-3033 ▪ **T +27 (0)21-529-3980**

L'Avenir Vineyards

This Stellenbosch winery has always retained a French accent, most obviously in its name, meaning 'the future'. If the first (Mauritian) owner was French-speaking but not French, Michel Laroche added that touch when he purchased the farm in 2005. A 2010 merger with French company Jeanjean formed a new group, AdVini, a leading French wine producer - and now owner of L'Avenir. The wines, by Dirk Coetzee and Mattheus Thabo, have their own French slant: from the classic varieties to SA's pinotage (with chenin, long a signature grape) the style is invariably one of elegant restraint.

Single Block range

★★★★☆ Pinotage Elegant example of pinotage from 20 year old single-vineyard. **12** supremely poised & polished, 100% new oak deftly woven into perfumed dark cherry profile. As previous, shows excellent long-term development potential. No **11**.

★★★★☆ Chenin Blanc Understated **13** (**★★★★**), genteel honey & nutty flavours sheathed in rich oak spice (all wood fermented, 50% new). Graceful & ageworthy, but shade off complexity of **11**. **12** sold out untasted.

Provenance range

★★★★ Cabernet Sauvignon Refined **12**, with all elements in place for rewarding development or enjoyment now if impatient. Less overtly fruity & slightly more restrained than **11**.

★★★★ **Pinotage** Fine fruit purity from careful vineyard selection, including oldest (1985) vineyard block. **12** perfumed & supple, harmonised oak enhances svelte texture.

★★★★ **Chenin Blanc** Unoaked, easy-drinking styling for **13** (★★★☆), dry, ample apple & honey flavours; initially bright & flavoursome but fades quite quickly. White peach & beeswax-toned **14**, also tasted, steelier, with good concentration & length, satisfying weight & freshness.

Merlot ★★★★ Partly oaked **13** is food styled, the dry chalky tannin anchoring sappy red-berry, polished leather & sweet tobacco flavours. Balanced, with solid dry farewell. Coastal WO. Also tasted: **Stellenbosch Classic 12** ★★★☆

Future Eternal range

★★★★ **Brut Rosé Méthode Cap Classique** Lively, fruity yet classy sparkler, **12** (★★★★) different blend to & shade off **10**. Pinot noir, chardonnay, pinotage & pinot meunier (36/33/25/6). Fine, savoury mousse with red berries & clean, enlivening acidity. Enjoy soon, solo or with canapés. No **11**.

Blanc de Blancs (NEW) ★★★☆ Trenchant bubbly from chardonnay, **11** bone-dry, flinty oystershell tones & fine bead tinged with baked apple & brioche. Needs food or time to gain more richness.

Far & Near range

Rosé de Pinotage ★★★☆ Sunset-hued preview, **14** al fresco quaffer with savoury cranberry nuance, piquantly dry twist on the tail. Also tasted: **Pinotage-Merlot 13** ★★★ **Sauvignon Blanc 14** ★★★ Not tasted: **Pinotage**, **Chenin Blanc**. — MW, CvZ

Location/map: Stellenbosch ▪ WO: Stellenbosch/Coastal ▪ Est/1stB 1992 ▪ Tasting & sales Mon-Fri 9–5 Sat 10–4 ▪ Fee R30 ▪ Closed Easter Fri/Sun, Dec 25 & Jan 1 ▪ Cellar tours by appt ▪ Child friendly ▪ Luxury 4-star Country Lodge ▪ Owner(s) AdVini ▪ Winemaker(s) Dirk Coetzee (Aug 2009), with Mattheus Thabo (Jan 2007) ▪ Viticulturist(s) Leigh Diedericks, with Johan Pienaar ▪ 64.9ha/27.26ha (cabs s/f, merlot, ptage, chenin, sauv) ▪ 250t/41,000cs own label 44% red 38% white 18% rosé ▪ IPW ▪ PO Box 7267 Stellenbosch 7599 ▪ info@lavenir.co.za ▪ www.larochewines.com, www.lavenir-lodge.com ▪ S 33° 53' 18.7" E 018° 50' 59.1" ▪ F +27 (0)21-889-5258 ▪ **T +27 (0)21-889-5001**

La Vierge Private Cellar

Prepare for exhilaration is the message from the Hemel-en-Aarde winery with some of the most original and evocative labels on the market, sourced from myth and legend. The focus here is on pinot noir and terroir expression through elevated, dryland-farmed vineyards planted on virgin soils (hence 'La Vierge') and now nearing maturity. The '13 Seduction, first vintage by self-confessed pinotphile Gerhard Smith, with eight crushes in New Zealand, is 'a first glimpse of what is to be expected'.

La Vierge range

★★★★ **La Vierge Noir Pinot Noir** (Ⓥ) The expected varietal elegance in **12** yet packed with flavour. Offers raspberries, cherries & a lovely oak savouriness, succulent & streamlined to the end.

La Vierge Collection

★★★★ **Nymphomane Cabernet Sauvignon-Cabernet Franc-Malbec-Merlot** Wonderful perfume, blackcurrants, dark cherries, oak-influenced spice layers, a cappuccino note on **12**. Creamy & rich yet well structured, more complex & concentrated than **11** (★★★☆).

★★★★ **Original Sin Sauvignon Blanc** Some grass, greenpepper lead into **14**, but the core is minerality, slatey & pure, focused. The acidity has an intriguing salty tone, perfect styling for seafood. With dab wooded semillon, as for also-tasted **13** (Walker Bay WO), vivid fynbos perfume, same appealing mineral flavours. No **12**.

Seduction Pinot Noir ★★★☆ Raspberries, some forest floor, white pepper, even violets, **13** offers the classic pinot styling as well as elegant & succulent accessibility. Only partial oak maturation to keep the freshness. Also tasted: **Last Temptation Riesling 14** ★★ Not retasted: **Anthelia Shiraz 11** ★★★☆ **Satyricon Sangiovese-Nebbiolo 11** ★★★☆ **Jezebelle Chardonnay 12** ★★★☆

— CR

Location: Hermanus ▪ Map: Elgin, Walker Bay & Bot River ▪ WO: Hemel-en-Aarde Ridge ▪ Est 1997 ▪ 1stB 2006 ▪ Tasting & sales Tue-Sun 10–5 ▪ Closed Good Fri & Dec 25 ▪ Cellar tours by appt ▪ La Vierge Restaurant & Champagne Verandah ▪ Tour groups by appt ▪ Owner(s) La Vierge Wines (Pty) Ltd & Viking Pony Properties 355 (Pty) Ltd ▪ Winemaker(s) Gerhard Smith (Nov 2012), with Alexander Grier (Nov 2013) ▪ Viticulturist(s) Petrus Bothma (2008) ▪ 44ha (pinot, sangio, shiraz, chard, riesling, sauv, sem) ▪ 160t 60% red 40% white ▪ PO Box 1580 Hermanus 7200 ▪ info@lavierge.co.za ▪ www.lavierge.co.za ▪ S 34° 22' 22.3" E 019° 14' 29.4" ▪ F +27 (0)28-312-1388 ▪ **T +27 (0)28-313-0130**

Lazanou Organic Vineyards

The organic ethos at this tiny family estate near Wellington goes way beyond the vineyards, encompassing home-grown food and harmony with nature at all levels (and a Jersey cow named Gertrude). Their popular Open Days allow visitors to partake of their bounty in al fresco splendour.

★★★★☆ **Syrah** Single-vineyard **11** outclasses **09** (★★★★) with understated elegance, succulent pure fruit & precise oaking. Rich & flavoursome, with a lovely moreish smoothness.

Viognier ★★★★ Exudes variety's aromatic appeal - rosepetal & litchi - in bright, fresh presentation, courtesy limy acidity & dry styling. **14** good fusion food partner. Not retasted: **Syrah-Mourvèdre 11** ★★★★ Not tasted: **Chardonnay, Chenin Blanc, Chenin Blanc-Chardonnay-Viognier**. — MW

Location/WO: Wellington ▪ Map: Paarl & Wellington ▪ Est 2002 ▪ 1stB 2006 ▪ Tasting & sales by appt ▪ Open days with wine & food pairing - booking essential ▪ Tour groups ▪ Farm produce ▪ Owner(s) Josef Lazarus & Candice Stephanou ▪ Winemaker(s) Rolanie Lotz (Jan 2011, consultant) ▪ Viticulturist(s) Johan Wiese (Jan 2006, consultant) ▪ 8.48ha/5.54ha (mourv, shiraz, chard, chenin, viog) ▪ 50t/6,000cs own label 50% red 50% white ▪ Organic certification by LACON ▪ PO Box 834 Wellington 7654 ▪ wine@lazanou.co.za ▪ www.lazanou.co.za ▪ S 33° 35' 59.58" E 018° 59' 36.12" ▪ F +27 (0)86-670-9213 ▪ **T +27 (0)83-265-6341**

☐ **Lazy Days** see Laborie Wine Farm
☐ **Le Bistro** see Zandvliet Wine Estate & Thoroughbred Stud

Le Bonheur Wine Estate

Part of the original Natte Valleij land grant, this estate on Stellenbosch's Klapmuts Hill was known as Oude Weltevreden until 1970, then became Le Bonheur ('Happiness') under Bergkelder part-ownership. It's now a Lusan property. Sakkie Kotzé, who managed cellar and vineyards for 20+ years, has retired, and Lauren Behrens, Rudi Buys and Jaco van der Berg have taken over his various roles. New, too, are cheese platters in the tasting centre, while the Friday outdoor film evenings are popular seasonal attractions.

★★★★ **Cabernet Sauvignon** Polished **10** (★★★★★) shows classic styling without sacrificing ripeness or approachability. Layers of dark fruit in seamlessly integrated oak & tannin framework. Elegant & balanced step up on **09**, for drinking pleasure over next 5 years.

★★★★ **Prima** Enduring Bordeaux red **09** continues in elegant but lively & fresh style. Bright & sappy liquid fruit pastille flavours streamlined by dusty, dry oak (40% new). Enjoyable now, life for 3-5 years.

★★★★ **Tricorne** Cab, cab franc, shiraz blend in slightly plusher mode for this winery. **09**'s bright, mint, spicy features enliven soft, fleshy core. Tasty if fairly straightforward.

★★★★ **Sauvignon Blanc** Lighter-style **14** (★★★★) is bright & flinty, with citrus, herbaceous tone & piquant acidity. Drier, tighter, with less breadth & grip than also-tasted **13**, for earlier enjoyment.

★★★★ **Single Vineyard Sauvignon Blanc** **12** more concentrated flinty vigour than standard bottling; firm mineral palate broadened by 6 months on lees, ripe length & moderate alcohol.

Also tasted: **Chardonnay 14** ★★★★ Discontinued: **Pinot Noir Rosé**. — MW

Location/map: Stellenbosch ▪ WO: Simonsberg–Stellenbosch ▪ Est 1790s ▪ 1stB 1972 ▪ Tasting & sales Mon-Fri 9–5 Sat/Sun 10–4 ▪ Fee R25/5 wines ▪ Closed Good Fri, Dec 25 & Jan 1 ▪ Cheese platters ▪ Conferences ▪ Outdoor film evenings, every last Friday of the summer months - booking essential ▪ Owner(s) Lusan Premium Wines ▪ Winemaker(s) Lauren Behrens (Oct 2013) ▪ Viticulturist(s) Rudi Buys & Jaco van der Berg (both Oct 2013) ▪ 163ha/75ha (cab, merlot, chard, sauv) ▪ 600t/60,000cs own label 30% red 70% white ▪ PO Box 104 Stellenbosch 7599 ▪ info@lebonheur.co.za ▪ www.lebonheur.co.za ▪ S 33° 50' 1.0" E 018° 52' 21.4" ▪ F +27 (0)21-875-5624 ▪ **T +27 (0)21-875-5478**

☐ **Leeumasker** *see* Maske Wines

Leeuwenberg

Five years since inception, Tanja Kastien-Hilka's negociant business is doing well, the original mostly German focus widened to include Switzerland, Denmark and the UK, with West Africa next. Tanja is now setting up an organisation locally 'to be more professional in sourcing wines'.

Flagship range

★★★★ **Two Barrels Shiraz** Improved since previewed last time, **11**'s tannins better integrated. Now shows lovely dark fruit, mocha chocolate, loads of spice. With 15% cab adding more structure.

Cellar Selection

★★★★ **Cellar Blend** Bordeaux mix cab, merlot & cab franc, delicious **11** rich, pure plum pudding & blackcurrant fruit, concentrated yet velvety. Different league to **09** (★★★). No **10**.

Chardonnay-Pinot Noir ⓝⓔⓦ ★★★☆ Coppery sheen on **13**, nicely balanced & silky, flowers & tangy red-berry flavours in appealing 50/50 blend. Not retasted: **Shiraz-Cabernet Sauvignon 11** ★★☆

Drie Kleine Leeuwen range

Merlot ⓝⓔⓦ **13** missed our tasting deadline. Not tasted: **Pinotage Rosé**, **Chardonnay Unwooded**. — CR

WO: Darling/Bot River/Western Cape ▪ Est/1stB 2010 ▪ Tasting only in Wiesbaden, Germany Mon-Fri 11-7 Sat 10-6 ▪ Closed all pub hols ▪ Owner(s) Tanja Kastien-Hilka ▪ Winemaker(s) Frank Kastien & Kobie Viljoen ▪ 4,000cs own label 70% red 30% white ▪ PO Box 422 Franschhoek 7690 ▪ sales@leeuwenbergwines.com ▪ www.leeuwenbergwines.com ▪ **T +49 (0)611-308-6778**

Leeuwenjacht

This entry-level brand, much favoured by restaurants around the country, is made by Fairview's Adele Dunbar, using classic varieties and combinations to make it accessible and friendly.

Leeuwenrood ★★★ 6-way southern French blend, **13** has a spicy nose complementing juicy berried fruit & a dry finish. WO W Cape. **Leeuwenblanc** ★★★ Mostly from viognier, tank sample **14** is a pleasant dryish sipper with lots of grape, rosepetal & litchi perfumes. Also tasted: **Nuance 13** ★★★ Discontinued: **Rosé**. — CM

Location: Paarl ▪ WO: Coastal/Western Cape ▪ Est 1692 ▪ 1stB 1989 ▪ Closed to public ▪ Winemaker(s) Adele Dunbar ▪ 20,000cs own label & 5,000cs for clients ▪ Brands for clients: Cubana ▪ PO Box 583 Suider-Paarl 7624 ▪ info@fairview.co.za ▪ www.spiceroute.co.za ▪ F +27 (0)21-863-2591 ▪ **T +27 (0)21-863-2450**

Leeuwenkuil Family Vineyards

Grapes from Willie and Emma Dreyer's vast vineyard holdings in Swartland and Paarl have been channelled anonymously into many vaunted brands over the years. They then founded their own Leeuwenkuil label, named for the historic home-farm. The wines may represent a mere drop in overall production but it's clearly a thoughtfully made, rather tasty and even impressive drop.

Heritage series ⓝⓔⓦ

★★★★ **Premium Shiraz** Bright, pure-fruited perfume from whole-berry fermentation on **12**. Red-fruit palate a touch stalky & herbaceous. Fresh acidity, fine dry tannins. Like Chenin, matured in larger old oak.

★★★★ **Premium Chenin** Stonefruit, thatch; hints of smoke & earth on **13**. More enigmatic, subtle & silky than standard (unwooded) version. Tight & restrained, needs time to blossom. Like Shiraz, natural ferment.

For more information, visit wineonaplatter.com

Leeuwenkuil range

★★★★ Family Reserve White **13**, pre-bottling, is usual half chenin plus 4 others. Citrus & stonefruit in lovely, complex harmony with a fine structure - freshness balanced with sumptuousness. Excellent value. Coastal WO.

Family Reserve Red ★★★★ Supple & easygoing **12** preview, a shiraz-based blend. Ripe, clean fruitiness balanced by freshness; ripe, melting tannins mingle happily with the sweet fruit. Coastal WO. Also tasted: **Shiraz 13 ★★★ Rosé 14 ★★ Chenin Blanc 14 ★★★** — TJ

Location: Swartland ▪ WO: Swartland/Coastal ▪ Est 2008 ▪ 1stB 2011 ▪ Closed to public ▪ Owner(s) Willie & Emma Dreyer ▪ Cellarmaster(s) Pieter Carstens (Aug 2008) ▪ Winemaker(s) Gustav Fouche & Johan Gerber (both Dec 2012), Corrien Geleijnse & Bernard Allison (both Jan 2012), Madré van der Walt (Sep 2013), with Jehan de Jongh (Aug 2008) ▪ Viticulturist(s) Koos van der Merwe (Dec 2008) & Claude Uren (Jan 2012) ▪ 4,550ha ▪ 36,500t/27m L ▪ 70% red 30% white ▪ Fairtrade, WIETA ▪ PO Box 249 Koelenhof 7605 ▪ kobus@leeuwenkuilfv.co.za ▪ F +27 (0)21-865-2780 ▪ **T +27 (0)21-865-2455**

Le Fût

Trevor and Joan Ernstzen indulged their love of wine just over a decade ago by buying and restoring an old Paarl wine farm. They combine running a special functions venue with tending vines. Most of the crop is sold, except for just enough for a fût or two of their own wine.

Shiraz Reserve **★★★** Development shows on interesting **07**. Not heavy (though big 15% alcohol) though shy on fruit, with more savoury, smoky & earthy notes to follow. — JP

Location/WO: Paarl ▪ Map: Paarl & Wellington ▪ Est 2004 ▪ 1stB 2005 ▪ Tasting by appt ▪ Conference/function/wedding venue ▪ Owner(s) Trevor & Joan Ernstzen ▪ Winemaker(s) Trevor Ernstzen (Nov 2004) ▪ Viticulturist(s) Joan Ernstzen (Nov 2004) ▪ ±17ha/9ha (shiraz, chenin, cbard, riesling) ▪ 80t/600cs own label 100% red ▪ PO Box 156 Paarl 7622 ▪ wine@lefut.co.za ▪ www.lefut.co.za ▪ S 33° 44' 34.38" E 019° 0' 39.90" ▪ F +27 (0)86-675-5114 ▪ **T +27 (0)83-561-1555**

☐ **Legacy** *see* DGB
☐ **Legends of the Labyrinth** *see* Doolhof Wine Estate

Le Grand Chasseur Wine Estate

Five generations of De Wets have farmed here, along the Breede River. There's much they're proud of - including concern for community welfare (like major support for the employees' school they founded in 1937); and 'keeping up with the times' (mechanical harvesters in the 1980s, computerised irrigation in the 1990s) . . . And their wine, offered for tasting at a venue on Robertson's main street.

Location/map: Robertson ▪ Est 1881 ▪ 1stB 1999 ▪ Tasting by appt ▪ Closed all pub hols ▪ Owner(s) Albertus de Wet ▪ Cellarmaster(s)/winemaker(s) Carel Botha (Jan 2011) ▪ Viticulturist(s) Francois Viljoen (Jan 1998, consultant) ▪ ±1,300ha/300ha (cab, merlot, ptage, ruby cab, shiraz, chard, chenin, cbard, muscadel w, nouvelle, sauv) ▪ ±4,500t ▪ IPW ▪ PO Box 439 Robertson 6705 ▪ cellar@lgc.co.za, sales@lgc.co.za ▪ www.lgc.co.za ▪ S 33° 48' 26.8" E 019° 52' 40.1" ▪ F +27 (0)23-626-1048 ▪ **T +27 (0)23-626-1048**

☐ **Le Grand Jardin** *see* Jean Daneel Wines

Leipzig Winery

Leipzig farm in secluded Nuy Valley near Worcester has a winemaking history dating from the 1890s to 1963. Current owners Francois and Lida Smit have revived the tradition, launched the first wines (including White Leipzig, once enjoyed by English royalty), and offer visitors a 'one-stop destination' - luxury accommodation, art tours, fine food and of course winetasting, to name a few.

Leipzig Winery range (NEW)

Cabernet Sauvignon ★★★ Blackcurrant & tobacco perfume, flavours on characterful **13**; enough ripe tannin for further development till 2019. **Master Blend ★★★** Cape Blend cab, merlot with 20%

pinotage, **13** vibrant berry highlight from unoaked merlot portion. Succulent texture, nice savoury tail with good tannic grip. WO W Cape. **White Leipzig ★★★** Venerable label returns with appealingly unforced **13**, deftly wooded blend mostly chardonnay & sauvignon; peach & oatmeal layered with citrus, fresh & light. WO W Cape. Also tasted: **Pinotage 13 ★★☆ Shiraz 13 ★★ Chardonnay 13 ★★☆ Chenin Blanc 13 ★★ Sauvignon Blanc 13 ★★ Viognier 13 ★★** — CR, CvZ

Location/map: Worcester ▪ WO: Stellenbosch/Nuy/Western Cape ▪ Est/1stB 2013 ▪ Tasting, sales & cellar tours Tue-Sat 10-3; or by appt ▪ Closed Ash Wednesday, Easter Mon, Dec 25 & Jan 1 ▪ Raven-ous restaurant Sat 11.30-2 ▪ Facilities for children ▪ Tour groups ▪ Conferences ▪ Weddings/functions ▪ Walks/hikes ▪ Mountain biking trail ▪ Guided tours by appt: historic buildings & art ▪ Leipzig Country House ▪ Owner(s) Francois & Lida Smit ▪ Cellarmaster(s)/winemaker(s) Mark Carmichael Green (Feb 2013, consultant) ▪ 10ha/4.5ha (sauv) ▪ 26t/2,917cs own label 49% red 51% white ▪ PO Box 5104 Worcester 6849 ▪ winery@leipzigcountryhouse.co.za ▪ www.leipzigcountryhouse.co.za ▪ S33° 38' 29.90" E 019° 38' 9.44" ▪ F +27 (0)86-295-5116 ▪ **T +27 (0)23-347-8422**

Le Joubert

A boutique wine label owned by ex-Gauteng motor trade entrepreneur Dawie Joubert and wife Alison. Self-taught Dawie makes the kind of traditional robust reds he likes to drink, plus a wooded viognier. All were sold out at press time with no new releases ready for review.

Location: Paarl ▪ Map: Paarl & Wellington ▪ Est 1693 ▪ 1stB 2007 ▪ Tasting & sales by appt ▪ Owner(s) Dawie & Alison Joubert ▪ Cellarmaster(s)/winemaker(s) Dawie Joubert ▪ 25ha/4ha (cab, p verdot) ▪ 20t/2,000cs own label 90% red 10% white ▪ PO Box 2963 Paarl 7620 ▪ alison@lejoubert.com, www.lejoubert.co.za ▪ S 33° 43' 29.02" E 018° 57' 16.61" ▪ F +27 (0)87-803-7886 ▪ **T +27 (0)21-870-1070/+27 (0)82-552-3671**

☐ **Lekker** *see* Thandi Wines

Le Lude Méthode Cap Classique

In 2009, Nic and Ferda Barrow, who own a portfolio of hotels and country houses, decided to build a specialist méthode cap classique cellar in Franschhoek to express their passion for wine. Paul Gerber was later appointed winemaker after internships at bubbly houses here and abroad. Traditionally made and matured a minimum of 36 months, the maiden releases are due this year.

Location: Franschhoek ▪ Est 2009 ▪ 1stB 2012 ▪ Tasting by appt only ▪ Owner(s) Nic & Ferda Barrow ▪ Winemaker(s) Paul Gerber (May 2010) ▪ Viticulturist(s) Eben Archer (2011, consultant) & Alain Deloire (2011, consultant/research) ▪ 6.2ha/3.4ha (pinot noir/meunier, chard) ▪ 100t/55,000 btls own label 100% MCC ▪ PO Box 578 Franschhoek 7609 ▪ paulgerberwyn@gmail.com ▪ www.lelude.co.za ▪ F +27 (0)44-279-1793 ▪ **T +27 (0)82-321-0820**

Le Manoir de Brendel

Christian and Maren Brendel, German proprietors of this exclusive Franschhoek guesthouse and winelands function venue, have consultant winemakers vinify 'at-home, in-house' wines from their small riverside vineyard. With no commercial considerations, they have the luxury of being able to bottle-age their wines for extended periods before offering them to guests and visitors.

Brendel Collection
Cabernet Sauvignon ⓥ **★★★** Mature **07** rhubarb & prune notes, firm tannin structure for food pairing. Not retasted: **Merlot 06 ★★☆ Pinotage 08 ★★★ Shiraz 06 ★★☆**

Le Manoir de Brendel Collection
Not tasted: **Shiraz.** — GdB, FM

Location/map/WO: Franschhoek ▪ Est/1stB 2003 ▪ Tasting daily 12-4 ▪ Fee R40pp, waived on purchase ▪ Sales daily 7.30-4.30 ▪ Closed Good Fri, Dec 25/26 & Jan 1; also closed when booked for weddings/conferences ▪ Facilities for children ▪ Gift shop ▪ Conferences: day package (60 pax)/overnight package incl 9 rooms ▪ Walks ▪ Weddings (up to 60 pax) with chapel & wooden terrace on the river ▪ 5-star guest house (9 suites) ▪ Salon treatments, booking essential ▪ Owner(s) Christian & Maren Brendel ▪ Winemaker(s) Cerina de Jongh & Gerda Willers ▪ Viticulturist(s) Paul Wallace (consultant) ▪ 30ha/±23ha (cab, merlot, ptage, shiraz, chard, chenin, sauv, sem) ▪ ±150t ▪ PO Box 117 La Motte

For more information, visit wineonaplatter.com

Franschhoek 7691 ▪ lmb@brendel.co.za ▪ www.le-manoir-de-brendel.com ▪ S 33° 52' 52.8" E 019° 3' 42.2" ▪ F +27 (0)21-876-4524 ▪ **T +27 (0)21-876-4525**

Lemberg Wine Estate

Originally established by pioneer winemaker Janey Muller in 1978 as the then smallest estate in the Cape, with a mere 11 ha of vineyards, this Tulbagh farm has been resuscitated by current owner Henk du Bruyn, who juggles his new passion with a medical career. Capital has been ploughed into the winery, visitor attractions and vineyards, and the results are showing.

Yellow Label range

★★★★ **Spencer** From pinotage. New-oak portion, no whole-berry fermentation distinguishes this from sibling. Step-up **12** more complex & sophisticated than **11** (★★★); curry spices, mulberry sweetness, enduring end.

★★★★ **Hárslevelü** Rare-in-SA white grape, long associated with Hungarian sweet white, here made dry & oxidatively. Waxy **13**, silk texture on a full body, savoury, drops sauvignon & semillon for freshness.

★★★★ **Lady** Innovative mix of oxidatively made (in older wood) viognier (59%), hárslevelü (33%), dashes semillon, sauvignon. **13** (★★★★★) supple honeysuckle, camphor & apricot glassful; more succulent & refined than ginger-spiced **12**.

★★★★★ **Surin** ⓐ Standout dessert from vine-dried sauvignon, older oak fermented. **12** (★★★★) barrel sample's decadent richness well refreshed by lively acidity, though touch more unctuous than **11**. Also tasted: **Pinot Noir 13** ★★★

White Label range

★★★★ **Sauvignon Blanc** ⓥ Fresh-cut grass & white peaches on crisp **14** preview. Bone-dry, interesting gravel grip & savoury seam, lingering finish.

Syrah ★★★ Whole-berry fermented with 14% carignan, only 5% new oak in super **13**. Smoky & vibrant, with firm tannins for winter fare. Also tasted: **Pinotage 13** ★★★★ **Cape Blend 13** ★★★ **Syrah Blanc de Noir 14** ★★★ — CvZ

Location/map: Tulbagh ▪ WO: Tulbagh/Western Cape ▪ Est 1978 ▪ Tasting, sales & cellar tours Mon-Fri 9-5 Sat/Sun 10–3 ▪ Fee R25 waived on purchase ▪ Closed Dec 25 ▪ Meals, cheese platters & picnics by appt - book prior to visit ▪ BYO picnic ▪ Table olives & olive oil ▪ Function venue (40-60 pax) ▪ Self-catering guest cottage (sleeps 4) ▪ Fly fishing (equipment available) ▪ Sunset rowboat trips by prior arrangement ▪ Owner(s) Henk du Bruyn ▪ Winemaker(s) Niël Russouw (Jan 2014) ▪ Viticulturist(s) Niël Russouw (Jan 2014) & consultants ▪ 21ha/9ha (grenache, ptage, pinot, shiraz, hárslevelü, sauv, viog) ▪ 100t/11,000cs own label 60% red 30% white 9% rosé 1% vine dried sauv ▪ IPW, Envirowines (2012) ▪ PO Box 221 Tulbagh 6820 ▪ suzette@lemberg.co.za ▪ www.lemberg.co.za ▪ S 33° 18' 8.27" E 019° 6' 23.06" ▪ F +27 (0)21-300-1131 ▪ **T +27 (0)21-300-1130**

☐ **Le Noe** *see* Barnardt Boyes Wines

Leopard Frog Vineyards

Fairtrade and, now, WIETA-accredited David Bate's output may be 'ridiculously small' but his creativity in crafting interesting wines (and latterly packaging them in eco-friendlier wood cases) is boundless. Witness a 17-vintage chardonnay (to celebrate the duration of David's SA residency), and a blend that reunites cab and its parents, cab franc and sauvignon blanc, debuting this edition.

Proprietor's Limited Releases

★★★★ **Tantra** ⓐ Cab franc's perfume & supple structure temper oak on Bordeaux red blend. Lower-key **06** (★★★) lacks gravitas & fruit of **05**.

Tendré ⓝ ★★ A Bordeaux blend with 15% sauvignon blanc! **11**'s chewy dark fruit wrapped around fairly elegant tannins make for an interesting drink. **Solstice** ⓝ ★★★ Surely a unique wine! From chardonnay, combination of 17 different vintages in this **NV** makes for a mature wine with flavours of toffee, oatmeal & lemon curd. Not retasted: **Tribe 07 ★★★ Kiss & Tell 06 ★★☆ Tao 09 ★★★☆ Ingénue 11 ★★☆ Titillation NV ★★★ Tryst MCC Blanc de Blancs Brut 08 ★★★** — CM

Location/WO: Stellenbosch ▪ Closed to public ▪ Owner(s) Dogwood Trust ▪ Cellarmaster(s)/winemaker(s) David John Bate (Jun 2005) ▪ 300cs own label 60% red 40% white ▪ Fairtrade; WIETA ▪ 8 Royal Ascot Lane Sandown Sandton 2196 ▪ info@leopard-frog.com ▪ www.leopard-frog.com ▪ F +27 (0)11-883-0426 ▪ **T +27 (0)11-884-3304**

Leopard's Leap Family Vineyards ⓆⓂ◎⑧

Owned by Hanneli Rupert-Koegelenberg and husband Hein, this previously export-only brand reaches more than 40 countries from its chic Franschhoek base. Here the focus is on encouraging visitors to experience the way wine and food enhance one another with, among others, a guided food-and-wine tasting, and cooking classes and demonstrations. This so impressed judges in the 2014 Drinks International Wine Tourism Awards, they named it as offering the Best Food & Wine Matching Experience.

Culinaria Collection

★★★★ Grand Vin Bordeaux-style quintet with notable leafy spice, violet fragrance of major partners cab franc, petit verdot. **12** lovely poise, freshness & flavour, with balanced tannin trim; good now, no hurry to drink up.

★★★★ Shiraz-Grenache **12**'s transparent ruby brilliance reflected in its light, fresh texture, fine peppery zest. Careful oaking (15% new) enriches, rounds & fills out the savoury persistence. Well conceived & satisfying.

Pinot Noir-Chardonnay ★★★☆ Pinot's dominance (60%) evident in salmon glow, full cherry fruit of **13** rosé, used oak fermented/matured for greater weight, food friendliness. Also tasted: **Chenin Blanc-Grenache Blanc 13 ★★★ Méthode Cap Classique NV ★★★☆** Not retasted: **Muscat de Frontignan 13 ★★★**

Family Collection

Shiraz-Mourvèdre-Viognier Ⓖ **★★★★** Exotic tang of viognier pervades sultry **11** & fills the already ample choc-mocha palate. 2 years in oak reflect wine's serious intent.

Classic range

Cabernet Sauvignon ⊘ **★★★☆ 12** full of delicious crunchy cassis flavours braced by firm but harmonious tannins. Good now & for few years. **Cabernet Sauvignon-Merlot ★★★ 12** wholesome 60/40 mix. Juicy mouthful black/red berries anchored by velvety tannins. **Chenin Blanc ★★★** Lively **14** has familiar guava, tropical fruit, briskly dry tail. Also tasted: **Merlot 12 ★★☆ Shiraz 12 ★★★ Chardonnay 14 ★☆ Sauvignon Blanc 14 ★★**

Lookout range

Semi Sweet ★★ Crisp red apples & marzipan in fruitily sweet **14**. Also tasted: **Pinotage Rosé 14 ★ Chenin Blanc-Chardonnay 14 ★★** Not retasted: **Cabernet Sauvignon-Shiraz-Cinsaut 12 ★★** — AL

Location/map: Franschhoek ▪ WO: Western Cape ▪ Est 2000 ▪ Tasting & sales Tue-Sat 9-5 Sun 11-5 ▪ Fee R25/5 wines ▪ Culinaria food & wine pairing R120pp Fri 10-11.30 only, booking essential ▪ Hands-on cooking classes ▪ Shop: lifestyle gifts, wine accessories, tableware, linen ware, kitchen utensils & equipment, food literature ▪ Rotisserie lunches Wed-Sun 11.30-3 ▪ Child friendly ▪ Owner(s) Hanneli Rupert-Koegelenberg & Hein Koegelenberg ▪ Cellarmaster(s) Eugene van Zyl (Nov 2002) ▪ 600,000cs own label 60% red 39% white 1% rosé ▪ PO Box 1 La Motte 7691 ▪ info@leopardsleap.co.za ▪ www.leopardsleap.co.za ▪ S 33° 52' 58.8" E 19° 04' 50" ▪ F +27 (0)21-876-4156 ▪ **T +27 (0)21-876-8002**

☐ **Leopard Spot** see Ayama Wines

☐ **Le Piquet** see Org de Rac

Le Riche Wines

This Stellenbosch winery - firmly settled in its own home after many years in rented space - is a quintessentially family one. Etienne le Riche founded the label after moving from Rustenberg in the mid-1990s, building his reputation as one of the Cape's leading exponents of fine, long-lived cabernet sauvignon. (Chardonnay is a relatively recent addition.) Son Christo took charge of winemaking in 2010 - assisted by the experienced Mark Daniels, and no doubt by Christo's redoubtable father and sister Yvonne. The latter is fully involved in the winery, giving 'opinion and direction when Christo's ideas become too extravagant'. The smallholding on which the new cellar was built has some vines, but grapes for the Le Riche cuvées continue to be sourced around Stellenbosch.

★★★★☆ **Cabernet Sauvignon Reserve** More elegant again after powerful **10**, yet still flavour-packed, **11** (★★★★) showcases cab's complexity. Loganberries, violets, creamy plums, a fennel seed nuance, masterly oaked, polished & supple after 24 months French barrels, 70% new.

★★★★☆ **Auction Reserve Cabernet Sauvignon** Name previously alluded to CWG **11** single-vineyard bottling, 24 months new French oak. Seductive cocoa-rich dark chocolate, blackcurrants & violets. The tannins are supple & savoury, with dried herb tones. Years off its peak, as befits its status.

★★★★ **Cabernet Sauvignon** Lovely plushness in **12**, blackcurrants & cedar on a bed of supple tannin, accessible & with a long future. Also-tasted **11** in similar style, a bit more savoury, hint of espresso, dried herbs.

★★★★ **Richesse** Within the illustrious line-up, **12** is for earlier drinking but at the cellar's high standard. Mainly cab, 16% merlot, dab others. Fruit rich, succulent, integrated oak, seamless.

Not tasted: **Chardonnay**. — CR

Location/WO: Stellenbosch ▪ Map: Helderberg ▪ Est 1996 ▪ 1stB 1997 ▪ Tasting, sales & cellar tours Mon-Fri 8.30-4.30 Sat by appt ▪ Closed all pub hols ▪ Owner(s) Etienne le Riche ▪ Cellarmaster(s) Etienne le Riche (Jan 1997) ▪ Winemaker(s) Christo le Riche (Jan 2010), with Mark Daniels (Sep 2000) ▪ 70t/9,000cs own label 90% red 10% white ▪ PO Box 5274, Helderberg 7135 ▪ wine@leriche.co.za ▪ www.leriche.co.za ▪ S 34° 0'52.87" E 018° 48' 9.06" ▪ F +27 (0)21-842-3472 ▪ **T +27 (0)21-842-3472**

☐ **Les Coteaux** *see* Mont du Toit Kelder
☐ **Les Fleurs** *see* Southern Sky Wines
☐ **L'Huguenot** *see* Leopard's Leap Family Vineyards

Libby's Pride Wines

Elizabeth Petersen's motto is 'Never think your dream is beyond your reach'. With star sign Leo, which she associates with strength and pride, she's intent on developing Libby's Pride into South Africa's most successful black-woman-owned wine business.

Cabernet Sauvignon ★★☆ Typical blackcurrant & touch of herbs on unwooded **13**, improvement on previous. **Shiraz** ★★ **13** unfettered by oak, offers uncomplicated sweet smoky plums. **Sauvignon Blanc** ★★★ Lemon-fresh **14** raises bar on last. Also tasted: **Merlot 13** ★★ **Signature Red 13** ★☆ **Chardonnay 14** ★★ — FM

Location: Wellington ▪ WO: Western Cape ▪ Tasting & sales by appt at Linton Park (see entry) ▪ Owner(s) Elizabeth Petersen ▪ Winemaker(s) JG Auret (2007, Linton Park) ▪ Viticulturist(s) Rudolf Jansen van Vuuren (2012, Linton Park) & Johan Viljoen (consultant) ▪ 720t/10,000cs own label 75% red 25% white ▪ info@libbyspridewines.com ▪ www.libbyspridewines.com ▪ F +27 (0)86-215-1811 ▪ **T +27 (0)82-745-5550**

Liberator

Rick the Cape Crusader, aka UK-based Richard Kelley MW, who lived and worked in the SA winelands for several years, returns regularly to 'liberate' hidden wine gems for export markets. Each wine is an 'Episode' with its own story told on the website.

For more information, visit wineonaplatter.com

★★★★ **The Francophile Chenin Blanc** Ample stewed apple flavours on **13** (★★★★). Mouthfilling, leesy mid-palate with dry, silky almond underlay shows clear nod to the Loire. Unoaked, approachable & balanced, but shade off **12**, both by DeMorgenzon.

★★★★ **Butch & The Sunrise Kid** Aromatic, flavoursome white blend, partly old-oaked, bright & balanced. **13** is 'declassified' Alheit chenin with roussanne, chardonnay & viognier from DeMorgenzon.

Also tasted: **The Francophile Syrah 13** ★★★ Not tasted: **The Connoisseur, The Bandolier, The Bird Has Flown, The Pie Chart**. — MW

WO: Western Cape/Stellenbosch ▪ Est 2010 ▪ 1stB 2008 ▪ Closed to public ▪ Owner(s) Richard Kelley & Eduard Haumann ▪ 50% red 50% white ▪ loirelover@hotmail.com ▪ www.theliberatorwine.com ▪ **T +44 (0)1476-870717**

☐ **Libertas** see Distell

Lieben Wines

Now in an advisory rather than full-time winemaking role at Goose Wines, Alwyn Liebenberg is devoting his considerable energies to his consulting work and own labels – the well-established Quinta do Sul, with port-styles from Calitzdorp family vines; and new Lieben ('Love'), beautifully and creatively packaged with an origami swan label, debuting with Alwyn's newest passion, pinot noir.

Lieben Wines range
★★★★ **Pinot Noir** **12** from 3 Walker Bay blocks, natural ferment, 30% new oak. Dense cherry & raspberry aromas & flavours, bright acidity & refreshing grape tannin grip. Impressive first attempt!

Quinta do Sul range
★★★★ **Cape Vintage** Traditional 'port' grapes plus shiraz, tannat. Very ripe & fruit-sweet **09** is plump & pliable, more Ruby in style, with less spirit attack & tannic grip than a typical Vintage.
The Library ★★★★ Idiosyncratic **NV** port-style billed as Vintage on label, actually blend of 10 vintages (2003-2012). Sweet crème de cassis & fruitcake, not as grippy as most SA examples but with fair elegance & length. Ready to enjoy. — CvZ

Location: Calitzdorp/Hermanus ▪ Map: Klein Karoo & Garden Route ▪ WO: Klein Karoo/Western Cape/Walker Bay ▪ Est 2005 ▪ 1stB 2008 ▪ Visits by appt ▪ Owner(s) Alwyn Liebenberg ▪ Cellarmaster(s)/winemaker(s) Alwyn Liebenberg (Jun 2005) ▪ 10ha/2.5ha (shiraz, souzão, tannat, tinta amarela/barocca/roriz, touriga) ▪ 5t/580cs own label ▪ 54 Siffie Crescent Vermont 7201 ▪ alwyn@thegoosewines.com ▪ www.quintadosul.co.za ▪ **T +27 (0)82-610-2279**

Lievland Estate

Early 18th-century Cape Dutch property Lievland, set among several Simonsberg red-wine luminaries, has always been synonymous with shiraz, even during its varietally and stylistically eclectic 80s/90s heyday. Bought in 2003 by US returnees, orthopaedic surgeon John Colley and wife Susan, it has since undergone low-key replanting, updating and a paring down of its portfolio.

Lievlander ★★★★ Shiraz-led blend with cab & dollop merlot. Spicily aromatic, properly dry **12** deftly seasoned & structured by some new oak. Also tasted: **Sauvignon Blanc 14** ★★★ Not retasted: **Merlot 11** ★★★ **Shiraz 11** ★★★ — IM

Location/map/WO: Stellenbosch ▪ Est/1stB 1982 ▪ Tasting, sales & cellar tours by appt T +27 (0)71-325-5382 ▪ Closed Dec 25 ▪ Summer picnic baskets by arrangement ▪ B&B accommodation ▪ Owner(s) Susan Colley ▪ Winemaker(s) Kowie du Toit (2004) ▪ Viticulturist(s) Conrad Schutte (2010, Vinpro) ▪ 50ha (cab, merlot, shiraz) ▪ 250t/10,000cs own label 95% red 5% white ▪ PO Box 66 Klapmuts 7625 ▪ lievland@icon.co.za ▪ www.lievland.co.za ▪ S 33° 50' 29.5" E 018° 52' 34.8" ▪ F +27 (0)86-628-1917 ▪ **T +27 (0)21-875-5226**

☐ **Like Father Like Son** see Bon Courage Estate

For more information, visit wineonaplatter.com

L'illa

The name (pronounced leeya) means 'island' in Catalan, and alludes to the wine's origin in Robertson's Eilandia ward and to the farm there, also Eilandia, of the Cilliers family for 6 generations. Nadia Cilliers married into the Newton Johnson clan in Hemel-en-Aarde and makes the wine in the eponymous cellar.

★★★★ **Noble Late Harvest** ⓐ Off 40 year old chenin, **12** has discreet but real charm. Delicate honeyed raisin notes supported by fine acid, giving gently sweet brightness & depth, if not intensity. 375 ml. — DS

Location: Hermanus ▪ WO: Eilandia ▪ Est/1stB 2006 ▪ Tasting & sales at Newton Johnson Vineyards ▪ Owner(s)/winemaker(s) Gordon & Nadia Newton Johnson ▪ Viticulturist(s) AA Cilliers (Jan 1973) ▪ (chenin) ▪ 220cs own label 100% white ▪ PO Box 225 Hermanus 7200 ▪ gordon@newtonjohnson.com, nadia@newtonjohnson.com ▪ www.newtonjohnson.com ▪ F +27 (0)86-638-9673 ▪ **T +27 (0)28-312-3862**

☐ **Limelight** *see* De Wetshof Estate
☐ **Lime Road** *see* Havana Hills
☐ **Limestone Rocks** *see* Springfontein Wine Estate

Limosin

Another of the brandies previously handled by Distell subsidiary Henry Tayler & Ries, (others are Chateau and Olof Bergh) which has reverted to owner Distell. Part of the brandy scene for many decades, Limosin boasts 3-year maturation in barrels from the Limousin oak forests of France, uniquely suited to brandy, imparting a silky golden smoothness and unique taste.

Limosin Extra Fine ⓐ ★★★ Uncomplex blended brandy, best for cocktails or with mixer. Caramel obvious on fruity nose. Rather sweet, with a dark, dense, spirity finish. — WB, TJ

☐ **Lindenhof** *see* Boland Kelder

Lingen

Vinification, tasting and sales for this boutique Stellenbosch label owned by the Krige family take place at neighbour Stark-Condé. Winemaker José Conde sees the wine as somewhat softer than his own but with the typical supple tannins and elegance for which Jonkershoek Valley is known. No wonder fans snap it up within weeks of release.

★★★★ **Lingen** A cab-led blend with 26% each shiraz & petit verdot, 5% petite sirah, from an interplanted 2 ha block. Elegant but tighter, more structured in **12**, with an underlying juicy core of dark fruit & pepper. — MW

Location: Stellenbosch ▪ WO: Jonkershoek Valley ▪ Est 2003 ▪ 1stB 2008 ▪ Tasting & sales at Stark-Condé Wines (see entry) ▪ Owner(s) JD Krige Family Trust ▪ Cellarmaster(s) José Conde (Jan 2003) ▪ Winemaker(s) José Conde (Jan 2003), with Elizma van Wyngaard (2012) ▪ Viticulturist(s) Andrew Klinck, with Kevin Watt ▪ 7ha/2ha (cab, p verdot, shiraz) ▪ 14t/508cs own label 100% red ▪ PO Box 389 Stellenbosch 7599 ▪ info@stark-conde.co.za ▪ www.stark-conde.co.za ▪ F +27 (0)21-887-4340 ▪ **T +27 (0)21-861-7700/+27 (0)21-887-3665**

Linton Park Wines

The UK-based diversified Camellia group own this venerable Cape Dutch property in Wellington, and continue to invest in people and place (including brand-new tasting facilities, open by appointment or every last Thursday to Saturday of the month). Winemaker JG Auret reveals additional planting is under way with a view to adding Rhône and Bordeaux-style blends to the range.

Reserve range
★★★★ **Cabernet Sauvignon** Dark, charry brooding quality to **10** (★★★☆). Extracted & firm, with profound oak spice notes. Last-tasted **08** more expressive & brighter.

★★★★ **Merlot** ⓥ **10** continues form of last-reviewed **05**. Earthy chocolate tones with graphite & tar grip. Firm dry tannin on a somewhat lean body indicative of 2 years French/American oak, third new.

★★★★ **Shiraz** ⓥ **08** (★★★★) dips on **07**. Spicy plum succulence doesn't match the oak tannin (2 years, third new) which results in a lean, dry astringency.

Linton Park range
Cabernet Sauvignon ★★★☆ **12** takes a pleasant step up. Ample rich fruitcake, with supple body. **Chardonnay** ★★★☆ Good form continues on broad, rich & creamy **13**. Fruit plays second fiddle to oak, 50% new for 12 months. Also tasted: **Café Cabernet 12** ★★★ Not retasted: **Merlot 09** ★★★★ **Shiraz 10** ★★★★ **De Slange Rivier 10** ★★★★ **Sauvignon Blanc 13** ★★☆

Louis Fourie 1699 range
Cabernet Sauvignon ★★★ Melange of dark berries, violets & spice on **13**. Taut, with firm tannin grip. Not retasted: **Chardonnay 13** ★★★ Occasional release: **Merlot**, **Shiraz**, **Chenin Blanc**, **Sauvignon Blanc**. — FM

Location: Wellington ▪ Map: Paarl & Wellington ▪ WO: Wellington/Western Cape/Paarl ▪ Est 1995 ▪ 1stB 1998 ▪ Tasting, sales & cellar tours every last Thu-Sat of the month 9-4, other days by appt only ▪ Closed all pub hols ▪ Meals/refreshments by appt ▪ 4x4 & MTB trails ▪ Annual harvest festival Mar/Apr ▪ Owner(s) Camellia PLC UK ▪ Winemaker(s) JG Auret (2007) ▪ Viticulturist(s) Rudolf Jansen van Vuuren (2012) & Johan Viljoen (consultant) ▪ 210ha/84ha (cab, merlot, pinot, shiraz, chard, sauv, viog) ▪ 720t/120,000cs own label 50% red 40% white 10% rosé ▪ Fairtrade ▪ PO Box 1234 Wellington 7654 ▪ sales@lintonparkwines.co.za, info@lintonparkwines.co.za ▪ www.lintonparkwines.co.za ▪ S 33° 36′ 40.1″ E 019° 2′ 15.0″ ▪ F +27 (0)21-873-0851 ▪ **T +27 (0)21-873-1625**

☐ **Lion Creek** *see* Napier Winery

☐ **Lion Ridge** *see* Valley Vineyards Wine Company

☐ **Lion's Drift** *see* Silkbush Mountain Vineyards

☐ **Lion's Pride** *see* Stellenrust

☐ **Lions River Vineyards** *see* Highgate Wine Estate

☐ **Liquor City** *see* Orange River Wine Cellars

☐ **Lisha Nelson Signature Wines** *see* Nelson Family Vineyards

Lismore Estate Vineyards

Few vineyards, even in the Cape, can have a lovelier setting than those of Californian expatriate Samantha O'Keefe, on the slopes of the Riversondend Mountains just outside the village of Greyton. 'This farm is our bountiful garden', says Samantha, who has worked long, hard and bravely to make it so, and to produce some fine cool-climate wines - the viogner perhaps the best known.

Location: Greyton ▪ Map: Southern Cape ▪ Est 2003 ▪ 1stB 2006 ▪ Tasting & sales by appt ▪ Facilities for children ▪ Tour groups ▪ Walking/hiking & mountain biking trails ▪ Owner(s)/winemaker(s) Samantha O'Keefe ▪ Viticulturist(s) Andrew Teubes (consultant) ▪ 232ha/12ha (shiraz, chard, sauv, viog) ▪ 45t/6,000cs own label 20% red 80% white ▪ PO Box 76 Greyton 7233 ▪ wine@lismore.co.za ▪ www.lismore.co.za ▪ S 34° 4′ 25.23″ E 019° 41′ 16.83″ ▪ **T +27 (0)82-343-7913**

☐ **Literature Wine** *see* Nordic Wines

Lithos Wines

Since last edition Tim Hoek, ex-Jordan winemaker/viticulturist, has overseen the clearing of land for more vines at the Sir Lowry's Pass boutique winery, and established a micro-brewery, while Lorraine Emery, co-owner with venture capitalist husband Sean, marketed the young Lithos brand 'with great success'. New tasting and visitor areas are next.

Location: Sir Lowry's Pass ▪ Map: Helderberg ▪ Est/1stB 2012 ▪ Tasting, sales & cellar tours Mon-Fri 8-5 by appt Sat/Sun by appt ▪ Fee R20, waived on purchase ▪ Closed all pub hols ▪ Owner(s) Sean & Lorraine Emery ▪ Winemaker(s)/

viticulturist(s) Timothy Hoek (Jan 2012) ▪ 16ha/2ha (ptage, shiraz) ▪ 20t/2,600cs own label 75% red 25% rosé ▪ Postal Suite 346 Private Bag X15 Somerset West 7129 ▪ winemaker@lithos.co.za ▪ www.lithos.co.za ▪ S 34° 6' 12.66" E 018° 55' 15.28" ▪ F +27 (0)860-552-5521 ▪ **T +27 (0)21-858-1851**

Litigo Wines

As the name suggests, a legal practitioner is behind this boutique brand. 'Being a trademark lawyer must unfortunately remain my day job,' says Eben van Wyk, who handcrafts (deftly, let the record show) tiny quantities of pinot noir - only 3 barrels of '13 - alongside Peter-Allan Finlayson of Crystallum, with 'as little as possible winemaking interference'.

★★★★☆ **Pinot Noir** Irresistible **13** offers customary sensual delight of ripe pure fruit, without lacking a serious dimension or elegance. Somehow combines restraint & exuberance, very winningly. Includes some whole bunches in the natural ferment. Sensitively, supportively oaked. Mostly Hemel-en-Aarde grapes. — TJ

Location: Cape Town ▪ WO: Hemel-en-Aarde Valley-Hemel-en-Aarde Ridge-Elandskloof ▪ Est 2011 ▪ 1stB 2012 ▪ Closed to public ▪ Owner(s) Eben van Wyk ▪ Winemaker(s) Eben van Wyk & Peter-Allan Finlayson (both 2011) ▪ 1.5t/ 160cs own label 100% red ▪ Postnet Suite 134, Private Bag X1005, Claremont 7735 ▪ info@litigowines.com ▪ www. litigowines.com ▪ F +27 (0)21-683-5952 ▪ **T +27 (0)82-803-4503**

☐ **Little Brown Job** *see* Cranefields Wine
☐ **Little J** *see* Joostenberg Wines
☐ **Little River** *see* De Meye Wines
☐ **Live-A-Little** *see* Stellar Winery
☐ **Living Rock** *see* Withington
☐ **Lodewijkx** *see* Eerste Hoop Wine Cellar

L'Olivier Wine & Olive Estate

Though mainly known as a tourist destination, with luxury accommodation and many amenities in a scenic Stellenboschkloof setting, family-owned L'Olivier does have 22 ha hectares under vine, from which boutique quantities are vinified offsite for the own label.

L'Olivier range

Chardonnay ⓝⓔⓦ ★★★ Preserved kumquats, toasted almonds; **13** boldly styled with enough freshening acidity to balance the oak. Softly rounded texture but finishes a bit short. Also tasted: **Cabernet Sauvignon 08** ★★★ **Sauvignon Blanc 13** ★★★ — CR, CvZ

Location/map: Stellenbosch ▪ WO: Western Cape ▪ Tasting & sales by appt only ▪ Fee R50 ▪ Accommodation in Manor House/Villa (sleeps 8) & two cottages (sleeps 6) ▪ Owner(s) Theuns Kuhn ▪ Viticulturist(s) Hendrik Pieterse ▪ 22ha (cab, chard, sauv) ▪ ±120t/2,945cs own label 30% red 70% white ▪ Stellenboschkloof Road Stellenbosch 7600 ▪ info@lolivierestate.com ▪ www.lolivierestate.com ▪ S 33° 55' 37" E 018° 46' 54" ▪ F +27 (0)86-519-0615 ▪ **T +27 (0)21-881-3218**

Lomond

Floral and avian names reflect the commitment to sustainable farming on this large property: 1,100ha in the Uilenkraal River Valley near fishing hamlet Gansbaai on Walker Bay. Member of the Biodiversity & Wine Initiative and Walker Bay Fynbos Conservancy, the Lomond joint venture (between Lomond Properties, Stellenbosch drinks giant Distell and a workers' trust) uses the cool coastal climate of the vaunted Cape Agulhas wine area and 120 ha of vines (selectively established on previously virgin land marked by an array of soil types) for wines that show impressive, occasionally profound, site and varietal expression.

★★★★ **Syrah** Tasty, lively **11** offers savoury mouthful of cured meat & spice flavours framed by appropriately chewy tannins. Ticks all boxes for current enjoyment, further 2/3 years.

★★★★☆ **Conebush Syrah 11** (★★★★) more powerful than **10**, though 15%+ alcohol tempered by gentle extraction, freshness. Displays usual spice, floral features associated with this single-vineyard bottling.

★★★★☆ **Cat's Tail Syrah 12** lovely follow-up to **11**. Enjoys real cool-climate scented purity, lightness of touch & freshness despite 15% alcohol. There's toothsome savouriness in the swish, plush texture & minerality in the prolonged tail.

★★★★ **SMV** (NEW) Commendably realised, approachable Rhône-style blend. **13** mainly shiraz, padded by 12% mourvèdre; full of life, energy & floral, spice fragrance (thanks to understated 6% viognier). Oak, 15% new French, equally in tune.

★★★★ **Pincushion Sauvignon Blanc 13** (★★★☆) riper vintage gives more voluptuous feel to tropical fruit; maintains fresh backbone, though little hot on finish. **12** vibrant & poised.

★★★★ **Sugarbush Sauvignon Blanc** Most enjoyable, distinctive of these **13** sauvignons. Heady quince, ripe lime scents & juicy flavours which linger deliciously long.

★★★★ **SSV White Blend 14** returns to SSV (was 'Buzzard's Trail' last edition) & with similar appeal, blend to **13**: 80% unoaked sauvignon with barrelled semillon & 4% viognier. Typical cool-climate white peach, lemongrass & honey ensemble carried lengthily by lovely freshness. Should age well for 2/3 years.

★★★★ **Snowbush** Unoaked sauvignon, nouvelle balanced by oaked semillon, viognier, in well-proportioned **13**. Good weight, zestily clean conclusion - if a bit light on fruit intensity compared to **12** (★★★★☆).

Also tasted: **Merlot 11** ★★★ **Pinot Noir 13** ★★★☆ **Sauvignon Blanc 14** ★★★☆ — AL

Location: Gansbaai ▪ Map: Southern Cape ▪ WO: Cape Agulhas ▪ Est 1999 ▪ 1stB 2005 ▪ Tasting & sales at Farm 215 Mon-Sun 9-4 by appt ▪ Closed all pub hols ▪ Guest accommodation, restaurant, conferences, hiking trail, conservation area (www.farm215.co.za) ▪ Owner(s) Lomond Properties, Distell & workers trust ▪ Cellarmaster(s)/winemaker(s) Kobus Gerber (2004) ▪ Viticulturist(s) Wayne Gabb (1999) ▪ 1,100ha/120ha (merlot, syrah, nouvelle, sauv) ▪ 750t 40% red 60% white ▪ ISO 9002, BWI ▪ PO Box 184 Stellenbosch 7599 ▪ lomond@capelegends.co.za ▪ www.lomond.co.za ▪ S 34° 34' 12" E 019° 26' 24.00" ▪ F +27 (0)21-882-9575 ▪ **T +27 (0)21-809-8330**

Londinium Wines

Despite living there himself for only two years (after 25 in New Zealand), Somerset West-born (and now -resident) Alan Bent named his wine business after his wife's home town, and the place where his maiden shiraz received the nod from some serious UK palates. His wine can be found at select outlets in Cape Town and the winelands.

The Dog's Bollocks Shiraz ⓥ ★★★ From Stellenbosch vines, **10** is high toned, with rum-&-raisin notes & curry leaf spicing, intense sweet-sour twist. For early drinking. — CvZ

Location: Somerset West ▪ WO: Stellenbosch ▪ Closed to public ▪ Owner(s) Alan & Christine Bent ▪ Cellarmaster(s) Alan Bent ▪ Winemaker(s) John Kotze ▪ 200cs own label 100% red ▪ PO Box 3747 Somerset West 7129 ▪ wineandwhales@telkomsa.net ▪ **T +27 (0)21-852-6545**

Longbarn Winery

David and Sue Power's Georgian-era barn has been refurbished and equipped as the boutique cellar on their serenely rural property in Wellington's Agter Groenberg. The sauvignon is now fermented with its own yeasts – 'takes much longer (about 3 months) but flavour is greater'.

Sauvignon Blanc ★★★ Fruity **14** preview packed with ripe tropical flavour & cooler greengage, all enlivened by lovely lime acid seam. Not tasted: **Pinot Noir**. — GM

Location/WO: Wellington ▪ Map: Paarl & Wellington ▪ Est/1stB 2006 ▪ Cellar tours by appt ▪ Owner(s) David & Sue Power ▪ Winemaker(s) David Power (Feb 2006) ▪ Viticulturist(s) David Power (Sep 2003) ▪ 69ha/4ha (pinot, sauv) ▪ 7t/280cs own label 100% white ▪ PO Box 1295 Wellington 7654 ▪ david@longbarn.co.za ▪ www.longbarn.co.za ▪ S 33° 34' 13.6" E 019° 3' 53.6" ▪ F +27 (0)86-611-1534 ▪ **T +27 (0)21-873-6396**

Long Beach

Entry-level brand by Robertson Winery for Vinimark, exported to Europe, Asia and the rest of Africa.

☐ **Longmarket** *see* Woolworths

Long Mountain Wine Company

The SA wine arm of international drinks company Pernod Ricard markets their Long Mountain and Gecko Ridge brands throughout Africa, tailoring their offering to each individual country's needs. New offices in Kenya, Angola, Nigeria and Ghana reinforce the commitment to the continent, while the ethos of social responsibility continues to be promoted through retail partnership initiatives.

Long Mountain range

Cabernet Sauvignon ★★ Slightly atypical **13** but pleasant mouthful of sweet black fruit with firm tarry finish. WO Breede River Valley, as most of these. **Chenin Blanc** ★★ Pleasant **14** tank sample shows promise of lively yellow fruit balanced with crisp acidity. Also tasted: **Pinotage 13** ★★ **Shiraz Reserve 13** ★ **Rosé 13** ★ **Chardonnay 14** ★ **Sauvignon Blanc 14** ★ Not retasted: **Merlot 12** ★★ **Ruby Cabernet 12** ★ Not tasted: **Pinotage Reserve**.

Gecko Ridge range

Pinotage ★★★ Juicy **13** shows red berried fruit backed with smoky coffee hints. Also tasted: **Cabernet Sauvignon 13** ★ **Chardonnay 14** ★ **Chenin Blanc 14** ★☆

Athena range (NEW)

Sparkling Rosé ★★ Aromatic medium-dry easy-drinker. **NV** with low alcohol. — CM

Location: Cape Town ▪ WO: Breede River Valley/Western Cape ▪ Est/1stB 1994 ▪ Closed to public ▪ Owner(s) Pernod Ricard ▪ Cellarmaster(s)/winemaker(s) Morne van Rooyen (Jan 2013) ▪ 50,000cs own label 55% red 40% white 5% rosé ▪ 2nd Floor, The Square, Cape Quarters, 27 Somerset Road, Cape Town 8005 ▪ morne.vanrooyen@pernod-ricard.com ▪ www.longmountain.co.za ▪ F +27 (0)86-775-3777 ▪ **T +27 (0)21-405-8800**

Longridge Wine Estate

Family-owned Longridge on the Helderberg benefits from what cellarmaster Jasper Raats calls the 'Helderberg Aircon' – False Bay, 5 km away as the crow flies and cold air rolling down the mountain. These conditions encourage ripe fruit at lower sugar levels and good natural acidity, resulting in a fresh, delicate chardonnay, velvety merlot and 'the biggest shift, a more pinot noir-like pinotage', enthuses Jasper, who believes these varieties, as well as chenin and other Bordeaux grapes, are particularly suited to their terroir.

Ultra Premium range

★★★★☆ **Ekliptika** (NEW) Stylish, sophisticated **12** blend of best batches cab, merlot, cab franc. Aromas of cardamon-spiced red & black fruit, tar & hints of toasty oak lead to dry, fresh palate which is both expansive & elegant, with integrated play of fruit & minerals, supportively oaked. Natural ferment.

★★★★ **Edelgoud** ⊘ A first in South Africa, Noble Late Harvest from verdelho? **11** a marriage of variety's spiced yellow peach & a deft brush of botrytis. Lightish body, crisply fresh & juicy.

Premium range

★★★★ **Pinotage** Elegant & full-bodied **12**, aromas of allspice, dark fruit & choc-coated banana. Rich, intense palate structured by finely grained tannin. Should improve with time in bottle.

★★★★☆ **Chardonnay** Natural ferment & 11 months in French oak give **12** complex aromas of hazelnut, lime, apple & honeysuckle. The palate is rich but no heavy, with a lingering mineral finish. No **11**. **10** (★★★★) also in rich style.

★★★★ **Chenin Blanc** Round, flavourful **12** with balanced, crisp palate & a flinty edge to its long finish. Natural ferment. **11** (★★★★☆) had less concentration.

Also tasted: **Cabernet Sauvignon 12** ★★★★ **Merlot 12** ★★★★ Not tasted: **Shiraz**.

Méthode Cap Classique range

★★★★☆ **Brut Vintage Reserve** Was just 'Brut'. In best years only. Finely textured & elegant **09** sparkling from chardonnay & pinot noir leaps forward from **08** (★★★☆). Aromas of pear, brioche & ripe apple, the palate both dry & generous. 60 months on lees, giving beautifully persistent, fine mousse.

Brut Rosé ★★★★ Frivolous **NV** bubbles from pinot noir & chardonnay, 40 months on lees. Aromas of strawberry, cherry & brioche; creamy & a little nutty. WO W Cape, as all these. **Brut** ★★★★ **NV** sparkler from chardonnay & pinot noir offering hazelnut, brioche & caramelised red apple notes. A fine persistent dry mousse, & a rusticity that is attractive.

Lifestyle range

Blanc ★★★ Thirst-quenching, dry, crisp & straightforward **13** an interesting unwooded 6-way white blend. WO W Cape, like the red. Not retasted: **Rouge 12** ★★☆

Discontinued: **Longridge Wine Estate range**. — JPf

Location: Stellenbosch ▪ Map: Helderberg ▪ WO: Stellenbosch/Western Cape ▪ Est 1841 ▪ 1stB 1992 ▪ Tasting & sales Mon-Sat 10-5 (last tasting at 4.30) ▪ Closed Easter weekend & Dec 25 ▪ Cellar tours by appt ▪ Longridge Restaurant T +27 (0)21-855-4082 ▪ Conferences, weddings & functions ▪ Owner(s) Van der Laan family ▪ Cellarmaster(s) Jasper Raats ▪ Winemaker(s) Jasper Raats, with Hendrien de Munck ▪ Viticulturist(s) Albert le Roux & Jasper Raats ▪ 38ha (cab, merlot, pinot, chard, chenin) ▪ 255t/27,200cs own label 53% red 45% white 2% MCC ▪ PO Box 2023 Dennesig 7601 ▪ info@longridge.co.za ▪ www.longridge.co.za ▪ S 34° 0' 55.2" E 018° 49' 60.0" ▪ F +27 (0)21-855-4083 ▪ **T +27 (0)21-855-2005**

☐ **Lookout** see Leopard's Leap Family Vineyards
☐ **Lord Somerset** see Somerset Wines

Lord's Wines

At 500m in the mountains above McGregor, boutique domaine Lord's is one of the highest and coolest in Robertson Valley and thus suited to pinot noir and chardonnay, utilised for both still and sparkling wines. Also in the purview of winemaker Ilse van Dijk-Schutte and viticulturist Jacie Oosthuizen is rare white grape nouvelle, aromatising the Sauvignon and starring solo in the Nectar dessert.

Sauvignon Blanc ★★★ Preview **14**, with dash nouvelle, steps up with stony mineral tones to broad fig appeal. Delicious in youth. **Méthode Cap Classique Brut** ★★★★ Traditional-method dry sparkler from 70% chardonnay with pinot, now **NV**. Apricot tang gets frisson from piercing, pinpoint mousse. Also tasted: **Pinot Noir Rosé 14** ★★ **Chardonnay Barrel Fermented 13** ★★★★ Not retasted: **Pinot Noir 11** ★★★ **Shiraz 11** ★★★ **Nectar Natural Sweet 12** ★★ — DS

Location/WO: McGregor ▪ Map: Robertson ▪ Est 2005 ▪ 1stB 2006 ▪ Cellar: Tasting, sales & cellar tours Mon-Fri 9-4 Sat 10-3 Sun by appt ▪ Lord's Wine Shop, Robertson: tasting & sales Mon-Fri 9-5 Sat/Sun 10-4; barrel tasting ▪ Closed Good Fri, Dec 25 & Jan 1 ▪ Tour groups by appt ▪ Farm produce ▪ Owner(s) 12 shareholders ▪ Cellarmaster(s)/winemaker(s) Ilse van Dijk-Schutte (Nov 2010) ▪ Viticulturist(s) Jacie Oosthuizen (Jan 2003) ▪ 33ha/13ha (pinot, shiraz, chard, nouvelle, sauv) ▪ 90t/13,200cs own label 50% red 45% white 5% rosé ▪ PO Box 165 McGregor 6708 ▪ ilse@lordswinery.com, sales@lordswinery.com ▪ www.lordswinery.com ▪ S 33° 59' 20.98" E 019° 44' 28.39" ▪ **T +27 (0)23-625-1265**

☐ **L'Ormarins** see Anthonij Rupert Wyne
☐ **Lorna Hughes** see Stonehill

Lorraine Private Cellar

Cellarmaster Johan de Wet is deeply attached to this land, where his family has been growing wine for five generations. Small wonder: the farm is situated in a fertile valley with clear rivers, diverse soils, late sunrises and long afternoon shadows cast by the Du Toitskloof Mountains - perfect conditions for vines.

Cape Harmony ★★★★ Aptly named, ripe-berried melange of cab, merlot & pinotage, **12** supple, supportive tannins & well-judged oak. Ready to enjoy. **Love Of My Life Pinotage Rosé** ★★☆ Tangy, sunset-hued picnic wine, **13** bright red-berry appeal, crisp balancing acidity for dryish, light sipping. Also tasted: **Chardonnay 12 ★★ Sauvignon Blanc 13 ★★** Not tasted: **Shiraz**, **Viognier**. — MW

Location: Rawsonville ▪ Map: Breedekloof ▪ WO: Goudini/Western Cape ▪ Est 1996 ▪ 1stB 2002 ▪ Tasting, sales & cellar tours Mon-Fri 8-1 ▪ Closed all pub hols ▪ Outdoor wine tasting & picnic by appt R200pp; or BYO picnic ▪ Tour groups ▪ Walks/hikes ▪ Conservation area ▪ Owner(s) Lorraine Trust (Johan & Lori Ann de Wet) ▪ Cellarmaster(s)/winemaker(s) Johan de Wet (Jan 2002) ▪ Viticulturist(s) Leon Dippenaar (2003, consultant) ▪ ±417ha/155ha (cab f, merlot, p verdot, ptage, ruby cab, shiraz, chard, chenin, nouvelle, sauv, viog) ▪ 2,000t total 50t/±8,400cs own label 45% red 50% white 5% rosé ▪ Fairtrade ▪ PO Box 2 Rawsonville 6845 ▪ info@lorraine.co.za ▪ www.lorraine.co.za ▪ S 33° 42' 43.14" E 019° 15' 40.83" ▪ F +27 (0)86-664-2279 ▪ **T +27 (0)23-349-1224**

☐ **Lorry** *see* Corder Family Wines

Lothian Vineyards

When the Wilson brothers bought an old protea farm on the banks of Elgin's Palmiet River in 2004 with the intention of establishing vineyards, they became the 3rd generation involved with wine – their Scottish grandmother owned Rust en Vrede in the 1950s and 60s and their mother supplied grapes to Spier. Launched after our deadline is a dry rosé from a small block of mourvèdre. Also-untasted Wildlife Series (Otter's Claw and Horny Owl) is mostly for early enjoyment and features 'ir-reverent labels aimed to elicit jovial conversation'.

Vineyard Selections

★★★★ Pinot Noir Elegant **12**, with balanced freshness & perfumed red fruit infused into silky tex-ture. Refined & persistent. Enjoyable now, with potential to age. Nudges next rung up.

Riesling ★★★ Semi-dry **13** lightish body & delicate flavours, creamy & rounded from lees-ageing, already quite developed terpene note. Pleasant aperitif for early enjoyment. **12** as yet unreleased. Not retasted: **Chardonnay 12 ★★★★** — MW

Location/WO: Elgin ▪ Map: Elgin, Walker Bay & Bot River ▪ Est 2004 ▪ 1stB 2010 ▪ Tasting first weekend in every month, or by appt ▪ Honey ▪ Conferences/functions ▪ Conservation area ▪ Luxury guesthouse (8 double en-suite bed-rooms) ▪ Owner(s) Wilson family ▪ Winemaker(s) Stefan Gerber (2010) ▪ Viticulturist(s) Kevin Watt (Mar 2009) ▪ 46ha/13ha (mourv, pinot, chard, riesling, sauv, viog) ▪ 60t 25% red 75% white ▪ IPW ▪ 68 Reservoir Rd Somerset West 7130 ▪ info@lothianvineyards.com ▪ www.lothianvineyards.com ▪ S 34° 11' 31.49" E 018° 58' 57.78" ▪ F +27 (0)86-718-1672 ▪ **T +27 (0)21-859-9901**

Louiesenhof Wines

Stephan Smit, the prime mover here, learnt eco-values in his early studies in Germany, inspiring a 'bio-organic wine' way back in 1991. Respect for the environment persists, as evidenced by the fact that Louiesenhof supports the Bottelary Hills Conservancy and strives to make wines 'in harmony with nature'.

Premier Collection

Shiraz ⓦ **★★★☆ 11** lovely dark-fruited nose has a green edge, following to rich full-bodied end. Not retasted: **Cabernet Sauvignon-Cabernet Franc 11 ★★★ Chardonnay Sur-Lie 11 ★★★☆**

Louiesenhof Wines range

Pinotage ⓦ **★★★** Attractive smoke & flint harmonise with clean berry aromas & firm tannins on **10**, good match for spicy food. **Perroquet Cape Tawny** ⓦ **★★★★ NV** rustic glow-inducing port-style from tinta, with savoury touches. Not retasted: **Cape Blend 10 ★★★ Chardonnay Sur-Lie 11 ★★★ Sauvignon Blanc 11 ★★★☆ Sweet Red NV ★★ Roobernet Cape Ruby 10 ★★★** Not tasted: **Perroquet Merlot Pétillant Rosé**.

Brandy range

3 Year Old Blended Brandy ⓦ **★★★** 100% potstill, from colombard (like next). Fresh & fruity, a touch sweet, with little oak influence. Ideal for mixing or cocktails. **Marbonne 16 Year Brandy** ⓦ

★★★ Less fresh than younger one, with earthy, oaky notes along with fruit & spice. Fairly rich & smooth, if not harmonious. — WB, JP, TJ

Location/map/WO: Stellenbosch ▪ Est 1991 ▪ 1stB 1995 ▪ Tasting & sales Mon-Fri 9–5 Sat/Sun 10-5 ▪ Fee R10pp ▪ Closed Good Fri, Ascension day & Dec 25 ▪ Bistro open daily 10-3, group bookings advised ▪ Play area for children ▪ Tour groups ▪ Gift shop ▪ Farm produce ▪ Conferences (20 pax) ▪ Conservation area ▪ Hiking & MTB trails ▪ Antique brandy kettle on display ▪ B&B guesthouse ▪ Owner(s) WS Smit Watergang Trust ▪ Cellarmaster(s) WS Smit ▪ Brandy master(s) Stefan Smit & Jos le Roux (both 1991) ▪ Winemaker(s) Jos le Roux ▪ Viticulturist(s) Stefan Smit (1991) ▪ 135ha (cabs s/f, merlot, ptage, shiraz, chard, chenin, pinot grigio, sauv) ▪ 900–1,000t/675,000L ▪ BWI, IPW, WIETA ▪ Koelenhof Road (R304) Stellenbosch 7601 ▪ info@louiesenhof.co.za ▪ www.louiesenhof.co.za ▪ S 33° 53' 34.7" E 018° 49' 35.3" ▪ F +27 (0)21-865-2613 ▪ **T +27 (0)21-865-2632 (office)/+27 (0)21-889-5550 (cellar)**

Louis

Cape Winemakers Guild member Louis Nel likens his negociant-style wine venture to a Jack Russell dog, small, energetic and nimble. His creativity and sales of the 3,000 cases of his own wines bears this out. Mentored by one of the industry's greats, Neil Ellis, Louis sagely notes that 'the causality of greatness is often an illusion' and continues to focus on getting the basics right.

Louis range

★★★★ **Cabernet Sauvignon** The ripe, lush aspects of impressively tasty **09** are checked by melting tannins, savoury acid & resolute dryness. Like **08** (★★★★☆), will benefit from few years - harmony will follow.

★★★★ **Cabernet Sauvignon-Merlot** ⓥ **12** (★★★★) has a core of dark fruit still tightly wrapped in fine-grained chalky tannins. Leaner & less approachable in youth than **08**.

★★★★ **Sauvignon Blanc** Tropical fruit mingles with grass, lemongrass & citrus on partly barrelled **14** from Darling. Intense, it's more refined than Buckleberry, but also powerful, with a forthright crisp acidity.

Black Forest range

Shiraz-Merlot ★★★★ Stylish, rather clever **13**, 90/10 blend, has choc & cherry - just like the gateau it's named for. Very soft, ripe & easy, though with some deftly placed savoury underpinning. WO W Cape.

Buckleberry range

Cold Fermented Sauvignon Blanc ★★★ Pleasant tropical quality to exuberantly fruity **14**, but there's also an assertively tangy, sour-tinged, green tug to it.

Titanic range

Cabernet Sauvignon Missed our tasting deadline. — TJ

Location: Stellenbosch ▪ WO: Stellenbosch/Western Cape/Darling ▪ Est/1stB 2007 ▪ Closed to public ▪ Owner(s) Louis Nel ▪ Cellarmaster(s)/winemaker(s) Louis Nel (Jan 2007) ▪ 15t/3,000cs own label 50% red 50% white ▪ 9 Forest Street Stellenbosch 7600 ▪ louis@louiswines.com ▪ www.louiswines.com ▪ **T +27 (0)82-775-8726**

☐ **Louis Fourie 1699** *see* Linton Park Wines

Louisvale Wines

An upgrade to the visitor facilities was under way at press time on this Devon Valley farm, where the focus has been on chardonnay since inception in 1989. It's still the only white grape planted, with different clones and blocks for longtime winemaker-viticulturist Simon Smith to work with, while some red grapes are brought in.

Louisvale Wines range

Chardonnay ★★★★ As usual, nuttier & richer than Chavant. **13** integrated oaking, balanced acidity, with a few grams of sugar adding to the silky texture. **Chavant** ★★★★ More characterful aromas & flavours than Unwooded version, stressing the ripe pear notes. Older-oaked **13** pleasingly restrained

& light-feeling, dry & rather elegant. Also tasted: **Dominique 13** ★★★☆ **Chardonnay Unwooded 14** ★★★ **Chardonnay-Pinot Noir 14** ★★☆

Stone Road range
Sauvignon Blanc ⊘ ★★★ Full-flavoured & tasty **14** offers plenty of tropical, but nicely green-tinged, character. Also tasted: **Cabernet Sauvignon 13** ★★ **Merlot 13** ★★ — TJ

Location/map: Stellenbosch ▪ WO: Stellenbosch/Coastal/Western Cape ▪ Est/1stB 1989 ▪ Tasting, sales & cellar tours Mon-Fri 10-5 ▪ Fee R20 ▪ Closed all pub hols ▪ BYO picnic ▪ Owner(s) Louisvale Wines (Pty) Ltd ▪ Directors Altmann Allers, Hendrik Kluever, Johann Kirsten & Zane Meyer ▪ Winemaker(s)/viticulturist(s) Simon Smith (Jul 1997) ▪ 34ha/23ha (cab, merlot, chard) ▪ 220t/16,000cs own label 50% red 50% white ▪ PO Box 542 Stellenbosch 7599 ▪ winery@louisvale.com ▪ www.louisvale.com ▪ S 33° 54' 32.3" E 018° 48' 24.3" ▪ F +27 (0)21-865-2633 ▪ T +27 (0)21-865-2422

Lourensford Wine Estate

On the edge of Somerset West lies businessman Christo Wiese's vast, multi-faceted estate, reaching far up the slopes of the majestic mountain amphitheatre. The conservation-minded property boasts one of the largest and most technologically advanced wineries in the country, together with a host of craft-orientated enterprises, eateries and galleries, as well as its imposing venue, The Laurent. The estate regularly hosts cycling and trail-running events, and its outdoor concert venue on the polo fields showcases world-famous performers. More attractions are in the offing, reveals CEO Koos Jordaan. 'We've got exciting plans to increase our tourist facilities.'

Winemaker's Selection range
★★★★☆ **Reserve Red Blend** Barrel selection of estate's best cab & merlot, 65/35 proportion in **11**. Sleek & muscular, dense core of dark fruit sheathed in dry, fine tannins (partly from 100% new French, 2 years). Youthful but polished, with pedigree to age. No **10**.

★★★★☆ **Chardonnay 13** (★★★★) serious oaking (70% new) dominates fresher tank-fermented portion, imparts richness but subdues subtle lime, hazelnut flavours. Similar creamy succulence but shade off captivating **12**.

★★★★☆ **Reserve White Blend** ⊘ **11** is back to form after **10** (★★★★). A blend of best barrel-fermented (older wood) sauvignon, chardonnay & viognier. Rounded, with superb balance & poise. Cellar or decant to reveal full potential.

★★★★☆ **Semillon Noble Late Harvest** An unctuously rich elixir, oak-fermented **12** is dessert on its own! Cornucopia of sweet caramel, pineapple, wild fynbos honey & toasted nut flavours, yet still vibrant, balanced & tangy. No **10**, **11** made.

Not tasted: **Merlot**, **Syrah**, **Sauvignon Blanc**, **Viognier**.

Lourensford range
★★★★ **Méthode Cap Classique Rosé** Tangy & vivacious **11** pink sparkling from pinot noir (92%) with splash chardonnay. Freshness focuses bright & savoury red fruit. Rich, creamy tone from partial oaking & 33 months on the lees.

★★★★☆ **Méthode Cap Classique** ⊘ Exuberant **09** bottle-fermented sparkling from chardonnay (7% oaked) & pinot noir. Fine, lazy mousse blossoms in the mouth with crisp appley brioche flavour & creamy texture from 48 months lees-ageing. Classy, with richness & finesse.

Shiraz-Mourvèdre-Viognier ★★★☆ Very rounded & approachable **12**, attractive dense colour with juicy-savoury red fruit coating amenable tannins & harmonious oak. Also tasted: **Shiraz 11** ★★★☆ **Chardonnay 13** ★★★☆ **Sauvignon Blanc 13** ★★★☆ Not retasted: **Cabernet Sauvignon 11** ★★★☆ **Merlot 11** ★★★☆

River Garden range
Rosé ★★★ Delightful al fresco/anytime pink, **14** dry & bright, lovely savoury red-berried flavour & freshness from merlot, mourvèdre & shiraz. **Chardonnay** ★★★ Unwooded **14** with some pinot noir

& splash viognier giving subtle waft of perfume. Smooth but fresh, glides across the palate with ethereal ease. Also tasted: **Cabernet Sauvignon-Merlot 13 ★★★ Shiraz-Cabernet Sauvignon 12 ★★★ Sauvignon Blanc 14 ★★** — MW

Location: Somerset West ▪ Map: Helderberg ▪ WO: Stellenbosch/Western Cape ▪ Est 1999 ▪ 1stB 2003 ▪ Tasting, sales & cellar tours daily 9-5 ▪ Fee R30 ▪ Closed Good Fri & Dec 25 ▪ Millhouse Kitchen ▪ Tour groups ▪ A-Place Interior ▪ Coffee Roastery ▪ Cheesery ▪ Function hall ▪ Conservation area ▪ Owner(s) Christo Wiese ▪ Winemaker(s) Hannes Nel (Nov 2002), with Timothy Witbooi (May 2005) ▪ Viticulturist(s) Piet Uys ▪ 4,000ha/135ha (cab, merlot, pinot, shiraz, chard, sauv, viog) ▪ 1,200t/240,000cs own label 40% red 58% white 2% rosé ▪ Brands for clients: Eden Crest (Checkers) ▪ BRC, BWI champion, HACCP, WIETA ▪ PO Box 16 Somerset West 7129 ▪ info@lourensford.co.za ▪ www.lourensford.com ▪ S 34° 4' 3.7" E 018° 53' 44.2" ▪ F + 27 (0)21-847-0910 ▪ **T +27 (0)21-847-2300**

Lovane Boutique Wine Estate

Lovane luxury guesthouse, chic conference venue and tiny cabernet-led vineyard between Stellenbosch heavyweights Overgaauw and Neethlingshof now belongs to chartered accountant and business change manager Theresa Visser and husband Hennie, who takes care of vines and wines under guidance of Philip Gous and wife Gail, who established the property in 2003.

★★★★☆ Isikhati ⓥ 09 (★★★★) cab-led blend, with telling input from petit verdot & cab franc; developed leafy features, tannins softened. 42 months cask. Less sprightly & refreshing than **07**. No **08**. **Cabernet Sauvignon Berries Only** ⓥ ★★★★ Perfumed **09**, more lissom than cellarmates, ready to enjoy after 3.5 years mainly older oak. **Petit Verdot Umama** ⓥ ★★★★ **08**'s pleasantly taut & lean profile will be appreciated by New-World-weary palates. **Unfiltered Blanc de Noir** ⓥ ★★★ Firm berry fruit & dry tail of **13** call for sushi. Not retasted: **Cabernet Sauvignon Iziko 08 ★★ Cabernet Sauvignon Umgidi 07 ★★★ Cabernet Sauvignon Tamkulu 08 ★★★★** Not tasted: **Cabernet Sauvignon Umbhidi Wholeberry, Cabernet Franc Iliwa, Summer Mist, Méthode Cap Classique, Sweet 77**. — JPf

Location/map/WO: Stellenbosch ▪ Est 2003 ▪ 1stB 2006 ▪ Tasting, sales & cellar tours Mon-Sun 10-5 ▪ Tasting fee R20, waived on purchase ▪ Closed all pub hols ▪ Conferences ▪ Lovane Guest House ▪ Owner(s) Hennie & Theresa Visser ▪ Winemaker(s) Philip Gous & Hennie Visser ▪ Viticulturist(s) Philip & Gail Gous, Hennie Visser ▪ 3.6ha/2.5ha (cabs s/f, p verdot) ▪ 20t/2,800cs own label 90% red 5% white 5% rosé ▪ PO Box 91 Vlottenburg 7604 ▪ info@lovane.co.za ▪ www.lovane.co.za ▪ S 33° 57' 09.74" E 018° 48' 02.38" ▪ F + 27 (0)21-881-3546 ▪ **T +27 (0)21-881-3827**

☐ **Loyal Brothers** *see* Govert Wines
☐ **Luca & Ingrid Bein** *see* Bein Wine Cellar

Luddite Wines

It's 15 years since winemaker Niels Verburg, viticulturist wife Penny and investor Hillie Meyer started out on a slope on Van der Stel Pass overlooking Bot River village. A farmstead, cellar and tasting locale have since been built, and the first (stellar-quality) home-vinified wines released. Farm produce, notably much-in-demand charcuterie from free-ranging pigs has been added, along with visitor amenities. A constant throughout has been wine made traditionally - without machinery and mechanisation — and, fans will be reassured, the Luddite way still reigns supreme.

★★★★☆ Shiraz Restrained **10** is complex, layered, refined & elegant. Velvety sweet/savoury fruit & vanilla oak seduce the senses yet are focused, with excellent tannin management & alcohol (15%) in perfect balance with the persistent liqueur-like blackberry finish. All Bot River fruit, 25% new oak.

★★★★☆ Saboteur Leashed power on **10** shiraz, cab, mourvèdre blend from 5 Bot River blocks (but WO W Cape). Textured mouthful of bright, succulent, rounded black fruit, fynbos & dried herbs. Firm oak backbone (95% new) yet silky, fine tannins & spicy cured meat lift on unflagging goodbye.

★★★★ Chenin Blanc Pineapple, orchard fruit & creamy citrus zest on expressive, broad, rich **13**, from 40-60 year old vines, naturally fermented in older oak, like debut **12** (★★★★). Balanced & complex from regular lees stirring, long finish. Overberg WO. — WB

Location: Bot River ▪ Map: Elgin, Walker Bay & Bot River ▪ WO: Walker Bay/Western Cape/Overberg ▪ Est/1stB 2000 ▪ Tasting, sales & cellar tours by appt ▪ Closed Dec 25 & Jan 1 ▪ Farm produce ▪ Walks/hikes ▪ Conservation area ▪ Owner(s) Niels Verburg & Hillie Meyer ▪ Cellarmaster(s)/winemaker(s) Niels Verburg (2000) ▪ Viticulturist(s) Penny Verburg (2000) ▪ 17ha/5.8ha (cab, mourv, shiraz, chenin) ▪ 30t/3,500cs own label 100% red + 4,000cs for clients ▪ Brands for clients: Elgin Vintners, Oneiric, Ridgelands ▪ PO Box 656 Bot River 7185 ▪ luddite@telkomsa.net ▪ www.luddite.co.za ▪ S 34° 12' 50.5" E 019° 12' 24.1" ▪ F +27 (0)28-284-9045 ▪ **T +27 (0)28-284-9308/+27 (0)83-444-3537**

LuKa Wine Estate

Pioneers of small-scale winegrowing around the upmarket resort town of Plettenberg Bay, Hennie and Anita Kritzinger's retirement venture is gaining devotees and visitors to the on-site tasting venue. Their Sauvignon Blanc missed our tasting deadline but appeared on track to greet the expected influx of festive season holidaymakers.

Location: Plettenberg Bay ▪ Map: Klein Karoo & Garden Route ▪ Est 2008 ▪ 1stB 2011 ▪ Tasting in Dec, Mar/Apr or by appt ▪ Owner(s) Hennie & Anita Kritzinger ▪ Cellarmaster(s)/winemaker(s) Anton Smal (Bramon Wines) ▪ Viticulturist(s) Hennie Kritzinger ▪ ±7ha/1.5ha (sauv) ▪ ±3t/422cs own label 100% white ▪ PO Box 2519 Plettenberg Bay 6600 ▪ henita@telkomsa.net ▪ www.lukawines.co.za ▪ S 34° 2' 28.14" E 023° 15' 57.56" ▪ F +27 (0)44-533-6782 ▪ **T +27 (0)82-457-8110/+27 (0)82-332-3299**

Lula by Rudera Wines

The name of this Rudera export brand captures the intended style, Lula being Xhosa for 'Easy'.

Pinotage ⓝⓔⓦ Dark-fruit aromas on **12**, with sweet light fruit. A trifle bony & awkward, with strong dry tannins. WO W Cape, like all. **Red** ⓝⓔⓦ ★★★ Pleasantly fruity Bordeaux blend, mostly cab; **12** easygoing & flavoursome, held together on a gentle structure. Unoaked, like Pinotage. Not retasted: **Merlot 12** ★★ Not tasted: **Syrah**, **Chenin Blanc**. — TJ

Lusan Premium Wines

Umbrella organisation for Alto, Le Bonheur, Neethlingshof, Stellenzicht (and its value brand Hill & Dale) and Uitkyk (including Flat Roof Manor). See entries.

Stellenbosch ▪ Closed to public ▪ imstrydom@distell.co.za ▪ F +27 (0)21-883-8941 ▪ **T +27 (0)21-883-8988**

☐ **Luscious Hippos** *see* United Nations of Wine

Lutzville Cape Diamond Vineyards

One of SA's largest wine producers, Lutzville Cape Diamond Vineyards delivers a polished performance as a company successfully evolved from the old co-operative system. Vinifying increasingly for the bulk-wine market overseas, cellarmaster Gideon Theron and his team (boosted by newcomer Andries Eygelaar ex Swartland) strive to maintain quality and value through developing close grower co-operation. This produces gems, mass-market and niche wines like the naturally sweet, low-alcohol Cape Elephant range, not tasted.

Francois Le Vaillant range

★★★★☆ **Noble Late Harvest** ⓖ Worthy addition to botrytis dessert category. From chenin, hedonistic **12** distinctive dried apricot & citrus peel flavour, lovely freshening acidity.

Not retasted: **Pinotage 12** ★★★★

The Diamond Collection

★★★★ **Oaked Chenin Blanc** ⓥ Finely integrated oak bolsters solid, ripe fruit on **13**, with mineral emphasis & silky texture. Hints of marzipan, white peach, with charming bitter twist at finish. From cooler Koekenaap & warmer Lutzville blocks.

★★★★ **Semillon** ⓖ **10** confirms team's assertion that their top whites can age with benefit. Restrained but interesting, with richness & length.

Sauvignon Blanc ★★★★ Arresting nettle/khaki bush aromas, ripe & generous fruit in **13** from Koekenaap vines. Creamy lees texture, salty mineral twist at finish. One to seek out. Also tasted: **Cabernet Sauvignon 12** ★★★☆ **Shiraz 12** ★★★★ **Ebenaezer 12** ★★★☆ Not tasted: **Chardonnay**.

Lutzville range

★★★★ **White Muscadel** ⊘ **10** rich & full but light-footed. Uncloying, delightful step up on last-tasted **07** (★★★).

Shiraz ★★★ Sweetly fruity, with hint of peppery spice, **13** ends with pleasant leathery tannin grip. Wholesome, juicy & appealing everyday tipple. **Shiraz Rosé** ★★★ Semi-sweet, with strawberries & roses, talcum-soft texture; **14** full, ripe & fruity. **Chenin Blanc** ★★☆ Shy peach & pineapple fruit, just-dry & juicy, with firm tangy acid grip; **14** delivers pleasant quaffing. Also tasted: **Cabernet Sauvignon 13** ★★☆ **Merlot 13** ★★★ **Pinotage 13** ★★☆ **Chardonnay 13** ★★★ **Sauvignon Blanc 14** ★★★ Occasional release: **Viognier**. — GdB

Location: Lutzville ▪ Map: Olifants River ▪ WO: Lutzville Valley ▪ Est 1961 ▪ 1stB 1980 ▪ Tasting, sales & cellar tours Mon-Fri 9-5 Sat 9-2 ▪ Closed Sun, Easter Sat, Dec 25 & Jan 1 ▪ Coffee shop Mon-Fri 9-4 Sat 10-1 ▪ Function/conference venue ▪ Owner(s) Lutzville Wingerde Beperk ▪ Cellarmaster(s) Gideon Theron (Nov 2005) ▪ Winemaker(s) Jaco van Niekerk (Sep 2009), Brenda Thiart (Nov 2011) & Andries Eygelaar (Jan 2014) ▪ Viticulturist(s) Gideon Engelbrecht (Sep 2009) ▪ 2,100ha (cab, merlot, ptage, pinot, ruby cab, shiraz, chard, chenin, cbard, nouvelle, sauv, sem, viog) ▪ ±46,000t/400,000cs own label 11% red 89% white ▪ BRC ▪ PO Box 50 Lutzville 8165 ▪ info@lutzvillevineyards.com ▪ www.lutzvillevineyards.com ▪ S 31° 33' 35.9" E 018° 21' 0.2" ▪ F +27 (0)27-217-1435 ▪ **T +27 (0)27-217-1516**

Lyngrove

In the Helderberg foothills between Somerset West and Stellenbosch, Lyngrove offers not only spectacular vistas of False Bay and Table Mountain — something guests and conference goers at the 5-star colonial-style establishment appreciate — but three-decades-old chenin vines too. Winemaker Danielle le Roux reveals that additional chenin (and pinotage) plantings ensure a continuation of the grape legacy.

Platinum range

★★★★ **Pinotage 12** echoes **10**'s subtle yet vibrant ripe blue & black fruit. Lithe & silky, with depth, breadth & well-integrated oak (40% new). Good focus & balance with long, rewardingly rich finish. Both a rung above **11** (★★★★).

★★★★ **Shiraz** Brooding spicy presence to **11** that improves on **10** (★★★★). Better concentration, balance & integration of French/American oak (25% new), with abundant juicy plum flavour.

★★★★ **Latitude 12** a welcome return to form for pinotage, cab, shiraz blend after **11** (★★★★). Bright cranberry succulence toned by 14 months in combo French/American wood (50% new). Structured & firm but fleshy.

Reserve range

Shiraz-Pinotage ★★★☆ Gentle texture to richly fruited **11**. Solid core & good focus. Long, dry tail. Also tasted: **Chardonnay 13** ★★★☆

Lyngrove Collection

Cabernet Sauvignon ★★★☆ Lipsmacking cherry plum notes on **12**. Smart & ripe but modest & approachable. Very drinkable. **Chenin Blanc** ★★★ Crisp tropical fruit populate vivacious **14**, unpretentiously light but focused. Also tasted: **Merlot 12** ★★★★ **Pinotage 13** ★★★ **Shiraz 12** ★★★☆ **Sauvignon Blanc 14** ★★★ — FM

Location: Somerset West ▪ Map: Helderberg ▪ WO: Stellenbosch ▪ Est/1stB 2000 ▪ Tasting & sales Mon-Fri by appt Sat/Sun 9-3 breakfast & wine tasting ▪ Guesthouse ▪ Conferences (12 pax) ▪ Winemaker(s) Hannes Louw & Danielle le Roux (Jun 2006) ▪ Viticulturist(s) André van den Berg ▪ 76ha (cab, merlot, p verdot, ptage, shiraz, chard, chenin, sauv)

▪ 100,000cs own label 70% red 20% white 10% rosé ▪ WIETA ▪ PO Box 7275 Stellenbosch 7599 ▪ wine@lyngrove.co. za ▪ www.lyngrove.co.za ▪ S 34° 1' 8.7" E 018° 48' 10.2" ▪ F +27 (0)21-880-0851 ▪ **T +27 (0)21-880-1221**

Lynx Wines

Spanish born and originally an engineer by profession, Franschhoek vintner Dieter Sellmeyer first made wine in 2002 with no greater ambition than having something for home consumption. 'We ended up with a wine but no name for it. We finally called it Xanache – after our three beautiful daughters Xan (Alexandra), Charlie and Anna who helped me make it.' Dieter was hooked and soon started taking winemaking seriously.

Premium range

★★★★ **Shiraz** Red fruit, sweet spices & subtle toasty vanilla charm from 30% American oak on **12**. Drying, firm acidity combines with overt pepperiness to enliven the palate, add freshness. Greater presence, more seriousness than soft & accessible **11** (★★★★).

★★★★ **Xanache** 4-way Bordeaux red with brooding dark fruit & black olive/meaty note, **12**'s dry tannins, leafy spice nuances, savoury finish make it one of the more structured of property's reds; add to its ageability.

★★★★☆ **The Lynx** Flagship, selection of best barrels; shiraz-led Rhône blend **11** (★★★★) very ripe elements & ample oak (2 years, 50% new). Approachable & supple, will reward fans of rich, modern style, though not in same league as **10**, a Bordeaux blend.

★★★★ **Viognier** Orange rind & bruised peach, nutty marzipan highlights, **13** (★★★★) 50% new wood more prominent than **12** but still integrated. Genteel sweetness balanced by acidity & subtle grip. Serious attempt well suited to the dinner table.

Cabernet Sauvignon ★★★☆ Easy, modern **12** has true-to-variety cedar notes, hints of cassis; medium body, sweet red fruits & fine dusty tannins; most elegant of the reds. Also tasted: **Cabernet Franc 12** ★★★ **Grenache 12** ★★★☆ **SMV 12** ★★★☆ Not tasted: **Sweet Lynx**. Discontinued: **Merlot**.

Classic range

Vino Blanco (NEW) ★★★☆ Viognier with few drops grenache blanc, balanced **14** has attractive florality, tangy apricot & pineapple flavour, refreshing savoury tail. Bring on summer! Also tasted: **Vino Tinto 12** ★★★★ **Blanc de Noir 14** ★★★ **Viognier Tardio 14** ★★★ — HJ

Location/map/WO: Franschhoek ▪ Est/1stB 2002 ▪ Tasting, sales & cellar tours Mon-Fri 10–5 Sat/Sun & pub hols by appt ▪ Fee R30 (tasting & tour) ▪ Owner(s) Vista Hermosa (Pty) Ltd ▪ Cellarmaster(s) Dieter Sellmeyer (Jan 2002) ▪ Winemaker(s) Helgard van Schalkwyk (Nov 2010) ▪ Viticulturist(s) Kevin Watt ▪ 26ha/11ha (cabs s/f, grenache, merlot, shiraz, viog) ▪ 90t/9,000cs own label 50% red 15% white 35% rosé ▪ IPW ▪ PO Box 566 Franschhoek 7690 ▪ winemaker@lynxwines.co.za ▪ www.lynxwines.co.za ▪ S 33° 51' 46.1" E 019° 2' 14.6" ▪ F +27 (0)21-867-0397 ▪ **T +27 (0)21-867-0406**

☐ **Maankloof** *see* Mountain River Wines

Maastricht Estate

Wheaty Louw's long-cherished dream of making wine carrying the name of the family's early 18th-century Dutch-named Durbanville grape-growing farm has been realised courtesy of recently graduated winemaker son Thys Jnr, who vinifies small parcels of wine alongside his cousin (also Thys Louw) at well-known Diemersdal nearby. Success may warrant an own cellar soon.

★★★★ **Shiraz** Soft **13** (★★★★) shows slightly confected ripe red fruit & some spice, with moderately firm palate. More of an easy-drinker than the intense & soulful **12**.

Sauvignon Blanc ★★★★ Greenpepper & grass with hint of Granny Smith apple on **14**. Bone-dry, with brisk acidity & fine sinewy mouthfeel. Very refreshing. Also tasted: **Cabernet Sauvignon 13** ★★★ **Pinot Noir 13** ★★★ **Pinotage 13** ★★★★ — JPf

Location: Durbanville ▪ WO: Durbanville/Western Cape ▪ Est 1702 ▪ 1stB 2009 ▪ Closed to public ▪ Owner(s) Wheaty Louw ▪ Cellarmaster(s) Thys Louw jnr (Jan 2009) ▪ Viticulturist(s) Wheaty Louw (1986) & Thys Louw jnr ▪ 105ha (cab, ptage, shiraz, sauv) ▪ ±1,100t/3,000cs own label 40% red 60% white ▪ wine@maastricht.co.za ▪ F +27 (0)86-521-9062 ▪ **T +27 (0)21-976-1995**

☐ **Mad About South African Wine** *see* Overhex Wines International
☐ **Mad Hatter's** *see* Wellington Wines
☐ **Phambili** *see* Wellington Wines
☐ **Maestro** *see* DeMorgenzon

Maiden Wine Cellars

Danie Hattingh's small negociant house was started in the mid-1990s with the US and UK as focuses, gradually expanded to include Malaysia and China. The US and Malaysia remain steady buyers of his Private Reserve red blend, while his newer occasional label Iwayini ('Wine') appeals to the Chinese.

Location: Gordon's Bay ▪ Est 1995 ▪ 1stB 1999 ▪ Tasting/tours by appt; also tailor-made wine tours (max 6 people) ▪ Owner(s) Danie Hattingh ▪ 3,700cs own label 100% red ▪ PO Box 185 Gordon's Bay 7151 ▪ mwines@mweb.co.za ▪ www.maidenwines.co.za ▪ F +27 (0)86-688-1177 ▪ **T +27 (0)82-554-9395**

Main Street Winery

This is a small-scale venture in a resurrected cellar on Paarl's main road which brand owner Marais de Villiers' shares with other artisan vintners. It's become increasingly part-time as he's been so busy with his 'hands-on, challenging' day job of providing equipment and advice to wine production start-ups; hence no Main Street wines for tasting.

Location: Paarl ▪ Est/1stB 1999 ▪ Tasting & tours by appt ▪ Owner(s)/winemaker(s) Marais de Villiers ▪ 200cs own label 100% red ▪ PO Box 2709 Paarl 7620 ▪ mainstreet@mweb.co.za ▪ F +27 (0)21-872-3006 ▪ **T +27 (0)21-872-3006**

Maison

Interior/homeware gurus Chris Weylandt and Kim Smith's chic Franschhoek estate's name aptly translates as 'Home', recalling travels and comforting memories of good wine and food shared with friends. Their own-brand wines, though often generous in alcohol, enjoy an elegance that make them fine partners for the newly expanded range of home-grown and -made goods at Maison's Deli.

★★★★ **Shiraz** **12** still very youthful, edgy. Slightly richer than **11**, with sweeter red berry fruit (1% raisined viognier co-fermented), but careful extraction, oaking allow for overall harmony.

★★★★ **Chardonnay** Elegant balance between lees richness & prolonged fresh thread on **13** highlight ripe but unshowy citrus tones. Sensitive oaking (27% new) completes this attractive package. Worth cellaring a few years, as was **12** (★★★★).

★★★★ **Single Vineyard Chenin Blanc Reserve** Barrel-fermented version ex same vineyard as unwooded; **13** the more expressive, if still understated. Lees enrichment, hint spicy oak augment chenin's more floral features.

★★★★ **Single Vineyard Chenin Blanc** Unoaked **13** tight & focused with underlying weight from 6 months on lees. Needs time for refined, subtle fruit to open up.

★★★★ **Straw Wine** **12** 500ml of peachy opulence spiced with intriguing ginger biscuit notes. Rich but uncloying thanks to firm acid thread. From air-dried chenin, aged year in older oak.

Méthode Cap Classique ★★★ Citrusy notes with unusual iodine salty tang on **09**. Brisk bubble & bone-dry. 100% chardonnay, barrel-fermented, 4 years on lees. Also tasted: **Blanc de Noir 14** ★★★★ **Viognier 13** ★★★ Not tasted: **Cape Ruby**. — AL

Location/map/WO: Franschhoek ▪ Est 2005 ▪ 1stB 2008 ▪ Tasting & sales Tue-Sun 10-5 ▪ The Kitchen @ Maison (fusion bistro, lunch 12-5) ▪ Deli (charcuterie, pâtés, preserves & more) ▪ Weddings & functions ▪ Owner(s) Chris Weylandt & Kim Smith ▪ Winemaker(s)/viticulturist(s) Antwan Bondesio ▪ 11ha/4.5ha (shiraz, chard, chenin, viog) ▪

50% red 50% white ▪ PO Box 587 Franschhoek 7690 ▪ reservations@maisonestate.co.za ▪ www.maisonestate.co.za ▪ S 33° 53' 09.7" E 019° 4' 39.80" ▪ F +27 (0)21-876-2116 ▪ **T +27 (0)21-876-2116**

Maison de Teijger

Working since 2004 in his De Tyger Street home's double-garage with a few tons of classic red varieties winkled from prime vineyards, Durbanville garagiste Charl van Teijlingen, wife Danél and children Matthew and Elda-Marie market their vinifications off-site through group tastings such as wine clubs. The latest vintages were yet to be bottled at press time.

Pinot Noir range

Elgin ⓠ ★★★☆ Last in regional selection now tasted, has lifted red cherry on **11** ex Elgin & from clone D115. Bright food-craving acidity refreshes. Not tasted: **Walker Bay**, **Durbanville Gold Screwcap**, **Durbanville Gold Foil**, **Durbanville Black Foil**, **Paarl**, **Coastal**.

Stellenbosch range

Petit Verdot ⓠ ★★★ Brooding fruit, tart & rich, following to bold tarry palate with good acid cleanout. **11** fine varietal exposition. Not tasted: **Cabernet Sauvignon**, **Cabernet Franc**, **Malbec**, **Merlot**, **Voorhout Bordeaux Blend**.

Durbanville range

Malbec ⓠ ★★★☆ Earthy, with strong coconut overlay, fresh **11** needs to shake oak dominance. Not tasted: **Cabernet Sauvignon (Fermicru XL)**, **Cabernet Sauvignon (NT 112)**, **Cabernet Franc**, **Malbec Diemersdal**, **Malbec Bloemendal**, **Merlot Klein Roosboom**, **Merlot Meerendal**, **Petit Verdot**, **Voorhout Bordeaux Blend**. — JP

Location: Durbanville ▪ Map: Durbanville, Philadelphia & Darling ▪ WO: Elgin/Bottelary/Durbanville ▪ Est/1stB 2004 ▪ Tasting by appt ▪ Owner(s)/cellarmaster(s) Charl van Teijlingen ▪ Winemaker(s) Charl van Teijlingen, with Danél, Matthew & Elda-Marie van Teijlingen (all 2004) ▪ 6-9t/650-800cs own label 100% red ▪ PO Box 2703 Durbanville 7550 ▪ charlvt@kingsley.co.za ▪ S 33° 49' 02.20" E 018° 39'01.56" ▪ F +27 (0)21-975-0806 ▪ **T +27 (0)83-456-9410**

Major's Hill Estate

Wine and brandy lovers will be equally at home on Dewald Louw's farm. Named Klipdrift, it's the birthplace of the famous namesake brandy, fondly known as 'Klippies', whose brand home is in Robertson village a few minutes away (see separate Klipdrift entry). The brandy's originator and some-time farm owner, major Kosie Marais, in turn gives his name to the wine range, available for tasting on the farm, and to the guest house perched on the major's favourite hill.

Location/map: Robertson ▪ 1stB 2002 ▪ Tasting & sales Mon-Fri 9.30–1; 2–5 Sat 10–4 ▪ Closed Easter Fri, Dec 25/26 ▪ Cellar tours by appt ▪ Facilities for children ▪ Major's Rest Guest House ▪ Owner(s) Dewald Louw ▪ Cellarmaster(s) Alkie van der Merwe ▪ Winemaker(s) Alkie van der Merwe (Jan 2003) ▪ Viticulturist(s) Acker Hattingh ▪ 52ha (cab, merlot, ptage, shiraz, chard, sauv) ▪ 15,000cs own label 60% red 40% white + 15,000cs for customers + 100,000L bulk ▪ PO Box 561 Robertson 6705 ▪ info@majorshill.co.za ▪ www.majorshill.co.za ▪ S 33° 49' 45.2" E 019° 53' 10.7" ▪ F +27 (0)23-626-6096 ▪ **T +27 (0)23-626-6093**

☐ **Makulu** see Imbuko Wines
☐ **Malagas Wine Company** see Sijnn
☐ **Malan de Versailles** see Versailles

Malanot Wines

'Wine is in my blood,' says newly inducted Cape Wine Master Marius Malan, referring to his family's grape-growing heritage in the Perdeberg area. With his own brands and business based in Stellenbosch, he consults to various clients keen to share his philosophy of natural winemaking. Exports are booming, and an online bulk-wine trading platform is being created to facilitate sales.

Malanot Wines range

★★★★ Family Reserve ⓐ From shiraz, aromatic nose of cinnamon, allspice & cloves, **10** is concentrated, elegant, with black cherries/cream balancing well-integrated oak (60% new French) & refreshing acidity.

★★★★ Cherry Blossom ⓐ Plenty of promise on dense & intense cab-based Bordeaux blend **11**. Masses of spicy appeal - liquorice & aniseed predominate - with black plums, cherry tobacco & gritty tannic finish.

Not retasted: **Flower Pot 13 ★★★★** Not tasted: **Vino Café Pinotage, Bush Pig**.

Vior range

Pinotage ⓐ **★★★☆** Well-made **12** shouts its varietal characteristics to the skies! Perfume, spice, smoked meat, black & red fruit. Not retasted: **Cabernet Sauvignon 11 ★★☆ Shiraz 11 ★★★ Red Blend 11 ★★★★** Not tasted: **Pinot Noir, Chardonnay**.

Cape Colony range

Malbec ⓐ **★★☆** Over-ripe & slightly unfocused **09** shows some dark chocolate & black fruit.

Chandos range

Pinotage Export only; not reviewed, as all. Not tasted: **Red Blend, Red Blend BIB**. — CM

Location: Stellenbosch ▪ WO: Western Cape ▪ Est/1stB 2006 ▪ Tasting & sales by appt ▪ Cellar tours by appt & during harvest only ▪ Owner(s) Malanot Wine Projects cc ▪ Cellarmaster(s)/winemaker(s)/viticulturist(s) Marius Malan (Jan 2006) ▪ 500t/40,000cs own label 80% red 20% white + 2,000cs for clients ▪ PO Box 592 Strand 7139 ▪ info@malanot.com ▪ www.malanotwines.co.za ▪ **T +27 (0)72-124-7462**

☐ **Malgas** *see* Sijnn
☐ **Malkopbaai** *see* Teubes Family Wines
☐ **Mamre Road** *see* Darling Cellars

MAN Family Wines ⓐ

MAN Family Vines is a negociant-type partnership between José Conde of Stark-Condé and Tyrrel and Philip Myburgh of Joostenberg, the name derived from the initials of their respective wives, Marie, Anette and Nicky. Most of the grapes are sourced from Agter Paarl and the focus is very much on delivering great quality relative to price. From 300 cases made in a tractor shed in 2001, the winery has kept on growing, with higher-level tier Tormentoso launched in 2011 and a dedicated bottling facility acquired in 2014.

Tormentoso range

Old Vine Cinsaut ⓝ **★★★★** Intense red berries, cherries, cranberries, honouring a former work-horse variety, newly fashionable. **13** spicy, juicy & light-textured, made for enjoyment. Well handled. Paarl WO. **Touriga Nacional** ⓝ **★★★★** Fruitcake & sweet spice draw you in, & though the tannins are a bit firm, the wine is young, has potential. Match **13** with rich dishes, or age for 2/3 years, it will repay you. Stellenbosch grapes. Also tasted: **Cabernet Sauvignon 13 ★★★☆ Bush Vine Pinotage 13 ★★★★ Syrah-Mourvèdre 13 ★★★ Old Vine Chenin Blanc 13 ★★★★** Not retasted: **Mourvèdre 12 ★★★**

Essay range

Syrah ★★★☆ Previously 'Shiraz'. **13** black plums, dried herbs, an espresso richness leads you into a silky smooth body, spicy & long. WO W Cape. Also tasted: **Chenin Blanc-Viognier 14 ★★★**

MAN Family Wines range

Bosstok Pinotage ★★☆ 'Bushvine'. **13** plums & sweet spice, cinnamon, nutmeg, hint of coffee, with a lively, juicy, fruity drinkability. **Free-Run Steen Chenin Blanc ★★★** From dryland bushvines, which explains the intensity of **14**'s flavours, pear & freshly mown hay, lovely typicity. Also tasted: **Ou Kalant Cabernet Sauvignon 13** ★★★ **Jan Fiskaal Merlot 13** ★★★ **Skaapveld Shiraz 13** ★★★ **Padstal Chardonnay 14** ★★★ **Warrelwind Sauvignon Blanc 14** ★★★ Discontinued: **Hanekraai Rosé.** — CR

Location: Stellenbosch/Paarl ▪ WO: Coastal/Western Cape/Paarl/Stellenbosch ▪ Est 2001 ▪ Tasting & sales by appt ▪ Owner(s) MAN Vintners (Pty) Ltd ▪ Cellarmaster(s) Tyrrel Myburgh (2001) ▪ Winemaker(s) Francois Bezuidenhout (Jul 2011) ▪ 250,000cs own label 60% red 40% white ▪ PO Box 389 Stellenbosch 7599 ▪ info@manwines.com ▪ www.manwines.com ▪ F +27 (0)21-887-4340 ▪ **T +27 (0)21-861-7759**

Manley Private Cellar

This exclusive all-in-one destination for visitors to the secluded Tulbagh Valley offers not only luxury accommodation, special functions venues (including a wedding chapel) and a restaurant, but also carefully crafted wines. The latter, vinified from small parcels of mainly red varieties, are increasingly finding favour overseas, prompting renewed focus on exports.

Pinotage ★★★ **12** is fruity & fresh, with lovely varietal flavours, coffee/mocha finish. **Shiraz** ★★★ Black fruit & spice combo in friendly **11**, easy, with good balance. **Sauvignon Blanc** (NEW) ★★★ From Durbanville fruit, **13** is refreshing, fragrant, with greenpepper & grass flavour. Also tasted: **Cabernet Sauvignon 11** ★★★ Not retasted: **Merlot 10** ★★★ **Thatch House Red 09** ★★★ Discontinued: **Semillon-Sauvignon Blanc.** — WB

Location/map: Tulbagh ▪ WO: Tulbagh/Coastal ▪ Est/1stB 2002 ▪ Tasting & sales Wed-Fri 10–4 Sat 10-3 ▪ Fee R25, waived on purchase ▪ Cellar tours by appt ▪ Closed Good Fri & Dec 25 ▪ Luxury B&B ▪ Restaurant ▪ Wedding & conference facilities ▪ Chapel ▪ Walks ▪ Owner(s) Manley Wine Lodge (Pty) Ltd ▪ Winemaker(s)/viticulturist(s) Stefan Hartmann ▪ 38ha/7ha (cab, merlot, ptage, shiraz) ▪ PO Box 318 Tulbagh 6820 ▪ bookings@manleywinelodge.co.za ▪ www.manleywinelodge.co.za ▪ S 33° 16' 15.8" E 019°8' 43.8" ▪ F +27 (0)23-230-0057 ▪ **T +27 (0)23-230-0582**

☐ **Manor House** *see* Nederburg Wines
☐ **MAN Vintners** *see* MAN Family Wines
☐ **Marais Family** *see* Wonderfontein
☐ **Marcel de Reuck** *see* Crows Nest

Marianne Wine Estate

It's a just over a decade since Bordeaux's Dauriac family put down New World roots on the Simonsberg. And now change is afoot: a wine portfolio restructuring will see the Floreal and Desirade blends moved to a flagship range, the single varieties and new easy-drinkers grouped as below. All equally at home on the dinner table, the choice dictated by budget or occasion. Extensions to the tasting area, with two boule courts, open this summer.

Marianne range

★★★★ **Cabernet Sauvignon** (Ⓩ) Dramatic **09** has plenty of fruit weight & power but also balance thanks to fresh acidity, firm tannins. **08** (★★), **07** & **06** available from tasting room, as are other older vintages.

★★★★ **Merlot** Cedar aromas entwine with savoury notes in **11**, smooth texture & fine tannins for graceful ageing. Similar meatiness seen in firmly structured **10**.

★★★★ **Floreal** Blend shiraz & merlot with dash of cab densely packed but relatively understated in context of house style. **11** has fine tannins guarding deep-piled fruit, needs time to open & unfurl. Also tasted: **Shiraz 11** ★★★★ **Rosé 14** ★★★ **Sauvignon Blanc 13** ★★★★ Not retasted: **Desirade 05** ★★★★ In abeyance: **Pinotage**. Discontinued: **Selena**, **Cape Blend**.

Natana range (NEW)

Syrah ★★★ Fruity but **13** also lithe, muscular. From Stellenbosch & Swartland. **Cuvée Rouge** ★★★ Plummy dry red with unobtrusive tannins for easy drinking. **13** from pinotage & shiraz. WO W Cape. — DS

Location/map: Stellenbosch ▪ WO: Simonsberg-Paarl/Western Cape ▪ Est/1stB 2004 ▪ Tasting, sales & cellar tours Mon-Sun 11–6 ▪ Fee R50/5 wines, waived on purchase ▪ Olivello Restaurant ▪ Tour groups ▪ Panoramic tasting deck ▪ Gift shop ▪ Deli ▪ Conference facilities ▪ 1hr 'grape to wine' tour ▪ 4-star accommodation ▪ Owner(s) Dauriac family ▪ Wine consultant Francois Haasbroek (Dec 2012) ▪ Viticulturist(s) Schalk Pienaar (Jan 2013) ▪ 36ha/±20ha (cab, merlot, ptage, shiraz, sauv) ▪ 100t/16,000cs own label 90% red 5% white 5% rosé ▪ PO Box 7300 Stellenbosch 7599 ▪ info@mariannewinefarm.co.za ▪ www.mariannewines.com ▪ S 33° 49' 57.6" E 018° 53' 37.4" ▪ **T +27 (0)21-875-5040**

☐ **Marimba** *see* Southern Sky Wines

Marklew Family Wines

Dudley and Lyn Marklew grew grapes on prime Simonsberg–Stellenbosch farm De Goede Sukses for 30 years before retiring in 2001. Children Bill and Haidee jumped at the chance of making boutique wine from a part of the crop, and duly renovated the 180-year-old cellar. Duan Brits, who vinified maiden crop 2003 to 2007, retuned in 2012 and at press time oversaw the first exports to China.

★★★★ **Cabernet Sauvignon 12** (★★★☆) first tasted since sumptuous **08**. Enticing ripe berry & savoury aromas lead to sweet-fruited, easygoing, succulent but simple palate.

★★★★ **Merlot** Last tasted was exemplary **08**. Latest very ripe **11** (★★★☆) much softer, with gentlest structure, hint of aromatic mint, & sweetish effect on finish.

★★★★ **Chardonnay 12** bursting with orange & ripe apple aromas & a good deal of friendly charm on flavourful palate. Not exactly refined or classic, but well balanced, with integrated modest oaking, good acidity.

Sauvignon Blanc (NEW) ★★★ **13** blends tropical, green notes. Flavourful, but unshowy, lightish & modest. Not retasted: **Cape Flora Pinotage 11** ★★★★ — TJ

Location/map: Stellenbosch ▪ WO: Simonsberg–Stellenbosch ▪ Est 1970 ▪ 1stB 2003 ▪ Tasting, sales & tours by appt ▪ Tour groups (max 20) ▪ Private/business functions for small groups ▪ Walks ▪ Mountain biking ▪ Conservation area ▪ Owner(s) Marklew family (Edward Dudley, Edward William, Lyn & Haidee) ▪ Winemaker(s) Duan Brits (2003-2007; Sep 2012) ▪ Viticulturist(s) Billy Marklew (Jun 2001), with Duan Brits (Sep 2012) ▪ 58ha/45ha (cabs s/f, merlot, ptage, shiraz, chard, sauv) ▪ ±300t/5,000cs own label 80% red 20% white ▪ BWI, IPW ▪ PO Box 17 Elsenburg 7607 ▪ wine@marklew.co.za ▪ www.marklew.co.za ▪ S 33° 50' 35.7" E 018° 51' 50.3" ▪ F +27 (0)21-884-4412 ▪ **T +27 (0)21-884-4412**

☐ **Marlbrook** *see* Klein Constantia Estate
☐ **Martinique** *see* Du Preez Estate
☐ **Marvelous** *see* Yardstick Wines

Mary Le Bow Trust

The grapes come from an Ashton farm owned by the Frater family, vinified by Bruce Jack of Flagstone fame – the late James Frater and Bruce having been good friends. James' mother Angela has distant ancestors buried in the crypt of London's St Mary le Bow Church, giving rise to the name.

★★★★ **Mary le Bow** (logo) Powerful **11** (★★★☆) roughly equal cab & shiraz, 23% petit verdot. Misses finesse of **09** & seems to be tending to an ever more imposing style. No **10**. — CE

Location: Somerset West ▪ WO: Western Cape ▪ 1stB 2005 ▪ Wine sales Mon-Fri 8.30-4 ▪ Owner(s) Frater family ▪ Winemaker(s) Bruce Jack ▪ 516cs own label 100% red ▪ PO Box 3636 Somerset West 7129 ▪ info@thedrift.co.za ▪ F +27 (0)86-563-9533 ▪ **T +27 (0)86-150-2025**

Maske Wines

Erich and Janine Maske have replanted their vineyards to ensure their Wellington export business keeps pace with demand. Emphasis remains on the 'common ground we have with people from all over the world'. Like the friends whose visit to a tattoo parlour gave name to a red blend...

For more information, visit wineonaplatter.com

Maske range

Tattoo Ⓐ ★★★ **11** shiraz & cab combo very ripe & fruit-sweet, easy to drink. WO W Cape. In abeyance: **Cabernet Sauvignon**, **Merlot**, **Chenin Blanc**.

Leeumasker range

Not tasted: **Cape Blend**. — CvZ

Location: Wellington ▪ Map: Paarl & Wellington ▪ WO: Western Cape ▪ Est/1stB 2000 ▪ Tasting & sales Mon-Sun by appt ▪ Closed Ash Wed, Easter Fri/Sun & Dec 25 ▪ BYO picnic ▪ Owner(s) Erich & Janine Maske ▪ Winemaker(s)/viticulturist(s) Outsourced ▪ 7ha/5ha (cab, merlot, chenin) ▪ 80% red 20% white, blends outsourced ▪ Klein Waterval PO Box 206 Wellington 7654 ▪ laureat@iafrica.com ▪ www.maskewines.co.za ▪ S 33° 40' 4.2" E 019° 2' 37.3" ▪ F +27 (0)21-873-3408 ▪ **T +27 (0)21-873-3407**

☐ **Mason's Hill** *see* Mason's Winery

Mason's Winery

Calling all sulphur-intolerant winelovers! Derek Clift, who tends small parcels of vines on his stone-mason family's Paarl Mountain farm (and quarry) for vinifying in shared cellar space in town, is a fellow sufferer so uses minimal amounts. Shiraz is a speciality that, with occasional other releases, can be found at local steakhouse Hussar's Grill.

Mason's Shiraz Ⓐ ★★★ Smoky, savoury, headily alcoholic & seriously oaked **11** - first tasted since **07**. Not tasted: **Klipkapper Chenin Blanc**. Occasional release: **Voëltjiegat Shiraz**. — IM

Location/WO: Paarl ▪ Map: Paarl & Wellington ▪ Est/1stB 2001 ▪ Tasting & sales by appt at Hussar Grill Paarl, adjacent to cellar ▪ Owner(s) JA Clift (Pty) Ltd - Clift family ▪ Cellarmaster(s)/winemaker(s)/viticulturist(s) Derek Clift (2001) ▪ 47ha/4ha (shiraz) ▪ 30t/2,000cs own label 100% red ▪ Main Street Suider-Paarl 7646 ▪ masons@cliftgranite.co.za ▪ www.cliftgranite.co.za ▪ S 33° 45' 20.5" E 018° 57' 42.6" ▪ F +27 (0)21-863-1601 ▪ **T +27 (0)83-228-7855**

☐ **Maties** *see* Stellenbosch University Welgevallen Cellar
☐ **Matys** *see* Diemersdal Estate

Matzikama Organic Cellar

Organically grown red-wine grapes from Klaas Coetzee's Olifants River vineyards, established in 1994 and originally contributing to his own brand, in recent vintages have been snapped up by nearby certified-organic Stellar Winery. Coetzee, now production head at Stellar, has resorted to buying in organic grapes for his latest bottlings.

Matzikama Organic Cellar range Ⓝⓔⓦ

The Tidal Phase Pinot Noir Ⓥ Ⓐ ★★★★ An organic cellar following nature's way for both wines in its stable, with noteworthy results. Lovely fruit purity in **14**, succulent berries, oak in gentle support, pinor noir at its essence. Very small production. WO Koekenaap. **The Moon Phase Shiraz** Ⓐ ★★★ Only 120 bottles of youthful **14** from Swartland fruit. Scrub & dried herbs, brambleberries, light textured despite 14.5% alcohol. Very supple, for early drinking. — CR, CvZ

Location: Vredendal ▪ Map: Olifants River ▪ WO: Swartland/Koekenaap ▪ Est/1stB 2001 ▪ Tasting by appt ▪ Owner(s)/winemaker(s)/viticulturist(s) Klaas Coetzee ▪ 12ha/2.5ha (cab, shiraz, tannat) ▪ 24t 100% red ▪ PO Box 387 Vredendal 8160 ▪ klaas@matzikamawyn.co.za ▪ www.matzikamawyn.co.za ▪ S 31° 36' 34.37" E 018° 44' 11.32" ▪ **T +27 (0)82-801-3737**

McGregor Wines

The unpretentious wines of this grower-owned winery are made just down the road from laid-back hamlet McGregor with its homely hostelries, excellent eateries, village markets, mountain walks and annual Ride2Nowhere mountain bike stage race, named for the cul de sac leading out of town.

McGregor range

Chardonnay ★★★ Waxy lemon fruit & hint of sweetness, **14** unwooded yet good body, rounded & pleasant. **Chenin Blanc ★★☆** Nice fruity notes on crisp, dry backdrop. **14** quaffable, with fair body. **Colombard ★★★** Light & cheerful, **14** off-dry with guava aromas. **Sauvignon Blanc ★★** Rather foursquare, but **14** shows well-modulated acid & some aromatic appeal. Not retasted: **Pinotage 12 ★★★ Ruby Cabernet 12 ★★ Shiraz 11 ★ Cabernet Sauvignon-Merlot 11 ★★★ Red Muscadel 13 ★★★ White Muscadel 08 ★★★ Cape Ruby 10 ★** Not tasted: **Pinotage Rosé**.

Winemaker's Reserve range

Not tasted: **Cabernet Sauvignon**. — GdB

Location: McGregor ▪ Map: Robertson ▪ WO: McGregor/Robertson ▪ Est 1948 ▪ 1stB 1978 ▪ Tasting & sales Mon-Fri 8–5 Sat 10–3 ▪ Closed Good Fri, Dec 25/26 & Jan 1 ▪ Cellar tours by appt ▪ BYO picnic ▪ Owner(s) 27 members ▪ Winemaker(s) Elmo du Plessis, with Jean-Prieur du Plessis ▪ 14,000t 22% red 78% white ▪ IPW ▪ PO Box 519 McGregor 6708 ▪ info@mcgregorwinery.co.za ▪ www.mcgregorwinery.co.za ▪ S 33° 56′ 5.4″ E 019° 50′ 56.3″ ▪ F +27 (0)23-625-1829 ▪ **T +27 (0)23-625-1741/1109**

MC Square

DRC-born Jean-Luc Sweerts calls himself a 'wine-creator' (and no doubt a 'vigneron' in his native French). The Somerset West-based label gets its name from an artful contraction of 'méthode cap classique', specialty of his, but he happily sources 'beautiful evocative names right here in Africa' for his other wines.

Location: Somerset West ▪ Est/1stB 1996 ▪ Closed to public ▪ Owner(s)/winemaker(s)/viticulturist(s) Jean-Luc Sweerts ▪ 200cs MCC Brut & 800cs Sophiatown ▪ PO Box 436 Somerset West 7129 ▪ mcsquare@iafrica.com ▪ **T +27 (0)83-303-5467**

☐ **Meander** *see* uniWines Vineyards

Meerendal Wine Estate

The dates 1702 and 1969 (founding and first bottled vintage) speak of heritage and tradition but any recent visitor to Durbanville's Meerendal will hardly recognise the estate for all the recent stylish revitalisation. In line with the slogan 'Home of Food & Wine', there's a restaurant, farmers market plus many other cellardoor amenities. Perhaps most visibly, the venerable Cape Dutch homestead has been converted into a boutique hotel. It's the venue, in quite spectacular fashion, for the Absa Cape Epic cycle tour prologue, the riders scooting through the building and down the front steps!

Prestige range

★★★★ Heritage Block Pinotage ⊘ Accomplished version from 1955-planted bushvines. Elegant **10** (★★★★☆) pays homage to Old World restraint with fairly moderate alcohol & proper dryness, while offering vibrant strawberry fruit. No **08**, **09**. Flavours on **07** were muted by firm tannins.

★★★★ Liza ⊘ Cape Blend of pinotage & 15% piquant shiraz. Moderate 13.2% alcohol, refreshing acidity contribute to elegant debut in mulberry-toned **11**. Polished tannins from older oak, refined conclusion.

★★★★ Blanc de Blancs Méthode Cap Classique Big emphasis on yeast in **09** from chardonnay, showing rich bakery aromas laced with baked apple. Expressive & generous, but retaining elegance. For early drinking.

Not retasted: **Bin159 Shiraz 07 ★★★★** Not tasted: **Merlot Reserve, Bin 242 Sauvignon Blanc, Natural Sweet**.

Standard range

★★★★ Pinotage Spicy oak on wild berries, ripe & full **12** (★★★★) avoids variety's high tone but harmony is some way off. Tasted pre-bottling, rating tentative. **11** was soft & pliable.

Cabernet Sauvignon ★★★☆ Leafy notes & blackcurrants on **12** barrel sample; dense & very ripe, full, with creamy tannins. **Pinotage Rosé** ★★★ **14** flavourful & overtly fruity with tangy acidity, crisp dry ending. Refreshing glassful for food or solo. **Sauvignon Blanc** ★★★☆ **14** young & nervous, but in a pleasant restrained style; long & balanced with satisfying weight. Not retasted: **Pinot Noir 11** ★★★☆ **Shiraz 10** ★★★☆ **Chardonnay Wooded 08** ★★★ **Chardonnay Unwooded 13** ★★★☆ Not tasted: **Merlot**. — GdB

Location/WO: Durbanville ▪ Map: Durbanville, Philadelphia & Darling ▪ Est 1702 ▪ 1stB 1969 ▪ Tasting & sales Mon-Sun 10-6 ▪ Closed Good Fri, Dec 25 & Jan 1 ▪ Cellar tours by appt ▪ Crown Restaurant & Wine Bar at Meerendal open daily; closed Sun/Mon evenings ▪ Facilities for children ▪ Tour groups ▪ Farmers market once a month ▪ Weddings/functions ▪ Walks/hikes ▪ Mountain biking ▪ Conservation area ▪ The Meerendal Boutique Hotel ▪ Owner(s) Coertze family ▪ Cellarmaster(s) Liza Goodwin (Sep 2006) ▪ Winemaker(s) Liza Goodwin (Sep 2006), with Piti Coetzee (Jan 2012) ▪ Viticulturist(s) Victor Rossouw (Feb 2007) ▪ 220ha/70ha (merlot, ptage, pinot, shiraz, chard, sauv) ▪ 500t/50,000cs own label 75% red 20% white 5% rosé ▪ IPW ▪ Private Bag X1702 Durbanville 7551 ▪ info@meerendal.co.za ▪ www.meerendal.co.za ▪ S 33° 47' 55.8" E 018° 37' 26.2" ▪ F +27 (0)21-975-1657 ▪ **T +27 (0)21-975-1655**

☐ **Meerhof Family Vineyards** *see* Antebellum Winery
☐ **Meerkat** *see* Welbedacht Wine Estate

Meerlust Estate

This beautiful Stellenbosch estate has belonged to the Myburgh family since 1757 and the gabled old manor house is (rather a rare thing, this) the home of current owner Hannes Myburgh — full of his artworks and older treasures. In the 1950s winemaking was reborn here, and Meerlust's reputation has long been high. Winemaker Chris Williams has brought new energy and added lustre since moving into the top cellar job just over a decade ago, and his wines show a fine balance between modern stylistics and classic ideals. But Chris is always quick to credit the sterling vineyard work of Roelie Joubert, and indeed to recognise the contribution of the whole team. There's a genuine, pervading concern for the social fabric, for the whole Meerlust community, which adds greatly to the place.

★★★★☆ **Cabernet Sauvignon** Epitome of seamless integration; all components of classy **11** - glossy cassis fruit, supple tannin, perfectly judged oak (70% new), freshening acid & balanced alcohol - are melded & polished. Impressive elegance & restraint. Needs & deserves time to realise potential.

★★★★☆ **Merlot** Tall, dark & handsome in refined house style, **12** minty notes with a piquant flavour profile lifted by 11% aromatic cab franc. Spicy oak (60% new) focuses the mineral centre. No **11**.

★★★★☆ **Pinot Noir** Ⓥ Initially reticent, youthful **12** from 26 year old vines takes time to reveal its utterly compelling, silken charm. Earthy core with profound, pure red fruit structured by supple tannins & fine, savoury acidity in seamless whole.

★★★★☆ **Rubicon** Ⓥ Sensational **09**, indisputably great vintage of venerable cab-dominated (70%) Bordeaux blend. Indulgently plush, with dark fruit that easily absorbs & integrates the oak influence (65% new) to produce an impressively complex, densely structured & promising masterpiece.

★★★★ **Red** Ⓥ Label used for 'declassified' Rubicon, in lesser years. Drinkable, plummy, fresh & fleshy **11** merlot-dominated & accessible, but lighter than flagship - for earlier drinking.

★★★★ **Chardonnay** Latest two releases more lightly fruited than broad, oxidative style of previous, **13** for earlier enjoyment. **12** similar but shade more complex. Year in barrel, half new. — DS

Location/map/WO: Stellenbosch ▪ Est 1693 ▪ 1stB 1975 ▪ Tasting & sales Mon-Fri 9—5 Sat 10—2 ▪ Fee R30 ▪ Closed all pub hols ▪ Cellar tours by appt ▪ Owner(s) Hannes Myburgh ▪ Cellarmaster(s) Chris Williams (Jan 2004) ▪ Winemaker(s) Altus Treurnicht (assistant, 2008) ▪ Viticulturist(s) Roelie Joubert (2001) ▪ 400ha/106ha (cabs s/f, merlot, p verdot, pinot, chard) ▪ 500t/50,000cs own label 90% red 10% white ▪ PO Box 7121 Stellenbosch 7599 ▪ info@meerlust.co.za ▪ www.meerlust.co.za ▪ S 34° 1' 1.7" E 018° 45' 24.7" ▪ F +27 (0)21-843-3274 ▪ **T +27 (0)21-843-3587**

Meinert Wines

Martin Meinert is well into his second quarter-century as owner of this family farm and boutique winery in Stellenbosch's Devon Valley. The first plot he bought in 1987 was known simply as 'Remainder of Farm 78'! Ten years later he gave up his prestigious security as Vergelegen winemaker (he'd helped plan both vineyards and cellar there) to realise his 'dream of a small private vineyard and winery'. Wines which had been sold off in bulk now appeared under his own label. Development continues (a new Elgin pinot noir this edition) but core values remain – restraint, dry elegance, and Martin's belief in 'the pleasure of wines that can age'.

Meinert Wines range

★★★★ Cabernet Sauvignon 11 has lots to offer, cherries, red berries, tobacco/oak spice, appealing dried herb nuance. Serious, no expense spared on oaking, but smooth, supple. Also-tasted **10** similar, extra year giving a more streamlined effect.

★★★★☆ Synchronicity Cab-led blend with merlot, 2 others, mainly new oak. Showy, ripe plums, berries, oak's savoury tones a counterpoint. **10** has excellent balance, carefully crafted tannins give immediate access, a long future. Powerful, impressive, individual.

★★★★ La Barry Sauvignon Blanc Named for Martin's wife (nee Barry), this suits her taste. Lemongrass & floral notes, some fynbos in **13**, dry & zesty, with suggestions of a mineral, wet pebble character. WO Elgin.

★★★★☆ Semillon Straw Wine Vine-dried grapes off the farm's only white-wine vineyard; oak fermented, just one barrel. Lemon & tangerine flavours in **13**, tangy freshness offsetting the sweetness, livening & extending the palate. Riveting intensity. In 375 ml.

Also tasted: **Merlot 11 ★★★★ Printer's Ink Pinotage 12 ★★★★** Not retasted: **La Barry Red 11 ★★★**

Family Collection

★★★★ Pinot Noir (NEW) Elgin-sourced **12** seductively perfumed, raspberries & cedar, crystallised violets. Despite 18 months oaking, retains the variety's signature succulence, elegance. Savoury enough to love food.

★★★★ Chardonnay ② **12** less oaky in youth than previous, but similar oatmeal & citrus notes. Mouthfilling, fresh & lively, with a lingering limy finish. WO Elgin, like Riesling.

Riesling ★★★ 13 off-dry style with varietal-true floral & pineapple perfume & flavours, made for enjoyment & food, the freshness balancing the touch of sugar. Also tasted: **The Italian Job 13 ★★★** — CR

Location/map: Stellenbosch ▪ WO: Devon Valley/Elgin ▪ Est 1987 ▪ 1stB 1997 ▪ Tasting Mon-Sat strictly by appt only ▪ Closed all pub hols ▪ Owner(s) Martin Meinert ▪ Cellarmaster(s)/winemaker(s) Martin Meinert (Nov 1997) ▪ Viticulturist(s) Henk Marconi (Jan 1991) ▪ 16ha/12ha (cabs s/f, merlot, p verdot, ptage, sem) ▪ 90t/8,000cs own label 67% red 33% white ▪ PO Box 7221 Stellenbosch 7599 ▪ info@meinertwines.com ▪ www.meinertwines.com ▪ S 33° 54' 1. 8" E 018° 48' 50.2" ▪ F +27 (0)21-865-2414 ▪ **T +27 (0)21-865-2363**

☐ **Melck's** see Muratie Wine Estate

Melkboomsdrift Wines

For a more personal encounter with the wines of the West Coast, traditionally associated with large wineries, visit boutique vintner Hilsa van den Heever at her Melkboomsdrift guest lodge and conference venue on the Olifants River near Lutzville. Hilsa has skipped the past few seasons of her all-red range but holds stock of some mature vintages.

Location: Lutzville ▪ Map: Olifants River ▪ Tasting & sales Mon-Fri 9-5 ▪ Melkboomsdrift Lodge serving farm breakfasts, with dinner & picnic baskets on request; also self-catering option ▪ Conference venue (20 max) ▪ Owner(s)/cellarmaster(s)/winemaker(s) Hilsa van den Heever ▪ Viticulturist(s) Jeff Joubert ▪ (cab, merlot, ptage, shiraz) ▪ PO Box 1124 Vredendal 8160 ▪ info@melkboomsdrift.co.za ▪ www.melkboomsdrift.co.za ▪ S 31° 36' 15.24" E 018° 24' 19.86" ▪ F +27 (0)27-217-2535 ▪ **T +27 (0)27-217-2624**

For more information, visit wineonaplatter.com

Mellasat Vineyards

Norfolk grain farmer Stephen Richardson's lifelong love of wine led him to buy a portion of Dekkersvallei farm below the Du Toitskloof Mountain pass in 1996. Having replanted vineyards, established an eclectic range of wines and married local chef Janet – doyenne of their seasonal pop-up restaurant – he's now a full-time Paarl winegrower.

Premium Exclusives

★★★★ **Tempranillo-Cabernet Sauvignon** Rich & earthy **11** packed with ripe fruit flavour, wafts of mountain fynbos & warm spice. Well structured, with fine tannins, complexity & great depth. Built to last.

★★★★ **Viognier** Barrel-fermented/matured in Romanian oak, **13** oozes peach blossom, clove & vanilla perfume. Mouthfilling & firm, with rich fruit flavours & delicious persistent spicy farewell.

Mellasat Premium range

★★★★ **'Sigma' White Pinotage** Pinotage vinified in Romanian oak as a dry white, **13** trumps **12** (★★★★) with more depth & spicy complexity. Fruity, full flavoured & creamy, long finish.

Also tasted: **Tuin Wyn 11** ★★★ Not retasted: **Chardonnay 12** ★★★★ Not tasted: **'M'**.

Dekker's Valley range

Revelation ★★★ Cab, shiraz, pinotage blend, **11** preview is fresh & vividly fruity, with supple tannins. Easy winter sipper. **White blend** ★★★ Chardonnay-led unoaked blend **14**, pre-bottling shows bright citrus, floral notes, but also gripping acidity. Also tasted: **Shiraz 12** ★★★ **Shiraz Rosé 14** ★★ Not retasted: **Chenin Blanc 13** ★★★ — WB

Location/WO: Paarl ▪ Map: Paarl & Wellington ▪ Est 1996 ▪ 1stB 1999 ▪ Tasting & sales Mon-Sat 9.30-5.30 Sun/pub hols 10-4 ▪ Closed Good Fri, Dec 25 & Jan 1 ▪ Cellar tours by appt ▪ Light lunches for groups/tours or private dinner functions by appt; picnics in summer & cheese platters in winter; pop-up seasonal restaurant & other food-based events ▪ Tour groups ▪ Conferences ▪ Paarl Ommiberg Festival ▪ Owner(s) Stephen Richardson ▪ Cellarmaster(s) Stephen Richardson (Jan 1999) ▪ Winemaker(s) Faizel Samuels (Jan 2014) ▪ Viticulturist(s) Poena Malherbe (Sep 1996) ▪ 13ha/8ha (cab, ptage, shiraz, tempranillo, chard, chenin, viog) ▪ 50t/3,500cs own label 40% red 50% white 10% rosé ▪ IPW ▪ PO Box 7169 Paarl 7623 ▪ mellasat@mweb.co.za ▪ www.mellasat.com ▪ S 33° 44' 30.0" E 019° 2' 31.0" ▪ F +27 (0)21-862-4525 ▪ **T +27 (0)21-862-4525**

☐ **Mentors** *see* KWV

☐ **Mercia Collection** *see* Mooiplaas Estate & Private Nature Reserve

Merwida Winery

Owned by cousins Schalk and Pierre van der Merwe, this cellar takes in grapes from several Breedekloof properties owned by the family, farming here for over 170 years. Their growing portfolio of own-label bottlings, geared to please those looking for good-value, lower-alcohol wines, is finding its way into a wider market.

★★★★ **Barbera** ⊘ Confirming quality of Italian variety from this site, **12** has new-oak-driven coffee notes over classy perfumed red fruit & roasted herbs. Crisp acidity & elegance well suited to oily food, as in **11**.

★★★★ **Chardonnay** ⊘ Citrus & peach with subtle supporting vanilla notes. **13** (★★★★) not quite the structure of **11**, more fruit driven, still pleasant, fresh & clean. **12** sold out untasted.

★★★★ **Sauvignon Blanc** ⊘ **14** generous tropical notes to zippy kiwi & green apple bouquet. Round & rich courtesy 3 months on lees, yet finishes fresh. Very appetising, like savoury **13**.

★★★★ **White Muscadel** ⊘ Unctuously sweet **13** (★★★★) not showing flair of earlier **11**. Sultana, honey & rosepetals warmed by alcohol. Might show better with time. No **12**.

Also tasted: **Cabernet Sauvignon 12** ★★★ **Pinotage 11** ★★★ Not retasted: **Pinotage Rosé 13** ★★★ In abeyance: **Cuvée Brut**. — HJ

Location: Rawsonville ▪ Map/WO: Breedekloof ▪ Est 1963 ▪ 1stB 1975 ▪ Tasting & sales Mon-Fri 8-12.30 & 1.30—5 Sat 9–1 ▪ Closed Easter Fri-Mon, Dec 25-Jan 1 ▪ Merwida Country Lodge T +27 (0)23-349-1435 ▪ Owner(s) Schalk & Pierre van der Merwe ▪ Cellarmaster(s)/viticulturist(s) Magnus Kriel ▪ Winemaker(s) Magnus Kriel (Dec 2000), with Sarel van Staden (Aug 1982) & Lodewyk Botha (Sep 2013) ▪ 630ha (cab, merlot, shiraz, chard, chenin, sauv, sem, viog) ▪ 15,000t/20,000cs own label 40% red 60% white ▪ ISO 22000, BWI, Fairtrade, IPW, WIETA ▪ PO Box 254 Rawsonville 6845 ▪ wines@merwida.com ▪ www.merwida.com ▪ S 33° 41' 24.9" E 019° 20' 31.1" ▪ F +27 (0)23-349-1953/+27 (0)86-538-1953 ▪ **T +27 (0)23-349-1144**

☐ **Metamorphic** *see* Hillcrest Estate

Metzer Wines

Somerset West-based Wade Metzer understands wine micro-biology even more than most Elsenburg graduates – and has a Swiss diploma to prove it. Science proves a good basis for his aim to craft wines expressing their origin, using simple, non-interventionist principles. Shiraz has been a focus as it responds so 'articulately' to different terroirs. Then comes innovative naming and packaging.

★★★★ **Vitamin B Syrah** ⓥ Clean black fruit, herbal & savoury notes on velvety **09** tasted a few years back.

★★★★ **Syrah** ⓥ 09 (★★★★★) offered perfumes of dark berries, flowers & spice a few editions back. Strikingly pure, vibrant & juicy fruit around a core of tannin. Helderberg grapes; **07** was from Swartland.

★★★★ **The Kitchen Sink Syrah** ⓥ **10** (★★★★) showed big, ripe fruity aromas & some sweet flavours on firm base, but a little more awkward & oaky than maiden **05**, with drying tannins.

Not retasted: **Vitamin B Blanc 11** ★★★★ — TJ

Location: Somerset West ▪ WO: Stellenbosch ▪ Est/1stB 2004 ▪ Tasting by appt ▪ Owner(s)/winemaker(s) Wade Metzer & Barry Holfeld ▪ 16t/2,400cs 100% red ▪ PO Box 35398 Northcliff 2115 ▪ metzerwines@gmail.com ▪ www. metzerwines.com, www.kitchensinkwines.com ▪ **T +27 (0)82-774-4121**

M'hudi Wines

The Rangaka family leapt into the world of wine despite knowing nothing about it. They moved across the country, bought a derelict Stellenbosch farm and started the first wine estate to be owned and managed by a black family in modern South Africa. M'hudi ('Harvester') is now part of giant Bidvest Food Services, and on the way 'to become a nationally recognisable brand in the on-trade'.

Platinum range

★★★★ **Cabernet Sauvignon** ⓥ Well-made **11** generous rendition of cab: lithely textured tannins support lush blackcurrant fruit, delivering great value & a properly dry finish.

★★★★ **Pinotage** ⓥ Vibrant, plush harmonious **11** made to charm with juicy, succulent red fruit & hint mocha for unpretentious enjoyment.

★★★★ **Shiraz** ⓥ Generously flavoured, harmonious **11**, plush, dense, dark fruit & ripe tannins exerting perfectly integrated savoury grip. Temptingly moreish.

M'hudi Wines range

Pinotage ★★★☆ Quite exotic spice, raspberry perfume, bright & fresh flavours on **12**. Year oak, 30% new, lends attractive extra dimension. Good now & for few years. Stellenbosch WO. Discontinued: **Merlot**, **Chenin Blanc**.

Say Lovey range ⓝⓔⓦ

Cabernet Sauvignon ★★ Leafy & somewhat lean **12**; simple sweet fruit, very dry tannins. Unoaked, as all wines below. **Pinotage** ★★★ **12** in modern, juicy-fruit, dry style for immediate enjoyment. **Shiraz** ★★★ Well-rounded & ready **12**, full of dark berries & spice. Hearty winter warmer. **Medley** ★★☆ Undisclosed blend offers plenty of ripe, juicy dark fruit on smoothly drinkable

12. Chenin Blanc ★★★ Medium-bodied **13** full of sunny ripe fruit, persisting on crisp, dry finish.
Sauvignon Blanc ★★☆ Gentle tropical tones on **13**. Fresh, dry but unharsh for easy sipping. — AL

Location: Stellenbosch ▪ WO: Paarl/Stellenbosch ▪ Est 2005 ▪ Closed to public ▪ Conferences (up to 70 pax) ▪ Owner(s) Rangaka family ▪ Winemaker(s) outsourced ▪ 70,000cs own label 80% red 10% white 10% rosé & sparkling ▪ WIETA ▪ PO Box 30 Koelenhof 7605 ▪ info@mhudi.com ▪ www.mhudi.com ▪ **T +27 (0)78-750-4494/+27 (0)73-833-2815**

☐ **Mia** *see* Nordic Wines
☐ **Michelle d'Or** *see* Fort Simon Wine Estate

Micu Narunsky Wines

This is Micu Narunsky's passion - less 'business' than following an 'inner instinct'. The Israeli-born jazz musician fell in love with wine while living in France before coming to South Africa. He makes his own range in rented space in Stellenbosch - near where his grandfather once made brandy.

★★★★ lemanjá ⓥ Attractively rustic, powerful **10** touriga-led red (with 30% tinta) shows violets, bergamot & black fruit. 15% alcohol noticeable but integrated in a rich, firm palate. Stellenbosch, Swartland grapes.

★★★★ La Complicité ⓥ Fresh & friendly, lightly oaked **11** aims higher than usual for colombard. Oak meshed with fruit; palate full but fresh. WO Stellenbosch. Last tasted was **06** (★★★) from muscat.

Olodum ★★★☆ Now bottled, **10** has tinta leading, 17% touriga in powerful, firm-tannined Swartland blend. Still an overripe impression, with notes of plum pudding & blackberry jam, unusually dry finish, like the other red. — JPf

Location: Somerset West ▪ Map: Helderberg ▪ WO: Coastal/Swartland/Stellenbosch ▪ Est 2005 ▪ 1stB 2006 ▪ Tasting by appt ▪ Owner(s)/cellarmaster(s)/viticulturist(s) Micu Narunsky ▪ Winemaker(s) Micu Narunsky, advised by Francois Naudé ▪ 4.8t/450cs own label 85% red 15% white ▪ PO Box 427 Somerset Mall 7137 ▪ micunarunsky@gmail.com ▪ www.micunarunsky.com ▪ S 34° 1' 52.20" E 018° 50' 46.73" ▪ **T +27 (0)73-600-3031/+27 (0)21-855-2520**

Middelvlei Estate

Two Momberg brothers bought this expansive farm in Stellenbosch's Devon Valley in 1919. It remains a Momberg family estate, run by another pair of brothers, Tinnie and Ben (with father Stiljan - who was sole owner since 1963 - a continuing influence). New is al fresco restaurant Boerebraai, with a resident expert barbecuing meat for serving with Ben's homemade pâté and ouma Annie's pumpkin fritters, while kids have fun feeding the farm animals.

★★★★ Shiraz Spicy, savoury **13** (★★★★) harmonious, smooth textured. Less depth than **10** but nicely integrated & pleasurable. **11**, **12** sold out untasted.

★★★★ Momberg Blackcurrant-scented, well-structured **12** Cape Blend cab, pinotage with dash shiraz in serious but succulent style, countered by refreshing acidity. Half American oak adds to accessibility & spiciness.

Chardonnay Unoaked ★★★ Named changed to confirm unwooded style. Rich butterscotch aromas & bold pineapple flavours in uncomplicated **14** sipper. Also tasted: **Cabernet Sauvignon 13 ★★★★ Free Run Pinotage 13 ★★★★ Pinotage-Merlot 13 ★★★** — IM

Location/map: Stellenbosch ▪ WO: Western Cape/Devon Valley ▪ Est 1941 ▪ 1stB 1973 ▪ Tasting & sales daily 10—4.30 ▪ Fee R15pp ▪ Closed Good Fri, Dec 25 & Jan 1 ▪ Cellar tours by appt ▪ Traditional lunchtime braai 7 days a week; evenings by prior arrangement for groups of 15+ ▪ Facilities for children ▪ Conferences ▪ Walking/hiking & MTB trails ▪ Cottage (2 pax) ▪ Owner(s) Momberg family ▪ Cellarmaster(s)/winemaker(s)/viticulturist(s) Tinnie Momberg (Feb 1992) ▪ 160ha/110ha (cab, merlot, ptage, shiraz, chard, sauv) ▪ 650t/60,000cs own label 95% red 5% white ▪ Other export brands: Hagelsberg, Red Falcon ▪ IPW, WIETA ▪ PO Box 66 Stellenbosch 7599 ▪ info@middelvlei.co.za ▪ www.middelvlei.co.za ▪ S 33° 55' 41.2" E 018° 49' 55.9" ▪ F +27 (0)21-883-9546 ▪ **T +27 (0)21-883-2565**

Migliarina Wines

Stellenbosch boutique vintner Carsten Migliarina always knew he wanted to make wine; his first was as a teenager using table grapes. The journey since has included wine courses, contract cellar work and stints as a sommelier locally and abroad. He exports (to Sweden, among others), and never stops looking for new wines to make - this edition a characterful chenin from Elgin.

★★★★ Shiraz Ripe flavours, definite oak presence & some richness on **12** from Stellenbosch, yet with some sure-footed elegance. It all adds up to an attractive fruity-savoury proposition.

★★★★ Chardonnay Quietly elegant, properly dry, harmonious **13** with notes of nut, citrus & oat-meal, the oaking unobtrusively supportive.

★★★★ Chenin Blanc ⓃⒺⓌ Bright, fresh floral & tropical aromas & flavours with green edge on very lightly oaked **13** - a good advertisement for Elgin chenin. A fine, even challenging, acidity balances the succulence. — TJ

Location: Stellenbosch ▪ WO: Elgin/Stellenbosch ▪ Est 2001 ▪ 1stB 2002 ▪ Closed to public ▪ Owner(s)/winemaker(s) Carsten Migliarina ▪ 2,400cs own label 65% red 35% white + 320cs for clients ▪ Brands for clients: Kap Hase, Fridhem Gaard ▪ PO Box 673 Stellenbosch 7599 ▪ carsten@migliarina.co.za ▪ www.migliarina.co.za ▪ **T +27 (0)72-233-4138**

☐ **Miko** see Mont Rochelle Hotel & Vineyards

Miles Mossop Wines

Miles Mossop is now established as one of the top winemakers in South Africa. It's evident in the wines he makes at Tokara and in his own range - named for his three children. What makes his wine-making so acute is his reliance on his gut-feel and his ability to take what nature offers and deliver wines of great polish as well as integrity. His new Introduction label comprises varietal wines from older blocks, generally in poorer soils and unirrigated. 'Made with the same philosophy as the other wines', they're intended to be fruit-forward, earlier drinking and more affordable. But, judging from the debut chenin (followed this year by a merlot), they're certainly not dumbed down.

Miles Mossop range

★★★★★ Max Quintessential Médoc styling in composed cab-led **10** with petit verdot, merlot, mal-bec: tightly structured, expressive blackcurrant fruit with classic hints of graphite, needing plenty time before broaching. Also-tasted **11** as ably executed if not quite as concentrated.

★★★★★ Saskia Masterly, seamlessly oaked chenin led **12** blend with viognier & dashes verdelho, clairette ex Stellenbosch, Swartland. Earlier-picked chenin brings freshness, while later botrytis adds richness & complexity to exceptionally concentrated & textured peach fruit.

★★★★★ Kika Unctuous botrytised chenin dessert. **13** in charmingly elegant style, flaunts well-structured layers of dense apricot fruit checked by fine acidity, ensuring perfectly poised balance.

The Introduction range ⓃⒺⓌ

★★★★★ Chenin Blanc Loire-like steeliness in ultra-tight, bone-dry **12** from old Stellenbosch & Perdeberg vines. Oak & lees maturation contribute to profound texture, racy mineral acidity promises to mask complex stonefruit flavours for a while yet. — IM

Location: Stellenbosch ▪ WO: Stellenbosch/Coastal ▪ Est/1stB 2004 ▪ Closed to public ▪ Owner(s)/winemaker(s)/viticul-turist(s) Miles Mossop ▪ 15t/2,750cs own label 36% red 55% white 9% NLH ▪ PO Box 7339 Stellenbosch 7599 ▪ miles@milesmossopwines.com ▪ www.milesmossopwines.com ▪ F +27 (0)21-808-5911 ▪ **T +27 (0)82-413-4335**

☐ **Milkwood** see Grape Grinder
☐ **Millberg** see Tulbagh Winery
☐ **Millbrook** see Valley Vineyards Wine Company
☐ **Millers Mile** see Klein Parys Vineyards
☐ **Stone** see Stettyn Cellar
☐ **Millstream** see DGB

Mimosa Boutique Wines

At Montagu's Mimosa Lodge the freshest seasonal ingredients are deliciously prepared by Swiss-born chef patron Bernhard Hess, who also handcrafts wines with consultant winemaker Lourens van der Westhuizen of Arendsig to complement the menu. For postprandial sipping, there are Mimosa 3 Year Old blended and 5 Year Old potstill brandies, neither tasted this edition.

★★★★ **Shiraz** Hedonistic, fragrant aromas of lavender, dried herbs & warm spice set the pace on **12**. Harmonious, smooth & flavoursome, with balance & poise. Drinks well & will reward ageing.

Chardonnay ★★★☆ Effortless barrel-fermented **13** a real crowd pleaser, packed with preserved pineapple fruit, lemon meringue pie & buttery oak. Also tasted: **Cabernet Sauvignon 12** ★★★☆ **Hess Reserve 12** ★★★☆ Not tasted: **Sauvignon Blanc**. — WB

Location: Montagu ▪ Map: Klein Karoo & Garden Route ▪ WO: Western Cape ▪ Est 2004 ▪ 1stB 2003 ▪ Tasting & sales daily 9-5 ▪ Tour groups ▪ Conservation area ▪ 4-star Mimosa Lodge: 23 rooms, conference centre, pool, boule pitch, wine cellar, tasting room & Ma Cuisine restaurant ▪ Owner(s) Bernhard Hess ▪ Cellarmaster(s)/winemaker(s)/viticulturist(s) Lourens van der Westhuizen (consultant) ▪ 5ha/3ha (cab, shiraz, chard, sauv) ▪ 20t/2,480cs own label 70% red 30% white ▪ PO Box 323 Montagu 6720 ▪ bernhard@mimosa.co.za ▪ www.mimosawines.co.za ▪ S 33° 47' 27.59" E 020° 6' 44.55" ▪ F +27 (0)86-535-0720 ▪ **T +27 (0)23-614-2351**

Miravel

When Maarten and Janine van Beuningen decamped from Zimbabwe to this 27 hectare Helderberg vineyard, they didn't know much about growing or making wine. A decade later, their grapes are sought after by high-end cellars and their own handcrafted wines are growing in stature.

★★★★ **Ella Family Reserve Cabernet Sauvignon** ⓥ Farm's best grapes. **10** demure cassis fruit tightly woven with fine tannins, will reward patience. 44% new casks, 2 years, whereas **08** (★★★☆) saw no new wood. No **09**.

Nigma ⓝ ⓥ ★★★☆ From sauvignon, piquant **12** layered with woodspice & gooseberry, 11 months on lees in seasoned cask smooths & broadens variety's edgier characters. **Sauvignon Blanc** ⓥ ★★★ Genial rather than steely; tropical **13** given girth by lees-ageing; brisk, fresh finish. Not retasted: **Merlot 10** ★★★★ **Pinotage 10** ★★★☆ **1952 Family Blend 10** ★★★☆ Not tasted: **Cabernet Sauvignon**. — DS

Location: Somerset West ▪ Map: Helderberg ▪ WO: Stellenbosch ▪ Est 2002 ▪ 1stB 2005 ▪ Tasting & sales Mon-Sat & pub hols by appt ▪ Closed Ash Wed, Easter Fri-Mon, Ascension Day, Pentecost, Dec 25/26 & Jan 1 ▪ Meals & cheese platters by prior arrangement ▪ Self-catering Fynbos Cottage ▪ Owner(s) Maarten van Beuningen ▪ Winemaker(s) Gerda Willers (whites) & Arno Cloete (reds, 2010) ▪ Viticulturist(s) Francois Hanekom (Apr 2007) & Paul Wallace (Jun 2004, consultant) ▪ 39ha/27ha (cab, merlot, p verdot, ptage, chenin, sauv) ▪ 175t/250cs (sauv) & 2,250L (cab, merlot, p verdot, ptage) own label 65% red 35% white ▪ PO Box 5144 Helderberg 7135 ▪ maarten@miravel.co.za ▪ www.miravel.co.za ▪ S 34° 1' 58.7" E 018° 46' 46.9" ▪ F +27 (0)21-842-3154 ▪ **T +27 (0)21-842-3154**

☐ **Mischief Maker** *see* Valley Vineyards Wine Company
☐ **Miss Molly** *see* Môreson
☐ **Misty Kloof's** *see* Goedverwacht Wine Estate

Mitre's Edge

Courtesy of a new photovoltaic array outputting on average 4,000 kWh/month, Bernard and Lola Nicholls have added solar energy to the portfolio of wine, accommodation and olive oil 'farmed' at their Simonsberg estate. Also seeing the light, as part of a rebranding process, are several top- and middle-tier varietal bottlings, an entry-level range named ME and, to follow, a 5-way Bordeaux red.

Flagship range

Cabernet Sauvignon ⓥ ★★★☆ Stern tannin softened by cushion of sweetness (sugar & fruit) in appealing, well-composed **08**. Not tasted: **Merlot**.

For more information, visit wineonaplatter.com

Mitre's Edge range

Cabernet Sauvignon ★★★★ Dense cassis & dark chocolate flavours still tightly coiled within **11**'s tannin structure, needing good few years to unfurl & show full potential. Third new oak well judged. **Viognier** ★★★☆ Peachy unwooded **14** technically off-dry but very well balanced so it feels brisk & vivacious, ends with lime cordial tang. Perfect for Thai curries. Also tasted: **Rosé 14** ★★ Not retasted: **Shiraz 08** ★★☆

ME Range

Classic Red ★★★ Was 'nvME Classic Red'. Crunchy red fruit & tealeaf tannins in cab-led **NV** blend, billed as a 'braai aperitif'. — MW

Location/map: Stellenbosch ▪ WO: Simonsberg-Paarl ▪ Est 1999 ▪ 1stB 2004 ▪ Tasting & sales by appt Mon-Fri 9-5 Sat 9-1 ▪ Cellar tours by appt ▪ Guest house B&B ▪ Olive oil ▪ Owner(s) Bernard & Lola Nicholls ▪ Winemaker(s) Lola Nicholls (2004), with Bernard Nicholls ▪ Viticulturist(s) Danie Kritzinger (consultant) ▪ Vineyard manager Bertus de Clerk ▪ 28ha/18ha (cabs s/f, malbec, merlot, p verdot, shiraz, chenin, viog) ▪ 28t/3,072cs own label 80% red 9% white 1% rosé ▪ PO Box 12290 Die Boord 7613 ▪ info@mitres-edge.co.za ▪ www.mitres-edge.co.za ▪ S 33° 49' 47.3" E 018° 52' 34.4" ▪ F +27 (0)21-875-5965 ▪ **T +27 (0)21-875-5960**

☐ **MM Louw** see Diemersdal Estate

Mofam Wines

Elgin vinegrowers and conservationists Derek and Sharon Moore use in-house and contracted experts to vinify a boutique wine range off their own vineyards to complement the varied offerings for guests visiting Mofam River Lodge. A pinot, shiraz and sauvignon missed our deadline.

Location: Elgin ▪ Map: Elgin, Walker Bay & Bot River ▪ Est 2005 ▪ 1stB 2010 ▪ Tasting daily 10-4 ▪ Flavours Restaurant ▪ Facilities for children ▪ Tour groups ▪ Conferences ▪ Walks/hikes ▪ Mountain biking trail ▪ Bass fishing ▪ Conservation area ▪ Mofam River Lodge 4-star B&B & self-catering chalets ▪ Owner(s) Derek & Sharon Moore ▪ Winemaker(s) Justin Hoy (reds) & Kosie van der Merwe (whites) ▪ Viticulturist(s) Chris Coetzee ▪ 260ha/20ha (pinot, shiraz, sauv, viog) ▪ 80t/1,872cs own label 66% red 33% white ▪ Global Gap ▪ PO Box 192 Elgin 7180 ▪ wines@mofam.co.za ▪ www.mofam.co.za ▪ S 34° 13' 42.06" E 018° 59' 18.30" ▪ F +27 (0)86-295-0084 ▪ **T +27 (0)21-846-8345**

MolenVliet Wine & Guest Estate

Two former SA rugby heroes, brand co-owner Ockie Oosthuizen and consultant winemaker Jan Coetzee have hands in these wines, enjoyed by (among others) guests using the wedding and conference facilities at Ockie and wife Susan's MolenVliet luxury lifestyle venue in Banhoek Valley.

★★★★ **Cabernet Sauvignon** Despite 16% alcohol, **07** achieved fine rounded balance previously.

★★★★ **Shiraz** **07** rich, bold & complex. Silky texture & lingering vanilla chocolate flavours.

★★★★ **Proprietors Blend** **05** classy Bordeaux red with enticing blackcurrant & mineral bouquet.

★★★★ **Diagonal Reserve** Full-bodied shiraz/cab-led **07**, upfront & perfumed with black fruit.

★★★★ **Meraz** Merlot & shiraz in equal proportion, finely structured **07** debut tasted for 2011 guide.

Not retasted: **Proprietors Selection 05** ★★★ — GdB

Location/map/WO: Stellenbosch ▪ Est/1stB 2005 ▪ Tasting & sales by appt ▪ Fee R50 ▪ Wedding/conference venue ▪ Self-catering accommodation/B&B ▪ Owner(s) Ockie & Susan Oosthuizen ▪ Winemaker(s) Jan Coetzee (2007, consultant) ▪ Viticulturist(s) Calvin Booysen (2005) ▪ 14ha/8ha (cab, merlot, shiraz) ▪ 13t/±2,500cs own label 100% red ▪ PO Box 6288 Uniedal 7612 ▪ info@molenvliet.co.za ▪ www.molenvliet.co.za ▪ S 33° 54' 52.9" E 018° 56' 30.6" ▪ F +27 (0)21-885-1684 ▪ **T +27 (0)21-885-1597**

Momento Wines

Well-travelled Marelise Jansen van Rensburg sources grapes from vineyards she discovers, sometimes in unexpected places, and vinifies in Bot River, where she has worked for the last eight years. Her focus is on winelovers who are thirsty for the new and the interesting out of the Cape. 'People who want to learn, explore, and appreciate purity and elegance in a wine.' Her approach: 'As little as possible fiddling by the winemaker.'

★★★★ **Grenache** A beautiful interpretation of Swartland grenache noir, **11** is elegant & subtle, a very special showcase for the 50+ year old bushvines so attractively depicted on the label.

★★★★ **Tinta Barocca** (NEW) **13** another exercise in 'hands-off' winemaking to give elegant, fresh & pure delight. Well structured, with a good but unaggressive grip. Delightful, but serious. Should keep.

★★★★☆ **Chenin Blanc-Verdelho** (NEW) Soulful **13** mostly old-vine chenin, naturally fermented in older oak. Lovely pure aromas seasoned with spice. Genuine freshness on perfectly poised mineral, dry, supple palate, with a kernel of sweet fruit. Delicious now & already showing complexity, but should mature many years. — TJ

Location: Bot River ▪ WO: Bot River/Swartland ▪ 1stB 2012 ▪ Private tastings on request ▪ Winemaker(s)/viticulturist(s) Marelise Jansen van Rensburg ▪ 2t/476cs own label 66% red 34% white ▪ marelise@momentowines.co.za ▪ www.momentowines.co.za ▪ **T +27 (0)82-968-8588**

☐ **Moments Collection** *see* Teddy Hall Wines
☐ **Monfort** *see* Ultra Liquors

Monis Wines

This fortifieds-only cellar is based in Paarl, but draws fruit from areas renowned for each style: muscadel from Breede River, Portuguese varieties for the port-styles from Calitzdorp and Paarl, and chenin for the sherry-styles from Stellenbosch. The fortifying brandy spirit is from parent group Distell's own distilleries.

Monis Wines

★★★★☆ **Wood Matured Muscadel** Flame-licked **04** 500ml of irresistible dried orange zest, spice, muscat complexity. Rich, silky sweetness disciplined by 5 years older oak, tangy acid. Breede River fruit.

★★★★ **Tawny Port** Gorgeous **96** ex Paarlberg tinta & cinsaut still selling.

Not retasted: **Vintage Port 06** ★★★★☆

Monis Sherry-Styles

★★★★ **Full Cream** Rich, with nuances of dried fruit, melon preserve, roasted hazelnuts giving complexity. Not overly sweet, with a nutty, savoury finish. Perfect for melon & ham.

Pale Dry ★★★★ Crunchy apple plus nuts & tealeaves, zesty palate is clean & refreshing. Satisfyingly dry, savoury finish; enjoy chilled. From chenin, matured under flor for 3 years in 59 year old solera barrels, fractional blend of vintages, as for all these. **Medium Cream** ★★★★ Brightly fruited nose is fresh, with hints of sweet candied fruit & roasted almonds. Smooth, long on flavour & intensity, yet still delicate & light. For solo sipping or soups. — WB, AL, CR

Location: Paarl ▪ WO: Stellenbosch/Breede River Valley/Calitzdorp ▪ Est 1906 ▪ Closed to public ▪ Owner(s) Distell ▪ Cellarmaster(s)/winemaker(s) Dirkie Christowitz (Aug 1979) ▪ 52,000cs 100% fortified ▪ PO Box 266 Paarl 7620 ▪ dchristowitz@distell.co.za ▪ www.moniswines.co.za ▪ F +27 (0)21-872-2790 ▪ **T +27 (0)21-860-1601**

Mon Rêve Estate

Entrepreneur Alex Kerrod, new owner of Mon Rêve Estate in the Simonsberg foothills, came to winegrowing via construction and latterly apple farming. Winemaker Marius Malan and viticulturist Stian Mooiplats are on board to help realise his vision 'to produce a limited quantity of great-quality wines'.

Location: Paarl ▪ Map: Paarl & Wellington ▪ Est 2009 ▪ 1stB 2011 ▪ Tasting, sales & cellar tours by appt ▪ Fee R20pp, waived on purchase ▪ Closed Easter Fri/Sun, May 1, Dec 25 & Jan 1 ▪ Facilities for children ▪ Owner(s) Rapitrade 652 (Pty) Ltd ▪ Winemaker(s) Marius Malan (Jan 2012) ▪ Viticulturist(s) Stian Mooiplats ▪ 12ha/±6ha (cab, merlot, shiraz, muscat d'A) ▪ 8,000L own label 94% red 6% white + 12,000L for clients ▪ PO Box 116 Franschhoek 7690 ▪ alexk@icon.co.za ▪ S 33° 49' 4.98" E 018° 54' 47.21" ▪ **T +27 (0)82-659-7649**

Mons Ruber Wine Estate

Family-owned Mons Ruber was among the first to re-apply for a distilling licence in the 1990s after long prohibition of private production, resurrecting their wood-fired copper potstill. There's history too in the tasting room, a 19th-century toll house, visited by at least one poet (CJ Langenhoven) and one princess (later Queen Elizabeth II).

Brandy range

★★★★ Estate Potstill Brandy ⓪ Muscat d'Alexandrie origin shows subtly on bright, grapey, floral fragrance. Easy, smooth & balanced, with effective oak maturation. Old-style label gives **03** vintage.

Buchu Brandy ⓪ **★★★** A quirky, light yellow medicinal brandy, infused (very noticeably) with round-leaf buchu plant. Fiery finish. From cinsaut. — WB, TJ

Location: De Rust ▪ Map: Klein Karoo & Garden Route ▪ Est ca 1850 ▪ 1stB 1985 wine/1995 brandy ▪ Tasting & sales Mon-Fri 9—5 Sat 9—1 ▪ Closed all pub hols ▪ Farm produce ▪ Hiking trail in proclaimed conservation area ▪ BYO picnic ▪ Owner(s) Radé & Erhard Meyer ▪ Winemaker(s) Radé Meyer ▪ Brandy master Radé Meyer (1990) ▪ Viticulturist(s) Radé Meyer (1990) & Johannes Mellet (consultant) ▪ ±1,800ha/38ha (cab, cinsaut, muscadel r/w, chard, chenin, hanepoot, palomino) ▪ ±500t/20,000cs own label 50% red 50% white & ±178cs brandy ▪ PO Box 1585 Oudtshoorn 6620 ▪ monsruber@gmail.com ▪ S 33° 32' 1.0" E 022° 28' 38.9" ▪ F +27 (0)86-566-6550 ▪ **T +27 (0)44-251-6550**

Montagu Wine Cellar

This popular Klein Karoo town's 'home' cellar, with its long-standing reputation for muscadel wines, has been renewing its cellar facilities in recent years. The latest investments: new grape delivery and run-off water treatment systems, the latter reflecting member growers' strong conservation ethic (together they protect over 38,000 ha of indigenous vegetation).

Cabernet Sauvignon ★★★ Fruitcake aromas, ripe juicy plums give **12** smooth-drinking appeal. WO W Cape. **Merlot-Ruby Cabernet ★★** Plums & dark berries on vanilla-spiced **12** combo, with friendly fruit-filled end. **Chenin Blanc ★★ 14** has peardrop aromas & light dry body, finishes on a zesty fresh note. Also tasted: **Colombar 14 ★★** Not retasted: **Late Harvest 12 ★★★** Not tasted: **Red Muscadel**, **White Muscadel**. Discontinued: **Sauvignon Blanc**. — WB, CR

Location: Montagu ▪ Map: Klein Karoo & Garden Route ▪ WO: Montagu/Western Cape ▪ Est 1941 ▪ 1stB 1975 ▪ Tasting & sales Mon-Fri 8—5 ▪ Closed all pub hols ▪ Farm produce ▪ Owner(s) 54 members ▪ Executive manager Jacques Jordaan (2013) ▪ Winemaker(s) Hermias Vollgraaff (Aug 2013) & Aldert Nieuwoudt (Nov 2011) ▪ Viticulturist(s) Johannes Mellet (2005, consultant) ▪ 620ha (11 varieties r/w) ▪ 16,000t/11,000cs own label 12% red 82% white 6% muscadel ▪ IPW ▪ PO Box 29 Montagu 6720 ▪ sales@montaguwines.co.za ▪ www.montaguwines.co.za ▪ S 33° 46' 37. 3" E 020° 7' 58.4" ▪ F +27 (0)23-614-1793 ▪ **T +27 (0)23-614-1125**

Mont Destin

Halfway between Stellenbosch and Paarl, and noted for its Luis Barragan architecture, Rhône-focused Mont Destin boutique cellar is owned by Ernest Bürgin and wife Samantha, whose handcrafting now includes a husk spirit, made from the skins of the flagship Destiny Shiraz. A unique feature available to visitors, al fresco bathing in wine, is now complemented by an equally unusual and indulgent chocolate essence bath.

Mont Destin range

★★★★★ Destiny Shiraz Just 3 barrels made. Signature layered complexity in **10** (★★★★★), molten plums, tobacco & nutmeg, cloves. Silky & seamless, polished, the oak (33% new) supple, melded. Not just carefully crafted, only released when ready. Nearly in **09**'s class.

For more information, visit wineonaplatter.com

★★★★☆ **Passioné** Ⓖ Shiraz with cinsaut, grenache, **10 (★★★★)** lacks **09**'s complexity. The fleshy ripeness is mirrored by dried herb, earthy notes, while firm tannins need rich dishes. Will age well.

Also tasted: **11 Barrels 13 ★★★**

Husk Spirit range Ⓝⓔⓦ

★★★★ **Spirit of Destiny** Ⓥ From shiraz husks, this hand-labelled spirit is smooth, gentle & flavoursome. Bright, with hint of smoke, perfect for late evening with an espresso. — WB, CR

Location/map: Stellenbosch ▪ WO: Paarl/Western Cape/Stellenbosch ▪ Est/1stB 1998 ▪ Tasting, sales & cellar tours by appt ▪ Closed all pub hols ▪ Open air wine bath ▪ Owner(s) Ernest & Samantha Bürgin ▪ Winemaker(s) Samantha Bürgin (May 1996) ▪ Viticulturist(s) Bertus de Clerk (2006, consultant) ▪ 10ha/7ha (cab, cinsaut, grenache, mourv, shiraz, viog) ▪ 15t/2,000cs own label 100% red ▪ IPW ▪ PO Box 1237 Stellenbosch 7599 ▪ info@montdestin.co.za ▪ www.montdestin.co.za ▪ S 33° 49' 58.9" E 018° 53' 27.8" ▪ F +27 (0)21-875-5870 ▪ **T +27 (0)83-288-4985**

Mont du Toit Kelder

Du Toits have been winefarming in the Cape since 1691, and since 1996 Johannesburg advocate Stephan du Toit's love for classic red wine has been expressed by continuing the tradition at the foot of the Hawequa Mountain (silhouetted on his labels). Said labels are set to become more visible, certainly in the Western Cape market, in a drive under new marketer Mark Tolmay. A mountain bike route, additional guest lodgings and a public post-harvest event are included in the planning.

Mont du Toit Kelder range

★★★★☆ **Mont du Toit** Flagship red in **08** regains form of **06** with 'secret blend' from Wellington fruit, after austere **07 (★★★★)**. Harmonious, moreish, with a velvety palate of ripe dark berries, supple tannins & firm structure from 2 years oak maturation.

★★★★ **Le Sommet** Ⓖ Powerfully built, austere **06** (first since **03**) another secret blend. Mature, should keep a few more years, but drying tannins (clearly partly from oak) likely to outlast the dark, sweet-edged fruit. Paarl WO.

Not tasted: **Hawequas**.

Les Coteaux range

★★★★ **Cabernet Sauvignon** Ⓖ **11** in established handsome, serious, classic style. Big, with plenty of flavour, but restrained thanks to dryness, balance & unshowy fruit. Should mature well, like most of these.

★★★★ **Cabernet Franc 12** offers gentle sweet red fruit in harmony with fragrant leafy herbs. A little lighter & juicier than the others, though as serious-minded; modest & sensitive oaking.

★★★★ **Sélection** Characterful **10** cab-based blend, bright, tasty fruit, with tobacco & dried herb notes. Elegant & light-footed with savoury notes on mouthfilling palate & long finish. **09** sold out untasted. WO Paarl.

Not retasted: **Merlot 11 ★★★ Shiraz 11 ★★★☆** — WB

Location: Wellington ▪ Map: Paarl & Wellington ▪ WO: Wellington/Paarl ▪ Est 1996 ▪ 1stB 1998 ▪ Tasting, sales & cellar tours Mon-Fri 9-4.30 Sat by appt ▪ Fee R15/R35 ▪ Closed all pub hols ▪ Hiking trails ▪ BYO picnic, picnic area by arrangement ▪ Guest cottages ▪ Owner(s) Stephan du Toit ▪ Cellarmaster(s) Bernd Philippi & Loftie Ellis (1997, consultants) ▪ Winemaker(s) Chris Roux (2012), with Abraham Cloete (Jan 2005) ▪ ±40ha/±28ha (alicante bouschet, cabs s/f, merlot, mourv, p verdot, shiraz, tinta barocca) ▪ ±165t/±16,000cs own label 100% red & ±2,000cs for clients ▪ IPW ▪ PO Box 704 Wellington 7654 ▪ kelder@montdutoit.co.za, marketing@montdutoit.co.za ▪ www.montdutoit.co.za ▪ S 33° 39' 27.72" E 019° 1' 45.81" ▪ F +27 (0)21-864-2737 ▪ **T +27 (0)21-873-7745**

☐ **Montebello** *see* Wine-of-the-Month Club

Monterosso Estate

Brothers Orneglio and Francesco De Franchi run the Stellenbosch grape and olive estate they grew up on after Italian-born father Socrate bought it in 1977, naming it after his Liguria home town. Small parcels of grapes (including sangiovese, naturalmente!) are vinified in the home-farm cellar.

Sangiovese Socrate ⊘ ★★★☆ **11** a step up. Fruitcake generosity cloaked in spicy, dry oak frame. Lithe & supple yet substantial. **Cabernet Sauvignon-Merlot** ⊘ ★★★ Cheery, light-bodied friendly appeal to 55/45 mix. Tobacco & dark fruit make **12** a good braai, pizza partner. Not retasted: **Chenin Blanc Old Bush Vine 13** ★★★ **Sauvignon Blanc 13** ★★★ — FM

Location/map/WO: Stellenbosch ▪ Est/1stB 2000 ▪ Tasting, sales & cellar tours by appt only ▪ Owner(s) Francesco & Orneglio De Franchi ▪ Cellarmaster(s)/winemaker(s) Orneglio De Franchi (Jan 2000) ▪ Viticulturist(s) Francesco De Franchi & Orneglio De Franchi (both Jan 2000) ▪ 83ha/60ha (cab, merlot, ptage, sangio, shiraz, chard, chenin, riesling, sauv, sem) ▪ 540t/760cs own label 60% red 40% white ▪ PO Box 5 Stellenbosch 7599 ▪ defranchivin@mweb.co.za, monterosso@mweb.co.za ▪ www.monterosso.co.za ▪ S 33° 54' 6.8" E 018° 50' 10.4" ▪ F +27 (0)21-889-7081/+27 (0)21-889-5021 ▪ **T +27 (0)21-889-7081/+27 (0)21-889-5021**

☐ **Montestell** *see* Boland Kelder
☐ **Montino** *see* Riebeek Cellars

Montpellier

Johannesburg advocate Lucas van Tonder continues to add to the attractions of his Tulbagh wine farm, which celebrated its 300th birthday last year. The stylish accommodation, landmark hillside chapel and nature walks have been joined by a deli, and the wedding venue revamped. And there's new energy and expertise in the cellar, with winemakers Flip Smith and Harold Versfeld intent on taking a venerable Cape name to new heights.

Location/map: Tulbagh ▪ Est 1714 ▪ Tasting, sales & tours Mon-Fri 9–5 Sat/Sun & pub hols 10-3 ▪ Pre-booked cheese platters & light meals available during tasting hours ▪ Tour groups: gazebo with pizza oven to be pre-booked ▪ Deli ▪ Olives ▪ Walking/hiking trails ▪ Renosterbos conservation area ▪ Guesthouse/B&B/self-catering ▪ Weddings: Dome & Cathedral venues ▪ Events ▪ Owner(s) Lucas J van Tonder ▪ Winemaker(s) Harold Versfeld (Sep 2014) & Flip Smith (Oct 2013) ▪ 482ha/60ha (cab, merlot, p verdot, pinot, shiraz, chard, chenin, gewürz, viog) ▪ 300t/4,400cs own label 48% red 27% white 25% MCC + 150,000L bulk ▪ PO Box 79 Tulbagh 6820 ▪ marica@montpellier.co.za ▪ www.montpellier. co.za ▪ S 33° 16' 30.4" E 019° 6' 40.0" ▪ F +27 (0)23-230-1574 ▪ **T +27 (0)23-230-0656**

Mont Rochelle Hotel & Vineyards

This gem of a boutique hotel and winery, in the mountains above Franschhoek village, no doubt will become even better known, having been bought by Sir Richard Branson in May 2014. As part of the Virgin Limited Edition portfolio, it offers world-class hospitality services. The 16 ha of vineyards and cellar return to the care of Dustin Osborne, back after a stint in Stellenbosch.

Mont Rochelle range

Cabernet Sauvignon ⊘ ★★★☆ Richly textured **07** retains supple elegance, with alcohol integrated into juicy fruit & structure. **Rosé** ⊘ ★★ Shiraz-based **11** is savoury & light. Pithy dry exit invites food. Not retasted: **Syrah 07** ★★★☆ **Artemis 08** ★★★ Not tasted: **Merlot, Barrel Fermented Chardonnay, Unwooded Chardonnay, Sauvignon Blanc.**

Miko Premier range

Not tasted: **Cabernet Sauvignon, Chardonnay Sur Lie.** — TJ

Location/map/WO: Franschhoek ▪ Est 1994 ▪ 1stB 1996 ▪ Tasting & sales 10–7 daily ▪ Fee available on request ▪ Wine tasting closed Dec 25 ▪ Cellar tours Mon-Fri 11, 12.30 & 3 Sat/Sun/pub hols 11 & 3 ▪ Miko Restaurant & Country Kitchen ▪ Mont Rochelle Hotel & Vineyard ▪ Picnics ▪ Walking/hiking trails ▪ Educational wine tastings - booking essential ▪ Owner(s) Virgin Limited Edition ▪ Cellarmaster(s)/winemaker(s)/viticulturist(s) Dustin Osborne ▪ 33ha/ 16ha (cab, merlot, shiraz, chard, sauv, sem) ▪ 100t/12,000cs own label 60% red 35% white 5% MCC ▪ PO Box 334

Franschhoek 7690 ▪ wine@montrochelle.virgin.com ▪ www.montrochelle.virgin.com ▪ S 33° 54' 52.1" E 019° 6' 21.9" ▪ F +27 (0)21-876-3255 ▪ **T +27 (0)21-876-2770**

☐ **Mon Vieux** *see* Boutinot South Africa
☐ **Moods** *see* Wineways Marketing
☐ **Mooiberg** *see* Zidela Wines

Mooi Bly Winery

Originally from Belgium, the Wouters family settled in Paarl and gained not only a son-in-law but a winemaker in Erik Schouteden, who was instrumental in planting tannat. One of the rarer varieties in the winelands, it and malbec set Mooi Bly apart, especially since both clearly are suited to the soils and climate.

Selection range

★★★★ **Malbec** Creamy salty liquorice, loads of spice threaded through the black plums yet **09** is polished, sleekly muscular, retains an elegant drinkability. Cellar with confidence.

Tannat ★★★★ Rarely bottled variety. Underbrush & smoked beef, smooth-textured **09**'s tannins are well integrated. Match with venison.

Cultivar range

Not tasted: **Cabernet Sauvignon**. — CR

Location/WO: Paarl ▪ Map: Paarl & Wellington ▪ Est/1stB 2005 ▪ Tasting, sales & cellar tours by appt ▪ Fee R50pp ▪ Closed Dec 25 & Jan 1 ▪ BYO picnic ▪ Walks ▪ 6 self-catering cottages ▪ Owner(s) Wouters family ▪ Cellarmaster(s)/winemaker(s) Erik Schouteden (Jan 2005) ▪ Viticulturist(s) Erik Schouteden (Feb 2001) ▪ 32ha/18ha (cab, malbec, shiraz, tannat, chard, chenin) ▪ 70t/6,000cs own label 50% red 50% white ▪ PO Box 801 Huguenot 7645 ▪ wine@mooibly.com ▪ www.mooibly.com ▪ S 33° 41' 7.0" E 019° 1' 21.9" ▪ F +27 (0)21-868-2808 ▪ **T +27 (0)21-868-2808**

Mooiplaas Estate & Private Nature Reserve

At family-owned Stellenbosch estate Mooiplaas, it all begins at the convivial langtafel – literally 'long dining table' – which is why the elegant, gabled manor house is regularly opened for luncheons and dinners. Visitors arrive as guests but leave as members of the Roos clan. 'Wonderful things happen when strangers sit around a table, break bread and drink wine,' says regular host, co-owner and cellarmaster Dirk Roos.

Mercia Collection

★★★★ **Tabakland Cabernet Reserve** Best cab barrels only for this new prestige label. **10** is intense & ripe, showing well-tuned black fruit with just enough vitality & freshness for a good future. Allow time for oak to integrate.

★★★★ **Watershed Syrah** Was 'Watershed Shiraz'. Robust but aristocratic **12**, with classy scrub & peppery aromas showing through; toasted coffee notes hopefully will integrate with time. No **10**, **11**.

★★★★ **Rosalind** Classy Bordeaux-style red, cab dominating still-youthful blend & character of **08**: lean & taut, with pleasing liquorice & meaty notes. Plenty in store.

★★★★ **Houmoed Bushvine Chenin Blanc** Seriously conceived, wooded **13** shows complex spicy fruit entwined with ginger, tiny twist of bitter almond at finish. Bone-dry & robust, oak needs to integrate further. Returns to form after lesser **12** (★★★☆).

★★★★ **Duel Méthode Cap Classique** Rich, creamy & very satisfying sparkling from pinot noir & chardonnay, 36 months on lees. Latest **NV** more classic: baked apples mingle with warm brioche aromas.

Classic range

★★★★ **Cabernet Sauvignon** Good varietal character, **07** chewy tobacco notes, malty finish. Ripe, concentrated but elegantly formed. Ready, don't keep too long.

★★★★ **Chenin Blanc Bush Vine** Honeyed botrytis notes over super-ripe tropical fruit. **13** (★★★★) unwooded but full bodied, slightly bland finish compared with **12** & previous.

Also tasted: **Pinotage 13** ★★★★ **Sauvignon Blanc 13** ★★★☆

Langtafel range

White ⊘ ★★★ Fresh & zesty sauvignon-led **13** combo with semillon, chenin, packed with flavour. Perfect for patio entertaining. WO W Cape, as all these. Not retasted: **Red 12** ★★★ **Rosé 13** ★★
— GdB

Location/map: Stellenbosch ▪ WO: Stellenbosch/Western Cape/Coastal ▪ Est 1806 ▪ 1stB 1995 ▪ Tasting & sales Mon-Fri 9–4.30 Sat 10–4 Sun 10.30-3.30 ▪ Fee R25/5 wines, waived on purchase ▪ Closed Easter Fri/Sun/Mon, Dec 25/26 & Jan 1 ▪ Gourmet picnic hampers & cheese platters, booking essential ▪ Langtafel (32 seater) luncheons or dinners every ±8-10 weeks in the manor house (a National Monument), enquire for dates ▪ Taste Experience presented by Dirk Roos in the 'voorkamer' (10-18 guests), booking essential ▪ Guest accommodation ▪ Walks/hikes ▪ Mountain biking ▪ Horse riding, riding lessons & trail rides ▪ 60ha private nature reserve ▪ Owner(s) Mooiplaas Trust ▪ Cellarmaster(s) Louis Roos (1983) ▪ Winemaker(s) Louis Roos (1983), with Dirk Roos ▪ Viticulturist(s) Tielman Roos (1981) ▪ 250ha/100ha (cabs s/f, p verdot, ptage, pinot, chard, chenin, sauv) ▪ 750t/50,000cs own label 57% red 41% white 2% rosé ▪ Other export brand: The Collection ▪ BWI, IPW ▪ PO Box 104 Koelenhof 7605 ▪ info@mooiplaas.co.za ▪ www. mooiplaas.co.za ▪ S 33° 55' 16.3" E 018° 44' 21.4" ▪ F +27 (0)86-604-4312 ▪ **T +27 (0)21-903-6273/4**

Mooiuitsig Wine Cellars

Mooiuitsig, the Jonker family's drinks enterprise, has a substantial portfolio (the sweeter toothed especially well catered for), its own distribution network and even retail outlets. Tastings are no longer available at the home farm, but accommodation is still offered in nearby Bonnievale village.

Location: Bonnievale ▪ Est 1947 ▪ Closed to public ▪ Stay-overs at De Rust Lodge info@outdoorarena.co.za; T +27 (0)23-616-2444 ▪ Owner(s) Jonker family ▪ Winemaker(s) Nico van der Westhuizen, with Carlo Schiocatti & Lazarus Kholomba ▪ Viticulturist(s) Casper Matthee ▪ 150ha total ▪ 2,900t ▪ PO Box 15 Bonnievale 6730 ▪ info@mooiuitsig.co. za ▪ www.mooiuitsig.co.za ▪ F +27 (0)23-616-2675 ▪ **T +27 (0)23-616-2143**

☐ **Mooiuitzicht** *see* Mooiuitsig Wine Cellars
☐ **Moonlight Organics** *see* Stellar Winery

Môreson

The 'Morning Sun' rose for owner Richard Friedman when he took over his parents' Franschhoek property just over twenty years ago. Wines had been made by the local cooperative but Richard built a cellar and surged to prominence with a solo, debut 1994 harvest. He and his family have since created an impressive wine and hospitality offering, and under the aegis of seasoned Clayton Reabow and newcomer Christelle Walters, a wine portfolio to match. The white wines are dominated by still and sparkling chardonnay (all clone material available in SA is grown and vinified on the estate), while the reds are being whittled down to just two: the Pinotage and a new pinotage-based blend.

Môreson range

★★★★ **Cabernet Franc** Niche red now entirely Franschhoek sourced, **11** has spearmint freshness rather than the herbaceousness of **10** (★★★★). Lithe, with lingering raspberry & plum flavours.

★★★★ **Pinotage** Including Stellenbosch grapes, **12** (★★★★★) has 10% cinsaut to add savoury note without detracting from the abundant dark fruit also evident in **11**. Soft, with understated oak.

★★★★ **Mata Mata** First vintage exclusively from Franschhoek grapes (40% merlot, 28% each cab & cab franc, malbec), **12** (★★★★★) has lovely black-fruit purity supported by soft tannins & fresh acidity. Even more balanced & elegant than **11**.

★★★★★ **Mercator Premium Chardonnay** Think pineapples & nectarines with a few squeezes of lime, elegant **13** is ripe & juicy but dry, rich & creamy but restrained, with fermentation (40% wild) in French oak (50% new) adding toasted almond & spice complexity.

For more information, visit wineonaplatter.com

★★★★ **Knoputibak** Conceived to showcase Franschhoek's regional identity, **13** (★★★★☆) is more refined than **12**, with 25% semillon (from 50 year old dryland bushvines) adding smooth beeswax texture to chardonnay's creamy lemon intensity.

Also tasted: **Dr Reason Why 13** ★★★☆ **Solitaire Blanc de Blancs Méthode Cap Classique NV** ★★★☆ Not retasted: **The Fudge 12** ★★★☆ Not tasted: **Magia, Sauvignon Blanc, Pink Brut Rosé.**

Miss Molly range

Not tasted: **In My Bed Cabernet Sauvignon-Merlot, Kitchen Thief Sauvignon Blanc, Hoity Toity Chenin Blanc-Viognier, Petit Rosé, Méthode Cap Classique.** — JG

Location/map: Franschhoek ▪ WO: Franschhoek/Coastal ▪ Est 1983 ▪ 1stB 1994 ▪ Tasting, sales & cellar tours daily 9.30–5 ▪ Fee R30 ▪ Closed Dec 25 ▪ Bread & Wine Restaurant daily 12-3 & The Farm Grocer (for lighter meals) daily 9.30-4.30 ▪ Charcuterie produced by Neil Jewell ▪ Exotic Plant Company ▪ Wine blending & breadmaking ▪ Owner(s) Richard Friedman ▪ Winemaker(s) Clayton Reabow (May 2007), with Christelle Walters (Jun 2014) ▪ Viticulturist(s) James McNaught Davis ▪ 35ha/±18ha (chard, chenin) ▪ ±120t 30% red 45% white 25% MCC ▪ Euro Gap, IPW ▪ PO Box 114 Franschhoek 7690 ▪ sales@moreson.co.za ▪ www.moreson.co.za ▪ S 33° 53' 11.9" E 019° 3' 30.6" ▪ F +27 (0)21-876-2348 ▪ **T +27 (0)21-876-3055**

☐ **Môrewag** see Blomendahl Vineyards

Morgenhof Wine Estate

As befits a property dating back to 1692, and under French ownership since 1993 (Anne Cointreau is from the famous French cognac and liqueurs family), classic traditions are often invoked here. Such as the generally restrained style of the winemaking, but also such factors as the lack of irrigation in the vineyards on the lower slopes of Stellenbosch's Simonsberg – where a diversity of aspects and soils (samples of the latter on display at the tasting centre) allow for careful matching of variety to site. Conservation responsibilities are not forgotten, with 29 of the estate's 200+ ha under natural fynbos. Watch out for a new varietal Cabernet Franc and a 'Pinotage to be reckoned with'.

Morgenhof Estate range

★★★★ **Cabernet Sauvignon** ② Youthful, unevolved **11** shows espresso, toasty oak & dark fruit. Classically structured, with a rich flavourful palate & fine tannins, leading to long finish. Needs 5+ years to develop.

★★★★ **Merlot** ② Attractive, youthful **10** (ex barrel) in house's classic style. Smart oaking does not intrude on the fruit & the palate is concentrated, with lots of energy & uplift; fine tannin & a dry finish.

★★★★ **The Morgenhof Estate** ② Flagship red from 5 Bordeaux grapes, toned 20 months in 40% new oak. **06** noticeable acidity but better integrated when revisited mid-2013. Delicious aromas persist, & firm tannin grip supports the fruit flavours.

★★★★ **Chenin Blanc** Delightful **13** (★★★★) well-structured & versatile food partner. Harmoniously fruity, though less convincing than **12** bottling.

★★★★ **Brut Reserve** ② Fresh **08** MCC bubbly from chardonnay & pinot with green apple, peach & delicate floral notes. Attractively tight, with a steely edge.

★★★★ **Cape LBV** ② **04** Late Bottled Vintage spent 6 years in oak barrels. Rich, full & intensely flavoured, with grippy tannins to balance the sweetness. From touriga.

Also tasted: **Merlot-Cabernet Franc 10** ★★★ **Chardonnay 13** ★★★☆ **Sauvignon Blanc 14** ★★★☆ Not tasted: **Noble Late Harvest.**

Fantail range

Pinotage ★★★ Pleasingly savoury **12** shows lovely bright fruit flavours underpinned by firm tannins. Stellenbosch WO, as most of these. Also tasted: **Pinotage Rosé 13** ★★★ **Sauvignon Blanc-Chenin Blanc 13** ★★★☆ Not retasted: **Cabernet Franc-Cabernet Sauvignon 11** ★★★ — IM

For more information, visit wineonaplatter.com

Location/map: Stellenbosch • WO: Simonsberg–Stellenbosch/Stellenbosch • Est 1692 • 1stB 1984 • Tasting & sales Mon-Fri 9–5.30 (Nov-Apr) & 9-4.30 (May-Oct); Sat/Sun 10–5 (Nov-Apr) & 10-3 (May-Oct) • Fee R25pp • Closed Good Fri, Dec 25 & Jan 1 • Cellar tours/viewing of underground barrel cellar on request • Cheese platters • Morgenhof Restaurant • Facilities for children • Gift shop • Conferences • Weddings/functions • Heli-pad • Conservation area • Morgenhof Manor House • Owner(s) Anne Cointreau • Winemaker(s) Andries de Klerk (Jan 2012) • Viticulturist(s) Pieter Haasbroek (Apr 1998) • 212ha/74ha (cabs s/f, malbec, merlot, chenin) • 410t/70,000cs own label 60% red 38% white 2% rosé • BWI, IPW • PO Box 365 Stellenbosch 7599 • info@morgenhof.com • www.morgenhof.com • S 33° 53' 38.5" E 018° 51' 39.2" • F +27 (0)21-889-5266 • T +27 (0)21-889-5510

Morgenster Estate

Developments at this beautiful property continue apace, led with energy by owner Giulio Bertrand. On the wine front, the first sauvignon and semillon are being planted for the white blend, while the olive groves are being extended by giulia, one of three patented olive varieties for which Morgenster holds propagation rights. With a few vintages here under his belt, cellarmaster Henry Kotzé reflects on what gives the wines their uniqueness and quality: 'All vineyards are grown on slopes of the Schapenberg with its specific mesoclimate; the collaboration with Cheval Blanc's technical team and Pierre Lurton has broadened my vision; and, of course, Mr Bertrand's commitment to quality.' Unusually, parcels of each vintage are held back, enabling Morgenster to offer a selection of vintages bottle-aged at the estate under ideal conditions.

Morgenster Estate range

★★★★☆ **Morgenster** Flagship, only-the-best Bordeaux blend. Seamlessly elegant yet taut **11** sees merlot (59%) play a greater role than in **10**. Cab & petit verdot in superb support, along with oak (60% new). Subtle, refined, poised & deeply rich. Lissom & svelte, with years of life ahead.

★★★★☆ **Lourens River Valley** Estate's second - very fine - claret, giving a plusher & more approachable take on Morgenster terroir in **11**. Cab franc makes up about two-thirds of the blend, with merlot, cab & petit verdot, showing rich fruitcake notes with light tannic grip, balanced by cocoa succulence.

★★★★ **White** Sauvignon leads with 51% but semillon's influence strongly felt in waxy lemon zest nuances on **13**, as in **12** (★★★★). Weighty, rich & textured, with oak (30% new) adding dimension & length. Schapenberg fruit.

Italian Collection

★★★★ **Nabucco** Intense pure cherry tobacco notes on vibrant, young **12**, maintaining tone of **11**. Focused, with firm core & long aftertaste. **10** (★★★★) had dabs merlot & cab but this is all nebbiolo. Also tasted: **Tosca 12** ★★★★☆ **Caruso 14** ★★★☆

NU Series 1

★★★★ **Merlot** Medium bodied & accessible, **13** (★★★☆) still has notable tannin grip to balance ripe cherry/cocoa succulence. Harmonious, as was slightly more impressive **12**.

Sangiovese (NEW) ★★★★☆ Ripe, pure blueberry & cherry notes on **14** pre-bottling sample. Youthful, bright, cheerful & friendly. **Sauvignon Blanc** (NEW) ★★★★ **14** is flinty, with zingy lemon zest & white pepper. Lively, pure & typical of the grape. Also tasted: **Cabernet Sauvignon 13** ★★★★ — FM

Location: Somerset West • Map: Helderberg • WO: Stellenbosch • Est 1993 • 1stB 1998 • Tasting & sales Mon-Sun 10–5 • Tasting fee R35 wine/R20 olive oil & olive products • Closed Good Fri & Dec 25 • Owner(s) Giulio Bertrand • Cellarmaster(s) Henry Kotzé (Oct 2009) • Winemaker(s) Henry Kotzé (Oct 2009), with consultant Pierre Lurton (Nov 1997, Château Cheval Blanc) • Viticulturist(s) Corius Visser (Apr 2014) • 200ha/30ha (cabs s/f, merlot, nebbiolo, p verdot, sangio) • ±200t own label 90% red 5% white 5% rosé • BWI, IPW • PO Box 1616 Somerset West 7129 • info@morgenster.co.za • www. morgenster.co.za • S 34° 5' 2.9" E 018° 53' 7.8" • F +27 (0)21-852-1141 • T +27 (0)21-852-1738

☐ **Mori Wines** see Casa Mori

☐ **Morkel** see Bellevue Estate Stellenbosch

Mostertsdrift Noble Wines

Unforeseen events caused winemaker Anna-Mareè Uys, brother and co-owner André Mostert and viticulturist father Nico Mostert to skip the 2014 harvest, but they hold stock of earlier-vintage reds and the ever-welcoming cellardoor on the northern edge of Stellenbosch town remains wide open to receive visitors with little pomp but lots of enthusiasm.

AnéRouge 🍷 ★★★ Mainly cab, rest merlot. Last-tasted **07**'s well-managed ripe fruit delivered balance & soft appeal. Not retasted: **Cabernet Sauvignon 07** ★★★ **Cape Blend 08** ★★★ Not tasted: **Merlot Rosé, Chardonnay, White Muscadel**. — IM

Location/map/WO: Stellenbosch ▪ Est/1stB 2001 ▪ Tasting, sales & cellar tours by appt ▪ Fee R10pp for groups ▪ Meals for groups by prior arrangement ▪ Facilities for children ▪ Conference venue ▪ Owner(s) André Mostert & Anna-Mareè Uys (Mostert) ▪ Cellarmaster(s)/winemaker(s) Anna-Mareè Uys (Jan 2001) ▪ Viticulturist(s) Nico Mostert (Jan 2001) ▪ 13ha/±8ha (cab, merlot, pinot, chard, hanepoot) ▪ ±80-100t/3,986cs own label 70% red 10% white 20% rosé + 15,000L bulk ▪ PO Box 2061 Dennesig Stellenbosch 7601 ▪ winemaker@mostertsdrift.co.za ▪ www.mostertsdrift.co.za ▪ S 33° 53' 31.7" E 018° 50' 17.6" ▪ F +27 (0)86-516-1730 ▪ **T +27 (0)73-194-9221**

Mount Abora Vineyards 🍷

Something of a shake-up sees Pieter de Waal and Krige Visser take full ownership of this Swartland label named after the imaginary landmark in Coleridge's poem 'Kubla Khan'. Both are longtime proponents of 'natural' and authentic winemaking - finding inspiration in the Rhône vigneron Alain Graillot, and in the Cape's cinsaut wines made 'before the days of small oak barrels, heavy extractions, high alcohols, enzymes and other winemaking wizardry'. Johan Meyer makes the wines in the Antebellum (formerly Meerhof) cellar in full accord with this vision and the precepts of the Swartland Independent Producers.

★★★★☆ **Saffraan** 🆕 One of the leaders in the revival of quality cinsaut - here unblended. Spicy & pure-fruited **13**, clean & refreshing, gently succulent, with sweet fruit on dry, subtly tannic palate; under 12% alcohol. A complete wine that takes modesty to a high level.

★★★★☆ **The Abyssinian** 🆕 Named for Coleridge's 'Abyssinian maid', from mourvèdre with cinsaut & shiraz. Whole-bunch ferment; maturation in older oak. **12** combines bright, fresh red fruit intensity with a lightness of touch & a modest 12.4% alcohol to make for great drinkability.

★★★★ **Koggelbos** Characterful **12** (★★★★★) chenin blanc is confident but unaggressive, with fine acid freshness balanced with oxidatively handled fruit & just 12.3% alcohol. Supple, silky & moreish. Vibrant minerality, as on **11**, & restraint make a good food wine. Will benefit from a few years in bottle, but tasty now. — TJ

Location: Riebeek-Kasteel ▪ WO: Swartland ▪ Est/1stB 2012 ▪ Tasting & sales at The Wine Kollective in Riebeek-Kasteel ▪ Owner(s) Vinotage (Pty) Ltd ▪ Winemaker(s) Johan Meyer ▪ 2,150cs own label 60% red 40% white ▪ PO Box 396 Riebeek Kasteel 7307 ▪ wine@abora.co.za ▪ www.abora.co.za ▪ **T +27 (0)82-413-6719/+27 (0)79-280-0237/+27 (0)83-357-3864**

☐ **Mountain Eye** *see* Kleinhoekkloof

Mountain Oaks Organic Winery 🍷

It was the wish to farm organically that led the Stevens family to the Slanghoek Valley, where the project was eased by conducive conditions. Today the farm is certified organic, and pre-booked tours and talks on organic farming are offered.

★★★★ **Pinotage** 🍷 🍃 After juicy **10**, **11** (★★★★) preview had ripe raspberry scent & delicious flavours, but perhaps not the depth for its ambitious structure. Drying tannin might resolve in time. Not retasted: **Eikenbosch Red 10** ★★★ **Le Jardin Rouge 11** ★★ Not tasted: **Le Jardin Rosé**. — TJ

Location: Rawsonville ▪ Map: Breedekloof ▪ WO: Slanghoek ▪ Est/1stB 2003 ▪ Tasting, sales & cellar tours by appt ▪ Farm tours & talks on organic farming by appt ▪ Farm produce ▪ Owner(s) Stevens family ▪ Viticulturist(s) Mark Stevens (2000) ▪ 200ha/16ha (cabs s/f, ptage, shiraz, chard, chenin) ▪ 20-30t own label 70% red 20% white 10% rosé ▪ SGS organic certification ▪ PO Box 68 Rawsonville 6845 ▪ eikenbosch@iafrica.com ▪ S 33° 38' 16.1" E 019° 13' 36.0" ▪ F +27 (0)86-613-6687 ▪ **T +27 (0)23-344-3107**

Mountain Ridge Wines

Founded in 1949 as Romansrivier Winery, and situated on De Liefde Road, Wolseley, Mountain Ridge and its 20 grower-owners are staying close to their roots (and, given their cellardoor wedding venue, punning on the themes of love and romance) for their new reserve and happy-occasion ranges. New, too, is Arno Albertyn, ex Knorhoek, taking over as cellarmaster/GM.

Romansrivier range (NEW)
Cabernet Sauvignon Reserve ★★★ Pleasing dark berry aromas introduce well oaked **11**. Robustly built, but the fruit weak at the core. Nice dry finish. Perhaps a few years will bring harmony. **Shiraz Reserve ★★★☆** Big, bold **11** has sweet, spicy-smoky fruit. Enticing & forward, with some juiciness, but nothing approaching refinement.

Mountain Ridge range
★★★★ Shiraz No longer 'Reserve', & likeable, friendly, old-oaked **11** (**★★★**) without the ambitions of big, dramatic **10**. Ripe, spicy & flavourful, but rather edgy; finishes on a sweet note.
Also tasted: **Sauvignon Blanc 14 ★★** Not retasted: **Cabernet Sauvignon 10 ★★★☆**

De Liefde range (NEW)
Aanstap Rooies Dry Red ★★ Fruity, cheerful **NV** (**12**) cab-merlot blend, with a bit of sweetness & a nice tug of tannin. **The Long & Wine'ing Road Dry White ★★☆ NV** (**14**), from chenin, with full tropical aromas & flavours balanced nicely with a good bracing freshness. **Smooch Vonkelwyn ★★** Mildly fruity, off-dry pink bubbly, **NV** - but the charming flavours disappear as quickly as the foam. — TJ

Location: Wolseley ▪ Map: Breedekloof ▪ WO: Western Cape ▪ Est 1949 ▪ 1stB 1976 ▪ Tasting & sales Mon-Fri 8–5 ▪ Closed all pub hols ▪ BYO picnic ▪ Ramkiekie Farmer's Market ▪ Wedding & function venue (140-160 pax) ▪ Owner(s) 20 members ▪ Cellarmaster(s) /GM Arno Albertyn (Jan 2014) ▪ Winemaker(s) Christo Stemmet (Jan 2010) ▪ Viticulturist(s) Pierre Snyman (consultant) ▪ 400ha (cab, shiraz, chenin, cbard) ▪ 9,000t/8,000cs own label 48% red 37% white 15% rosé ▪ IPW ▪ PO Box 108 Wolseley 6830 ▪ sales@mountainridge.co.za ▪ www.mountainridge.co.za ▪ S 33° 28' 26.04" E 019° 12' 10.44" ▪ F +27 (0)23-231-1102 ▪ **T +27 (0)23-231-1070**

Mountain River Wines

Run from one of historic Paarl Main Street's elegantly restored homes, De Villiers Brits' negociant business, founded in the early 1990s when newly democratic SA's wine exports took off, has carved a place for both its bulk and bottled wines in markets as diverse as the UK, India, China and Russia.

Mountain River range
★★★★ Pinotage ⊘ **09** (**★★★☆**), successor to ageworthy **06**, high-toned raspberry fruit, vanilla fudge nose, black fruit pastille core & coconut tail ex 20% American oak.
Not retasted: **Chardonnay 12 ★★★☆**

Maankloof range
Shiraz ★★ Balanced, dark-fruited **13**, pleasant undemanding drinking with touch of spicy oak in dry finish. **Sauvignon Blanc ★★★** Light **14** vibrantly fresh & grassy, perfect with braaied crayfish. Also tasted: **Pinotage 13 ★★** Not tasted: **Cabernet Sauvignon**, **Chenin Blanc**.

Zaràfa range
Cabernet Sauvignon ★★ Rustic, outdoorsy **13**, berry jam flavours & dry tannins, tart farewell with 14.2% alcohol glow. **Rosé ★★** Fresh & dry **14** with piquant & pithy farewell. Light uncomplicated quaffer. Also tasted: **Pinotage 13 ★★ Shiraz 13 ★★ Sauvignon Blanc 14 ★★★**

For more information, visit wineonaplatter.com

Ukuzala range

Not tasted: **Dry Red**, **Dry White**. — MW

Location: Paarl ▪ WO: Western Cape ▪ Est 1993 ▪ 1stB 1998 ▪ Closed to public ▪ Owner(s) De Villiers Brits ▪ Cellar-master(s) De Villiers Brits, with consultants ▪ 1.2ha (shiraz) ▪ 60,000cs own label 60% red 40% white ▪ 146 Main Road Paarl 7646 ▪ dev@mountainriverwines.co.za, mattie@mountainriverwines.co.za ▪ www.mountainriverwines.co.za ▪ F +27 (0)21-872-3255 ▪ **T +27 (0)21-872-3256/7**

☐ **Mountain Shadows** *see* Wineways Marketing
☐ **Mountain Stream** *see* Ashton Kelder

Mount Babylon Vineyards

A pioneer in Hemel-en-Aarde Ridge, Mount Babylon Vineyards is both the realisation of a dream and 'our own little "Heaven on Earth"' of vines, fynbos and birdsong for Johan Holtzhausen, corporate financier and winemaker (with neighbour Jean-Claude Martin of Creation Wines), and his family.

★★★★ **SMV** ⓐ Bright & refreshing **07** (★★★☆) mocha, chocolate aromas; harmonious but lacking complexity of maiden **06** (from shiraz, with malbec, viognier). Like next, tasted a few years back.

★★★★ **Pioneer Brut Reserve** ⓐ Polished **07** a rare 100% shiraz blanc de noir MCC sparkling. Apricot-tinged, with berry hints, intriguing nuttiness & herbal persistence. — TJ

Location: Hermanus ▪ Map: Elgin, Walker Bay & Bot River ▪ Est 2002 ▪ 1stB 2007 ▪ Tasting, sales & cellar tours by appt ▪ Cheese platters ▪ Owner(s) Johan Holtzhausen ▪ Winemaker(s) Jean-Claude Martin (2008, consultant) & Johan Holtzhausen ▪ Viticulturist(s) Johan Pienaar (2002, consultant) ▪ 65ha/7ha (pinot, shiraz, viog) ▪ ±38t/±400cs own label 90% red 10% white ▪ PO Box 7370 Stellenbosch 7599 ▪ info@mountbabylon.co.za ▪ www.mountbabylon.co.za ▪ S 34° 19' 44.0" E 019° 19' 34.3" ▪ F +27 (0)21-855-2768 ▪ **T +27 (0)21-855-2768/+27 (0)84-511-8180**

Mount Pleasant Vineyards

Former London banker Alfred Legner relishes country life in arty Darling, where he is an active music patron and tender of a small walled village vineyard, source of his and business partner Pascale Palmer's shiraz, made, with a new chenin from a local vineyard, by Malmesbury's Hofstraat Kelder.

Darling Pascale's Shiraz ⓐ ★★★☆ Named for Mount Pleasant co-owner Pascale Palmer. Leafy nuance to **11**'s black cherry & spicy red fruit. Showy, with tight tannins, deserves time or a good meal. **Darling Pascale's Chenin Blanc** ⓝⓔⓦ ★★★☆ Oak-touched **13** has chenin's stonefruit, herbal & subtle wet wool nuances. Fresh & zippy, showing coastal influence, hides few grams sugar well to finish with savoury flair. — HJ

Location/WO: Darling ▪ Est 2009 ▪ 1stB 2011 ▪ Closed to public ▪ Owner(s) Pascale Palmer & the Legner family ▪ Winemaker(s) Wim Smit (Dec 2010, Hofstraat) ▪ Viticulturist(s) Alfred Legner (Jun 2006) ▪ 0.2ha/0.1ha (shiraz) ▪ 2t/ha 66cs own label 100% red ▪ 11 High Street Darling 7345 ▪ info@darlingmusic.org ▪ **T +27 (0)72-015-1653**

Mount Rozier Estate

Under ownership since 2012 of nearby Journey's End, Mount Rozier extends the UK's Gabb family landholding from which both labels can draw (the latter as an entry-level range). The site is on Schapenberg, the famously windy hill overlooking False Bay between Somerset West and Sir Lowry's Pass, known for quality-enhancing cool conditions and stony soils.

Merlot ⓥ ★★★ Pleasantly fresh & flavourful **11** shows sweet plum fruit & decent grip. **Sauvignon Blanc** ★★★ Bold, rich style in **13** - no shortage of flavour. A crowd pleaser. Also tasted: **Cabernet Sauvignon** ⓥ **12** ★★★★ Not retasted: **Shiraz 11** ★★★ **Chardonnay 12** ★★★ — IM

Location: Sir Lowry's Pass ▪ Map: Helderberg ▪ WO: Stellenbosch ▪ Est/1stB 2011 ▪ Tasting & cellar tours by appt only ▪ Wine sales Mon-Fri ▪ Owner(s) Gabb family ▪ Winemaker(s) Leon Esterhuizen ▪ Viticulturist(s) Lodewyk Retief ▪ 40ha/30ha (cab, malbec, merlot, p verdot, shiraz, chard) ▪ 200t/25-30,000cs ▪ HACCP, IPW, WIETA ▪ PO Box 3040 Somerset West 7129 ▪ wines@mountrozier.co.za ▪ www.mountrozier.co.za ▪ S 34° 6' 21.22" E 018° 54' 35.80" ▪ F +27 (0)86-540-1929 ▪ **T +27 (0)21-858-1929**

Mount Vernon Estate

This property in the Simonsberg-Paarl ward is owned by the Hooper family, who run liquor distributors E Snell. The name was inspired by George Washington's home in Virginia, but also reflects the middle name of every Hooper male, given in memory of Vernon Edward Hooper – the crest on the elegant labels is his rank insignia as a sergeant major in World War II.

Location: Paarl ▪ Map: Paarl & Wellington ▪ Est 1996 ▪ 1stB 2005 ▪ Tasting, sales & cellar tours Mon-Fri 10-5 Sat 10-3 ▪ Owner(s) David & Debbie Hooper ▪ Cellarmaster(s) Debbie Hooper (Jan 2003) ▪ Winemaker(s) Debbie Hooper (Jan 2003), with Philip du Toit (Jan 2005) ▪ Viticulturist(s) Philip du Toit (Jun 1997) ▪ 110ha/27.5ha (cab, malbec, merlot, p verdot, ptage, shiraz, chard) ▪ 210-225t/2,000cs own label 80% red 15% white 5% rosé ▪ PO Box 348 Klapmuts 7625 ▪ john@mountvernon.co.za ▪ www.mountvernon.co.za ▪ S 33° 48' 57.8" E 018° 52' 51.9" ▪ F +27 (0)86-618-9821 ▪ **T +27 (0)21-875-5073**

Mulderbosch Vineyards

Charles Banks of Terroir Capital is very much a visible owner of Mulderbosch. His interest in and understanding of wine ensures he has a vision for the top-ranked Stellenbosch winery to further grow and improve. Andy Erickson, consultant winemaker at Banks' Californian wineries, visits twice a year to give guidance. Both Mulderbosch winemakers, Adam Mason and Mick Craven, have the opportunity of working in California, 'where we have the privilege to be exposed to different vineyards, fresh ideas'. Meantime, the Mulderbosch range continues to be redefined; a méthode cap classique is a work in progress; new plantings include bushvine chenin and more cabernet franc. The Chardonnay's three trophies on the 2014 Trophy Show were complemented by a 'best in Stellenbosch' vote for Mulderbosch pizzas and a marked rise in visitor numbers.

Mulderbosch Vineyards range

★★★★☆ **Faithful Hound** Classically styled **12**, cabs s/f-based with input from other Bordeaux trio. Oak-dusted dark fruits refrained in sweet flesh & trimmed with fine tannin. An assembly of refinement that drinks well now & can be matured with confidence until around 2020. WO W Cape.

★★★★ **Chardonnay** Eminently satisfying **13**. Elegant pickled lime, nutty contributions in polished harmony with rich texture, poised freshness & lengthy tail. Possibly even better by 2017. 28% older French oak.

★★★★☆ **Chardonnay Barrel Fermented** Ⓥ Elegant & complex, **12** shows seamless integration between mineral, limy fruit & oak (50% new, 18 months). Expansive mouthfeel, good length though still tight core of flavour. Will reward cellaring. No **11**.

★★★★ **Chenin Blanc Steen op Hout** As in **12**, latest **13** abounds with inviting ripe yellow peach aromas, juicy flavours. Just 10% oaked for extra bounce in this moreish mouthful. WO W Cape.

★★★★ **Sauvignon Blanc** Sauvignon's natural vigour neatly anchored but not diminished by extended lees-ageing. **13** interesting lees, artichoke features; cool, clean & with impressive persistence. WO W Cape. **12** (★★★★☆) had splash semillon.

★★★★ **Faithful Hound White** (NEW) Promising **13** oaked semillon & sauvignon (57/43). Waxy, carpet-pile textured semillon ex Franschhoek old vines, enlivened by tangy, blackcurrant-toned sauvignon. Deserves year/2 to fully harmonise, grow. Distinctive addition to this quality category.

★★★★ **Sauvignon Blanc Noble Late Harvest** Ⓥ Yellow-gold **11**. Botrytis & oak nicely judged not to swamp sauvignon (& a little chenin) fruit. Lightish body; sweetness cut by tangy acid. No **10**. WO W Cape.

Also tasted: **Cabernet Sauvignon Rosé 14** ★★★

1000 Miles range

★★★★☆ **Single Vineyard Chenin Blanc - Block S2** Was 'Sonop'. Now bottled, **13** palest & most delicate of trio, but also persuasive. Similar floral, red apple features as last year, more nuanced & lengthy. Lovely refined, refreshing wine. This & next 2 vinified same way; partial natural ferment in barrel/aged 10 months.

★★★★☆ **Single Vineyard Chenin Blanc - Block W** Was 'Rustenhof'. **13**, previewed last time, more oxidative, reflected in pale golden hue. Luscious, rich, but with incisive cleansing & balancing thread of savoury acid, tang of fragrant tangerine peel. Promises great complexity with the lengthy ageing it just begs.

★★★★☆ **Single Vineyard Chenin Blanc - Block A** Was 'Eikenhof'. Like Block W, oxidative but much steelier, with firm pithy finish. Hint of bruised apple, even oak spice but, as suggested when previewed last year, **13** slowest to evolve, maybe longest lived.

★★★★☆ **Sauvignon Blanc 13** shows more youthful restraint than **12** (★★★★★); distinctive lime zest, blackcurrant intensity yet to unfold. Sleek & taut rather than zesty, with cool resonance in its endless fantail persistence. 14 months in 500L French oak seamlessly absorbed. Lovely prospects. WO W Cape. — AL

Location/map: Stellenbosch ▪ WO: Stellenbosch/Western Cape/Coastal ▪ Est 1989 ▪ 1stB 1991 ▪ Tasting & sales Tue-Sun & pub hols 10-6 ▪ Fee R50-R70 ▪ Closed Mon, Easter Fri-Mon, Dec 25 & Jan 1 ▪ Pizzas & cheese boards, cappuccinos, artisanal beer, juice ▪ Olive oil ▪ Bocce ball courts (Italian boule) ▪ Conservation area ▪ Owner(s) Terroir Capital ▪ Winemaker(s) Adam Mason (Dec 2011), with Mick Craven (Jan 2013) ▪ Viticulturist(s) Adam Mason (Jun 2013) ▪ 80ha/45.2ha (cabs s/f, merlot, p verdot, shiraz, chard, chenin, sauv, viog) ▪ BWI ▪ PO Box 12817 Die Boord Stellenbosch 7613 ▪ info@mulderbosch.co.za ▪ www.mulderbosch.co.za ▪ S 33° 56' 56.00" E 018° 45' 57.00" ▪ F +27 (0)21-881-3514 ▪ **T +27 (0)21-881-8140**

Mullineux & Leeu Family Wines

Since scooping their Platter's Winery of the Year title in 2014, Swartland 'revolutionaries' Chris and Andrea Mullineux have not been resting on their laurels. Firstly, the Mullineux & Leeu name change to reflect their new partnership with Indian businessman Analjit Singh ('singh' the Hindu word for lion, 'leeu' in Afrikaans'). Secondly, the securement of Roundstone, a farm on the slopes of Swartland's Kasteelberg, which will remain the winegrowing duo's firm winegrowing focus even as they develop new wines in Franschhoek. 'We are now busy with plans to carefully and thoughtfully plant Roundstone over the next few years,' says US-born Andrea, proud to have added a couple of new wines to the Terroir Specific range this year and her first Cape Winemakers Guild auction bottling, from rare red-skinned semillon.

Mullineux Terroir Specific range

★★★★☆ **Granite Syrah** An illuminating demonstration of the effect of terroir in this range of wines. **12** from single Perdeberg vineyard on granite-based soils is very tightly focused & flinty, least expressive of the quartet of Syrahs. Intense fruit & oak tannins, slow evolving, but like siblings below, built for a decade. Infanticide now, but richly rewarding in the future.

★★★★★ **Schist Syrah 12** (★★★★★) perfumed red berries & white pepper aromas provide a glimpse of future delights from single-vineyard Kasteelberg fruit. Palate bound up in dry, chalky tannins from schist-derived soils (same as **11**), a structured vintage & vinification techniques (the latter identical for all these reds). Pedigree to age.

★★★★☆ **Iron Syrah** (NEW) Iron-rich soils in the Malmesbury hills impart a distinct ferrous, meaty tone to **12**. Very tightly coiled & unyielding in youth, with muscular intensity. All elements in place & keepability evident, built for a decade.

★★★★★ **Schist Chenin Blanc 13** (★★★★★) from 2 old schist-based Kasteelberg vineyards. Natural ferment, & old oak (as for all Mullineux whites). Understated & refined, with similar mineral undertone to stellar **12**. Subtler than Quartz sibling but equally focused & ageable.

★★★★☆ **Quartz Chenin** **13** reflecting quartz-based soil of single parcel of Kasteelberg vines. Same winemaking regime as Schist but more expressive & fresher, with brighter acidity & spicy baked apple, almond flavours. Silk textured & intense, good length & ageing potential.

Mullineux Family Wines range

★★★★☆ **Syrah** Consummate blend of 9 vineyards & the characteristics of schist-, granite- & iron-based soils. **12** appealing garrigue scrub, graphite/gun oil & white pepper tones woven into concentrated fruit & tannin structure. The most balanced in youth of the Syrahs; eminently ageworthy.

★★★★☆ **CWG Auction Reserve The Gris Semillon** **13** Andrea Mullineux's first CWG Auction wine, from rare 'gris' (red-skinned) semillon. Tiny crop yields finely nuanced greengage, starfruit flavours, with an orange peel & flor sherry tone & silky texture. Lovely freshness, some minerality. Contemplative wine, deserves ageing.

★★★★☆ **White Blend** One of the Cape's top examples of this genre. **13** is a chenin-led blend, with clairette & viognier (13/7) from 8 vineyards. Feisty & fresh, leavened by a waxy almond undertone & gentle baked apple aromas. Youthful & complex, will unfurl beautifully over 3-5 years.

★★★★★ **Straw Wine** Star amongst the Cape's vin de paille-style dessert wines. Naturally older-barrel-fermented **13** decadently sweet (269 g/l sugar) & viscous, threaded with chenin's pervasive & piquant freshness. Lingering nougat, honey & dried fruit flavours drawn to long & tangy conclusion.

Kloof Street range

★★★★ **Swartland Rouge 13** a shiraz-led blend, with carignan & a splash each of cinsaut, mourvèdre & grenache. Well crafted, bright & sappy, younger accessible than the other reds.

★★★★ **Old Vine Chenin Blanc 14** from two old (35 & 39 years) Perdeberg vineyards, returns to form after **13** (★★★★). Initially closed, decanting rewards with rich & focused fruit. Elegant & finely woven, with pervasive lemony freshness. — MW

Location: Riebeek-Kasteel ▪ Map/WO: Swartland ▪ Est 2007 ▪ 1stB 2008 ▪ Tasting, sales & tours by appt ▪ Owner(s) Mullineux & Leeu Family Wines (Pty) Ltd ▪ Cellarmaster(s) Chris & Andrea Mullineux (May 2007) ▪ Winemaker(s) Andrea Mullineux (May 2007), with Tremayne Smith ▪ Viticulturist(s) Chris Mullineux (May 2007), with Rosa Kruger ▪ 28ha (carignan, cinsaut, mourv, shiraz, chenin, clairette, viog) ▪ 160t/16,000cs own label 58% red 40% white 2% dessert ▪ PO Box 369 Riebeek-Kasteel 7307 ▪ info@mlfwines.com ▪ www.mullineuxwines.com ▪ S 33° 22' 34.13" E 018°50' 23.74" ▪ F +27 (0)86-720-1541 ▪ **T +27 (0)22-448-1183**

Muratie Wine Estate

Visiting Stellenbosch family farm Muratie is like stepping back into history, from the gnarled oaks to the cobwebbed tasting room and old tartrate-encrusted fermenters, where lunches are held. History is also commemorated in the naming of the wines, all the important figures are there, with their colourful stories on the back labels. But, as evidenced by the ratings below, there's nothing old-fashioned about the viticulture, winemaking practices or equipment (a state-of-the-art crusher inaugurated recently), or the quality of the terroir-focused wines, now made by Hattingh de Villiers after the untimely passing of Francois Conradie in January 2014.

Premium range

★★★★ **Martin Melck Cabernet Sauvignon** Blackcurrants, black plums & fruitcake richness greet you, deep & luscious, **11**'s spicing continuing into the flavours. Styling is bold, hedonistic, befitting a big personality.

★★★★ **George Paul Canitz Pinot Noir** Ripeness shows in **12**'s cherry, plummy fruit without compromising the structure. Remains sleek, streamlined, finishing savoury-dry. Drink now & for 5+ years.

★★★★☆ **Ronnie Melck Shiraz** Honours family patriarch & industry luminary who loved shiraz. Usual bold styling in **11**, rich & deep, creamy plums with an array of spices, scrub, a touch of well-cured venison. Succulent, smooth-textured but there's underlying power.

★★★★☆ **Ansela van de Caab** Cab-led Bordeaux blend generously oaked because **11**'s fruit richness accepts it. Opulent dark plums, berries, a savoury almost peppery seam of spice, yet enough succulence to give current drinking pleasure. Very good ageing potential.

★★★★ **Isabella Chardonnay** ⓧ Boldly styled **12** has perfumed richness, tropical fruit, but the palate's savoury, nutty tones confirm pleasurable food compatibility.

★★★★ **Laurens Campher** ⊘ Chenin-led oaked blend, dried peach & beeswax in **13** (★★★★☆), as if tapping into artisanal winemaking; wonderfully nutty flavours, silky, long & savoury, better than **12**. So interesting, sip it & let your thoughts take flight.

★★★★ **Lady Alice Méthode Cap Classique** Different character in **11** bubbly, attractively so. Almost meaty perfume from 85% pinot noir (rest chardonnay), burnt match top note, then citrus kicks in on the palate. Fresh & vibrant. Simonsberg—Stellenbosch WO.

Also tasted: **Alberta Annemarie Merlot 11** ★★★☆

Fortified Wines

★★★★☆ **Amber Forever** Fortified dessert from muscat d'Alexandrie. Wonderful floral & fruit styling in **13**, jasmine scented, grape/fresh pear & apricot flavours, all seamed with ginger, adding an exotic note. Richly sweet & distinctive, irresistible. WO W Cape.

★★★★ **Cape Ruby** ⓧ Deep rich fruitcake & brandy, this port-style **NV**'s perfume is seductive & the flavours don't disappoint either. Nutty, a savoury underpin, finishes with enlivening alcohol grip.

★★★★ **Ben Prins Cape Vintage** Richer than **09**, opulent fruitcake-styled **10**'s (★★★★★) oak & spirit perfectly judged, adding structure, spice, livening grip to the sweetness. Portuguese varieties. WO Simonsberg—Stellenbosch.

Melck's range

Blended Red ★★★ Was 'Shiraz-Cabernet Sauvignon'. Those varieties joined by merlot in **13**, but the styling remains unchanged, juicy plums, touch of oak, ripe & appealing. Also tasted: **Cabernet Franc Rosé 14** ★★ **Sauvignon Blanc 14** ★★★ WO W Cape for this range. — CR

Location/map: Stellenbosch ▪ WO: Stellenbosch/Western Cape/Simonsberg–Stellenbosch ▪ Est 1685 ▪ 1stB ca 1920 ▪ Tasting & sales daily 10–5 ▪ Fee R30/5 wines R50/chocolate pairing experience ▪ Closed Good Fri, Dec 25 & Jan 1 ▪ Cellar tours by appt ▪ Farm Kitchen Wed-Sun 12-3 ▪ Cheese platters ▪ Function venue ▪ Art gallery/exhibition ▪ Guest cottage ▪ Harvest festival ▪ Live music ▪ Mountain biking ▪ Owner(s) Melck Family Trust ▪ Winemaker(s) Hattingh de Villiers (Jul 2014) ▪ Viticulturist(s) Paul Wallace ▪ 110ha/42ha (cab, merlot, p verdot, pinot, shiraz, chard, hanepoot, port) ▪ 300t/ 40,000cs own label 60% red 14% white 6% rosé 20% other ▪ BWI, IPW ▪ PO Box 133 Koelenhof 7605 ▪ info@muratie.co. za ▪ www.muratie.co.za ▪ S 33° 52' 14.8" E 018° 52' 35.1" ▪ F +27 (0)21-865-2790 ▪ **T +27 (0)21-865-2330/2336**

Mvemve Raats ⓧ

Accolades and international honours continue to fall the way of this collaboration of two good friends. Mzokhona Mvemve and Bruwer Raats (of Raats Family Wines) source the grapes for their wine from carefully selected Stellenbosch vineyards and each variety is vinified separately before the all-important blending begins. Quality is paramount and vintages may be skipped (as happened in 2010) if the wine isn't up to the stellar standards of their 'blend of stars'.

★★★★☆ **MR de Compostella** Masterly **12** maintains recent form in 5-way cab franc-dominated (just) Bordeaux blend. Waves of black fruit, soft cedar & perfumed spice, velvety tannins, polish, vanilla – all with wonderful texture & length at the finish. Benchmark Cape wine. — CM

Location/map/WO: Stellenbosch ▪ Est/1stB 2004 ▪ Tasting & sales by appt ▪ Closed all pub hols ▪ Owner(s) Bruwer Raats & Mzokhona Mvemve ▪ Cellarmaster(s)/viticulturist(s) Bruwer Raats & Mzokhona Mvemve (both Jan 2004) ▪ Winemaker(s) Bruwer Raats & Mzokhona Mvemve (both Jan 2004), with Gavin Bruwer Slabbert (Feb 2010) ▪ (cabs s/f, malbec, merlot, p verdot) ▪ 10t/900cs own label 100% red ▪ PO Box 2068 Dennesig Stellenbosch 7601 ▪ braats@mweb. co.za ▪ www.raats.co.za ▪ S 33° 58' 16.6" E 018° 44' 55.3" ▪ F +27 (0)86-647-8500 ▪ **T +27 (0)21-881-3078**

For more information, visit wineonaplatter.com

MVH Signature Wines

The name behind the initials of this new boutique venture is Matthew van Heerden, who fans will recognise from memorable bottlings at Helderberg wineries Uva Mira and latterly Webersburg. Specialising in pinot noir and chardonnay, Matthew is fully behind the new impetus in SA winemaking: 'Small barrel-lot production, native yeast fermentation and minimal intervention allow my wines to express specific grape characteristics and provide a quality framework for each of them.'

Location: Stellenbosch ▪ Est/1stB 2013 ▪ Tasting & sales at Webersburg (see entry) ▪ Owner(s) Matthew van Heerden ▪ Winemaker(s)/viticulturist(s) Matthew van Heerden (Jan 2013) ▪ 5t/400cs own label 50% red 50% white ▪ IPW ▪ PO Box 3428 Somerset West 7129 ▪ mvhwines@gmail.com ▪ F +27 90)21-881-3217 ▪ **T +27 (0)21-881-3636/ +27 (0)82-520-9338**

☐ **Mwitu** see Jacques Germanier
☐ **My Best Friend** see Zandvliet Wine Estate & Thoroughbred Stud

My Wyn

My Wyn ('My Wine') is the brand of boutique vintner Jacoline Haasbroek, who vinifies in a tiny, hospitable Franschhoek mountainside cellar. ('Handy, helpful' husband Johan advises other growers.) She hopes lucky number five (turning 50 in 2015, her 15th harvest) keeps her firing on all cylinders (late bottling sometimes precludes submissions, including a new MCC bubbly, for this guide).

Location/map: Franschhoek ▪ Est/1stB 2001 ▪ Tasting, sales & cellar tours Mon-Fri 10-1 Oct-Apr; after hours, weekends & pub hols by appt or as indicated on the gate ▪ Fee R50pp, waived on purchase ▪ Sunset MCC tastings on koppie (15min walk, weather permitting) by appt only ▪ Cheese platters by prior booking ▪ Owner(s) Jacoline Haasbroek ▪ Winemaker(s) Jacoline Haasbroek (2001) ▪ 1,250cs own label 40% red 20% white 20% port 20% MCC ▪ IPW ▪ PO Box 112 Franschhoek 7690 ▪ tastewine@telkomsa.net ▪ www.mywynfranschhoek.co.za ▪ S 33° 53' 29.3" E 019° 8' 3.6" ▪ F +27 (0)86-608-0233 ▪ **T +27 (0)21-876-2518/+27 (0)83-302-5556**

☐ **Mzansi** see Kingsriver Estate
☐ **Mzanzi's** see Goedverwacht Wine Estate

Mzoli's Wines

The shisa nyama ('buy and barbecue') offered at Mzoli's Place in Cape Town's Gugulethu has become a must-see attraction for tourists and locals alike, often featured in guide books, websites and travel shows. The man behind it is Mzoli Ngcawuzele, also co-founder of the Gugulethu Wine Festival, whose own wines are geared at unpretentious enjoyment.

Madala ⓐ ★★★☆ 'The Elder' most serious wine in meat-friendly range. Cab & merlot in **11**, layers of black berry, spice & liquorice. Good grip; long, velvety finish. Not retasted: **Mandisi Merlot 11 ★★★ Unathi 09** ★★☆ Not tasted: **One One Five Rosé**. — FM

Location: Cape Town ▪ Map: Cape Peninsula ▪ WO: Darling ▪ Meals & tasting daily 11-8 ▪ Owner(s) Mzoli Ngcawuzele ▪ NY 115 Shop No 3 Gugulethu 7750 ▪ mzoli@darlingwine.co.za ▪ www.mzoliwine.co.za ▪ S 33° 58' 34.9" E 018° 34' 11.1" ▪ **T +27 (0)21-638-1355/+27 (0)82-487-0980**

Nabygelegen Private Cellar

James McKenzie continues to improve facilities on his boutique heritage estate in Wellington, adding a gift shop as well as an increased range of food options for visitors. The Snow Mountain range is proving popular, made from fruit sourced from long-term leased vineyards at high altitude.

Nabygelegen Private Cellar range
★★★★ **Merlot** ⓐ Forthright minty choc chip notes on **12** before sweep of ripe black fruit (plums & cherry yoghurt) heads through to vanilla finish. Well-structured wine, plenty of drinking pleasure.

★★★★☆ **1712** Majestic **11**, first tasted since **07**, merlot-dominated Bordeaux blend starts mint-choc-chip before unfolding into dark berries & cherries, hints of polish & leather. Smooth, silky tannins & back to mint for finish. Very satisfying - cries out for roast lamb!

★★★★ **Scaramanga Red** Thoroughly enjoyable **13** continues good form with black cherry yoghurt flavours offset by masses of spice, perfume & backed by soft tannins. Cab, merlot & malbec with 20% tempranilho.

★★★★ **Scaramanga White** ⑭ Fabulous Cape white blend **14** comes charging out the blocks with lots of fresh & dried apricots, resinous texture, light perfume & spice. Mainly chenin with chardonnay & 10% verdelho, wooded, 30% new American.

Also tasted: **Chenin Blanc 14** ★★★☆ **Lady Anna 14** ★★★ Not retasted: **Sauvignon Blanc 13** ★★★

Snow Mountain range

★★★★ **Syrah 13** maintains standards with perfumed nose yielding to peppered meats, intense black fruit, liquorice, juniper berries. WO Coastal, as are all these.

The Mistress ⑭ ★★★ Light & aromatic **13** from unwooded pinot noir made for easy-drinking. Bursts with exotic Indian spice notes - perfect with curry! Also tasted: **Pinot Noir 13** ★★★★ **Chardonnay-Pinot Noir 14** ★★★ Not retasted: **Chardonnay 12** ★★★☆ — CM

Location: Wellington ▪ Map: Paarl & Wellington ▪ WO: Wellington/Coastal/Western Cape ▪ Est 2001 ▪ 1stB 2002 ▪ Tasting, sales & cellar tours Mon-Fri 10-5 Sat 10-1 ▪ Closed all pub hols ▪ Tour groups ▪ Conferences/functions ▪ Small weddings ▪ Walks/hikes ▪ Mountain biking trail ▪ Self-catering luxury accommodation ▪ Owner(s) James McKenzie ▪ Cellarmaster(s) James McKenzie (Jan 2002) ▪ Winemaker(s) Charles Stassen (consultant), with Maria Bosman (Jan 2002) ▪ Viticulturist(s) Johan Wiese (May 2001, consultant) ▪ 35ha/17ha (cab, merlot, p verdot, tempranillo, chenin, sauv) ▪ 180t/24,000cs own label 50% red 50% white ▪ PO Box 302 Wellington 7654 ▪ marketing@nabygelegen.co.za ▪ www.nabygelegen.co.za ▪ S 33° 37' 54.7" E 019° 3' 51.2" ▪ F +27 (0)86-561-7761 ▪ **T +27 (0)21-873-7534**

☐ **Naked Truth** see PicardiRebel

Namaqua Wines

One of SA's largest and most successful wineries, on both local and export fronts, Namaqua operates from two cellars (Vredendal and Spruitdrift) with a host of winemakers under production chief Len Knoetze. Despite doing their bit to popularise wine with the ubiquitous 5L bag-in-box, it's not just about mass production here. After investment in hi-tech winemaking equipment comes the appointment of two additional new viticulturists, to both up across-the-board quality and explore the potential of some of its 200 member-growers' premium West Coast vineyards. This promises exciting developments in their already internationally awarded Winemakers Reserve range.

Spencer Bay Winemakers Reserve range

★★★★ **Cabernet Sauvignon 11** (★★★) more savoury, lacks generosity of **08** & **09**. Firm oak tannins (18 months new) & brisk acidity restrain fruit in youth. Needs time or food. **10** sold out untasted.

★★★★ **Pinotage** After modern, mulberry-centred **10**, **11** (★★★) shows retro stewed fruit & banana; leaner & savoury styling with over-generous acidity.

★★★★ **The Blend** Cassis & firm tannins dictate the styling of the **11** cab-led 5-way Bordeaux blend. Core of dark fruit still tightly coiled though less masked by oak than other reds. Will reward 3-5 years cellaring.

Pinot Noir ⑭ ★★★ Appealing red berry aromas, dry supple tannins, stewed red-fruit palate with smoky overlay. **12** ticks most boxes - just needs bit more complexity. Also tasted: **Shiraz 11** ★★★★

Namaqua range

★★★★ **Noble Late Harvest** ⊘ Returns with a delightfully tangy flourish in **13** (★★★★☆), first since **10**. Old-oak-matured semillon's intense glacé pineapple & lemon flavours infused in a decadently smooth & rich texture. A lingering beauty at a mere 8% alcohol.

★★★★ **Red Muscadel** Sunset orange fortified dessert with spicy choc orange flavours. Oak-aged **13** (★★★) more robust & spirituous than delicately balanced previous **NV**, still a good winter warmer.

Beach Braai (NEW) ★★ Aptly named **NV** from cab, wearing variety's smiley face: rounded, affable & medium bodied, dry savoury finish. **Pinotage** ⊘ ★★★ Lush plummy flavours boosted by few grams sugar, spicy **11** soft tannins for easy drinkability. **Chenin Blanc** (NEW) ★★ **14** undemanding, light bodied & genial, with crunchy acidity & hint of Golden Delicious apple. **Guinevere Méthode Cap Classique** ★★★ Orange hues on **07** sparkler from 60% pinot noir with chardonnay, fine bubbles, tangy red berry tone. Refreshing aperitif style. **Cape Ruby** (NEW) ★★ **NV** from undisclosed varieties pleasant enough but could do with more of Ruby-style port's ripe fruit, warmth & generosity. Also tasted: **Cabernet Sauvignon 12** ★★★ **Merlot** ⊘ **12** ★★★ **Shiraz 12** ★★ **Sauvignon Blanc 14** ★★ **Sauvignon Blanc-Semillon 14** ★★★ **Chenin Blanc-Sauvignon Blanc 14** ★★☆ **White Muscadel 12** ★★★☆ **Hanepoot Jerepigo NV** ★★★

Cellar Door range

Pinotage (NEW) ★★★ **12** loads of banana, spicy plummy fruit & mocha nuance, dry cinnamon-dusted tannins. Bright, pleasant everyday red. **Pinotage-Malbec** (NEW) ★★☆ Unusual blend in **11** is earthy, dark fruited, with dry tannins & frisky acid needing time to integrate.

Gôiya range

Sauvignon Blanc-Chardonnay ★★★ Enduring entry-level brand; first tasted since **07**, **14** 50/50 will appeal widely: creamy, rounded & plumped by touch sugar, has drinkability in its DNA. — MW

Location: Vredendal ▪ Map: Olifants River ▪ WO: Olifants River/Western Cape ▪ Est/1stB 2002 ▪ Tasting & sales Mon-Fri 8–5 Sat 9–3 ▪ Closed Easter Fri-Mon, Ascension day & Dec 25/26 ▪ Cellar tours Mon-Fri 10 & 3, book ahead ▪ Die Keldery Restaurant T +27 (0)27-213-3699/8 Mon-Fri 8-5 & dinner Thu-Fri 7-10 Sat 9-3 Sun buffet 11-3 booking required ▪ Facilities for children ▪ Conferences ▪ Owner(s) 200 members ▪ Production manager Len Knoetze ▪ Winemaker(s) Driaan van der Merwe, Dewald Huisamen, Alwyn Maass, Roelf Retief, Koos Thiart, Johan Weideman, Reinier van Greunen & Jaco Theron ▪ Viticulturist(s) Stoney Steenkamp, Dirk de Bruyn & Marina Cornellisen ▪ 4,990ha ▪ 113,692t/9.3m cs 20% red 80% white ▪ PO Box 75 Vredendal 8160 ▪ info@namaquawines.com ▪ www. namaquawines.com ▪ S 31° 42' 34.9" E 018° 30' 15.6" ▪ F +27 (0)27-213-3476 ▪ **T +27 (0)27-213-1080**

Napier Winery ⓠ ⑪ ⑩ ⑤

Family-owned Napier Winery in the Groenberg foothills takes its name from Sir George Napier, governor of the Cape Colony, who in 1840 oversaw the naming of the nearby town after the Duke of Wellington, vanquisher of Napoleon. Sir George also gives his name to the potstill brandy debuting this edition, traditionally made from estate chenin vines over 35 years old.

Napier range

★★★★ **Cabernet Sauvignon** Vibrant & focused single-vineyard **12** bursts with ripe blackcurrant fruit, bolstered by liquorice & aromatic oak spices. Elegantly formed, with presence & attitude.

★★★★☆ **Red Medallion 09** cab-led Bordeaux blend shows ripe intensity of top vintage. Finely tuned, noble of stature, with lingering tobacco aromas. Also-tasted **10** follows excellent form in slightly tweaked 5-way blend, possibly even riper than previous.

Not tasted: **St Catherine**, **Greenstone**.

Lion Creek range

Cabernet Sauvignon-Shiraz ⑦ ★★★☆ Plush & juicy **12**, sprinkle of white pepper on ripe red cherry & plum fruit, thickish tannins. Also tasted: **Cabernet Sauvignon 12** ★★★ **Chenin Blanc-Sauvignon Blanc 13** ★★★

Brandy range (NEW)

★★★★ **Sir George Potstill Brandy** From 100% chenin, vibrant gold potstill, matured 5 years. Fresh apple, caramel on nose mingle with dried peach & pear on palate. Well structured, with sweet tobacco edge & lemondrops on finish. Smooth & elegant; appropriately packaged. — WB, GdB

Location: Wellington ▪ Map: Paarl & Wellington ▪ WO: Wellington/Western Cape ▪ Est 1989 ▪ Tasting, sales & cellar tours Mon-Fri 8–5 Sat 10–3 ▪ Fee R15 ▪ Closed Easter Fri-Mon, Dec 25/26 & Jan 1 ▪ Tapas platters, preferably pre-booked ▪ Conferences ▪ Owner(s) Michael & Catherine Loubser ▪ Cellarmaster(s)/winemaker(s)/viticulturist(s) Leon Bester (Apr 2000) ▪ 135ha/±89ha under vine ▪ 70% red 30% white ▪ Other export brand: Sir George ▪ PO Box 638 Wellington 7654 ▪ info@napierwinery.co.za ▪ www.napierwinery.co.za ▪ S 33° 38′ 37.0″ E 019° 2′ 24.8″ ▪ F +27 (0)21-864-2728 ▪ **T +27 (0)21-873-7829**

☐ **Natana** *see* Marianne Wine Estate
☐ **Nativo** *see* Hughes Family Wines

Natte Valleij Wines

Among Stellenbosch's oldest farms, Natte Valleij has been home to the Milner family since the 1960s. Brothers Marcus (also De Meye winemaker) and Alexander (the 'Brit' in Boer & Brit) this year celebrate a decade of handcrafting under the estate and Swallow labels with new open cement fermenters based on a Portuguese design, growing exports to Europe, the first cinsaut off old Darling blocks, and the label's first white wine: 'based on the history of the farm, it is 100% hanepoot'.

Location/map: Stellenbosch ▪ Est 1715 ▪ Tasting, sales & cellar tours Mon-Sat by appt ▪ Closed all pub hols ▪ Facilities for children ▪ Conference/indaba venue ▪ Art gallery & art classes ▪ Artifacts & various paintings ▪ Natte Valleij B&B/self-catering cottages ▪ Owner(s) Milner family ▪ Winemaker(s) Alexander Milner (2005), with Marcus Milner (2010) ▪ 28ha total ▪ 15t/2,000cs own label 100% red ▪ PO Box 4 Klapmuts 7625 ▪ alex@boerandbrit.com ▪ www.nattevalleij.co.za ▪ S 33° 50′ 3.6″ E 018° 52′ 43.2″ ▪ **T +27 (0)21-875-5171**

☐ **Natural Star** *see* Stellar Winery

Naughton's Flight

Francis Naughton worked for many years for SFW (precursor of Distell) following his 'flight' from his native Ireland (he retains plenty of the accent and a bit of the blarney he brought with him). With him from the start has been consultant Ronell Wiid in the cellar, making boutique-scale wines.

Tribua ⓐ ★★★★☆ **09** from shiraz & mourvèdre, viognier. Engaging, ripe flavours: sweet fruit in modestly oaked, dry, firm package. WO Coastal. Not retasted: **Shiraz 08** ★★★★ **Délice 09** ★★★ Not tasted: **Viognier**. — TJ

Location: Constantia ▪ WO: Stellenbosch/Coastal ▪ 1stB 2003 ▪ Closed to public ▪ Owner(s) Francis Naughton ▪ Winemaker(s) Ronell Wiid (consultant) ▪ (carignan, mourv, shiraz, viog) ▪ ±20,000 btls ▪ 25 Willow Rd Constantia 7806 ▪ naughts@mweb.co.za ▪ F +27 (0)21-794-3928 ▪ **T +27 (0)21-794-3928**

☐ **Naughty Girl** *see* Alvi's Drift Private Cellar

Nederburg Wines

Nederburg is the biggest brand of South Africa's biggest producer-wholesaler, Distell, vinifying close to 3 million cases annually. The land of the original Paarl estate was granted in 1791 and named after the then commissioner-general of the Dutch East India Company, and the fine Cape Dutch homestead that is now a central focus of the modern Nederburg (including the setting for its famous annual auction) was built in 1800. Latterly, Nederburg went through a lacklustre spell in the 1990s but subsequent to the appointment of Romanian-born cellarmaster Razvan Macici in 2001, it has enjoyed a major resurgence. For a large-volume winery which emphatically aims to cater for all sectors of the market, the very great number of awards that Nederburg now reaps is quite simply astonishing.

Ingenuity range

★★★★☆ **Red Italian Blend** Was 'Red'. Sangiovese & barbera, & a dollop nebbiolo, **11** does not disappoint. Great aromatic complexity with rich berries, chocolate, nuts & spices on the palate, taut, polished tannins, lingering finish. **12** similar quality & vibrant personality, just younger.

★★★★☆ **Red Spanish Blend** ⒩ Gorgeous local take on tempranillo (85%) & graciano, **12** invites comparison with a vivacious & poised Flamenco dancer. Richly textured red summer berries, supple fine-grained tannins, great freshness to finish. Paarl grapes, combo French & American oak, new, 15 months.

★★★★★ **White Blend** Adds 'Blend' to name. Splendid 8-part sauvignon-led blend which includes aromatic varieties, some oaking. Focused & impressive **13** (★★★★★) offers intense floral & fruity notes, spice & vibrant freshness, depth & impeccable balance. Will age gracefully like **12**.

Heritage Heroes range

★★★★ **The Brew Master** Saluting Nederburg founder Johann Graue, **11** cab-led 4-way Bordeaux blend has captivating blackcurrant ripeness & tobacco, with firm tannin grip & texture. Will cellar well.

★★★★☆ **The Motorcycle Marvel** Enchanting Rhône-style blend from grenache, carignan, shiraz & dollops of mourvèdre & cinsaut gives **11** concentrated earthy hedgerow fruit, black pepper & cloves. Spice & smooth tannins round off this flavour blast.

★★★★ **The Anchorman** Four different fermentation techniques on **13** (★★★★★) up the ante on **12**, capturing chenin's character admirably. Fascinating interplay between focused & pure crunchy apple flavours, creamy vanilla & almond powder; restrained & harmonious.

★★★★ **The Beautiful Lady** From gewürztraminer, semi-sweet **13** (★★★☆) allures with typical rosepetal fragrance but lacks a bit of freshness to balance the sugar. Off the precise mark of **12**. WO Stellenbosch.

★★★★☆ **The Young Airhawk** Bright & sprightly barrel-fermented sauvignon **13** is variety-true, with tightly wound citrus, spicy orchard fruit & creamy flavours. Shows outstanding complexity, depth & clarity. A long lime zest finish.

Manor House range

★★★★ **Cabernet Sauvignon** Sappy ripe blackcurrant & plummy fruit on **12** from Philadelphia, perfect foil for firm tannins, vanilla oaking rounds out long finish. Made to drink on release, & to cellar few years.

★★★★ **Shiraz** Bright scrub & hedgerow fruit mingle with cinnamon & clove spice in **12**, supported by a peppery texture, velvet end. Also-tasted **13** is fresh, perfumed & in the same vein, with vivid fruit flavours, fluid texture. Both from Philadelphia, great promise.

★★★★ **Fairtrade Shiraz-Mourvèdre** Attractive savoury thread in previewed **12**'s dense, sweet earthy red & black berries from mix of Groenekloof barrels: dried herbs, allspice, fynbos. Complexity bodes well for ageing.

★★★★ **Sauvignon Blanc** Tropical fruit with whiffs of greenpepper, fresh thyme, **14** also has lemon appeal; racy & inviting, with a mouthwatering goodbye. WO Coastal.

II Centuries range

★★★★☆ **Cabernet Sauvignon** Premium-priced flagship cab - only 516 cases. Understated, regal **10** (★★★★★) from Paarl deserves 'king cab' epithet. Complex, layered, rich, with intense but not heavy ripe berry flavours. Super oaking & tannin structure, a vibrant lift to the enduring finish. Previously made was **08**.

Private Bin range for Nederburg Auction

★★★★ **Cabernet Sauvignon Private Bin R163** ⊘ Bettering last-tasted **07**, perfumed **10** (★★★★☆) from Paarl shows refinement, soft texture with dark brooding palate full of blackberry & chocolate, fine ripe tannins. Plush & silky, with a unflagging finish. Brilliant with richly sauced lamb.

★★★★ **Merlot Private Bin R181** ⊘ First tasted since **07**, **10** (★★★★★) an excellent expression of the variety. Plump berries, spicecake, concentrated layers of integrated vanilla oak, supple tannins all wrapped in a herbal sheath - harmonious & elegant. Moreish & a joy to drink.

★★★★ **Pinot Noir** (NEW) Full & opulent opaque ruby, foot-stomped & handcrafted **12** entices with classic pinot flavours of ripe strawberry, cherry, savoury mushroom. Elegant and finessed, with an attractive tangy acid. Perfect for duck.

★★★★ **Petit Verdot Private Bin R104** Not seen since **03**, firm & taut **10** is like a racehorse waiting for the start. Mouthcoating tannins balanced by dark chocolate, berry fruit & meaty flavours. Great texture, well judged oaking (24 months). Paarl WO.

★★★★☆ **Pinotage Private Bin R172** ⊘ Alluring & youthful **11** is classy, dense, with a creamy complex core of vanilla-seamed dark fruit, polished elegance. Broad & rich, finishing long with a lingering sweetness. A firm spine from all-new barrels. WO Groenekloof.

★★★★☆ **Shiraz Private Bin R121** ⊘ Rich & dark blackberry fruit, cured meat, leather & coriander lead the way on broad-shouldered **11** from Paarl. Mouthfilling, with savoury, nutty, creamy ending showing a hint of black pepper & smoke. Serious & for the long haul, as was last-tasted **09**.

★★★★☆ **Sauvignon Blanc Private Bin D234** ⊘ With usual Old World refinement, **13** from Darling shows intense & exotic nose of perfumed citrus, basil & wet stone. Brisk, bright mineral acidity, with great depth & breadth from regular lees stirring. Mouthfilling texture, balance & length complete the drama.

★★★★★ **Eminence** ⊘ Gorgeous Natural Sweet from Paarl muscat de Frontignan. Richer of the dessert wines & flamboyantly ripe, **13** (★★★★★) beguiles with usual candied pineapple, apricot, ginger & honeysuckle. Pure, balanced & focused, unctuous but not weighty, unflagging. As silky as was **12**.

★★★★☆ **Edelkeur** ⊘ Noble Late Harvest from unoaked chenin. Packed with melon, apricot fruit & herb-tinged honey, but light-footed thanks to mineral acidity. Extremely long finish on **13**, with great lift & grip, as on **12** (★★★★★). Low alcohol, 375 ml only, like Eminence. Durbanville WO.

Not tasted: **Grenache Private Bin**, **Cabernet Sauvignon-Merlot Private Bin R109**, **Cabernet Sauvignon-Shiraz Private Bin R103**, **Chardonnay Private Bin D270**, **Sauvignon Blanc Private Bin D215**, **Semillon Private Bin D266**, **Viognier Private Bin D212**, **Sauvignon Blanc-Chardonnay Private Bin D253**, **Sauvignon Blanc-Semillon Private Bin D252**, **Gewürztraminer Special Late Harvest Private Bin S354**.

Winemaster's Reserve range

★★★★ **Edelrood (Cabernet Sauvignon-Merlot)** ⊘ Ever-dependable Bordeaux-style red, **12** brims with ripe berry perfume, silk texture, perfectly judged oaking. Over-delivers every time.

★★★★ **Special Late Harvest** Ex-tank **14** from chenin will delight its fans. Sweet & fragrant, with apricot & pineapple flavours, lemon blossom wafts & a tangy farewell. Chill for spicy Cape Malay fare. Coastal WO.

★★★★★ **Noble Late Harvest** ⊘ The only botrytis dessert from Nederburg freely available. **13** (★★★★☆), unwooded chenin (80%) & muscat de Frontignan, satisfies with a mouthful of gingered apricot & honey; steely-tangy & richly aromatic. As great a bargain as **12** was. Coastal WO.

Shiraz ★★★☆ **13** is succulent, spicy-savoury & well-balanced, smooth. Fabulous expression, juicy & rich - just delicious! **Baronne (Cabernet Sauvignon-Shiraz)** ⊘ ★★★★ Longtime friend. Well-matched varieties, **13**'s lush spicy berries are backed by velvety harmonious tannins. Slips down easily. **Chardonnay** ★★★☆ Soft, citrus-fruited **13** is soft, creamy & oh so delicious. Zesty lift to finish. Also tasted: **Cabernet Sauvignon 13** ★★★☆ **Merlot 13** ★★★☆ **Pinotage 13** ★★★☆ **Cabernet Sauvignon Rosé** **Pinot Grigio 14** ★★★☆ **Riesling 14** ★★★ **Sauvignon Blanc 14** ★★★

56Hundred range

Chenin Blanc ★★★ Dry **14** is as ripe, fresh & crunchy as a Granny Smith apple, with friendly 12.5% alcohol. Coastal WO. Also tasted: **Cabernet Sauvignon 13** ★★★

Fair Selection

Cabernet Sauvignon ⓃⒺⓌ ★★★ Sweet, soft, inviting **13**, balanced for easy drinking. Lovely fresh flavours. WO Groenekloof & Fairtrade accredited, as all these. Also tasted: **Pinotage 13** ★★★ Not tasted: **Sauvignon Blanc**.

Foundation Collection

Merlot ★★★ Juicy, fruity **13** is just-dry, sweet-fruited & tasty - perfect for parties. **Duet (Shiraz-Pinotage)** ★★★ With 60% dominance, shiraz rules in **13**. Chocolate-rich dark fruit is tempered by pinotage's fresh juicy texture. Fun in a bottle! **Rosé** ★★☆ Nicely packaged **14** appeals with semi-sweet red berry flavours from the two cabs & merlot. **Stein** ★★★ **14** chenin semi-sweet is pure drinking pleasure: luscious & fresh mouthful from the peach orchard. Made for spicy fare. **Chenin Blanc** ⓃⒺⓌ ★★★ Semi-sweet **14** is kissed by the sun, bursting with ripe orchard fruit flavours, bright acidity & clean finish. **Lyric (Sauvignon Blanc-Chenin Blanc-Chardonnay)** ★★★ Sauvignon leads the **14** blend with herbal tones & just-dry tropical flavours, finishing with a tangy lime twist. Serve well chilled. **Première Cuvée Brut** ★★★ **NV** dry sparkling is frothy & zesty, with citrus & apple flavours. Real party animal. Also tasted: **Cabernet Sauvignon 13** ★★★ **Pinotage 13** ★★★ **Shiraz 13** ★★★ **Shiraz-Viognier 13** ★★★ **Cabernet Sauvignon-Shiraz 12** ★★★ **Chardonnay 14** ★★★ **Sauvignon Blanc 14** ★★★ **Chardonnay-Viognier 14** ★★★ **Sauvignon Blanc-Chardonnay**

Brandy range

★★★★ **Solera Potstilled Brandy** Ⓥ Lightish gold colour good intro to lightly elegant style of this 100% potstill brandy, aged up to 12 years in solera. Smooth, balanced, serene & complete; fine fruity flavours. — WB, TJ

Location: Paarl ▪ Map: Paarl & Wellington ▪ WO: Western Cape/Paarl/Coastal/Groenekloof/Philadelphia/Stellenbosch/Darling/Durbanville ▪ Est 1791 ▪ 1stB ca 1940 ▪ Tasting & sales Mon-Fri 8–5 Sat 10–2 (May-Sep)/10–4 (Oct-Apr) Sun 11–4 (Oct-Apr) ▪ Various tasting fees, waived on purchase of R100+ ▪ Closed Good Fri, Dec 25 & Jan 1 ▪ Cellar tours Mon-Fri 10.30 & 3 Sat 11 Sun 11 (Oct-Apr) ▪ Large groups/foreign language tours by appt only ▪ Visitors' centre: wine tasting, cheese & wine pairing ▪ Historic Manor House (national monument) featuring The Red Table restaurant, open Tue-Sun T +27 (0)21-877-5155 ▪ Tour groups ▪ Gifts ▪ Conferences ▪ Museum ▪ Conservation area ▪ Owner(s) Distell ▪ Cellarmaster(s) Razvan Macici (2001) ▪ Winemaker(s) Wilhelm Pienaar (reds, 2009) & Natasha Williams (whites, 2013), with Samuel Viljoen (reds) ▪ Viticulturist(s) Unathi Mantshongo & Henk van Graan ▪ 1,100ha (cab, carignan, grenache, malbec, merlot, p verdot, ptage, shiraz, tannat, tempranillo, chard, riesling, sauv, sem) ▪ 18,000t/2.8m cs own label ▪ ISO 0001:2008, ISO 14001:2004, BWI, HACCP, IPW, BRC, SGS organic ▪ Private Bag X3006 Paarl 7620 ▪ nedwines@distell.co.za ▪ www.nederburg.co.za ▪ S 33° 43' 15.4" E 019° 0' 9.4" ▪ F +27 (0)21-862-4887 ▪ **T +27 (0)21-862-3104**

Neethlingshof Estate   Ⓥ Ⓨ ⓒ Ⓐ ♿

Colourful characters have shaped the history of this Lusan-owned Stellenbosch estate over past three centuries, including Maria Magdalena Marais, after whom their delectable desert wine is named, and her son-in-law, the dapper Johannes Henoch Neethling, dubbed 'Lord Neethling'. Today the grounds host music concerts during the annual Woordfees cultural festival, the tasting centre offers new tapas, wine and music evenings in summer, the The Lord Neethling restaurant is under new management and, in the cellar, the ever-delightful Gewürztraminer is receiving a packaging facelift.

Short Story Collection

★★★★ **Owl Post Pinotage** Inky colour hints at density (& youth) of **12**, packed with black plums & cherries, soft & ripe but fresh, with oak (65% Hungarian) lending support. Wines all estate-grown.

★★★★☆ **Caracal** 31% malbec adds plenty of stuffing to dark, concentrated **12**; cab-led, so packed with cassis but beautifully cushioned by soft merlot (13%) & enlivened by cab franc. Aged in 65% new oak for 14 months. Elegant with long, fresh finish.

★★★★ **Six Flowers** Floral **13** chardonnay/chenin-led sextet has hints of wild fynbos & dried herbs on the nose, a bouquet indeed. Zesty orange & lime on the palate are rounded out by creamy oak. Deserves more time to bloom.

★★★★☆ **Maria** Among SA's most consistently fine botrytised rieslings. **14** preview promises all the caramelised pineapple tang & crème brûlée unctuousness of its delicious predecessors, with dense raisin sweetness balanced by zesty citrus as well as rapier-like acidity to finish clean & fresh.

Neethlingshof range

★★★★ **Gewürztraminer** ⊘ Mouthwatering acidity makes slightly off-dry **14** seem refreshingly dry, brimming with litchis & infused with ginger. Jasmine nose is beguiling rather than blowsy.

★★★★ **Sauvignon Blanc Single Vineyard** ⓧ **13** exudes sauvignon's vibrant freshness, with clean flinty tone & loads of stonefruit. More intense & structured than sibling, with long mineral finish.

Cabernet Sauvignon ★★★★ **11** is a big step up, with a pleasant minty freshness enlivening dense black berries & plums, while cinnamon & pencil shaving notes linger. Balanced, with firm but ripe tannins. **Shiraz** ★★★★ Opulent **11** has all the concentrated black fruit of previous with added interest of liquorice, coffee grinds & a pinch of pepper on its very long finish. **Chenin Blanc** ★★★★ Enjoyable **14** brims with Golden Delicious apple & yellow pear, ripe fruitiness balanced by citrus acidity with a hint of guava flavour & texture. Also tasted: **Pinotage 13** ★★★ **Cabernet Sauvignon-Merlot 12** ★★★★ **Chardonnay Unwooded 14** ★★★ **Sauvignon Blanc 14** ★★★★ Not retasted: **Malbec 12** ★★★★ **Merlot 12** ★★★ — JG

Location/map/WO: Stellenbosch ▪ Est 1692 ▪ 1stB 1880 ▪ Tasting & sales Mon-Fri 9–5 Sat/Sun 10-4 ▪ Fee R35pp ▪ Closed Good Fri & Dec 25 ▪ Public cellar tours daily at 10; private cellar tours by appt ▪ 'Flash Food & Slow Wine' pairing R65pp - booking recommended for 6+ ▪ Jungle gym ▪ Tour groups ▪ Conferences ▪ Conservation area ▪ Annual music concert in conjunction with Die Woordfees (Mar); Wednesday night live music during summer months ▪ Lord Neethling Restaurant & Palm Terrace ▪ Owner(s) Lusan Premium Wines ▪ Cellarmaster(s) De Wet Viljoen (Jun 2003) ▪ Winemaker(s) Monique Fourie ▪ Viticulturist(s) Hannes van Zyl & Nico Nortje ▪ 273ha/95ha (cabs s/f, malbec, merlot, p verdot, ptage, shiraz, chard, chenin, gewürz, riesling, sauv, viog) ▪ 1,400t/100,000cs own label 55% red 45% white ▪ BWI champion, WIETA ▪ PO Box 104 Stellenbosch 7599 ▪ info@neethlingshof.co.za ▪ www.neethlingshof.co.za ▪ S 33° 56' 28.2" E 018° 48' 6.7" ▪ F +27 (0)21-883-8941 ▪ **T +27 (0)21-883-8988**

Neil Ellis Meyer-Näkel   ⓠ

When reputed Werner Näkel of Weingut Meyer-Näkel in Germany's Ahr Valley visited SA for the first time in the mid-1990s, he was 'captured by the overwhelming beauty' of Stellenbosch and vowed to make wine here. In 1998 he and old friend Neil Ellis launched their flagship Bordeaux blend Zwalu ('New Beginning'), and later a second wine, simply known as Z, most years a varietal cabernet.

★★★★ **Zwalu** Cab dominates on **11**, cab franc adds graceful leafy presence & shiraz supports the sweet berry fruit. Ripe & tasty, already approachable, but firm enough grip for a good few years. Not tasted: **Z**. — TJ

Location: Stellenbosch ▪ WO: Jonkershoek Valley ▪ Est/1stB 1998 ▪ Tasting & sales at Neil Ellis Wines (see entry) ▪ Owner(s) Neil Ellis Meyer-Näkel (Pty) Ltd ▪ Winemaker(s) Werner Näkel & Warren Ellis (2006) ▪ Viticulturist(s) Pieter Smit & Warren Ellis ▪ 7,000cs own label 100% red ▪ PO Box 917 Stellenbosch 7599 ▪ tasting@neilellis.com ▪ www. neilellis.com ▪ F +27 (0)21-887-0647 ▪ **T +27 (0)21-887-0649**

Neil Ellis Wines

To celebrate his 40th year in winemaking (having earned his spurs at KWV, Groot Constantia and Zevenwacht), and his 30th year flying 'solo' at what is now a highly reputed family business, unassuming yet enormously influential industry doyen Neil Ellis moved the remaining production facilities from Stellenbosch's Jonkershoek Valley to the newer premises on Helshoogte Pass nearby. 'As of 2015, all winemaking, tasting and administration are under one roof,' says daughter and brand manager Margot Ellis, whose brother Warren has quickly made a name for himself since taking over wine and vine responsibilities while his father focuses more on strategy and tactical decision making. Their vision today is pretty much the same as 30 years ago: 'To make distinctive, refined wines that are expressive of their terroir and rank amongst South Africa's finest.'

For more information, visit wineonaplatter.com

Vineyard Selection

★★★★☆ **Cabernet Sauvignon 11** shows its beautifully handled all-new oak maturation, but the 5-10 years in bottle it deserves should resolve that. Altogether impressive, from the rich fruit aromas & flavours to the genuinely dry finish. From Jonkershoek Valley, like fine **10** (★★★★★).

★★★★☆ **Grenache** ⓥ Fragrant & expressive **11** from low-yield old Piekenierskloof vines. Composed yet intense, shows real presence. Lovely fruit purity & a silky & seamless structure. One to savour over 5+ years.

★★★★ **Pinotage** Ripe, pure-fruited **12** ex Jonkershoek shows friendly plushness now, but there's a good future ahead. Tannins a little austere, almost at odds with the sweet fruit (but bone-dry).

★★★★☆ **Rodanos** Shiraz (80%, Groenekloof) & grenache (Piekenierskloof). **10** (★★★☆) impresses less than complex **09**. Might develop, but in youth it shows modest fruit & little focus, with the oak rather obvious.

★★★★ **Amica** Fresh **13** from sauvignon, 33% semillon. Neither dominant, but oak shows though none new used - mostly natural ferment in older barrels. Silky & gentle. Needs year/2 to harmonise. WO Coastal.

Not tasted: **Syrah**.

Premium range

★★★★ **Cabernet Sauvignon** Fresh, darkly bright fruit on **12**, supported by clever oaking. Balanced, firm, savoury, juicy - not demanding, but serious enough; good now, should develop. WO Stellenbosch, as next.

★★★★ **Cabernet Sauvignon-Merlot 12** - the cab franc a small minority - has clean, delicious fruit flavours, unobscured by masterly oaking, discreet tannins. No great depth, but most drinkable.

★★★★☆ **Aenigma Red** Pleasing, charmingly perfumed **12** (★★★☆), mainly Stellenbosch shiraz & cab as was **11** - but this perhaps more simple, weak-centred. Decent grip; very drinkable.

★★★★☆ **Stellenbosch Chardonnay** ⊘ Mostly barrel ferment, some natural yeast, on expressive but unshowy **13**. The oaking is subtle & supportive of the fruit, combining to give citrus, nut & oatmeal notes. With a quiet intensity of flavour, restrained & elegant, & a lingering finish.

Also tasted: **Shiraz 12 ★★★ Aenigma White 13 ★★★** Not tasted: **Pinotage**, **Groenekloof Sauvignon Blanc**. — TJ

Location/map: Stellenbosch ▪ WO: Western Cape/Stellenbosch/Jonkershoek Valley/Groenekloof/Piekenierskloof/Coastal ▪ Est 1986 ▪ 1stB 1984 ▪ Tasting & sales Mon-Fri 9.30-4.30 Sat/pub hols 10–5 ▪ Fee R25 premium range/R35 vineyard selection range ▪ Closed Good Fri, Dec 25/26 & Jan 1 ▪ Antipasto platters ▪ Tour groups ▪ Owner(s) Neil Ellis Wines (Pty) Ltd ▪ Winemaker(s)/viticulturist(s) Warren Ellis (2006) ▪ 100,000cs own label 50% red 50% white ▪ Brands for clients: Woolworths ▪ WIETA ▪ PO Box 917 Stellenbosch 7599 ▪ info@neilellis.com ▪ www.neilellis.com ▪ S 33° 55' 34.92" E 018° 53' 32.46" ▪ F +27 (0)21-887-0647 ▪ **T +27 (0)21-887-0649**

Nelson Family Vineyards

The Nelson family's peaceful Paarl property plays host to many a perfect wedding as well providing the venue for a wide variety of other events. Wine-wise, daughter and winemaker Lisha continues to craft the wines, currently enjoying success overseas, particularly in the UK.

Lisha Nelson Signature Wines

★★★★☆ **Cabernet Franc** ⓥ Pungent varietal aromas on **10** before generous mouthful of intense fruit. Mid-2013 still-taut tannins & new French oak needed time to settle.

★★★★ **Dad's Blend** ⓥ Cab franc-dominated **09** Bordeaux blend with tomato leaf giving way to blackcurrants, capsicum, hint of coffee.

Nelson Estate range

Rosé ★★★ Fresh & fruity **14** pitches strawberries & candyfloss against lively acidity for balanced dry quaffing. Not retasted: **Shiraz 08** ★★★★ **Cabernet Sauvignon-Merlot 08** ★★★★ **Sauvignon Blanc 13** ★★★ Not tasted: **Chardonnay**.

Nelson's Creek range

Chenin Blanc ★★★ Candied oranges & perfume give way to peardrops & fruit salad in lightish, easy-drinking **14**. Also tasted: **Pinotage Rosé 14** ★★★ Not retasted: **Shiraz 11** ★★★★ — CM

Location: Paarl ▪ Map: Paarl & Wellington ▪ WO: Paarl/Western Cape ▪ Tasting, sales & cellar tours by appt only ▪ Closed all pub hols ▪ Facilities for children ▪ Tour groups ▪ Conferences ▪ Weddings ▪ Walks/hikes ▪ Mountain biking trails ▪ Guest accommodation ▪ Owner(s) Alan Nelson ▪ Cellarmaster(s) Lisha Nelson (Nov 2007) ▪ Winemaker(s) Lisha Nelson (Nov 2007), with Solly Hendriks (Apr 2011) ▪ Viticulturist(s) Petrus de Villiers ▪ 142ha/46ha (cabs s/f, merlot, p verdot, ptage, shiraz, chard, chenin, sauv, sem) ▪ 210t/9,340cs own label 30% red 60% white 10% rosé ▪ IPW ▪ PO Box 2009 Windmeul 7630 ▪ lisha@nelsonscreek.co.za ▪ www.nelsonscreek.co.za ▪ S 33° 39′ 31.2″ E 018° 56′ 17.3″ ▪ F +27 (0)21-869-8424 ▪ **T +27 (0)21-869-8453**

New Beginnings Wines

This small cooperative belongs to empowered vineyard staff, nurtured by exporters FMS Food & Beverages. A revival of a dormant label (though new to the guide) is blended range Skipper's, which so impressed its Japanese prospects, a tentative order was promptly doubled. A Dry White will join this line-up, a Merlot will be delivered into the Family Collection, and a Renaissance Collection will form the top tier. Exotic but lively is the Côte d'Ivoire market, now graced by private label OloPam.

Family Collection

Pinotage ★★★ Cheery raspberry appeal to easy, light & sweet-fruited **12** from Darling. **Chardonnay** ★★★ Broad marmalade interest to structured yet fresh **13** off Klein Karoo vines. Also tasted: **Chenin Blanc 13** ★★★ Not retasted: **Cabernet Sauvignon 10** ★★★ Not tasted: **Shiraz, Pinotage Rosé, Shiraz Rosé**.

Skipper's Collection (NEW)

Classic Dry Red ★★★ Light-bodied **10** from Darling has blueberry tang & succulence on defined frame. — FM

Location: Cape Town ▪ Map: Cape Peninsula ▪ WO: Darling/Stellenbosch/Paarl/Klein Karoo ▪ Est 1996 ▪ 1stB 1999 ▪ Tasting by appt only ▪ Owner(s) Klein Begin Farming Association ▪ Brand manager FMS Food & Beverages SA cc ▪ 13ha/10ha (cab, ptage, shiraz, chard, chenin) ▪ 20,000cs own label 70% red 25% white 5% rosé ▪ Unit 6, Tafelberg Hof, Upper Wandel Street, Gardens, Cape Town 8001 ▪ info@fms-wine-marketing.co.za ▪ www.fms-wine-marketing.co.za ▪ S 33° 55′ 58.08″ E 018° 24′ 47.16″ ▪ F +27 (0)21-413-0825 ▪ **T +27 (0)21-426-5037**

☐ **New Cape Wines** *see* Eagle's Cliff Wines-New Cape Wines
☐ **New Gate** *see* Ernst Gouws & Co Wines

Newstead Lund Family Vineyards

Ex-international polo player Doug Lund and wife Sue were among the pioneers of the Plettenberg Bay wine district when they first planted vines in 2006. New Zealand was their inspiration to make wine and choose sauvignon, chardonnay and pinot noir, there being significant similarities in geography and climate. Vinification of the much-pampered grapes is by local go-to vini man Anton Smal.

★★★★ **Méthode Cap Classique Brut** (NEW) **12** dry sparkling from chardonnay shows fresh limes & red apples with hints of smoke. Fruit forward & crisp, great balance. Superb first effort!

Chardonnay ★★★ **13** fruity & fresh, gets extra weight, breadth from 4 months lees-ageing & small wooded portion. Now bottled, shows property's smoked salt notes. **Sauvignon Blanc** ★★★★ **13**, retasted as bottled wine, less green fruit, more seashell minerality, smoke & peat. Palate still understated, lean & zippy, as befits cool coastal origin. — HJ

Location/WO: Plettenberg Bay ▪ Map: Klein Karoo & Garden Route ▪ Est 2008 ▪ 1stB 2012 ▪ Tasting & sales Tue-Sat 11-3.30
▪ Closed Dec 25 ▪ Cellar tours by appt only ▪ Farm to fork lunches, booking required ▪ Tour groups ▪ Gift shop ▪ Farm produce
▪ Walks ▪ Mountain biking/guided cycle tours ▪ Owner(s) Doug & Sue Lund ▪ Cellarmaster(s)/winemaker(s) Anton Smal
(Jan 2011, consultant) ▪ Viticulturist(s) Doug Lund & Gift Lwazi ▪ 11ha/5ha (pinot, chard, sauv) ▪ 24t/4,500cs own label
white & MCC ▪ PO Box 295 The Crags 6602 ▪ info@newsteadwines.com ▪ www.newsteadwines.com ▪ S 33° 57' 7.24" E
023° 28' 18.66" ▪ **T +27 (0)44-534-8387 (office)/+27 (0)84-586-1600/+27 (0)83-616-0010**

Newton Johnson Vineyards

Dave Johnson and wife Felicity (née Newton) founded this estate in the Hemel-en-Aarde area in the mid-1990s, when only the earliest pioneers were already here. Two generations are now fully involved (and the next one no doubt learning) making this a quintessential family operation. Thoughtful, intelligent work in the expanding vineyards and winery (where natural processes rule: gravity rather than mechanical pumping, no yeast inoculation, for example) have brought an ever-growing reputation for quality. While other varieties are far from neglected, as the ratings below reveal, a particular passion for pinot noir prompted small bottlings of the three single-vineyard wines going into the Family Vineyards blend — giving 'a sense of place and perspective to the variations in the granitic soils of our vineyards'.

Family Vineyards range

★★★★★ **Pinot Noir** As with **12** & **11**, **13** combines fruit from estate's best sites into a stunning whole. As before, a triumph of subtle insistence, pure fruit integrated with succulent acidity, understated tannins & sensitive oaking in an elegant composition. With a power that belies its demure demeanour.

★★★★☆ **Granum** Ⓝ Scintillating debut **12** shows this cellar equally adept with Rhône & Burgundy varieties. Shiraz with 12% mourvèdre, year in barrel, 21% new; fine expression of violets & forest floor fruit characters in deft, elegant composition, with brilliant balance, echoing length of flavour.

★★★★☆ **Chardonnay** Exquisitely textured **13**, interleaving crisp citrus fruit, wood spice, acid & stern minerality with poise, aplomb. Fun candyfloss fillip on tail. Thrilling follow-up to subtly assertive **12** (★★★★★).

Newton Johnson range

★★★★☆ **Block 6 Pinot Noir** The factotum of the single-vineyard trio, from the estate's oldest pinot block in clay soil; the NJ family's favourite component of the blended (W Bay) wine. **13** both perfumed & dark fruited, supple, smooth & silky, with more gravitas than Mrs M but less persistence & intensity than Windansea.

★★★★☆ **Mrs. M Pinot Noir** From a free-draining vineyard without clay, dedicated to the late Moya McDowall. **13** light on its feet, pretty rather than punchy, still serious. Like all these pinots, fermented with natural yeast; year in oak, 20-35% new. Moderate 12.8% alcohol, as for Block 6.

★★★★★ **Windansea Pinot Noir** Rich, fragrant & warmly sensuous if grapes grown in shallow clay soil not picked too ripe - happily the case in well-judged **13** (★★★★★), most structured of the single-vineyard bottlings (a notably succulent mineral acidity), with a bigger 13.9% alcohol. **12** was our Red Wine of the Year last time.

★★★★ **Walker Bay Pinot Noir** Ⓥ Mostly off younger vines & flatter slopes, but **12** very attractive. Fresh clean aromas of berries, tinged with earthiness. Gentle balance, with bright acidity & understated tannins.

★★★★ **Full Stop Rock** Suave **11** from shiraz/syrah with dollops mourvèdre & grenache. Less generous than cellar siblings but has a lean, muscled elegance, finishes dry. Mostly seasoned oak. WO Walker Bay.

★★★★ **Southend Chardonnay** Butterscotch & peanut brittle aromas herald **13** from neighbour farm's grapes. Full & broad, brash even, a praise singer for more regal Family Vineyards offering.

For more information, visit wineonaplatter.com

★★★★ **Sauvignon Blanc** Emphatic **14**'s grassier edges smoothed by smidgeon oaked semillon; myriad flavour components in precise balance. Elgin grapes with 38% from home vineyards.

★★★★☆ **Resonance** 23% wood-matured Elgin semillon with own sauvignon; complex, reverberating flavours including blackcurrant in a waxy, earthy, lightly tannic grip. Brush of botrytis adds a honeyed patina. **13** exceptional, as was **12**. WO Cape South Coast. — DS

Location: Hermanus ▪ Map: Elgin, Walker Bay & Bot River ▪ WO: Upper Hemel-en-Aarde Valley/Walker Bay/Cape South Coast ▪ Est 1996 ▪ 1stB 1997 ▪ Tasting & sales Mon-Fri 9—4 Sat 10—2 ▪ Closed all pub hols ▪ 'Restaurant @ Newton Johnson': lunch 12-3 Wed-Sun (Apr-Nov)/Tue-Sun (Dec-Mar) & dinner Fri-Sat 6-9 ▪ Owner(s) Newton Johnson family ▪ Cellarmaster(s) Gordon Newton Johnson (Jan 2001) ▪ Winemaker(s) Gordon Newton Johnson (Jan 2001) & Nadia Newton Johnson (Aug 2006) ▪ Viticulturist(s) Dean Leppan (Sep 2010) ▪ 140ha/18ha (grenache, mourv, pinot, shiraz, chard, sauv) ▪ 240t/20,000cs own label 50% red 50% white ▪ PO Box 225 Hermanus 7200 ▪ wine@newtonjohnson.com ▪ www. newtonjohnson.com ▪ S 34° 22' 9.7" E 019° 15' 33.3" ▪ F +27 (0)86-638-9673 ▪ **T +27 (0)28-312-3862**

☐ **New World Collection** see Zidela Wines

Nicholson Smith

No longer is Nicholson Smith merely the Gauteng and Mpumalanga agent for Nabygelegen. Owner Jason Neal has teamed up with the Wellington estate's owner/cellarmaster, James McKenzie, to come up with this eponymous range of easily accessible wines, showing 'great body, great fruit'.

Pandora's Box range
The Persian Connection Shiraz ⊘ ★★☆ Spice, red fruit, crisp acidity abound in early-drinking **NV**, firm enough for food. **The Gooseberry Sauvignon Blanc** ★★ Faint candy store aromas, soft acidity for casual quaffing; **NV** refreshing grassy tones, grapefruit flavours up the appeal. Also tasted: **The Black Bird Merlot NV** ★★ **Lock 1855 Merlot-Cabernet Sauvignon** ⊘ **NV** ★★☆

Bella Vino range
Sultry Red ★★ **NV** blend of merlot (87%), petit verdot with dark berry & choc appeal, enough grip for the BBQ but also good solo quaffing. Also tasted: **Sublime White NV** ★★ — WB, CvZ

Location: Johannesburg ▪ WO: Western Cape ▪ Est 1997 ▪ 1stB 2012 ▪ Closed to public ▪ Owner(s) Jason Neal ▪ Winemaker(s)/viticulturist(s) James McKenzie (2012) ▪ 40,000cs own label 70% red 20% white 10% other ▪ PO Box 1659 Jukskei Park 2153 ▪ jason@nicholsonsmith.co.za ▪ www.nicholsonsmith.co.za ▪ F +27 (0)11-496-2952 ▪ **T +27 (0)11-496-2947**

Nick & Forti's Wines

Started just over ten years ago as a celebration of 'life, friendship and superb wine', the venture between restaurateur Fortunato 'Forti' Mazzone and Saronsberg winery owner Nick van Huyssteen continues to flourish. The range, made by Dewaldt Heyns at Saronsberg, is available at the winery and Forti's Pretoria restaurant, Ritrovo, his stores and the selected outlets and restaurants he supplies.

★★★★ **Shiraz** Complexity sets **12** apart from **11** (★★★★). Juicy yet gentle black berry & layered liquorice depth. Lean & lithe with muscle & leashed power. Long aftertaste.

★★★★ **Viognier** ⓥ Peach pip & shortbread, rich consistency & resonating savoury length on **09**. Rung up on **08** (★★★★☆), with peach & pine nut opulence.

Epicentre ★★★★ Elegantly constructed Bordeaux quintet with cab leading in **12**. Toned, ripe cassis & spice make it ultra food friendly. — FM

Location: Tulbagh/Pretoria ▪ WO: Coastal ▪ Est/1stB 2004 ▪ Tasting at Saronsberg Cellar (see entry) ▪ Owner(s) Fortunato Mazzone & Saronsberg ▪ Winemaker(s) Dewaldt Heyns (2004) ▪ 4,000cs own label 85% red 15% white ▪ Box 25032 Monument Park Pretoria 0105 ▪ ritrovo@mweb.co.za ▪ www.saronsberg.com ▪ F +27 (0)12-460-5173 ▪ **T +27 (0)12-460-4367**

Nico van der Merwe Wines

Nico van der Merwe, longtime cellarmaster at Saxenburg, has produced his own premium wines since 1999, and the past few years have seen his ambition of owning his own cellar slowly come together. The tiny Mas Nicolas spread on Stellenbosch's Polkadraai Hills is up and running, and receiving visitors by appointment. Its affable owner's winemaking philosophy is based on traditional methods, hands-on involvement - and an aversion to screwcaps. A spell of ill health last year caused him to 'stand still,' but at press time he was mobile again and anticipating to be up to speed soon.

Flagship range

★★★★☆ Mas Nicolas Cape Cab & shiraz (50/50) from same vineyards since maiden **99**. Elegant anniversary **09** has intriguing nose of florals, dark berries & earth. Understated layers of intense black fruit, plum, savoury coriander-spiced meat & oak flavours add to great depth.

Nicolas van der Merwe range

★★★★☆ Syrah ② Big, muscular (15.5% alcohol) **07** set new standard for label previously. Larger-than-life fruit demanded attention, needed time - contrast with open-textured **06** (**★★★★☆**).

★★★★☆ Red Voluptuous merlot-led Bordeaux-style **09** radiates pure red berry, graphite & spice. Elegant, mouthfilling, intense fruit concentration & super balance. Finishes with a lovely vanilla spice grip from year oaking.

★★★★ White ⊘ **13** (**★★★★★**) ups ante on **12**, with bright aromas of green apple, dusty lemon & lime, from near-equal sauvignon (Stellenbosch) & barrel-fermented semillon (Darling). Displays vibrancy & fine minerality. Made for ageing.

★★★★ Méthode Cap Classique Brut NV (10) sparkling from chardonnay oozes personality with tiny, lazy, pearly bubbles, crunchy green apple, lemon curd & creamy yeast flavours rounding out the palate. More presence, interest than last-tasted **08** (**★★★★**).

Robert Alexander range

★★★★ Shiraz Savoury **13** shows complexity in ripe black fruit, fynbos, dried herbs, cured meat, along with richness & depth; good balance & length. Super value too - stock up! No **10-12**.
Also tasted: **Merlot 13 ★★★★**

Cape Elements range

Cape Elements ★★★★ Was 'Shiraz-Cinsaut-Grenache' which still the blend in **11**. Fresh, juicy & bright, with dark berry & spice flavours, great depth. Delightful all-year appeal. WO W Cape. — WB

Location/map: Stellenbosch ▪ WO: Stellenbosch/Western Cape ▪ Est/1stB 1999 ▪ Tasting & sales by appt only ▪ Owner(s) Nico & Petra van der Merwe ▪ Cellarmaster(s)/winemaker(s) Nico van der Merwe ▪ 50t/4,000cs own label 80% red 20% white ▪ PO Box 12200 Stellenbosch 7613 ▪ nvdmwines@vodamail.co.za ▪ S 33° 57' 48.2" E 018° 43' 51.8" ▪ F +27 (0)21-881-3063 ▪ T +27 (0)21-881-3063

Nico Vermeulen Wines

Veteran vintner Nico Vermeulen, whose 30+ years in wine include early associations with L'Ormarins (now Anthonij Rupert Wyne), former Savanha Wines and Havana Hills and latterly Wedderwill, since 2003 has made time for this small family label, latterly based at Ruitersvlei, and a bulk-wine export business, scaled back for now.

★★★★ The Right Red ② Shiraz from Stellenbosch & Paarl perfect for hearty meals. Preview **10** plush & juicy, bold & tannic but, like **08**, not for long keeping. No **09**.

The Right White ② **★★★★** Sauvignon from Durbanville coated with honeyed bottle-age, layered with asparagus in **12**, liveliness abetted by grapefruit acidity. Amenable solo or with food. Not tasted: **The Right Two Reds**, **The Right Two Whites**. — DB

Location: Paarl ▪ WO: Coastal ▪ Est/1stB 2003 ▪ Closed to public ▪ Owner(s)/viticulturist(s) Nico Vermeulen ▪ Winemaker(s) Nico Vermeulen, with Judy & Izelle Vermeulen ▪ 3,000cs own label & 240,000L bulk export ▪ 3 Pieter

Hugo Str Courtrai Suider-Paarl 7646 ▪ nicovermeulen@webmail.co.za ▪ F +27 (0)21-863-2048 ▪ **T +27 (0)21-863-2048/+27 (0)82-553-2024**

Niel Joubert Estate

Home-farm Klein Simonsvlei since last edition lamented the passing of owner and patriarch Niel Joubert, his wisdom, warmth and dry wit to be celebrated with a single-barrel bottling of shiraz ('The challenge is to find the one that most fits the profile!'). Passing of the baton to son Daan coincides with a French-inspired white blend in the making, and, underlining continuity, the 20th running of the Niel Joubert Plaaswedloop, an exclusive athletic event presided over by majestic mountains.

Christine-Marié range

★★★★ **Cabernet Sauvignon** ⓥ Refined, elegant flagship, **09** has poise, balance & structure, with enticing blackcurrant fruit. Step up from last-tasted **06** (★★★★).

★★★★ **Shiraz 08** shows development, but retains concentration & ripeness. Exotic tobacco aromas & silky tannins, well-judged oak add to appeal.

★★★★ **Méthode Cap Classique** ⓥ Opulent & attractive **09** dry bubbly from chardonnay, harbours powerful yeasty influence. Rich, creamy & persistently dry. Improves on **08** (★★★★).

Not retasted: **Merlot 06** ★★★★ **Chardonnay 08** ★★★★ **First Kiss Fortified Chenin Blanc 09** ★★★★ Not tasted: **Viognier**.

Niel Joubert Estate range

Shiraz ★★★★ Ripe & plummy **12**, with smoky bacon & tobacco notes, pleasant weight & texture, sweet baked-fruit finish. **Sauvignon Blanc** ★★★ Perfect for summer picnic hampers, as usual. **14** lively, herbaceous & light, with gentle acidity. Also tasted: **Merlot 12** ★★★ **Pinotage 12** ★★★ **Rosé 13** ★★★ **Chardonnay 13** ★★★ **Chenin Blanc 14** ★★★ Not retasted: **Cabernet Sauvignon 11** ★★★ — GdB

Location: Paarl ▪ Map: Paarl & Wellington ▪ WO: Paarl/Western Cape ▪ Est 1898 ▪ 1stB 1996 ▪ Tasting & sales Mon-Fri 9-4 by appt ▪ Closed all pub hols ▪ Owner(s) Joubert family ▪ Cellarmaster(s) Ernst Leicht ▪ Winemaker(s) Ernst Leicht, with Niel Joubert jnr (May 2011) ▪ Viticulturist(s) Daan Joubert ▪ 1,000ha/300ha (cab, merlot, ptage, shiraz, chard, chenin, sauv) ▪ 1,953t/±160,000cs own label 49% red 50% white 1% rosé ▪ Other export brand: Hunterspeak ▪ Global Gap, IPW ▪ PO Box 17 Klapmuts 7625 ▪ wine@nieljoubert.co.za ▪ www.nieljoubert.co.za ▪ S 33° 49' 54.7" E 018° 54' 3.2" ▪ F +27 (0)86-599-0725 ▪ **T +27 (0)21-875-5936**

☐ **Niels Verburg** *see* Luddite Wines

Nietgegund

Having bought a small Blaauwklippen Valley property amidst several red-wine luminaries in 2001, Stellenbosch lawyer Jan Dreyer couldn't not plant vines of his own. Managed and made by consultants, his niche red named Pro Amico (a legal term) may loosely translate as 'for a friend', but back-label QR codes enable ordering by all.

★★★★ **Pro Amico** ⓥ Merlot spiced by 10% shiraz; serious intent evident in firm structure & judicious oaking (30% new). **10** provisionally rated preview needed time to settle last edition. — WB

Location/WO: Stellenbosch ▪ Est 2004 ▪ 1stB 2008 ▪ Closed to public ▪ Owner(s) Nietgegund Boerdery (Edms) Bpk ▪ Winemaker(s) Ronell Wiid (Jan 2013, consultant) ▪ Viticulturist(s) Francois Hanekom (Sep 2006, consultant) ▪ 3.4ha/1ha (cab, merlot, shiraz) ▪ 4t/100cs own label 100% red ▪ IPW ▪ PO Box 12684 Die Boord 7613 ▪ jan@dreyer.za.net ▪ **T +27 (0)21-880-0738**

Nietvoorbij Wine Cellar

Charmingly set on an avenue of oaks, Nietvoorbij Cellar is owned by the Agricultural Research Council. During harvest many hundreds of tiny experimental batches are vinified here for clients by winemaker and Elsenburg graduate Craig Paulsen. The knowledge gained is used to develop an increasing range of good-quality (often good-value) wines for the Nietvoorbij commercial label.

Location/map: Stellenbosch ▪ Est 1963 ▪ 1stB 1992 ▪ Tasting & sales Mon-Fri 9–4 ▪ Closed Sat/Sun & all pub hols ▪ Owner(s) Agricultural Research Council ▪ Winemaker(s) Craig Paulsen, with Sifiso Mbhele ▪ Viticulturist(s) Guillaume Kotze ▪ 32ha (cabs s/f, malbec, merlot, ptage, shiraz, chard, sauv, viog) ▪ 75t/6,000cs own label 56% red 40% white 4% port ▪ Private Bag X5026 Stellenbosch 7599 ▪ cellar@arc.agric.za, winesales@arc.agric.za ▪ www.arc.agric ▪ S 33° 54' 43.5" E 018° 51' 48.9" ▪ T +27 (0)21-809-3091/3084/3140

Nieuwedrift Vineyards

Johan Mostert's vineyards, tucked into a bend of the Berg River near Piketberg, are really a sideline to his wheat farming business, but he takes them seriously. He vinifies a small portion of the crop under his own label, and this time allowed the white and pink to ferment spontaneously.

Shiraz ★★★★ Previewed **12** mixes oily oak & sweet black berries, tobacco with tarry liquorice; pleasantly full & long. **Chenin Blanc** ★★★★ Fresh & fruity **14** preview has a nice creamy texture, lightish body & salty-mineral finish. Step up on previous. Also tasted: **Blanc de Noir** **14** ★★★★ **Méthode Cap Classique 12** ★★★ — GdB

Location: Piketberg ▪ Map/WO: Swartland ▪ Est/1stB 2002 ▪ Tasting, sales & cellar tours Mon-Fri 9–1 & 2–6 Sat 9–2 ▪ Closed Easter Fri/Sun, Dec 25/26 & Jan 1 ▪ Meals on request; or BYO picnic ▪ Facilities for children ▪ Tour groups ▪ Conferences ▪ Owner(s)/viticulturist(s) Johan Mostert ▪ Cellarmaster(s) Johan Mostert (Jan 2002) ▪ 151ha/31ha (shiraz, chard, chenin, cbard) ▪ 410t total 10t/1,316cs own label 28% red 40% white 16% rosé 16% MCC ▪ PO Box 492 Piketberg 7320 ▪ nieuwedrift@patat.za.net ▪ S 32° 58' 28.1" E 018° 45' 10.6" ▪ F +27 (0)88-022-913-1966 ▪ T +27 (0)22-913-1966/+27 (0)82-824-8104

19th Wines

(NEW)

Veteran vintner and entrepreneurial wine man Ernst Gouws and winemaker son Ernst jnr (Ernst Gouws & Co Wines) researched the perfect wine for enjoyment at the '19th hole' by asking 300 golfers at two golf days to taste-test eight wines. Their favourites – a 2013 sauvignon and 2010 shiraz-merlot – will inform future offerings of The 19th Wines duo, available exclusively at leading golf clubs countrywide and exported to Mauritius, The Netherlands and Denmark.

Location: Stellenbosch ▪ Est 2012 ▪ 1stB 2013 ▪ Closed to public ▪ Owner(s) Ernst Gouws snr, Ernst Gouws jnr & 2 directors ▪ Winemaker(s) Ernst Gouws snr, Ernst Gouws jnr ▪ 3,000cs own label 50% red 50% white ▪ PO Box 580 Stellenbosch 7599 ▪ ernst@the19th.co.za ▪ www.the19th.co.za ▪ F +27 (0)86-768-6376 ▪ T +27 (0)21-886-6830

Nitida Cellars

Bought by engineer Bernhard Veller and wife Peta as a residence, the run-down Durbanville sheep farm has been transformed into a prime family-oriented wine and lifestyle destination, with nature playing a major role in the process through conservation, social responsibility projects as well as the many outdoor activities on offer. Bernhard's guiding hand is everywhere and especially in the wines, of which three have female names (and a story) to honour women. Only making wines that 'we love to drink', and bottling only the best, is the philosophy. Bernhard's membership of the prestigious Cape Winemakers Guild since 2005, and many awards and accolades, show the validity of that approach.

★★★★ **Cabernet Sauvignon** Remarkably pure cassis nose on **12**, proliferating on palate into black & red cherries with fresh leafiness & hints of cigarbox & leather. WO Coastal (30% ex Stellenbosch).

★★★★☆ **Calligraphy** Heady aromas of blackberries, violets & truffle on merlot-dominated **12**, liquid fruitcake with dark spices & hints of tobacco & leather from 27% cab franc, 14% cab & 4% petit verdot. Still extremely youthful, deserves more time to soften.

★★★★ **Riesling** Promising even better ageing potential than **13**, intensely floral, ginger-spiced **14** (★★★★★) walks tightrope between racy acidity & lime cordial sweetness, fruitily sweet-sour but finishing pleasingly dry.

★★★★ **Sauvignon Blanc** 'Green but ripe' **14** with 4% semillon has grassy nose but Golden Delicious rather than Granny Smith apple flavours, with sugar snap peas & bean sprouts adding vegetal interest.

★★★★ **Club Select Sauvignon Blanc** Ⓥ Special selection to highlight cool terroir, which **13** reveals in its minerality, lime essence note. Elegant, flavour packed & briskly fresh, will age beautifully.

★★★★ **Semillon** Dash of sauvignon boosts acidity to balance creamy texture of **13**, a soft dumpling of a wine studded with dried apple & nuts, drizzled with orange blossom honey.

★★★★★ **Coronata Integration** Epitomising complexity, **13** (★★★★★) combines tank-fermented sauvignon for green apple, lime & grapefruit zestiness with barrel-fermented semillon for creamy, zabaglione-like texture, counselled into a happy marriage by 8 months in older barrels. Graceful, like complex **12**.

Matriarch in Red ⊕ ★★★ 'Weird & wonderful' sparkling shiraz, **12** full bodied with ripe plums & a hint of sweet barbecue smoke, finishing dry. Definitely different, worth trying. Also tasted: **Shiraz 12** ★★★★ **Chardonnay 14** ★★★★ **The Matriarch 13** ★★★☆ Occasional release: **Modjadji Semillon Noble Late Harvest**. Discontinued: **Pinotage**. — JG

Location: Durbanville ▪ Map: Durbanville, Philadelphia & Darling ▪ WO: Durbanville/Coastal ▪ Est/1stB 1995 ▪ Tasting & sales Mon-Fri 9–5 Sat 11–4 Sun 11-3 ▪ Fee R20/4 wines R50/range ▪ Wine & nut/dehydrated products paired with 4 wines R50 ▪ Closed Good Fri, Dec 25/26 & Jan 1 ▪ Cassia Restaurant T +27 (0)21-976-0640; conference & function venue at Cassia (200 pax) ▪ Tables at Nitida T +27 (0)21-975-9537, www.tablesatnitida.co.za ▪ Facilities for children ▪ Mountain biking: Vellerdrome track for novice riders; part of Hillcrest/Majik forest trail (www.tygerbergmtb.co.za) ▪ Conservation area ▪ Annual festivals: Season of Sauvignon (Oct); Feast of the Grape (Mar); Soup, Sip & Bread (June) ▪ Owner(s) Bernhard & Peta Veller ▪ Cellarmaster(s) Bernhard Veller ▪ Winemaker(s) Brendan Butler (2013) ▪ Viticulturist(s) Bernhard Veller & Brendan Butler ▪ 35ha/16ha (cabs s/f, p verdot, riesling, sauv, sem) ▪ 150t/18,000cs own label 30% red 70% white + 3,000cs for clients ▪ Brands for clients: Woolworths, Checkers ▪ PO Box 1423 Durbanville 7551 ▪ info@nitida.co.za ▪ www. nitida.co.za ▪ S 33° 50' 3.8" E 018° 35' 37.0" ▪ F +27 (0)21-976-5631 ▪ **T +27 (0)21-976-1467**

☐ **Nixan Wines** see Blue Crane Vineyards

Noble Hill Wine Estate

Reinforced glass allows patrons at American-family-owned Noble Hill in the Simonsberg-Paarl foothills a glimpse into the barrel maturation cellar which lies beneath the verandah that is home to the popular restaurant. Enjoyment and pairing of food and wine is central to the offering here. Keeping it natural extends from enriched organic fertilisers in the vineyards (with ground broken on a new bushvine mourvèdre block) to the local artisan cured ham, cheese and bread on offer.

Noble Hill range

★★★★ **Cabernet Sauvignon 10** picks up where **09** left off. Ripe blackberry fruit & cedary notes. Squeeze of tannin from 18 months in French oak, 30% new. Focused & powerful but softly textured.

★★★★ **Merlot** Vivacious & pure mulberry & blueberry with choc notes on **11**. Friendly & succulent but not lacking power & depth. Sleek yet yielding with long, rewarding tail. Oak uniform on Cab, Syrah & Blend.

★★★★ **Estate Blend** Cab leads 3-way blend with merlot & cab franc on **11** which matches **10**. Fruitcake spice & light chalky grip, with inky intensity. Sleek, with defined earthy tail.

Mourvèdre Rosé ★★★ Juicy peach & nectarine vivacity on **14** coral pink quaffer. Unfussy, dry & refreshing. **Viognier** ★★★★ **13** shows what viognier can do & raises bar. Cornucopia of ripe yellow fruits yet fresh, vibrant & balanced by judicious oak - just 15% new. Elegant, refined & long. Coastal WO. Also tasted: **Syrah 10** ★★★★ **Chardonnay 13** ★★★★ **Sauvignon Blanc 14** ★★★★ Not tasted: **Syrah-Mourvèdre-Viognier**, **The Longest Day Sauvignon Blanc**.

Bloem range
Syrah-Mourvèdre ★★★ Smoky bramble & blackcurrant with spice. Light meaty note. Uncomplicated & easy drinking. Not retasted: **Chenin Blanc-Viognier 13** ★★★

Austin range
Not tasted: **Cabernet Sauvignon-Merlot**. — FM

Location: Paarl ▪ Map: Franschhoek ▪ WO: Simonsberg-Paarl/Western Cape/Coastal ▪ Est/1stB 2001 ▪ Tasting & sales daily 10–5 ▪ Fee R30, waived on purchase ▪ Cellar tours by appt only ▪ Food & wine pairing option ▪ Hitachino Nest Japanese craft beer available at winery ▪ cosecha Restaurant ▪ Picnic baskets ▪ Facilities for children ▪ Farm-produced extra virgin olive oil ▪ Conservation area ▪ Owner(s) Noble Hill Trust ▪ Winemaker(s) Kristopher Tillery ▪ Viticulturist(s) Rodney Zimba (2001) & Johan Viljoen (consultant) ▪ 50ha/30ha (cabs s/f, merlot, mourv, p verdot, shiraz, sauv, viog) ▪ PO Box 111 Simondium 7670 ▪ info@noblehill.com ▪ www.noblehill.com ▪ S 33° 49' 38.0" E 018° 56' 12.1" ▪ **T +27 (0)21-874-3844**

Noble Savage

These fun wines from Bartinney Private Cellar, branded as a 'sexy blend of mischief', are best enjoyed at Bartinney's wine bar in Stellenbosch town centre (they're not available from the farm). Winemaker Ronell Wiid says sales are skyrocketing, keeping her out of mischief as she tries to meet the demand.

★★★★ **Cabernet Sauvignon-Merlot** ⊘ Sweet, ripe black berries on **11** (★★★☆) make for attractive mouthful though firm tannins slightly dominate, lacking focus of **10**.

Cabernet Sauvignon Rosé ⊘ ★★★☆ Exuberant & happy **13** explodes in the mouth with lashings of strawberry & raspberry fruit. Hint of sweetness balanced by refreshing acidity. Step up on previous. Also tasted: **Sauvignon Blanc 14** ★★☆ — CM

Nomada Wines

Riaan Oosthuizen now advises eight small wine producers and still runs an ostrich business, so little wonder that he's not had much time to make his own wine. He and wife Gina's boutique cellar and tasting room still operate, however, from rented premises on Morgenster farm in Durbanville.

Location: Durbanville ▪ Map: Durbanville, Philadelphia & Darling ▪ Est/1stB 2007 ▪ Tasting Tue-Sun 10-4 ▪ Owner(s) Riaan & Gina Oosthuizen ▪ Winemaker(s)/viticulturist(s) Riaan Oosthuizen (2007) ▪ 66ha/7ha (cabs s/f, merlot, chenin, sauv) ▪ 55t total 10t/2,000cs own label 40% red 60% white + 6,000cs for clients ▪ Brands for clients: Klein Roosboom Wines, Red White Pink Wines, Schaap Wines (Netherlands), Signal Gun Wines ▪ PO Box 5145 Tygervalley 7536 ▪ nomadawines@gmail.com ▪ S 33° 50' 15.70" E 018° 36' 23.88" ▪ **T +27 (0)83-280-7690**

☐ **Non Pareil** *see* L'Olivier Wine & Olive Estate

Nordic Wines

Having started their wine venture (with luxury guest farm accommodation) as Wedgewood Wines in Malmesbury, negociants Peter Tillman and Norwegian partner Wiggo Andersen subsequently established an HQ in Robertson. Sourcing wines for export under various labels, mainly to Scandinavia (hence the revised house name), opportunities in Norway are being explored.

Location: Robertson ▪ Est 2007 ▪ 1stB 2010 ▪ Closed to public ▪ Wine orders Mon-Fri 9-5 from export offices: Nordic Wines, Robertson ▪ Owner(s) Wiggo Andersen & Peter Tillman ▪ Winemaker(s)/viticulturist(s) consulting ▪ Other export brands: By Norwegians, Cape to Cape, Frogner, Literature Wine, Mia, Selma, Wedgewood ▪ PO Box 896 Robertson 6705 ▪ info@nordicwines.co.za, peter@nordicwines.co.za, alison@nordicwines.co.za ▪ www.nordicwines.co.za ▪ F +27 (0)23-626-1031 ▪ **T +27 (0)23-626-1413/+27 (0)83-283-5354**

☐ **Nuts About** *see* Chateau Naudé Wine Creation

Nuweland Wynkelder

Owner/winemaker Juan Louw's boundless enthusiasm results in an eclectic range, all handcrafted in minuscule quantities, and mostly available only ex cellardoor and the family farmstall/wine house on

Route 27. He wants to make wines to suit everyone's taste, and can't resist small parcels from neighbouring farms when he spots something interesting or old. He skipped the '14 vintage and is bottling '13 pronto to keep up with demand, especially for the sweets.

Genade Water range

★★★★☆ **Straw Wine** Pale amber **13** barrel sample from 50% sauvignon, with chenin, bukettraube, hanepoot. Vivid apricot & tangerine throughout, very sweet (270 g/l sugar) but rescued by a seam of limy acidity. Hedonistic & scrumptious. No **09-12**. Swartland WO.

★★★★ **Muskadel** ⑩ Oaked (15 months 3rd fill) fortified blend of red & white muscat de Frontignan giving **13** preview liquidised raisin sweetness, mouthcoatingly rich & full bodied. Goudini grapes.

Hanepoot ⑩ ★★★☆ Fortified sun-dried grapes give the amber colour, fruit concentration of ginger biscuit, & barley sugar perfume. Tank sample **13**'s flavours stamp it as an individual. Very sweet, serve well chilled. Note: this range was 'Premium'. Also tasted: **Haasbek Tinta Barocca 13 ★★★★ Juan II 13 ★★★** Not retasted: **Wilna 12 ★★★★** Discontinued: **18 Mei Grenache Noir, Van Reenen Ruby Cabernet, Bosstok Rosé, Sauvignon Blanc, Muscat d'Alexandrie, Muscat de Frontignan**.

Louw range

Mariëtha Merlot ⑩ ★★★ Named after winemaker's mother. **13** pulpy red berries with a thread of freshness adding appeal, tannins in balance, promising longevity. **Olmo Ruby Cabernet** ⑩ ★ Dusty oak, sour cherries & fynbos, followed by a savoury & austere palate. **13** could soften over time, still young. **Granietmyn Shiraz** ⑩ ★★★ Red berries & scrub in a smooth, juicy, below 12.5% alcohol package, already drinking well. **13** from dryland bushvines. Also tasted: **Koffieklip Chenin Blanc 12 ★★★ Gesuierde Sauvignon Blanc 14 ★★★** Not tasted: **Rooipad Cabernet Sauvignon, Makstok Pinotage.** Discontinued: **Droëland Merlot, Oustok Cinsaut Rosé, Semi-Soet Merlot Rosé, Semi-Soet Bukettraube, Rolbos Chardonnay, Probus Viognier, Ruby Cabernet Jerepigo, Bukettraube Jerepigo.** — CR

Location: Malmesbury ▪ Map: Durbanville, Philadelphia & Darling ▪ WO: Malmesbury/Swartland/Coastal/Goudini ▪ Est 2007 ▪ 1stB 2008 ▪ Vygevallei farmstall & Nuweland wine house (R27): Tasting & sales Mon-Sat 10-6 Sun 10-4 ▪ Closed Dec 25 & Jan 1 ▪ Cellar tours by appt only ▪ Restaurant ▪ Facilities for children ▪ Tour groups ▪ Gifts ▪ Art ▪ Farm produce ▪ Conferences ▪ Owner(s) Juan Louw ▪ Winemaker(s)/viticulturist(s) Juan Louw (Jan 2007) ▪ 300ha/96ha (cab, merlot, ptage, tinta barocca, chenin, sauv) ▪ 560t/1,500cs own label 45% red 35% white 20% dessert ▪ PO Box 283 Malmesbury 7299 ▪ juan@nuweland.za.net ▪ www.nuweland.za.net ▪ S 33° 24' 03.87" E 018° 16' 41.73" ▪ **T +27 (0)78-111-7913**

☐ **Nuwe Wynplaas** see Group CDV

Nuy Wine Cellar

Renowned as a producer of some of South Africa's consistently finest fortifieds under long-serving cellarmaster Wilhelm Linde — at the helm for 32 years before retiring in 2003 — this grower-owned Nuy Valley winery, under equally steady successor Christo Pienaar, is adding barrel selection reds to its honours roll.

★★★★ **Pinotage Barrel Selection** Earthy strawberries & vanilla from 70% new oak, some American, **13**'s tannins still firm but should soften over next year/2. **10** (★★★) was leaner but pleasant, satisfying. **11, 12** sold out untasted.

★★★★ **Barrel Selection Syrah** Cranberries & some smoky savoury notes, sweetish palate from vanilla oakiness. **12** tannins still pushy but few years patience will be rewarded. **11** sold out untasted.

★★★★ **Red Muscadel** Lovely light-hearted **13** fortified winter drink packed with raisins, sunshine & honey, with a delicate acid balance. Perfect with a ripe cheese after a meal.

★★★★☆ **Red Muscadel Limited Release** Only 1,500 bottles of this fortified & barrel-matured **NV** nectar released to mark Nuy's 50th anniversary. Enticing Indian spices, tobacco & tea leaves followed by an ambrosial raisin mouthful. Rich & refined, with subtle tannic grip. Do try to cellar some.

★★★★☆ **White Muscadel** Demonstrating this team's mastery of fortified muscadel, **13** (★★★★★) a deliciously decadent yet light-footed glassful of honeyed raisins, marmalade & jasmine, silky smooth & delicately balanced, with flavours that last & last. Like **12**, will develop for ages.

Chardonnay ★★★★ Attractive lemon cream biscuit aroma, lemon zest & vanilla flavours on **13**. **Chant de Nuit** ★★ Unique **NV** white blend with distinctive pineapple aroma from splash Ferdinand de Lesseps. Quaffing with a difference. Also tasted: **Rouge de Nuy NV** ★★ **Chenin Blanc 14** ★★★ **Blanc de Blanc NV** ★★★ **Sauvignon Blanc 14** ★★ **Sauvignon Blanc Sparkling Vin Sec 14** ★★★ Not retasted: **Cabernet Sauvignon 12** ★★ **Colombar Semi-Sweet 13** ★★★ Not tasted: **Barrel Selection Cabernet Sauvignon**. Discontinued: **Pinotage**. — DB

Location/map: Worcester • WO: Nuy • Est 1963 • Tasting & sales Mon-Fri 9–4.30 Sat 9–12.30 • Closed Good Fri, Dec 25/26 & Jan 1 • Owner(s) 19 members • Cellarmaster(s) Christo Pienaar (Sep 2003) • Winemaker(s) Charl Myburgh (Dec 2012) • Viticulturist(s) Pierre Snyman (Vinpro) • 770ha (cab, merlot, muscadel, ptage, shiraz, chard, chenin, cbard, nouvelle, sauv) • 16,600t/10,000cs own label • PO Box 5225 Worcester 6849 • wines@nuywinery.co.za • www.nuywinery.co.za • S 33° 39' 8.7" E 019° 38' 30.9" • F +27 (0)23-347-4994/+27 (0)86-520-1782 • **T +27 (0)23-347-0272**

☐ **Oak Lane** see Beau Joubert Vineyards & Winery

Oak Valley Wines

This large family estate in Elgin was founded in 1898 by Sir Antonie Viljoen. There were vines in the earlier years, but for much of the 20th century the focus was on flowers, fruit and livestock. It was not until the 2003 vintage that current owner Anthony Rawbone-Viljoen released wines under an own label (made at neighbouring Paul Cluver). Pieter Visser, winemaker/viticulturist since inception, sadly passed away in April 2014. Successor Quentin Gobregts is a qualified accountant who moved to Australia to study oenology and later make wine there. Also new are a Riesling (untasted), and The Pool Room's head chef, Jacques Theron, a locavore who doubtless will relish working with estate produce such as free-range beef, acorn-fed pork and home-grown (in a 250m2 garden) vegetables.

★★★★ **Pinot Noir** Maraschino cherry aromas on **12** promise perhaps more than the palate delivers. Light spice notes, touches of savoury & game. Fine texture, restrained oaking & modest alcohol.

★★★★ **The Oak Valley Blend 08** (★★★☆) mostly merlot, cab franc, splash cab. Brooding dark berries, savoury & some minerality, pleasantly soft & ready to enjoy. Misses some of the fruit intensity of **07**.

★★★★☆ **Chardonnay** Creamy & open textured (80% malo) with generous ripe pear & hazelnut, enveloped in a waxy embrace. **13** (★★★★) oak more evident, shade less verve & elegance than **12**.

★★★★☆ **Mountain Reserve White Blend** Was 'The OV'. Polished **10** (★★★★★) sauvignon-led blend with oaked semillon, step up on **09**. Finely balanced, complex layers of stonefruit, waxy lanolin & flinty minerality woven into svelte texture. Accomplished blend showcasing Elgin's fine-boned elegance.

Not retasted: **Sauvignon Blanc 12** ★★★☆ Not tasted: **Shiraz**. — MW

Location/WO: Elgin • Map: Elgin, Walker Bay & Bot River • Est 1898 • 1stB 2003 • Tasting & sales Mon-Fri 9–5 Sat/Sun 10–4 • Closed Dec 25/26 & Jan 1 • The Pool Room Restaurant • Deli: artisanal breads, homegrown free-range meats & charcuterie • Self-catering 1-bedroom cottage • Walks/hikes • MTB trail • Conservation area • Owner(s) AG Rawbone-Viljoen Trust • Winemaker(s) Quentin Gobregts • Viticulturist(s) Quentin Gobregts, assisted by Kevin Watt • 30ha (cabs s/f, merlot, pinot, shiraz, chard, riesling, sauv, sem) • ±100t/±15,000cs own label 50% red 50% white • BWI champion, GlobalGap, IPW, WIETA • PO Box 30 Elgin 7180 • wines@oak-valley.co.za • www.oakvalley.co.za • S 34° 9' 24.4" E 019° 2' 55.5" • F +27 (0)21-859-3405 • **T +27 (0)21-859-4110**

Obikwa

Distell entry-level brand named for the indigenous Obikwa people and sold in more than 40 countries. Widely sourced, and made for early enjoyment.

Shiraz ★★ Glühwein-spiced **14** perfect for relaxed fireside sipping with friends. **Pinotage Rosé** ⊘ ★★★ Clean, fresh, dry finish on food-friendly **14**, less sweet than you might expect from its boiled sweet, strawberries-&-cream aromas. **Moscato** ★★★ A truly grapey wine from white muscat de Frontignan, sweet yet fresh, **14** low-alcohol (7.5%) quaffer has a lovely clean finish. **Pinot Grigio** ★★ With appealing lemon blossom nose, pineapple & apricot flavours, **14** seems drier than previous vintage, slight pétillance adding to impression of freshness. Also tasted: **Cabernet Sauvignon** ⊘ **14** ★★★ **Merlot 14** ★★ **Pinotage** ⊘ **14** ★★★ **Chardonnay 14** ★★★ **Chenin Blanc 14** ★★★ **Sauvignon Blanc 14** ★★★ **Cuvée Brut** ⊘ **14** ★★★ — JG

Observatory Cellar

Among the first with a 'natural and green' philosophy, and terroir-expressive wines of high quality, Observatory makes a welcome return to the guide in the hands of new brand owner Joe van der Westhuizen (the farm, in the neighbourhood of some of South Africa's wine greats, is jointly owned). Joe is refurbishing the facility, 'typical of a 1920s Swartland Perdeberg cellar' and, with down-the-road winemaker Christa von La Chevallerie, producing small quantities from own vineyards, some planted around 1950.

Observatory Cellar range (NEW)

Chardonnay ★★ Unwooded & just-dry, **14** has an idiosyncratic spearmint bouquet, shows gentle citrus flavours, the smoothly rounded texture making it easy to drink. **Chenin Blanc** ★★★★ Combo old oak & Swartland fruit gives **14** distinctive quince, melon & dry toast aromas; lean & linear if quite neutral flavours, lovely vinosity & smooth finish. — CR, CvZ

Location: Malmesbury ▪ Map/WO: Swartland ▪ Est 2011 ▪ 1stB 2014 ▪ Tasting, sales & cellar tours by appt ▪ Owner(s) Joe van der Westhuizen & Mechtild Braxmaier ▪ Cellarmaster(s) Christa von La Chevallerie (Jan 2014, consultant) ▪ Winemaker(s) Christa von La Chevallerie (Jan 2014, consultant), with Joe van der Westhuizen (Nov 2011) ▪ Viticulturist(s) various ▪ 71ha/20ha (ptage, shiraz, chard, chenin) ▪ 8t/±580-600cs own label 40% red 60% white ▪ PO Box 16306 Vlaeberg 8018 ▪ wine@theobservatorycellar.com ▪ www.theobservatorycellar.com ▪ S 33° 31' 17.4" E 018° 46' 59.7" ▪ T +27 (0)62-071-4258/+27 (0)83-628-9313

☐ **Ocean Basket** see Simonsvlei International
☐ **Odd bins** see Shoprite Checkers
☐ **Oggendau** see Eerste Hoop Wine Cellar

Old Bridge Wines

Export-focused producer and negociant sourcing wines for various brands, including private labels for specialised corporate clients. The wines include limited-edition African Gold Collection mainly for US, Europe and Asia; Big Six Collection, boxed sets for local game lodges/retreats and export; and Old Bridge.

St Francis Bay ▪ Closed to public ▪ Owner(s) Paulinas Dal Mountain Vineyards (Pty) Ltd ▪ 40,000cs 60% red 40% white ▪ PO Box 45 De Rust 6650 ▪ rickety@iafrica.com ▪ T +27 (0)82-777-1519

☐ **Old Brown** see Sedgwick's Old Brown

Oldenburg Vineyards

Adrian Vanderspuy returned to his native Banhoek Valley from many years overseas, to buy the neglected Oldenburg farm in 2003 and thus 'participate in two very positive stories, the rise of South Africa and its wine industry's renaissance'. With vineyards 'back to life', the seasoned Philip Costandius now takes charge of them and cellar, and the old homestead becomes a 'short-stay luxury villa'.

★★★★ **Cabernet Sauvignon** Opaque **11** (★★★★★) has classic claret tones, New World generosity. Flint, cigarbox, blackcurrant & liquorice nuances, successfully walks tightrope between power, concentration & Banghoek's finesse. Top effort still in its infancy - give plenty of time. **10** was unshowy & brooding.

★★★★ **Cabernet Franc** Characteristic cab franc florals & pencil lead joined by gunsmoke & black berries in tightly packed **11**. Fruit intensity, impressive structure hint at future pedigree of the site. Decant now, or cellar few years. Step up on brash **10** (★★★★).

★★★★ **Merlot** Fruity **11** followed by herbaceous **12** (★★★☆), bouquet garni, crushed leaf, sugared plum nuances, with hints capsicum, cedar. There's good acidity, with dry tannins, but needs year/2 to meld.

★★★★ **Chardonnay** Barrel fermented/aged **13** best to date. Subtle & delicate bouquet lime, blossom & tangerine. Vanilla, buttery tones from 50% new oak noticeable, but balanced by pure fruit core, zippy acidity. **12** (★★★★) slightly astringent.

★★★★ **Chenin Blanc** Bruised apple, sweet muesli, toasted oak & honey on **13** (★★★☆). Similar sweet-sour impression as in **12**, needs year/2 for oak to knit.

Also tasted: **Syrah 11** ★★★★ **Rhodium Red Blend 11** ★★★★ In abeyance: **Cabernet Sauvignon Barrel Selection**. — HJ

Location/map/WO: Stellenbosch ▪ Est 1960s ▪ 1stB 2007 ▪ Tasting & sales Mon-Fri 10-4.30 Sat & pub hols 10-4 (Oct-May)/by appt (Jun-Sep) ▪ Fee R30 ▪ Closed Good Fri, Dec 25/26 & Jan 1 ▪ Refreshments for sale: cheese platters, biltong, etc. ▪ Luxury accommodation in The Homestead (exclusive use, sleeps up to 12 in 6 bedrooms) ▪ Owner(s) Adrian Vanderspuy ▪ Winemaker(s)/viticulturist(s) Philip Costandius ▪ 50ha/30ha (cabs s/f, merlot, shiraz, chard, chenin) ▪ 227t/8,000cs own label 57% red 43% white ▪ PO Box 2246 Dennesig 7601 ▪ cellardoor@ oldenburgvineyards.com ▪ www.oldenburgvineyards.com ▪ S 33° 55' 7.61" E 018° 56' 8.75" ▪ F +27 (0)21-885-2665 ▪ T +27 (0)21-885-1618

☐ **Old Man's Blend** see Groote Post Vineyards

Old Vines Cellars

'2015 will be MAJOR as we will be celebrating 20 years of Old Vines Cellars,' says Irina von Holdt co-owner with daughter Françoise Botha. 'We'll be marking the release of our first wine, the iconic Blue White, South Africa's first wine in the brilliant royal blue bottle. It created a sensation at the time (and gave rise to a bunch of "me-too's"). Our purpose had been to attract attention to the wine — we saw it as the renaissance of SA chenin. We still believe it to be this country's flagship white wine. The blue bottle is gone, but we are doing our best to make sure that chenin gets its due by being better and better each year.'

Old Vines range

★★★★ **Barrel Reserve Chenin Blanc** Hefty dollop of oak & oxidative styling lend **13** honeyed, buttery flavours. Gentle acidity, ripe, complex fruit & creamy lees texture combine in appealing harmony. Bottelary grapes. No **11**, **12**.

★★★★ **Chenin Blanc** Ⓐ Ageworthy unwooded version. **12** (★★★★★) a rich silky texture threaded with vibrant acidity. Elegantly understated, more intensity & length than previewed **11**.

Baron von Holdt ★★★★ First since **09**, cab-led Bordeaux blend **12** is well formed, with savoury stewed fruit. Barrel sample, but showing development. In abeyance: **Vintage Brut**.

Spring Valley range

Merlot Telltale leafy notes on solid & fruity **13** with strong tannin presence. Preview too unformed to rate. **Shiraz-Merlot** ★★★ Convincing weight, black fruit & liquorice, tangy conclusion on youthful & oak-spicy **13** tank sample from various vineyard sites (WO Coastal, as all these). Also tasted: **Chenin Blanc-Sauvignon Blanc 14** ★★★ Occasional release: **Pinotage**, **Sauvignon Blanc**. — GdB

Location: Cape Town ▪ WO: Stellenbosch/Coastal ▪ Est/1stB 1995 ▪ Closed to public ▪ Owner(s) Irina von Holdt & Françoise Botha ▪ Winemaker(s) Irina von Holdt ▪ 14,000cs own label 40% red 60% white + 4,000cs for clients ▪ 50 Liesbeek Rd Rosebank 7700 ▪ info@oldvines.co.za ▪ www.oldvines.co.za ▪ F +27 (0)21-685-6446 ▪ **T +27 (0)21-685-6428**

Olifantsberg Family Vineyards

Exciting progress at the Leeuwerik family farm on Breedekloof's Brandwacht mountain. Recent high-lying, shale-based, mainly Rhône reds and whites have nearly doubled plantings, and more than trebled production in the refurbished fermentation cellar (formerly a glass blowing studio). Cultivation on virgin soil is balanced by sustainable farming practices and conservation of indigenous vegetation.

★★★★ **Blanc de Noir** (NEW) Seriously conceived blush from shiraz, dry **13** is distinctly un-tutti-frutti. Partial older oaking adds breadth & lees lends texture to restrained but elegant fruit. Impressive debut.

★★★★☆ **Blanc** (NEW) Striking oxidatively styled (in older oak) chardonnay-based blend with roussanne, grenache blanc & chenin, **13** breaks into big league with complex layers of brioche, pineapple & marmalade on full, ripe body, with creamy mouthcoating but lively texture. 15% Paarl grapes.

Pinotage ★★★★ Typically wild & high toned but **13** also juicy & well structured, with soft acid, gentle tannins & ripe berry fruit. Naturally fermented, as all the new vintages. Not retasted: **Cabernet Sauvignon 10** ★★★ **Syrah 11** ★★★★ Occasional release: **Chardonnay**. Discontinued: **Chenin Blanc-Chardonnay**. — GdB

Location: Worcester ▪ Map: Breedekloof ▪ WO: Breedekloof/Western Cape ▪ Est 2003 ▪ 1stB 2005 ▪ Tasting & sales Mon-Fri by appt ▪ Owner(s) Paul J Leeuwerik ▪ Cellarmaster(s)/winemaker(s)/viticulturist(s) Jacques du Plessis (Nov 2009) ▪ 95ha/18ha (carignan, grenache n/b, mourv, ptage, shiraz, chard, chenin, rouss) ▪ 100t/±13,000cs own label 50% red 50% white ▪ PO Box 942 Worcester 6849 ▪ duplessis.je@gmail.com ▪ www.olifantsbergwines.com ▪ S 33° 35' 42.76" E 019° 21' 42.39" ▪ **T +27 (0)79-376-1466**

Olof Bergh Solera

Previously handled by Distell subsidiary Henry Tayler & Ries, Olof Bergh brandy (like siblings Chateau and Limosin) has reverted back to owner Distell's distribution. It is a local rarity, being matured using the solera system of racking brandies from different distillations down tiers of brandy barrels, for a final product of greater character and age than the usual blended brandy. Its 'home' distillery is in Goudini in Breede River Valley, where the grapes are sourced.

Olof Bergh Solera Brandy (℧) ★★★ Blended brandy, sippable but best for cocktails & mixers. Straightforward, with nice fruity fragrance to sniff & some caramel & oak vanilla coming through. Clean, dry finish. — WB, TJ

☐ **OloPam** *see* New Beginnings Wines

Olsen Wines

A decades-old partiality for pinotage persuaded American physicist Greg Olsen (the third civilian in space, in 2005) to eventually buy a Klein Drakenstein property (co-owned with daughters Kimberly and Krista). Father-and-son team Gawie and Armand Botha not only tend these Paarl vines, but have recently helped their entrepreneurial boss root pinotage in Montana.

Orbit Pinotage ★★★★ New name for what was just 'Pinotage' & higher rating for **10**, with candyfloss, fruit pastille aromas, commendably dry & savoury finish, structure to improve 3+ years.
Chardonnay (⊕) ★★★★ Year new oak for ambitious **13**, giving toasty lemon cream nuances; broad buttery palate buoyed by citrus acidity. Balanced & lightish, dry tasting despite few grams sugar.
Chenin Blanc (⊕) ★★★★ **14** unoaked to showcase very attractive fruit: floral & tropical combo, a honey undertone; brisk, persistent saline tail. Would rock a plate of oysters. Also tasted: **Soyuz Shiraz** (NEW) **11** ★★ — CvZ

Location/WO: Paarl ▪ Map: Paarl & Wellington ▪ Est/1stB 2002 ▪ Tasting by appt only ▪ Fee R30pp ▪ Light meals for groups of ±10 by appt ▪ Farm-style jams ▪ Owner(s) Greg Olsen & daughters ▪ Cellarmaster(s)/viticulturist(s) Armand Botha (2000) ▪ Winemaker(s) Armand Botha (2007) & Loftie Ellis (consultant) ▪ 30ha ▪ 1,000cs own label 90% red 10% white ▪ Europgap registered ▪ PO Box 9052 Huguenot 7645 ▪ olsenwines@mweb.co.za ▪ www. olsenprivatevineyards.co.za ▪ S 33° 44' 4.7" E 019° 3' 5.0" ▪ F +27 (0)21-862-2589 ▪ **T +27 (0)21-862-3653**

Onderkloof

Originally a grape and milk farm, Onderkloof on Schapenberg Hill was acquired by Swiss-born Beat Musfeld and wife Heidi in 1997 and the first vintage vinified in a new cellar two years later. Since 2012 the Musfelds' Geisenheim-trained son Yves has been making the wine, overseeing vineyard revitalisation and managing the visitor facilities, including four guest cottages with False Bay vistas.

Cabernet Franc ⓝⓔⓦ ★★★ Naturally fermented & aged in French oak (15% new) 2 years, **11** ripe plum nose with more savoury leather/tobacco notes on palate, 14.9% alcohol showing on finish. **Sir Lowry** ⓝⓔⓦ ★★★ Naturally fermented & aged in French barrels (10% new) 2 years, **11** blend of 50% merlot, 35% shiraz & 14% petit verdot has cooked plum & berry notes on nose, drying out on palate. **Bottleneck Rosé** ⓝⓔⓦ ★★★ Named after an unexpected ton of ripe cab franc that couldn't be vinified as red wine, **14** is fairly rich, with ripe red berry fruit & spice, finishing dry with lingering zip. Not retasted: **Chenin Blanc 12** ★★★ **Sauvignon Blanc 13** ★★★ **Floreal Blanc de Blanc 13** ★★★ Not tasted: **Cabernet Sauvignon**. — JG

Location: Somerset West ▪ Map: Helderberg ▪ WO: Stellenbosch/Western Cape ▪ Est 1998 ▪ 1stB 1999 ▪ Tasting, sales & cellar tours by appt ▪ Conservation area ▪ Self-catering cottages ▪ Owner(s) Beat Musfeld ▪ Winemaker(s) Yves Musfeld (Jan 2012) ▪ Viticulturist(s) Botha Marais (Aug 2012) ▪ 64ha/12ha (ptage, shiraz, chenin, muscat d'A, sauv) ▪ 75t ▪ PO Box 90 Sir Lowry's Pass 7133 ▪ info@onderkloof.com ▪ www.onderkloof.com ▪ S 34° 6' 37.9" E 018° 53' 49. 2" ▪ **T +27 (0)21-858-1538**

☐ **Ondine** *see* Ormonde Private Cellar

Oneiric Wines

Oneiric, 'of or pertaining to dreams', describes Matt and Jennifer Pascall and family's aspiration to bottle wines from their Elgin property on the border of the Kogelberg Biosphere under an own brand. Middle child Shan is the MD and prime mover, bringing boundless enthusiasm and a fresh perspective to the young brand. Vinification is by contracted specialists and, for visitors, the cellardoor offers a gift shop with arts and crafts, scenic walks and other allures.

Location: Elgin ▪ Map: Elgin, Walker Bay & Bot River ▪ Est 2007 ▪ 1stB 2009 ▪ Tasting & sales by appt only ▪ BYO picnic ▪ Gift shop ▪ Walks/hikes ▪ Conservation area ▪ Owner(s) Pascall family ▪ Winemaker(s) Niels Verburg (2014, consultant) & Jean Smit (2009, consultant) ▪ Viticulturist(s) Paul Wallace (Aug 2007, consultant) ▪ 64ha/8ha (cab, merlot, syrah, chard, sauv) ▪ ±90t/5,000cs own label 65% red 35% white ▪ shan@oneiric.co.za ▪ www.oneiric.co.za ▪ S 34° 14' 31.0" E 019° 03' 05.8" ▪ **T +27 (0)71-481-9560**

☐ **One World** *see* Koopmanskloof Wingerde

Oom Tas

Distell big-volume white depicts winefarmer 'Uncle Tas' beaming from retro label.

Oom Tas ★ Amber hue implies sweetness but latest **NV** is bone-dry, dilute. 1L,2L & 5L bottles. — MW

☐ **Opener's** *see* Waterstone Wines

Opstal Estate

Seventh-generation Slanghoek Valley winemaker and enthusiastic marketer Attie Louw is determined to make father Stanley's farm a 'destination of choice' with his hip-and-happening

combination of live music, good food and fine wine. A red blend is set to join the newly minted Heritage collection, debuting last edition with a five-star chenin honouring great-grandfather Carl Everson. No better inspiration for the circumspect renewal of 30-plus-year-old vines 'to maintain balance and quality' and trialling of other blocks.

Heritage range

★★★★★ **Carl Everson Chenin Blanc** From 34 year old home vineyard, naturally vinified. Stellar debut with **12**; Serious **13** (★★★★☆) does not disappoint. Complex layers of tropical & green fruit, honey - packed with flavour, the dry end belying the rich palate. Only older oak.

Opstal Estate range

★★★★ **Hanepoot** Great typicity of raisin, spice & fragrant, floral lift, following to sun-drenched viscosity. **13** fortified dessert has wonderful cleansing acidity to balance the sweet richness.

Syrah-Viognier Blush ★★★ Fragrant strawberry & musk on co-fermented **14** rosé lead to bright juicy palate, barely pink in hue, dry. **The Mill Iron** ★★★ Potpourri-scented **14**, fresh & fruity off-dry sipper from viognier, muscat d'Alexandrie & colombard, lovely balance & playfulness. Also tasted: **Cabernet Sauvignon 12** ★★★☆ **Sauvignon Blanc 14** ★★★ **Sauvignon Blanc Sparkling Sec 14** ★★☆ Not retasted: **Chardonnay Barrel Dessert 11** ★★★☆

Sixpence range

Cabernet Sauvignon-Merlot ★★★ Breezy, red-fruited sipper, **13** ends just-dry. Breedekloof WO, like next. Also tasted: **Sauvignon Blanc-Semillon 14** ★★★ — WB

Location: Rawsonville • Map: Breedekloof • WO: Slanghoek/Breedekloof • Est 1847 • 1stB 1978 • Tasting, sales & cellar tours Mon-Fri 9–5 Sat 11–3 Sun by appt • Closed Easter Fri-Mon, Dec 25/26 & Jan 1 • Cheese platters • Restaurant Wed-Sun 9–5 • Facilities for children • Tour groups • Gift shop • Farm produce • Conferences • Conservation area • MTB trail • Quarterly music/theatre shows with dinner • Quarterly farmers market • Owner(s) Stanley Louw • Winemaker(s) Attie Louw (Sep 2010) • Viticulturist(s) Gerhard Theron (Jan 2002) • 419ha/101ha (cab, ptage, shiraz, chard, chenin, muscat d'A, sauv, sem, viog) • 1,500t/15,000cs own label 20% red 55% white 20% rosé 5% dessert • BWI, IPW, WIETA • PO Box 27 Rawsonville 6845 • wine@opstal.co.za • www.opstal.co.za • S 33° 38' 19.8" E 019° 13' 40.8" • F +27 (0)23-344-3002 • **T +27 (0)23-344-3001**

☐ **Oracle** *see* Distell

Orangerie Wines

As well as supplying grapes to others from this large and venerable Perdeberg farm, young Pieter Euvrard has made some wines in his tiny cellar using a minimal-intervention approach. There have been recent plantings on the farm of scarcer varieties, and more will follow.

Location: Malmesbury • Map: Swartland • Est 1707 • 1stB 2009 • Tasting, sales & cellar tours by appt only • Paardeberg Conservation Area • Owner(s)/viticulturist(s) Loffie & Pieter Euvrard • Winemaker(s) Pieter Euvrard (2009) • 200ha/70ha (cab, malbec, merlot, mourv, ptage, shiraz, chard, chenin, rouss, sauv, verdelho, viog) • 15t/600cs own label 60% red 40% white • PO Box 92 Malmesbury 7299 • orangeriewines@yahoo.com • www.orangeriewines.co.za • S 33° 32' 20.8'' E 018° 49' 55.6'' • F +27 (0)22-487-3046 • **T +27 (0)22-482-2169**

Orange River Wine Cellars

Mother Nature can be cruel, and when your catchment straddles the banks of the mighty Orange River - meandering 400 km through the arid vastness and red Kalahari desert soils of the Northern Cape - there's a lot that can suffer the consequences. The mercury plummeted to minus 10 Celsius in places and frost hit the budding vines, reducing last year's yields to 'just' 123,000 tons. Not that it dampened enthusiasm at this enormous grower-owned winery, with five cellars — Grootdrink, Groblershoop, Keimoes, Kakamas and Upington — each with multiple winemakers and dedicated viticulturist. Quality improves incrementally as experimentation is encouraged and, with 200 ha of new plantings underway, there's more scope. It's not just local markets which appreciate ORC's pocket friendliness (Best Value Cellar 2012), expanding export markets do too.

Reserve range

★★★★ **Straw Wine** Welcome return to form for **13**, all-chenin air-dried & older-barrel-fermented dessert. Mango & sun-dried pineapple sweetness balanced by fresh acid. Clean finish.

Also tasted: **Lyra 11** ★★★ **Chenin Blanc de Barrique 13** ★★★

Orange River Wine Cellars range

★★★★ **Soet Hanepoot** Latest **NV** raises the bar. Richly sweet, with bold muscat flavour, it's balanced, clean & dry to end.

★★★★ **Red Muscadel** ⊘ Tawny hue seduces, along with grapey, floral scent & raisined flavour on **12** - as did **11**. Harmonious fortification & ripe typicity of muscat. Honeyed memory lingers.

★★★★ **White Muscadel** Broad, rich barley sugar, sun-dried pineapple & muscat typicity to **13** (★★★★☆) fortified, which improves on lighter **12** (★★★★) & seamless **11**. Elegant, long & beautifully balanced, its dry finish is focused by flavours that linger long.

Ruby Cabernet ⊘ ★★★ Seamless & succulent **13** offers light fruitcake enjoyment. Easy-drinking quaffer. **Chardonnay** ⊘ ★★★ Fresh tangerine vibrancy to **13**, with pleasant creamy note from lees stirring & oak fermentation. **Chenin Blanc** ★★☆ Melon & tropical fruit on light but lively **14**, effortless & fresh. **Sparkling Brut** ★★★ **14** all-chenin sparkler a notch up. Vibrant sherbet & apple/pear crunch with good acidity. Nice length. **Nouveau Blanc Natural Sweet** ★★ Ripe peach, pineapple simplicity to **14** low-alcohol sweetie from chenin. Good swimming pool fare. Also tasted: **Colombard** ⊘ **14** ★★★ **Sauvignon Blanc 14** ★★★ **Sparkling Rosé 14** ★★★ **Sparkling Doux 14** ★★☆ **Rosé Natural Sweet 14** ★★★ **Red Jerepigo NV** ★★★★ **White Jerepigo NV** ★★★★ Not retasted: **Cabernet Sauvignon 12** ★★★ **Shiraz 12** ★★★ **Cape Ruby 12** ★★★ Not tasted: **Pinotage.** — FM

Location: Upington ▪ Map: Northern Cape, Free State & North West ▪ WO: Northern Cape ▪ Est 1965 ▪ 1stB 1968 ▪ Tasting & sales Mon-Fri 8—4.30 Sat 8.30—12 ▪ Fee R10/5 wines ▪ Closed all pub hols ▪ Cellar tours Mon-Fri 9, 11 & 3 (Jan-Mar) ▪ Owner(s) ±890 shareholders ▪ Cellarmaster(s) Gert Visser ▪ Cellar managers Bolla Louw (Kakamas), Johan Dippenaar (Keimoes), Johan Esterhuizen (Upington), Jim de Kock (Grootdrink), Riaan Liebenberg (Groblershoop), with winemakers (in same cellar order) George Kruger/Marko Pentz/Stephan Steenkamp; Rianco van Rooyen/Mariken Jordaan; Jopie Faul/Cobus Viviers/Philane Gumede; Rudi de Wet ▪ Viticulturist(s) Henning Burger (viticultural services manager), with (in same cellar order) Ockert Vermeulen, Chris Kalp, Francois Ozrovech, Dirk Sutherland ▪ 4,200ha (ptage, ruby cab, shiraz, chard, chenin, cbard, muscat varieties) ▪ 123,000t/20m L own label 10% red 50% white 20% rosé 20% other + 30m L for clients/bulk ▪ Other export labels: Island View, Gilysipao, Star Tree ▪ Ranges for customers: Country Cellars & Carnival (Spar); Seasons Collection (Liquor City) ▪ ISO 9001:2008 & 2011, PAS 22000:2010, FSSC 20000, PAS 220:2008, BRC, IPW, HACCP, WIETA ▪ PO Box 544 Upington 8800 ▪ info@orangeriverwines.com ▪ www.orangeriverwines.com ▪ S 28° 26' 33.0" E 021° 12' 30.6" ▪ F +27 (0)54-332-4408 ▪ T +27 (0)54-337-8800

☐ **Oranjerivier Wynkelders** *see* Orange River Wine Cellars

Org de Rac

Imposing hillside winery Org de Rac aptly positions itself as the 'green heartbeat' of the Swartland, having helped pioneer eco-friendly winefarming in the region. Since the maiden bottling ten years ago, the portfolio has expanded greatly and today includes an unusually varied cellardoor offering, various oils, a new husk spirit with the Dalla Cia family, debut 3L bag-in-box for the Swedish market, and a first 'port' (untasted by us) - all made and run as naturally and sustainably as possible.

Reserve range

★★★★ **Cabernet Sauvignon** ⊘ Classy blackcurrant & damson fruit with iodine, tobacco & earth notes on **13** show promise of improvement with time in bottle. Generous body & length. No **12**.

For more information, visit wineonaplatter.com

★★★★ **Shiraz** Smoky, spicy & plump, **13** is youthful but has bright future. Honest, ripe fruit & chalky tannins need time to integrate, but the right components are in place.

Also tasted: **Merlot** 13 ★★★

Org de Rac range

★★★★ **La Verne Méthode Cap Classique**   Commendable all-chardonnay sparkling, showing rich, leesy brioche with baked apple fruit. **11** lively mousse, refreshing acidity & lingering creamy finish.

Shiraz-Cabernet Sauvignon-Merlot (NEW) ★★★ Export-only **14** has sweet currants, caramel/toffee oak notes; juicy but ends abruptly. **Lightly Wooded Chardonnay** ★★★★ Oak-spiced, with good varietal fruit, salty-mineral finish, **14** well-rounded & plump enjoyment. Also tasted: **Cabernet Sauvignon** 13 ★★★ **Merlot** 13 ★★★ **Shiraz** 13 ★★★ **Unwooded Chardonnay** 14 ★★★ Not tasted: **Merlot Rosé**.

Le Piquet range (NEW)

Cabernet Sauvignon-Merlot ★★★ Convincing cassis fruitiness on lighter body of **13** thank sample. Sweet vanilla spice, soft tannins, ripe & accessible. **Cabernet Sauvignon-Merlot-Shiraz Reserve** ★★★★ Jammy sweetness on intensely ripe **13** preview has strong savoury edge. A fruit bomb, bit over the top but doubtless will have its fans.

Green Shebeen range

The Blend   ★★★ NV amiable cab/merlot packed with juicy fruit & easy tannins. Discontinued: **Cabernet Sauvignon**, **Rosé**, **Chardonnay**.

Husk Spirit range (NEW)

★★★★ **Le Genio** Husk spirit from **14** merlot nicely done. Nutty, with floral violet & lavender scents; elegant, creamy, some roasted nut, sweet berry fruit complexity. Smooth & long marzipan tail. — WB, GdB

Location: Piketberg ▪ Map/WO: Swartland ▪ Est 2001 ▪ 1stB 2005 ▪ Tasting, sales & tours Mon-Fri 9–5 Sat 9–1 ▪ Closed Good Fri, Dec 25 & Jan 1 ▪ Meals/refreshments/cheese platters by prior arrangement; or BYO picnic ▪ Tour groups ▪ Weddings/functions/conferences ▪ Walks/hikes ▪ Mountain biking ▪ Conservation area ▪ Game viewing ▪ Owner(s) Nico Bacon ▪ Winemaker(s) Jurgen Siebritz (Sep 2014) ▪ Viticulturist(s) Ettienne Swarts (Nov 2013) ▪ 59ha (cab, grenache, merlot, mourv, shiraz, chard, chenin, rouss, verdelho) ▪ 500t/62,500cs own label 85% red 10% white 5% rosé ▪ Other export brand: Abbotsville ▪ SGS (Organic) ▪ PO Box 268 Piketberg 7320 ▪ wine@orgderac.co.za ▪ www.orgderac.co.za ▪ S 32° 57' 44.3" E 018° 44' 57.4" ▪ F +27 (0)22-913-3923 ▪ **T +27 (0)22-913-2397/3924**

Origin Wine   (♀)

Headquartered on Stellenbosch's Bottelary Road, Origin Wine's 10 million case production caters to diverse local and international markets, and includes Fairhills, among the leading Fairtrade brands.

Location/map: Stellenbosch ▪ Est/1stB 2002 ▪ Tasting strictly by appt ▪ Owner(s) Bernard Fontannaz ▪ Cellarmaster(s) Hermias Hugo (2011) ▪ Winemaker(s) Seugnét Rossouw (2007), with Ferdi Coetzee & Terence Capes ▪ Game 10m cs ▪ 50% red 40% white 10% rosé ▪ BRC, DLG, Fairtrade, HACCP, IFS, WIETA ▪ PO Box 7177 Stellenbosch 7599 ▪ info@originwine. co.za ▪ www.originwine.co.za, www.fairhills.co.za, www.stormhoek.co.za, www.streetart.co.za ▪ S 33° 52' 39.07" E 018° 48' 35.50" ▪ F +27 (0)21-865-2348 ▪ **T +27 (0)861-ORIGIN/+27 (0)21-865-8100**

Ormonde Private Cellar   (♀) (🍴) (👜) (📷) (👤)

It was this Basson-family-run property that opened Darling up as a quality wine area, planting the first classic grapes when the area was supplying distilling wine to the local cooperative. Its five ranges, differently priced and positioned, are premium range Ormonde, carrying the property's name, and with blends honouring historical family members; Ondine, named after the famous ballet about a water nymph, used here as dedication to the Basson women; Alexanderfontein refers to the farm where the Basson family grew up; and Chip Off The Old Block's wines are vineyard selections from the oldest vines, in honour of the Basson generations to come.

Ormonde Premium Blends range

★★★★☆ **Vernon Basson** After lighter **07** (★★★★), velvety **08** marks return to a richer style, with concentrated cassis of cab lifted by leafy freshness of cab franc to ensure elegance, while lengthy bottle-maturation has added notes of meaty, leathery complexity.

Not retasted: **Theodore Eksteen 08** ★★★☆

Ormonde Single Barrel range

★★★★ **Shiraz** ⊘ With layered black plums & cocoa meatiness throughout, barrel-selection **09**'s oak foundation adds a serious note to the plush palate, assures future development.

★★★★ **Chardonnay** Still-vibrant **11** bursts with zesty lime intensity, balanced by oatmeal softness of integrated oak, making it an elegant wine with a subtle but lingering grapefruit finish. **10** skipped.

Not retasted: **Cabernet Sauvignon 08** ★★★☆ **Pinot Noir 10** ★★★★ Not tasted: **Sauvignon Blanc**.

Chip Off The Old Block range

Merlot ⊘ ★★★☆ Smooth & supple **11** shows lovely black plum purity, veering to prune, very appealing. **Sauvignon Blanc** ★★★☆ Tasted shortly after bottling, still-subdued **14** already shows appealing lime & gooseberry notes with a tangy finish. Also tasted: **Cabernet Sauvignon 11** ★★★ **Shiraz 12** ★★★

Ondine range

★★★★ **Cabernet Franc** ⊘ **10** follows smoothly in footsteps of rich yet elegant **09**. Perfumed nose hints at blackcurrants & ripe black fruit to come, leaving molten dark chocolate in their wake.

Chenin Blanc ★★★ Good length & acidity on zippy **13**, boasting appealing white peach notes as well as tangy hint of apricot. **Semillon** ★★★ As bright yellow suggests, **13** fairly weighty, more pungent thatch notes than its grassy predecessor. Also tasted: **Merlot 11** ★★★★ **Chardonnay 13** ★★★★ **Sauvignon Blanc 13** ★★★★ Not retasted: **Malbec 10** ★★★ **Pinot Noir 10** ★★★

Alexanderfontein range

Shiraz ★★★ Less quirky than its Chip stablemate, **13** bursts with pure mulberry & black plum fruit, finishing with a pinch of white pepper. **Sauvignon Blanc** ⊘ ★★★☆ Zesty **14** seduces with lime & passionfruit intensity, mouthwatering acidity & good length. Also tasted: **Cabernet Sauvignon 13** ★★★ **Merlot 13** ★★★ **Chardonnay 14** ★★★ **Chenin Blanc 14** ★★★ — JG

Location: Darling ▪ Map: Durbanville, Philadelphia & Darling ▪ WO: Darling/Coastal ▪ 1stB 1999 ▪ Tasting & sales Mon-Fri 9—4 Sat & pub hols 9—3 ▪ Closed Good Fri, Dec 25/26 & Jan 1 ▪ Vineyard tours by appt ▪ Chocolate & wine tasting by appt R50pp ▪ Cheese & wine tasting by appt R55pp - tasting fee applies to Ormonde range only ▪ Picnic baskets by appt; or BYO picnic ▪ Facilities for children ▪ Walks ▪ Owner(s) Basson family ▪ Winemaker(s) Michiel du Toit ▪ Viticulturist(s) Theo Basson ▪ ±300ha (cabs s/f, merlot, mourv, p verdot, pinot, shiraz, chard, chenin, sauv, sem) ▪ 1,000t/70,000cs own label 40% red 60% white ▪ BWI ▪ PO Box 201 Darling 7345 ▪ info@ormonde.co.za ▪ www.ormonde.co.za ▪ S 33° 22' 20.2" E 018° 21' 23.6" ▪ F +27 (0)22-492-3470 ▪ **T +27 (0)22-492-3540**

Osbloed Wines

Somerset West-based Bertus van Niekerk sources grapes widely for his growing boutique range but labels - beautifully illustrated by artist wife Selma Albasini, who sadly passed away last year - nod to his former clerical past in their biblical names. Multi-talented oenology student son Hendrik assists in the creation of a range that's interesting, varied and authentic — everything wine should be.

Icon range

★★★★ **Wonderbare Raadsman** 13 (★★★★) a cornucopia of bright red berry fruits, succulent & delicious. Light, gentle & yielding but with structure & length. Lighter than introductory **12**, blend of pinotage & parents cinsaut & pinot noir.

Calico range

Ebony ★★★ Fynbos note to **13** from cab franc, with deep, black & blue berry palate. Cocoa nuance adds interest. Good structure, definition & length. **Auburn** ★★☆ Tangy fresh berry-packed mouthful on unfussy **13** pinot noir.

Farm Animals range

★★★★ **Osbloed** ⓧ Textured five-way Bordeaux/shiraz blend from Philadelphia grapes. **12** ups game on **10** (★★★★). Serious & brooding, dark fynbos-tinged tobacco & hedgerow fruit.
Not tasted: **Hanekam**, **Blommetjie**.

Horses of the Apocalypse range

★★★★ **Black Horse Cabernet Sauvignon** Pure typicity to nose & palate of **13**, which improves on **12** (★★★★). Balanced, poised & yet fresh. Yielding but defined structure, good length.

Red Horse Cinsaut Noir ★★★☆ **13** vibrant spicy red fruit echoes **12**. Bright & breezy, medium bodied & easy drinking. Also tasted: **White Horse Chardonnay 12** ★★☆ **Pale Horse Riesling 13** ★★★ — FM

Location: Somerset West • Map: Helderberg • WO: Coastal/Durbanville/Stellenbosch/Elgin • Est 2009 • 1stB 2010 • Tasting, sales & cellar tours daily - please call ahead • Tasting fee R20, waived on purchase • Owner(s) Bertus van Niekerk • Cellarmaster(s) Bertus van Niekerk (Jan 2010) • Winemaker(s) Bertus van Niekerk (Jan 2010), with Hendrik van Niekerk (2011) • 600cs own label 75% red 25% white • 33 Eagle Crescent Somerset West 7130 • bertus@osbloed.com • www.osbloed.com • S 34° 5' 26.22" E 018° 51' 55.87" • T +27 (0)83-400-2999

Oude Compagnies Post Private Cellar   ⓠ ⓞ

The Swanepoel family owners honour their Tulbagh farm's history as a 17th-century border outpost of the Dutch East India Company (VOC) and wine producer since the mid-19th century. The latter role sees the drift towards a Rhône style continuing this edition with two new wines evoking the farmstead and its montane surrounds. Much of the boutique production goes overseas.

Compagnies Wijn range

The Homestead ⓝ ★★★☆ Evocative cinnamon & mulled wine scents on **13** shiraz, grenache, mourvèdre blend. Rich but not overly heavy; lively acid & rounded tannins add satisfying drinkability. **The Buchu Trail** ⓝ ★★★ Fruit-forward shiraz-mourvèdre blend. **13** good savoury substance; like all reds, burly tannins need cutting with rich meat dishes. **Mourvèdre-Merlot** ★★★ Rich & meaty **12** has balanced freshness, lively tannins. **Ruby Blanc** ★★ More ruby than blanc, **14** rosé has billowing pinotage fruit, full body & dryish tail. Also tasted: **Cabernet Sauvignon 11** ★★ **Pinotage Grand Reserve 09** ★★ **Shiraz 11** ★★ Not tasted: **Merlot**, **Mourvèdre**, **Pinotage**, **Caap Ensemble**, **Cabernet Sauvignon-Merlot**, **Buchu Berg**. — AL

Location/map/WO: Tulbagh • Est 1996 • 1stB 2003 • Tasting, sales & cellar tours by appt • Walking trail (flower season Sep-Oct) • Hiking trail 1-2 days (sleepover on Obiqua mountain in own tent) • Mountain bike (difficult) & 15km off-road motorbike trails • Owner(s) Jerry Swanepoel Family Trust • Cellarmaster(s) Jerry Swanepoel • Winemaker(s) Jerry Swanepoel, with Ervin Koen (Jul 2011) • Viticulturist(s) Marius Robert (consultant) • 235ha/18ha (cab, grenache, merlot, mourv, ptage, shiraz) • 70t/10,000cs own label 90% red 10% rosé + 20,000L bulk • Other export brand: Buchu Berg • PO Box 11 Tulbagh 6820 • swanepoel@intekom.co.za • S 33° 14' 56.9" E 019° 6' 49.1" • F +27 (0)23-230-0840 • T +27 (0)23-230-0840

For more information, visit wineonaplatter.com

Oude Denneboom

The tranquil De Waal family property in Voor Paardeberg offers peace seekers a trio of countryside attractions: restored 19th-century cottages in a small game reserve stocked with African antelope beside vineyards producing a select range of wines (aptly labelled in celebration of the local fauna).

Grysbok Chenin Blanc ★★★★ Exuberant, tropical **14**'s upfront juicy fruit is crisply fresh & pleasingly concentrated. Also tasted: **Black Harrier Shiraz 13 ★★★★** Not tasted: **Eland**, **Steenbok**. — IM

Location/WO: Paarl ▪ Map: Paarl & Wellington ▪ 1stB 2003 ▪ Tasting by appt ▪ 4-star self-catering cottages ▪ Private game reserve ▪ Owner(s) Niel de Waal ▪ Cellarmaster(s)/viticulturist(s) Willem de Waal ▪ 199ha/±55ha (cab, mourv, ptage, shiraz, chenin, nouvelle, viog) ▪ 500t/1,000L own label 70% red 30% white ▪ Global GAP ▪ PO Box 2087 Windmeul 7630 ▪ info@oudedenneboom.co.za ▪ www.oudedenneboom.co.za ▪ S 33° 37' 47.28" E 018° 51' 55.08" ▪ F +27 (0)86-552-2695 ▪ **T +27 (0)21-869-8072**

☐ **Oude Kaap** *see* DGB

Oude Meester

Venerable Oude Meester brandy was launched in 1946, heralding the arrival of Distillers Corporation (now Distell) as one of SA's leading producer-wholesalers. The current range consists of four variants: Souverein and Reserve 12 Year Old for those preferring extra-long barrel-aged premium brandies, Demant launched in 2006 to celebrate the diamond jubilee and containing 5–10 year old potstill brandy, and VSOB, the standard blended brandy for mixing or drinking solo.

★★★★☆ Demant ⑦ Fine value offered with this 5-10 year matured potstill brandy. Stressing a fresh, lighter elegance rather than full richness, like all in this range. Satisfying blend of maturing floral notes along with fruitier youthful ones.

★★★★★ Souverein ⑦ A fairly recent label & amongst the elite of the Cape's older potstill brandies - minimum 18 years in oak. Lightish amber colour to yellow rim. Thrilling floral & spice notes, more delicate than Reserve, even more complex. Not a roughness or jagged edge. Serene, silken, very long.

★★★★☆ Reserve 12 Year Old ⑦ Molten gold colour. Aromas suggest some development - nutty & spicy along with fruit & honeysuckle. Fuller, richer than Demant, as elegant & dry, with restrained oak backing. Complex, lingering, mellow finish.

VSOB ⑦ **★★★★** Standard blended brandy, first step of a ladder of quality in this range. Good fruity nose & palate, a little dry oak, some sweet forcefulness. Great for mixing, but not impossible to sip solo. — WB, TJ

Oude Molen Distillery

With a distinguished history — established in Stellenbosch in the early 20th century by French-born René Santhagens, initiator of the Cape's strict Cognac production methods, using copper potstills — Oude Molen is now based in Elgin, in a forest setting. Visitors can see old Big Bertha and Long Tom potstills which are still used to make award-winning brandies by production manager Eddie Beukes, and master blender Andy Neill, advised by former KWV chief distiller Kobus Gelderblom.

★★★★ 100 Reserve ⊘ Potstill component of this blended brandy oak-matured 5 years before blending. Attractive dried fruit notes & touch of creamy vanilla for smooth sipping, even without a mixer (43% alcohol). New blend tasted.

★★★★☆ René Single Cask ⑦ All potstill, minimum 6 year maturation. Label shows cask & bottle numbers (about 600 bottles in each). More refined than Solera; a touch little less showy on the nose, but loads of fruit & flowers, with hints of prune & caramel. Rich, but some real finesse, & a long, soft finish.

★★★★ VOV Rare Vintage Selection ⑦ 14 years matured pure potstill. Lightish colour, medium rich; shows more oak & more sweetness than others in range. Lovely aromas & flavours: fruit, flowers, nuts, vanilla.

For more information, visit wineonaplatter.com

Solera Grand Reserve ⊘ ★★★☆ 100% potstill matured for consistency in a solera system. Nutty sherry notes, some jasmine fragrance as part of a pleasing complexity. Smooth & subtly persistent. — WB, TJ

Location: Elgin ▪ Map: Elgin, Walker Bay & Bot River ▪ Tasting, sales & distillery tours Mon-Fri 9–4 Sat/Sun & pub hols by appt ▪ Fee R50pp (incl tour & tasting) ▪ Closed Dec 25 & Jan 1 ▪ Tour groups ▪ Gift shop ▪ Conferences ▪ 4x4 trail ▪ MTB trail ▪ Brandy master(s) Kobus Gelderblom (Jun 2013, consultant) ▪ PO Box 494 Grabouw 7160 ▪ info@ oudemolen.co.za ▪ www.oudemolen.co.za ▪ S 34° 8' 27.77" E 019° 1' 15.64" ▪ F +27 (0)21-859-3192 ▪ **T +27 (0)21-859-2517**

☐ **Oude Rust** *see* Mooiuitsig Wine Cellars
☐ **Out of Africa** *see* Jacques Germanier

Overgaauw Wine Estate

Photograph portraits of four generations of winemaking van Veldens appear on each Overgaauw back label (including young David, the current winemaker), testifying to the long history of this family estate in the Stellenboschkloof. More than a century, in fact, although the first own-label wine was in 1970. The family have been amongst the pioneers in many significant areas of Cape wine – including the use of Portuguese 'port' varieties, the making of Bordeaux blends and of wines from chardonnay and sylvaner, and the Cape's first varietal merlot bottling, celebrating its 30th anniversary this edition.

Overgaauw Estate range

★★★★ Cabernet Sauvignon Unlike previous, serious-minded **12** not at all burly, though also fragrant. Savoury & vinous, with sweet fruit & dry tannins in quietly refined whole. Needs a few years to show best.

★★★★ Merlot Enticing red fruit & fragrant dry herbs on tasty, convincing & deft **12**, 30th vintage of this, SA's first varietal merlot. Much more harmonious, balanced than **11** (★★★). Subtle dry tannins. Restrained oaking, like all these reds.

★★★★☆ Tria Corda **12** blends cab, merlot & touch cab franc, as did big & bold **11** (★★★★), but this, though fully ripe, returns to the more graceful, restrained classicism of **09**. Subtle dry tannins in balance with the sweet ripe fruit & savoury vinosity. Already delicious, can only gain with a good few years in bottle.

★★★★ Cape Vintage The oldest current port-style release in the winelands? Mature **94**, from sextet port varieties, as pleasant & moderate as usual in its levels of sweetness, richness, power & grip.

Chardonnay ★★★★ Peach, pear & citrus notes on softly creamy, judiciously oaked, balanced & very approachable **13**. Also tasted: **Touriga Nacional 13** ★★★★ **Sauvignon Blanc 14** ★★★ Not tasted: **Sylvaner**

Shepherd's Cottage range

Cabernet Sauvignon-Merlot ★★★☆ Easygoing **13** touch ingratiatingly sweet (though firmly built) for those who like an element of austerity; dead right for others. — TJ

Location/map/WO: Stellenbosch ▪ Est 1905 ▪ 1stB 1970 ▪ Tasting & sales Mon-Fri 9–4 Sat 10–2 ▪ Fee R20pp for groups of 6+ ▪ Closed Easter Fri-Mon, Dec 25/26 & Jan 1 ▪ Restaurant open for lunch Thu-Sun from 12.30 (Sep-Mar only) T +27 (0)79-904-2995, booking essential ▪ Owner(s) Braam & David van Velden ▪ Winemaker(s) David van Velden (Jan 2003) ▪ Viticulturist(s) David van Velden; Vinpro ▪ 100ha/60ha (cabs s/f, merlot, ptage, touriga, chard, chenin, sauv, sylvaner) ▪ 60% red 40% white ▪ Other export brand: Sandrivier ▪ HACCP, IPW ▪ PO Box 3 Vlottenburg 7604 ▪ info@overgaauw.co.za, restaurant@overgaauw.co.za ▪ www.overgaauw.co.za ▪ S 33° 56' 52.1" E 018° 47' 33.4" ▪ **T +27 (0)21-881-3815**

Overhex Wines International

Key appointments continue the forward momentum of this modern, social-media-savvy, globally operating Worcester-based wine business. Among them: founding owner now executive chairman Gerhard van der Wath, focusing on new international ventures, and celebrated Jean Daneel Wines cellarmaster Jean Daneel advising on winemaking. The jovial elephant perched on a stool perfectly depicts their mantra: balance in all things, from ethical trading and staff empowerment to amenable, well-priced wines to a family-friendly cellardoor welcome.

Balance Winemaker's Selection

Pinot Noir (NEW) ★★★ On nose rather subdued, **14** promises bright cranberry & other red berry fruit. **Shiraz** ★★★ Steak-friendly **13** sees simple mocha berry flavours of previous elevated by pepper spice & savoury edge. Medium bodied, with long finish. **Pinot Grigio** (NEW) ★★★ **14** has generous Apple Danish flavours; pleasant oily texture balanced by acidity. **Sauvignon Blanc** ★★★ Pineapple & gooseberry nose invites first sip of **14**; lovely acid balance & long finish invite 2nd sip, then 3rd... Also tasted: **Cabernet Sauvignon** 13 ★★★ **Merlot** 13 ★★★ **Chardonnay** 14 ★★★ **Chenin Blanc** 14 ★★★ Not retasted: **Pinotage** 12 ★★★

Balance Best Blends

Pinotage-Shiraz ★★ Ripe dark fruits of **13** have almost a cooked, jammy quality. Complete with vanilla pod! **Shiraz Rosé** ★★ Nicely balanced **14** has raspberry nose leading to ripe red berries. Dry & tangy with bright acidity. **Chardonnay-Pinot Noir** (NEW) ★★★ 85% chardonnay dominates 15% pinot noir in citrus **14**. Oranges & lemons galore with pithy texture/bitterness on finish. **Chenin Blanc-Colombar** ★★★ In **14** 20% colombard adds guava to sweet-sour grenadilla tang with leesy pithiness on lingering finish. Also tasted: **Cabernet Sauvignon-Merlot** 13 ★★ **Shiraz-Merlot** ⊘ 13 ★★★ **Sauvignon Blanc-Semillon** ⊘ 14 ★★★ Not retasted: **Semi-Sweet Muscat** 13 ★★★

Balance Buddy range

Sweet Rosé ⊘ ★★★ NV party pink has 15% chenin added to pinotage, candyfloss nose, sweet but not cloying thanks to nice acidity. Also tasted: **Sweet White NV** ★★ **Sweet Red NV** ★★

Balance Sparklings

Lusciously Fruity Sparkling ★★ Rosepetal & apricot aromas on this friendly **NV** sparkler. Initial fizz masks sweetness then muscat grapiness comes through. Also tasted: **Sweet Temptation Sparkling NV** ★★ **Boldly Brut Sparkling NV** ★★

Willow Way Fairtrade range (NEW)

No. 1 Willow Way Shiraz-Mourvèdre ★★★ Fairtrade feelgood factor adds to appeal of juicy maiden **13** with dense cherry/berry fruit, peppery spice, plus hint of dark chocolate from 5% mourvèdre as well as six-month exposure of 15% of wine to new French oak staves. **No. 2 Willow Way Chardonnay-Pinot Grigio** ★★★ **14** marriage of chardonnay with 20% pinot grigio has apple & citrus notes on nose & palate; medium-bodied & creamily smooth.

Discontinued: **Haven Point Fairtrade range**. — JG

Location/map: Worcester ▪ WO: Western Cape ▪ Est/1stB 2006 ▪ Tasting & sales Mon-Thu 8–5 Fri 8-4 Sat/Sun 9-4 ▪ Closed Easter Fri-Tue, Jun 30-Jul 21 & Dec 22-Jan 6 ▪ Cellar tours by appt ▪ Bistro Wed-Sun 10-4 ▪ Facilities for children ▪ Tour groups ▪ Conferences ▪ Weddings & functions ▪ Owner(s) G van der Wath ▪ Cellarmaster(s) Gert van Wyk ▪ Winemaker(s) Willie Malan (2002) & Ben Snyman (Dec 2010), with Dirk Rust (Jan 2012) ▪ Viticulturist(s) Pierre Snyman & Dirk Bosman (both Vinpro) ▪ 10,100t ▪ 36% red 63% white 1% rosé ▪ ISO 22000, Fairtrade, WIETA ▪ PO Box 139 Worcester 6849 ▪ marketing@overhex.com ▪ www.overhex.com ▪ S 33° 39' 28.6" E 019° 30' 55.8" ▪ F +27 (0)23-347-1057 ▪ **T +27 (0)23-347-5012**

Overmeer Cellars

Enduring no-frills range (since 1996) from Distell. Modest alcohol levels and 3/5L packs for all.

Selected Red ★★ Medium-bodied, slightly herby **NV** pizza/pasta wine. All, except **Stein**, in 3L & 5L packs. **Stein** ★★ Pleasant, undemanding semi-sweet white, **NV**, juicy & rounded. Only in 5L pack. Also tasted: **Rosé NV** ★★ **Premier Grand Cru NV** ★ **Late Harvest NV** ★★ — WB

☐ **Over the Mountain** *see* Seven Springs Vineyards

☐ **Overvaal** *see* Hartswater Wine Cellar

Paardebosch Wines

Swartland property Paardebosch was acquired by Des Kruger, a local lawyer, and Wiggo Anderson, an exporter of fine South African wines to Norway, in 2011. David Sadie, one of the pre-eminent young winemakers at work in the district, was appointed as winemaker in 2014 and he has been charged with overseeing an extensive rehabilitation programme. David is committed to the 'natural' ideals of Swartland Independent Producers.

★★★★ **Pinotage** Bright, dark fruit on perfumed **12** - less rustic than **11** (★★★), no less charming. Ripe, but refined. Dry tannins mingle happily - if not yet harmoniously - with the deep flavour. Old oak.

★★★★ **Chenin Blanc** ⊘ Drops 'Shani' name in **14** preview. Less quirky than last **11** (★★★★), but also has oxidative element, with fynbos notes. Not intense, but a fresh, mineral vitality. Older-oak maturation; unfined/filtered.

Rosé (NEW) ★★★☆ Shiraz, carignan & 3 other red varieties, naturally fermented in old oak, on unusually characterful **14** tank sample. Lovely gentle fruit, with earthy element too. Rounded & textured, notably fresh. Discontinued: **Malbec, Phoenix White Blend.** — TJ

Location: Malmesbury ▪ Map/WO: Swartland ▪ Est/1stB 2011 ▪ Tasting & sales Mon-Sat by appt ▪ Closed all pub hols ▪ BYO picnic ▪ Walks/hikes ▪ Owner(s) Wiggo Anderson & Des Kruger ▪ Winemaker(s)/viticulturist(s) David Sadie (2014) ▪ 45ha/16ha (malbec, ptage, chenin, sem) ▪ 17t/1,900cs own label 35% red 65% white ▪ alison@nordicwines.co.za, deskruger21@gmail.com, dtsadie@gmail.com ▪ S 33° 32' 41.41" E 018° 49' 36.14" ▪ **T +27 (0)82-565-4218/+27 (0)23-626-1413**

PaardenKloof

The first wholly black-owned wine estate in the Overberg, PaardenKloof takes its name from a valley on the northern face of Babylonstoren Mountain, which separates Bot River from Hemel-en-Aarde. Most of the 1,430 ha, fynbos-rich property is conserved but ±23 ha of vineyard were established from 2004 and the first vintage pressed in 2008. Only ±40% of the harvest is vinified by contracted winemakers for the boutique label, the balance sold to other premium brands. The wines, extensively bottle-matured before release, are available from selected Cape Town and Johannesburg retailers, and the PaardenKloof Wine Club. An on-site tasting venue was set to open at press time.

PaardenKloof Private Collection (NEW)

★★★★☆ **Renosterveld Cabernet Sauvignon** Bright & concentrated red berry fruit, wild strawberry & exotic dried flower aromas & flavours on debut **09**, with outstanding structure & dimension: broad, lush & sumptuous with persistence.

Peter Clarke Collection

★★★★ **The Long Road Shiraz** Was 'Die Lang Pad'. Ripe plum, fynbos & white pepper aromas on **09**. Perfectly judged oak provides framework for lush, bright fruit, rounded mouthfeel & a finish that keeps on going. Hearty **08** (★★★★) had obvious 15% alcohol.

★★★★ **Bend In The Road Sauvignon Blanc** (NEW) ⊘ Cool-climate expression on **13**, with fresh lime & grapefruit on the nose. Bright & focused, with clean, refreshing orchard & fynbos flavours with a brisk zesty conclusion.

Also tasted: **Gaiety Sauvignon Blanc 2012** ★★★ — WB

Location/WO: Bot River ▪ Map: Elgin, Walker Bay & Bot River ▪ Est 2003 ▪ 1stB 2007 ▪ Tasting & tours by appt ▪ Sales Mon-Fri 9-5 ▪ Winemaker(s) Kobie Viljoen & Niels Verburg (cab/shiraz), Adam Mason (sauv/pinot) ▪ Viticulturist(s) Kevin Watt (Dec 2006) ▪ 23.6ha (cab, pinot, shiraz, sauv) ▪ BWI, IPW, WIETA ▪ PO Box 381 Bot River 7185 ▪ info@paardenkloof.co.za ▪ www.paardenkloof.co.za ▪ S 34° 17' 44.1" E 019° 14' 5.4" ▪ F +27 (0)28-284-9419 ▪ **T +27 (0)28-284-9824**

Packwood Wines

Packwood, on the periphery of Knysna Forest, is a country estate owned by Peter and Vicky Gent (originally from England), complete with luxury accommodation, dairy herd and small vineyard, grapes which Vicky herself now vinifies under the direction of estimable Teddy Hall (Teddy Hall Wines).

★★★★ Sauvignon Blanc Rounded & riper-style **13** (★★★), melon & granadilla perfumes, bountiful fruit with softer acid underpin than **12**, less of variety's tangy verve.

Pinot Noir (NEW) **★★★** Pleasantly savoury **13**, earthy & meaty notes, some stewed red fruit & a structure which would benefit from more of the area's fleet-footed freshness. **Gent Méthode Cap Classique ★★★** Piquant red berry/cherry fruit & rose hue on **12** sparkler from pinot noir (70%), chardonnay; sweeter profile with just enough tangy acidity to keep the spirits high. — MW

Location/WO: Plettenberg Bay ▪ Map: Klein Karoo & Garden Route ▪ Est 2006 ▪ 1stB 2009 ▪ Tasting & sales Mon-Fri 11-3 Sat/Sun & pub hols by prior arrangement ▪ Cheese & wine lunch - book ahead ▪ Small tour groups by appt ▪ Farm produce ▪ Hikes ▪ Mountain biking trail ▪ 4-star country house & self-catering cottages ▪ Owner(s) Peter & Vicky Gent ▪ Winemaker(s) Vicky Gent, advised by Teddy Hall (consultant) ▪ Viticulturist(s) Vicky Gent (Jan 2006) ▪ 380ha/3.5ha (pinot, chard, sauv) ▪ 5t/10,000cs own label 30% red 70% white ▪ PO Box 622 Knysna 6570 ▪ vicky@packwood.co.za ▪ www.packwood.co.za ▪ S 34° 0' 18.77" E 023° 13' 43.33" ▪ **T +27 (0)44-532-7614**

☐ **Paddagang** *see* Tulbagh Winery

Painted Wolf Wines

Highly intelligent and social, the African Wild Dog, aka Painted Wolf, is also endangered. In a bid to help reverse this, Jeremy Borg and his team tithe a percentage of their annual profits to conservation efforts. Paarl-based, they also travel regularly to unlock new markets, most recently Japan, and forge new partnerships with those who share their passion for nature and their philosophy of interesting wines of quality, offering value, and in the spirit of suitability and fun.

Black Pack range

★★★★ Stellenbosch Pinotage Lovely nose, showing fresh banana loaf, brooding fruit; seriously oaked **11** has better balance & composure of fruit & oak than **10** (★★★☆).

★★★★ Pictus III Flagship blend of Swartland shiraz, mourvèdre & grenache. **11** combines power & charm in rich-fruited & polished style. New oak (70%) is evident, but seductive.

★★★★ Roussanne **12** shy peach, dried apricot & lovely composure - floral but also nutty, following to distinct wet stone & pith, yet juicy & rich. Better than **11** (★★★★). Older large oak well integrated. WO Paarl.

Not retasted: **Chenin Blanc 12 ★★★★** Not tasted: **Merlot**, **Shiraz**. Discontinued: **The Chase**.

Pack range

★★★★ Lycaon Grenache (NEW) **13** from Swartland, with dollop shiraz, is smooth, fragrant & earthy, with delicate wafts of dried lavender. Succulent & understated, shows a silky tannin structure & savoury finish.

★★★★ Guillermo Pinotage Intense aromas of red candy, some coconut & wood. **12** is fragrant, packed with black fruit, not overly sweet. Plush & composed, juicy & warm, spicy end.

★★★★ Penny Viognier Organically grown, wild yeast fermented preview **14** oozes exuberant fruit flavours, creamy peach melba with supportive vanilla oak & great textured mouthfeel.

Also tasted: **Rosalind Pinotage Rosé 14 ★★★**

Cape 'Hunting' Blends

★★★★ Lekanyane 'Peleton Blanc' for export. Back-to-form **13** equal blend of chenin, roussanne & viognier. Ripe stonefruit, hay & Swartland sunshine! Intense, exudes bold fragrance, with rounded mouthfeel & creamy oak. Better balanced than **12** (★★★☆).

Madach ★★★★ 'Peloton Rouge' for export. Plums & ripe berry allure on **12** from mix pinotage, grenache, cinsaut. Savoury & juicy, showing toasty oak; dry finish.

The Den Comfort Wines
Cabernet Sauvignon ★★★ Ripe & easy-drinking, lightly oaked **13** charms with milk chocolate, mulberry & red cherry freshness. 'Drink around the fire at the Kruger Park' says winemaker. **Rosé** ★★★ Soft, delicate **14** from Paarl pinotage, light fruited & pretty pink. Also tasted: **Pinotage 13** ★★★ **Chenin Blanc 14** ★★★★ Not tasted: **Sauvignon Blanc**. — WB

Location: Paarl • Map: Paarl & Wellington • WO: Coastal/Swartland/Paarl/Stellenbosch • Est/1stB 2007 • Tasting & sales by appt Mon-Sun 10-5 • Fee R25 • Closed Easter Fri-Mon, Dec 25 & Jan 1 • Lunch by appt (parties of 6 or less) • Owner(s) Jeremy & Emma Borg, & 16 'pack members' • Cellarmaster(s) Rolanie Lotz & Johan Gerber (consultants) • Winemaker(s) Jeremy Borg • ±65ha/40ha (grenache, merlot, mourv, ptage, shiraz, chenin, sauv, viog) • 80t/40,000cs own label 75% red 20% white 5% rosé • Other export brand: Jemma • PO Box 1489 Suider Paarl 7624 • sales@paintedwolfwines.com • www.paintedwolfwines.com • S 33° 46' 14.8" E 018° 57' 14.6" • T +27 (0)21-863-2492

☐ **Palesa Fairtrade** *see* uniWines Vineyards
☐ **Pandora's Box** *see* Nicholson Smith
☐ **Pantére** *see* Knorhoek Wines
☐ **Papillon** *see* Van Loveren Family Vineyards

Paradisum

Peter-Allan Finlayson of Crystallum (see entry) first thought of this as a Swartland project, but grenache from Hemel-en-Aarde joins the blend from the 2012 vintage. Always keen to try new projects, Peter-Allan wanted, he says, 'to work with Swartland fruit and also try out different techniques, like whole-bunch fermentation, some of it in small barrels'.

★★★★ **Paradisum** Ⓖ Gently perfumed, complex aromas on **11** from shiraz, 20% mourvèdre; palate a touch less charming - rather elegant, yes, with fresh acidity, subtle oak & restrained, firm grip, but less generosity. — TJ

☐ **Paradyskloof** *see* Vriesenhof Vineyards
☐ **Parker Family** *see* Altydgedacht Estate

Paserene

'Wine is a massively complex, sophisticated and living thing that you can drink. It excites me just thinking about it,' says Vilafonté and now own-label winemaker Martin Smith. Having worked a decade in California for Louis Vuitton Moët Hennessy, Martin sees himself as a 'swallow', hence the reference to Passeriformes, the order of birds which includes martins and swallows. Working with Cape Town creatives on the packaging, his intention is to offer 'art on the outside and inside of the bottle', and to 'express myself in the way I see fit'.

★★★★ **Marathon** Previewed **13** secret red blend well handled; plummy/prune fruit & cedar, well-judged tannins providing a supple platform for current enjoyment plus drinking till 2020.

Chardonnay ★★★☆ Ex-tank **13** almond & citrus zest styling, over-ripe tangerine note giving an impression of sweetness although bone-dry. Natural ferment/matured 16 months in old oak. WO Elgin. — CR, CvZ

Location: Stellenbosch • WO: Western Cape/Elgin • Est/1stB 2013 • Closed to public • Owner(s)/viticulturist(s) Martin Smith • Cellarmaster(s)/winemaker(s) Martin Smith (Jan 2013) • 6t/560cs own label 60% red 40% white • greatscottsouthafrica@yahoo.com • T +27 (0)71-379-2674

Passages Wine

American couple Ron Gault (eminent banker) and Charlayne Hunter-Gault (eminent journalist) arrived in South Africa in the early 1990s. Later, Cape wine became part of their 'embrace of new beginnings' – with the US intended as the Passages label's prime market. Ron is also a partner in the smart Epicurean brand.

Pinotage ★★★★ 13 as cheery as previous: bright red fruit with lurking dark liquorice nuance. Soft textured & easy. Wellington WO. **Chardonnay ★★★** Unresolved tension between fruit & acid on **13**. Fresh & juicy citrus with toasty oak appeal. Coastal WO. Not retasted: **Merlot 11 ★★★★ Cabernet Sauvignon-Merlot 09 ★★★** — FM

WO: Stellenbosch/Wellington/Coastal ▪ 1stB 2006 ▪ Closed to public ▪ Owner(s) Ronald T Gault & Charlayne Hunter-Gault ▪ Cellarmaster(s)/winemaker(s) Ernst Gouws (2007, consultant) ▪ (cab, merlot, ptage, chard) ▪ ±10,000cs own label 70% red 30% white ▪ gaultronald@gmail.com ▪ www.passageswine.com

Paul Cluver Estate Wines

Cluver family farm De Rust, dating from 1896, lies in the Kogelberg Biosphere in cool-climate Elgin. Visionary Paul Cluver snr pioneered commercial winefarming here in the late 1980s and became a leader in environmental and social sustainability. The younger generation, who subscribe to the same principles, took over in 2003 (4 of the 5 siblings are involved here) and continue to build the reputation of the thriving and diverse business. Son-in-law and winemaker Andries Burger has two new team members, Drew Harty (wines) and Rudi Zandberg (vines), and an equal number of outsize (5T) French casks specifically to ferment pinot noir. These joining seasoned German barrels for riesling. In other tweaking, Burgundy guru Martin Prieur flies in twice a year to advise. A mountain bike park is now open in the al fresco amphitheatre, its creative bridge designs by multi-talented Paul snr winning recognition as a Design Capital of the Year project.

★★★★ Pinot Noir 4 clones for this bottling; **13** raises bar on also-tasted **12 (★★★★)** with perfumed red fruit, silkier tannins than any pinot in this stable. Lovely elegant intensity without sacrificing flavour & balance. **12** tight, firm chalky tannins, needs time to unwind & show more fruit.

★★★★ Seven Flags Pinot Noir Selected barrels of 113 clone. New oak woven into pure fruit, with appealing sultry, smoky aromas. **12** restrained yet intense, with good length. Will reward cellaring.

★★★★ Chardonnay 13 (★★★★★) up a notch from steely **12**, showing more fruit intensity & generosity but retaining elegant restraint. Tangy lime & hazelnut threaded into rich, creamy texture from 40% malolactic ferment, 9 months on lees. Refined, balanced & tempting - but worth cellaring.

★★★★ Gewürztraminer ⊘ Semi-dry styled but beautifully balanced **13 (★★★★★)** betters **12**. Spicy ginger & jasmine blossom, quivers with sweet/sour tension. A bit more breadth than previous, with creamy gingerbread substrate. Classy fusion food partner.

★★★★ Close Encounter Riesling 13 more sugar (34.2 g/l sugar) than sibling but equally balanced, actually tastes drier courtesy racy acidity. A delicate bouquet of sweetness & freshness in featherlight (8.34% alcohol) delivery.

★★★★ Dry Encounter Riesling Driest of the Cluver rieslings, 8.7 g/l sugar offset by piquant lime, kiwi & starfruit in **13**. Creamy, light yet intense, with zesty balance & lingering farewell.

★★★★ Sauvignon Blanc Herbaceous, lemon tones on **13**. Usual dab oaked semillon adds depth & texture. Feisty passionfruit freshness & clean-cut acidity. Good length on this food partner.

★★★★☆ Riesling Noble Late Harvest ⊘ Slimline elegant packaging & appealingly low 9% alcohol belie the riveting freshness & intensity of dried apricot, lime & botrytis flavours on scintillating **12** icon dessert wine, partly wooded. **11 (★★★★★)** was 2013 edition's White Wine of the Year.

Village Pinot Noir ⊛ **★★★★** Smoky cherry fruit ex 3 clones, **13** supple, juicy tannins, mid-palate creaminess enhancing drinkability. Flavoursome, cheerful, earlier accessible than siblings. — MW

Location/WO: Elgin ▪ Map: Elgin, Walker Bay & Bot River ▪ Est 1896 ▪ 1stB 1997 ▪ Tasting & sales Mon-Fri 9–4 Sat/Sun (summer) 9–3 & Sat/Sun (winter) 10-2; tasting centre closed Sundays for period of 6 weeks in winter, phone ahead to confirm ▪ Fee R50 for groups, limited to 10 pax per group ▪ Closed Easter weekend, Dec 25/26 & Jan 1 ▪ Conservation area (part of Kogelberg Biosphere UNESCO heritage site) ▪ MTB track & bike park open to public, fee payable ▪ Open air amphitheatre hosting concerts Nov-Feb ▪ Fresh Restaurant T +27 (0)71-563-6020, booking essential ▪ Owner(s) Cluver family ▪ Cellarmaster(s) Andries Burger (Nov 1996) ▪ Winemaker(s) Andries Burger (Nov 1996), with Drew Harty (Oct 2013) ▪ Viti-culturist(s) Rudi Zandberg (Dec 2013) & Kevin Watt (Mar 2005, consultant) ▪ 80ha (pinot, chard, gewürz, riesling, sauv) ▪ 20% red 80% white ▪ Brands for clients: Woolworths, ScruCap ▪ BWI champion ▪ PO Box 48 Grabouw 7160 ▪ info@cluver. com ▪ www.cluver.com ▪ S 34° 10' 6.2" E 019° 5' 8.1" ▪ F +27 (0)21-844-0150 ▪ **T +27 (0)21-844-0605**

☐ **Paul de Villiers** *see* Landskroon Wines
☐ **Paulina's Reserve** *see* Rickety Bridge Winery
☐ **Paul René** *see* Wonderfontein

Paul Wallace Wines

'One heck of a busy year,' say leading viticultural adviser Paul Wallace and wife Nicky, 'but loving the realisation of our dreams.' Mrs W since the last edition resigned from a full-time job to focus on developing the Elgin-based Paul Wallace Wines family label, including the launch of two new wines (a third, Noble Late Harvest, still fermenting away at press time), opening of a tasting venue, and renovation of labourers' cottages into a homestead 'so we can finally live on our farm!'

★★★★ **Black Dog Malbec 10**'s leaner (13% alcohol) frame shows less of the concentration of **09**, more herbaceous & minty profile. Good dry structure, with variety's prominent tannins.

Brave Heart Pinot Noir ⒩ ★★★☆ Elgin's elegance on **13**, from 7 year old vines. Black cherries, jammy currants & spicy touch from 50% new oak, slight farmyard undertones. Finishes dry, with stalky tealeaf notes. Unevolved, deserves time for fruit flavours to develop. **Little Flirt Sauvignon Blanc** ⒩ ★★★☆ Intended to 'charm & captivate' - & does! Aromatic cool grassy notes on a riper citrus base, well structured, dry & savoury. **13** released after year to show variety's ability to gain complexity in bottle. — HJ

Location/WO: Elgin ▪ Map: Elgin, Walker Bay & Bot River ▪ Est/1stB 2004 ▪ Tasting facility open most Saturdays, other days by appt or when open sign is displayed ▪ Tapas ▪ Owner(s)/viticulturist(s) Paul Wallace ▪ Winemaker(s) Paul Wallace, advised by various other winemakers ▪ 25ha/10.5ha (malbec, pinot, sauv) ▪ 90t/1,000cs own label 90% red 10% white ▪ BWI, IPW ▪ PO Box 141 Elgin 7180 ▪ wallovale@mweb.co.za ▪ www.wallovale.co.za ▪ S 34° 12' 58.67" E 19°03' 32.18 ▪ F +27 (0)86-646-3694 ▪ **T +27 (0)21-848-9744/+27 (0)83-255-1884/+27 (0)82-572-1406**

☐ **Pavillion** *see* Boschendal Wines
☐ **Peacock Ridge** *see* False Bay Vineyards
☐ **Pearlstone** *see* Rhebokskloof Wine Estate
☐ **Pearly Bay** *see* KWV
☐ **Pecan Stream** *see* Waterford Estate
☐ **Pegalle** *see* Bonview Wines
☐ **Pella** *see* Super Single Vineyards
☐ **Peloton** *see* Painted Wolf Wines
☐ **Percheron** *see* Boutinot South Africa

Perdeberg Winery

Originally one of the large co-ops that dotted the winelands, this unpretentious producer with a Voor Paardeberg cellar, consistently delivers arguably some of the best value in the industry. Although the vast vineyard tracts of the 30 member-owners cover most major varieties, the winery remains synonymous with chenin. Wines are released under their own three-tiered labels (with fetching new labels) as well as customer, partnership and themed ranges: Waka Waka, David Frost Signature, Bottelary and Saam (see separate entries).

Dryland Collection

★★★★ **Cabernet Sauvignon** Substantial, expressive **12** shows class after promising **11** debut. Dense & dark, with plush, supple fruit core & solid tannin backbone. Good value, too.

★★★★ **Pinotage** Stylish expression of variety, **12** emphasises vibrant red fruit while reining in wilder tendencies. Elegant & plush, like **11**.

★★★★ **Shiraz** Rhône-like pepper & scrub spice up big, opulent & fruity **12**. Hefty tannin & appealing sinuous minerality should integrate & soften with time. Confirms class of **11**.

★★★★ **Joseph's Legacy** Shiraz-led blend with cab, petit verdot & mourvèdre, **12** is easily as good as maiden **10** (no **11**). Seamless & elegant, showing mineral core clad in dark fruit, with fragrant highlights. Coastal WO.

★★★★ **Chenin Blanc** (NEW) Enticingly layered stone & tropical fruit celebrate **13** newcomer's oak-free handling. Rich, ripe yet crisp, with delightful bitter twist on lengthy finish. Great value.

★★★★ **Barrel Fermented Chenin Blanc** Less obvious oak on **13** produces better balance than **11** (★★★★). Generously ripe fruit takes centre stage, creamy lees texture provides the encore. No **12**.

Pinot Noir-Chardonnay (NEW) ★★★☆ Cheerful, bone-dry rosé. **14** generous fruit & perfume, crisp finish. Coastal WO. **Sauvignon Blanc** (NEW) ★★★ Pungent khaki bush with bellpeppers, **13** full bodied, nicely balanced, with softer acid. Promising newcomer. **Chardonnay-Viognier** (NEW) ★★★ Promising fruit on **13**, but somewhat let down by emphatic oak on nose & palate.

Reserve range

★★★★ **Méthode Cap Classique Chenin Brut** (NEW) Impressive first release **12** presents crunchy apple fruit over shortbread & brioche, delivered on a fine creamy mousse. Underscores chenin's great versatility.

★★★★☆ **Weisser Riesling** (②) Impressive Natural Sweet shows this noble variety to benefit. Piercing acid scythes through layers of honeyed raisin essence. **11** vinified in seasoned barrels.

Also tasted: **Méthode Cap Classique Pinot Noir Rosé 12** ★★★★ Discontinued: **Pinotage**, **Shiraz**, **Chenin Blanc**, **Chardonnay-Viognier**.

Popular range

Sauvignon Blanc ★★★ Generously aromatic **14** with candied fruit aroma, not especially concentrated but fresh & crisp. **Soft Smooth Red** ★★★ Sweetish, light **13** shiraz blend, fruity & fresh. Not tasted: **Cabernet Sauvignon**, **Merlot**, **Pinotage**, **Shiraz**, **Cabernet Sauvignon-Merlot**, **Chenin Blanc**, **Sparkling Rosé**, **Sparkling Chenin Blanc**. In abeyance: **Rosé**. — GdB

Location: Paarl ▪ Map: Paarl & Wellington ▪ WO: Paarl/Coastal ▪ Est 1941 ▪ 1stB 1942 ▪ Tasting & sales Mon-Fri 8—5 Sat 9.30–2 ▪ Closed Easter Fri-Mon, Dec 25/26 & Jan 1 ▪ Cellar tours Mon-Fri by appt ▪ Meals, pre-booked week in advance, for groups of 10+ ▪ BYO picnic ▪ Annual October festival ▪ Owner(s) 30 members ▪ Cellarmaster(s) Albertus Louw (Oct 2008) ▪ Winemaker(s) Riaan Möller (Dec 2006) & Carla Herbst (Jun 2008) ▪ Viticulturist(s) Jaco Engelbrecht (Nov 2011) ▪ 6,000ha/2,564ha (cab, cinsaut, merlot, ptage, shiraz, chard, chenin, sauv) ▪ 18,000t/300,000cs own label 63% red 37% white ▪ BWI, HACCP, IPW, WIETA ▪ PO Box 214 Paarl 7620 ▪ info@perdeberg.co.za ▪ www.perdeberg.co.za ▪ S 33° 39′ 30.00″ E 018° 49′ 37.00″ ▪ F +27 (0)21-869-8245 ▪ **T +27 (0)21-869-8244**

☐ **Pernod Ricard** *see* Long Mountain Wine Company

Peter Bayly Wines

In secluded Groenfontein Valley near Calitzdorp, Peter and Yvonne Bayly are fulfilling their dream of 'living free range', handcrafting port-style wines – including a new pink version – and a country red from Portuguese varieties planted in ancient red soils.

★★★★ **Cape Vintage** (②) Port-style **09**, touriga (45%) with tinta & souzão. Choc/savoury flavours, balanced fortification & sugar; tad firmer than **07**, inviting cellaring - though hard to resist. No **08**.

III ★★★★ Big improvement on **12** for this savoury-fruited wine, older-oak-matured touriga with tinta & souzão. Well-worked tannins & acidity. Very pleasant tipple. Also tasted: **Cape Pink** (NEW) **13** ★★★ **Cape White NV** ★★★ Not retasted: **Cape Late Bottled Vintage 08** ★★★ — CM

Location/WO: Calitzdorp ▪ Map: Klein Karoo & Garden Route ▪ Est 2002 ▪ 1stB 2004 ▪ Tasting, sales & tours by appt ▪ Owner(s) Peter Bayly Wines (Pty) Ltd ▪ Winemaker(s)/viticulturist(s) Peter Bayly ▪ 6.6ha/1.2ha (tinta, touriga, souzão) ▪ ±8t/±1,320cs own label ▪ PO Box 187 Calitzdorp 6660 ▪ info@baylys.co.za ▪ www.peterbayly.co.za ▪ S 33° 27' 16.70" E 021° 45' 34.86" ▪ F +27 (0)86-513-2727 ▪ **T +27 (0)44-213-3702**

☐ **Peter Clarke Collection** *see* PaardenKloof

Peter Falke Wines

Owned by Germany-based sports-footwear king Franz-Peter Falke, the focus is on terroir wines in Stellenbosch's predominantly red-wine 'Golden Triangle' area. The very able Louis Nel (Louis Wines) now advises the team, who relaunched the PF Cabernet and prepared to unveil a Signature MCC sparkling as the guide went to press.

Signature range
★★★★ **Exclusive Blend** Was 'Signature Blend'. Bold but nicely paced Bordeaux quintet, **12** cab-dominant. Sumptuous ripe fruit is freshened by balanced acid, lively tannins. Enjoyable now; good prospects. No **10**, **11**.

Also tasted: **Syrah 12 ★★★★**

PF range
Cabernet Sauvignon ★★★☆ Returns after a short break. **13** lively youngster. Plenty ripe, juicy cab fruit backed by brisk grape tannins. Will benefit from few years' ageing. **Blanc de Noir ★★★ 14** from cab, perfect warm-weather partner. Lightish, fresh, with gentle black fruit persistence. Also tasted: **Pinot Noir 13 ★★★ Ruby Blend 12 ★★★☆ Sauvignon Blanc 14 ★★★** — AL

Location/map/WO: Stellenbosch ▪ 1stB 2003 ▪ Tasting & sales Tue–Sun 11-7 Mon by appt ▪ Fee R45 ▪ Closed Good Fri, Dec 25/26 & Jan 1 ▪ Cellar tours by appt 11-4 ▪ Cheese platters & refreshments ▪ Owner(s) Franz-Peter Falke ▪ Winemaker(s) Louis Nel (2013, consultant) ▪ Viticulturist(s) / GM Werner Schrenk (Jan 2009) ▪ 24ha/±5ha (cab, shiraz) ▪ 100t/12,000cs own label 65% red 25% white 10% rosé ▪ PO Box 12605 Stellenbosch 7613 ▪ marketing@peterfalkewines.co.za ▪ www.peterfalkewines.com ▪ S 34° 0' 2.1" E 018° 50' 19.3" ▪ F +27 (0)21-881-3667 ▪ **T +27 (0)21-881-3677**

☐ **Petit** *see* Ken Forrester Wines

Pfeifer's Boutique Wines

Co-owner and winegrower Pascal Pfeifer advises that vintages 2005 to 2007, the last Caelum Syrah made, are still available from his family's Helderberg farm.

Location: Somerset West ▪ Map: Helderberg ▪ Est 2000 ▪ 1stB 2003 ▪ Tasting & sales by appt ▪ Closed Easter Fri/Sun, Dec 25 & Jan 1 ▪ Owner(s) Pascal & Maya Pfeifer ▪ Winemaker(s)/viticulturist(s) Pascal Pfeifer (Jun 2006) ▪ 1.675ha/1.4ha (shiraz) ▪ 14-16t/±150cs own label 100% red ▪ IPW member ▪ PO Box 5238 Helderberg 7135 ▪ enquiries@pfeifersvineyard.co.za ▪ www.pfeifersvineyard.co.za ▪ S 34° 01' 10.98" E 018° 47' 17.06" ▪ F +27 (0)86-616-8850 ▪ **T +27 (0)21-842-3396**

☐ **Philip Jonker** *see* Weltevrede Estate

Philip Jordaan Wines

Amiable Philip Jordaan established his own brand while long-serving cellarmaster (26 years!) at Breedekloof winery Du Toitskloof, continuing to vinify small parcels of special wines after his retirement in 2010. He's taking a 'wine sabbatical' but promises his fans it will be a short one.

Est/1stB 1998 ▪ For wine orders call T +27 (0)82-573-0620 ▪ Owner(s)/cellarmaster(s)/winemaker(s) Philip Jordaan ▪ Viticulturist(s) Leon Dippenaar ▪ P/Bag X15 Hermanus 7640 ▪ **T +27 (0)82-573-0620**

Phizante Kraal

Changes and improvements continue at the Durbanville boutique winery owned by André and Ronelle Brink, who sell most of their grapes but keep back slightly more each year for their

Diemersdal-vinified own label. Now there's a new tasting room, and a restaurant offering 'contemporary country-style cooking', in a renovated cowshed dating back to 1767.

★★★★☆ **Sauvignon Blanc** ⊘ **14 (★★★★)** a fine bargain, complex & intriguing, with a range of flavours, though palate more about texture & good mouthfeel than fruit intensity. **13** also delicious.

Cabernet Sauvignon ★★★ Ripe but minty red fruit on well-oaked **12**, with an uncomplicated soft palate. Also tasted: **Shiraz 12 ★★★ Chenin Blanc 14 ★★★** — JPf

Location/WO: Durbanville ▪ Map: Durbanville, Philadelphia & Darling ▪ 1stB 2005 ▪ Tasting & sales Mon-Fri 9-4 Sat 10-2.30 ▪ Fee R15 ▪ Restaurant Mon-Fri b'fast 8.30-10.30 lunch 12-2.30 Sat brunch 10-2.30 ▪ Owner(s) André & Ronelle Brink ▪ Winemaker(s) Thys Louw (Jan 2005, Diemersdal) ▪ Viticulturist(s) André Brink ▪ 50ha (cab, shiraz, chenin, sauv) ▪ 2,000cs own label ▪ PO Box 8 Durbanville 7551 ▪ wines@phizantekraal.co.za ▪ www.phizantekraal.co.za ▪ S 33° 47' 47.35" E 018° 40' 13.83" ▪ F +27 (0)21-975-3589 ▪ **T +27 (0)21-825-0060**

PicardiRebel

The PicardiRebel nationwide drinks chain offers wine shoppers a number of affordable options under house brand/occasional label Coast.

Est 1994 ▪ PO Box 1868 Cape Town 8000 ▪ F +27 (0)21-469-3434 ▪ **T +27 (0)21-469-3301**

Pick n Pay

A wide range of producers' own brands appear on the shelves of this national supermarket chain, along with an own portfolio mostly sourced from Robertson Winery, Swartland Winery and Orange River Wine Cellars. Managed by Pick n Pay Corporate Brands' Neil Cooke, the selection includes boxed and bottled single varieties and blends, a handful of carbonated sparklings and low-alcohol options, the latter proving exceptionally popular, especially the Extra Light White.

Enquiries Neil Cooke ▪ Pick n Pay Corporate Brands PO Box 1960 Bedfordview 2008 ▪ ncooke@pnp.co.za ▪ www.picknpay.co.za ▪ F +27 (0)86-616-5949 ▪ **T +27 (0)11-856-7000**

☐ **Pick's Pick** see Butcher Shop & Grill
☐ **Piekeniers** see Tierhoek
☐ **Pierneef Collection** see La Motte
☐ **Pierre Jourdan** see Haute Cabrière
☐ **PK Morkel** see Bellevue Estate Stellenbosch

Place in the Sun

Deon Boshoff, appointed cellarmaster of Distell's Adam Tas production facility at the tender age of 32, is the son of farm employees and learned his trade on a bursary open to the community. So it's appropriate that the Fairtrade-accredited brand for which he now vinifies aspires to unlock opportunities for those involved in its making by contributing a portion of sales.

Merlot ★★★ Interesting spice, rock candy, farmyard & red berry combo in **13**, dry & shy on fruit/weight but appetising. **Sauvignon Blanc** ⊘ **★★★★** Fans of 'green-style' sauvignon will enjoy **14**, the full smoky, flinty, nettly, limy, appley monty in austere, bone-dry package. Also tasted: **Cabernet Sauvignon 13 ★★★ Shiraz 13 ★★★** Not retasted: **Chardonnay 13 ★★★** — HJ

Location/WO: Stellenbosch ▪ Est/1stB 2010 ▪ Closed to public ▪ Owner(s) Distell ▪ Cellarmaster(s)/winemaker(s) Deon Boshoff (2010) ▪ Viticulturist(s) Annelie Viljoen (2010) ▪ 1,000t ▪ ISO 9001 & ISO 14001 (pending), Fairtrade, IPW ▪ PO Box 184 Stellenbosch 7599 ▪ dboshoff@distell.co.za ▪ www.placeinthesun.co.za ▪ **T +27 (0)21-809-7000**

Plaisir de Merle   ⓠ ⑾ ⌂ ◎ ⑧ ⑥

This Simonsberg-Paarl farm has been in the stable of Distell (then Stellenbosch Farmers' Winery) since 1964, with winemaker Niel Bester in charge of the cellar since the maiden Plaisir de Merle-branded vintage of 1993. Fruit from the extensive vineyards, which include some of the Cape's more unusual varieties, is also delivered to other cellars under Distell ownership.

★★★★ **Shiraz** Coconut & minty spice winning over sweet, slightly jammy red fruit when **10** (★★★★) tasted mid-2013. More awkward than affable **09**. WO Simonsberg-Paarl, like Grand Plaisir.

★★★★ **Grand Plaisir** Cab-based Bordeaux sextet with shiraz. Maturing savoury features on **08**; charry oak hints too. Good flavour concentration, rounded tannins & fresh core allow for current drinking.

★★★★ **Chardonnay** Assured **13** in generous, opulent style but retains good varietal definition; pickled lime, oatmeal tones, lees-enriched substance & mineral lift. 8 months in oak, half new.

★★★★ **Sauvignon Blanc** Exuberant **14** loaded with a tropical/fig fullness, controlled (just) by a flinty edge & almost unhinged by 14% alcohol... One third Darling grapes.

Also tasted: **Cabernet Sauvignon 11** ★★★☆ **Merlot 12** ★★★☆ **Petit Plaisir 12** ★★★★ **Grand Brut Méthode Cap Classique 11** ★★★ — DS

Location: Paarl ▪ Map: Franschhoek ▪ WO: Western Cape/Paarl/Simonsberg-Paarl ▪ Est/1stB 1993 ▪ Tasting, sales & cellar tours Mon–Fri 9–5 Sat/Sun 10–4 (Nov–Mar) & Sat 10–2 (Apr–Oct) ▪ Tasting fee R50 ▪ Closed Easter Fri & Dec 25 ▪ Cheese platters available during trading hours R80 ▪ Children welcome ▪ Gifts ▪ Manor House (sleeps 8) can be booked for functions, conferences & weddings ▪ Owner(s) Distell ▪ Cellarmaster(s) Niel Bester (1993) ▪ Viticulturist(s) Drikus Heyns & Freddie le Roux ▪ 974ha/400ha (cabs s/f, malbec, merlot, p verdot, pinot, shiraz, chard, sauv) ▪ 800t/ 80,000cs own label 80% red 20% white ▪ ISO 9001:2008, ISO 14001:2004, BRC, BWI, SGS, WIETA ▪ PO Box 121 Simondium 7670 ▪ info@plaisirdemerle.co.za ▪ www.plaisirdemerle.co.za ▪ S 33° 51' 0.0" E 018° 56' 36.2" ▪ F +27 (0)21-874-1689 ▪ **T +27 (0)21-874-1071**

Plettenvale Wines

Inspired by 'super wines' from small vineyards on a 2007 Tuscan walking and cooking tour, Gloria Strack van Schyndel accepted the challenge of becoming a small-scale vigneron on her Plettenberg Bay property. Clearing alien vegetation, braving crop-marauding birds and aided by experienced consultants, she has conquered a recalcitrant climate to produce a boutique range.

Brut Rosé Methode Cap Classique ★★★ Tawny-hued **12** (subsequent disgorgement of chardonnay & pinot (32%) sparkling tasted this edition) has lively, firm bubbles & savoury notes of salted biscuits, iodine & marmalade best enjoyed soon. Not retasted: **Chardonnay 13** ★★★ Not tasted: **Dry Rosé**. — HJ

Location/WO: Plettenberg Bay ▪ Map: Klein Karoo & Garden Route ▪ Est 2008 ▪ 1stB 2011 ▪ Tasting & sales by appt ▪ Self-catering cottages ▪ Owner(s) Gloria Strack van Schyndel ▪ Winemaker(s) Anton Smal (consultant) ▪ Viticulturist(s) Paul Wallace (Nov 2007, consultant) ▪ 5.3ha/2.3ha (pinot, shiraz, chard) ▪ PO Box 2103 Plettenberg Bay 6600 ▪ info@plettenvalewines.co.za ▪ www.plettenvalewines.co.za ▪ S 34° 04' 53.9" E 023° 19' 41.4" ▪ F +27 (0)44-533-9146 ▪ **T +27 (0)44-533-9146/+27 (0)82-322-0765**

☐ **Poetry** *see* Flagstone Winery
☐ **Poker Hill** *see* Somerbosch Wines
☐ **Polkadraai** *see* Stellenbosch Hills Wines
☐ **Polo Club** *see* Val de Vie Wines
☐ **Pomüla** *see* Imbuko Wines

Pongrácz

Specialist méthode cap classique bubbly brand named after Desiderius Pongrácz, Dachshund-loving aristocrat who fled the Hungarian uprising, settled in Stellenbosch in 1958 and went on to become chief viticultural adviser to Distillers Corporation, Distell's precursor.

★★★★ **Desiderius** 2nd disgorgement of **08** (★★★★★) follows previous impressive form: 70% chardonnay with pinot noir offer delightful brioche & lemon shortbread. Silky mousse carries to lengthy roasted nut finish. First since **03**.

★★★★ **Pongrácz Brut** Latest **NV** pinot noir/chardonnay (55/45) bubbly shows improved form. Appealing baked apple fruit & shortbread borne on fine, creamy mousse. Polished, subtle & lingering.

Pongrácz Brut Rosé ★★★★ Dry pinot noir-chardonnay **NV** bubbly with prominent strawberry fruit & gentle mousse. Pleasant if uncomplicated. From widely sourced fruit, as for all. — GdB

☐ **Porcelain Mountain** *see* Porseleinberg

Porcupine Ridge

This is Boekenhoutskloof's original 'value' range, and it continues to build its reputation. The Rhône-inspired offerings, sourced in Swartland, are the more interesting, yet most of these wines over-perform in terms of price.

★★★★ Syrah ⊘ Peppery black fruit abounds in layered, complex **13** that raises bar on **12** (**★★★★**). Underlying concentration, richness & generosity still reined-in mid-2014 but will unfurl & reward given time.

Syrah-Viognier ⊘ **★★★★** Smoky violet delicacy vies with bold, earthy black fruit on **13**, which ratchets up quality. Long, focused & dry with silky tannins. **Viognier-Grenache Blanc ★★★★** Ripe honeyed nectarine on big **13** blend. Polished & poised, with oak supporting rich fruit beautifully. Succulent long tail. Also tasted: **Cabernet Sauvignon** ⊘ 13 **★★★★** **Merlot** ⊘ 13 **★★★★** **Sauvignon Blanc 14 ★★★** — FM

Porseleinberg

The Swartland's Porcelain Mountains which give this property its name are mere hills, in fact — but ambitions soar! A few organic shiraz vineyards were established before Boekenhoutskloof acquired the farm in 2009 and appointed Callie Louw to manage a major planting programme based on organic, even biodynamic, principles (chickens and Nguni cattle play their part too). Most of the fruit will be delivered to the parental Franschhoek winery, but Callie is crafting his one exquisite wine from the older vines, in accord with the 'natural' approach of the Swartland Independent Producers.

★★★★ Porseleinberg ⊛ **10** from syrah/shiraz tasted young, **11** held back for now, but **12** (**★★★★★**) is superb! Many years ahead of it, but already complexity on perfumed aromas & super-subtle but intense palate, with a truly rare refinement. Also rare is lack of oak influence - in concrete 'egg' for year. Tiny yield, bunch-pressed. Bone-dry; 13.5% alcohol; big tannins also a touch dry - give them time. — TJ

Location: Malmesbury • WO: Swartland • Est 2009 • 1stB 2011 • Closed to public • Owner(s) Boekenhoutskloof Winery Pty Ltd • Winemaker(s)/viticulturist(s) Callie Louw (Jun 2009) • 85ha/30ha (shiraz) • 6t/600cs own label 100% red • Organic EU Control Union • PO Box 433 Franschhoek 7690 • callie@porseleinberg.com • www.porseleinberg.com • F +27 (0)86-566-9332 • **T +27 (0)79-884-2309**

☐ **Porter Mill Station** *see* Tulbagh Winery
☐ **Porterville Cellars** *see* Tulbagh Winery
☐ **Postcard Series** *see* Stark-Condé Wines

Post House Vineyards

Having set up home in an old post office building next to the Helderberg village of Raithby, boutique owner/winemaker Nick Gebers naturally chose a philatelic theme for his wines. From the appropriately inky Penny Black to the new Chinese-inspired Golden Monkey, each carries a historical explanation and a yarn to entertain you while you sip.

★★★★ Bulls Eye Was 'Cabernet Sauvignon'. **12**, still from that grape, steps up on **11** (**★★★★**) with greater purity of fruit, classy oak. Rich, ripe & aromatic, with solid tannins, massive concentration. Needs time to soften & round out.

★★★★ Missing Virgin Foursquare Cape Blend pinotage & petit verdot, **12** has intense ripe berry fruit on robust tannins. Hefty 15.5% alcohol, opaque & dense. Not for the faint of heart.

★★★★ **Penny Black** Blockbuster shiraz/Bordeaux/chenin blend is almost too dense & heavy to enjoy. **12** has the subtlety of a falling anvil, packing 15% alcohol, thick blackcurrant & chalky tannins. **11** sold out untasted.

★★★★ **Stamp Of Chenin** Full & yeasty, with candied fruit, **13** shows serious intent. Barrel ferment & maturation bolsters rather than dominates structure. Weighty mouthfeel, savoury finish.

★★★★☆ **Treskilling Yellow** Now bottled, **12** Noble Late Harvest chenin delivers on promise, improves on **10** (★★★★). Spicy mulled honey, dried apricots & orange zest in a rich, rounded body with delicate but effective acidity. 19 months small oak. No **09**, **11**.

Golden Monkey ★★★ Rhône-style blend mostly shiraz with 20% mourvèdre, 6% grenache in **12**. Dusty, tarry notes over mulberry & old leather; tad awkward with astringent tannins. WO Coastal. Also tasted: **Black Mail 11** ★★★☆ **Merry Widow 12** ★★★☆ **Blueish Black 13** ★★★☆ **Blueish White 13** ★★★ Discontinued: **Sauvignon Blanc**. — GdB

Location: Somerset West ▪ Map: Helderberg ▪ WO: Stellenbosch/Western Cape/Coastal ▪ Est/1stB 1997 ▪ Tasting, sales & cellar tours Mon-Fri 9-5 Sat by appt ▪ Fee R30 ▪ Closed all pub hols ▪ BYO picnic ▪ Guest house ▪ Owner(s) Nicholas Gebers ▪ Cellarmaster(s) Nick Gebers ▪ Winemaker(s) Nick Gebers, with Riana Theart ▪ 70ha/39ha (cab, merlot, p verdot, ptage, shiraz, chenin, sauv) ▪ 200t/16,000cs own label 65% red 35% white ▪ PO Box 5635 Helderberg 7135 ▪ info@posthousewines.co.za ▪ www.posthousewines.co.za ▪ S 34° 1' 8.1" E 018° 48' 41.6" ▪ F +27 (0)21-842-2409 ▪ **T +27 (0)21-842-2409**

☐ **Post Tree** *see* Valley Vineyards Wine Company
☐ **Pot Luck Club** *see* Almenkerk Wine Estate
☐ **Pride of Kings** *see* Waterstone Wines
☐ **Private Collection** *see* Saxenburg Wine Farm
☐ **Prohibition** *see* Camberley Wines
☐ **Protea** *see* Anthonij Rupert Wyne
☐ **Provenance** *see* Saronsberg
☐ **Provoyeur** *see* Devonvale Golf & Wine Estate

Pulpit Rock Winery

Lying on the foothills of the Swartland's Kasteelberg, Pulpit Rock takes its name from a distinctive craggy outcrop on that mountain. The Brink family have grown grapes here for over half a century, but made their own wine first in 2004. Their style is fruit driven, something they believe is dictated by the soil and climate, whose diversity also gives a unique character.

Reserve range

★★★★ **Pinotage** Youthful **12** (★★★★★) has a real sense of place: pure, unshowy perfume; big but beautifully proportioned, oak (80% new) just needs time to integrate. Follows sturdy **10**.

★★★★ **Chardonnay** Citrus, spice & noticeable toasty oak (though just 10% new French) promising introduction to retasted **12** (★★★). Palate less impressive, rather heavy, sweet, with roughish tail. Lacks focus of last **09**.

Petit Verdot ★★★★ Deep hued, with lifted violet aromas, **12** is sturdily built yet balanced, with a sound core of acid. All-new French oak well absorbed. **Louisa** ★★★★ Harmonious pinotage-based blend with cab, malbec & petit verdot. **12** full bodied, rounded; a hint of oak vanilla lifting overall savoury profile. Also tasted: **Cabernet Sauvignon 12** ★★★ **Shiraz 12** ★★★ Discontinued: **Merlot**.

Brink Family range

Pinotage ★★★ Youthfully approachable **13**. Enjoyable juicy red fruit with bit of backbone to allow for further year/two. **Chardonnay** ★★★ Tiny 10% oaked portion in **14** allows full rein to exuberant melon, orange zest features. Fruit further highlighted by few grams sugar. Also tasted: **Cabernet**

Sauvignon 13 ★★★ **Merlot 12** ★★ **Shiraz 12** ★★★ **Chenin Blanc 14** ★★★ Not retasted: **Pinotage Rosé 13** ★★

Swartland Stories
Chenin Blanc-Viognier ★★★ Refreshing, crisp **14** with twist sun-dried apricot. Fruitily dry. Also tasted: **Shiraz-Pinotage-Grenache 13** ★★ — AL

Location: Riebeek West ▪ Map/WO: Swartland ▪ Est 2003 ▪ 1stB 2004 ▪ Tasting & sales Mon-Fri 9—5 Sat 10—2 ▪ Closed Easter Fri-Sun, Dec 25/26 & Jan 1 ▪ Cellar tours by appt ▪ BYO picnic ▪ Walks/hikes ▪ MTB trail ▪ Annual olive festival (May) ▪ Self-catering accommodation ▪ Owner(s) Brink family ▪ Winemaker(s) Riaan van der Spuy (Dec 2011) ▪ Viti-culturist(s) Marco Roux (Dec 2008, consultant) ▪ 600ha/450ha (cab, grenache, merlot, mourv, p verdot, ptage, shiraz, chard, chenin) ▪ 650t/30,000cs own label 70% red 29% white 1% rosé + 200,000L bulk ▪ Other export brand: Cape Tranquility ▪ PO Box 1 Riebeek West 7306 ▪ info@pulpitrock.co.za ▪ www.pulpitrock.co.za ▪ S 33° 20' 47.4" E 018° 51' 14.1" ▪ F +27 (0)22-461-2028 ▪ **T +27 (0)22-461-2025**

☐ **Pure African** *see* Bellevue Estate Stellenbosch

Quando Vineyards & Winery

The original Bruère family arrived in the Robertson area from France in the 1700s. Sixth generation Martin and Fanus Bruwer have been making and bottling under the Quando label since 2001. With such experience under his belt, Fanus is happy to say 2014 was one of the best white-wine vintages 'over the past century, thanks to a long spring with sufficient rain to allow slow ripening.'

Mourvèdre Rosé ★★★ Salmon glints & strawberry tones on dry & zesty **14**, a crowd pleaser. **Sauvignon Blanc** ★★★★ Riverine home-farm vineyard delivers exuberant **14**; ladles of peach focused by crisp nettly acidity. **Chenin Blanc-Viognier** ★★★★ Unwooded **14** has rich & creamy oatmeal character, with dried fruit intensity. Attractive blend of 32 year old chenin with 14% viognier. Not retasted: **Pinot Noir 12** ★★★ Not tasted: **Natural Sweet Sauvignon Blanc**. — DS

Location: Bonnievale ▪ Map/WO: Robertson ▪ Est/1stB 2001 ▪ Tasting & sales by appt ▪ Closed all pub hols ▪ Owner(s) F M Bruwer cc ▪ Cellarmaster(s)/winemaker(s) Fanus Bruwer (Jan 1991) ▪ Viticulturist(s) Martin Bruwer (Jan 1991) ▪ 190ha/80ha (mourv, chenin, sauv) ▪ 6,000cs own label 10% red 90% white ▪ PO Box 82 Bonnievale 6730 ▪ info@quando.co.za ▪ www.quando.co.za ▪ S 33° 56' 9.6" E 020° 1' 28.8" ▪ F +27 (0)23-616-2752 ▪ **T +27 (0)23-616-2752**

☐ **Quay 5** *see* Two Oceans
☐ **Quest** *see* Du Toitskloof Winery
☐ **Quinta do Sul** *see* Lieben Wines

Quoin Rock Winery

Ownership might now rest with a wine-loving Ukranian businessman but the quality continuity is there in winemaker Narina Cloete and viticulturist Nico Walters. They are both familiar with the almost schizophrenic profile of the home-owned vineyards and wines, cool climate from Agulhas and warmer-fruited Stellenbosch, yet both fit perfectly into the range, each area used to express certain wine styles. Of the distinctive wine names, Oculus is a design feature in the cellar, and The Centaur, The Nicobar and The Mendi are ships which sank off Cape Agulhas, yet another link to that area. The upgrading and rejuvenation continues, begun with the change of ownership and designed to reposition Quoin Rock as a top-end producer locally and internationally. The tasting centre is next, closed for major renovation until Spring 2015.

★★★★☆ **Syrah** ⓐ Muscular, handsome **11** has rejected the pretty side of shiraz, gone for character, structure & the longer haul. With 13% mourvèdre.

★★★★ **The Centaur** ⓐ Great care in shiraz-led **09**: whole-berry natural ferment, long skin contact, new oak maturation, result is crimson-hued brambleberries & black pepper, fine-grained tannins.

For more information, visit wineonaplatter.com

★★★★ **Chardonnay** Style switches from svelte to flamboyant in naturally fermented **13**, sumptuous pear & butterscotch tone well freshened by citrus, but unashamedly oaked & ample. WO W Cape. Follows cool-fruited **12** (★★★★★).

★★★★☆ **The Nicobar Reserve Sauvignon Blanc** Distinctive wooded sauvignon only in the best years. With a lime pickle & pine nut intro, **12** draws you in to a vital, zesty palate, lipsmacking freshness. Threaded throughout & taking a bow on the finish is a lovely pure minerality.

★★★★☆ **Sauvignon Blanc** With 'Cape South Coast' prefix previously, now unnoted WO Coastal. **13** (★★★★) steely & dry with oystershell & flint nuances. Attractively taut & food styled, with grapefruit pithiness, but lacks gravitas & wow factor of **12**.

★★★★ **Cape South Coast Cap Classique** With a touch of pinotage to pinot noir & chardonnay, latest **NV** sparkler gains more red berry profile but the elegance, finely crafted bubbles & refined palate remain intact, memorable.

★★★★☆ **Vine Dried Sauvignon Blanc** Barrel-aged **13** (★★★★) unctuously smooth & rich, with subtle fig & barley sugar flavours. Shade off acid & fruit intensity of **12**, still decadently delicious dessert, on its own or with cheeses. Simonsberg—Stellenbosch WO.

Discontinued: **Merlot, The Mendi, The Oculus.** — MW

Location/map: Stellenbosch ▪ WO: Simonsberg—Stellenbosch/Stellenbosch/Western Cape/Coastal/Cape South Coast ▪ Est 1998 ▪ 1stB 2001 ▪ Tasting & sales will reopen Spring 2015 ▪ Fee R35 ▪ Closed Easter Fri/Sun, Dec 25/26 & Jan 1 ▪ Cheese platters ▪ Owner(s) Quoin Rock Wines (Pty) Ltd ▪ Winemaker(s) Narina Cloete (Jun 2010) ▪ Viticulturist(s) Nico Walters (Sep 2012) ▪ 193ha/15ha (cabs s/f, merlot, mourv, shiraz, sauv, viog) ▪ 200t/22,000cs own label 55% red 35% white 7% MCC 3% dessert ▪ PO Box 1193 Stellenbosch 7599 ▪ tasting@quoinrock.co.za ▪ www.quoinrock.com ▪ S 33° 52' 42.5" E 018° 52' 2.3" ▪ F +27 (0)21-888-4744 ▪ **T +27 (0)21-888-4740**

Raats Family Wines

In pursuit of only the very best chenin, Bruwer Raats seeks out specific soil combinations planted with older vines. Three different vineyards of this soil dotted around Stellenbosch are under long-term contract and provide the grapes for his top wine, a perennial high-flyer in many international competitions and tastings. Continuing his fascination with the Loire, his other focus is cabernet franc, either singly or as the dominating grape in Bordeaux blends, both under the Raats label and for Mvemve Raats (listed separately), his winemaking collaboration with friend Mzokhona Mvemve.

★★★★☆ **Cabernet Franc** Exquisitely balanced, elegantly intense **12** follows seamlessly on from stellar **11** (★★★★★), with signature tomato leaf, liquorice, perfume & dark cooked berries. Supportive acidity freshens & lengthens while assertive yet plushy tannins promise future enjoyment.

★★★★ **Dolomite Cabernet Franc** Quiet **13** shows dark berried fruit enlivened with perfume & tealeaf notes. Also-tasted **12** seems livelier, with ripe black fruit dancing on the palate, both wines ending softly yet positively.

★★★★ **Red Jasper** Smart & accomplished **12** (★★★★★) radiates ripeness (blackberries & currants), well reined in by chewy tannins & enlivened by balancing acidity. Cab franc-led Bordeaux blend as is shyer, also-tasted **13**, both styled for serious contemplation, deserving good food & friends.

★★★★☆ **Old Vine Chenin Blanc** Slow-starting **13** opens up with glorious flavours of yellow fruit, creamy notes, crunchy apples, flowers & just a hint of spice. Endless finish changes & evolves, cleaned up by lick of fresh acid in tail. 3 different Stellenbosch blocks, average age 45. Only 30% oaked, French, none new.

★★★★ **Original Chenin Blanc** Unwooded **13** improves deliciously on **12** (★★★★) with fresh flavours of yellow peaches & perfumed pears, bouncy acidity & lengthy finish. A cut above your everyday sipper. Coastal WO. — CM

Location/map: Stellenbosch ▪ WO: Stellenbosch/Coastal ▪ Est/1stB 2000 ▪ Tasting & sales by appt only ▪ Closed all pub hols ▪ Owner(s) Bruwer Raats ▪ Cellarmaster(s) Bruwer Raats (Jan 2000) ▪ Winemaker(s) Gavin Bruwer Slabbert

(Feb 2010) ▪ Viticulturist(s) Bruwer Raats (Jan 2000) & Gavin Bruwer Slabbert (Feb 2010) ▪ 30ha (cab f, chenin) ▪ 150t/20,000cs own label 40% red 60% white ▪ PO Box 2068 Dennesig Stellenbosch 7601 ▪ braats@mweb.co.za ▪ www.raats.co.za ▪ S 33° 58' 16.6" E 018° 44' 55.3" ▪ F +27 (0)86-647-8500 ▪ **T +27 (0)21-881-3078**

☐ **Racetrack** *see* Damarakloof
☐ **Radford Dale** *see* Winery of Good Hope

Rainbow's End Wine Estate

The Malan family unearthed their pot of gold on a high-altitude fruit farm in Stellenbosch's Banhoek back in the 1970s. Years of part-time, hands-on cultivation, conversion and conservation by civil engineer father Jacques and wife Ingrid, latterly joined by sons Anton (accountant/winemaker) and Francois (winemaker/viticulturist), have seen a collection of mostly Bordeaux reds, now headed by an impressive reserve bottling, sold locally and abroad.

Reserve range ⓃⒺⓌ

★★★★☆ **Family Reserve Bordeaux Blend** Impressive **11** opaque, boldly styled blend 5 Bordeaux varieties. Resolute, ripe tannins frame complex melange sweet dark red fruit & spice. Accessibility aided by some sweetness; carries heftiness well.

Estate range

★★★★ **Cabernet Sauvignon** Dense, compact core pure blackcurrant in classic **12**, firmly underpinned by tannins from half new oak, which will need time to resolve. Same bold 2 year oaking regime for all reds.

★★★★ **Cabernet Franc** Spicy, aromatic **12**, full bodied, with gorgeously ripe, elegant fruit framed by sturdy tannins.

★★★★☆ **Limited Release Cabernet Franc** Single-vineyard bottling. **12** densely ripe & complex red fruit with finely integrated tannins. Still youthful, will benefit from time in bottle.

★★★★ **Merlot** Dense, seriously styled **12**'s savoury plum fruit seasoned by spicy oak. Resolute tannins ensure properly dry finish.

★★★★☆ **Shiraz** Deeply coloured **12**'s (★★★★) overtly spicy dark fruit exhibits more charm & ease than the range's cabs, though perhaps not as regal as **11**. Supple tannins smoothly harmonious.

Also tasted: **Mystical Corner 13** ★★★★ Not retasted: **Rosé 12** ★★★ — IM

Location/map: Stellenbosch ▪ WO: Banghoek ▪ Est 1978 ▪ 1stB 2002 ▪ Tasting, sales & tours by appt ▪ Fee R25, waived on purchase of 4+ btls ▪ Closed Dec 25 & Jan 1 ▪ Sales also via website, delivery free of charge ▪ Conservation area ▪ Owner(s) Malan family ▪ Cellarmaster(s) Anton Malan (Nov 2000) ▪ Winemaker(s) Anton Malan (Nov 2000) & Francois Malan (Jan 2005) ▪ Viticulturist(s) Francois Malan (Jan 2005) ▪ 52ha/21.6ha (cabs s/f, malbec, merlot, p verdot, shiraz) ▪ 120t/8,200cs own label 90% red 10% rosé ▪ IPW, WIETA ▪ PO Box 2253 Dennesig 7601 ▪ info@rainbowsend.co.za ▪ www.rainbowsend.co.za ▪ S 33° 56' 25.8" E 018° 56' 42.6" ▪ F +27 (0)21-885-1722 ▪ **T +27 (0)21-885-1719/+27 (0)83-411-0170/+27 (0)82-404-1085**

☐ **Rain Song** *see* Ses'Fikile

Raka

Out on a limb in every sense, ebullient Piet Dreyer, squid fisherman extraordinaire, burst onto the wine scene a little over a decade ago to considerable acclaim. His unabashed enthusiasm and desire to learn quickly triumphed over lack of experience, and the family-run winery and vineyards near Stanford produced highly rated wines from the start. Those early years are remembered and celebrated in the new Five Maidens, a limited release of only 4,000 bottles – 1,000 for each of Piet's children. Eldest scion Gerhard's son Pieter was born the past year, and of course is his granddad's darling, regularly taken around the farm and, naturally, to the harbour.

★★★★ **Cabernet Sauvignon** Ⓠ **10** has trademark ripe dark berry fruit, concentrated flavours & gentle oak spice. Elegant, with a super balance, freshness & structure.

★★★★☆ **Cabernet Franc** 🏵 **11** follows on stellar **09** (★★★★☆) with class, elegant perfume, concentrated berry flavours, herbal edge & dusty tannins. Oak is in perfect harmony with the fresh & intense fruit, balanced by a fine acid structure.

★★★★ **Malbec** Occasional label. Youthful **12** (★★★☆) chunky, with dark fruit, heavy tannins needing time. Not same quality & complexity as last-made **09**.

★★★★ **Mourvèdre** 🏵 Meaty, fragrant coriander spice allures on **11**. Firmly structured & made for food, the sweet-savoury marriage is harmonious & moreish. A lifting sour cherry finish delights.

★★★★ **Petit Verdot** 🏵 Deep ruby-hued **10** offered intense dark cherry & blackcurrant with great fruit purity previously. Rich, complex savoury support & refreshing acidity. Should be drinking well.

★★★★☆ **Biography Shiraz** ⟋ Flagship offers a kaleidoscope of black berry, violet, vanilla & white pepper aromas & flavours in **11**. The lush texture, seamless & complex structure adds to elegance & refinement, though does not have the texture & depth of exceptional **10** (★★★★★).

★★★★ **Quinary** ⟋ Five-way Bordeaux-style red shows silky, harmonious berry & vanilla flavours in **10**. Good balance, with mouthfilling savoury fruit & velvety tannins from mostly older oak barrels.

★★★★☆ **Five Maidens** (NEW) Knockout **11** 5-way cab-led Bordeaux-style commemorates 10 years of the Dreyer family in wine. Elegant intensity, without excess weight. Pristine black fruit is complemented by buffed tannins from 24 months in new French oak. Great vibrancy & persistence.

★★★★ **Figurehead Cape Blend** 🏵 Five Bordeaux varieties & a dollop of pinotage, **09** is now settled & balanced. Big & bold, with with smooth & appealing spicy fruit flavours.

Rosé Dry ⟋ ★★★ **14** easy, fruity dry pink from 7 different varieties; red-berried fun for salads & seafood in summer. **Chenin Blanc** ★★★★ Zippy apple & vanilla on uncomplicated, nicely rounded **13**. Easy & appealing. Coastal WO. Also tasted: **Barrel Select Merlot 12** ★★★★ **Spliced 11** ★★★ **Sauvignon Blanc 14** ★★★★ **Shannonea Dry White Blend 13** ★★★ Not retasted: **Pinotage 11** ★★★★ **Sangiovese 12** ★★★ — WB

Location: Stanford ▪ Map: Elgin, Walker Bay & Bot River ▪ WO: Klein River/Western Cape/Coastal/Cape South Coast ▪ Est/1stB 2002 ▪ Tasting & sales Mon-Fri 9–5 Sat 10–2.30 ▪ Tasting fee: 4 wines on daily tasting list free, other wines R10/wine ▪ Closed Sun, Good Fri & Dec 25 ▪ Cellar tours & large groups by appt ▪ BYO picnic ▪ Conservation area ▪ Owner(s) Piet Dreyer ▪ Winemaker(s) Josef Dreyer (Jan 2007) ▪ Viticulturist(s) Pieter Dreyer (Jan 2007) ▪ 760ha/62ha (5 Bdx, mourv, ptage, sangio, shiraz, sauv, viog) ▪ 350t/30,000cs own label 75% red 17% white 8% rosé ▪ BWI, IPW ▪ PO Box 124 Caledon 7230 ▪ info@rakawine.co.za ▪ www.rakawine.co.za ▪ S 34° 23' 56.1" E 019° 37' 26.7" ▪ F +27 (0)86-606-5462 ▪ **T +27 (0)28-341-0676**

Rall Wines

Donovan Rall finished his winemaking studies in 2005, went travelling to gain work experience for a period, and then made his first own-label wines in 2008. Grapes are sourced mostly from Swartland and until recently he made only one white blend and one red though tiny bottlings of verdelho and grenache noir are set to join the range. He is one of the more prominent figures among a group of young winemakers who have re-energised the local wine scene in recent times.

★★★★☆ **Rall Red** Deliberate focus on Swartland's delicacy gains impetus in scintillating **12**; higher percentage stems in ferment adding fresh natural tannin to frame pretty red & black berry fruit, with dash white pepper. 85% shiraz, rest grenache. 18 months older oak. Gear up on **11** (★★★★).

★★★★★ **Rall White** Super silky, the mineral texture of **13** (★★★★☆) has great depth; supportive older oak & seamless acid spine underlie poise, balance, in a salty-tang finish. Naturally fermented blend chenin, verdelho, chardonnay & viognier from Swartland & Stellenbosch, as was **12**. To cellar, & savour. — DS

Location: Swartland ▪ WO: Swartland/Coastal ▪ Est/1stB 2008 ▪ Tasting, sales & cellar tours by appt ▪ Owner(s)/ winemaker(s)/viticulturist(s) Donovan Rall ▪ 10t/1,000cs own label 50% red 50% white ▪ info@rallwines.co.za ▪ www.rallwines.co.za ▪ **T +27 (0)72-182-7571**

☐ **Ralph Parker** *see* Altydgedacht Estate

Rannoch Farm ⓃⒺⓌ

Proud of their Scottish heritage, owners Rory and Ricky Antrobus named their Helderberg farm after Loch Rannoch in Scotland. 'The island in the middle of our lake and the surrounding scenery are reminiscent of the highlands,' explains viticulturist Rory, who nurtures a single hectare of cabernet for optimum fruit quality. 'Avondale in Paarl has been making our wine successfully for the past four years and this partnership should continue into the future.'

★★★★ **Cabernet Sauvignon** Fruit's the hero in **09**, cassis & black cherries, dark chocolate, creamy-rich, & enough savoury tannin to make it serious, a food partner. Plushly elegant, at perfect drinking age. — JG, CR

Location/WO: Stellenbosch ▪ Est 1999 ▪ 1stB 2003 ▪ Closed to public ▪ Owner(s) Rory & Ricky Antrobus ▪ Winemaker(s) Corné Marais, with Ivan September (both Jan 2010, Avondale) ▪ Viticulturist(s) Rory Antrobus (Mar 1999) ▪ 8ha/1ha (cab) ▪ 6t/500cs own label 100% white ▪ PO Box 5667 Helderberg 7135 ▪ rory@gmint.co.za ▪ **T +27 (0)21-842-3601**

☐ **Raoul's** *see* Beaumont Wines

Rare Earth Wines ⓆⓎⓐ

On Plettenberg Bay's wine route, John 'Chick' Legh's polo estate is home to two Rare Earth Retreats: the Redford Farm Country House and Rondebosch Wine Estate, with almost 4 ha of sauvignon blanc, chardonnay and pinot noir vinified by consultant Anton Smal. A tasting venue is now open by appointment, and visitors can pre-book cheese hampers to enjoy al fresco on the scenic property.

★★★★ **Champu** ⓃⒺⓌ Unlike its bold packaging & out-there name, **12** MCC sparkler from chardonnay is classic, restrained; subtle green apple & toasted brioche; comes alive on finish with burst of zesty bubbles, long bone-dry finish. Perfect solo sipper, or elegant meal companion.

SAV ★★★★ Was 'Sauvignon Blanc' when previewed last time, now-bottled **13** matches expectations with creamy texture, subtle pea & melon tones, enlivening acidity. — CvZ

Location/WO: Plettenberg Bay ▪ Map: Klein Karoo & Garden Route ▪ Est 2009 ▪ 1stB 2012 ▪ Tasting by appt only ▪ Cheese hampers to be pre-booked for summer picnics ▪ Guest house (Rare Earth Retreats www.rare-earthretreats.co.za) ▪ Owner(s) John Legh ▪ Cellarmaster(s)/winemaker(s) Anton Smal (2012, consultant) ▪ Viticulturist(s) Doug Lund (2009, consultant) ▪ 16.23ha/3.99ha (pinot, chard, sauv) ▪ 27t/1,110cs own label 100% white ▪ PO Box 295 The Crags 6602 ▪ dltadmin@iafrica.com ▪ S 33° 55' 58.32" E 023° 26' 21.40" ▪ F +27 (0)44-534-8387 ▪ **T +27 (0)44-534-8387**

☐ **Ready Steady** *see* Southern Sky Wines
☐ **Rebourne Fairtrade** *see* Imbuko Wines
☐ **Rebus** *see* Romond Vineyards
☐ **Red Chair** *see* Rooiberg Winery

RED ESCape

Made by Stellenzicht, RED ESCape is positioned as an antidote to the demands of 24 x 7 connectedness, the unserious packaging promising a convivial, any-occasion red.

Red Blend ⓈⒼ ★★ Several grains sugar notwithstanding, **11** shiraz & pinotage comes across as firm, even stern, more food wine than solo boot-me-up. Try with cherry-choc mousse, says winemaker. — DC, JP

☐ **Red Falcon** *see* Middelvlei Estate
☐ **Red Gold** *see* Bushmanspad Estate
☐ **Red Tape** *see* Tanja Beutler Wine Collection
☐ **Red White Pink** *see* Nomada Wines

Reiersvlei

'Enjoyment of life' caused Russell and Elize Inggs to postpone their bottling dates, hence no new vintages from their Great Karoo wine farm, named after its resident grey herons. With some of the highest vineyards in South Africa (860m average), the Inggs practice a minimum-interference approach to achieve 'an honest reflection of our terroir'.

Touriga Nacional Ⓥ ★★★ Friendly **11** has spice & orange peel lift, well-behaved tannins, juicy conclusion masking high alcohol. **Red Muscadel** Ⓥ ★★★ **12** fortified dessert with sweet toffee apple flavour enlivened by tangy acid & gentle tannic grip. Not retasted: **Shiraz 11 ★★ Sauvignon Blanc 12 ★★★ Cape Vintage Port 10 ★★** Not tasted: **Pinotage.** — HJ, CvZ

Location: Prince Albert ▪ Map: Klein Karoo & Garden Route ▪ WO: Prince Albert Valley ▪ Est 1999 ▪ 1stB 2010 ▪ Tasting, sales & cellar tours Tue-Fri 10-3 Sat 10-2; or by arrangement ▪ Closed Sun-Mon, Easter Fri-Mon, Dec 25/26 & Jan 1 ▪ Light refreshments for group tastings, booking essential ▪ Owner(s) Reiersvlei Investments CC (Russell & Elize Inggs) ▪ Cellarmaster(s)/winemaker(s)/viticulturist(s) Russell Inggs (Sep 2007) ▪ 113ha/9ha (cab, p verdot, ptage, red muscadel, shiraz, tinta, touriga, sauv) ▪ 70t/3,600cs own label 90% red 10% white ▪ PO Box 33 Prince Albert 6930 ▪ reier@absamail.co.za ▪ S 33° 16' 50" E 022° 14' 38" ▪ F +27 (0)23-541-1983 ▪ **T +27 (0)23-541-1983/1556**

☐ **Releaf Organic** *see* Imbuko Wines

Remhoogte Wine Estate

It's 20 years since the bottling of the first wines under the ownership of Murray Boustred, who moved with his wife and young family from Johannesburg to this Simonsberg farm in 1994. (The Dutch name Remhoogte refers to the days of oxwagons applying the brakes as they descended into Stellenbosch.) The estate, with title deeds dating back to 1812, was in a run-down state but under the Boustreds old vineyards have been revived and new ones planted. All grown up now, the younger generation is fully involved: Chris as winemaker/viticulturist, and Rob driving sales and marketing.

Reserve range

★★★★☆ **Sir Thomas Cullinan** Flagship Bordeaux red; merlot's dominance (65% in **11**, balance cab) reflection of winemaker Chris Boustred's love of Pomerol, St Emilion. Fuller, richer than **10**, more obvious lush dark fruit, but great balance, fresh tannins ensure no heaviness. French oak polished, 40% new.

★★★★☆ **Honeybunch Chenin Blanc** Single old vineyard, harvested on morning side only, yields intense honeyed fragrance, creamed honey succulence on just-dry **13**. Richness reined in by firm line savoury acid. Natural ferment, 11 months on lees in French oak, 20% new.

Estate range

★★★★ **Terroir Cabernet Sauvignon** Ⓥ **11** in classic style (but 15.2% alcohol!). Impressively plush with brooding dark fruit, dusty oak, controlled by cab's fine grip. Sensitively oaked, like whole range.

★★★★ **Aspect Merlot** Name refers to important southwest orientation of this high-lying vineyard. Main reason for this fine **12**; freshness, flesh, fine tannin & perfectly ripe fruit give a lesson in high-quality merlot.

★★★★ **Bushvine Pinotage 12** more restrained, sophisticated than **11** (★★★★). Pinot noir-like in its fragrance, silky delicacy despite substantial alcohol. Beautifully polished, seamless feel enhanced by carefully judged oak (20% new).

★★★★ **Valentino Syrah** Ⓥ Elegant **11** quality climb. Complex vinification in larger French oak, natural ferment. Pure & delicate, with lingering white spice, fine tannin trim. More persistent than **10** (★★★★).

★★★★ Estate Blend Powerful **07** (★★★★) even more demanding than bold **06**. Merlot, shiraz, cab, pinotage deliver plush black fruit concentration, well-rounded mouthfeel; tannins a satisfyingly dry finish.

Lifestyle range

★★★★ Chenin Blanc ⊘ Serious chenin offering amazing value. **13** starts quietly; layers of juicy honey, lemon & subtle toast (small portion oaked) richness follow. Concentration, depth, augur well for greater future pleasure.

Also tasted: **Soaring Eagle 12 ★★★☆** — AL

Location/map: Stellenbosch • WO: Simonsberg–Stellenbosch • Est 1994 • 1stB 1995 • Tasting & sales Mon-Fri 9–5 Sat 10-4 • Closed Easter Fri-Sun, Dec 25/26 & Jan 1 • Cellar tours by appt • Picnic baskets, booking required • Functions • Walking/hiking trails • Game • Guest cottage • Owner(s) Murray Boustred Trust • Cellarmaster(s) Chris Boustred (Jan 2011) • Winemaker(s)/viticulturist(s) Chris Boustred (Jan 2007) • 55ha/25ha (cab, merlot, ptage, shiraz, chenin) • 130t/10,000cs own label 80% red 20% white • BWI, IPW • PO Box 2032 Dennesig 7601 • info@remhoogte.co.za • www.remhoogte.co.za • S 33° 53' 4.2" E 018° 51' 4.6" • F +27 (0)21-889-6907 • **T +27 (0)21-889-5005**

Re'Mogo Wines

Founded in 2004 by black entrepreneurs to establish business interests in wine, among other sectors, Re'Mogo (Setswana for 'standing together', illustrated on the label by giraffes with necks intertwined) is fronted by Thamsanqa Hombana. Based in Khayamandi, Stellenbosch, and Gugulethu, Cape Town, the brand currently sources wines from Olifants River.

Location/map: Stellenbosch • Est 2004 • Tasting & sales Mon-Fri & pub hols 9-3 Sat 9-12 by appt only • Owner(s) Re'Mogo Holdings Trust & Re'Mogo Holdings (Pty) Ltd • Winemaker(s) Klaas Coetzee (Stellar Winery) • 50% red 50% white • George Blake Street Stellenbosch 7599 / NY147 No. 7 Gugulethu 7750 • remogo.holdings@gmail.com • www. remogo.co.za • S 33° 55' 9.47" E 018° 51' 7.90" • F +27 (0)86-610-7047 • **T +27 (0)82-638-6774**

☐ **Renosterbos** see Hofstraat Kelder

Restless River ⊕ ⊕ ⊕

Big Ethel joined Craig and Anne Wessels at their boutique winery in time for last harvest – a magnificent old 1 ton basket press, lovingly restored, which in time will crush the fruit from 2 ha of pinot noir newly planted on different soils using different clones. Their cab, hugely challenging to grow successfully in cool Hemel-en-Aarde, is now properly on the map, selling out before release. Chardonnay, commoner in the area, gets the same intricate attention and is shaped by the same belief that 'the quality of a message is not improved by the volume with which it is delivered'.

★★★★☆ Cabernet Sauvignon Open, powerful but not ostentatious style, with crème de cassis, cherries & subtle notes of toasty oak (33% new). **11** soft, creamy, with fine tannin & very good breadth, substantial richness. No **10**.

★★★★☆ Chardonnay Showing power with Old World restraint, focused **11** has intricate layers of melon, hazelnut & vanilla infused yellow apple. Tight, intense flavours, with great lift & delineation. Exceptionally balanced, but needs & deserves time to fully unfold. Walker Bay WO. Also-tasted **12** similar but slightly riper, an extra dimension of lemon & crushed stones showing in slightly longer finish. Both gently, judiciously oaked (27-30% new). — JPf

Location: Hermanus • Map: Elgin, Walker Bay & Bot River • WO: Upper Hemel-en-Aarde Valley • Est 1999 • 1stB 2005 • Tasting, sales & tours daily by appt • Closed all pub hols • Charcuterie, cheese platters & refreshments - booking essential • BYO picnic • Owner(s) Craig & Anne Wessels • Winemaker(s) Craig Wessels (Jan 2005) • Viticulturist(s) Kevin Watt (2012) • 20ha/7ha (cab, pinot, chard) • 10t/1,000cs own label 50% red 50% white • PO Box 1739 Hermanus 7200 • anne@restlessriver.com • www.restlessriver.com • S 34° 21' 26.11" E 19° 16' 32.80" • **T +27 (0)28-313-2881/+27 (0)82-650-3544**

Retief Wines

Originally home to a blacksmith, now a mainly table grape farm, this boutique winery in Paarl has added a warm welcome to its beautiful mountain views in the form of a recently-opened tasting and sales venue and bistro-style restaurant. 'Just follow the brick road,' quips prime mover, Graham Retief.

Retief range

Three Oaks Cabernet Sauvignon (NEW) ★★★ **12** promising blackcurrant aromas, but palate dominated by rugged tannins, need time to settle, soften. Also tasted: **Above The Mist Merlot 12** ★★★ **Wagon Trail Shiraz 12** ★★★

Stubborn Man range (NEW)

Chardonnay Unwooded ★★★★ Fruit-forward & easygoing **14** with juicy apple & pear notes; full & round but nicely lifted; uncomplicated & very enjoyable lunch wine. — JPf

Location/WO: Paarl ▪ Map: Paarl & Wellington ▪ Est 1747 ▪ 1stB 2004 ▪ Tasting & sales Tue-Fri 10-5 Sat 10-6 Sun 10-3 ▪ Closed Mondays, Dec 25 & Jan 1 ▪ Bistro Tue-Fri 11-9.30 Sat 8-10 Sun 8-4 ▪ Owner(s) Pearl Mountain Wines (Pty) Ltd ▪ Winemaker(s) Robert Frater (2004, De Zoete Inval) ▪ Viticulturist(s) Graham Retief ▪ 11.8ha (cab, merlot, shiraz, chard, chenin, sauv) ▪ 92t/13,300cs own label 75% red 25% white ▪ PO Box 709 Northern Paarl 7623 ▪ info@pearlmountain.co. za ▪ www.pearlmountain.co.za ▪ S 33° 41' 44.4" E 018° 57' 11.1" ▪ F 021-872-9983 ▪ **T 021-872-9088**

☐ **Reuben's** see Goose Wines
☐ **Revelation** see Osbloed Wines

Reverie

Jacques de Klerk (also Winery of Good Hope winemaker) describes his boutique label from Swartland as a 'liquid art project', striving to reflect a seldom-seen side of chenin. The well-received debut vintage (2012) features on top restaurant lists, and the larger 2013 bottling is selling locally under an exclusive deal with a leading national retailer, with exports to the UK and US planned.

★★★★ **Chenin Blanc** As unmanipulated as **12** (gently foot-crushed, natural ferment, no additives bar a little sulphur etc), old-oaked **13** (★★★★) amongst the least assertive of Swartland chenins, but worth lingering over to find its gentle, delicate, subtly fruit-filled force. 12.2% alcohol. — TJ

Location: Somerset West ▪ WO: Swartland ▪ Est 2011 ▪ 1stB 2012 ▪ Tasting & sales by appt ▪ Closed all pub hols ▪ Owner(s) Jacques de Klerk ▪ Cellarmaster(s)/viticulturist(s) Jacques de Klerk (Nov 2011) ▪ Winemaker(s) Jacques de Klerk (Nov 2011), with Amelie de Klerk (Nov 2011) ▪ (chenin) ▪ 125cs own label 100% white ▪ 5 Birkenhead Road Somerset West 7130 ▪ reveriechenin@gmail.com ▪ **T +27 (0)82-783-7647**

Reyneke Wines

'We've made great progress. We're nearly back where we started,' chuckles co-owner and viticulturist Johan Reyneke, who's long since shifted Stellenbosch family farm Uitzicht towards organic practices and then further - it is registered as biodynamic, a rare distinction in the Cape. An Environmental Philosophy post-grad with Twitter handle @ZAVineHugger, Johan's passionate concern for the vines and well-being of the land is matched in the cellar by the brilliance of Rudiger Gretschel, chief guru at wine company Vinimark (which has an interest in the Reyneke brand). Together they are building this into unquestionably one of the Cape's top wineries. No wonder Johan can report that they're 'making big headway in America with our vinehugger brand'. But people have also always been respected here - employees are the farm's cornerstone, hence the name of a wine whose profits last year paid for a new house for a staff member.

Biodynamic range

★★★★ **Pinotage** (◎) Usual perfumed complexity introduces **12**. Forthcoming sweet fruit, its purity unchallenged by maturation in large older casks; big tannins; good dry finish. Few years will give big benefits.

★★★★☆ **Syrah** ✓ ◎ Lovely fragrance on **12**, with ripe berries & a touch of flowers & herbs. Very well balanced, with both generous sweet fruit & a savoury, vinous succulence, all supported by a sound structure, leading to a lingering dry finish. Only old oak used. Extraordinary quality:price ratio.

★★★★☆ **Reserve Red** ◎ No **11**, but masterly **12** worth waiting for. Unlike **10** with some cab, this pure syrah/shiraz - lighter, even more elegant & fine. Less sweet-fruited than the Syrah, but more complex & subtly intense, melding structural austerity with grace. Already complex, but will develop.

★★★★ **Cornerstone** ◎ **12** cab with merlot & cab franc. Bolder & more fruity than the syrahs, but same dry restraint. New-oak touch adds tobacco notes & dries the tannins. **11** (★★★★☆) charmed more. Needs time.

★★★★☆ **Chenin Blanc** ◎ Like **12** (★★★★★), **13** an exercise in lightly oaked elegance, containing a kernel of sweet fruity power (ripe apple, peach, melon) in its subtle presentation. Characteristically well balanced. Length of flavour speaks to its inherent intensity.

★★★★★ **Reserve White** ◎ As always, **13** from straight sauvignon, naturally fermented in barrel. Exciting emergent complexity - jostling floral, citrus, blackcurrant notes along with evidence of the mostly new oak that should integrate. The austere element of **11**, the forwardness of **12** (★★★★☆). Achingly long finish.

★★★★☆ **Sauvignon Blanc** ✓ ◎ Vibrant **13** just a touch less rich & complex than Reserve - also oaked, but less obviously so. With delicate aromas & quiet finesse & fine balance on the silky, dry palate, it's the opposite of showy, but greatly rewards attention. Like **12** (★★★★) includes brought-in grapes, so WO W Cape.

Organic range
Sauvignon Blanc-Semillon (NEW) ✓ ★★★ In house style, **13** blend somewhat understated - restrained, dry & elegant though certainly not without charm & vitality. WO W Cape. Also tasted: **Shiraz-Cabernet Sauvignon** ✓ **12** ★★★ Discontinued: **Chenin Blanc-Sauvignon Blanc-Chardonnay**. — TJ

Location/map: Stellenbosch ▪ WO: Stellenbosch/Western Cape/Coastal ▪ Est 1863 ▪ 1stB 1998 ▪ Tasting, sales & cellar tours Mon-Fri 10-4 Sat & pub hols by appt ▪ Paintings by Mila Posthumus on display ▪ Owner(s) Reyneke Wines (Pty) Ltd ▪ Cellarmaster(s) Rudiger Gretschel ▪ Winemaker(s) Rudiger Gretschel, with Jessica Garlick (Jan 2014) ▪ Viticulturist(s) Johan Reyneke ▪ 40ha/32ha (cabs s/f, merlot, ptage, shiraz, chenin, sauv) ▪ 270t/30,000cs own label 70% red 30% white + 2,000cs for clients ▪ CERES (organic), Demeter (biodynamic), IPW, WIETA ▪ PO Box 61 Vlottenburg 7604 ▪ wine@reynekewines.co.za ▪ www.reynekewines.co.za ▪ S 33° 57' 27.7" E 018° 45' 7.0" ▪ F +27 (0)21-881-3285 ▪ **T +27 (0)21-881-3517/3451**

Rhebokskloof Wine Estate ⓘ 🍴 ◎ ⓑ ♿

Centuries-old Paarl estate Rhebokskloof is owned by Siebrits and Albie Laker of civils group ASLA, who are determined that it should become a South African Top 10. Extensive replanting and repositioning are under way, cellarmaster since harvest 2013 Francois Naudé introducing several new wines (including a non-alcoholic sparkling). Shiraz, Rhône blends (red & white), chardonnay and chenin will be the future focuses. There's a new hotel school, plus 'possibly the best mountain bike/hiking trail in the Cape — truly testing with fantastic views!'

Mountain Vineyards Reserve range
★★★★ **Black Marble Hill Syrah** Serious (21 months new oak) shiraz - best portion of best vineyard - in etched black glass bottle. Suave, smoky **12** concentrated yet not weighty; savoury tang adds freshness.

★★★★☆ **The Rhebok** (NEW) Seamless & impressive new flagship, Cape Blend of shiraz, pinotage (40%) & dash mourvèdre in **12**. Thrilling integration of sultry plum/mulberry fruit, fine-grained new wood & bold 14.5% alcohol.

★★★★ Sandstone Grove Chardonnay Leesy oatmeal gloss of **13** overlays beautifully harmonious lemon & lime fruit features, both depth & length of flavour up on reticent **12** (★★★★). 30% new cask, 10 months.

Design Shiraz ⓝ **★★★☆** Inspired by Cape Town's status as World Design Capital, selection of different blocks to be highlighted on label each vintage. 60% new-oak veneer to **12**'s red berry fruit.

Rhebokskloof range

★★★★ Méthode Cap Classique New livery for dry sparkling from chardonnay - regal blue with trademark 'R' - mirrors serious **08**. 5 years on lees give developed richness cleaned by pin-point mousse. Lifts bar on **07** (★★★★).

Pinotage ★★★☆ Affable **12** brims with plummy pleasure; weighty, but a fresh tail lifts the ensemble. WO Coastal. **Viognier ★★★☆** Plump, sweet peach pip character of **13** kept just this side of blowsy by firm old-oak support. **Rosé Sparkling** ⓝ **★★★** Pretty in pink, a wedding sparkler; **14** fresh, fruity & sweet. Physics 101 needed to open new-fangled, resealable plastic cork! Also tasted: **Shiraz 11 ★★★★ The MGS 11 ★★★★ Chardonnay 13 ★★★★** Not retasted: **Viognier-Shiraz 12 ★★**

Pearlstone range

Cabernet Sauvignon-Shiraz ⓝ **★★★** 60:40 blend, asphalt & heavy char features of **12** obscure shy mulberry fruit. WO Coastal. **Bosstok Chenin Blanc ★★★ 14** starts quietly, then vibrant melon fruit lifts thatchy edge. Perdeberg bushvines. Also tasted: **Cabernet Sauvignon-Merlot 12 ★★★ Rosé 14 ★★** Not retasted: **Pinotage 11 ★★★ Shiraz 11 ★★★ Sauvignon Blanc 13 ★★** Discontinued: **Sparkling Rosé**. — DS

Location: Paarl • Map: Paarl & Wellington • WO: Paarl/Coastal/Western Cape • 1stB 1975 • Tasting & sales Mon-Fri 9-5 Sat/Sun 10-3 • Fee R15/5 wines • Cellar tours by appt • Rhebokskloof Restaurant open daily for b'fast & lunch; dinner Fri & by appt • Facilities for children • Tour groups • Gifts • Weddings, functions & conferences • Mountain bike & hiking trails • Live concerts • Hotel school • Owner(s) Siebrits & Albie Laker, ASLA Group • Cellarmaster(s) Francois Naudé (Nov 2012) • Winemaker(s) Rolanie Lotz (Jan 2007) • Viticulturist(s) Karin Louw (Jan 2007) • 180ha/30ha (cab, carignan, durif, grenache n/b, mourv, p verdot, ptage, shiraz, chard, chenin, marsanne, rouss, viog) • 250t/30,000cs own label 75% red 20% white 5% rosé + 3,000cs for buyers own brands • PO Box 2637 Paarl 7620 • info@rhebokskloof.co.za • www.rhebokskloof.co.za • S 33° 41' 6.1" E 018° 55' 56.6" • F +27 (0)21-869-8386 • **T +27 (0)21-869-8386**

☐ **Rhinofields** *see* Durbanville Hills

Rhino of Linton Park   ⓠ

Once a plentiful fynbos type in the Cape, renosterveld today is highly endangered - much like the rhinos which share the name. Wellington producer Linton Park merges a variety of interests in The Rhino label, in that it is Fairtrade accredited, forms part of the home-farm's employee empowerment scheme, and benefits Save The Rhino through the donation of a portion of profits.

Red Rhino range

Cabernet Sauvignon ⓥ **★★★** Sweet dark fruitcake ease to light-bodied **13**. Unoaked, as all these. **Shiraz** ⓥ **★★★** Sweet plum & blueberry spice on unfussy, quaffable **13**. Not retasted: **Merlot 12 ★★★ Pinotage 12 ★★★ Cape Red 12 ★★★**

Pink Rhino range

Natural Sweet ⓝ **★★** Berry cordial & candyfloss simplicity to **NV** light, pink sweetie. Wellington WO. Also tasted: **Rosé** ⓥ **NV ★★☆**

White Rhino range

Sauvignon Blanc ⓥ **★★★** White pepper & flint vibrancy on **14**, up a notch on previous. Also tasted: **Chenin Blanc 14 ★★★ Cape White 14 ★★** Not retasted: **Chardonnay 12 ★★★** — FM

Location: Wellington ▪ WO: Western Cape/Wellington ▪ Tasting & sales by appt at Linton Park (see entry) ▪ Owner(s) Camellia PLC UK ▪ Winemaker(s) JG Auret (2007) ▪ Viticulturist(s) Rudolf Jansen van Vuuren (2012) & Johan Viljoen (consultant) ▪ PO Box 1234 Wellington 7654 ▪ sales@lintonparkwines.co.za, info@lintonparkwines.co.za ▪ www. rhinowines.com, www.lintonparkwines.co.za ▪ F +27 (0)21-873-0851 ▪ **T +27 (0)21-873-1625**

Richard Kershaw Wines

Owner, winemaker and Master of Wine Richard Kershaw established his boutique winery to create clonally selected, site-specific, cool-climate wine paradigms from noble grapes capable of producing world-class examples. He chose Elgin Valley for its higher altitude, ocean proximity, specific cloud cover sequencing, high cold-units and a large diurnal range, believing these factors would allow his preferred varieties to show a sense of place. Launched in 2013 to local and international acclaim, his Chardonnay has since been joined by an exceptional Syrah and, in cyberspace, a direct-to-customer Clonehead club. The first export orders have been received, and the focus now is on 'cementing strategies and striving hard to make even better wines'.

Clonal Selections

★★★★☆ **Elgin Syrah** 🆕 Ethereal allspice & white pepper notes to finely etched, iodine-tinged dark berry fruit flavours in fantastic **12** debut. Exceptional food partner - savouriness & tempered tannins perfectly complement richer dishes (duck, pork belly), amplify the 'umami' tone of both food & wine. 50% new casks for 15 months.

★★★★★ **Elgin Chardonnay** Minimal intervention delivers a maximal taste experience: no pumps used, no enzymes, acid or yeasts added... The stellar **13** is refined, but rich, complex & earthy, with a taught minerality & judicious oak (33% new). Like **12**, precise, classy & delicious, now & for many years. — DS

Location/WO: Elgin ▪ Est/1stB 2012 ▪ Tasting by appt ▪ Owner(s) Richard Kershaw ▪ Cellarmaster(s) Richard Kershaw (2012) ▪ 20t/±2,500cs own label 45% red 55% white ▪ PO Box 77 Grabouw 7160 ▪ info@richardkershawwines.co.za ▪ www.richardkershawwines.co.za ▪ F +27 (0)86-637-6202 ▪ **T +27 (0)21-848-9114**

☐ **Richard's** *see* Richard Kershaw Wines

Richelieu

This South African-owned brand straddles both Cognac and the Cape. The product of a French company founded in 1962 by the late Anton Rupert of Distillers Corporation (now Distell) to produce a richer, sweeter brandy akin to cognac, the brand now comprises three brandies: Richelieu XO Cognac Fine Champagne is Cognac-grown, distilled and matured for 25+ years (entitling it to be labelled 'cognac'); and Richelieu International and new 10 Year Old, which are local.

★★★★ **10 Year Vintage Brandy** Ⓐ At least ten years maturation on both the potstill (30%) & spirit content. Elegant but rich; harmonious & dry, with integrated vanilla oak colouring the apricot & prune complexity.

Richelieu International Ⓐ ★★★ Grapey, fruity aromas on this blended brandy - a mixer will tame its rather sweet aggression. — WB, TJ

Rickety Bridge Winery

A venerable Franschhoek property granted to the widow Paulina de Villiers in 1797, Rickety Bridge in recent years has been transformed under British owner Duncan Spence. Luxury accommodation and varied, family-welcoming cellardoor facilities have been created, and the wine team under Wynand Grobler have steadily ratcheted up the bar. Noteworthy this edition are two partners for the strikingly packaged Foundation Stone Red, the pink moving from the Rickety Bridge range, the new white an unusual and delicious blend featuring rarely seen ugni blanc/trebbiano.

For more information, visit wineonaplatter.com

Icon Wines

★★★★☆ **The Bridge** ⓘ Flagship from cab, naturally fermented, seriously oaked (100% new, 25 months). **09** restrained & subtle, with firm structure; shows wonderful integration of cool fruit & fine wood tannin.

Paulina's Reserve range

★★★★ **Cabernet Sauvignon** Slight meaty **11** restrained yet sufficiently fruit filled & oak spiced. Firm tannins add freshness, grip, for food & ageing potential. Slightly more open than iron-fisted **10**.

★★★★ **Chenin Blanc** ⓘ Quietly beguiles with subtle honey & flowers, bright dry finish; large-format oak (100% new) smartly used to provide weight, depth & vanilla patina. **12** more convincing than **11** (★★★★).

★★★★ **Sauvignon Blanc** ⓘ Opposite to prevailing green, spiky styles: 30% barrel-fermented for broadness, softer white asparagus & tinned pea tones. **12** tasty mouthful, very satisfying. WO W Cape.

★★★★ **Semillon** 10 months small French barrels have given **11** oxidative styling; lovely & lean, unlike oak-sweet **10** (★★★★), unusual & distinctive.

Foundation Stone range

★★★★ **White** ⓝ Complex & compelling **13** blend led by chenin, 15% each ugni blanc/trebbiano, roussanne & grenache blanc, drop viognier. White peach, apricot, nutty persistence. Barrel fermented/aged before blending. Worth seeking out. WO W Cape.

Red ⓘ ★★★★ Was 'The Foundation Stone'. Franschhoek, Swartland, Breede River fruit for **13**, savoury shiraz-led 6-way blend. Individual, friendly; nudges next level. Also tasted: **Rosé 14** ★★★

Rickety Bridge range

★★★★ **Merlot** Now from Franschhoek Valley fruit, **12** plum, dark chocolate & cherries, compact & intense. Less svelte than **10** but should reward more with 3+ years ageing. No **11**.

★★★★ **Shiraz** **12** smoky & tarry; ripe, plush & long with bright acidity, tannic grip refreshes. Like savoury **11**, needs year/2 to meld. WO W Cape.

★★★★ **Méthode Cap Classique Brut Rosé** Now **NV**, with onion skin hue, energetic bubble with savoury cherry styling from 53% pinot (rest chardonnay). Smoky, with enough personality for solo enjoyment. Oaked 6 months, year on lees.

Also tasted: **Pinotage 13** ★★★ **Chardonnay 13** ★★★★ **Chenin Blanc 14** ★★★ **Sauvignon Blanc 14** ★★★ **Natural Sweet Chenin Blanc 13** ★★★★ Not retasted: **Méthode Cap Classique Blanc de Blancs 09** ★★★★ — CvZ

Location/map: Franschhoek ▪ WO: Franschhoek/Western Cape/Coastal ▪ Est 1990 ▪ Tasting, sales & cellar tours Mon-Sat 9–7 (Dec-Mar) 9-5 (Apr-Nov) Sun 10-5 ▪ Closed Dec 25 & Jan 1 ▪ Fee R20, waived on purchase ▪ Paulina's at Rickety Bridge ▪ Facilities for children ▪ Gift shop ▪ Conferences ▪ Weddings ▪ Rickety Bridge Manor House ▪ Owner(s) DS Sarnia (Pty) Ltd ▪ Cellarmaster(s)/winemaker(s) Wynand Grobler (Nov 2007) ▪ 91ha/39ha (cab, merlot, shiraz, chard, chenin, sauv, sem) ▪ 195t/28,000cs own label 45% red 45% white 10% rosé ▪ PO Box 455 Franschhoek 7690 ▪ info@ricketybridge.com ▪ www.ricketybridge.com ▪ S 33° 53′ 58.5″ E 019° 5′ 27.6″ ▪ F +27 (0)21-876-3486 ▪ **T +27 (0)21-876-2129**

Rico Suter Private Cellar

This large family property in Breedekloof has reverted to being a red-wine-only producer (unless a drop of viognier blended with shiraz counts), including a new cinsaut – the grape currently a favourite of many local sommeliers. Rico, with input from son Carlo, vinifies them, other son Bruno cares for the vines.

★★★★ **Cabernet Sauvignon-Syrah** **12** (★★★★) 70/30 blend with touch of cab's herbaceousness & slightly astringent tannins; needs year/two to harmonise & fresh, juicy fruit centre to unfurl. Shade off last-featured **06**.

Cinsaut (NEW) (V) ★★★★ Engaging, characterful **12**, perfumed red fruit with mocha overtone, bone-dry & very quaffable. **Syrah-Viognier** (NEW) ★★★★ Viognier's spicy perfume more evident than dominant partner (93%). **12** ripe & round mouthful of red fruit in a supple structure. Ready now & good for next 3-5 years. Also tasted: **Pinotage 12** ★★★★ Not retasted: **Cabernet Sauvignon 05** ★★★ **Petit Verdot 04** Discontinued: **Syrah**, **Cabernet Sauvignon-Petit Verdot**, **L'Amitié**, **Sauvignon Blanc**, **Viognier-Chenin Blanc**. — MW

Location: Worcester ▪ Map/WO: Breedekloof ▪ Est/1stB 2004 ▪ Tasting, sales & tours by appt ▪ Tour groups ▪ Olive oil, dried prunes ▪ Walking/hiking & mountain biking trails ▪ Bird watching ▪ Guesthouse (bookings: erika@ ricosuterwines.com) ▪ Owner(s) Suter Family Trust ▪ Cellarmaster(s) Rico Suter, advised by Carlo Suter ▪ Winemaker(s) Rico Suter ▪ Viticulturist(s) Bruno Suter (2004) ▪ 750ha/45ha (cab, cinsaut, p verdot, ptage, shiraz, sauv, viog) ▪ 8-15t/ha 8,850L own label 100% red ▪ PO Box 38 Breervier 6858 ▪ rico@ricosuterwines.com ▪ S 33° 31' 39.00" E 019° 15' 13.00" ▪ F +27 (0)86-642-6591 ▪ **T +27 (0)23-355-1822**

Ridgeback

The association with the Rhodesian Ridgeback dog in the name and branding of this Paarl property reflect the experience of the man who came south to establish it in 1997. Here almost as long, Toit Wessels celebrates 15 years as viticulturist (he's now also winemaker and GM). No doubt this background directs his determination to produce 'deep, rich wines of consistent quality' primarily through continuous - and seemingly successful - vineyard work. He's no less proud of having received WIETA ethical trade accreditation.

★★★★ **Cabernet Sauvignon** Ample cassis flavour in streamlined & supple **12**. Sheathed power, suave tannins enveloped in oak's creamy succulence. Charming in youth & with 4-6 years development potential.

★★★★ **Cabernet Franc 12** first tasted since **08**. Polished but taut, with pervasive green walnut & perfumed piquancy woven into dry chalky tannins. Tight fruit core judiciously oaked, with long perfumed farewell. Future rewards in store.

★★★★ **Shiraz 11** (★★★★) appealing spicy dark chocolate aromas; ripe & rich style, with enough savoury, pliable tannins to anchor fruit. Less complex than **09**. **10** sold out untasted.

★★★★ **Journey** A merlot-led Bordeaux blend in **13**. Flavoursome dark berry fruit clothes fine amenable tannins. Vibrant & juicy, dry finish. Well crafted, could grace a table now & over the next few years.

★★★★ **His Master's Choice** Bold & flavoursome shiraz-led quartet with mourvèdre, grenache & viognier. **11**, first since **08**, aromatic & savoury, firm fleshed & toned structure. Like the dog on the apt label, needs few years to grow into its paws.

★★★★ **Chenin Blanc** (V) Barrel-fermented, lees-enriched, balanced **13** from bushvines focuses on mouthfeel; gets greater richness & complexity from tiny addition of Natural Sweet wine prior to bottling.

★★★★ **Viognier** (V) Flamboyant but beautifully balanced **13** (★★★★★) raises the bar on **12**. Exudes pineapple & dried peach zested with tangy acidity. Deft oaking (fermentation & maturation) provides rich substrate. Fabulous to enjoy now with spicy cuisine.

★★★★ **Natural Sweet Viognier** Vivacious return in **14** after **11** (★★★★). A delicately crafted tightrope act of sweet but piquant, light (10.5% alhohol) but intense. Delicious dessert style that exudes florality & clean-cut freshness.

Sauvignon Blanc ★★★ **14** tropical basket of fruit in fresh & gently crisp delivery for appealing summer enjoyment. Also tasted: **Merlot 12** ★★★★ **SGMV 13** ★★★ Not retasted: **Vansha Red 12** ★★★ **Vansha White 13** ★★★ Discontinued: **Shiraz Rosé**. — MW

Location: Paarl ▪ Map: Paarl & Wellington ▪ WO: Paarl/Western Cape ▪ Est 1997 ▪ 1stB 2001 ▪ Tasting & sales Mon-Sat 10-5 (summer)/10-4 (winter) Sun 10-4 ▪ Fee R25/5 wines, R50/10 wines ▪ Closed Good Fri, Dec 25 & Jan 1 ▪ Cellar tours by appt ▪ The Deck Restaurant Tue-Sun 9.30-3.30 ▪ 4-star/5-room Ridgeback Guest House ▪ Hiking trails ▪ Children's play area ▪ Owner(s) Kilimanjaro Investments ▪ Cellarmaster(s)/winemaker(s) Toit Wessels (Jan 2007) ▪ Viticulturist(s) Toit Wessels (Mar 2000) ▪ 65ha/35ha (cabs s/f, grenache, merlot, mourv, p verdot, shiraz, sauv, viog) ▪ 300t/30,000cs own label 60% red 35% white 5% sweet ▪ BWI, WIETA ▪ PO Box 2076 Windmeul Paarl 7630 ▪ tasting@ridgeback.co.za ▪ www. ridgebackwines.co.za ▪ S 33° 40' 24.9" E 018° 54' 53.5" ▪ F +27 (0)21-869-8146 ▪ **T +27 (0)21-869-8068**

☐ **Ridgelands** *see* Luddite Wines

Riebeek Cellars

While tiny producers in this part of the Swartland take the headlines, large wineries like Riebeek Cellars play a vital part in the scheme of things – not only in supplying grapes to some well-known Cape brands, but also in offering affordable good value, with easygoing, often slightly sweet and simply fruity wines. Not that ambition is lacking, as shown in the more serious-minded A Few Good Men wines, which the winemakers say, 'give us the opportunity to slow down the process'. Certain labels were recently upgraded to reflect the Riebeek Valley and its people - 'Our lifestyle in a bottle'.

A Few Good Men range

★★★★ **Shiraz** ⊘ **12**, like **10** (★★★★), has modest spicy oaking - allowing the lovely ripe red/ black fruit to shine. Big, but also delicious & harmonious. Fine, savoury tannins support the sweet fruit. No **11**.

Chardonnay ★★★ Rich, well-oaked **11** fruity & lightly spicy. No pretensions to interest or seriousness. Finishes in rather cloying fashion. Not retasted: **Cabernet Sauvignon 11** ★★★ **Merlot 10** ★★★ **Pinotage 11** ★★★

Kasteelberg range

Shiraz ★★★★ Ultra-ripe **12** powerful (16% alcohol!) & a touch too sweet, with its all-new oak only too evident. But lovely intense fruit, trying to get out, silky tannins. More showy & impressive than Few Good Men version, but less eminently drinkable. Also tasted: **Viognier 12** ★★★ Not retasted: **Chenin Blanc 10** ★★★★ **Kasteelberg Méthode Cap Classique NV** ★★★ **Soet Steen NV** ★★★★

Riebeek Collection

Cabernet Sauvignon ★★★ Clean-cut, pleasing **13** with sweet berry fruit supported by sufficient structure. **Shiraz** ★★★ As usual (this being the Swartland!) this **13** is the pick of the range. Fairly bold & ripe, finishing a little too sweet, but with good varietal character, & lovely succulent tannins. **Chenin Blanc** ★★★ Attractive guava character on **14**; nicely balanced; easygoing but not without a crisp bite. **Sauvignon Blanc** ★★ Forward, fruity **14** quaffer. Fleeting flavours, but lively enough. Also tasted: **Merlot 13** ★★★ **Cabernet Sauvignon-Merlot 13** ★★★ **Shiraz-Cinsaut** ⊘ **13** ★★★ **Chardonnay 13** ★★★ Not retasted: **Pinotage 12** ★★ **Pinotage Rosé 13** ★★★ **Pieter Cruythoff Brut NV** ★★★ **Cape Ruby Port NV** ★★★

Montino range

Not retasted: **Petillant Natural Sweet Rosé NV** ★ **Petillant Light NV** ★★ **Petillant Natural Sweet Red-Rosso NV** ★ — TJ

Location: Riebeek-Kasteel ▪ Map/WO: Swartland ▪ Est 1941 ▪ Tasting & sales Mon-Fri 9-5 Sat 9-4 Sun 10.30-4 (wine boutique) ▪ Closed Good Fri, Dec 25 & Jan 1 ▪ Cellar tours by appt ▪ BYO picnic ▪ Owner(s) ±40 shareholders ▪ Cellarmaster(s) Zakkie Bester (Dec 1999) ▪ Winemaker(s) Eric Saayman & Alecia Boshoff (Jan 1997/Dec 2004), with Daniel Slabber (May 2013) ▪ Viticulturist(s) Tharien Hansen (Jul 2013) ▪ 1,200ha (cab, carignan, merlot, mourv, ptage, shiraz, tinta amarela, chard, chenin, sauv, viog) ▪ 17,000t/300,000cs own label 50% red 40% white 10% rosé & ±80,000cs for clients ▪ Brands for clients: Broken Rock, Rocheburg, Royal, Steenbok ▪ BWI, Fairtrade, HACCP, WIETA ▪ PO Box 13 Riebeek Kasteel 7307 ▪ info@riebeekcellars.co.za ▪ www.riebeekcellars.com ▪ S 33° 22' 58.0" E 018° 54' 54. 5" ▪ F +27 (0)22-448-1281 ▪ **T +27 (0)22-448-1213**

Rietvallei Wine Estate

Family-owned Rietvallei is one of the oldest wine estates in Robertson, growing, vinifying and marketing under the Special Select, Classic Estate, Innings (with cricket heroes Mark Boucher and Jacques Kallis), Stonedale and John B labels.

Location/map: Robertson ▪ Est 1864 ▪ 1stB 1975 ▪ Tasting & sales Mon-Fri 8.30–5 Sat 10–2 ▪ R25pp for groups of 15+ ▪ Closed Easter Fri/Sun, Dec 25 & Jan 1 ▪ Cellar tours by appt ▪ Cheese platters, book ahead for groups of 6+ ▪ Farm produce ▪ Conservation area ▪ Owner(s) Kobus Burger ▪ Cellarmaster(s)/winemaker(s) Kobus Burger (2003) ▪ Viticulturist(s) Wilhelm Treurnicht ▪ 215ha/130ha (cab, red muscadel, shiraz, chard, sauv) ▪ 2,500t/110,000cs own label 40% red 50% white 5% rosé 5% fortified + 950,000L bulk ▪ PO Box 386 Robertson 6705 ▪ info@rietvallei.co.za ▪ www.rietvallei.co.za ▪ S 33° 49' 25.7" E 019° 58' 39.4" ▪ F +27 (0)23-626-4514 ▪ **T +27 (0)23-626-3596**

☐ **Rijckholt** see Zandvliet Wine Estate & Thoroughbred Stud

Rijk's

Rijk's owner Neville Dorrington originally made his money manufacturing luxury leather goods but chose to abandon Cape Town for some country living in 1996. Opting for unfashionable Tulbagh, he bought a large plot of virgin land and, though advised to plant fruit, set about establishing vineyard. Today the property specialises in chenin, pinotage and shiraz and Dorrington, along with winemaker Pierre Wahl, have pretty much confounded conventional wisdom making seriously good versions of all three varieties - a point underlined by the extra 4 ha of pinotage being planted at press time.

Reserve range

★★★★☆ **Pinotage** Distinguished from Private Cellar & Touch of Oak versions by more new oak. **10**'s weight & extraction a nod to the warm vintage, yet it retains the breeding, structure of its terroir. True to variety, with brooding dark fruit, tarry grip. Exceptional **09** (★★★★★) was tightly coiled, measured.

★★★★ **Shiraz** Heady fruit pastille, violets & liquorice perfume, plush core & firm tannins, silky finish to **10**. Like **09**, handles 66% new French oak with aplomb.

★★★★ **Chenin Blanc** **09** will reward fans of fully ripe, barrel-fermented chenins with brush of sweetness. Still youthful, with sun-dried apricots, marmalade & butterscotch, yet drinks well already. Slight heat from 14.9% alcohol, shade off fine expression of **08** (★★★★★).

Private Cellar range

★★★★ **Pinotage** Like **09**, **10** has floral notes to its wild black berries & spice, coffee & vanilla from 50% new oak, mix French/American. Appetising, silky, well structured. Less powerful than Reserve, more elegant than Touch of Oak.

★★★★ **Shiraz** Commanding **08** (★★★★★) improves on excellent **07**. Ripe yet unshowy, with similar vibrancy & malleable tannins but a greater presence.

★★★★ **Chenin Blanc** Though barrel fermented/aged, less new wood than for Reserve. **11** expressive yellow fruit, noticeable but integrated oak. As extravagant as **09** (no **10**), slightly sweet finish.

Touch of Oak range

★★★★ **Pinotage** **12** (★★★★☆) varietally true banana, spiced mulberries & smoke; surprisingly bold, concentrated & serious for this range. Some Swartland fruit. **11**, though less typical of grape, more satisfying.

★★★★☆ **Chenin Blanc** While generous, **12** not in the same ageworthy style as **11**. Simpler, more accessible, with oak hardly noticeable, great fruit purity & zippy conclusion. WO Coastal.

Also tasted: **Shiraz 11 ★★★** — HJ

Location/map: Tulbagh ▪ WO: Tulbagh/Coastal ▪ Est 1996 ▪ 1stB 2000 ▪ Tasting & sales Mon-Fri 10–4 Sat 10–2 ▪ Fee R10/wine, waived on purchase ▪ Closed Easter Fri-Mon, Dec 25 & Jan 1 ▪ Cellar tours by appt ▪ Rijk's Guest House ▪ Conferences ▪ Owner(s)/viticulturist(s) Neville Dorrington ▪ Winemaker(s) Pierre Wahl (Jan 2002) ▪ 135ha/36ha (carignan, grenache noir, mourv, ptage, shiraz, tinta amarela, chard, chenin, viog) ▪ 210t/24,000cs own label 75%

red 25% white ▪ IPW ▪ PO Box 400 Tulbagh 6820 ▪ wine@rijks.co.za ▪ www.rijks.co.za ▪ S 33° 16' 1.5" E 019° 8' 42.0" ▪ F +27 (0)23-230-1650 ▪ **T +27 (0)23-230-1622**

Rivendell

Located near Bot River, Heimo and Maria Thalhammer's Rivendell boutique winery offers visitors a variety of food options to pair with the wines. A new home for the Bistro has opened further up on the farm, leaving the winetasting area free to serve simpler fare. The wines continue to be vinified by specialist winemakers.

★★★★ Shiraz Violets & perfume intro to **13** (★★★☆), which just misses fine texture of **12** but still pleases with meaty flavours, mixed with black plums & spice.

★★★★ Sauvignon Blanc 14 shines brightly with lots of gooseberries & guavas on the nose before lashings of tinned grapefruit, threaded with bracing acidity; dies away for soft finish. Tad less impressive than stellar **13** (★★★★★).

Rosé ★★★☆ 14 absolutely nails it in terms of happy red berry fruit with sherbet twist & zippy, fresh dry tail. Walker Bay WO. — CM

Location: Bot River ▪ Map: Elgin, Walker Bay & Bot River ▪ WO: Bot River/Walker Bay ▪ Est 2008 ▪ 1stB 2011 ▪ Tasting & sales daily 9-5 ▪ Cheese platters ▪ Restaurant open for b'fast, lunch & dinner; cater for functions of various sizes ▪ Picnics in summer, to be pre-booked ▪ Facilities for children ▪ Tour groups ▪ Venue for weddings & seminars with fully equipped kitchen (94 pax inside) ▪ Walks/hikes ▪ Owner(s) Whales & Castle Investments (Pty) Ltd, with shareholders Heimo & Maria Thalhammer ▪ Winemaker(s) Kobie Viljoen (Mar 2010, consultant) & PJ Geyer (Feb 2013, Barton) ▪ Viticulturist(s) Schalk du Toit (Mar 2008, consultant) ▪ ±8ha/±4ha (shiraz, sauv) ▪ 32t/1,000cs own label 33% red 67% white ▪ PO Box 181 Onrusrivier 7201 ▪ office@rivendell-estate.co.za ▪ www.rivendell-estate.co.za ▪ S 34° 18' 5. 22" E 019° 8' 32.23" ▪ F +27 (0)28-284-9597 ▪ **T +27 (0)28-284-9185/9597**

☐ **River Garden** *see* Lourensford Wine Estate

☐ **River Grandeur** *see* Viljoensdrift Wines & Cruises

☐ **Riverscape** *see* Viljoensdrift Wines & Cruises

☐ **River's End** *see* Stellar Winery

☐ **Robert Alexander** *see* Nico van der Merwe Wines

Robertson Wide River Export Company

Joint venture between Robertson Winery and Vinimark, handling all the cellar's exports under labels such as Robertson Winery, Kaapdal, Kleindal, Silversands and Veldt. See Vinimark for contact details.

Robertson Winery

'We're all about innovation,' says marketing manager Ankia Niemann of this dynamic grower-owned winery in Robertson. One of the largest producers in Africa, they make a multitude of different wines and ranges, tailoring their products to suit markets in over 40 different countries and launching new ones (such as a lightly sparkling sauvignon) when they feel the time is right. All can be sampled at the town centre tasting room boasting 'the friendliest staff in Robertson', some of whom have been with the winery for more than 20 years.

Constitution Road range

★★★★☆ No. 1 Constitution Road Shiraz Iron fist in a velvet glove, **11** picks up where **10** left off. Supple texture to layers of single-vineyard fruit. Rich, ripe black fruit & superb balance. Deep cocoa, spice nuance. Oak (2 years, new, mix French/American) adds silky tannin, breadth, depth & length.

Vineyard Selection range

★★★★ Prospect Hill Cabernet Sauvignon 12 continues soft breadth of **11** (★★★☆) but improves due to depth, good oak & long, textured finish with typical blackcurrant & bramble notes.

★★★★ **Wolfkloof Shiraz** From cool Langeberg slope, **12** continues powerful modern style of **11**. Earthy nuance to blue/black fruit. Just 40% new oak makes for greater harmony on layered palate, acidity adds tangy freshness.

★★★★ **Kings River Chardonnay** Single block on Kings River farm, **13** repeats last-tasted **11**'s rating with rich, creamy marmalade notes well supported by mix new & old oak. Curvaceous but well structured; fresh yet elegant & long.

★★★★ **Retreat Sauvignon Blanc 13**, now bottled, & showing some secondary development of fig, grass & grapefruit vivacity. Good palate weight & density with moderate 13% alcohol.

Also tasted: **Phanto Ridge Pinotage 12** ★★★★

Winery range

Cabernet Sauvignon ★★★ Appealing black fruit tang to pleasantly light-bodied **13**. Light oak note is from tank staves, as with most reds in range. **Pinot Noir** ★★★ Cherry & tobacco leaf liveliness on **13**, with light smoke & forest floor nuance. Light bodied yet firm, with inky tail. **Ruby Cabernet** ⊘ ★★★ Dried thyme, fynbos & brambly fruit on **14** preview. Light tannic grip but tail-waggingly friendly. **Pinot Grigio** ★★☆ Zippy & clean **14** shows light kiwi & melon charm. Modest 12.5% alcohol, less than previous. **Viognier** ★★★ Lightly rounded body on unwooded **14** displaying typical stonefruit vibrancy & leesy spice. **Gewürztraminer Special Late Harvest** ★★★ Delicate yet delicious gewürztraminer abundance of rosepetals & honeysuckle on **13**. Deft balance of fruit & acid makes for clean, dry, balanced tail. Also tasted: **Merlot 13** ★★★ **Pinotage 13** ★★★ **Shiraz 13** ★★★ **Cabernet Sauvignon-Shiraz 13** ★★★ **Chardonnay 14** ★★☆ **Chenin Blanc** ⊘ **14** ★★★ **Sauvignon Blanc 14** ★★★ **Beaukett** ⊘ **14** ★★★ Not retasted: **Méthode Cap Classique 07** ★★★ Occasional release: **Red Muscadel**, **White Muscadel**, **Cape Ruby**.

Chapel range

Cabernet Sauvignon-Merlot ★★ Bright red-berry charm to now-bottled **13** uncomplicated quaffer, light smoke & choc notes. Unwooded. **Natural Sweet** ★★ Dried herb sheen to low-alcohol **NV** rosé's red berry twist. Poolside staple. Also tasted: **Extra Light NV** ★☆ **Chenin Blanc-Colombar 13** ★★ **Semi-Sweet NV** ★★

Natural Sweet range

Rosé ★★ Easy-drinking, strawberry-hued **NV** pink for the sweet-toothed. Low alcohol (7.5%), as all these. Also tasted: **Red NV** ★★ **White NV** ★★

Light Cultivar range

Extra Light Sauvignon Blanc ★★ Good typicity of granadilla zip & zing on 8% alcohol **14**. Also tasted: **Extra Light Merlot 13** ★☆ **Pinotage Rosé 13** ★★ **Light Chenin Blanc 14** ★★

Sparkling Wines

Brut ★★★ Lively apple crunch with some lees backing on **NV** fizz. Simple & unfussy, it's ideal for celebrations. Also tasted: **Sweet Red NV** ★★ **Sweet Rosé NV** ★★ **Sweet White NV** ★★

One-Litre Combibloc range

Merlot ⊘ ★★★ First listing in guide for old favourite, **13** fruitcake & blackcurrant, with earthy cocoa depth. Good grip & breadth, long tail. **Chardonnay** ⊘ ★★★ Lively nectarine & citrus to fresh **14**, some lees-ageing adds breadth. **Fruity Late Harvest** ★★☆ Tangy peach & floral nuances to lightly sweet & juicy **NV**. **Natural Sweet Rosé** ★★ Undemanding **NV** pink with sweet cherry & plum succulence. Also tasted: **Cabernet Sauvignon** ⊘ **13** ★★★ **Smooth Dry Red NV** ★★ **Sauvignon Blanc** ⊘ **14** ★★★ **Crisp Dry White NV** ★★ **Crisp Extra Light NV** ★ **Selected Stein NV** ★★ Not retasted: **Natural Sweet White NV** ★★ **Smooth Sweet Red NV** ★★

Two-Litre Certified Cultivar Slimline range

Shiraz ★★★ Coffee & pepper zip to **13**, some backbone from French & American oak staves, medium bodied & supple. **Chenin Blanc ★★★** Juicy melon on lively **14**, with light sweetness broadening the palate. Also tasted: **Cabernet Sauvignon 13 ★★★ Merlot 13 ★★★ Sauvignon Blanc 14 ★★☆** Not retasted: **Ruby Cabernet 13 ★★★ Chardonnay 13 ★★★**

Three-Litre Cultivar Slimline range

Shiraz ★★★ French & American oak staves lend **13** a mocha note - but ample berry fruit & spice. Good food wine. Also tasted: **Cabernet Sauvignon 13 ★★★ Chardonnay 14 ★★☆ Sauvignon Blanc 14 ★★☆ Sauvignon Blanc Extra Light 14 ★★ Natural Sweet White NV ★★** Not retasted: **Merlot 13 ★★**

Three-Litre Blended range

Smooth Dry Red ★★ Easy-drinking & light-bodied **NV** displays some bright red-fruit appeal. **Johannisberger Semi-Sweet White ★★** Apple & peach vibrancy to refreshing **NV** quaffer which improves on previous. **Natural Sweet Red (Slimline Packed) ★★** Light cherry, berry sweetness to **NV** easy-drinker. Also tasted: **Crisp Dry White NV ★★ Refreshing Extra Light NV ★ Natural Sweet Rosé (Slimline Packed) NV ★★ Johannisberger Semi-Sweet Red NV ★★**

Brandy range ⑲

★★★★ 7 Year Potstilled for minimum 7 years (38% alcohol). Caramelised nuts, fragrant dried peaches, sultanas on the nose. On the mellow palate hints of apple & pear, marzipan creaminess & long smooth finish. Elegant & fresh. Variety/ies undisclosed, as for 5 Year.

5 Year ★★★★ Blended brandy with potstill content matured for at least 5 years. 43% alcohol. Caramel, fresh herbs on the nose with apricot, peardrops on the palate. Long & fresh. For mixing. — WB, FM

Location/map/WO: Robertson ▪ Est 1941 ▪ 1stB 1987 ▪ Tasting & sales Mon-Fri 9–5.30 Sat/pub hols 9-3 Sun 9–1 ▪ Closed Good Fri, Dec 25 & Jan 1 ▪ Cellar tours by appt ▪ Conferences ▪ Small wine museum ▪ Owner(s) 43 members ▪ Cellarmaster(s) Bowen Botha (Jan 1982) ▪ Winemaker(s) Francois Weich (Sep 1997), Jacques Roux (Jan 2001), Thys Loubser & Olivia Poonah (both Jan 2012) ▪ Viticulturist(s) Briaan Stipp (May 2005) ▪ 2,200ha (cab, shiraz, chard, chenin, sauv) ▪ 35,100t ▪ ISO 22000, WIETA ▪ PO Box 556 Robertson 6705 ▪ info@robertsonwine.co.za ▪ www.robertsonwinery.co.za ▪ S 33° 48' 36.8" E 019° 52' 51.4" ▪ F +27 (0)23-626-6807/+27 (0)23-626-4788 (sales) ▪ **T +27 (0)23-626-7080/+27 (0)23-626-8817 (sales)**

Robert Stanford Estate

Established in 1855, this hillside property once owned by the entrepreneur Sir Robert Stanford is one of Walker Bay's oldest, and home to winegrowing since the 1890s. More recent rejuvenation has added a varied visitor offering, including country-style restaurant, art studio and distillery.

Sir Robert Stanford Estate range

★★★★ Shiraz ⑫ Potentially boisterous blackberry fruit of **10** cajoled into order by layers of warm spice; lovely composure & unwavering length of flavour swaddle 14.9% alcohol.

★★★★☆ The Hansom ⑫ Cab-led **10** (★★★★) blend is piled high with bramble fruit, but derailed by weighty 15.3% alcohol, whereas understated **09**'s notable alcohol & smidgen sugar didn't jar. Not tasted: **Rosé**.

Cutters Cove

Not tasted: **Shiraz-Viognier**. — DS

Location: Stanford ▪ Map: Elgin, Walker Bay & Bot River ▪ WO: Walker Bay ▪ Est 1855 ▪ 1stB 2008 ▪ Tasting & sales Fri-Mon 10-3.30 ▪ Closed Good Fri, Dec 25 & Jan 1 ▪ Madre's Kitchen Thu-Mon 8-4 ▪ Facilities for children ▪ Gift shop ▪ Farm produce ▪ Conservation area ▪ Art studio ▪ Tractor tours/vineyard walks by appt ▪ Owner(s) Kleinrivier Beleggings (Pty) Ltd ▪ Winemaker(s) Johan Joubert (2009/10 vintages, Kleine Zalze) & Van Zyl du Toit (Allée Bleue) ▪ Viticulturist(s) Jan Malan (Jan 2003) ▪ 176ha/60ha (pinot, shiraz, chenin, sauv) ▪ 320t/2,500cs own label 40% red 30% white 15% rosé 15% MCC

▪ BWI champion ▪ wines@robertstanfordestate.co.za ▪ www.robertstanfordestate.co.za, www.madreskitchenstanford.co.za ▪ S 34° 25' 49.41" E 019° 27' 49.98" ▪ F +27 (0)86-655-6944 ▪ **T +27 (0)28-341-0647**

Robin Hood Legendary Wine Series

Mark Simpson, owner of fun-styled Robin Hood Legendary Series and upmarket Arumdale Cool Climate Wines (see entry for tasting details), says the quartet of Robin Hood wines is specially designed to accompany a casual meal: Maid Marian with hors d'oeuvres, Little John fish or white meat, Robin Hood pizza or pasta, and Friar Tuck after-supper cheese (or even curry/masala). Bon appétit!

Robin Hood ★★ Driest of range, **NV** from cab & shiraz. Black fruit, some spice, palatable quaffer. Elgin grapes, as all unless noted. **Maid Marian ★★** Rosé from shiraz. Light flowers & berries before sticky toffee-apple sweetness. **NV** with some Paarl fruit. **Little John ★★★** Mainly sauvignon with 10% Paarl viognier adding lift & interest. **NV** off-dry flavours of green fruit with a peachy finish. **Friar Tuck ★★** From shiraz & cab, **NV** super-ripe black berries with short, sweet finish. — CM

☐ **Rocheburg** see Riebeek Cellars
☐ **Rockfield** see Du Preez Estate

Romond Vineyards

The past year proved successful for André and Rhona Liebenberg's Helderberg boutique winery, with a number of positive reviews resulting in increased sales. In response, new labels are being added though we'll taste them only next edition.

Rebus range

★★★★ Fanfaronne ⓖ Fragrant **09** (★★★★★) best yet; complex, classic cab franc leads Bordeaux blend with cab, merlot. Savoury fruit balances firmly structured tannins. Step up from **07**; no **08**.
Pinotage ⓖ **★★★★ 09** fruity but serious, balanced & juicy, with delicious grip to finish. Like Impromptu, tasted a few years back. Not retasted: **Impromptu 10 ★★★★** — IM

Location: Somerset West ▪ Map: Helderberg ▪ WO: Stellenbosch ▪ Est 1993 ▪ 1stB 2003 ▪ Tasting, sales & tours by appt Mon-Sat 10-5.30 Sun 11-5.30 ▪ Fee R40, waived on purchase ▪ Closed Easter Fri-Sun, Dec 25/26 & Jan 1 ▪ Olive oil ▪ The Vintner's Loft self-catering apartment ▪ Owner(s) André & Rhona Liebenberg ▪ Winemaker(s) André Liebenberg ▪ Viticulturist(s) Francois Hanekom (May 2007) ▪ 11.5ha/9.5ha (cabs s/f, merlot, ptage) ▪ PO Box 5634 Helderberg 7135 ▪ info@romond.co.za ▪ www.romondvineyards.co.za ▪ S 34° 1' 52.61" E 018° 49' 59.67" ▪ F +27 (0)21-855-0428 ▪ **T +27 (0)21-855-4566**

☐ **Roodeberg** see KWV

Roodezandt Wines

Under stalwart cellarmaster Christie Steytler (this harvest his 35th here), grower-owned Roodezandt remains a steady producer of bulk wine — well over 20 million litres — to local and overseas brand owners - so much so additional storage capacity has been required. But Christie and team also welcome visitors to the cellar in Robertson town to taste and buy their own affordable bottlings.

Balthazar range

★★★★ Chardonnay Brut Méthode Cap Classique ⓖ Elegant top-label sparkling. **09** shows appealing marzipan notes, toned yet generous body, nutty conclusion.

Roodezandt range

Cabernet Sauvignon ★★★ Polished **12** takes step up with more varietal typicity. Lovely herb & redcurrant notes, balanced & nicely dry conclusion. **Chenin Blanc ★★★** Mouthwatering fruit salad nose & light, fresh palate make for amiable **14** summer sipper for early enjoyment. Also tasted: **Sauvignon Blanc 14 ★★★** Not retasted: **Syrah 11 ★★★ Special Late Harvest 11 ★★★ Red Muscadel 12 ★★★**

For more information, visit wineonaplatter.com

Keizer's Creek range

The Red ★★ Unwooded plush-fruited **NV** blend offers light, uncomplicated party fun. Near-equal pinotage, cab & merlot. — HJ

Location/map/WO: Robertson ▪ Est 1953 ▪ Tasting & sales Mon-Fri 9-5 ▪ Cellar tours by appt Mon-Fri 8-12 & 2-5 ▪ Closed all pub hols ▪ Sales (at cellar price) also from La Verne Wine Boutique Mon-Fri 9-5.30 Sat 9-5 ▪ Facilities for children ▪ Owner(s) 60 members ▪ Cellarmaster(s) Christie Steytler (May 1980) ▪ Winemaker(s) Jean du Plessis (2012), with Tiaan Blom (Oct 2005) ▪ Viticulturist(s) Jaco Lategan (Dec 2006) ▪ 1,800ha (cab, merlot, ptage, ruby cab, shiraz, chard, chenin, cbard, muscadel w, sauv) ▪ 30,000t/23m L bulk ▪ BSCI, HACCP, IPW, WIETA ▪ PO Box 164 Robertson 6705 ▪ info@roodezant.co.za ▪ www.roodezant.co.za ▪ S 33° 48' 33.2" E 019° 52' 47.3" ▪ F +27 (0)23-626-5074 ▪ T +27 (0)23-626-1160

Rooiberg Winery

Formerly a co-operative, Robertson's progressive grower-owned private company Rooiberg is driven by three P's: profit, people and planet, CEO Johan du Preez says. To this end comes concerted expansion in China, the US, Africa and Russia (among more than 20 international markets receiving their bulk and bottled wine). Contract crushing is done for others (including black economic empowerment companies), and sustainable winegrowing includes some organic production and conservation of over half its combined landholding.

Reserve range

★★★★ **Pinotage** ⊘ **13**, from barrel, a touch more feistily tannic than previous but the well-handled, ripe, smoky/savoury black fruit is in place & will pleasurably unfold over the next couple of years.

★★★★ **Shiraz** ⊘ Plush new-leather aroma on **13** preview, with heather & hay. Dry tannins mask dark berry fruit mid-2014, but should retreat given time. Meantime match with rich venison dishes.

★★★★ **Chardonnay** ⊘ Citrus tang on base of subtle vanilla from new-barrel ferment, soft honey flavours & lemon zest, lime marmalade on long clean finish. **13** better realised than **12** (★★★★).

Cabernet Sauvignon ★★★★ Always one of the region's more accomplished & appealing. Preview **13** classic pencil shavings & cedar combo, savoury black fruit on a wine which deserves keeping few years to show best. Also tasted: **Merlot 13** ★★★★ **Cape Blend 13** ★★★★

Rooiberg range

★★★★ **Red Muscadel** Perfect for fireside sipping, or over ice for a summer pleaser, **13** fortified oozes raisin sweetness, balanced by crisp sultana-toned acidity to long fruity finish. Delicious!

Cabernet Sauvignon ★★★ **12**, now bottled, offers savoury smoked beef aroma, firm tannins, concludes with tangy cranberry notes & black pepper. Serve with hearty stews. **Cabernet Sauvignon-Merlot (Roodewyn)** ⊘ ★★★ Clean flinty aroma, ripe mulberry juiciness & hint of cloves, **13** soft & chocolate-laced for dessert partnering. **Chenin Blanc** ★★★ Fresh white peach aroma, crisp acidity, green apple flavours. **14** ends nice & dry. Serve chilled. **Brut Sparkling** ★★ Clean, simple **NV** carbonated sparkler from sauvignon blanc, with crisp lively bubbles for birthday toasts. **Rosé Natural Sweet** ★★ **14** no-pretensions pretty pink party pleaser from red muscadel, to serve well chilled. **Blanc Natural Sweet** ★★★ Honey-sweet **14**, with big grapey flavours from white muscadel. Also tasted: **Merlot 13** ★★ **Pinotage 12** ★★★ **Mountain Red 13** ★★ **Chardonnay** ⊘ **14** ★★★ **Colombar 14** ★★★ **Sauvignon Blanc 14** ★★ **Flamingo Sparkling NV** ★★ **Vin Doux Sparkling NV** ★★ **Red Natural Sweet 13** ★★ Not retasted: **Shiraz 12** ★★★ **Cape Vintage 12** ★★★ Discontinued: **Pinotage Rosé, Chenin Blanc-Sauvignon Blanc.**

Red Chair range

Sauvignon Blanc Light ⊘ ★★ Appealing grassy intro to **13**, pleasantly light & lean. Not retasted: **Pinotage 12** ★★★ — DB

Location/map/WO: Robertson ▪ Est 1964 ▪ 1stB 1974 ▪ Tasting & sales Mon-Fri 9–5.30 Sat 9–4 ▪ Fee R10pp for tour groups ▪ Closed Good Fri, Dec 25 & Jan 1 ▪ Bodega de Vinho restaurant & bakery Mon-Fri 8–5.30 Sat 9–4 ▪ Facilities for children ▪ Tour groups ▪ Gift shop ▪ Rooiberg Conservancy ▪ Owner(s) 30 members ▪ Cellarmaster(s) André van Dyk (Oct 2002) ▪ Winemaker(s) André Scriven (Jan 2008), with Pieter Rossouw (Jan 2013) ▪ Viticulturist(s) Hennie Visser (2007, Vinpro consultant) ▪ 667ha (cab, merlot, ptage, ruby cab, shiraz, chard, chenin, cbard, sauv) ▪ 13,000t/300,000cs own label 35% red 65% white ▪ Other export brands: African Dawn, Amandalia, Cape Avocet, Finch Mountain, Table View, Tembana Valley, Zebra Collection ▪ Brands for clients: AlexKia, Cape Dreams, Ferling Noble, Headbutt, Woolworths ▪ ISO 9001:2000, BWI, HACCP, IPW, SGS Organic ▪ PO Box 358 Robertson 6705 ▪ info@rooiberg.co.za ▪ www.rooiberg.co.za ▪ S 33° 46' 35.3" E 019° 45' 42.9" ▪ F +27 (0)23-626-3295 ▪ **T +27 (0)23-626-1663**

☐ **Rooi Kalahari** *see* Die Mas van Kakamas

Rosendal Winery

This mainly direct-to-customer wine business vinifies a range of wines to please the palates of its 10,000-plus customers in southern Africa and Scandinavia, while its tourism facilities near Robertson have much to offer visitors: a comfortable tasting and sales venue for winelovers; guest house, spa, restaurant, gallery, coffee shop and boutique for the rest.

Reserve range

★★★★ Hilltop Shiraz (NEW) From Stellenbosch fruit, **12** structured for the long haul, with firm tannin giving form to dense & fruit-filled core.

★★★★ Serenity Chardonnay (NEW) Poised **13**, judicious marriage spicy new oak (50%), creamy texture (9 months sur lie) & ebullient lemon & lime aromas, tastes. Bright & easy yet complex solo sipper.

Also tasted: **Classic Cuvée 11 ★★★ Black Eagle 08 ★★★★** Not tasted: **Cabernet Sauvignon, Merlot, Blue Mountain, Cape Francolin, Leopard's Eye, Sauvignon Blanc.** Note: range merges previous 'Reserve Limited' & 'Hilltop' line-ups.

Barony range

August Cabernet Sauvignon (NEW) **★★★** Cassis & graphite notes, austere, grippy mouthfeel - **11** is classic cab but beginning to tire, enjoy soon. **Bønne Pinotage** (NEW) **★★★** Mocha-infused **12** packed with mulberry fruit, brisk acidity ensures drinkability. Also tasted: **Cecile Sauvignon Blanc 13 ★★★★** Not tasted: **Heidi Shiraz**.

Rosendal range

Merlot (NEW) (bottle) **★★★ 12** black fruit, sweet vanilla oak, commendable grip without the greenness the variety often shows in SA. **Syrah** (NEW) **★★★** Hemel-en-Aarde Valley grapes in solid **11**, generous, with toasty oak & roasted nuts bouquet, leathery beef carpaccio flavours. **Chenin Blanc** (NEW) **★★★** Waxy & creamy **13** laced with refreshing lemon, making a good match for avocado ritz, say team. Not tasted: **Chardonnay, Riesling, Sauvignon Blanc.** — CvZ

Location/map: Robertson ▪ WO: Western Cape ▪ 1stB 2003 ▪ Tasting, sales & cellar tours Mon-Sat 8-5 Sun 9-1 ▪ Fee only charged for groups of 10+ ▪ Wine & Lindt chocolate tastings ▪ Restaurant & guesthouse ▪ Spa & wellness centre ▪ Conferences ▪ Owner(s) Geir Tellefsen & Sissel Anderssen ▪ Cellarmaster(s)/winemaker(s) Therese de Beer (Jan 2012) ▪ 18ha ▪ 80% red 15% white 5% rosé ▪ PO Box 3 Suite 128 Roggebaai 8012 ▪ info@rosendalwinery.com ▪ rosendalwinery.com ▪ S 33° 48' 7.8" E 019° 59' 19.0" ▪ F +27 (0)21-424-1570 ▪ **T +27 (0)21-424-4498 (sales)/ +27 (0)23-626-1570 (farm)**

Ross Gower Wines

The cellar on this small Elgin property was built by the late Ross Gower and his family using the uncommon but eco-friendly rammed-earth technique, resulting in ultra-thick walls which provide a constant temperature year round. 'Ideal conditions, especially for bubbly,' says matriarch Sally Gower, who has taken over the reins and intends specialising in MCC sparkling with the assistance of ex-Mulderbosch winemaker and now Kanu viticultural consultant, Mike Dobrovic.

For more information, visit wineonaplatter.com

Pinot Noir Méthode Cap Classique Brut ⓥ ★★★★ Fruity champagne-method sparkling **08**, dapper & appealing aperitif or food partner. **Chardonnay Méthode Cap Classique** ⓥ ★★★★ Bottle-fermented **11** bubbly offers fresh, creamy quaffability for any occasion. — HJ

Location/WO: Elgin ▪ Map: Elgin, Walker Bay & Bot River ▪ Est 2003 ▪ 1stB 2004 ▪ Tasting & sales by appt ▪ Glen Stuart self-catering cottages ▪ Conservation area ▪ Owner(s) Gower family ▪ 83ha/±7ha (shiraz, sauv) ▪ 20,000cs own label 5% red 10% white 85% MCC ▪ PO Box 161 Elgin 7180 ▪ info@rossgowerwines.co.za ▪ www.rossgowerwines.co.za ▪ S 34° 14' 17.7" E 019° 7' 3.7" ▪ F +27 (0)86-611-2179 ▪ **T +27 (0)21-844-0197**

☐ **Rowlands** *see* Southern Sky Wines
☐ **Royal** *see* Riebeek Cellars, Valley Vineyards Wine Company
☐ **Ruby Ridge** *see* Govert Wines

Rudera Wines ⓥ

Initially at the forefront of developing chenin into a highly reputed grape, Rudera since also estab-lished a reputation for cabernet and shiraz/syrah. Quality and classic styling have always been attrib-ute, and with the excellent Chris Keet (Keet Wines) as adviser, the standard is maintained. At the cellardoor outside Stellenbosch, owner Riana Hall is raising winetasting to an artform, offering six dif-ferent set options - including pairings with food or chocolate, and a sensorial tasting - plus bespoke variants like vegetarian, vegan and food intolerance. 'And we welcome kids.'

★★★★☆ **Cabernet Sauvignon** Though ripe-fruited & powerful, savoury **12** from a mix of Stellenbosch & Paarl grapes is nicely balanced between youthful exuberance & disciplined constraint, built on firm foundations of concentration & structure. The dry finish is crucial.

★★★★☆ **Platinum Cabernet Sauvignon 09** is acquiring the deeper, more complex character of maturity (but many years to go). Velvet textured, with firm tannic structure, it's a little more substantial in all ways than the straight Cab - generally bigger but still with some grace. Handles 50% new oak well; dry. A serious wine. **08** sold out untasted.

★★★★ **Syrah** Fragrant floral notes lift red/black fruit on good, serious **12**. Supportive oaking. Ripe & rather big - 14.5% alcohol glows on the finish. Like **11** (★★★★★) will benefit from some time in bottle.

★★★★ **De Tradisie Chenin Blanc** Richness & breadth on **11**, with notes of ripe apple, earth & smoky melon. Touch drier than Robusto, with balancing acid core. Like next, natural ferment; oaked (10% new). WO Stellenbosch.

★★★★☆ **Robusto Chenin Blanc** Sweet-fruited, rich & full-bodied but effectively dry **12**, despite some residual sugar which adds to the wine's harmony, with the richness balanced by a light intensity, even an element of austerity. Lingering finish testimony to the quality of the ripe grapes. Stellenbosch WO.

★★★★☆ **Noble Late Harvest** ⓥ Oak-matured **10** dessert from chenin with smatterings chardon-nay, viognier & sauvignon. Excellently balanced, with right hint of honeyed botrytis adding complexity to luscious ripe peach & tart apricot.

Not retasted: **Platinum Chenin Blanc 09** ★★★★ — TJ

Location/map: Stellenbosch ▪ WO: Western Cape/Stellenbosch/Elgin ▪ Est 1999 ▪ 1stB 2000 ▪ Tasting by appt only ▪ Fee R50pp/5 wines, waived on purchase ▪ Specialised tastings (min 4/max 16 pax): food & wine pairing R280pp; chocolate & wine pairing R180pp; sensorial tasting R100pp ▪ Owner(s) Riana Hall ▪ Cellarmaster(s) Chris Keet (2011, consultant) ▪ 15ha/10ha (cab, shiraz, chenin) ▪ ±120t/15,000cs own label 50% red 50% white ▪ IPW ▪ PO Box 589 Stellenbosch 7599 ▪ riana@rudera.co.za ▪ www.rudera.co.za ▪ S 33° 56' 26.5" E 018° 54' 14.3" ▪ **T +27 (0)21-882-8214**

☐ **Rudi Schultz Wines** *see* Schultz Family Wines
☐ **Ruins** *see* Bon Cap Organic Winery

Ruitersvlei Wines

Rejuvenation continues at the scenically situated estate on the Paarl Mountain slopes, as a new winemaker (seasoned Nico Vermeulen) takes the reins and oversees a range reshuffle with, among others, a new Bordeaux blend and rosé in prospect, along with 'lots of exciting changes'.

Ruitersvlei range

Cabernet Sauvignon ★★★☆ Plummy & spicy aromas, **11** contrasting dry palate with tannins asking for steak on the braai. WO W Cape, as next. Not retasted: **Merlot 11** ★★★ **Sauvignon Blanc 13** ★★ Not tasted: **Pinotage**, **Shiraz**, **Private Collection**, **Chenin Blanc**. — CvZ

Location: Paarl • Map: Paarl & Wellington • WO: Western Cape/Paarl • Tasting & sales Mon-Sun 9-5; in season (from mid Sep) tastings continue till 10pm at restaurant • Restaurant: mountainside@ruitersvlei.co.za • Weddings & conferences • 11 guest rooms • Owner(s) Ruitersvlei Holdings (Pty) Ltd • Winemaker(s) Nico Vermeulen • 120ha • PO Box 532 Suider-Paarl 7624 • marketing@ruitersvlei.co.za • www.ruitersvlei.co.za • S 33° 45' 10.8" E 018° 54' 28.0" • F +27 (0)21-863-1443 • **T +27 (0)21-863-1517**

☐ **Runner Duck** *see* Vergenoegd Wine Estate
☐ **Running Duck** *see* Stellar Winery

Rupert & Rothschild Vignerons

Founded in 1690, French Huguenot farm Fredericksburg has since 1997 once more had a French connection. In that year, the late SA businessman Anton Rupert and the late Baron Edmond de Rothschild of Bordeaux's Château Clarke established this Simonsberg winery. The families' association and their goals continue under the Rupert family and Baron Benjamin de Rothschild. Producing world-class wine in an environmentally sustainable manner is close to their hearts; to this end the winery was the first to be awarded Environmental Management certification. Their staff also benefit from this, and from the Dennegeur community initiative, established with the two Franschhoek-based Rupert properties. In the newly renovated tasting centre, international wines from the Rothschild portfolio may now be sampled with complementary food pairings.

★★★★☆ **Baron Edmond** Generously scented merlot-cab blend plus a little cab franc, with dark, ripe fruit & spicy cedarwood, **11** immediately impresses. Medium bodied & beautifully balanced, if slightly less intense than **10**. Worth cellaring until around 2020. Stellenbosch & Darling fruit.

★★★★ **Classique** Very youthful 6-way cab-led **12** (★★★★) blend with merlot & dollop shiraz; less convincing than **11**, needs time for refreshing but prominent acidity to integrate.

★★★★☆ **Baroness Nadine** Creamily oaked multi-region chardonnay, **12** a refined, classy act. Elgin fruit's steely lime acidity & minerality complements & tightens richly rounded tropical flavours from Robertson & Barrydale vineyards to create a winning combination. — IM

Location: Paarl • Map: Franschhoek • WO: Western Cape • Est 1997 • 1stB 1998 • Tasting & sales Mon-Fri 10-4.30 Sat 10-4; cellar tours at 11 & 3 • Closed all religious holidays, Dec 26 & Jan 1 • Owner(s) Rupert family & Baron Benjamin de Rothschild • Winemaker(s) Yvonne Lester (Sep 2001), with Clive Radloff (Jun 1997) • 90ha (cabs s/f, merlot, p verdot) • 1,200t/170,000cs own label 95% red 5% white • ISO 14001, HACCP, IPW • PO Box 412 Franschhoek Valley 7690 • info@rupert-rothschildvignerons.com • www.rupert-rothschildvignerons.com • S 33° 50' 14.5" E 018° 56' 51.1" • F +27 (0)21-874-1802 • **T +27 (0)21-874-1648**

☐ **Rupert Wines** *see* Anthonij Rupert Wyne

Russo Family Vintners

Henk and Terèsa Rossouw bought a Durbanville smallholding in 2004, and feel inspired by one of the Cape's first winemakers, Pierre Rousseau, who arrived in 1688. The potential for fine Bordeaux-style red was early identified. Now the whole family (including dog) is involved, and caught up in the dream. Current releases are Russo Bordeaux blend and Cabernet Franc, both '08.

Location: Durbanville ▪ Map: Durbanville, Philadelphia & Darling ▪ Est 2004 ▪ 1stB 2007 ▪ Tasting, sales & tours Mon-Fri 9–4 Sat by appt ▪ Closed all pub hols ▪ Owner(s) Henk & Terèsa Rossouw ▪ Winemaker(s) Terèsa Rossouw (2007) ▪ 6.5ha/4ha (cabs s/f, malbec, merlot, p verdot) ▪ 35t/800cs own label 100% red ▪ PO Box 4402 Tyger Valley 7536 ▪ teresa@russowines.co.za ▪ www.russowines.co.za ▪ S 33° 48' 37.9" E 018° 37' 04.3" ▪ F +27 (0)21-979-1996 ▪ **T +27 (0)21-979-1960**

Rustenberg Wines

This beautiful estate on the lower slopes of Stellenbosch's Simonsberg is one of the great names in Cape wine history, though it was split in two in 1810. It seems that, remarkably, wine has been bottled here continuously since Schoongezicht farm was bought in 1892 by John X. Merriman, the Cape's last prime minister. That farm and Rustenberg itself were both acquired by industrialist Peter Barlow in the 1940s and reunited. It remains in the hands of the Barlow family, with owner Simon Barlow as fully involved as ever — particularly on the viticultural side, and with Peter's grandson Murray, Diners Club Young Winemaker of the Year 2013, in charge of the cellar and intent on keeping in step with modern styles while preserving the estate's rich heritage.

Site Specific range

★★★★☆ **Peter Barlow** ⓖ 100% cab from estate's finest red vineyard. **08** a few years back had restrained power & regal bearing, gorgeous fruit still masked by polished oak. Should reward ageing.

★★★★☆ **Five Soldiers** ⓖ Supremely elegant & complex single-vineyard **11** exhibits all prerequisites for world-class chardonnay: oak plays supporting role to intense, layered citrus core, bound by intricate minerality & precise acidity.

Not tasted: **Buzzard Kloof Syrah**.

Regional range

★★★★ **Merlot** ⓖ Maiden **10** previewed few years back poised & well structured, with delicious concluding fruit acid grip.

★★★★ **John X Merriman** ⓖ Lighter, savoury **11** (★★★★) blend of all the Bordeaux red varieties would need the greater fruit density of **10** to provide flesh & cope with firm tannins.

★★★★ **RM Nicholson** ⓖ **10** cab, shiraz, merlot-led blend with pure fruit & hint of oaky vanilla tasted from barrel few years back. Balanced, firm & rich.

★★★★☆ **Straw Wine** ⓖ Delicately sweet, honeyed **11** from air-dried chenin, viognier & crouchen in lighter dessert style. Thread of bright acidity sustains delightful savoury finish. Coastal WO.

Not retasted: **Stellenbosch Shiraz 11 ★★★★** Not tasted: **Stellenbosch Chardonnay, Stellenbosch Roussanne, Sauvignon Blanc**.

Ida's / Est.1682 range

Not retasted: **Red 12 ★★☆ White 12 ★★☆** — IM

Location/map: Stellenbosch ▪ WO: Stellenbosch/Simonsberg–Stellenbosch/Coastal/Western Cape ▪ Est 1682 ▪ 1stB 1892 ▪ Tasting & sales Mon-Fri 9–4.30 Sat 10–4 Sun 10-3 ▪ Closed Good Fri, Dec 25 & Jan 1 ▪ Garden ▪ Weddings ▪ Owner(s) Simon Barlow ▪ Cellarmaster(s) Murray Barlow (Nov 2011) ▪ Winemaker(s) Randolph Christians (Nov 1995), with Gareth le Grange (2003) & Craig Christians (Jun 2012) ▪ Viticulturist(s) Simon Barlow (Aug 1987), with Tessa Moffat ▪ 1,200ha/±154ha (cabs s/f, grenache n/b, malbec, merlot, mourv, p verdot, shiraz, chard, rouss, sauv, sem) ▪ ±1,050t/154,000cs own label 51% red 47% white 2% other ▪ BWI, IPW ▪ PO Box 33 Stellenbosch 7599 ▪ wine@rustenberg.co.za ▪ www.rustenberg.co.za ▪ S 33° 53' 44.8" E 018° 53' 33.6" ▪ F +27 (0)21-809-1219 ▪ **T +27 (0)21-809-1200**

Rust en Vrede Estate

Owner Jean Engelbrecht continues to build on - and not simply maintain - the already excellent reputation of this historic Stellenbosch property. Many recent accolades, including top ratings in this guide, are further justification for his conviction that the Helderberg soils are perfect for shiraz, cabernet and merlot, and the Estate blend the best possible reflection of the harmony of site and grape. The property's substantial status rests in the capable hands of former Diners Club Winemaker of the Year Coenie Snyman, one of just four custodians of its wines over the more than three decades of Engelbrecht family piloting. And with the elegant restaurant serving equally refined fare, the future seems assured.

Estate Vineyards range

★★★★ **Cabernet Sauvignon** 12 (★★★★☆) a notch up on **11**. Ripe black fruit & spice with inky depths & elegant, broad layers. There's a restrained violet/herb delicacy too. Complexity & structure gained from 18 months French oak (25% new) & 9 months in bottle. Rewarding & long.

★★★★★ **Single Vineyard Cabernet Sauvignon** 11 (★★★★) continues oaky note of **10**. Cassis & cocoa richness with grip & backbone but juicy too. Complex, layered & serious, it needs time. Long maturation in bottle before release, as for all.

★★★★ **Merlot** Rounded yet deep, **13** is layered with cherry & tobacco leaf intricacy. As refined & sleekly succulent as **12**. Dense, broad & superbly poised with a long aftertaste.

★★★★ **Syrah** Name change from 'Shiraz' coincides with improvement by **12** (★★★★★) on **11** with clarity of (black) fruit expression. Seductive, ripe, with grip, concentration, refinement & class. French oak (25% new) provides polished support. Harmonious throughout.

★★★★★ **Single Vineyard Syrah** Effortlessly classy **12** is seamlessly elegant & harmonious yet powerful. Restraint evident in well-judged ripeness of berries, lively acidity & smart combo French/American oak (50% new). Lithe & supple, with great density & depth. Stellar **11** (★★★★★) a hard act to follow.

★★★★☆ **1694 Classification** Pricey limited release honouring date property was granted. **10** & also-tasted **11**, both near-equal shiraz-cab blends, pulsate with life & sophistication. Brooding yet delicate ripe dark fruit, layered with cocoa, liquorice & dried herb nuances. Statuesque yet supple & lissom. 18 months French oak, 65% new. 1,590/2,150 bottles.

★★★★☆ **Estate** Beguiling **11** continues standard of previous classy cab (63%), shiraz, merlot blends. Cassis purity, seamlessly knit with oak (French & American). Squeeze of tannin in silky & genteel texture. Long, rich & refined. — FM

Location/map/WO: Stellenbosch ▪ Est 1694 ▪ 1stB 1979 ▪ Tasting, sales & cellar tours Mon-Sat 9–5 ▪ Fee R40/4 wines & R70/6 wines, waived on purchase ▪ Closed Easter Fri/Sun, Dec 25 & Jan 1 ▪ Rust en Vrede Restaurant ▪ Gift shop ▪ Owner(s) Jean Engelbrecht ▪ Cellarmaster(s) Coenie Snyman (Dec 2006) ▪ Winemaker(s) Coenie Snyman (Dec 2006), with Roelof Lotriet (Nov 2011) ▪ Viticulturist(s) Dirkie Mouton (Jun 2010) ▪ 50ha/45ha (cab, merlot, shiraz) ▪ ±300t/40,000cs own label 100% red ▪ IPW ▪ PO Box 473 Stellenbosch 7599 ▪ info@rustenvrede.com ▪ www.rustenvrede.com ▪ S 33° 59' 54.0" E 018° 51' 22.5" ▪ F +27 (0)21-881-3000 ▪ **T +27 (0)21-881-3881**

☐ **Rusthof** see Mooiuitsig Wine Cellars
☐ **Rustler** see Flagstone Winery
☐ **Ruyter's Bin** see Stellenrust

Saam Mountain Vineyards   ⓘ

Describing itself as 'the home of ethical winemaking', Saam ('Together') unites Perdeberg Winery and 3rd-generation family growers on farms from Paarl to Durbanville in a WIETA- and BSCI-accredited export venture.

Saam Premium Collection

Shiraz-Mourvèdre-Petit Verdot (NEW) ★★★☆ Full-bodied & ripe **12**, with supple tannins & stewed fruit flavours. Coastal WO. Not tasted: **Koopmanskraal Shiraz**. Note: range was 'Saam Single Vineyard Selection'.

Saam range

Chenin Blanc ★★★ Appealing ripe stonefruit & tangy acid, **14** dry & medium bodied. Also tasted: **Cabernet Sauvignon** 13 ★★★ **Pinotage** 13 ★★★ Not tasted: **Shiraz**. — GdB

eat, drink, sleep, breathe

(S 34 25' 38.5" E 19 24' 32.7")

SPRINGFONTEIN
WINE ESTATE

Stanford, Western Cape
Telephone: 028 341 0651 | Fax: 028 341 0112
http://www.springfontein.co.za/ info@springfontein.co.za

AS GOOD AS GOLD

The Tulbagh Valley is home to Oakhurst Olives. Here, on the farm Lemoendrif, the Du Toit family produces multi-award winning Extra Virgin olive oil, Kalamata and natural green table olives in harmony with Mother Nature.

Total dedication to quality in every step from planting to hand-harvesting, to processing and packaging ensure premium quality and pure enjoyment.

A clutch of gold medals and awards won at competitions across the globe – from New York to Sydney and South Africa – attest to our unwavering commitment and fuels our passion to keep striving for the best.

info@oakhurstolives.co.za
+ 27 83 269 6999
www.oakhurstolives.co.za
 www.facebook.com/oakhurstolives
 @OakhurstOlives

NOTHING ADDED EXCEPT NATURE ITSELF

SA CHAMPIONS HAILED IN INAUGURAL STANDARD BANK
Chenin Blanc
TOP 10 CHALLENGE

The winners of the inaugural **Standard Bank Chenin Blanc Top 10 Challenge** have been revealed. The announcement made in Stellenbosch has again highlighted the excellence of these South African white wines.

"Finally South Africa's iconic white wines are getting the recognition they deserve and this Top Ten is just a snapshot of the greatness that awaits wine drinkers," says winemaker Ken Forrester, chairman of the Chenin Blanc Association. "Behind these ten great wines are another ten and behind them another ten, Chenin Blanc is an exciting journey and a grape whose time has come."

There were 126 wines entered for assessment by a panel of experienced wine judges. The wines were tasted blind and narrowed down over another two tastings to arrive at the 10 best scoring wines.

The Top 10 wines are listed below, followed by the cellar door price and an extract from the panel tasting report:

- **Bellingham The Old Orchard's 2013** (R150) – "Rich and ripe"
- **Kleine Zalze Family Reserve 2013** (R141) – "Very stylish"
- **KWV The Mentors 2012** (R160) – "Concentrated and pure"
- **Perdeberg The Dry Land Collection Barrel Fermented 2013** (R73) – "A powerful but well balanced wine"
- **Remhoogte Honeybunch Reserve 2013** (R150) – "A good line of acidity ensures balance"
- **Rijk's Cellars Private Cellar 2009** (R130) – "A blockbuster"
- **Simonsig Chenin Avec Chêne 2010** (R110) – "Really well executed"
- **Spier Woolworths Private Collection Barrel Fermented 2013** (Woolworths price: R109.95) – "Totally seductive"
- **Stellenrust 2014 (R44)** – "Really flavourful"
- **Villiera Traditional Barrel Fermented 2014** (R94.50) – "Shows real finesse and balance"

"There's general consensus that [Chenin Blanc] is a 'first division' grape," says judging panel chairman Christian Eedes. Pointing out the disproportionately large number of old vines compared to other varieties, he adds: "The potential is obvious."

"Variations in soil, aspect and micro-climate across often very short distances... coupled with increasingly confident and imaginative winemaking, means that Chenin Blanc will always manifest a plethora of styles, drinking well from bargain basement to top-end," says Eedes.

Also on the panel were wine judging authorities: London-based wine writer Jamie Goode; Cape Wine Master Alan Mullins, head of the Woolworths (SA) Wine Department; Carrie Adams, partner at Norman Goodfellows Fine Wine & Spirit Merchants; Higgo Jacobs, certified with the Court of Master Sommeliers; and, associate judge Gregory Mutambe, sommelier from the Twelve Apostles Hotel and Spa.

Willie du Plessis, Head of Business Banking Western Cape at Standard Bank, congratulated the winners of the inaugural event: "Standard Bank is proud to be associated with such a prestigious event that aims to celebrate and honour the finest Chenin Blanc wines produced in our country. South Africa is known for its top quality wines and has claimed a spot as one of the biggest wine producers in the world. It is up to the future generation of wine producers to work hard to uphold our status and further steer South Africa to even greater heights, by innovating and producing wines of the highest quality and standards.

"We have great talent in our country and it need to be nurtured – the Standard Bank/Chenin Blanc Top Ten Challenge does exactly that. We would like to congratulate all the winners and encourage them to continue breaking new ground and actively contribute to the economy and job creation."

Standard Bank announced its support as headline sponsor in a three-year agreement earlier this year. Winners will receive R20 000 each and the money must be used to reinforce the economic and social benefits in the workplace to the workforce.

Grant Thornton audited the competition.

**For more information about Chenin Blanc visit www.chenin.co.za
or send e-mail to Ina Smith on ina.smith@iafrica.com**

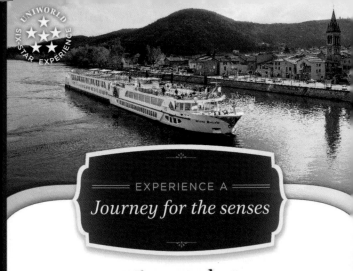

Pick n Pay

Whether you like them bold, flashy, seductive or smooth,
everyone loves a little Italian.

Vino, plonk, nectar of the gods, no matter what you call it, we stock a range of Italian cultivars, exclusive to Pick n Pay – simply for the love of wine.

From the classic Chianti that sits firm on the palate, to the lightly sparkling Lambrusco, you'll find a little Italian to fall in love with at Pick n Pay.

For great wine pairing ideas visit www.picknpay.co.za/wine

lighting the way

Whether for a private home, a commercial business or a wine farm, you can draw smart energy from the sun for less.

soventix
Powerful Returns

Tel: +27 (0) 21 852 7333
Email: r.jacklin@soventix.com
www.soventix.co.za

Soventix SA (Pty) Ltd, a subsidiary of Soventix GmbH in Germany is involved with the development and realisation of roof top and carport solar photovoltaic plants from residential to agricultural as well as large scale solar farms. Whether you finance the solar plant yourself or sign a power purchase agreement, Soventix will ensure you're protected from the rising costs of energy for the next 30 to 40 years. Not only will you be saving on your energy bills, but you'll also be contributing to a more sustainable environment. Renewable energy is the future and is becoming more affordable than energy from non-renewable sources.

CONTEMPORARY
DINING

For an intimate and elegant restaurant that offers classical cuisine with a contemporary twist. Level Four, located at 54 on Bath hotel in Rosebank, creates a fusion of flavours that will charm even the most refined palate.

---

54 Bath Avenue, Rosebank, 2196, Johannesburg
PO Box 3046, Saxonwold, 2132
Tel: +27 11 344 8500
Email: 54onbath.reservations@tsogosun.com

Follow us on Twitter @54onBath
facebook.com/54onBath

54
ON BATH

LEVEL FOUR
RESTAURANT & CHAMPAGNE BAR

ANOTHER TSOGO SUN EXPERIENCE

LUCE

AT HYDE PARK

Luce at Hyde Park offers authentic Italian cuisine.
Our fresh and seasonal produce, meats and homemade pasta
will dazzle and delight diners.

Southern Sun Hyde Park Sandton, 1st Road, Hyde Park, Sandton
t: +27 (0)11 341-8080, e: sshydepark.reservations@tsogosun.com

Onda enables sulphur-free winemaking and is a unique, patented tank system with three key characteristics:

■ Injection of technical gases from below (compressed air, nitrogen, argon and carbon dioxide).
■ Punching down and mixing of the must cap, without the assistance of pumps.
■ Great flexibility of use during each phase of winemaking.

The system was developed by Ghidi Metalli Srl and designed with scientific support by the Faculty of Agriculture's Course of Viticulture and Oenology at Pisa University in Italy.

Enoveneta has done extensive research, development and production of machinery and technological solutions for winemaking over the past 50 years, and offers:

■ A wide range of highly advanced machines that are customized and affordable.
■ Several winemaking solutions, from harvesting wagons in various versions to custom-made conveyor tanks.

Passion meets experience in the production of wine processing equipment, beer micro-breweries and olive oil plants, ensuring top-quality output.

TOSCANA ENOLOGICA MORI SA (PTY)LTD

TOSCANA ENOLOGICA MORI SA (PTY) LTD, Unit 2, The Vineyards, Cincaut Avenue, Saxenburg Park 1, Kuilsriver, Western Cape
T. +27 21 905 9705 **W.** www.tem-sa.co.za **E.** piero.viglietti@tem-sa.co.za

J.
Joostenberg

Come rain or shine...
YOUR TABLE IS WAITING.

Joostenberg Bistro, Deli, Events, Wines & Butchery

Klein Joostenberg, R304, Muldersvlei, Stellenbosch
T 021 88 44 141 | **E** bistro@joostenberg.co.za
GPS 33 49'30.26" S   18 47'37.64" E
f /JoostenbergBistroEventsVenue 🐦 joostenberg_b
www.joostenberg.co.za | *Booking recommended for the bistro.*

AT HOME WITH NATURE AND WINE

Situated in the heart of the Winelands, in one of the most beautiful and heritage conscious towns, Protea Hotel Stellenbosch is located between two international golf courses and is a mere 35km from Cape Town International Airport. Strand Beach, where the mountains and ocean finally meet, is only a 10-minute drive away. Guests seeking the magnificent backdrop of mountain ranges, a scenic drive along the coast or a wine tasting at the many surrounding wine farms, will not be disappointed with the array of things to do in the area.

The Bellezza Health & Skincare Clinic provides relaxing massages, facials and manicures to pamper the most stressed and weary holidaymaker.

Let executive chef Billy Ward tantalise your taste buds with either the themed seasonal dining options in the Cultivar Restaurant or a warm family grill option at The Vineyard Restaurant and Lounge.

The 180-bedroom hotel offers guests the most comfortable beds in the Winelands. The 88 well-appointed deluxe rooms each have a small kitchenette and lounge. All rooms have air conditioning, selected satellite TV channels, an electronic safe and tea- and coffee-making facilities. Friendly, efficient staff are at your service.

If you need a quiet and tranquil getaway still close enough to all the action of the city, the Protea Hotel Stellenbosch is the place to be!

WOODED WHITE

South African **brandy** is made by distilling the **finest quality wine** followed by at least three years of maturation.

Chenin blanc and colombar are the most popular varietals, sourced mainly from warmer wine growing regions.

A **proud heritage** and comprehensive legislation ensure that South African brandy is widely regarded as the world's finest. Indeed, both the IWSC and ISC 2014 **World Champion brandies** are South African! Share the spirit, proudly.

SA
BRANDY
FOUNDATION

SHARE THE SPIRIT

Liebherr innovates again:
wine cabinet with TipOpen technology.

- Two independently adjustable temperature zones ranging between $+5°C$ and $+20°C$
- Ideal for stroring red and white wine
- The wine cabinet can be perfectly integrated into a handle-free kitchen
- Innovative TipOpen technology: when lightly tapped, the glass door automatically opens
- The SoftClosing system automatically shuts the door

ORG de RAC
Organic Wine Estate

WEDDING & FUNCTION VENUE

SEE ME

FEEL ME

TOUCH ME

HEAL ME

Green Heartbeat of the Swartland

SITUATED NEAR PIKETBERG ON THE N7

TO VELDDRIF — PIKETBERG
TO HOPEFIELD — N7
MOORREESBURG
MALMESBURY
N7
CAPE TOWN

www.orgderac.co.za
www.facebook.com/OrgderacWines
twitter.com/OrgdeRacWines

FOR STOCKISTS GO TO:
http://www.orgderac.co.za/where-to-buy.html

KLEINE ZALZE
STELLENBOSCH

A unique Cape Winelands experience

AWARD WINNING WINES - TERROIR RESTAURANT - KLEINE ZALZE LODGE

Kleine Zalze, Strand Road (R44), Stellenbosch, 7600, South Africa | www.kleinezalze.co.za

ARNISTON
SPA HOTEL
★ ★ ★ ★

The hotel is set in the Overberg in one of the Cape's most exquisite locations with the Indian Ocean splashing on your doorstep.

Offering 60 luxurious rooms with breathtaking sea views and mouth-watering meals, complimented by award-winning wines from the region.

Tel: (028) 445 9000 | info@arnistonhotel.com
www.arnistonhotel.com

Mariella's Restaurant

Botterberg Road, Philadelphia
South 33°70′17" East 18°57′33"

Phone: +27 (21) 972 1103
Fax: +27 (21) 972 1894

Email: mariellas@capaia.co.za
Web: www.capaia.eu

CAPAIA
WINES

PONT DE VAL

RIVERSIDE BISTRO

A TASTE OF THE **FRENCH COUNTRYSIDE**
JUST AN HOUR FROM **JOBURG**
ON A **TRANQUIL STRETCH** OF THE **VAAL RIVER**

Wine Tasting • Lavish Cheese Platters
Gourmet Baguettes • Riverside Picnics
Open-air Lounges • River Cruises

Reservations essential. Tel: 016 004 0019
Open Sat, Sun & public holidays from 10 AM

GPS Co-ordinates: S26°46 '23.5 " E27°40 '46.0" or S26°46.392' E27°40.767'

www.pontdeval.co.za

Situated within the Cote de Val Estate.

Location: Paarl ▪ WO: Paarl/Coastal ▪ Tasting & sales at Perdeberg Winery (see entry) ▪ Owner(s) 30 members ▪ Cellarmaster(s) Albertus Louw (Oct 2008) ▪ Winemaker(s) Riaan Möller (Dec 2006) & Carla Herbst (Jun 2008) ▪ PO Box 214 Paarl 7620 ▪ info@perdeberg.co.za ▪ www.perdeberg.co.za ▪ F +27 (0)21-869-8245 ▪ **T +27 (0)21-869-8244**

☐ **Sabi Sabi** *see* Stellenrust

Sadie Family Wines

Eben Sadie's vision of rescuing the venerable and largely neglected old bushvine vineyards in the winelands and honouring them through wine, is being realised both on a broad and personal scale. With viticulturist Rosa Kruger, he helped spearhead an awareness which lead to action among likeminded winemakers, and the fruits can be seen in many wine ranges — including Eben's own Old Vine Series, the latest vintages of which sold out before their official release. Each wine in the series is named after a vineyard site, with the story explained on the back label. All blocks date back to the last century. The oldest is 'T Voetpad, planted 1900–1928 on the vines' own roots, ungrafted, and Mev Kirsten from the 1920s, the oldest chenin vineyard in the country. Sadie Family, our prestigious Winery of the Year for 2015, cannot be commended enough for bringing these priceless gems to winelovers at prices that offer astonishing value. Eben's other wine venture is Sequillo (listed separately), with its own message.

Signature Series

★★★★☆ **Columella** Seamless, confident **12** blend syrah (76%), mourvèdre, splash grenache flaunts fragrantly spicy garrigue scrub & dark fruit. Different soil types contribute to blend: schist for fresh acidity, granite spiciness, & iron clay structure, to remarkably supple wine. Minimal new oak.

★★★★★ **Palladius** Astonishingly layered, complex & harmonious **12** blend of 8 varieties, led by chenin, roussanne, skilfully matured 2 years on lees in concrete 'eggs', older casks & barrels. Intense flavours, lemon, herbs, even some florality & white pepper spice, all sewn together by pithy mineral thread.

Old Vine Series

★★★★☆ **Pofadder** ⊘ Remarkably delicate, transparent **13** (★★★★★) honours old-vine cinsaut's vibrant, pure red fruit & sensuous gossamer-like texture. Unfined/filtered & no new oak for extra-ethereal fruit expression. From a vineyard near Riebeek-Kasteel, like **12** & previous.

★★★★☆ **Soldaat** Deeply satisfying, richly supple, earthy **13** from Piekenierskloof. Old bushvine grenache's expressive fruit purity & smooth vinosity untrammeled by new oak or winemaking tricks. An absolute delight.

★★★★☆ **Treinspoor** Guileless, almost rugged **13** from old tinta barocca vines has authentic presence & intrigue; taut, grainy tannins frame ample bright red fruit & sweet spiciness. Like **12** (★★★★) needs time to reveal more charming side.

★★★★★ **Skurfberg** Fine dryland chenin from Olifants River. **13** (★★★★☆) generously weighty, rounded mouthfeel & gradually unfurling stonefruit sweetness, edged by light spice & lemon. Broad, rich texture focused by enticing minerality & fresh acidity. Same minimal handling as pure **12**.

★★★★☆ **Kokerboom** ⓃⒺⓌ Profound blend semillon blanc & gris from old Olifants River vines yields bone-dry, salty, fino-like tanginess in **13** (5th vintage but new to this guide). Abundant white pepper spiciness & sweet yellow fruit beneath steely phenolic breadth, focused by lemon & lime. A revelation!

★★★★☆ **'T Voetpad** Field blend chenin, semillon & palomino, with splash muscat d'Alexandrie from isolated century-old vineyard. Charmingly rich & voluptuous **13** boasts expressive ripe red apple flavours underpinned by remarkable minerality & soft citrus twist.

★★★★☆ **Skerpioen** Cooler site & exceedingly chalky soils interplanted with old-vine chenin & palomino ensures ample acidity in almost equal **13** (★★★★★) blend. Spicy intrigue adds to quiet complexity, while lower acid, higher alcohol than **12** leaves softer, sweeter than usual impression.

Not tasted: **Mev. Kirsten**. — IM

Location: Malmesbury ▪ Map: Swartland ▪ WO: Swartland/Olifants River/Swartland-Voor Paardeberg/Piekenierskloof ▪ Est 1999 ▪ 1stB 2000 ▪ Tasting by appt only ▪ Owner(s) The Sadie Family (Pty) Ltd ▪ Winemaker(s)/viticulturist(s) Eben Sadie (1999) ▪ 25ha (cinsaut, grenache n/b, mourv, syrah, tinta barocca, chenin, clairette, palomino, rouss, sem, verdelho, viog) ▪ 60t/8,000cs own label 50% red 50% white ▪ PO Box 1019 Malmesbury 7299 ▪ office@thesadiefamily.com ▪ www. thesadiefamily.com ▪ S 33° 31' 31.0" E 018° 48' 18.1" ▪ F +27 (0)86-692-2852 ▪ **T +27 (0)76-151-7131**

☐ **Safari** *see* De Zoete Inval Estate
☐ **Sainsbury** *see* Bosman Family Vineyards
☐ **Saints** *see* DGB

Saltare

Anniversary wishes are due to Christoff and Carla Pauw, who bottled the first wines under their Stellenbosch boutique brand ten years ago. 'Dancing' (what the Latin name means) reflects the happy occasion when the Pauws and friends crushed the grapes for the first of winemaker Carla's beloved bubblies – still a major focus here, with a new Blanc de Blancs 'completing the Saltare MCC quartet'. More cause for celebration is the opening of a tasting venue across the Eerste River from the cellar.

★★★★ **Syrah** Fresh, incisive & youthful **11** from Swartland, seasoned in older oak, expressive, ripe red fruit underpinned by grip from splash carignan.

★★★★ **Specialis** ② Perfumed **08** blend merlot & cab plus a little cab franc. Juicy ripe fruit firmly underpinned by fresh, brisk acidity. WO Paarl. Previous was lavish **06** (★★★★).

★★★★ **Chenin Blanc** Pale gold, richly textured **12** from old Swartland vines naturally fermented in older barrels, freshened by extended lees-ageing. Not quite as concentrated & focused as **11** (★★★★★).

★★★★ **Old Vines Chenin Blanc 12** from old Perdeberg bushvines, naturally fermented in seasoned oak. More tightly focused, with greater depth than **11** (★★★★) from Paarl. Rich, full-bodied tropicality & engagingly rounded mouthfeel.

★★★★ **Méthode Cap Classique Brut Rosé** Exhilaratingly austere, pale salmon **NV** sparkling gets firm backbone from Stellenbosch pinot noir, while 2 years on lees adds some breadth to bone-dry bubbles. Try with fresh strawberry soup, suggests winemaker.

★★★★ **Méthode Cap Classique Brut Reserve** Aims to show more mature style of sparkling, with **NV** spending longest (up to 48 months) on lees. 60:40 chardonnay, pinot blend dry, focused & fresh, with gentle richness. Robertson, Stellenbosch grapes, like Brut Nature.

★★★★ **Méthode Cap Classique Brut Nature** Plenty brioche & creamy, persistent mousse in fine, delicate **NV**, finer than last. Barrel-fermented & reserve portions, & lengthy lees gives richness to bone-dry finish.

★★★★☆ **Méthode Cap Classique Blanc de Blancs** ⑭ Classy, charming pale gold **NV** sparkler from Robertson chardonnay flaunts persistent pinpoint bubbles. Rich, tasty & very fine, with engaging depth & creaminess. No dosage, as for all the MCCs. — IM

Location/map: Stellenbosch ▪ WO: Swartland/Western Cape/Paarl/Stellenbosch/Robertson ▪ 1stB 2005 ▪ Tasting & cellar tour by appt ▪ Tasting & sales also every Sat at Stellenbosch Slow Food Market, Oude Libertas ▪ Owner(s) Christoff & Carla Pauw ▪ Cellarmaster(s)/winemaker(s) Carla Pauw (2005) ▪ 19t/2,200cs own label 15% red 15% white 70% MCC ▪ PO Box 2290 Dennesig Stellenbosch 7601 ▪ info@saltare.co.za ▪ www.saltare.co.za ▪ S 33° 56' 15. 85" E 018° 52' 7.69" ▪ F +27 (0)88-021-883-9568 ▪ **T +27 (0)21-883-9568**

☐ **Sandrivier** *see* Overgaauw Wine Estate
☐ **Sandveld** *see* Tierhoek

Santa Cecilia

Witty non-conformists Anton Espost and Thys Greeff make a little wine in a cellar in Swartland's Riebeek-Kasteel, where minimal intervention is the word ('perhaps out of laziness'). Their Santa

Cecilia bottlings celebrate chenin and now include an Oppie Dop (skin-contact) version; the 'anarchist' range Tres Estrellas (currently El Presidente and El Pervertido) has labels printed in Spanish and Russian to recognise the role of those languages 'in making the world a more interesting place'.

Location: Riebeek-Kasteel ▪ Map: Swartland ▪ Est/1stB 2008 ▪ Tasting facility in The Wine Kollective: Mon-Sat 10-5 Sun 10-3 ▪ Closed Good Fri, Dec 25 & Jan 1 ▪ Gifts ▪ Farm produce ▪ Adjacent Bar Bar Black Sheep Restaurant ▪ Overnight facility 'The Santa Cecilia Boudoir' ▪ Owner(s) Anton Espost & Thys Greeff ▪ Winemaker(s) Anton Espost ▪ Viticulturist(s) Thys Greeff (Feb 2008), Outback Viticulture ▪ 2,000cs own label 30% red 70% white ▪ PO Box 61 Riebeek-Kasteel 7307 ▪ espost@telkomsa.net ▪ S 33° 23' 1.48" E 018° 53' 46.54" ▪ **T +27 (0)22-448-1008/+27 (0)82-776-9366**

Sarah's Creek

In Malherbe hands since 1888, DCM Boerdery's wine brand is named Sarah's Creek after the stream on the Robertson home farm where, generations ago, a young daughter was habitually waylaid by dragonflies and birds. 'Our handcrafted wines are the result of the same love of nature and simplicity.'

Location: Robertson ▪ Closed to public ▪ Owner(s) Dirk C Malherbe ▪ Winemaker(s) Marga Malherbe ▪ 20ha (cab, merlot, sauv) ▪ PO Box 6531 Welgemoed 7538 ▪ info@sarahscreek.co.za ▪ www.sarahscreek.co.za ▪ **T +27 (0)76-838-6507**

Saronsberg

Saronsberg — named for the mountain rising above the estate — helped bring red-wine renown to Tulbagh this century. Pretoria businessman Nick van Huysteen bought two farms here in 2002 — one rising up the lower slopes, the other stretching down the valley. But a terrible fire quickly made a replanting programme necessary, to accompany the building of a fine cellar and an airy, art-filled tasting room. Dewaldt Heyns has been cellarmaster and chief viticulturist from the start, building a good name for his wide range, especially those based on shiraz, the estate's most-planted grape. This is hot-summer country (but winters are icy!), and Saronsberg reds are appropriately ripe and powerful, but Heyns increasingly manages to infuse them with a supple liveliness and a touch of grace.

Saronsberg range

★★★★★ **Shiraz** Rich, ripe & supple, with a genuine gracefulness & vibrancy rare in big, robust wines. **12** (★★★★☆) fits well into this character, speaking of masterly work in vineyard & cellar. Plentiful new oak not obvious. Balanced & assured. Like **11**, should develop & keep many years.

★★★★☆ **Full Circle** Generous but light-feeling shiraz-led blend with grenache, mourvèdre, viognier - generally the most complex & refined in this range, remarkably fresh given big 14.5% alcohol, all-new oak & few grams sugar. Both **11** & **12** tasted, & both good examples, with lingering sweet-fruited flavours - **12** perhaps a shade more intense, complete.

★★★★ **Sauvignon Blanc** Plenty of flavour on **14** (★★★☆), delivered with panache, though without real depth & interest. Finishes with crisp green kick. WO Coastal, as was **13**.

★★★★ **Viognier** Peachy, floral **13** (★★★☆) perhaps less exuberant than **12**. Flavourful, but heavy texture, obvious oak & a few grams of residual sugar lessen freshness. (Tasted as unfinished sample.)

★★★★ **Brut Méthode Cap Classique** Fine mousse on **10**, & lovely brioche-redolent development from 3 years on lees. Full flavoured & gently rich, but elegant & dry. Mostly chardonnay, drop pinot noir.

★★★★ **Six Point Three Straw Wine** Name now reflects the 6.3 (Richter scale) magnitude of the 1969 Tulbagh earthquake. **07** from air-dried sauvignon, naturally fermented & nearly 3 years in new oak (well integrated). Intriguing, gorgeous & sweet; not intense, but balanced & fresh.

Not retasted: **Grenache 11** ★★★☆ Not tasted: **Seismic**.

Provenance range

★★★★ **Shiraz** ⊘ **12** (★★★★☆) reflects Heyns's mastery of this variety in a warm climate. Great comeback after **11** (★★★☆), which was less satisfying than **10**. Supple & flavourful, with clean, spicy, sweet fruit balanced with ripe tannins & succulent acidity. Mostly own-farm grapes, but WO Coastal.

★★★★ **Rooi 12** (★★★☆) from all five Bordeaux red grapes, as was **11**. Fruity & ripe, overtly friendly but with firm enough tannic grip. Rather simple, with sweetish finish. WO Coastal.

Earth in Motion (NEW) ★★★ Another reference to Tulbagh 1969 earthquake. Flavoursome **14** chenin & sauvignon. Finishes fairly soon, with a green snap. Also tasted: **Shiraz Rosé 14** ★★☆ — TJ

Location/map: Tulbagh ▪ WO: Tulbagh/Coastal/Western Cape ▪ Est 2002 ▪ 1stB 2004 ▪ Tasting & sales Mon-Fri 8–5 Sat 10–2 ▪ Fee R50pp ▪ Closed Easter Fri/Sun, Ascension day, Dec 25 & Jan 1 ▪ Cellar tours by appt ▪ Olive oil ▪ BYO picnic ▪ Art works & sculptures on display ▪ Christmas in Winter Tulbagh festival (Jun) ▪ Self-catering guest cottages ▪ Owner(s) Saronsberg Cellar (Pty) Ltd ▪ Cellarmaster(s) Dewaldt Heyns (2003) ▪ Winemaker(s) Dewaldt Heyns (2003), with Jolandie van der Westhuizen (2011) ▪ Viticulturist(s) Dewaldt Heyns (2003) & Chris Immelman (2012) ▪ 550ha/50ha (shiraz) ▪ 500t own label 70% red 30% white ▪ BWI, WIETA ▪ PO Box 361 Tulbagh 6820 ▪ info@saronsberg.com ▪ www.saronsberg. com ▪ S 33° 14' 48.2" E 019° 7' 2.0" ▪ F +27 (0)23-230-0709 ▪ **T +27 (0)23-230-0707/+27 (0)23-004-0435**

☐ **SA Rugby** *see* Ernie Els Wines

Sauvignon.com

With its pixellated vine leaf logo and active social media presence (especially on Facebook, where promotions are tailored to its many and growing export markets), Sauvignon.com is the brainchild of Diemersdal's internet-savvy cellarmaster, Thys Louw.

Cabernet Sauvignon ★★★ Easy-drinking fun, with telltale redcurrant & cherry notes. **13** fruity & uncomplicated. **Sauvignon Blanc** ★★☆ **14** fantail of tropical, herbal & grassy notes, juicy palate. Succulent summer wine. — JPf

Location: Durbanville ▪ WO: Western Cape ▪ Est/1stB 2010 ▪ Closed to public ▪ Owner(s) Thys & Tienie Louw ▪ Winemaker(s) Thys Louw & Mari Branders (both Jan 2010) ▪ Viticulturist(s) Div van Niekerk (Jan 2010) ▪ 40% red 60% white ▪ PO Box 27 Durbanville 7551 ▪ info@sauvignon.com ▪ www.sauvignon.com ▪ F +27 (0)21-979-1802 ▪ **T +27 (0)82-442-1317**

Savage Wines

Duncan Savage, who has earned an enviable reputation as winemaker at Cape Point Vineyards launched his own label in 2013. 'Savage by name but not by nature', is the motto, and he makes two blends, a Rhône-style red and Bordeaux-inspired white, both exceptionally well executed and exuding a quiet but persuasive confidence. Grapes are sourced from a number of high-altitude and maritime blocks around the winelands, but he's reluctant to go into more detail – 'lots of tiny parcels' is about all he'll share. The current vintage's sauvigon blanc component, though, is identified as being from one of the Cape best known and reputed vineyards: Kaaimansgat.

★★★★☆ **Red** Southern Rhône in styling, **11**'s shiraz/syrah (62%), grenache, cinsaut trio is joined by mourvèdre in subtle harmony for **12**. Intense wafts of aromatic spiciness mingle with piercing bramble, black cherry & plum. Delicious now & for many years. WO W Cape, as for White.

★★★★☆ **White** Near-equal blend of Kaaimansgat sauvignon & Villiersdorp semillon, **13** underscores very auspicious **12** debut. Intricate weave of tropical & stonefruit, creamy-chalky lees-driven texture & vibrant acidity. Combo new/old large-format oak. For keeping. — GdB

Location: Cape Town ▪ WO: Western Cape ▪ Est 2006 ▪ 1stB 2011 ▪ Closed to public ▪ Owner(s) Duncan Savage ▪ Winemaker(s)/viticulturist(s) Duncan Savage (Jan 2006) ▪ 20t/2,000cs own label 40% red 60% white ▪ info@ savagewines.com ▪ **T +27 (0)21-785-4019**

Savanha

This Spier-owned, mainly exported premium wine brand 'celebrates the vibrant energy of the South African sun, in a fun, relaxed and social way'.

Naledi range

★★★★ **Cabernet Sauvignon** Naledi is Sotho for 'star' & **12** shines brightly: attractively compact berry fruit woven with firm tannins, dry & tangy, & in need of a few years to soften. WO Coastal.

★★★★ **Chardonnay** Citrus fruit of sumptuous **13** layered with leesy oatmeal & oak vanilla in bold, rich New World style. Barrel fermented/aged, 70% new wood. Tygerberg grapes.

Winemakers Selection
Cabernet Sauvignon-Merlot ⊘ ★★☆ Welcoming meaty/bacon fullness in previewed **12**. WO W Cape & for export, as next. Not retasted: **Chardonnay-Chenin Blanc 13** ★★☆

Savanha Sun range
Shiraz-Cabernet Sauvignon-Pinotage ⊘ ★★ Light-hued **12** ex tank offers cinnamon spice & plummy fruit, dry finish. Unwooded. These all WO W Cape. **Pinotage Rosé** ⊘ ★★ Previewed **13** just-dry, savoury-tinged cherry styling that welcomes food; chill & bring on the tapas. **Chenin Blanc** ⊘ ★★ **13** is bottled sunshine, with fleshy apricot tang. For export, as all. Not retasted: **Shiraz 12** ★★ **Pinotage-Shiraz 12** ★★ **Chardonnay 13** ★★☆ **Sauvignon Blanc 13** ★★ **Chenin Blanc-Sauvignon Blanc 13** ★★ Not tasted: **Cabernet Sauvignon**, **Merlot**.

Frieda's Vine
Shiraz-Mourvèdre ⊘ ★★☆ Vanilla whiffs to berry-laden **12**, tad sweet but enough grip for food. Fairtrade certified & for export, like next. Not retasted: **Chenin Blanc-Viognier 13** ★★☆ — DS

Saxenburg Wine Farm

The Swiss Bührer family's highly regarded estate in Stellenbosch's Polkadraai area has been producing standout wines under cellarmaster Nico van der Merwe since its modern reincarnation exactly a quarter century ago. In this time it has built an enviable reputation for classical styling, consistent quality and well-defined, focused product ranges. 'Wine is a place,' Nico believes, 'so we continue to work with the unique terroir we have been blessed with.' Several hectares were recently planted, and the aim is to produce more chardonnay to meet rising demand, mostly from overseas. Missing our tasting deadline is Drunken Fowl, 'a "baby shiraz" giving a humorous twist to the very traditional Estate versions'. Featuring a caricature of Saxenburg's famous guinea fowl emblem, the wine hopes to 'truly over-deliver on value for money'.

Saxenburg Limited Release
★★★★★ **Shiraz Select** ⊘ Stunning depth & complexity of **09** (★★★★★) excites. Beautifully judged weight & structure underscore rich, complex fruit in a dry, concentrated package. Complete & integrated now, with great ageing potential. Just a shade off magnificent **07**. No **08**.

Private Collection
★★★★☆ **Cabernet Sauvignon 11** (★★★★) supple, plush & balanced, fruits of the forest & dark chocolate combining with firm oak & mouthwatering final grip. Misses the complexity & intensity of **10**.

★★★★ **Merlot 11** offers layers of silky black fruit, warm spice, dark chocolate with firm backbone & long spicy Christmas cake finish.

★★★★☆ **Shiraz** Vibrant **11** back on form after **10** (★★★★) blip. Bold & intense flavours of wild berry fruit, pepper, spicy oak & liquorice. Seamless on the palate, with great balance & good ageing potential.

★★★★☆ **Chardonnay** Opulent yet elegant barrel-fermented **13** maintains the pattern. Offers many intense layers of dense, buttery citrus, crushed stone, vanilla & flowers; bold precise oaking (year French, only 10% new). A keeper.

★★★★ **Sauvignon Blanc** Consistent & dependable. **14** preview is dry, with concentrated grapefruit & lime flavours, & a good whiff of sea air. Refreshing minerality on the finish.

★★★★ **Méthode Cap Classique NV (10)** bubbly from chardonnay is dry, vibrant, with fine mousse & creamy texture from 36 months lees-ageing. Intense flavours of lemon curd & apple pie leave you wanting more.

Also tasted: **Pinotage 12** ★★★☆ Not tasted: **Le Phantom Brut Cap Classique**.

Guinea Fowl range

Red ★★★ 2nd-tier merlot, cab & shiraz blend, **13** tank sample is fresh & fruity, delicious everyday tipple. Also tasted: **White 14** ★★★ Not tasted: **Rosé**.

Concept range

Grand Vin Blanc ★★★ Fun & fruity entry-level **NV** from sauvignon & chenin, bursts with ripe fruit & zesty acidity. Also tasted: **Grand Vin Rouge NV** ★★ — WB

Location: Kuils River ▪ Map/WO: Stellenbosch ▪ Est 1693 ▪ 1stB 1990 ▪ Tasting & sales Mon-Fri 9–5 Sat/Sun 10–5 ▪ Fee R20/R35 ▪ Closed Good Fri, Dec 25 & Jan 1 ▪ Cheese platters ▪ Wedding/function venue ▪ Gifts ▪ Conservation area ▪ Game park ▪ Saxenburg guest cottages ▪ Owner(s) Adrian & Birgit Bührer ▪ Cellarmaster(s) Nico van der Merwe (Nov 1990) ▪ Winemaker(s) Nico van der Merwe (Nov 1990), with Edwin Grace (Jan 2005) ▪ Viticulturist(s) Donovan Diedericks (Apr 2008) ▪ 195ha/85ha (cabs s/f, malbec, merlot, ptage, shiraz, chard, chenin, sauv, viog) ▪ 650t/100,000cs own label 78% red 20% white 2% rosé ▪ Other export brands: Bosman's Hill, Gwendolyn ▪ PO Box 171 Kuils River 7580 ▪ info@saxenburg. co.za ▪ www.saxenburg.co.za ▪ S 33° 56' 47.9" E 018° 43' 9.4" ▪ **T +27 (0)21-903-6113**

☐ **Say Lovey** *see* M'hudi Wines

Scali

Scali (reference to the mostly shale – 'skalie'- soils) is based on Schoone Oord farm in Voor Paardeberg, owned by Willie and Tania de Waal, Willie the 5th generation here. Grapes went to some bigger local cellars but in 1999 the De Waals bottled their first commercial wine, and volumes since have grown steadily. Official organic certification was achieved in 2011. The new Sirkel ('Circle') label features an organic, earlier-ready pinotage (a white partner on the way). The brand logo, 'Guardians of Man', is stamped by hand on the label, 'creating an income earning opportunity for the local community, especially during winter months'.

Scali range

★★★★ **Pinotage 10** mulberry, dark chocolate & liquorice flavours in a firm tannin framework. Big boned, ripe style & with silky texture & some savoury, earthy charm. Potential to develop. **09** sold out untasted.

★★★★ **Syrah** Balsamic hints on **09** (★★★★) not out of sync with dominant white pepper, wild scrub & lily aromas. Dry texture, with dusty tannins (3 years older oak) in balance with fruit. Good food wine. Shade off stellar **08** (★★★★☆) & **07**.

★★★★☆ **Blanc** ⊘ **13** first tasted since **09**. Characterful, complex chenin-led blend, with equal chardonnay, roussanne, viognier & dash sauvignon. Oxidative style, but pervasive pine freshness & dried peach, citrus peel flavours. Clean, dry farewell.

Ancestor ⊛ ⊘ ★★★★ Engaging sparkling chenin using méthode ancestrale (natural ferment started in tank & completed in bottle). **13** sweetish, soft, like spiced apple pie in a bottle. Lots of personality, good partner for pâté or dessert.

Sirkel range ⊛

Pinotage ⊘ ★★★ High-toned **13**, with cherry, raspberry fruit drop flavours & smooth, supple texture. Pleasantly rustic, fresh & ready to enjoy with hearty fare. — MW

Location: Paarl ▪ Map: Paarl & Wellington ▪ WO: Voor Paardeberg ▪ Est/1stB 1999 ▪ Tasting, sales & cellar tours Mon-Sat by appt ▪ Closed all pub hols ▪ Self-catering cottage ▪ Owner(s) Willie & Tania de Waal ▪ Cellarmaster(s)/ winemaker(s) Willie & Tania de Waal (Aug 1999) ▪ Viticulturist(s) Willie de Waal (Feb 1991) ▪ 270ha/70ha (cab, merlot, ptage, shiraz, chard, chenin, rouss, sauv, viog) ▪ 45t/6,000cs own label 67% red 33% white ▪ CERES (vyds, wines certified organic) ▪ PO Box 7143 Paarl 7620 ▪ info@scali.co.za ▪ www.scali.co.za ▪ S 33° 36' 70.6" E 018° 51' 49.5" ▪ F +27 (0)86-617-5040 ▪ **T +27 (0)21-869-8340**

☐ **Scarborough Affair** *see* Clive Torr Wines

For more information, visit wineonaplatter.com

☐ **Scarlett Organic** *see* Seven Sisters
☐ **Schalk Burger & Sons** *see* Welbedacht Wine Estate

Schalkenbosch Wines

Debuting in the 2004 edition with the then farm manager's words - 'The love affair has begun' - we noted that vine and cellar establishment on the unyielding Tulbagh slopes was less like True Love and more like Romancing the Stone. Today Schalkenbosch wines are well entrenched and export focused (mainly Europe, but also new markets), and the guest lodgings, for whose benefit the brand was mostly founded, still welcome an upmarket clientele.

Schalkenbosch range

★★★★ **Cumulus** After impressive deep berry flavours on **10**, similar dark fruit from Bordeaux quintet less intense on **11** (★★★★). Boldly structured, with densely layered tannins which may benefit from few years' ageing.

★★★★ **Stratus** Shiraz-led flagship, **11** (★★★★) less characterful than **10**. Light spice, red berries given push by few grams sugar, but still dominated by 50% new French/American oak. May gain greater harmony in short term.

Also tasted: **Viognier 14** ★★★ Not tasted: **Cuvée Brut Cap Classique**.

Edenhof range

Nighthawk 409 ★★★★ Grenache with shiraz, mourvèdre, drop viognier. Approachable, flavoursome **12**. Despite 14.5% alcohol, light-textured, good freshness. **Sauvignon Blanc** ★★★ Balanced fruit, spicy oak (40% barrel fermented new French) in **14**. Unshowy & good presence as food partner. Also tasted: **Pinotage 12** ★★★ **Shiraz 13** ★★ **Cabernet Sauvignon-Merlot 12** ★★★ **Chardonnay 14** ★★★ **Blanc de Blancs 13** ★★ Not retasted: **Merlot 11** ★★★ Not tasted: **Cabernet Sauvignon**.

Isis range

Rosé ⊘ ★★★ Spicy, crisp & dry, **14** will make pleasing partner to simple summer dishes. Also tasted: **Dry Red 13** ★★★ **Dry White 13** ★★ — AL

Location/map: Tulbagh ▪ WO: Tulbagh/Western Cape/Coastal ▪ Est 1792 ▪ 1stB 2002 ▪ Tasting, sales & tours by appt ▪ Closed all pub hols ▪ Tour groups ▪ Walking/hiking & mountain biking trails ▪ Conservation area ▪ Self-catering cottages ▪ Owner(s) Platinum Mile Investments ▪ Viticulturist(s) Johan Wiese & Andrew Teubes ▪ 1,800ha/37ha (cab, shiraz) ▪ 140t/20,000cs own label 80% red 18% white 2% rosé ▪ BWI champion ▪ PO Box 95 Tulbagh 6820 ▪ info@schalkenbosch.co.za ▪ www.schalkenbosch.co.za ▪ S 33° 18' 49.7" E 019° 11' 59.9" ▪ F +27 (0)86-519-2605/+27 (0)86-654-8209 ▪ T +27 (0)23-230-0654/1488

Schenkfontein Kelders

A sibling to separately listed Winkelshoek, and historically a supplier of bulk wine to one of the majors, family-owned Schenkfontein is stepping into the bottled wine arena with a trio of varietal releases (the Chardonnay untasted) made from Schenkfontein estate grapes and partner farms in the area between Piketberg and Citrusdal. The new venture is part of winemaker/viticulturist Hendrik Hanekom's desire 'to achieve greater heights', and his plans include enlarging the cellar, launching additional labels and opening a visitor venue on the farm on the eastern slopes of Piketberg.

Shiraz ★★★ Unwooded **14** showcasing plush dark plums, a hint of scrub for complexity; smooth & rounded, very appealing. **Chenin Blanc** ⊘ ★★★ Lovely melon & mango perfume on **14** in total contrast to the flavours: hay, an asphalt minerality, almost smoky. Distinctive, would show even more over time. — CR, CvZ

Location: Piketberg ▪ WO: Swartland ▪ Est 2000 ▪ 1stB 2014 ▪ Closed to public ▪ Cellarmaster(s)/winemaker(s)/viticulturist(s) Hendrik Hanekom (Nov 2010) ▪ 500ha/51ha (ptage, shiraz, chenin) ▪ 500t/150,000L own label 30% red 70% white ▪ PO Box 2 Eendekuil 7335 ▪ hendrik@winkelshoek.co.za ▪ www.winkelshoek.co.za ▪ F +27 (0)22-942-1488 ▪ T +27 (0)22-942-1484

Schultz Family Wines

Rudi Schultz's 'day job' is the illustrious one of being winemaker for Thelema – but it allows him a little time for his own label. Here he's 'attempting to make hand-crafted ultra-premium wines at sensible prices'. The range is even expanding, says Rudi: 'We will be releasing a small bottling of cabernet sauvignon from the same property where the syrah is sourced'.

★★★★ **Syrah** Smoky bacon, black pepper & lavender notes on **12**. The palate is generous & well focused but needs some years to open up & integrate the fine tannin.

★★★★☆ **Reserve Syrah** Best 4 barrels go into this bottling. **12** similar aromatic profile to sibling wine, but more intensity & fruit concentration, & longer finish. Very well integrated oak (50% new; 15% new for Syrah), giving riper, rounder tannin structure. Natural ferment; 15% whole bunch. — JPf

Location/WO: Stellenbosch ▪ Est 2002 ▪ Tasting by appt ▪ Closed all pub hols ▪ Owner(s) Rudi Schultz ▪ Cellarmaster(s)/winemaker(s) Rudi Schultz (Jan 2002) ▪ Viticulturist(s) Dirkie Morkel ▪ 12t/1,000cs own label 100% red ▪ 8 Fraser Road Somerset West 7130 ▪ rudi@thelema.co.za ▪ F +27 (0)21-885-1800 ▪ **T +27 (0)82-928-1841**

Scrucap Wines

Guests of LUX* Resorts on Indian Ocean islands are invited to 'say farewell to corks and Old World wines and say hi to Scrucap, a collection of South African wines specially selected' for the hotel group. Consultant Kent Scheermeyer says the aim is to offer 'fresh, sexy' wines - a goal that should be met, considering the elite Cape sources: De Grendel, Paul Cluver, Mullineux & Leeu Family Wines, Steenberg and Winery of Good Hope.

★★★★ **Pinot Noir 12** from De Grendel, elegantly crafted, with lovely silky texture. Fresh balance, layers of polished leather, red fruit & a delicate waft of incense perfume. Alluring now but will continue to charm for many years. Step up on **11** (★★★☆). WO W Cape.

★★★★ **Swartland Blend** As with **12**, LUX* guests will be transported back to the Old World on tasting **13**, classy shiraz blend by Mullineux & Leeu, with Rhône-like spicy flavour melange, supple structure.

★★★★ **Chardonnay 13** from Elgin's Paul Cluver, exudes rich & ripe pear & lime flavours. Part ferment in old oak provides subtle hazelnut undertone. Vivacious, fresh & balanced with a long finish. Better than **12** (★★★☆).

★★★★ **Riesling 13** by riesling star Paul Cluver, subtle perfumed lime & kiwifruit in tangy balance with creamy undertone from semi-sweet styling. Beautifully light, fresh & delicious, especially at modest 10.6% alcohol.

★★★★ **Sauvignon Blanc** Feisty & flavoursome **13** by Paul Cluver raises the bar on **12** (★★★☆). Cream texture threaded with racy passionfruit flavours, vivacious balance, long tangy farewell.

★★★★ **Popcap Brut** Méthode cap classique bubbly from chardonnay, lighter styled, fresh & crisp. An excellent aperitif, **13**'s zesty citrus broadened by year on lees & 10% oak-aged reserve wine. By Steenberg. WO W Cape.

Merlot ⓃⒺⓌ ★★★ Good food styling in **12** ex De Grendel, smoky red berry/cherry flavours with herbaceous nuance, dry, piquant & fresh. **Chenin Blanc** ★★★☆ Chenin specialists The Winery of Good Hope made firm & tasty **13**, showing some depth & character along with appealing fruity-dry flavour. Also tasted: **Three Valleys Blend 12** ★★★★ **Rosé 14** ★★★ **Sauvignon Blanc 13** ★★★★ Not retasted: **Shiraz 11** ★★★ — TJ, DS, MW

WO: Elgin/Western Cape/Coastal/Durbanville/Swartland/Stellenbosch ▪ Est 2011 ▪ Closed to public ▪ Cellarmaster(s) Andries Burger (Paul Cluver Estate Wines), JD Pretorius (Steenberg Vineyards), Charles Hopkins (De Grendel Wines) & Edouard Labeye (Winery of Good Hope) ▪ 20,000cs own label 40% red 40% white 10% rosé 10% MCC ▪ ksconsult@mweb.co.za ▪ www.luxislandresorts.com ▪ **T +27 (0)83-484-8781**

Seal Breeze Wines

After 25 years as a nine-to-fiver, Joan Wiggins reclaimed the family winegrape farm on the diamond-rich West Coast. Mentored by ex-Le Bonheur winemaker Sakkie Kotzé, and with barrels donated by Beyerskloof's Beyers Truter, she now shares her joy with annual harvest helpers (Journey of Hope breast cancer survivors) and buyers of her 1.5L magnums (whom she surprises with a sparkler in each bottle!).

Shiraz ★★★★ Star of the range. Pre-bottling, **13** rich & ripe red fruit with white pepper, cardamom & clove dusting. Supple, silky; succulent, very long, spicy farewell. Different league to previous, as all these reds. **Sauvignon Blanc ★★★** Previewed **14** cool & fresh expression of the variety, balanced, with immediate 'drink me' appeal & clean greengage/starfruit flavours. Drink now! Also tasted: **Cabernet Sauvignon 13 ★★★ Merlot 13 ★★★★** — MW

Location: Lutzville ▪ Map: Olifants River ▪ WO: Lutzville Valley ▪ Est 2004 ▪ 1stB 2005 ▪ Tasting, sales & cellar tours Mon-Fri 9–4 Sat 9–12 ▪ Closed Easter Fri-Mon, Ascension Day, Dec 25 & Jan 1 ▪ Meals/refreshments by prior arrangement ▪ Facilities for children ▪ Tour groups ▪ BYO picnic ▪ Owner(s)/viticulturist(s) Joan Wiggins ▪ Cellarmaster(s) Joan Wiggins (Feb 2004) ▪ Winemaker(s) Joan Wiggins (Feb 2004), with Toy Brand (Feb 2006) ▪ ±92ha/±70ha (cab, merlot, shiraz, chenin, cbard, hanepoot, sauv) ▪ 1,200t/1,560cs own label ▪ PO Box 33 Lutzville 8165 ▪ jwiggins@kingsley.co.za ▪ www.sealbreezewine.co.za ▪ S 31° 34' 50.1" E 018° 19' 9.8" ▪ F +27 (0)27-217-1458 ▪ **T +27 (0)84-505-1991**

☐ **Season's Collection** *see* Orange River Wine Cellars
☐ **Secateurs** *see* AA Badenhorst Family Wines
☐ **Secret Cellar** *see* Ultra Liquors

Sedgwick's Old Brown

Venerable Distell brand, blend of jerepiko and dry sherry, in 200 ml, 375 ml, 750 ml, 1L and 2L.

Sedgwick's Old Brown ⊘ **★★★** Fortified winter warmer since 1961. Latest **NV** deep amber brown, combo raisins, sherry & candied fruit, ending savoury. — CR

☐ **Selma** *see* Nordic Wines
☐ **Semara** *see* Wine-of-the-Month Club

Sequillo Cellars

This venture by Swartland's original winemaking star, Eben Sadie, is quite separate from Sadie Family Wines. Sequillo, Latin for 'an arid dry place of great purity', aims to showcase Swartland terroir. Varieties used are Rhône/Mediterranean because they best suit conditions here and are blend-compatible, all handled with minimal intervention in the dryland vineyards and cellar. Labels have line-drawn designs which change each year and always contain a message about the natural way of farming versus its alternative. The blends might be tweaked occasionally, but the main focus never wavers: integrity and balance.

★★★★☆ Sequillo Red ⓦ Changing blend, mainly Rhône varieties, shiraz-led in **11** with cinsaut & 4 others. Reflecting the area & varieties, there is dusty cocoa, a core of dark wild fruit & then the clincher, juicy freshness & impressively supple tannins.

★★★★☆ Sequillo White ⓦ Chenin & clairette blanche in a 5-part oaked blend selected to showcase the area. Made for enjoyment (says the winemaker) but **12**'s multi-layers impress as well. There's melon & quince, crushed almonds & tangy acidity promising a fine future. — CR

Location: Malmesbury ▪ Map/WO: Swartland ▪ Est/1stB 2003 ▪ Tasting by appt only ▪ Closed all pub hols ▪ Owner(s) Eben Sadie Trust ▪ Cellarmaster(s)/winemaker(s) Eben Sadie (Jan 2003) ▪ 20ha (carignan, grenache, mourv, syrah, chenin, clairette, rouss, viog) ▪ 45t/6,000cs own label 50% red 50% white ▪ PO Box 1019 Malmesbury 7299 ▪ info@sequillo.com ▪ www.sequillo.com ▪ S 33° 31' 31.0" E 018° 48' 18.1" ▪ F +27 (0)86-692-2852 ▪ **T +27 (0)76-151-7131**

☐ **Sereia** *see* Anatu Wines

Ses'Fikile

Brand owner and former teacher Nondumiso Pikashe partners with winemaker Banele Vakele to produce her wines, whose name translates as 'We Have Arrived, In Style', for local and overseas markets.

Rain Song range (NEW)
Cabernet Sauvignon ★★★ Rich cassis flavours, yet an appealing elegance, giving **12** good drinkability. Tannins amenable, don't hamper. **Rosé** ★★ **14** semi-sweet charmer, strawberries & Turkish Delight, friendly 10% alcohol. Also tasted: **Pinotage 12** ★★ **Ruby Cabernet 13** ★★ **Shiraz 11** ★★☆ **Colombard 13** ★★ — CR, CvZ

Location: Upington ▪ Est 2008 ▪ Tasting by arrangement in Gugulethu ▪ Owner(s) Ses'Fikile Wine Services ▪ Winemaker(s) Banele Vakele ▪ 50,000cs own label 70% red 30% white ▪ PO Box 38055 Pinelands 7430 ▪ sesfikile@gmail.com

---

☐ **7even** see Zevenwacht

Seven Sisters

Seven indeed, from the West Coast village of Paternoster, and by their wines shall you know their names. Sister Vivian (Kleynhans) took the lead in launching the range for their company, African Roots, nearly a decade back. The winery was more recently established - in Stellenbosch - and a restaurant is set to open there in the course of this year.

Sweet Rosé Twena ★★★ Natural Sweet style **14** pink from mainly Swartland pinotage, with jammy berry flavours. Not retasted: **Cabernet Sauvignon Carol 12** ★★★ **Merlot June 12** ★★ **Pinotage-Shiraz Dawn 12** ★★☆ **Bukettraube Odelia 13** ★★ **Moscato Yolanda 12** ★★ **Sauvignon Blanc Vivian 13** ★★★ — GdB

Location/map: Stellenbosch ▪ WO: Swartland/Western Cape ▪ Tasting & sales at Seven Sisters Farm, Welmoed Rd, off Annandale Rd, Lynedoch, Stellenbosch - phone ahead ▪ Owner(s) African Roots Wine ▪ Winemaker(s) Vivian Kleynhans ▪ PO Box 4560 Tygervalley 7536 ▪ vivian@africanrootswines.com ▪ www.sevensisters.co.za ▪ S 33° 59' 23. 41" E 018° 46' 34.35" ▪ F +27 (0)86-514-5569 ▪ **T +27 (0)71-049-4109/+27 (0)83-624-0391**

Seven Springs Vineyards

Planning and preparation are vital. It's what has seen British-based, social-media-savvy owners Tim and Vaughan Pearson establish vines on their 8 ha of Bokkeveld shale soils at the foot of Shaws Mountain between Hermanus and Caledon, and vinify a well-regarded boutique range offsite. Cellar plans are final – but first an access road needs to be built!

★★★★ Pinot Noir Ⓥ Intense pure fruit expression on **12** follows debut 11 (★★★★). Pared down yet supple frame holds ripe, smoky raspberry fruit gently. Light & elegant.

★★★★ Chardonnay 12 improves on 11 (★★★★) in its refinement & restraint. Rich mandarin & cream notes with subtly supportive oak (older barrels only, year). Malo eschewed, so vibrantly fresh & seamlessly long.

Unoaked Chardonnay ★★★☆ Lively pithy grapefruit zing to **13**, crisp & focused but with leesy interest & body. Also tasted: **Syrah 12** ★★★★ Not retasted: **Sauvignon Blanc 12** ★★★★ — FM

Location: Hermanus ▪ WO: Overberg ▪ Est 2007 ▪ 1stB 2010 ▪ Closed to public ▪ Owner(s) Tim & Vaughan Pearson ▪ Winemaker(s) Riana van der Merwe (Nov 2009) ▪ Viticulturist(s) Peter Davison (Jul 2007, consultant) ▪ 12ha/±8ha (pinot, syrah, chard, sauv) ▪ ±67t/10,000cs own label 60% red 40% white ▪ Other export brand: Over the Mountain ▪ Private Bag X15 Suite 162 Hermanus 7200 ▪ tim@7springs.co.za ▪ www.7springs.co.za ▪ F +27 (0)86-571-0623 ▪ **T +27 (0)28-316-4994 (office)/+27 (0)82-487-7572 (winemaker)**

Seven Steps Wines

A brand created by two entrepreneurs, Pragasen Ramiah and Travis Braithwaite, who is also the winemaker, sourced from across the winelands. The name comes from the last remaining concrete evidence of the old District Six in Cape Town.

Syrah ★★★★ Last **08** rose geranium scent, meaty hint, charry oak smoothed by few grams sugar. Not tasted: **Sauvignon Blanc**. — CR

Location: Cape Town ▪ WO: Western Cape ▪ Est/1stB 2009 ▪ Tasting by appt only ▪ Owner(s) Travis Braithwaite & Pragasen Ramiah ▪ Cellarmaster(s)/winemaker(s) Travis Braithwaite ▪ (shiraz, sauv) ▪ 1,600cs own label 30% red 70% white ▪ PO Box 981 Sea Point Cape Town 8060 ▪ info@sevenstepswines.com ▪ www.sevenstepswines.com ▪ F +27 (0)86-625-0109 ▪ **T +27 (0)82-368-5270**

☐ **Sgt Pepper** *see* Teddy Hall Wines

Shannon Vineyards

Located in Elgin and owned by James and Stuart Downes, Shannon first built an enviable reputation on the quality of the grapes supplied to several of South Africa's leading winemakers. Then, in 2009, the brothers' own label, vinified in Hemel-en-Aarde Valley by Gordon and Nadia Newton Johnson, debuted with a stellar trio of releases. Shannon wines have since enjoyed a 'second' reputation as among South Africa's finest, and most expressive of their cool, meticulously nurtured and very beautiful origin. The Downes are proud and grateful to have a merlot and pinot noir selected and launched by Woolworths (see entry), 'a positive endorsement of our boutique wine business'.

★★★★☆ **Mount Bullet Merlot** Among SA's top examples. **11** has a noble bearing & athletic build, & suave fruit. Beautifully dry & authoritative, will only show better with cellaring.

★★★★☆ **Macushla Pinot Noir Noble Late Harvest** 'My Darling' deliciously idiosyncratic dessert, naturally fermented in older oak. **12** (★★★★), first tasted since **09**, so easy to drink now, next year... or in 10.

Not tasted: **Rockview Ridge Pinot Noir**, **Sanctuary Peak Sauvignon Blanc**, **Semillon**. — CvZ

Location/WO: Elgin ▪ Map: Elgin, Walker Bay & Bot River ▪ Est 2000 ▪ 1stB 2003 ▪ Tasting & sales by appt ▪ Owner(s) Stuart & James Downes ▪ Winemaker(s) Gordon Newton Johnson & Nadia Newton Johnson ▪ Viticulturist(s) Kevin Watt (consultant) ▪ 75ha/15.5ha (merlot, pinot, sauv, sem) ▪ 100t/6,000cs own label 66% red 34% white ▪ BWI, Global GAP, IPW, Tesco's Natures Choice ▪ PO Box 20 Elgin 7180 ▪ james@shannonwines.com ▪ www.shannonwines.com ▪ S 34° 11' 3.9" E 018° 59' 3.6" ▪ F +27 (0)21-859-5389 ▪ **T +27 (0)21-859-2491**

☐ **Shepherd's Cottage** *see* Overgaauw Wine Estate

Ship

Another piece of Distell-owned South African wine patrimony, launched in 1929.

Ship ★★ Raisiny jerepiko-style fireside comforter. **NV**. — DB

Shoprite Checkers

Southern African supermarket chain Shoprite Checkers' virtual wine route offers selections from 80+ local and around 50 international fine-wine producers, plus significant Nederburg Auction labels. But the house wines, handpicked by a panel and labelled 'Odd Bins', remain a top seller.

Enquiries: Stephanus Eksteen ▪ 160,000cs own label 50% red 40% white 10% rosé ▪ PO Box 215 Brackenfell 7561 ▪ seksteen@shoprite.co.za ▪ www.shoprite.co.za ▪ F +27 (0)21-980-4421 ▪ **T +27 (0)21-980-4000**

☐ **Short Story** *see* Neethlingshof Estate
☐ **Short Street** *see* Valley Vineyards Wine Company
☐ **Shortwood** *see* Imbuko Wines
☐ **Signal Cannon** *see* Vondeling

Signal Gun Wines

The range launched in 2006 by MJ de Wit as a hobby, with grapes off the old Hooggelegen family farm in Durbanville, soon developed into project Ke-Monate ('That's Nice!'), with tasting room, restaurant and, happily, more wines. Lighter-styled Tin Hill recalls nearby Hoogeberg, an outcrop devoid of old prospectors' hoped-for ore but rich in fauna and flora.

De Wit Family Reserves

B Loved Méthode Cap Classique (NEW) ★★★★ Only 300 bottles of fresh, pink-tinged bubbly from chardonnay & pinot noir. Delightful **12** offers crunchy apple & lime frothiness. Also tasted: **Sea Smoke Sauvignon Blanc 13** ★★★★ Not retasted: **WRM Shiraz 10** ★★★☆

Signal Gun range

Rosé ★★★★ **13** from merlot; dry, rosepetals on the nose, spicy, with gorgeous lift. **Chardonnay** ★★★☆ Unoaked **13**, shows tropical & ripe apple notes, hint of lemon, smooth & creamy. Also tasted: **Sauvignon Blanc 13** ★★★★ Not retasted: **Merlot 12** ★★★★ **Shiraz 11** ★★★☆

Tin Hill range (NEW)

Pinotage ★★★☆ Dark & dusty **13**'s ripe plum fruit overpowered by chunky tannins. Needs time or food. **Merlot-Cabernet Sauvignon** ★★★ 60/40 blend **13** sweet fruited, with hint of oak spice, good balance for easy drinking. **Sauvignon Blanc** ★★★ Green-toned **13** all grass & greenpepper, lees-ageing gives some complexity, brisk tangy exit. **Muy-Scatty** ★★★ Charming name for light off-dry blend muscat d'Alexandrie & sauvignon; **13** soft & fruity, with fragrant floral perfume. — WB

Location/WO: Durbanville ▪ Map: Durbanville, Philadelphia & Darling ▪ Est/1stB 2006 ▪ Tasting & sales Tue-Sat 9.30-5 Sun 9.30-4 ▪ Fee R20 ▪ Closed Good Fri, Dec 25 & Jan 1 ▪ Ke-Monate Restaurant ▪ Conferences ▪ Conservation area ▪ Owner(s) WRM de Wit ▪ Cellarmaster(s)/winemaker(s) Riaan Oosthuizen (2011), MJ de Wit (Jan 2006) ▪ Viticulturist(s) Walter Smith ▪ 210ha/95ha (cab, merlot, ptage, shiraz, chard, sauv) ▪ 19t/2,000cs own label 50% red 50% white ▪ PO Box 364 Durbanville 7551 ▪ wine@signalgun.com ▪ www.signalgun.com ▪ S 33° 49' 13.26" E 018° 36' 40. 32" ▪ F +27 (0)86-611-8747 ▪ **T +27 (0)21-976-7343**

Signal Hill Wines

Named after a peak above Cape Town, Signal Hill is situated in the city centre and has a remarkable and unique focus on tiny bottlings off metropolitan vineyards. Founder of the business and originator of the concept is the irrepressible and innovative Frenchman, Jean-Vincent Ridon. Limited space has prompted the decision to vinify wider-sourced wines (like the Grenache Noir) off-site, Jean-Vincent says, but this in no way diminishes his or longtime winemaker Laurence Buthelezi's enthusiasm, and talks are in progress with city officials to plant more vines. 'To come, malbec and durif!'

Single Barrel range

★★★★ **Pinot Noir** (Ⓟ) **10** lighter-footed style than **08** standard bottling, also from Stellenbosch fruit, with more appetising acidity & cranberry flavours imparting an elegant cool-climate feel.

★★★★ **1771 Heritage Vine** (Ⓟ) One 240 year-old city centre chenin vine bore 20 bottles of this intriguing **11** curiosity: full of flavour, with a sweet impression despite low alcohol & sugar.

★★★★☆ **Pineau de Ludovic** (Ⓟ) Contemplative **NV** aperitif; chenin-colombard blend spent a decade in barrel. 200g/l sugar & 16% alcohol on complex & delicious fortified wine. Stellenbosch/Paarl fruit.

Not tasted: **Kalk Bay Blanc de Noir**.

Signal Hill range

★★★★ **Grenache Noir** Pioneer varietal bottling in SA. Vinous **13**, from Durbanville vines, remarkably bright & pure, ripe red fruit with supple tannins providing savoury grip. Occasional release, last was **07** (★★★☆).

★★★★☆ **Camps Bay Vineyard** (Ⓟ) **10** (★★★★), from mourvèdre, just 250 bottles off coastal suburban vines. Fine **09** was maiden harvest.

★★★★☆ **Clos d'Oranje** From tiny apparently ungrafted shiraz vineyard in Oranjezicht, Cape Town. Both **08** & **09** spicily vibrant, authentic & convincing. Sweetly ripe core red fruit underpinned by supple, integrated tannins in harmonious artisan wine.

★★★★ **Grenache Blanc** ⓥ **08** subtle scents, silky, & savoury mineral core. From Piekenierskloof.

★★★★ **Méthode Cap Classique Pinot Noir** ⓥ **06** sparkling disgorged on demand. Lovely mature aromas. Bone-dry, unsulphured.

★★★★ **Crème de Tête Muscat d'Alexandrie NLH** ⓥ Last tasted was hedonistic **03**.

★★★★★ **Eszencia** ⓥ Magnificent **NV** (**02**), probably a one-off, sweet & rich, electrified by nervy acidity.

★★★★☆ **Vin de l'Empereur Solera** ⓥ Unctuous **NV** from 8 year-old solera of Constantia muscat d'Alexandrie.

Not retasted: **Olympia Cabernet Franc 08** ★★★ **Straw Wine 01** ★★★★ Not tasted: **Malbec, Pinot Noir, Petit Verdot, Syrah, The Threesome, Rosé de Saignée, Empereur Rouge, Mathilde Aszú 6 Puttonyos, Vin de l'Empereur**.

Discontinued: **Buthelezi range**. — IM

Location: Cape Town ▪ Map: Cape Peninsula ▪ WO: Coastal/Stellenbosch/Stellenbosch/Paarl/Durbanville/Piekenierskloof/Constantia ▪ 1stB 1997 ▪ Tasting, sales & cellar tours Mon-Fri 11-6 Sat 12-4 in season ▪ Closed all pub hols ▪ Cheese platters, charcuterie & tapas during open hours ▪ Owner(s) Signal Hill Wines cc ▪ Cellarmaster(s) Jean-Vincent Ridon ▪ Winemaker(s)/viticulturist(s) Laurence Buthelezi ▪ 2ha (cab f, mourv, pinot, shiraz) ▪ 75% red 20% white 5% rosé ▪ Heritage Square, 100 Shortmarket Street, Cape Town 8001 ▪ info@winery.co.za ▪ www.winery.co.za ▪ S 33° 55' 15.06" E 018° 25' 5.54" ▪ F +27 (0)21-422-5238 ▪ **T +27 (0)21-424-5820**

☐ **Signatures of Doolhof** *see* Doolhof Wine Estate

Sijnn

Nothing that co-owner and winemaker David Trafford does is without careful thought, as befits his architectural training. Sijnn (pronounced 'sane') might look like an almost hobbyist project because of the family holiday home there, but planting warm-country varieties in a cool climate like that of Malgas at the Breede River estuary (which he has) makes sense in the context of global warming. It's also part of the 'search for excellence outside the traditional areas' because David believes 'that's where real interest lies'. A cellar was completed last year (previously vinification was at De Trafford in Stellenbosch) and there is much excitement about crushing this year's harvest on-site.

★★★★★ **Syrah** Poor, stony soils of this remote vineyard perfectly suited to shiraz. **12** (★★★★☆) flourishes same spicy scintillation, freshness as **11** though is more textured, richer, with firmer yet still fine structure to match & less accessible in youth. Time should see it reach even greater heights.

★★★★ **Touriga Nacional** Moves up scale of quality & intensity in **12** (★★★★☆). Beguiling perfume of violets & spice (from 2% shiraz inclusion?) but bigger, stronger-boned than **11**. Needs year/two for dense tannic wall to come down; will improve for much longer.

★★★★ **Sijnn** ⓥ Allsorts blend with shiraz, touriga playing important roles, **10** is individualistic. Scrub & coffee, wild berries, it's hard to pin down but very easy to enjoy. The savoury oak grip makes it ideal for food.

★★★★★ **White** Chenin (76%), viognier (20%) & roussanne in **13** blend of intrigue & harmony. Much appeal in the delicate yet flavoursome floral, spicy ensemble & gently creamy mouthfeel, both energised by refreshing mineral thread. Belies 14% alcohol. Natural ferment in small & 700L French oak; unfiltered.

Also tasted: **Cabernet Sauvignon 11** ★★★★ **Low Profile 12** ★★★★ **Saignée 12** ★★★★ — AL

Location/WO: Malgas ▪ Map: Southern Cape ▪ Est 2003 ▪ 1stB 2007 ▪ Tasting at Sijnn Sat 10-3 or by appt ▪ Sales only at De Trafford (see entry) ▪ Closed all pub hols ▪ Owner(s) David & Rita Trafford, Simon Farr, Quentin Hurt ▪ Winemaker(s) David Trafford ▪ Viticulturist(s) Schalk du Toit (2002, consultant) ▪ 125ha/16ha (cab, mourv, shiraz, touriga nacional, trincadeira, chenin, rouss, viog) ▪ 60t/5,400cs own label 73% red 20% white 7% rosé ▪ PO Box 495 Stellenbosch 7599 ▪ info@sijnn.co.za ▪ www.sijnn.co.za ▪ F +27 (0)86-542-3959 ▪ **T +27 (0)21-880-1611**

Silkbush Mountain Vineyards

Well-established and -reputed as a supplier of top-quality grapes to some of the Cape's majors, this Californian-owned spread below Breedekloof's Sybasberg (Silkbush Mountain) exports its own-brand wine to the US but is also now establishing a presence in Gauteng. Range expansions are planned.

Viognier ⓐ ★★★ Unwooded **12** a textbook for the variety: apricot & peach perfumes, light-textured palate adorned with floral notes & fresh acidity. Perfect summer wine. Not retasted: **Pinotage 09** ★★★☆ **Shiraz 10** ★★★ — GM

Location: Wolseley ▪ WO: Breedekloof ▪ Est 2000 ▪ 1stB 2007 ▪ Closed to public ▪ Kingsbury Cottage (self-catering), www.silkbush.net/kingsbury ▪ Owner(s) Silkbush Holdings LP ▪ Winemaker(s) Bennie Wannenburg (2007, consultant) ▪ Viticulturist(s) Anton Roos (2000) ▪ 143ha/87ha (cabs s/f, malbec, merlot, mourv, p verdot, ptage, shiraz, sauv, sem, viog) ▪ 1,200t/10,000cs own label 100% red ▪ Other export brand: Lion's Drift ▪ PO Box 91 Breërivier 6858 ▪ anton@silkbush.net ▪ www.silkbush.net ▪ F +27 (0)86-520-3261 ▪ **T +27 (0)83-629-1735**

☐ **Silverhurst** *see* High Constantia Wine Cellar

Silvermist Vineyards ⓠ ⓜ ⓐ ⓞ

Silvermist, in the mountains above Constantia, is the only organically certified wine estate in the area and part of the Table Mountain National Park. Viticulturist/winemaker Gregory Louw and his team spent over a decade clearing alien vegetation and planting vines, and latterly are bottling the fruits of their labour. Top fine-dining restaurant La Colombe is now established here, and the Silvermist Eatery has a larger venue among the vines from which to offer wine tasting and sales, meals and picnics, and views over Constantia Valley and False Bay.

★★★★ **Cabernet Sauvignon** ⓐ A liqueur richness, blackcurrant, cedar - youthful **10** ticked all the cab boxes mid-2012 but needed time for new oak to integrate. Serious effort, with a savoury undertone bridling the fruit. WO Coastal.

★★★★ **Rocket Dog Red** ⓐ ⓢ **11**'s cab gets 25% shiraz blended in at bottling. Sweet-oak-infused, New-World, suavely approachable style. Dual Constantia-Coastal WO.

★★★★☆ **Single Vineyard Sauvignon Blanc** ⓢ Gets 'Single Vineyard' designation from **14**, a classy step up on **13** (★★★☆), from low-yielding vines. Lovely stonefruit intensity in piquant balance with fine mineral thread. Vivacious yet focused, pure fruit unfettered by oak.

Sauvignon Blanc ⓝ ★★★☆ Mostly cool & herbaceous tones but also hints of ripe tropical fruit, **14** really tangy mouthful especially given modest alcohol; racy freshness favours food. — MW

Location: Constantia ▪ Map: Cape Peninsula ▪ WO: Constantia/Constantia-Coastal/Coastal ▪ Est 1984 ▪ 1stB 2010 ▪ Tasting & sales Mon-Sun 10-4.30 ▪ Silvermist Mountain Lodge ▪ Conferences ▪ Weddings/functions ▪ La Colombe Restaurant, www.lacolombe.co.za or reservations@lacolombe.co.za ▪ Silvermist Eatery open daily 8-5.30 ▪ Picnics ▪ Walks/hikes ▪ Conservation area ▪ Owner(s) Constantia Ridge Estates (Pty) Ltd ▪ Cellarmaster(s)/winemaker(s)/viticulturist(s) Gregory Brink Louw (Jan 2005) ▪ 22ha/6ha (cab, shiraz, sauv) ▪ 5.2t/580cs own label 30% red 70% white ▪ Certified organic (CERES-19340) ▪ PO Box 608 Constantia 7848 ▪ silvermistvineyards@gmail.com ▪ www.silvermistvineyards.co.za ▪ S 34° 0' 51.93" E 018° 24' 5.13" ▪ F +27 (0)21-794-7602 ▪ **T +27 (0)21-794-7601**

☐ **Silver Myn** *see* Zorgvliet Wines
☐ **Silversands** *see* Robertson Wide River Export Company

Silverthorn Wines

One of South Africa's relatively few bubbly-only producers, Robertson boutique house Silverthorn was founded by Karen and John Loubser (he the champagne-loving MD and sometime winemaker of Steenberg, in far-off Constantia). Later investment meant they were able to create a full portfolio of

sparklings of their own, including an unusual rosé from shiraz. Now into their second decade of production, Karen and John say they are on a 'thrilling odyssey of discovery', amazed at how much more
there is to learn and enjoy. Fortunately for us, volumes now top 21,000 bottles.

★★★★ **The Genie** Playful, delightful & charming **NV** MCC rosé, most unusually made from shiraz.
Latest (**12**) gently spiced red fruit, scented nose with round yet fresh, crisp & lipsmacking dry palate.

★★★★☆ **Jewel Box** Balance & class are obvious in second disgorgement of chardonnay-driven **10**
bubbly with 40% pinot. Finer, more integrated aromas & flavour, complex & subtle notes of brioche,
nuts, a new slight saline nuance. Palate long & seamless, with the richness of ±40 months on lees yet
vibrantly fresh & full of potential. WO W Cape.

★★★★☆ **The Green Man** MCC sparkler from Robertson chardonnay, 32 months on lees for **11**,
offering the usual sophistication, intensity & elegance. Slightly more prominent yeasty brioche is complicated by ripe apple, lemon & white flowers. Fresh & steely, like **10** (★★★★★), with typical blanc de
blanc undeviating focus. — JPf

Location: Robertson ▪ WO: Robertson/Western Cape ▪ Est 1998 ▪ 1stB 2004 ▪ Closed to public ▪ Owner(s) Silverthorn
Wines (Pty) Ltd ▪ Cellarmaster(s)/winemaker(s)/viticulturist(s) John Loubser (1998) ▪ 10.5ha/4ha (cab, shiraz,
chard) ▪ 50t/3,500cs own label 66% white 34% rosé ▪ IPW ▪ PO Box 381 Robertson 6705 ▪ john@silverthornwines.co.
za, karen@silverthornwines.co.za ▪ www.silverthornwines.co.za ▪ **T** +27 (0)21-788-1706

☐ **Simelia** *see* Woestkloof Estate
☐ **Simonay** *see* Simonsvlei International
☐ **Simonsbosch** *see* Koelenhof Winery

Simonsig Landgoed

This large and dynamic family estate in the foothills of the Simonsberg is welcoming the third generation of Malans into its management, with a new brand manager in the person of the eldest son of
CEO Francois and grandson of visionary founder Frans. (As well as being a pioneer of the Wine of Origin legislation and the Stellenbosch Wine Route, the latter made the Cape's first champagne-method
sparkling wine, and perhaps the first seriously oaked white.) Johan Malan continues to preside over
the cellar, and reports on continuing upgrades there. It's not only family at Simonsig, of course, and in
2014 the WIETA audit was successfully completed - 'to give further recognition to our longstanding
commitment to uplifting the standards of living of our staff'.

★★★★☆ **Red hill Pinotage** Finely crafted, with dense ripe fruit, intriguing aromatic spiciness &
silky texture, single-vineyard **11** maintains stellar standard. Blackberry, plum pudding & cinnamon,
with noble oak showing through at lingering finish.

★★★★☆ **Merindol Syrah** Intensely concentrated, generously ripe, yet retaining a nervous spiciness,
12 easily upholds the standard of this premium, single-vineyard classic. Seamlessly constructed & carefully detailed, showing garrigue scrub with aromatic tobacco.

★★★★☆ **CWG Auction Reserve Heirloom Shiraz** Smoky, decadently fruity, with delightful tarry
liquorice notes, **12** impresses at every level. More approachable than expected, with sweet, juicy
charm, but undoubted class showing in peacock's tail finish.

★★★★☆ **Tiara** Stand-out cabernet-led, 4-way Bordeaux blend, **11** faithfully follows long line of aristocratic predecessors. Inky/iodine notes mingle subtly with plush, ripe berry fruit. Big bodied yet
already approachable & supple.

★★★★ **Frans Malan Cape Blend** Respected pioneering Cape Blend has lower 64% pinotage with
cab & dash of merlot in **11**. Oak vanilla spices up generous bramble & blackcurrant fruit, supported by
ripe, soft tannins.

★★★★ **Aurum Chardonnay** ⊘ Prime vintage **09** (★★★★) swamped by potent oak, buttery/
yeasty lees notes mid-2013. Weighty, rich & ripe, may emerge in time, like last-tasted **07**.

★★★★ **Chenin Avec Chêne** ⓐ **12** (★★★☆) more rigorously oaked than previous, but ripe tropical fruit still holds centre stage. Leaner than **10**.

★★★★ **Roussanne** ⓝ Intriguing candy/lemon zest with honeyed notes on limited-release **13**, opens into sweet clove & cinnamon spiciness. Ripe & robust but elegantly weighted, easily handling year in oak.

★★★★☆ **CWG The Red Ox Chenin Blanc-Roussanne** ⓝ Seductively ripe & rich barrel-fermented roussanne, with 14% oxidative chenin, **13** oozes charm & character. Subtle but substantial glacé fruit, mouthcoating texture & delightful salty-mineral finish; complex & finely detailed.

★★★★ **Kaapse Vonkel Brut Rosé** Pale blush **13** MCC sparkling from pinot noir & pinotage is reliably appealing, finely balanced & fruity. Baked apple & shortbread on delicate mousse, with a lingering green apple finish.

★★★★☆ **Cuvée Royale** Prestige blanc de blanc MCC bubbly from partially oaked chardonnay. **10** is packed with character & yeasty appeal. Rich & savoury yet focused & elegant. Deft cellar touch shows in perfectly poised, balanced special occasion bubbly. No **09**.

★★★★ **Kaapse Vonkel Brut** Eminently satisfying pioneer MCC bubbly delivers familiar appletart flavours & aromas in **12**. Dry & freshly crisp. Pinot & chardonnay with dash of pinot meunier. WO W Cape.

★★★★ **Vin de Liza** ⓐ Noble Late Harvest from sauvignon & semillon. After simpler **09** (★★★★), **10** satisfies with silky, gently unctuous charm.

★★★★ **Cape Vintage Reserve** ⓐ First recorded since **94** (LBV), all-shiraz port-style **09** is liquid Christmas pudding, complete with brandy! Dense, spicy & rich, made for cold winter nights.

Pinotage ★★★ Typical high-toned aromas introduce **12**, unwooded as always, spicy berry fruit, good body & generous finish. **Cabernet Sauvignon-Shiraz** ★★★ Fruit-driven **13** shows peppery notes, lightish body. Fresh & youthful. **Chenin Blanc** ⓥ ⓣ ★★★★ Ripe & cheerful **14**, with pineapple & peach fruit, firm acidity. Great value. **Gewürztraminer** ★★★★ Intensely fragrant, full & floral **14**, semi-sweet, ripe & appealing. **Sunbird Sauvignon Blanc** ★★★ Vinous & fruity aromas, fresh acidity, appealing lees texture. **14** is ripe & full flavoured. **Sensation Sweet Red** ⓝ ★★☆ Nicely weighted but very jammy-sweet (54 g/l sugar). **13** from cab & shiraz, with overt red berry fruit. Also tasted: **Labyrinth Cabernet Sauvignon 10** ★★★★ **Mr Borio's Shiraz 12** ★★★☆ **Adelberg Cabernet Sauvignon-Merlot 12** ★★☆ **The SMV 13** ★★★☆ **Chardonnay 13** ★★★ **Adelberg Sauvignon Blanc 14** ★★★ Not retasted: **Straw Wine 11** ★★★☆ — GdB

Location/map: Stellenbosch ▪ WO: Stellenbosch/Western Cape ▪ Est 1953 ▪ 1stB 1968 ▪ Tasting & sales Mon-Fri 8.30–5 Sat 8.30–4 Sun 11-3 ▪ Fee R30pp (incl glass) ▪ MCC tour & tasting; MCC & cake pairing, book ahead ▪ Closed Good Fri, Dec 25 & Jan 1 ▪ Cellar tours daily at 11 & 3 (booking advised) ▪ Cuvée restaurant ▪ Facilities for children ▪ Tour groups ▪ Gifts ▪ Farm produce ▪ Conferences ▪ 4x4 Landrover experience ▪ Labyrinth vineyard ▪ Owner(s) Pieter, Francois & Johan Malan ▪ Cellarmaster(s) Johan Malan (1981) ▪ Winemaker(s) Debbie Thompson (Nov 1999) & Hannes Meyer (Jul 2009), with Charl Schoeman (Dec 2012) ▪ Viticulturist(s) Francois Malan (Jan 1981) & Tommie Corbett (Nov 2008), with Conrad Schutte (Vinpro) ▪ 300ha/210ha (cab, merlot, ptage, pinot, shiraz, chard, chenin, sauv) ▪ 2,700t/340,000cs own label 31% red 41% white 2% rosé 26% MCC ▪ BWI, HACCP 2009, IPW, SANAS, WIETA ▪ PO Box 6 Koelenhof 7605 ▪ wine@simonsig.co.za ▪ www.simonsig.co.za ▪ S 33° 52' 12.1" E 018° 49' 31.7" ▪ F +27 (0)21-888-4909 ▪ **T +27 (0)21-888-4900/99**

Simonsvlei International

⬭ 🍴 🥤 📷 🚻 ♿

Constituted in the aftermath of World War II to grow quality wines on a larger and sustainable scale, Simonsvlei took its name from the father of the South African wine industry, Simon van der Stel, and this Paarl area's vlei (wetlands) landscape. Co-founder Sonny le Roux in 1945 expressed a vision of 'quality wines at affordable prices' and that's still the mantra today. A 'rainbow' offering aims to please everyone, from grandpa and grandma with their sweet tooth to junior jungle-gymming outside the cellardoor while dad and mom taste the charming easy-drinkers.

Hercules Paragon range

★★★★ SMCV Shiraz, mourvèdre, cinsaut & viognier **12** blend is a delight, with soft & supple tannins, packed with perfumed berry, savoury & earthy flavours. Invites spicy grilled meat dishes.
Cabernet Sauvignon ★★★☆ Flagship of range, featuring occasional bottlings. **09**, bold fruit profile & big oak vanilla. Also tasted: **Shiraz 12 ★★★☆ Sauvignon Blanc 14 ★★★☆**

New Generation range

Ja-Mocha Pinotage ★★★☆ Will please fans of 'coffee' pinotage. Bright, ripe red-berry fruit with strong whiffs of espresso on now-bottled **12**. Smooth & rounded, with a firm grip. Not retasted: **Toffee Chunk Syrah 12 ★★★☆**

Premier range

Pinotage ★★★ Vibrant sweet ripe plum aromas on easy **13**, delights with berry & spicy coffee flavours. Try with biltong. **Shiraz** ⊘ **★★★☆** Sweet-spicy mulberry on fresh & fruity **13**. Fynbos & white pepper add to savoury tail. Over-delivers - stock up! **Chenin Blanc** ⊘ **★★★★** Ripe tropical fruit & zingy pineapple flavours on unpretentious & vibrant **14**, balanced by a mouthwatering fresh goodbye. Also tasted: **Cabernet Sauvignon 13 ★★★ Cabernet Sauvignon-Merlot 13 ★★★ Chardonnay 13 ★★★ Humbro Red Jerepiko NV ★★★**

Lifestyle range

Shiraz ⊘ **★★★ 13** rich brambleberry fruit, peppery spices with a tasty savoury goodbye. Over-achieves at the price. **Chenin Blanc** (NEW) **★★☆** Tropical fruit riot on **14**, bright & breezy fun! **Sauvignon Blanc** (NEW) **★★☆** Easy, lean-fruited, light & bright **14**. **Simonsblanc ★★★ NV** from chenin & colombard, light, easy & fresh, with a zingy tail. Also tasted: **Cabernet Sauvignon 13 ★★★ Merlot 13 ★★★ Pinotage 13 ★★ Simonsrood** ⊘ **NV ★★★**

Simonay range

Dry Red ★★ Was 'Classic Red'. Soft berry flavour, smooth **NV** (up a notch) party wine. 5L bag-in-box, as all in this range. Also tasted: **Dry white NV ★☆ Natural Sweet Rosé NV ★★** — WB

Location: Paarl = Map: Paarl & Wellington = WO: Western Cape = Est/1stB 1945 = Tasting & sales Mon-Fri 8–5 Sat 8. 30–4.30 Sun (Sep-Apr) 11–3 = Fee R20pp = Cellar tours by prior arrangement = Closed Good Fri, Dec 25 & Jan 1 = Eat@ Simonsvlei restaurant serving hot meals, snacks & refreshments = BYO picnic = Playground for children = Conference/ function venue (80 pax) incl. equipment, break-away areas, lunches, etc. = Conservation area = Owner(s) 65 share-holders = Winemaker(s) Ryan Puttick (Nov 2010), with Mari de Jager (Jan 2012) = Viticulturist(s) Ryan Puttick (Nov 2010) & Francois van Zyl = 1,158ha (shiraz, chenin) = 7,400t = 55% red 45% white = Brands for clients: Kelvin Grove, Ocean Basket, Woolworths = BWI, Fairtrade, HACCP, IPW, WIETA = PO Box 584 Suider-Paarl 7624 = info@simonsvlei.co. za = www.simonsvlei.com = S 33° 47' 24.9" E 018° 55' 49.1" = F +27 (0)21-863-1240 = **T +27 (0)21-863-3040**

☐ **Simplicity** *see* Weltevrede Estate

☐ **Simply Red/White** *see* PicardiRebel

☐ **Simply Wines** *see* Dorrance Wines

☐ **Since 1922** *see* Villiersdorp Cellar

☐ **Sir George** *see* Napier Winery

☐ **Sirkel** *see* Scali

Sir Lambert Wines

Named after 19th century seafarer Sir Robert Lambert and the namesake seaboard town where the vines are grown, this is a joint venture between Diemersdal cellar chief Thys Louw and two partners. Hand harvested (exclusively by locals, as part of the winery's support for the Lamberts Bay community), the grapes are from a 10-ha block just 3 km from the cold Atlantic ocean.

★★★★ Sauvignon Blanc Reflecting its maritime terroir, **14** is a refreshing melange of lemongrass, unripe tropical fruit & crushed stone; usual lovely depth & vinosity without sweetness, the sense of lightness aided by modest alcohol.

Not tasted: **The Admiral's Shiraz**. — JPf

Location/WO: Lamberts Bay • Map: Olifants River • Est 2004 • 1stB 2007 • Tasting by appt in Lamberts Bay or Mon-Sat/pub hols 9-5 Sun 10-3 at Diemersdal • Closed Good Fri, Dec 25 & Jan 1 • Xamarin Guest House & Restaurant • BYO picnic • Conference & function venue (up to 250 people) • Game drives • Golf course • Tour groups • Conservation area • 4x4 trail • Facilities for children • Owner(s) John Hayes, Johan Teubes & Thys Louw • Winemaker(s) Thys Louw & Mari Branders • Viticulturist(s) Johan Teubes (2004) • 10ha (shiraz, sauv) • 60t/6,000cs own label 10% red 90% white • PO Box 27 Durbanville 7551 • info@sirlambert.co.za • www.sirlambert.co.za • S 32° 5' 52.40" E 018° 18' 19.50" • F +27 (0)21-979-1802 • **T +27 (0)21-976-3361**

☐ **Sir Robert Stanford Estate** *see* Robert Stanford Estate
☐ **Six Hats** *see* Citrusdal Wines
☐ **Sixpence** *see* Opstal Estate
☐ **1685** *see* Boschendal Wines
☐ **Sixty 40** *see* Boland Kelder

Sizanani Wines   ⓠ

The employees of Stellenbosch estate Bellevue previously had a minority stake in the Sizanani brand but full ownership was acquired in 2011, giving them real control over their future. The wine portfolio, focused mainly on export markets, has included a pinotage, red blend, chenin, sauvignon and rare-in-SA cabernet franc rosé.

Location: Stellenbosch • Est 2005 • 1stB 2006 • Tasting & sales at Bellevue Estate Stellenbosch • Owner(s) Stellenbosch Wine & Logistics (Pty) Ltd • CEO Annelize Tities • Winemaker(s) Wilhelm Kritzinger & Anneke Potgieter (both 2005, Bellevue) • Viticulturist(s) Dirkie Morkel (Feb 2005, Bellevue) • 4,000cs own label 40% red 40% white 20% rosé • PO Box 33 Koelenhof 7605 • annelizepebbles@gmail.com • www.sizanani-wines.co.za • F +27 (0)21-865-2899 • **T +27 (0)21-865-2055/+27 (0)72-511-8899**

Skaap Wines   �址 ⓗ ⓞ ⓑ

Dutch banker Thierry Schaap has dryland vines on his prime Schapenberg site (Schaap and Schapen, meaning 'sheep', pure coincidence; 'Skaap' the Afrikaans version). Thierry and team are committed to sustainable farming, including local Sir Lowry's Pass village community involvement with a soup kitchen, children's foundation and amateur artists (whose beadwork is featured on the label).

★★★★ Skaap 42 Sauvignon Blanc From own & Durbanville grapes, **13** intense grassy & floral nose, tropical melon & citrus flavours with a flinty core, initial pétillance melting into satin texture.

Skaap 41 Shiraz ★★★☆ Now with 'Skaap 41' prefix, **12** has glossy dark fruit as well as wildflowers, white pepper & whiff of smoke. Not tasted: **Méthode Cap Classique Brut**. — JG

Location: Sir Lowry's Pass • Map: Helderberg • WO: Durbanville/Coastal • Est/1stB 2011 • Private functions (lunch/dinner) by appt • Swimming pool • Tour groups • Local art on display & for sale • Conferences (up to 18 pax) • Walks/hikes • Mountain biking trail • Conservation area • 5-bedroom guesthouse, dining room with chef & 2 self-catering lodges • Owner(s) Thierry Schaap • Cellarmaster(s)/winemaker(s) Riaan Oosthuizen (Jan 2011) • 17ha/4ha (shiraz, sauv) • 1,100cs own label 30% red 70% white • BWI, IPW • PO Box 3794 Somerset West 7130 • info@skaapwines.com • www.skaapwines.com • S 34° 06' 11.35" E 018° 55' 05.87" • **T +27 (0)21-858-1982/+27 (0)83-452-2083**

Skilpadvlei Wines   ⓠ ⓧ ⓗ ⓞ ⓑ ⓖ

A multi-faceted offering at the fourth-generation Joubert family farm on a ridge in the Polkadraai Hills overlooking Stellenbosch. Grapes, olives, tomatoes and wine spring from the site where turtles were found in the 1800s, giving the farm its name. Amenities include a wedding and conference venue, accommodation and popular family restaurant.

Skilpaddop Dry Red ★★★ Improved **10** equal blend of melot & pinotage is ripe & juicy, with good body. **ML Joubert ★★★★** Usual shiraz, cab, merlot combo in **12**, full & ripe, with oak-mocha spicing. **Sauvignon Blanc ★★★** Blast of khaki bush from **14** glass; well weighted, pleasant herbaceous conclusion. Also tasted: **Cabernet Sauvignon-Shiraz 12 ★★★ Chenin Blanc 14 ★★☆** — GdB

Location/map/WO: Stellenbosch ▪ Est 2004 ▪ 1stB 2001 ▪ Tasting & sales Mon-Sat 8-5 Sun 8-4 ▪ Fee R20 ▪ Closed Dec 25/26 & Jan 1/2 ▪ Restaurant Mon-Sat 8-late Sun 8-4 ▪ Facilities for children ▪ Gift/décor shop ▪ Conferences ▪ Weddings & functions ▪ B&B guesthouse & self-catering cottages ▪ Owner(s) WD Joubert ▪ Cellarmaster(s) Koewie du Toit (consultant) ▪ Viticulturist(s) Johan Pienaar & Eben Archer (consultants) ▪ 78ha/55ha (cab, merlot, ptage, shiraz, chenin, sauv) ▪ 652t/12,000cs own label 80% red 20% white ▪ PO Box 17 Vlottenburg 7604 ▪ info@skilpadvlei.co.za ▪ www.skilpadvlei.co.za ▪ S 33° 57' 31.5" E 018° 45' 52.4" ▪ F +27 (0)21-881-3538 ▪ **T +27 (0)21-881-3237**

☐ **Skipper's** *see* New Beginnings Wines
☐ **Skoon Vallei** *see* Eerste Hoop Wine Cellar

Slaley

One of the few cellardoors where you can taste and buy older vintages across a range of reds and whites, all at peak drinking age. Besides its popular bistro and live music over weekends, the Hunting family's picturesque Stellenbosch farm offers a variety of outdoor activities, like orchard lunches, cheese tastings in the vineyards, and pre-booked slides into the dam, or sundowners there.

Hunting Family range

★★★★ Merlot ⓐ Dark chocolate & meat extract add complexity to **07**'s rich dark fruit, while the serious oak regime (28 months, 40% new) provides spice & deep muscle tone for further cellaring.

★★★★ Shiraz ⓐ Luscious berries & spice array, touch of wintergreen, doesn't quite cloak **06**'s (**★★★☆**) dry tannins, less seductive than **04**. No **05**.

★★★★ Reserve Noble Late Harvest Chardonnay ⓐ Last was **07**, decadent & irresistible, concentrated honey/raisin character (from vine-dried grapes) perfect match for strong cheeses.

Not retasted: **Pinotage 07 ★★★★ Cabernet Sauvignon-Merlot 07 ★★★ Chardonnay 10 ★★★☆**

Broken Stone range

★★★★ Pinotage ⓐ Vanilla from 70% American barrels enriches **06**'s mulberry fruit while leaving the supple juiciness intact. Admirable intensity yet elegant (13% alcohol), polished. No **05**.

Sauvignon Blanc ★★★ Brimstone whiff, light passionfruit nuance on modest, restrained **13**. Not retasted: **Cabernet Sauvignon 06 ★★★★ Shiraz 07 ★★★ Cabernet Sauvignon-Shiraz-Pinotage 07 ★★★★**

Social range

Lindsay's Whimsy Rosé ★★☆ Dry **13** from pinotage, full bodied & packed with strawberry fruit. Weightier style is deliberate, says team, so wine will 'stay wine as opposed to water if you add ice'! Not retasted: **Lindsay's Whimsy Cape Blend 10 ★★★** — GdB

Location/map: Stellenbosch ▪ WO: Simonsberg–Stellenbosch ▪ Est 1957 ▪ 1stB 1997 ▪ Tasting & sales Tue-Sun 10–4 ▪ Fee R20, waived on purchase ▪ Closed Good Fri, Dec 25/26 & Jan 1 ▪ Cellar tours by appt ▪ Bistro: light meals during tasting hours ▪ Farm produce ▪ Venue & conference facility with AV capacity ▪ Owner(s) Hunting family ▪ Winemaker(s) Etienne Malan (Feb 2013) ▪ Viticulturist(s) Etienne Malan (Dec 2013) ▪ 240ha/51ha (cab, merlot, ptage, shiraz, chard, sauv) ▪ 320t/24–30,000cs own label 90% red 9% white 1% rosé ▪ IPW ▪ PO Box 119 Koelenhof 7605 ▪ info@slaley.co.za ▪ www.slaley.co.za ▪ S 33° 51' 53.7" E 018° 50' 51.1" ▪ F +27 (0)86-529-2347 ▪ **T +27 (0)21-865-2123**

Slanghoek Winery

At the foot of the Slanghoek mountains lies this efficient and modern grower-owned winery. One of the biggest local concerns, they're associated with a variety of popular events and activities like the Mountain to Mountain MTB Classic, Slanghoek Triathlon and Blend & Bottle. The Private Selection

and Vinay own-brands continue to be popular both locally and overseas, and to keep their many fans well supplied they recently extended their fermentation capacity by an impressive 6 million litres.

Private Selection

★★★★ **Crème de Chenin** ⊘ Appealing **13** Natural Sweet, the chenin spiced with a dash of muscat d'Alexandrie, shows ripe apricot & dried fruit. Tangy acid firms out palate, tempers 85 g/l sugar. Easily outdoes last **10** (★★★☆).

★★★★ **Noble Late Harvest** ⊘ Rich, honeyed **13**, first since **07**, has commendable concentration & focus. Delicious. From chenin with 10% muscat d'Alexandrie, 9 months in new French oak.

Cabernet Sauvignon ★★★ Appealing fruit-driven styling for new bottling of **12**, light but pleasantly chewy tannins, prominent vanilla the only quibble. **Pinotage** ★★★ Attractive spicy berry fruit with oak aromas, **12** light bodied & juicy. **Shiraz** ★★★ Stylish & well balanced, follow-on bottling of **10** notably lighter bodied than previous, overtly fruity with gentle tannins. **Chardonnay** ★★★ Nice weight & balance, oak a pleasant backdrop. **14** has usual few grams sugar but profile is less Rubenesque, more food friendly. **Hanepoot Jerepigo** ★★★★ Wholesome, rich & aromatic fortified dessert. **14** ex tank is very sweet but fresh, showcasing the ripe & pure muscat fruitiness. **Cape Ruby** ★★★ Port-style fortified from all-new-oaked touriga. **13** dense, taut, with restrained 112 g/l sugar. Also tasted: **Merlot 12** ★★☆ **Camerca 11** ★★★ **Chenin Blanc 14** ★★ **Sauvignon Blanc 14** ★★★ **Cuvée Brut NV** ★★ **Vin Doux NV** ★★ **Special Late Harvest 14** ★★★ **Red Muscadel 14** ★★★ **Red Jerepiko 14** ★★★

Vinay range

Crispy White ★★ NV as advertised: off-dry but crisp & tangy, fair fruit anchoring the freshness. Also tasted: **Smooth Blended Red NV** ★★ **Natural Sweet Rosé NV** ★★ — GdB

Location: Rawsonville ▪ Map: Breedekluof ▪ WO: Slanghoek ▪ Est 1951 ▪ 1stB 1970 ▪ Tasting & sales Mon-Fri 9–5 Sat 10–1 ▪ Closed Easter Fri/Sun, Dec 25 & Jan 1 ▪ Cellar tours by appt ▪ Picnic baskets, booking required ▪ Slanghoek MTB Route, fee R20: 13km ride with optional extra, more challenging 4km ▪ Owner(s) 25 producers ▪ Cellarmaster(s) Pieter Carstens (Aug 2002) ▪ Winemaker(s) Nico Grundling (Dec 2002), with Jacques de Goede & Jaco Theron (Dec 2001/Oct 2007) ▪ Viticulturist(s) Callie Coetzee (Nov 2010) ▪ 1,830ha ▪ 30,000t/80,000cs own label 25% red 55% white 10% rosé 10% fortified ▪ Other export brand: Zonneweelde ▪ ISO 22000, BWI, IPW ▪ PO Box 75 Rawsonville 6845 ▪ info@slanghoek.co.za ▪ www.slanghoek.co.za ▪ S 33° 39' 1.1" E 019° 13' 49.0" ▪ F +27 (0)23-344-3157 ▪ **T +27 (0)23-344-3026**

☐ **Slent** see Ayama Wines

Slowine

Slowine is a collaboration between owner Villiersdorp Cellar and shareholder wineries Luddite and Beaumont. Their motto urges us to decelerate and relax... with slow food, slow wine and slow living. Appropriately, the emblem on the label is the Common Padloper ('Road Walker') Tortoise, whose folkloric cousin famously beat the hare.

Pinotage ⑭ ★★★ Hint of banana adds to plum pudding appeal of **13**, ripe & fruity with soft powdery tannins. **Rosé** ★★★ Candy-pink quaffer from shiraz. **14** may smell like candyfloss but red cherry flavours add zest for overall dry profile. Cape South Coast WO. **Chenin Blanc-Sauvignon Blanc** ★★★ Floral & grassy **14** pre-bottling is like a relaxed stroll through a meadow, with peachy softness underfoot & lime freshness on the breeze. Also tasted: **Cabernet Sauvignon 13** ★★★ **Merlot 13** ★★★ **Shiraz 13** ★★★ **Chenin Blanc** ⊘ **14** ★★★★ **Sauvignon Blanc 14** ★★★ — JG

Location/map: Villiersdorp ▪ WO: Western Cape/Cape South Coast ▪ Est/1stB 2005 ▪ Tasting & sales at Villiersdorp Cellar (see entry) ▪ Owner(s) Villiersdorp Cellar ▪ Shareholders Beaumont Wines & Luddite Wines ▪ Technical team: Sebastian Beaumont & Niels Verburg ▪ Winemaker(s) Christo Versfeld, with André Bruyns (Dec 2009) ▪ Viticulturist(s) André Bruyns (Dec 2009) ▪ 300ha (merlot, chenin, sauv) ▪ 3,600t/40,000cs own label 40% red 40% white 20% rosé ▪ BWI, IPW ▪ PO Box 14 Villiersdorp 6848 ▪ marketing@slowine.co.za ▪ www.slowine.co.za ▪ S 33° 59' 11.2" E 019° 17' 48.5" ▪ F +27 (0)28-840-1833 ▪ **T +27 (0)28-840-1120**

Snowfield Boutique Winery

Raised in sunny Swartland, Bi-Anne du Toit completed her studies in winemaking in 2003 and, after marrying sheep farmer Louis, found herself in Sutherland, officially South Africa's second-coldest town. Undeterred, she made a Cape Ruby named Anti-Freeze and planted a few rows of mourvèdre with the intention of adding other varieties. Meanwhile she brings in grapes for her Snowfield and ZAHarmonie labels, both temporarily out of stock at press time.

Location: Sutherland ▪ Est 2012 ▪ 1stB 2011 ▪ Tasting, sales & cellar tours Mon-Sat by appt ▪ Fee R50pp ▪ Closed Easter Fri/Sun & Dec 25 ▪ Meals/refreshments by appt ▪ Picnic baskets to be pre-booked ▪ Owner(s) Bi-Anne du Toit ▪ Winemaker(s) Bi-Anne du Toit (Aug 2008) ▪ (mourv) ▪ 1t/118cs own label 60% red 40% port ▪ PO Box 154 Sutherland 6920 ▪ bianne@snowfieldboutiquewinery.co.za ▪ www.snowfieldboutiquewinery.co.za ▪ S 32° 28' 42.18" E 020° 38' 31.94" ▪ F +27 (0)23-571-1137 ▪ **T +27 (0)23-571-1137/+27 (0)78-165-8429**

☐ **Snow Mountain** *see* Nabygelegen Private Cellar
☐ **Social** *see* Slaley
☐ **Soek Die Geluk** *see* Goedverwacht Wine Estate

SoetKaroo Wine Estate

Susan Perold, winemaker at this micro estate in Prince Albert, calls her and husband Herman's business 'a hobby that got out of hand'. Their focus is on fortified dessert wines, which they handcraft with 'meticulous/neurotic quality control'. An 'increasing tendency to cultivarism' sees red muscadel's debut as a solo act this edition. Previously it was blended with the rare-in-Cape red hanepoot.

Red Muscat de Frontignan (NEW) ★★★★ Very sweet fortified with mix of muscat & raisin flavours, full bodied, long finish. Serve **14** with cheese or drink or its down after a meal, in place of dessert!
Also tasted: **Red Muscat d'Alexandrie 13** ★★★★ Not tasted: **Cape Vintage Touriga Nacional**, **Cape Vintage Petit Verdot**. — CR

Location: Prince Albert ▪ Map: Klein Karoo & Garden Route ▪ WO: Western Cape ▪ Est 2000 ▪ 1stB 2004 ▪ Tasting & sales Mon-Sat 9-1; afternoons by appt ▪ Closed Dec 25 ▪ Owner(s) Herman & Susan Perold ▪ Cellarmaster(s)/winemaker(s) Susan Perold (Jan 2007) ▪ 2t ▪ 56 Church Str Prince Albert 6930 ▪ perold@netactive.co.za ▪ www.soetkaroo.co.za ▪ S 33° 13' 21.9" E 022° 1' 48.0" ▪ F +27 (0)86-524-3801 ▪ **T +27 (0)23-541-1768**

☐ **Soleil de Karusa** *see* Karusa Vineyards
☐ **Solidus** *see* Claime d'Or
☐ **Solms-Astor** *see* Solms-Delta

Solms-Delta

The past is revered at the progressive Franschhoek property owned by the Solms, Astor and staff families - the museum, rural music programme, social history tourism, indigenous culinary garden, traditional cuisine, and, of course, wine, all reflect a commitment to the social history of the (very ancient) terroir. One of the more recent attractions, a music museum, explores the multiple layers of influence that combined over 4 centuries to create the rich musical traditions of the modern Cape. In addition to a formal exhibition space, which includes an interactive display of indigenous instruments, the centre has a workshop where local musicians make and play indigenous instruments. The facility also serves as a base for archiving and displaying the knowledge accumulated during the archaeological fieldwork on the property - an empowering, hopefully seminal resource for the wider community.

Solms-Delta range
★★★★ **Hiervandaan** (Ⓥ) Shiraz (portion vine-dried) blended with grenache & carignan, seasoned with 1% mourvèdre & 35% new oak. **11** as piquant & refreshing as **10**, with similar firm persistence.
★★★★ **Lekkerwijn** (✓) Serious, dry rosé from grenache, mourvèdre & viognier, partly fermented & matured in seasoned oak. **13** juicy, with invigorating zing & flavours of plum, spice & raspberry.

★★★★☆ **Amalie 13** grenache blanc-led white blend with widely sourced chenin, roussanne & viognier, partly barrel fermented. Aromas of pear, apricot blossom & nut. The dry, broad palate is ripe but with refreshing acidity, subtle oak not obscuring the fruit.

★★★★ **Koloni** Flamboyant **12** with exuberant aromas & flavours from muscat d'Alexandrie & vine-dried muscat de Frontignan. Unoaked, unlike previous. Though off-dry (13 g/l sugar), tastes much drier.

★★★★☆ **Gemoedsrus** Ⓥ 'Peace of Mind' is a quirky take on port: vine-dried shiraz stiffened with husk spirit. **10** (★★★★) laced with cigarbox & cloves; lively but not as charming as **09**.

Not tasted: **Africana**.

Solms-Astor range

Cape Jazz Shiraz ★★★ Unusual, crowd-pleasing off-dry **NV** sparkling red; with low alcohol, fresh acidity & little tannin should go with hot dishes. Not retasted: **Langarm 12** ★★★★ **Vastrap 12** ★★★ — JPf

Location/map: Franschhoek ▪ WO: Western Cape ▪ Est 1690 ▪ 1stB 2004 ▪ Tasting & sales daily 9–5 ▪ Fee R20pp ▪ Closed Dec 25 & Jan 1 ▪ Cellar tours by appt ▪ Cheese platters, picnics & set menus for tour groups ▪ Fyndraai Restaurant ▪ Conferences ▪ Weddings/functions ▪ Walking farm tours ▪ Dik Delta fynbos culinary garden ▪ Cape music museum, social history museum & archaeological sites ▪ Harvest festival (Mar) ▪ Summer music concerts ▪ Owner(s) Solms & Astor Family Trusts and Wijn de Caab Workers' Trust ▪ Winemaker(s) Hagen Viljoen (Nov 2012), with Joan Heatlie (Aug 2012) ▪ Viticulturist(s) Rosa Kruger (Jul 2011) ▪ 78ha/33ha (grenache n/b, mourv, ptage, shiraz, chenin, macabeo, muscat d'A, muscat de F, rouss, sem, viog) ▪ 370t/80,000cs own label 63% red 33% white 4% rosé ▪ BWI, IPW, WIETA ▪ PO Box 123 Groot Drakenstein 7680 ▪ info@solms-delta.co.za ▪ www.solms-delta.co.za ▪ S 33° 51' 51.0" E 018° 59' 23.8" ▪ F +27 (0)21-874-1852 ▪ **T +27 (0)21-874-3937**

Somerbosch Wines

The laid-back lifestyle of which brothers Marius, Japie and Wrensch Roux are proponents is reflected in their Helderberg winery's wines and welcome (further enhanced by decadent wine and ice-cream pairings). Equally representative is the name of their flagship, Kylix, an ancient Greek earthenware drinking vessel, broad-based and shallow for sipping supine.

Somerbosch range

★★★★ **Kylix** Ⓥ First since **04**, **10** mainly cab with shiraz, merlot. Spicy pencil shaving notes on backdrop of dark berries. Well made, should age rewardingly.

Merlot ★★★★ Always approachable label, **11**'s chocolate-infused red fruit is firm yet friendly, buffed by older French & American oak. **Shiraz-Merlot** ★★★ Equal marriage, some oak-ageing in **13** yields cheery, spicy lick-your-lips combo. **Sauvignon Blanc** ★★☆ Green apple, citrus & capsicum flavours supported by racy acidity in **14**, all shouting for butter-grilled seafood. Also tasted: **Pinotage 12** ★★★ **Chenin Blanc 14** ★★★ Not retasted: **Cabernet Sauvignon 10** ★★☆ **Shiraz 10** ★★★ **Late Bottled Vintage Port 06** ★★★ Not tasted: **Chardonnay, Méthode Cap Classique Brut**.

Poker Hill range

Shiraz-Merlot ★★★ Equal blend in lightly wooded **13** for youthful enjoyment around the BBQ or with pizza. Not tasted: **Semillon-Chenin Blanc**. — GM

Location/WO: Stellenbosch ▪ Map: Helderberg ▪ Est 1950 ▪ 1stB 1995 ▪ Tasting & sales daily 9-5 ▪ Fee R20/6 wines, waived on purchase of any 3 btls; R40pp/ice cream & red wine tasting ▪ Closed Dec 25 & Jan 1 ▪ Cellar tours by appt ▪ Somerbosch Bistro: b'fast & lunch daily ▪ Facilities for children ▪ Farm produce ▪ Conferences ▪ Owner(s) Somerbosch Wines cc ▪ Cellarmaster(s)/winemaker(s)/viticulturist(s) Marius & Japie Roux (both 1995) ▪ 55ha/43ha (cab, merlot, shiraz, sauv) ▪ 350t 55% red 45% white ▪ PO Box 12181 Die Boord 7613 ▪ enquiries@somerbosch.co.za, sales@somerbosch.co.za ▪ www. somerbosch.co.za ▪ S 34° 0' 28.6" E 018° 49' 6.9" ▪ F +27 (0)21-855-4457 ▪ **T +27 (0)21-855-3615**

Somerset Wines

Value-for-money wines sourced from established wineries, and all with easy names, designed to remove mystique and complication from the drinking experience - this is due to the marketing savvy and experience of co-owner Boetie Rietoff. In the wine industry for over 40 years, he gives a portion of the sales to local charities and communities in need.

Lord Somerset range

Sauvignon Blanc ⊘ ★★★ A jolly quaffer, **14** is crisp & dry with fresh apple fruitiness. **Soft Smooth Red** ★★ Slightly more tannic than name suggests, ample sweetness adds to appeal of latest **NV**. Also tasted: **Merlot-Cabernet Sauvignon** ⊘ **12** ★★★ Not retasted: **Cabernet Sauvignon 12** ★★☆ **Shiraz 12** ★★☆ **Chenin Blanc Bushvine 13** ★★☆

Lady Somerset range

Stylish Elegant Red ⊘ ★★★ Pick of the latest red crop, plump **NV** has soft stewed plums from merlot, hints of smoke & pepper from shiraz. **Sparkling Blush** (NEW) ⊘ ★★★ Foam enlivens glacé cherry sweetness of prettiest pale pink **NV**, low alcohol of 9.5% ensuring drinkability. Also tasted: **Crisp Dry White NV** ★★ **Natural Sweet Red NV** ★★★ **Natural Sweet Rosé NV** ★★★ **Natural Sweet White NV** ★★★ — JG

Location: Somerset West ▪ Map: Helderberg ▪ WO: Western Cape ▪ Est 2010 ▪ 1stB 2011 ▪ Tasting & sales Mon-Fri 8. 30-5 Sat 9-1 ▪ Closed all pub hols ▪ Tour groups ▪ Wine shop ▪ Owner(s) Boetie Rietoff, Greig Rietoff ▪ Cellarmaster(s) Francois van Zyl ▪ Winemaker(s) Ryan Elan-Puttick, with Jeff Wedgwood (consultant) ▪ 200,000cs 80% red 20% white ▪ PO Box 2240 Somerset West 7129 ▪ info@somersetbeverages.co.za ▪ www.somersetwines.com ▪ F +27 (0)21-852-9563 ▪ **T +27 (0)21-851-8188**

Somfula Wines

Swartland-based Nokubonga 'Bongi' Somfula developed a love of wine while working as a wine label designer in Cape Town. Her goal is to become a recognised brand locally and overseas, and build a network of agents. Current releases include a Cabernet, Merlot, Chardonnay and Natural Sweet Red. Recently she started supplying Pick n Pay and Cape Town's Hotel School, and now intends to export.

Location: Riebeek West ▪ Est/1stB 2009 ▪ Tasting by appt ▪ Closed Easter Fri/Sun/Mon, Dec 25/26 & Jan 1 ▪ Owner(s) Nokubonga Somfula ▪ 60% red 20% white 20% rosé ▪ c/o PO Box 1 Riebeek West 7306 ▪ info@somfulawine.co.za ▪ www.somfulawine.co.za ▪ F +27 (0)86-293-3443 ▪ **T +27 (0)79-464-0204**

☐ **Sonata** *see* Waterstone Wines

Sonklip Wine

Engineer Frik Kirsten's later-in-life winemaking was inspired by a 2008 garagiste course and the 'thinking-out-the-box' approach of top Cape vintner Eben Sadie (whose vaunted Mev. Kirsten old-vine chenin comes from Frik's Stellenbosch family farm, Westridge). Frik elected to age his four 2012 varietal wines longer and blend them, and the result is reviewed below.

Sonklip range (NEW)

Red Blend ★★★ Malbec (50%) leads cab, shiraz & soupçon viognier in old-oak-matured **12**. Meat, smoke, liquorice - all dark tones but attractively so. Has succulent appeal, is smooth & tasty; designed to please. — CR, CvZ

Location/map: Stellenbosch ▪ WO: Western Cape ▪ 1stB 2009 ▪ Tasting & cellar tours for groups only, by appt ▪ Owner(s)/winemaker(s) Frik Kirsten ▪ 200cs own label 100% red ▪ PO Box 6198 Uniedal 7612 ▪ frik.kirsten@gmail. com ▪ S 33° 56' 3.55" E 018° 53' 44.95" ▪ F +27 (0)21-887-5869 ▪ **T +27 (0)21-887-5869**

☐ **Sonop Organic** *see* Jacques Germanier

Sophie & Mr P

'A dapper couple' is an apt description for Mr P and Sophie Te'blanche, the nattily packaged and affordably priced pinot noir and sauvignon blanc created in Elgin's top-ranked Iona cellar (Sophie Te'blanche the vernacular name for sauvignon). Grapes either 'declassified' from Iona or selected from Cape South Coast vineyards also give life to cousins Sophie Le Rouge and Rosé.

Mr P Pinot Noir ★★★ Pleasant if simple cherry features on **13**. Lacks joie de vivre of **12**. **Sophie Te'blanche** ★★★ **14** vivacious youngster from sauvignon, easygoing tropical flavours, clean, dry. Also tasted: **Sophie Le Rouge 12** ★★ **Sophie Le Rosé 13** ★★ — AL

Location: Elgin ▪ WO: Cape South Coast ▪ Est/1stB 2009 ▪ Closed to public ▪ Owner(s) Andrew Gunn ▪ Cellarmaster(s) Werner Muller (May 2011) ▪ (cab, merlot, pinot, shiraz, sauv) ▪ 150t/20,000cs own label 10% red 85% white 5% rosé ▪ PO Box 527 Grabouw 7160 ▪ orders@sophie.co.za ▪ www.sophie.co.za ▪ F +27 (0)28-284-9078 ▪ **T +27 (0)28-284-9678**

☐ **Sopiensklip** *see* Springfontein Wine Estate
☐ **Southern Cape Vineyards** *see* Barrydale Winery & Distillery

Southern Right

In the 21 years since Hemel-en-Aarde Valley boutique vintners Southern Right embarked on their mission of redefining pinotage, co-owner Anthony Hamilton Russell believes, their 'unusual and very "Old World" expression has changed numerous consumers' views on the grape into something much more positive'. Their other wine, Sauvignon Blanc, is listed by quality restaurants globally, often by the glass. Both wines, from the 2014 vintage, will carry a new neck label to indirectly indicate to consumers Southern Right's more classic styling and philosophy.

★★★★ **Pinotage** Pinot noir-like **13** reflection of its cooler, maritime climate. Lifted cherry notes, minerality enhanced by tiny splashes malbec, shiraz, petit verdot. Fruitier, less grippy & readier than **12**.
★★★★☆ **Sauvignon Blanc** Starts with tropical ebullience, zesty greenpepper note, but **14** (★★★★) fades somewhat in face of overly bracing acid, bone-dry finish. **13** less flamboyant than previous but still accomplished. Walker Bay WO. — AL

Location: Hermanus ▪ Map: Elgin, Walker Bay & Bot River ▪ WO: Hemel-en-Aarde Valley/Walker Bay ▪ Est 1994 ▪ 1stB 1995 ▪ Tasting, sales & cellar tours Mon-Fri 9-5 Sat 9-1 ▪ Closed Easter Fri/Mon, Dec 25/26 & Jan 1 ▪ Fynbos reserve, renosterveld reserve & 3 wetlands ▪ Quad bike route ▪ Owner(s) Mark Willcox, Mikki Xayiya & Anthony Hamilton Russell ▪ Winemaker(s) Hannes Storm (2004) ▪ Viticulturist(s) Johan Montgomery (2005) ▪ 447ha/±36ha (ptage, sauv) ▪ 225-280t/30-40,000cs own label 20% red 80% white ▪ PO Box 158 Hermanus 7200 ▪ hrv@hermanus.co.za ▪ S 34° 24' 3.2" E 019° 13' 0.4" ▪ F +27 (0)28-312-1797 ▪ **T +27 (0)28-312-3595**

Southern Sky Wines

Andrew Milne, formerly in advertising, events and marketing, has made full use of these skills in his Paarl-based negociant bulk and bottled wine business. Having established a steady export market, primarily in south-east Asia, he is now focusing on local sales and 'a fresh look' for brand and labels.

Signature Selection
Tara Hill ⓥ ★★★★ Cab (88%) & petit verdot blend from Stellenbosch & Paarl. Serious effort, ably executed. **09** noble fruit on nose, quite fresh but well formed, smooth & concentrated.

Imagine range
Shiraz ⓥ ★★★ Ideal braai mate, ready-to-drink **08** has meaty charred oak notes already embedded. Just add T-bone steak. Not retasted: **Cabernet Sauvignon 08** ★★★

Marimba range
Cabernet Sauvignon ⓥ ★★ A savoury version, **09** concentrated black cherry fruit, ends with a dried-fruit tang.

Almara range
Cabernet Sauvignon ★★ Mediumweight **10** cab offering typical blackcurrant flavour & crisp acidity.

Ready Steady range
Red ⓠ ★★ Lightish, juicy & pleasant **NV**, chiefly cinsaut & 3 others, mostly unwooded. — GdB, HJ

Location: Paarl ▪ Map: Paarl & Wellington ▪ WO: Western Cape ▪ Est/1stB 2002 ▪ Tasting & sales by appt ▪ Owner(s) Andrew Milne ▪ Winemaker(s) Andrew Milne (Jan 2003) ▪ 10,000cs own label 95% red 5% white ▪ Other export brands: Golden Chalice, Hawk's Head, Les Fleurs, Rowlands ▪ PO Box 1312 Paarl 7624 ▪ andrew@ssw.co.za ▪ www. ssw.co.za ▪ S 33° 45' 8.78" E 018° 57' 42.55" ▪ F +27 (0)21-863-0444 ▪ **T +27 (0)21-863-4440**

South Hill Vineyards

This Elgin winefarm (with added attractions like art gallery, function venue and guesthouse - and now the new Gallery Restaurant) was, not long ago, home to neglected apple and pear trees - doomed, happily, to be replaced by vines. The new Kevin King label, reserved for limited edition wines, is named after the farm's owner.

Kevin King range 🆕
★★★★ **KK Bazza** **12** pinot noir shows mouthwatering blackberry, tar, ink & violets. Soft, open & approachable, with sweet ripe tannin. Shows vigour, balance & depth. Older oak; just 13.2% alcohol.
★★★★ **KK Micah** Peppery, leathery **12** a compact, elegant & understated shiraz-led blend with mourvèdre & barbera. Precise, fresh & fairly intense, though unlingering. Only older oak.

South Hill range
★★★★ **Cabernet Sauvignon** Subtle pencil shaving, cassis & blackberry notes on elegant, fresh **11**. Fruit not obstructed by sensitive oaking (none new); well structured, with ripe, fine tannin.
★★★★ **Sauvignon Blanc 13** shows cool-climate aromas & flavours of cut grass, fresh asparagus & flint. Good mouthfeel, with a precise, laser-like acidity & finely chiselled finish.
Also tasted: **Cabernet Sauvignon Rosé 13** ★★★☆ Not retasted: **Blanc de Blancs Méthode Cap Classique 08** ★★★☆ — JPf

Location/WO: Elgin ▪ Map: Elgin, Walker Bay & Bot River ▪ Est 2001 ▪ 1stB 2006 ▪ Tasting Mon-Sun 10-4 ▪ The Gallery @ South Hill (original artworks) ▪ Gallery Restaurant open Wed-Sun for lunch ▪ The Guest House and Pumphouse Cottage ▪ Function venue for conferences & weddings ▪ Conservation area ▪ Owner(s) South Hill Vineyards (Pty) Ltd ▪ Winemaker(s) Sean Skibbe (Jun 2005) ▪ Viticulturist(s) Andrew Teubes (Mar 2006, consultant) ▪ 57ha/28ha (cab, pinot, shiraz, chard, riesling, sauv, sem, viog) ▪ 130t/7,000cs own label 20% red 80% white ▪ PO Box 120 Elgin 7180 ▪ info@southhill.co.za ▪ www.southhill.co.za ▪ S 34° 14' 6.22" E 019° 6' 32.77" ▪ F +27 (0)86-530-4065 ▪ **T +27 (0)21-844-0888**

Spekulasie Landgoed

Swartlanders Johan and Linza Louw handcraft a small quantity of wine on their dryland bushvine estate, Spekulasie (most grapes go to Darling Cellars). The couple's bottlings, 'Old World styled and food friendly', are named after family members, notably Jan Pieterzoon, who founded the vinegrowing tradition in 1659.

De Beatrix ⓠ ★★★★ From shiraz, sparingly oaked in older wood. Lighter-styled **12** perfumed glassful of cherry, sweet spice, cinnamon & smoked meat, moderate alcohol & satisfying full conclusion. Not retasted: **De Pieterzoon 12** ★★★ **The Elizabeth 13** ★★★ — GdB, GM

Location/map/WO: Swartland ▪ Est 2008 ▪ 1stB 2010 ▪ Tasting, sales & cellar tours Mon-Sat/pub hols by appt ▪ Fee R20pp ▪ Light meals & refreshments by appt only ▪ Facilities for children ▪ Conferences/weddings ▪ Hiking trails ▪ Conservation area ▪ Accommodation ▪ Owner(s)/cellarmaster(s)/viticulturist(s) Johan & Linza Louw ▪ Winemaker(s) Linza Louw ▪ 220ha/27ha (cab, merlot, ptage, shiraz) ▪ ±120t/200cs own label 75% red 25% rosé ▪ PO Box 173 Malmesbury 7299 ▪ spekulasie@cornergate.com ▪ www.spekulasie-estate.co.za ▪ S 33° 23' 23.43" E 018° 35' 7.58" ▪ **T +27 (0)82-559-6066/+27 (0)72-375-7078**

□ **Spencer Bay** *see* Namaqua Wines

Spice Route Winery

Spice Route grew out of the conviction of Fairview's Charles Back that the Swartland was under-uti-lised. He acquired property in the region in the late 1990s, keeping some old vines but also going on to pioneer some lesser-known Mediterranean varieties. Ever the pragmatist, however, Charles believes 'wine on its own is not a strong enough drawcard to appeal to the average tourist'. Hence the creation of a brand home in Paarl featuring a restaurant, 'bean-to-bar' chocolate maker, brewery, distillery and glass blowing studio, among others. Oh, and a tasting room. 'The success of inner-city markets point to a consumer hankering to connect with product. We're taking it one step further.'

★★★★ **Grenache** (NEW) Earthy, savoury **12** is smooth, with ripe dark berry flavours complemented by hints of fynbos. Unobtrusive oak (only older barrels). Good structure & length.

★★★★ **Terra de Bron Mourvèdre** (NEW) Dusty mulberry fruit on preview **12** - great integration of supple tannins already, with touches of cured meat & lavender to add to complexity. Finishes dry & long.

★★★★ **Pinotage** Consistent & appealing, **12** with usual seductive sweet logan/blackberry note, bold but unobtrusive structure & subtle oaking, leaving succulent, pure, fresh fruit. From trellised & bushvines.

★★★★☆ **Terra de Bron Syrah** (NEW) **09** gorgeous expression of Swartland - rich, dark berries framed by lush structure of 21 months new oak. Smooth, creamy & elegant, with unflagging liqueur-like blackberry ending. For the long haul. Preview **12** (★★★★) from Darling not as complex, compelling.

★★★★ **Chakalaka** **12** is a compact, meaty, delicious 6-way shiraz/mourvèdre-led blend. Plentiful restrained sweet fruit, violet perfume & fragrant spice; harmonious, groomed & well built.

★★★★☆ **Chenin Blanc** ⊘ Now bottled, **13** is lush & silky, with kaleidoscopic crème brûlée, lemon, honey & vanilla. Still fresh & vibrant, with restrained oak & smooth complexity.

★★★★ **Sauvignon Blanc** From Darling fruit, **14** attracts with tropical fruit aromas & herbaceous notes. Restrained, juicy acidity, refined & very enjoyable. **13** sold out untasted.

★★★★☆ **The Amos Block Sauvignon Blanc** (NEW) ⊘ Excellent varietal expression from oldest sauvignon vineyard in SA, planted 1965, hand-picked **14** is complex, intense, shows wonderful con-centrated flavours of citrus & greenpepper. Elegant, never-ending finish. Outstanding value.

★★★★ **Viognier** Spicy & fragrant oak-dusted peach melba builds in the mouth on **13**. Broad & rich, satisfying, with invigorating freshness & zippy citrus finish.

Not tasted: **Mourvèdre**, **Malabar**. Discontinued: **Shiraz**. — WB

Location: Malmesbury/Paarl ▪ Map: Paarl & Wellington ▪ WO: Swartland/Darling ▪ Est/1stB 1998 ▪ Tasting & sales Mon-Sun 9-5, last tasting 30min before closing ▪ Closed Good Fri, Dec 25 & Jan 1 ▪ Spice Route Restaurant ▪ Tour groups by appt ▪ Red Hot Glass Studio ▪ DV Artisan Chocolate Roastery & Espresso Bar ▪ Cape Brewing Company ▪ Bar-ley & Biltong Emporium ▪ Wilderer's Distillery & La Grapperia Restaurant ▪ Owner(s) Charles Back ▪ Winemaker(s) Charl du Plessis (Dec 2001), with Licia Solomons (Jan 2006) ▪ 112ha (barbera, cab, carignan, grenache, merlot, mourv, petite sirah, ptage, sangio, shiraz, tannat, zin, chenin, rouss, sauv, sem, viog) ▪ 900t 60% red 40% white ▪ Fairtrade, IPW, WIETA ▪ PO Box 583 Suider-Paarl 7624 ▪ info@spiceroute.co.za ▪ www.spiceroutewines.co.za ▪ S 33° 45' 50.5" E 018° 55' 9.7" ▪ F +27 (0)21-863-3797 ▪ **T +27 (0)21-863-5200**

Spier

Having the Enthoven family as owners has focused the activities and direction of this dynamic Stellenbosch farm and business, because they are concerned about quality, conservation, community development and upliftment. Creative Block is one example, where local artists create small-format works which Spier markets on their behalf; others are the conservation area allowing raptor rehabili-tation, and the Eagle Encounter; a heritage walk (because Spier is one of the oldest wine estates in Stellenbosch); not to forget the amphitheatre which showcases local artists. It is also a tourist destination, with hotel and hospitality attractions, including spa, restaurants, deli and picnic venue on the Eerste River bank. Heading up the wine operation is Frans Smit, who gives his name to the estate's pinnacle wine and this year celebrates 20 vintages at Spier.

Frans K. Smit range

★★★★☆ **CWG Frans Smit Auction Reserve** ⑭ Classic Bordeaux-styled red, near-equal cab & merlot, dash cab franc, all from Helderberg. Burly **10** also shows a 'feminine' side with alluring spice & savoury notes to dark berry fruit, but it's finely packed in a muscular frame, & needs time. 18 months oak, 70% new.

★★★★☆ **Frans K. Smit** ⑫ Generous flagship Cape Blend (4 Bordeaux reds plus shiraz, pinotage) honours the cellarmaster. Inky **08**, suave forest floor fruit nestle in savoury tannins, 30 months 100% new oak still settling. A blockbuster from any angle. Coastal WO.

21 Gables range

★★★★ **Cabernet Sauvignon** ⑭ One for the long haul; serious Stellenbosch fruit treated accordingly. **11** lavished 2 years 70% new French oak, which guards sleeping cassis/blackberry fruits in youth.

★★★★☆ **Pinotage** Outstanding expression of the variety; **12** has a clove-studded baked plum core laced with freshness, & finesse. Bold enough to contain 14.5% alcohol but the fineness of structure & bone-dry finish keep it from being a fruit bomb. Home grapes.

★★★★ **Chenin Blanc** Full throttle **13** is showy, but risks losing nuance of the grape. Technically dry again, loads of new oak & oodles of summer fruits provide bags of flavour. Tygerberg vines.

★★★★ **Sauvignon Blanc** ⑫ Wake-me-up **13** like a dip in an icy lake, riveting grassy attack to tangy asparagus/canned pea fruit, super length of flavour. Refreshing, to say the least!

Creative Block range

★★★★ **5** Merlot & cab lead 5-way Bordeaux blend. Lots of power lurks in tightly toned **12**, with a fresh underlying minerality. Needs time to relax, & yield. All reds in this range WO Coastal.

★★★★ **3** Shiraz & mourvèdre seasoned by splash viognier; 60% new oak, some American. **12** delectably spicy & meaty, but sleek & smooth with a savoury/green olive farewell.

★★★★ **2** ⑫ Strident grassy muscularity of dominant sauvignon gets width & balance from 14% unoaked semillon in **13**; satisfying, but a yard off mineral **12** (★★★★☆).

8 ⑭ ★★★★ A United Nations of wine! Pinotage & shiraz in the vanguard, supported by cab & merlot with splashes petit verdot, mourvèdre, cab franc & viognier in the mix. **12** in dense tannic grip, needs time for berry fruit to emerge.

Private Collection

★★★★ **Shiraz** ⑫ Energised spice of **11** captured in firm structure; maintains freshness with 50% new wood & 14.6% alcohol well contained. This range for export only.

Not retasted: **Cabernet Sauvignon** 11 ★★★☆ **Merlot** 11 ★★★☆ **Pinotage** 11 ★★★☆ **Chardonnay** 12 ★★★☆ **Sauvignon Blanc** 13 ★★★☆

Collaborative Series ⑭

★★★★☆ **Noble Late Harvest** A joint project between Spier & activist-poet Breyten Breytenbach's Pirouge Collective. Amber **09** folds apricot, tangerine & candied lemon into sweet, mellow whole. Mere 500 x 375 ml bottles from Stellenbosch chenin, 3 years in older wood.

Ideology ⑭

Wild Ferment Pinotage ★★★☆ Wild tropical tones to **12**; spicy fruit still jousting with toasty oak (20 months, 60% new) in youth. Paarl grapes. **'Rhône-Style Blend'** ★★★☆ Fresh-tasting blend cinsaut, mourvèdre & shiraz with dash of viognier. **12** open grained, delicate fruit not swamped by old oak. This, next WO Coastal. **Chardonnay-Pinot Noir** ★★ Cask fermented & matured 6 months, pearl-pink **13** lacks fruit verve. **Weisser Riesling** ★★★☆ Semi-dry **12** a fascinating exhibition of floral, quince & stonefruit interest; for jaded palates. Tygerberg vines. **Wild Ferment Sauvignon Blanc** ★★★☆ **12** tiny production of spontaneously wood-fermented Elim sauvignon; thatch-like fruit coddled in creamy oak, gentle acidity.

Vintage Selection

Cape Late Bottled Vintage ⓝ ★★★☆ Venerable **07** a blend tinta & touriga, 7 years in wood. Brandied toffee & rich, sweet Christmas cake features call for a winter's hearth. Ex Stellenbosch. Not retasted: **Malbec-Cabernet Franc-Petit Verdot 12** ★★★ **Shiraz-Mourvèdre-Viognier 12** ★★★☆ **Chardonnay-Chenin Blanc-Viognier 13** ★★★ Not tasted: **Cabernet Sauvignon, Sauvignon Blanc**.

Signature range

Cabernet Sauvignon-Merlot-Shiraz ⓝ ★★★ Supple tannins allow cassis fruit to shine in **13**, nicely poised, alcohol in check. **Chardonnay-Pinot Noir** ⓝ ★★☆ **14** onion skin hue leads out strawberry features, lowish alcohol for lunchtimes. WO Coastal. **Chardonnay** ⓥ ★★★ Lipsmacking loquat character to lightly wooded **14**; a tasty, very tasty crowd pleaser! **Chenin Blanc** ⓥ ★★★ Sunshine in a glass; **14** packed with succulent peach & melon, decidedly moreish. Also tasted: **Cabernet Sauvignon 13** ★★★ **Merlot 13** ★★★ **Pinotage 13** ★★★ **Shiraz 13** ★★★ **Sauvignon Blanc 14** ★★★ **Méthode Cap Classique 12** ★★★★ — DS

Location/map: Stellenbosch ▪ WO: Western Cape/Coastal/Stellenbosch/Tygerberg/Elim/Paarl ▪ Est 1692 ▪ 1stB 1770 ▪ Tasting 10–4.30 & sales 9–5 daily ▪ Tasting from R38 ▪ Facilities for children ▪ Tour groups ▪ Farm produce ▪ Conferences ▪ Manor House & Heritage Walk ▪ Conservation area ▪ 4-star Spier Hotel ▪ Eight Restaurant, Eight to Go & Spier Hotel Restaurant ▪ Owner(s) Enthoven family ▪ Cellarmaster(s) Frans Smit (Dec 1995) ▪ Winemaker(s) Johan Jordaan (reds, Jul 2007) & Jacques Erasmus (whites, Apr 2007) ▪ Wine procurement/winemaker(s) Johan de Villiers, Anton Swarts & Lizanne Jordaan ▪ Viticulturist(s) Johann Smit (Dec 1999) ▪ 650ha (barbera, cabs s/f, malbec, merlot, mourv, p verdot, ptage, shiraz, chard, chenin, sauv, sem, viog) ▪ 3,850t own label 65% red 31% white 3% rosé 1% MCC ▪ ISO 22000:2005, BWI, Fairtrade, IPW, Organic, WIETA ▪ PO Box 99 Lynedoch 7603 ▪ info@spier.co.za ▪ www. spier.co.za ▪ S 33° 58' 24.63" E 018° 47' 2.23" ▪ F +27 (0)21-809-1930 ▪ **T +27 (0)21-809-1100 (wine tasting)**

Spioenkop Wines

Introduced to and familiarising himself with SA by importing top brands into Belgium and working a few seasons at, among others, L'Avenir (with similarly impassioned self-taught Francois Naudé), Koen Roose-Vandenbroucke with wife Hannelore and partner bought vineyard land on Spioenkop Hill in Elgin 10 years ago. The winemaker/viticulturist is committed to artisan tools and techniques, guided as much by his winegrowing philosophy and individualistic character as by the 'dangerously steep' terroir. The aim, he says, is to specialise in pinotage and pinot noir (debut release of the latter maturing at press time), and allow Elgin 'elegance, minerality, sensuality and purity' to shine through (though some Stellenbosch fruit features for now). Below ratings speak of some success!

1900 range

★★★★☆ **Pinotage** Serious, elegant **13** entrances, like good pinot noir, with ethereal, floral, black cherry fragrance, silky, fresh feel. Harmony of optimally ripe fruit, fine tannin & well-judged oak (40% new) allows for current drinking, but also years to go. Elgin & Stellenbosch grapes, like standout **12** (★★★★★) & all these.

★★★★ **Chenin Blanc** **13**'s riveting acidity, concentration & length tempered by tropical juicy appeal, botrytis & oxidative hints. Partly barrel fermented for structure. Good few years potential.

★★★★ **Sauvignon Blanc** Elegant yet steely **13** returns to form after less composed **12** (★★★☆). Refreshing winter melon notes gain juiciness from 5% splash semillon. Incisively dry, long.

For more information, visit wineonaplatter.com

Spioenkop range

★★★★ **Pinotage** Eye-catching luminosity on pinot noir-like **13**. Fresh, linear, with pure cherry raspberry flavours; nice grippy tannins on dry finish. Subtle oaking (40% new). Just 12% alcohol, ideal lunchtime red.

★★★★☆ **Chenin Blanc** Austere yet compelling **13** from young Elgin vines. Tighter than '1900' version with purity & precision in its orange pith character. Palate tension, finishing tannic grip suggest this is a long runner & worth the wait. Portion oaked; natural ferment (as are all).

★★★★ **Riesling 13** (★★★★☆) best to date; like maiden **11** shows great poise, elegance after slightly ponderous **12** (★★★★). Mouthwatering melange lime, flint, hint smoky slate. Racy tension, purity, tangily dry finish cap this delicious individual. Perfectly built for long ageing. Moderate 12% alcohol.

★★★★☆ **Sauvignon Blanc** Distinctive **13** shows similar expressive yet intricate lime, winter melon, pineapple as **12**. Lovely rich mouthfeel contrasted by zesty mineral finish. Power with elegance. — AL

Location: Elgin ▪ Map: Elgin, Walker Bay & Bot River ▪ WO: Elgin/Western Cape ▪ Est 2008 ▪ 1stB 2010 ▪ Tasting, sales & cellar tours by appt only ▪ Fee R20, waived on purchase (case of wine) ▪ Closed all pub hols ▪ Facilities for children ▪ BYO picnic ▪ Hiking trails ▪ Conservation area ▪ Weddings/functions ▪ Self-catering cottage ▪ Owner(s) Valuline 119 (Pty) Ltd, 5 shareholders ▪ Cellarmaster(s)/winemaker(s)/viticulturist(s) Koen Roose-Vandenbroucke (2008) ▪ ±47ha/10ha (ptage, pinot, chenin, riesling, sauv) ▪ 40t/5,000cs own label 20% red 80% white ▪ PO Box 340 Grabouw 7160 ▪ info@spioenkopwines.co.za ▪ www.spioenkopwines.co.za ▪ S 34° 14' 14" E 019° 3' 50" ▪ **T +27 (0)21-859-1458/+27 (0)79-491-6613/+27 (0)72-440-2944**

☐ **Splattered Toad** *see* Cape Point Vineyards

Spookfontein Wines

Family-owned Spookfontein boutique winery in Upper Hemel-en-Aarde Valley has opened its doors to the public, welcoming visitors with a range of wines from organically farmed grapes. Craig Sheard continues to vinify as naturally as possible, employing biodynamic practices wherever possible.

★★★★ **Phantom** Merlot-led (with cab & cab franc) **08** raises the bar on **07** (★★★★☆). Poised & lengthy, but greater grip & just the right amount of flavour without seeming worked.

Rosé ★★ **14**, from merlot, like an extremely light, slightly insipid, dry red wine. **Méthode Cap Classique** ★★★☆ Dry bubbly **06** from old-oaked pinot noir, has gained gold colour & some brioche developmental character, along with its ripe yellow apple notes. Rich & flavoursome, brightly balanced, if not exactly crisply fresh. **Late Bottled Vintage** ★★★☆ Pretty, easygoing **NV** from 18% 2008 cab with 2009 & 2012 merlot, bottled in 2014. Berry fruit in pleasing balance with light tannin grip & lively acidity. Alcohol & sugar pretty modest for port-style. Also tasted: **Cabernet Sauvignon 09** ★★★ **Cabernet Franc 09** ★★★ **Merlot 09** ★★★☆ Not tasted: **Pinot Noir**. — TJ

Location: Hermanus ▪ Map: Elgin, Walker Bay & Bot River ▪ WO: Upper Hemel-en-Aarde Valley ▪ Est 2000 ▪ 1stB 2004 ▪ Tasting & sales Tue-Sun 10.30-4.30 ▪ Closed Dec 25/26 & Jan 1 ▪ Two self-catering guest cottages ▪ Conservation area ▪ Owner(s) Spookfontein Wines cc (Mike Davis) ▪ Winemaker(s) Craig Sheard (Feb 2006) ▪ Viticulturist(s) Andries Gotze (Jan 2000) ▪ 313ha/±12ha (cabs s/f, merlot, pinot) ▪ 50t/2,000cs own label 100% red ▪ PO Box 12031 Mill Street Cape Town 8010 ▪ craig@spookfontein.co.za ▪ S 34° 21' 19.5" E 019° 17' 20.8" ▪ **T +27 (0)82-265-1071**

Spotswood Wines

Father and son Bill and Nick Spotswood's boutique property on Stellenbosch's Blaauwklippen Road is planted with (amongst others) durif — a rare variety in SA. It and most of the grapes are vinified by Guy Webber at nearby Stellenzicht; the viognier (of which more is being established) is made by Tamboerskloof's Gunter Schultz. Watch for a chardonnay rolling out this year.

Durif ★★★☆ From the variety also known as petite sirah. Very ripe **12**, with dark fruit & meaty aromas. Big & forthright, packed with flavour, but quite juicy, reined-in enough for hearty drinkability. **Dry Rosé** ★★★ Dry? **14** only just, in fact. Some richness, breadth & power behind the pleasant fruitiness. Also tasted: **Shiraz 12** ★★★ **Viognier 14** ★★★ Occasional release: **Shiraz Reserve**. — TJ

Location/map/WO: Stellenbosch ▪ Est 2007 ▪ 1stB 2008 ▪ Tasting & sales by appt ▪ Owner(s) Spotswood family ▪ Winemaker(s) Guy Webber (Jan 2012, consultant) & Gunther Schultz (consultant) ▪ Viticulturist(s) Bill Spotswood (Sep 2007) ▪ 7.05ha/3ha (durif, shiraz, chard, viog) ▪ 28t/3,000cs own label 72% red 6% white 22% rosé ▪ Suite 200 Private Bag X4 Die Boord 7613 ▪ nick@limpro.co.za ▪ S 33° 59' 2.0" E 018° 51' 35.0" ▪ F +27 (0)21-880-2893 ▪ **T +27 (0)21-880-2893**

Springfield Estate

It certainly ain't broke, this highly regarded family estate in Robertson — so why fix it? The news Springfield offers seems as unchanging as the splendid mountain views: perhaps some vines pulled up and others planted, perhaps a bit of new equipment to assist cellarmaster and viticulturist Abrie Bruwer in his work of making 'the hundreds of little choices' that lead to quality. But that's about it. Jeanette, Abrie's sister, meanwhile manages the marketing side of things — but also lends an experienced hand in the rougher side of farming, alongside the estate's 'team of dedicated workers'. And someone must be ready to chase away the occasional Springbok, descendant of a herd introduced many decades ago, escaping into a vineyard to nibble the vines growing in the lime-rich soils.

★★★★☆ **Méthode Ancienne Cabernet Sauvignon** From single vineyard, planted 1979. Whole berries naturally fermented in new oak, adds polish & structure to **08**. Further bottle-maturation buffs tannins & fruit to a suave savoury conclusion. Succulent & ready to enjoy now & for a few years. No **07**.

★★★★ **Whole Berry Cabernet Sauvignon** Gentle winemaking coaxes lovely fruit purity & freshness from old vines in fine **12** vintage. Elegant restraint, more structured than **11** (★★★★), all elements in place, just needs time.

★★★★ **The Work of Time** Powerful, food-styled **08**, Bordeaux blend of cab franc, merlot, cab & petit verdot (31/30/25/14); similar winemaking to Méthode Ancienne. Muscular & brooding, with liquorice mixed in with the savoury tones. No **07**.

★★★★☆ **Méthode Ancienne Chardonnay** Meagre yield made naturally 'in ancient style of Burgundy'. **11** complex layers of flavour, with opulent yeasty brioche tone & pervasive tangy freshness. Mouthfilling presence & long persuasive farewell. One to contemplate & savour. No **10**.

★★★★ **Wild Yeast Chardonnay** ⊘ Flamboyant **12** (★★★★★) surpasses form of **10** (★★★★) & **09**. Unoaked & slow natural ferment with a concentrated burst of pure, rich fruit threaded with tangy lime & burnished orange. Full malolactic fermentation & big alcohol add mouthfilling texture. **11** sold out untasted.

★★★★ **Special Cuvée Sauvignon Blanc** From 23 year old vines in sandy soils - estate's prime sauvignon site; **14** real intensity at pleasingly low 12.4% alcohol. Similar feisty acidity, but richer, better balanced than sibling, from a different clone.

Pinot Noir ⃝ ★★★ Translucent garnet hues on attractive **10** from shy-bearing venerable vines; tealeaf, dried prune & cranberry aromas; light & leanish flavours, piquant farewell. For earlier enjoyment with food. **Life From Stone Sauvignon Blanc** ★★★★ The name says it all; extremely rocky site yields this vibrantly 'wild' version, **14** with flinty herbaceous tone & racy freshness looking for food or year/2 for acid & fruit to fully meld. — MW

Location/map/WO: Robertson ▪ Est/1stB 1995 ▪ Tasting & sales Mon-Fri 8–5 Sat 9–4 ▪ Closed Easter Fri/Sun, Dec 25 & Jan 1 ▪ Cellar tours by appt ▪ BYO picnic ▪ Owner(s) Bruwer family ▪ Cellarmaster(s)/viticulturist(s) Abrie Bruwer ▪ Winemaker(s) Abrie Bruwer, with Johan van Zyl ▪ 150ha (cabs s/f, merlot, p verdot, chard, sauv) ▪ IPW ▪ PO Box 770 Robertson 6705 ▪ admin@springfieldestate.com ▪ www.springfieldestate.com ▪ S 33° 50' 12.1" E 019° 54' 54.0" ▪ F +27 (0)23-626-3664 ▪ **T +27 (0)23-626-3661**

Springfontein Wine Estate

Limestone soils and vineyards lying next to the sea are what attracted the Weber and Schneider families to this unique Stanford site, and prompted a relocation from Germany to live in South Africa. Where Jürgen Schneider reprised his role as chef, at the cellar's restaurant. It quickly became clear

that pinotage and chenin in particular thrive here and the range currently comprises three of the former plus a number of blends where it makes its presence felt, and two differently styled chenins. In the capable hands of ex-Nederburg winemaker Tariro Masayiti, this planned specialisation is bound to run smoothly.

Single Vineyard range

★★★★ Jonathan's Ridge Pinotage Ripe style, pruney fruit, spices from French, American, Hungarian oak. Preview **11** has expected smooth flavourful drinkability, supple tannins, but lacks polish of **10** (★★★★★).

★★★★ Jonathan's Ridge Mendocino Pinotage ⓧ Blueberries & salty liquorice, while the good tannin foundation offsets **10**'s ripeness. Adds restraint & focus without losing the polished varietal succulence.

★★★★ Jil's Dune Chenin Blanc Pre-bottled **13** has some botrytis, natural ferment in barrel, aged 14 months, giving stonefruit & wild honey flavours, a shortbread savoury tone, all refreshed by brisk acidity.

Estate Wines

★★★★ Ikhalezi Noble Late Harvest ⓧ From chenin. Amber-hued **07** (★★★★★) is one of a kind. Astonishingly rich at 372 g/l sugar, it is so refreshed by racy acidity that it drinks beautifully; syrupy, tangy apricot with an added savoury roasted almond tone from new oak. 375 ml. Even better than gorgeous **06** preview.

Ulumbaza Red of Springfontein ⓝ **★★★☆ 11** mix of cab, shiraz, merlot & pinotage shows blackcurrants & blueberries, tobacco & spice, a luscious mouthfeel & drinkability. Good enough to drink solo. **Ulumbaza Pink of Springfontein** ⓝ **★★** Mainly merlot with pinotage; **13** forthcoming red berries, dry, lightish (12.5% alcohol) & easy-drinking. **Ulumbaza White of Springfontein** ⓝ **★★★** Semillon-based with chardonnay & 12% blanc de noir pinotage so that each wine in this range contains pinotage. **13** pear & winter melon flavours, zesty & elegantly structured. Unwooded. Not tasted: **Special Red**.

Terroir Selection

★★★★ Cabernet Sauvignon ⓧ Powerful blueberry/mulberry perfume demands attention, but the underpin is layers of complexity. Provençal herbs, liquorice, cappuccino, **10** (★★★★★) is on another level to **09**, the final seduction a succulent, well-toned body, polished & long.

★★★★ Petit Verdot ⓧ Fynbos & black pepper, hedgerow berries, there's a sense of wildness in **10** which will settle over time, its deep muscle tone promises a long future. Smooth & supple, already appeals.

★★★★ Chenin Blanc Now bottled, complex **12**'s quince almond & thatch gets to the essence of crafted chenin, something very pure here, doubtlessly influenced by natural ferment in barrel. Improves on **11** (★★★★).

Blanc de Pinotage ⓝ **★★★☆** No trace of pink in the colour & berries with unexpected buttered toast flavours from the old barrel ferment. **13** striking new take on blanc de noir, very attractive & altogether more serious. Also tasted: **Pinotage 10 ★★★☆ Chardonnay 12 ★★★ Sauvignon Blanc 13 ★★★☆** Discontinued: **Chardonnay Wild Yeast**.

Limestone Rocks range ⓝ

★★★★ Gadda da Vida Pinotage Natural ferment, aged 16 months new American barrels, **09** is showy, rich black plums, heaps of spice, some vanilla; the 15% alcohol not intrusive. Creamy, flavour-packed drinkability, it's inviting, seductive. — CR

Location: Stanford ▪ Map: Elgin, Walker Bay & Bot River ▪ WO: Walker Bay ▪ Est 1996 ▪ 1stB 2004 ▪ Tasting, sales & cellar tours Mon-Fri 8-5 Sat/Sun 9-4 ▪ Closed Dec 25 & Jan 1 ▪ Springfontein Eats Restaurant ▪ Tour groups ▪ Farm produce ▪ BYO picnic ▪ Walking/hiking trail ▪ Springfontein Guest House ▪ Owner(s) Johst & Jennifer Packard Weber,

Jürgen & Susanne Schneider, with family & friends ▪ Cellarmaster(s) Tariro Masayiti (Jan 2013) ▪ Winemaker(s) Tariro Masayiti (Jan 2013), with Luzaan du Pisanie (Jun 2014) ▪ Viticulturist(s) Hildegard Witbooi (Oct 2013), with Vusumzi Rigala (Jul 2014) ▪ 500ha/25ha (cab, p verdot, ptage, chard, chenin) ▪ 145t/20,000cs own label 76% red 22% white 2% rosé ▪ PO Box 71 Stanford 7210 ▪ info@springfontein.co.za ▪ www.springfontein.co.za ▪ S 34° 25' 38.5" E 019° 24' 32.7" ▪ F +27 (0)28-341-0112 ▪ **T +27 (0)28-341-0651/+27 (0)72-371-7546**

Spring Grove Wines

Banhoek's Spring Grove, originally part of the Zorgvliet property, was purchased by David Parodi and family ten years ago. After uprooting the vineyards, their Italian heritage encouraged them to include sangiovese and pinot grigio in the replant. The wines are made at Zorgvliet by Bernard le Roux.

★★★★ **Sangiovese** ⊘ Preview **13** fragrant & appealing; like last-tasted **10** (★★★★), fruit almost leaps from glass except it's varietally correct sour cherries, not berries, tailored & toned in older oak to lengthy dry conclusion.

★★★★ **Sauvignon Blanc** ⓧ **10** still selling, few years back oozed gooseberry, melon & citrus; good fruit/acid balance & lingering mineral conclusion. Stellenbosch WO.

Pinot Grigio ★★☆ **14** preview has nutty, sweet nectarine & tangerine appeal; tad broad for grigio, needs more zing. Not retasted: **Shiraz 09** ★★★★ Not tasted: **Viognier**. — CvZ

Location/map: Stellenbosch ▪ WO: Banghoek/Stellenbosch ▪ 1stB 2005 ▪ Tasting & sales by appt ▪ Owner(s) Parodi family ▪ Winemaker(s) Bernard le Roux (Dec 2013) ▪ Viticulturist(s) Hannes Jansen van Vuuren (Mar 2008) ▪ 10ha/6. 4ha (sangio, shiraz, pinot gris, sauv, viog) ▪ 41t/25,200L bulk ▪ PO Box 670 Vereeniging 1930 ▪ hannes@zorgvliet.com ▪ S 33° 54' 46.50" E 018° 56' 13.6" ▪ F +27 (0)86-697-3938 ▪ **T +27 (0)82-856-8717**

☐ **Spring Valley** see Old Vines Cellars
☐ **Spruitdrift** see Namaqua Wines
☐ **Stablemate** see Excelsior Estate

Stanford Hills Winery

It's a life less ordinary for Peter and Jami Kastner on their property near Walker Bay, producing indigenous flowers for export, roses for the local market, olives and wine. The tasting room affords a view of the unspoilt surrounds and the comestibles on offer are delicious (the pork pie particularly good).

★★★★ **Chardonnay** ⓧ **12** (★★★★) overtly oxidative, yeasty & bready notes to go with ripe citrus. **11** was fresher.

Jacksons Pinotage ★★★☆ Hint of mocha but mostly sweet red cherry fruit on **13**; smooth, slightly viscous, with hint of aniseed. **Veldfire Shiraz** (NEW) ★★★ More approachable (& pocket friendly) than sibling, **12**'s dark fruit is slightly dominated by smoky, almost charry wood notes. Also tasted: **Veldfire Pinotage 13** ★★★ **Shiraz 13** ★★☆ **Sauvignon Blanc 14** ★★★ — JG

Location: Stanford ▪ Map: Elgin, Walker Bay & Bot River ▪ WO: Walker Bay ▪ Est 1856 ▪ 1stB 2002 ▪ Tasting & sales & restaurant Thu-Mon/pub hols 9-5 Tue/Wed by appt only ▪ Grappa, olive oil, preserves ▪ Restaurant (exec chef Bridget Bartelman): breakfast & lunch, chalkboard menu changes daily ▪ Functions & events (up to 100 pax) ▪ Hiking/mountain biking trails ▪ Horse riding ▪ Fishing ▪ Whale watching flights from own airfield ▪ 5 self-catering cottages & main farmhouse (sleeps up to 32 pax) ▪ Owner(s) Stanford Hills Estate (Pty) Ltd ▪ Cellarmaster(s)/winemaker(s) Peter Kastner (Apr 2005) ▪ Viticulturist(s) Peter Kastner ▪ 131ha/12ha (ptage, shiraz, chard, sauv) ▪ 60t/4,000cs own label 66% red 34% white ▪ PO Box 1052 Stanford 7210 ▪ info@stanfordhills.co.za ▪ www.stanfordhills.co.za ▪ S 34° 25' 21. 4" E 019° 28' 25.7" ▪ F +27 (0)28-341-0286 ▪ **T +27 (0)28-341-0841**

Star Hill

Financial services practitioners Grant Hatch and Christopher Palmer Tomkinson contract Arendsig winegrower Lourens van der Westhuizen to help them realise the viticultural potential of their quartzite-rich fruit and vine farm on a high Langeberg Mountain plateau. Some wines appear under the rare Tradouw Highlands Wine of Origin seal; all are worth seeking out.

★★★★ Shiraz Single-vineyard **11** is meaty, peppery, shows scrub nuances, the fruit a dark-toned underpin. Tannin grip adds definition, ensures longevity.

★★★★ Fountainhead Cab-led 4-part Bordeaux-style blend, **12** shows intense cassis & cedar. There's enough plush fruit to cloak the tannins without losing the backbone grip that promises a future. WO W Cape.

Chenin Blanc ★★★☆ Older-barrel-fermented **12** quince preserve & almonds, enough backing freshness to balance the textural richness, finishes smooth & long. Oak well judged. Montagu grapes. Also tasted: **Viognier 12 ★★★★** Not tasted: **Sauvignon Blanc**. — CR

Location: Montagu ▪ Map: Klein Karoo & Garden Route ▪ WO: Tradouw Highlands/Montagu/Western Cape ▪ Est 2005 ▪ 1stB 2009 ▪ Tasting & sales daily 9-3 ▪ Closed Dec 25 ▪ Cellar tours by appt ▪ Akkerboom farm stall & restaurant ▪ Facilities for children ▪ Gifts ▪ Farm produce ▪ Conference facilities on Killarney farm ▪ Walks/hikes ▪ Mountain biking ▪ Akkerboom self-catering cottages (www.akkerboomcountrycottages.com) ▪ Owner(s) Grant Hatch & Christopher Palmer Tomkinson ▪ Winemaker(s)/viticulturist(s) Lourens van der Westhuizen (consultant) ▪ 15ha (shiraz, chenin, sauv, viog) ▪ 1,000cs own label 40% red 60% white ▪ PO Box 342 Montagu 6720 ▪ starhill@tradouw.co.za ▪ www.starhillwines.com ▪ S 33° 54' 46.86" E 020° 29' 32.31" ▪ F +27 (0)28-572-1644 ▪ **T +27 (0)28-572-1610**

Stark-Condé Wines

This family business started when yachtsman and global traveller Hans-Peter Schröder, after living two decades in Tokyo, in the late 1980s returned to SA with a Japanese wife and family, and decided to put down roots, buying venerable Oude Nektar wine farm and nursery in Jonkershoek, Stellenbosch. Enter son-in-law, Kansas City-born José Conde, a designer quick to learn the craft of fine wine, scoring five stars in this guide with his maiden '98 Cabernet. José has since handcrafted a succession of remarkable wines, especially cabernet, shiraz and, latterly, pinot noir. Wife Marie (also the 'M' in MAN Family Wines) has placed her own stamp of excellence on the popular and trendy Postcard Café. Authentic Japanese touches alone make this a must-visit, let alone the mountain vistas, extraordinary even by Cape standards, and rendered, stylishly of course, in José's label designs.

Three Pines range

★★★★★ Cabernet Sauvignon Superlative **12** from best cab block on Jonkershoek home-farm mountain slopes. More fruit depth & intensity than house's other cab, sheathed power in firm fruit & oak (70% new 22 months) tannin structure. Ageworthy. With small additions of merlot & petit verdot.

★★★★☆ Syrah From elevated single vineyard on Oude Nektar estate, **12** (**★★★★**) less overt fruit & elegant balance in youth than acclaimed **11** (**★★★★★**) or fine **10**. Slow evolving, bound up in firm dry tannin structure. From a quality lineage, however, can be cellared with confidence.

Stark-Condé range

★★★★ Cabernet Sauvignon Standout **12** (**★★★★☆**) from 4 own-farm blocks (but WO Stellenbosch), with splashes petit verdot, cab franc, merlot & 1st-time malbec. Fruit intensity & freshness, authoritative tannin stamp & serious but integrated oak. Poised & cellarworthy step up on **11**.

★★★★ Syrah **12** more compact & restrained than spicy & accessible predecessor but with good depth of fruit from 2 vineyard sites, tannins in streamlined formation. Future pleasure in store. Own vines (certified as WO Stellenbosch).

★★★★ The Field Blend **13** (**★★★**) aromatic own-vineyard blend roussanne, chenin, viognier & verdelho. Really creamy mouthfeel, from 40% natural ferment in mostly older oak, lacks zing of **12** but retains intrinsic interest, appeal.

Occasional release: **Oude Nektar**.

Postcard Series

★★★★ Rowey Vineyards Pinot Noir Alluring perfume of red fruit & cedar on **13** (**★★★★☆**) from Elgin. Shows some fruit richness but also a firm structure of oak (30% new) & gatekeeper tannins needing to let down their guard. Shade off **12**.

★★★★☆ **Round Mountain Pinot Noir** Striking **13**, white pepper perfumes & flavours from organically farmed Overberg vineyard. Lovely fruit purity & intensity, silkily presented. So balanced & svelte, already tempts, but with life for good few years.

Pinot Noir ★★★★ Fine core of smoky cherry fruit & bright acidity, but youthful **13** still tight & firm mid-2004, with chalky tannins. Give time to settle, harmonise. WO Elgin. Also tasted: **Chenin Blanc 13** ★★★★ **Sauvignon Blanc 13** ★★★ Note: range was 'Pepin Condé'. — MW

Location/map: Stellenbosch ▪ WO: Jonkershoek Valley/Stellenbosch/Elgin/Overberg ▪ Est/1stB 1998 ▪ Tasting & sales Mon-Sun 10–4 ▪ Fee R30pp ▪ Closed Good Fri, Dec 25 & Jan 1 ▪ Postcard Café Tue-Sun 9.30-4 ▪ Owner(s) Jonkershoek Cellars (Pty) Ltd ▪ Cellarmaster(s) José Conde (1998) ▪ Winemaker(s) José Conde (1998), with Elizma van Wyngaard (2012) ▪ Viticulturist(s) Andrew Klinck, with Kevin Watt ▪ 250ha/40ha (cabs s/f, merlot, p verdot, shiraz) ▪ 150t/ 12,000cs own label 80% red 20% white ▪ PO Box 389 Stellenbosch 7599 ▪ info@stark-conde.co.za ▪ www.stark-conde.co.za, www.postcardcafe.co.za ▪ S 33° 57' 13.83" E 018° 54' 37.59" ▪ F +27 (0)21-887-4340 ▪ **T +27 (0)21-861-7700/+27 (0)21-887-3665**

☐ **Starlette** *see* Allée Bleue Wines
☐ **Star Tree** *see* Orange River Wine Cellars

Steenberg Vineyards

Much more than a wine farm, this is a destination and lifestyle centre, with a premium housing estate around an 18-hole championship golf course, hotel and spa, two top-rated restaurants, and of course, a winery and upmarket tasting room. With an understanding of the prevailing weather conditions and soil, the main focus has been on sauvignon and semillon, varietally and in blends, to local and international acclaim. With room for some classic reds plus nebbiolo, one of few local bottlings. It has a history that preceded Groot Constantia's granting of land, and after various corporate ownerships culminating in Graham Beck in 2005, this is now a well-oiled operation, led by MD and ex-cellar-master John Loubser. Always looking forward, plans have included replanting of the original sauvignon and semillon vineyards to get even greater quality and terroir matching, and using the facilities to explore wine-and-food matching.

Icon range

★★★★☆ **Magna Carta** Sauvignon's pristine flinty herbaceous fruit, layered with 40% semillon's richness, combine perfectly with steely acidity & stony minerality of very fine **12**. Like **11**, eminently drinkable on release but rewards ageing. Semillon barrel fermented (45% new); blend 9 months in older oak.

Ultra Premium range

★★★★☆ **Nebbiolo** Perfect foil after a few steely sauvignons! Deceptively pale **12** blossoms to show bright & savoury sour cherry features amongst the suave smoky depth of flavour, all given definition by firm tannin & acidity associated with the variety. Only seasoned casks. Fabulous with food.

★★★★ **Catharina** Selection of best of vintage; perfumed eucalyptus in powerful yet graceful blend. **12** shows deft touch - merlot fruit lifted by 35% cab (plus splash shiraz). 80% new oak well integrated.

★★★★ **The Black Swan Sauvignon Blanc** Successor to fabled 'Reserve' & includes low yields of old Block 28, giving spine & heft to grassy fruit ex younger vines; **13** cool-climate style filled out by 10% semillon. Now unoaked.

★★★★☆ **Semillon** ⓦ **12** (★★★★) shows the texture of barreled semillon, but not as rich, complex & weighty as **11**; usual minerality & savoury acidity keep the focus though.

★★★★ **1682 Pinot Noir MCC** Fragrant, beautifully textured dry rosé bubbly. **11** yeasty (on lees 3 years) but firm, bright & assertive. Less sumptuous than **10** (★★★★★). Widely sourced grapes.

Occasional release: **Sauvignon Blanc-Semillon**.

For more information, visit wineonaplatter.com

Super Premium range

★★★★ **Merlot** ⓐ Unequivocal **11** (★★★☆) brims with trademark minty character that permeates its medium structure; more overt & less refined than **10**, will still be loved by many.

★★★★ **Shiraz** Alluring **12** elegant & expressive, with plenty of meat spice & earthiness in its smooth texture. Medium-weight, there's no threat of taste fatigue.

★★★★ **1682 Chardonnay MCC** Blanc de blancs sparkler in fresh, crisp, lighter style. **13**'s citrus zing tempered a year on lees; gets breadth from 10% oak-aged reserve wine. A super aperitif. WO W Cape.

Sauvignon Blanc ★★★☆ Sauvignon's fresh minerality with gravitas derived from lees-ageing & oak-fermented 12% semillon component; **14** steely & stylish. **Sparkling Sauvignon Blanc** ⓝⓔⓦ ★★★ Funky fizz in orange finery; **NV** tastes of, well, bubbly sauvignon! Bottle fermentation too brief to qualify as MCC, or to mask grassy fruit. Also tasted: **HMS Echo Red Blend 12 ★★★☆ HMS Sphynx Chardonnay 14 ★★★☆ HMS Rattlesnake Sauvignon Blanc 13 ★★★☆**

Klein Steenberg range

Sauvignon Blanc ★★ Light **14** with a dash of semillon & a splash of fruity colombard. This range WO Western Cape. Also tasted: **Cabernet Sauvignon 12 ★★☆ Cabernet Sauvignon-Merlot-Cabernet Franc 12 ★★★ Rosé 14 ★★** — DS

Location: Constantia ▪ Map: Cape Peninsula ▪ WO: Constantia/Western Cape/Coastal ▪ Est 1990 ▪ 1stB 1996 ▪ Tasting & sales Mon-Sun 10–6 ▪ Tasting fees: R20pp, R40pp for flagship range, waived on purchase ▪ Closed Good Fri & Dec 25 ▪ Cellar tours 11 & 3 daily ▪ Bistro Sixteen82; Catharina's at Steenberg ▪ Steenberg Hotel & Spa; conferences; world-class golf course, walking trail ▪ Extensive merchandising area ▪ Annual festivals: Constantia Fresh (Feb), Constantia Food and Wine (Apr) ▪ Conservation area ▪ Owner(s) Graham Beck Enterprises ▪ Cellarmaster(s) JD Pretorius (Mar 2009) ▪ 60ha (cab, merlot, nebbiolo, shiraz, sauv, sem) ▪ 312t/70,000cs own label 40% red 60% white ▪ WIETA ▪ PO Box 224 Steenberg 7947 ▪ info@steenbergfarm.com ▪ www.steenbergfarm.com ▪ S 34° 4' 17.0" E 018° 25' 31.1" ▪ F +27 (0)21-713-2201 ▪ **T +27 (0)21-713-2211**

☐ **Steenbok** *see* Riebeek Cellars
☐ **Steenhuis** *see* Wine-of-the-Month Club
☐ **Steenrust** *see* Stellenrust
☐ **STELL** *see* Stellenrust

Stellar Winery   ⓛ

It started in 2002 as a Vredendal winery, with tanks 'beneath the stars', vinifying some 1,000 tons of grapes to internationally recognised organic principles but struggling to find markets for its ambitiously big-production Stellar Organics brand. Today, two fully operational cellars (the other at Trawal) handle nearly 12,000 tons from over 200 ha for a global market absorbing 2.5-million bottles a year, making it the world's largest producer of no-sulphur-added wines. Now Fairtrade accredited (workers own nearly 30% of the business), Stellar continues to expand its already varied varietal, price and style offering.

River's End range ⓝⓔⓦ

Pinot Noir ★★★ Lightly oaked **13** from Koekenaap joins new wave of budget-priced pinot bottlings in SA. Faint cherry & scrub attractions, soft tannins, not complex but will be welcomed by pinotphiles.

Sensory Collection

Chardonnay ⓝⓔⓦ ⓢ ★★ Wax & spearmint nuances on **13**, oak-aged (French, year); slippery lanolin palate, few grams sugar smooth & plump the tail. WO Koekenaap.

Stellar Organic Reserve range

Cabernet Sauvignon-Pinotage ⓢ ★★★ Lightly oaked 70/30 combo takes step up in **12**, delivers spicy complexity, balanced juicy enjoyment plus sufficient grip for food. Also tasted: **Sauvignon Blanc-Semillon** ⓢ **14 ★★★** Not retasted: **Pinot Noir 11 ★★**

Stellar Organics range

Chardonnay ⊘ ★★★ Gently oaked **14** is a lemon-toned, buttery crowd pleaser with pleasant sweet-fruit finish, zippy acidity. **Chenin Blanc-Sauvignon Blanc** ⊘ ★★ Mostly chenin **14**, faintly peachy summer quaffer. **Chardonnay-Pinot Noir Sparkling** (NEW) ★★★ Partridge-eye hue, ripe strawberry flavour on lively **13** bubbles. For celebrations - & soft cheeses. Also tasted: **Sauvignon Blanc** ⊘ **14** ★★★ **Sparkling Extra Dry** ⊘ **13** ★★★ Not retasted: **Cabernet Sauvignon 13** ★★★ **Merlot 13** ★★ **Pinotage 13** ★★★ **Shiraz 13** ★★★ **Rosé 13** ★★ Not tasted: **Chenin Blanc**.

Stellar Organics No-Sulphur-Added

Cabernet Sauvignon ⊘ ★★★ Slight malty top notes on unoaked **14**'s juicy black berries not a distraction; satisfying grip & length. **Rosé** ⊘ ★★ Strawberry & cream infused dry **14** for uncomplicated summer fun. Also tasted: **Pinotage** ⊘ **14** ★★ Not retasted: **Merlot 13** ★★ **Shiraz 13** ★★ Not tasted: **White**.

Live-A-Little range

Slightly Sweet & Sassy Sparkling (NEW) ★★ Frothy, light & pink **NV** with strawberry & musk notes. A breakfast bubbly - try with bacon & French toast, say the team. **Somewhat Sweet & Soulful** (NEW) ★★★ Sweetish **NV** red has enough grip, personality to enjoy solo or with the BBQ. Also tasted: **Wildly Wicked White** ⊘ NV ★★ **Slightly Sweet & Shameless** ⊘ NV ★★★ Not retasted: **Really Ravishing Red NV** ★★★ **Rather Revealing Rosé NV** ★★

Heaven on Earth range

★★★★ **Natural Sweet** ⊘ ⊘ Delicious & stylish dessert from air-dried muscat d'Alexandrie, unwooded (unlike previous). Muscat, citrus zest complexity, satin texture seamed with lime acidity in latest **NV** bottling. — CvZ

Location: Vredendal ▪ Map: Olifants River ▪ WO: Western Cape/Koekenaap ▪ Est 2000 ▪ 1stB 2001 ▪ Tasting & sales Mon-Fri 8–5 ▪ Closed all pub hols ▪ Cellar tours by appt ▪ Owner(s) Rossouw family, Stellar Empowerment Trust & others ▪ Cellarmaster(s) Berty Jones (Oct 2008) ▪ Winemaker(s) Klaas Coetzee (Aug 2010) & Mauritius Naude ▪ Viticulturist(s) Klaas Coetzee ▪ ±68ha/Stellar Farming & ±149ha/Independent organic producers (cab, merlot, ptage, ruby cab, shiraz, chenin, chard, muscat d'A, sauv) ▪ 11,900t ▪ Other export brands: African Star, Firefly, Ithemba, Moonlight Organics, Natural Star, Running Duck, Sunshine ▪ PO Box 4 Klawer 8145 ▪ info@stellarorganics.com ▪ www.stellarorganics.com ▪ S 31° 42' 24.70" E 018° 33' 33.70" ▪ F +27 (0)86-635-1968 ▪ **T +27 (0)82-317-6494**

Stellekaya Winery

Situated at trendy Bosman's Crossing in Stellenbosch, where neighbours include Dalla Cia, High Road and Vilafonté, Stellekaya ('House of Stars') produces only two whites, otherwise the focus is on red, with a range of single varieties as well as blends. From KwaZulu-Natal, winemaker Ntsiki Biyela believes in hands-on experience, which has included a vintage in Tuscany to better understand sangiovese, main component of the Hercules blend, and a crush in Bordeaux, where she had the distinction of creating her own wine at Chateau d'Arsac as part of the Winemakers' Collection project.

Fusion Collection

★★★★ **Orion** ⊘ Flagship cab-led Bordeaux blend. Heaps of concentration in **08**, intense blackcurrants & cigarbox, yet the palate remains juicy, streamlined, with supple tannins.

Aquarius ⊘ ★★★★ Bordeaux blend equal cab, merlot, cab franc in youthful but focused **13**; classic graphite & cassis notes, plump plum core; pleasantly firm for food pairing or ageing few years. Also tasted: **Cape Cross 09** ★★★★ Not retasted: **Hercules 09** ★★★★

Premium Eclipse Collection

★★★★ **Cabernet Sauvignon** ⊘ With dash cab franc & half the oak barrels new, **09** improves on **08** (★★★☆), showing depths of mellow dark berries & cigarbox, crafted oaking. Expect a long future.

★★★★ **Merlot** Such power in the berry, Mint Crisp flavours, one almost forgets how well made **08** is. Oak is in careful support, mainly older barrels, to retain the supple sleekness, fruit focus.

★★★★ **Shiraz** Piquant red berries & cedar are **09**'s main focus, its youth apparent in the fruit's succulence. Tailored tannins give it a built-in future but it already drinks beautifully.

Pinot Grigio (NEW) ★★★ From Elgin, lees-aged 2 months to add weight & texture to cool-climate zip; **14** dry, with appealing floral & ginger spice. Also tasted: **Pinotage** ⊘ 11 ★★★★ Not tasted: **Pinot Noir**.

Boschetto range

White ★★★ Mouthwatering zestiness on **14** chenin gives way to exuberant pineapple, apple & pear. Delicious solo or with summer salads. Also tasted: **Red** ⊘ 11 ★★★★ — GM

Location/map: Stellenbosch ▪ WO: Stellenbosch/Western Cape/Elgin ▪ Est 1998 ▪1stB 1999 ▪ Tasting, sales & cellar tours Mon-Fri 10–4 ▪ Closed all pub hols & Dec 16 to 3rd week of Jan ▪ Private luncheon & wine tasting with winemaker by arrangement (min 6 pax) ▪ Vineyard tours for groups of 10+ with tasting, cheese & biscuits - booking essential ▪ Owner(s) Dave & Jane Lello ▪ Winemaker(s) Ntsiki Biyela (Feb 2004) ▪ Viticulturist(s) Paul Wallace (Jan 2005, consultant) ▪ 23ha/15ha under vine ▪ 12,000cs own label ▪ Brands for clients: The Grand Beach Café ▪ IPW ▪ PO Box 12426 Die Boord Stellenbosch 7613 ▪ info@stellekaya.co.za ▪ www.stellekaya.co.za ▪ S 33° 56' 27.6" E 018° 50' 47.3" ▪ F +27 (0)21-883-2536 ▪ **T +27 (0)21-883-3873**

Stellenbosch Family Wines

Believing that 'good wine is a constant reminder that God loves us and loves to see us happy', the De Vries, Van Wyk and Truter families of Stellenbosch have created an own wine brand, proceeds contributing to selected faith-based projects. 'Family' it certainly is: shareholders Michelle-Lize van Wyk and Christel Truter design the front labels and handle the marketing (respectively); grapes and cellar space are sourced from Koelenhof Winery, and that sterling cellar's winemaker/GM, Andrew de Vries, assists, but the actual vinification is by his son Carlo – aged 10!

Cabernet Sauvignon ★★★ **13** vivid red berries, juicy & vibrant, on a foundation of amenable tannins, ending dry, food friendly. **Merlot** ★★★ Spiced plums lead you in to softly rounded, juicy drinkability; **13** has just enough tannin grip to handle food. **Pinot Noir** ★★ Raspberries & sweet spice, a nuance of mixed herbs & light texture; **13**'s tannic grip still youthful, needing year or 2 to soften, meld. **Family Blend** ★★ Merlot/cab show their compatibility in the plummy/berry character; gentle spice & structured by oak staves in **13**. **CMP Legacy Red** ★★ **13** mainly cab with merlot & pinot noir. Red berries & gentle savoury spice, a slight herbaceous note, but the palate is accessible, drinks easily. **Chardonnay** ★★★ Peach & pineapple attraction in **13**; fresh & lightly oaked to give gentle flavour, allow the fruit to take the lead. — CR, CvZ

Location/map/WO: Stellenbosch ▪ Est/1stB 2013 ▪ Tasting by appt ▪ Fee R20/6 wines ▪ Sales Mon-Sat 8-6 by appt ▪ Owner(s) Renata de Vries, Michelle-Lize van Wyk & Christel Truter ▪ Winemaker(s) Carlo de Vries, with Andrew de Vries (both Jan 2013, consultants) ▪ 2,900cs own label 90% red 10% white ▪ c/o PO Box 1 Koelenhof 7605 ▪ koelwyn@icloud.com ▪ www.stellenboschfamilywines.co.za ▪ S 33° 50' 5.2" E 018° 47' 52.7" ▪ **T +27 (0)82-835-7107**

Stellenbosch Hills Wines

The winery in Stellenbosch's Vlottenburg area recently welcomed a new grape-supplying member, a not only rare but also remarkable occurrence in that Erik Phinallephe rose from labourer to managing partner of the farm where he'd worked 18 years. Also noteworthy here are biltong-and-wine pairings, an art gallery in a refurbished wine tank, and one of the Cape''s very few varietal bottlings of muscat de Hambourg.

1707 Reserve range

★★★★ **Red** Seriously vinified (100% new oak) & impressive blend shiraz & Bordeaux grapes in **10**. Generous & spicy, with complex layers of fruit in better balance with wood than last **08** (★★★☆). Not retasted: **White 12** ★★★★

Stellenbosch Hills Cultivar Collection

★★★★ **Muscat de Hambourg** 12 (★★★) engagingly sweet & grapey but misses depth & complexity of **10**, which took the jerepiko-style desert to a new level. No **11**.

Pinotage ★★★ Smoky, mocha-toned **12** for easy everyday drinking. **Chenin Blanc** ★★★ Charmingly versatile, flavourful **14** sufficiently light & crisp for easy sipping, but serious enough as food partner. **Sauvignon Blanc** ★★★ Pleasingly fresh & harmonious **14** has decent palate weight & plenty of flavour. Also tasted: **Merlot 11** ★★☆ **Shiraz 11** ★★☆ Not retasted: **Cabernet Sauvignon 11** ★★★

Polkadraai range

Pinotage-Merlot ★★☆ Mocha-laced **13** in popular, easy-quaffing blend. Polkadraai Hills WO, as all this range. **Pinot Noir Rosé Sparkling** ★★★ Light, sweet **14** sparkler, raspberry pink, fresh & very fruity. Also tasted: **Polka Sauvignon Blanc 14** ★☆ **Chenin Blanc-Sauvignon Blanc 14** ★★☆ Not retasted: **Polka Merlot-Shiraz 12** ★★ — IM

Location/map: Stellenbosch ▪ WO: Stellenbosch/Polkadraai Hills ▪ Est 1945 ▪ 1stB 1972 ▪ Tasting & sales Mon-Fri 9–5 Sat 10–3 ▪ Fee R15; R40 wine, biltong & droëwors tasting ▪ Closed Sun & all pub hols ▪ The Tank art gallery ▪ Owner(s) 16 members ▪ Cellarmaster(s) PG Slabbert (Jan 1997) ▪ Winemaker(s) Juan Slabbert (Jan 2009) ▪ Viticulturist(s) Johan Pienaar & Eben Archer (consultants) ▪ 715ha (cab, merlot, ptage, shiraz, chard, chenin, Muscat de Hambourg, sauv) ▪ 8,000t/20,000cs own label 68% red 30% white 2% other ▪ IPW ▪ PO Box 40 Vlottenburg 7604 ▪ info@ stellenbosch-hills.co.za ▪ www.stellenbosch-hills.co.za ▪ S 33° 57′ 38.2″ E 018° 48′ 1.8″ ▪ F +27 (0)21-881-3357 ▪ **T +27 (0)21-881-3828**

Stellenbosch Reserve

Previously 'Stellenbosch Ridge', this sophisticated blend (soon to be joined by a chardonnay, merlot and cab) is Rust en Vrede proprietor Jean Engelbrecht's homage to Stellenbosch, 'a unique town [and] birthplace and home to many of South Africa's greatest leaders, intellectuals, artists, scientists, sportsmen and winemakers'.

★★★★☆ **Stellenbosch Reserve** Restraint & gentility mark polished **12** 4-way Bordeaux blend. Cab reined in to 42% (63% previously), with merlot doubled to 33%. Rich cocoa tang to abundant yet serious black fruit, balanced by 18 months French oak. Taut & chiselled, it deserves time. — FM

Location/map/WO: Stellenbosch ▪ Est 2004 ▪ 1stB 2005 ▪ Tasting & sales at Guardian Peak (see entry) ▪ Owner(s) Jean Engelbrecht ▪ Winemaker(s) Coenie Snyman (Jan 2005) ▪ Viticulturist(s) Dirkie Mouton (Jan 2010) ▪ 14t/3,000cs own label 70% red 30% white ▪ IPW ▪ PO Box 473 Stellenbosch 7599 ▪ info@thestellenboschreserve.com ▪ www. thestellenboschreserve.com ▪ S 34°0′ 40.19″ E 018° 50′ 31.99″ ▪ F +27 (0)21-881-3000 ▪ **T +27 (0)21-881-3881**

Stellenbosch University Welgevallen Cellar

In the premises where Abraham Perold crossed pinot noir and hermitage (cinsaut) to create pinotage in the 1920s, Stellenbosch University oenology students today still learn their winecraft. Respect for tradition is an important part of this, the commercial label, as is value for money.

Die Laan range

Cape Blend Ⓐ ★★★★ Well-constructed, ripe **10** from cab & pinotage with splash petit verdot is appetisingly fresh & savoury. Not tasted: **Pinotage, Rosé, Chardonnay, Sauvignon Blanc, Viognier**. Occasional release: **Rector's Reserve**.

Maties range

Not tasted: **Rooiplein**. — IM

Location/map/WO: Stellenbosch ▪ Est 2001 ▪ 1stB 2009 ▪ Tasting Mon-Fri 9-4 ▪ Fee R10pp ▪ Closed all pub hols & Dec 15-Jan 10 ▪ Owner(s) Stellenbosch University ▪ Cellarmaster(s)/winemaker(s) Riaan Wassüng (Jan 2004) ▪ Viticulturist(s) Vaatjie Jacobs (Jan 1973) ▪ 11ha/10ha (cab, ptage, shiraz, chard, sauv) ▪ 4,600cs own label 68% red 32% white ▪ Department of Viticulture & Oenology Private Bag X1 Matieland 7602 ▪ winesales@sun.ac.za, rfw@sun.ac.za ▪ http://academic. sun.ac.za/viti_oenol/ ▪ S 33° 56′ 22.38″ E 018° 52′ 1.92″ ▪ **T +27 (0)21-808-2925/+27 (0)83-622-6394**

Stellenbosch Vineyards

Progressive global wine business Stellenbosch Vineyards, marketing big brands in over 60 countries, has its origins in the amalgamation of two stalwart Stellenbosch wineries Welmoed and Helderberg. Based at the former and having sold the latter (to Boekenhoutskloof), Stellenbosch Vineyards was known until 2013 as The Company of Wine People after a merger with Vinfruco in 2004. It subsequently became one of South Africa's top five wine exporters through brands Kumkani (since transferred to a black empowerment partner), Arniston Bay and Versus (both mainly exported). Latest innovations include The Flagship label for top-end, limited-release bottlings, joining established brands Credo, Four Secrets and Welmoed (all separately listed). Also new is the 1690 Wine Club (offering discounts and special tastings), bistro-style eatery and revamped tasting venue.

Stellenbosch Vineyards range

★★★★ **Hayden's Red** ⊘ **11** Bordeaux blend has improved since previewed last time. Smooth & rich with mouthfilling depth, creamy texture & supporting tannins. Similar profile to **10** (★★★★).

Hayden's White ★★★☆ **13** seduces with asparagus, grapefruit & tropical complexity, pebbly conclusion. Mainly sauvignon & 3 others, 40% barrel fermented for extra mouthfeel. Also tasted: **Bushvine Pinotage 12** ★★★☆ Not tasted: **Bushvine Chenin Blanc**. Note: range was listed under Welmoed as 'Heyden's Courage'. — WB

Location/map/WO: Stellenbosch ▪ Est 2004 ▪ Tasting & sales Mon–Fri 9–5.30 Sat 9–5 Sun 10–4 ▪ Fee R20pp ▪ Closed Dec 25 & Jan 1 ▪ Bistro-style restaurant ▪ Facilities for children ▪ Owner(s) 200+ shareholders ▪ Winemaker(s) Abraham de Villiers (Dec 2004) & Bernard Claassen (Feb 2005), with Felicity Seholoba (Jan 1993), Rudolph Steenkamp (2013) & Stefan Niemandt (2013) ▪ Viticulturist(s) Francois de Villiers (1998) ▪ 5,500t ▪ 55% red 35% white 10% rosé ▪ ISO 22000, Fairtrade, IPW, WIETA ▪ PO Box 465 Stellenbosch 7599 ▪ info@stellvine.co.za ▪ www.stellenboschvineyards.co.za ▪ S 33° 59' 26.06" E 018° 46' 2.21" ▪ F +27 (0)21-881-3102 ▪ **T +27 (0)21-881-3870**

Stellendrift - SHZ Cilliers/Kuün Wyne ⓠ

Wine's in Stellenbosch-based Fanie Cilliers' blood — his forebears were French vignerons before they fled to the Cape in 1700; by 1709 they had 8,000 vines under cultivation. Recently production has been scaled down, but Fanie's goal remains 'more mature, softer wines, competitively priced'.

Stellendrift range

Josué Merlot ★★ Tomato leaf, eucalyptus & bacon crackers on savoury **11**; austere dusty palate demands food. **Giant Sauvignon Blanc** ★★★☆ Passionfruit & lime on generously aromatic **14**, with full & juicy palate to match. Fine balance & length for enjoying solo or with summer salads. Not retasted: **Kruispad Pinotage 05** ★★★ **VOC Syrah 09** ★★★★ **Rosa Rosaceae Red Select 06** ★★★ Not tasted: **Reserve Cabernet Sauvignon**, **Merlot-Cabernet Sauvignon Blitz**, **Cape White Savour**. In abeyance: **Cape Huguenot Merlot-Pinotage**.

Cilliers Cellars range

Not retasted: **Jacko's Pinotage-Cabernet Sauvignon 05** ★★ Not tasted: **De Reijgersdaal Cabernet Sauvignon**, **Elizabeth Couvret Merlot**.

De Oude Opstal range

Not retasted: **Merlot-Cabernet Sauvignon 04** ★★★ In abeyance: **Cabernet Sauvignon Reserve**. — HJ

Location/map/WO: Stellenbosch ▪ Est 1995 ▪ 1stB 1996 ▪ Tasting, sales & cellar tours by appt ▪ Owner(s) Fanie Cilliers (SHZ Cilliers/Kuün Wines) ▪ Winemaker(s)/viticulturist(s) Fanie Cilliers (Nov 1995) ▪ 2,200cs own label 90% red 10% white ▪ PO Box 6340 Uniedal 7612 ▪ fcilliers@vodamail.co.za ▪ www.stellendrift.co.za ▪ S 33° 58' 54.92" E 018° 46' 15.91" ▪ F +27 (0)21-887-6561 ▪ **T +27 (0)21-887-6561/+27 (0)82-372-5180**

Stellenrust

Winemaker Tertius Boshoff and viticulturist Kobie van der Westhuizen are the dynamic duo driving Stellenrust. It's one of the Cape's larger family estates — with half of the 500 hectares of vines spread over Stellenbosch's 'Golden Triangle', the other vineyards high on the Bottelary Hills (now with upgraded tasting venue). The home-farm is old, with some pretty venerable vines. Other grape sources are now also on their radar, Tertius expressing excitement about 'projects germinating in Swartland and Elgin, among others'. Continuing critical and commercial success sees certain of their wines flying business/first class with Emirates and Lufthansa, and a second successive chenin trophy in the International Wine & Spirit Competition.

Super Premium range

★★★★☆ **Cabernet Franc** Elegant & convincing as ever, **11** offers fallen-leaf fragrance & under-stated but forceful fruit. Modest, unobtrusive oaking in house style - as is the general restraint. All in balance, with early complexity; slightly austere dry tannins should grow more harmonious with a year or 2.

★★★★ **Old Bushvine Cinsaut** Fresh, bright red fruit on **12**, with a delicately forceful charm. Supple & deceptively easy-drinking - but repays attention beyond the immediate pleasure it gives. Lingering flavours.

★★★★ **Cornerstone Pinotage** Full, ripe berry fragrance & flavours on **12** off old bushvines (**11** sold out untasted). Richer, sweeter-fruited than others here, but well structured, with disciplined tannins. Delicious.

★★★★ **Peppergrinder's Shiraz** As usual, 1952 vines give wild berry note & white pepper, spice aromas in **11**. Less austere in youth than previous, still refined & subtle, though already tasty. Good supportive oaking.

★★★★☆ **Timeless** Blend of cab with merlot & cab franc (the last adding herbal fragrance to the berry fruit). **11** almost ripely showy & rich by Tertius Boshoff's standards, but with his trademark firm structuring, finesse & properly dry finish, plus a tangy vitality. More approachable than **10** (★★★★).

★★★★ **JJ Handmade Picalot** Pinotage gives perfume to interesting ripe, fruit-filled (very tasty) **11** blend with cab & merlot. Firmly built, but the tannins not drying as in less well balanced **10** (★★★★☆). As usual the oak supportive rather than insistent. Should develop a good few years.

★★★★ **Barrel Fermented Chardonnay** Butterscotch & toast on youthful **13**, then concentrated citrus & stonefruit on generous palate, mouthwatering acidity focusing the flavours; green-lime finish. Judicious oaking.

★★★★☆ **49 Barrel Fermented Chenin Blanc** Changing number gives vine age. Natural ferment & time in oak (some new) on **13**. Botrytised portion adds a sweet & honeyed note, but lemony acid brings vitality to the lusciousness. Glamorous, elegant & complex. The endless finish also noted on **12** (★★★★★).

★★★★ **Chenin d'Muscat Noble Late Harvest** (ℚ) Old chenin & muscat vineyards yield a light & vivacious elixir in **09**. Gentle apricot, almond & hint of perfume, subtly oaked.

Premium range

★★★★ **Chenin Blanc** (✓) (⑨) Very worthy junior version of the grander Chenin. Ripe, gently rich **14** (★★★★), with minimal supportive oak, has greenish acidity to enliven it. **13** was particularly radiant.

Shiraz (✓) ★★★★ Charming sweet fruit & spice on silky, fresh & refined **12**, which slips down only too easily. All of these wines have restraint & a dry finish, making them all the more drinkable. Sensitive, modest oaking, as elsewhere in range. Also tasted: **Cabernet Sauvignon** (✓) **12** ★★★★ **Merlot 12** ★★★ **Pinotage** (✓) **13** ★★★★ **Simplicity 13** ★★★ **Chardonnay** (✓) **14** ★★★★ **Sauvignon Blanc** (✓) **14** ★★★★

For more information, visit wineonaplatter.com

Kleine Rust range

Pinotage-Shiraz ★★★ Was 'Red'. Plentiful fruit aromas on **13**, with a sweet edge to its charm, but also a trace of the house's elegance. Fairtrade certified, as all except Semi-Sweet. Also tasted: **Pinotage Rosé 14 ★★★ Chenin Blanc-Sauvignon Blanc 14 ★★★ Semi-Sweet 14 ★★★** — TJ

Location/map/WO: Stellenbosch ▪ Est/1stB 1928 ▪ Tasting & sales (Hberg & Btlry) Mon-Fri 10—5 Sat 10-3 ▪ Closed Ash Wed, Easter Fri-Mon, Ascension Day, Dec 25/26 & Jan 1 ▪ Cellar tours by appt ▪ Farm-style platters & pre-arranged lunches/dinners ▪ BYO picnic ▪ Tour groups ▪ Grape 'stompings' ▪ Gifts ▪ Conferences ▪ Weddings/functions (300+ pax) ▪ Walking/hiking & mountain biking trails ▪ Art exhibition ▪ Owner(s) Stellenrust Family Trust ▪ Cellarmaster(s) Tertius Boshoff (Jan 2004) ▪ Winemaker(s) Tertius Boshoff (Jan 2004), with Christo van Rooyen (Feb 2012) ▪ Viticulturist(s) Kobie van der Westhuizen (Jan 2000) ▪ 500ha (cab, cinsaut, merlot, ptage, shiraz, chard, chenin, muscat d'A, sauv) ▪ 1,700t/ 300,000cs own label 69% red 30% white 1% rosé + 40,000cs for clients ▪ Other export brands: Steenrust, STELL, Steynsrust, Xaro ▪ Brands for clients: Cape Hill, Embrace, Lion's Pride, Ruyter's Bin, Sabi Sabi private game lodge ▪ HACCP 2005, Fairtrade ▪ PO Box 26 Koelenhof 7605 ▪ info@stellenrust.co.za ▪ www.stellenrust.co.za ▪ S 33° 59' 18.0" E 018° 50' 57.9" (Hberg) S 33° 51' 44.41" E 018° 46' 34.11" (Btlry) ▪ F +27 (0)21-880-2284 ▪ **T +27 (0)21-880-2283**

Stellenzicht Vineyards

On the northern slopes of the Helderberg, with (as its name implies) a good view of Stellenbosch town, Stellenzicht benefits from being in the viticulturally auspicious 'Golden Triangle'. International banker and financier Hans-Joachim Schreiber purchased the property in 1981, and some 18 years later joined with the forerunner of Distell to form Lusan Premium Wines, with Stellenzicht among its properties. Winemaker Guy Webber and team have gained a name for pinotage, adding to their recognition as significant producers of shiraz/syrah. A trailer-load of fruit is said to have overturned rather messily near their top shiraz site, hence the colourful name Plum Pudding Hill.

Stellenzicht Specialities range

★★★★ Plum Pudding Hill Syrah ⓥ Was 'Syrah', now named after wine's single-vineyard source, which also produced benchmark **94**. Current **07**, with savoury worn-in leather character & briskly dry finish, ready to enjoy.

Discontinued: **Rhapsody, Sémillon Reserve.**

Golden Triangle range

★★★★ Cabernet Sauvignon 11 big step up after awkward **10** (★★★). Plentiful fresh, crunchy cassis fruit lifted by whiff oak vanilla (74% new barrels, including American). Well-judged tannins but will still benefit from few years' ageing.

★★★★ Pinotage Very ripe & richly textured **12**; generous mulberry fruit enhanced by complementary oaking (30% new), polished tannins. Better balance than **11** (★★★).

Also tasted: **Shiraz 11 ★★★ Sauvignon Blanc 14 ★★☆**

Discontinued: **Cellarmaster's Release range.** — AL

Location/map/WO: Stellenbosch ▪ Est 1982 ▪ 1stB 1989 ▪ Tasting & sales Mon-Fri 9—5 Sat/Sun 10—4 ▪ Fee R25 ▪ Closed Good Fri, Dec 25 & Jan 1 ▪ Cellar tours by appt ▪ BYO picnic ▪ Owner(s) Lusan Premium Wines ▪ Winemaker(s) Guy Webber (Oct 1998), with Nataleé Botha (Aug 2010) ▪ Viticulturist(s) Quintus van Wyk ▪ 228ha/99ha (cabs s/f, malbec, merlot, p verdot, ptage, shiraz, chard, sauv, sem, viog) ▪ 1,000t/40,000cs own label 85% red 15% white + BRC, HACCP, WIETA ▪ PO Box 104 Stellenbosch 7599 ▪ info@stellenzicht.co.za ▪ www.stellenzicht.co.za ▪ S 33° 59' 50. 0" E 018° 51' 59.8" ▪ F +27 (0)21-880-1107 ▪ **T +27 (0)21-880-1103**

Sterhuis

Stellenbosch's Bottelary Hills are home to the Kruger family farm, whose name (literally 'Star House') was given by early colonists because it appears as if Venus rises above it. The boutique winery reflects winemaker Johan's focus on restrained and elegant wines, now including an Elgin pinot noir. Volumes of sparkling, sauvignon, chardonnay and chenin are up, to meet 'dramatic higher demand, locally and abroad', and a reserve bubbly is in the offing.

★★★★ **Cabernet Sauvignon** ⓧ Good varietal character & freshness on **07** tasted a few years back.

★★★★☆ **Chardonnay Barrel Selection** Focused **12** (★★★★★) confirms quality lineage - **11** was also a serious offering. Finely tuned, limy intensity woven into rich & creamy framework from natural ferment in oak (40% new) & 14 months on the lees. Streamlined, will age elegantly.

★★★★ **Chenin Blanc Barrel Selection** Was 'Chenin Blanc'. **13** (no **12** made) more oak & slower evolving than sibling below. Opulent & contemplative, with spiced apple & nutty nuance. Textural, subtle & ageworthy.

★★★★ **Sauvignon Blanc** Vivacious **14**, now unwooded, has lovely fruit focus & silky tone. Mouthfilling, fresh & tangy, with some clean minerality. Great food partner now & for the next few years.

★★★★☆ **Astra White** ⓧ A third each of best barrels chenin, sauvignon & chardonnay. Oak spice & white chocolate lead to toasty, sweet-fruited & vanilla-rich **09**. Bold in flavour & aroma with loads of oak tones needing to meld. Palate cleansed by tart orange peel & fresh lemon/lime zing.

★★★★ **Chenin Blanc** ⊘ Name change from 'Chenin-Viognier' but **13** still has 15% oak-fermented viognier adding perfumed lift to riper profile, with nutty lees substrate. Balanced, more fruit-driven & brighter than serious stablemate, equally satisfying. Raises bar on **12** (★★★☆).

★★★★ **Blanc de Blancs Méthode Cap Classique 10** bubbly from oak-fermented chardonnay has a sumptuous honeycomb texture courtesy 36 months on lees. Infused with clean citrus flavours, extra–dry, but with balancing creaminess, freshness & length.

Elgin Pinot Noir ⑯ ★★★★ **13** from low-yielding vines. Lithe & silky structure, fresh, with perfumed berry, damp earth aromas. Well crafted, shows potential to develop. Also tasted: **Merlot-Cabernet Sauvignon 12** ★★★☆ Not retasted: **Merlot 09** ★★★★ **Unwooded Chardonnay 13** ★★★★ Discontinued: **Astra Red**. — MW

Location/map: Stellenbosch ▪ WO: Bottelary/Stellenbosch/Elgin ▪ Est 1980 ▪ 1stB 2002 ▪ Tasting, sales & cellar tours by appt ▪ Closed Christian hols ▪ Facilities for children ▪ Conservation area ▪ Owner(s) Kruger family ▪ Winemaker(s) Johan Kruger ▪ 100ha/40ha under vine ▪ 300t/12,000cs own label 25% red 75% white ▪ PO Box 131 Koelenhof 7605 ▪ johan@sterhuis.co.za ▪ www.sterhuis.co.za ▪ S 33° 54' 43.1" E 018° 46' 4.2" ▪ F +27 (0)21-906-1195 ▪ **T +27 (0)83-411-0757**

Stettyn Cellar   ⓠ ⓢ ⓞ ⓐ ⓑ

A handful of grape-growing Klein Drakenstein foothill farms — including 18th-century Stettyn, home to eight generations of the Botha family — feed this cellar, given multi-million rand upgrades in recent years after becoming a supplier to, among others, FirstCape, South African 'superbrand' in the UK, and exporting to Germany and China.

Stettyn range

Reserve Straw Wine ⑯ ★★★★ Varietal mix dried on straw, then year small oak. **NV** shows richness & concentration, sultanas, dried peach & pineapple, yet a surprising elegance. Sweet but refreshed by limy acidity. **Reserve Cape Vintage** ⑯ ★★★ From touriga. Cocoa-rich dark chocolate, prunes & savoury meat extract. **08** showing none of its age, the palate is juicy, silky smooth, sweet. Not retasted: **Reserve Shiraz-Cabernet Sauvignon 11** ★★★☆ Note: range was 'Signature Reserve'. WO W Cape for all.

Griffin range

Cabernet Sauvignon ⑯ ★★★ Blackcurrants & cherries, a mint nuance, the oak adding some savoury flavours but no edges. **11** drinks easily. **Merlot** ⑯ ★★★ Herbaceous notes accompany the red berry perfume, but **12**'s palate is welcoming, juicy & fruity-fresh. **Shiraz** ⑯ ★★★ Made for easy drinking, smooth & round, but you get a bonus — the lovely perfume! **13** plums & spice, a note of violets & dried herbs whets the appetite. Also tasted: **Sauvignon Blanc 14** ★★★ Not retasted: **Pinot Grigio 13** ★★★

For more information, visit wineonaplatter.com

Stone range

Red ★★★ Friendly & fruity for fireside fun. Cab with splashes cab franc, souzão, petit verdot & ruby cab in previewed **NV**. Not retasted: **White NV** ★★★ Note: range was 'Millstone'. — CR

Location/map: Worcester ▪ WO: Western Cape/Worcester ▪ Est 1964 ▪ 1stB 1984 ▪ Tasting & sales Mon-Thu 8–5 Fri 8-4.30 Sat (Oct-Mar) 10-1 ▪ Closed all pub hols ▪ Cellar tours from 1.30-4 by appt ▪ BYO picnic ▪ Facilities for children ▪ Vineyard tours R200pp ▪ Owner(s) 4 major producers (3 family owned) ▪ Cellarmaster(s) Albie Treurnicht (Nov 2000) ▪ Winemaker(s) Albie Treurnicht (Nov 2000), with JM Crafford (Nov 2012) ▪ Viticulturist(s) Pierre Snyman (Vinpro) ▪ 400ha (cab, merlot, ptage, shiraz, chard, chenin, sauv) ▪ 7,500t/19,000cs own label 25% red 75% white + 6.1m L bulk ▪ Brands for clients: FirstCape, Felicité, The Griffin Range ▪ ARA, BEE, HACCP, IPW, WIETA ▪ PO Box 1520 Worcester 6849 ▪ info@stettyncellar.co.za ▪ www.stettyncellar.co.za ▪ S 33° 52' 14.8" E 019° 22' 2.3" ▪ F +27 (0)86-771-3568 ▪ **T +27 (0)23-340-4220**

☐ **Steynsrust** see Stellenrust
☐ **Steytler** see Kaapzicht Wine Estate

St Francis Point Vineyards

In 2009 Ian and Jean Fynn established a small sauvignon blanc, semillon and chardonnay vineyard to complement their olive groves and preserved tracts of indigenous forest in the exclusive Eastern Cape coastal enclave of St Francis Bay. Kept busy by their Five Elements eatery, they hope to have a maiden wine available soon.

Location: St Francis Bay ▪ Map: Klein Karoo & Garden Route ▪ Est 2009 ▪ Tasting by appt ▪ Five Elements restaurant: www.five-elements.co.za ▪ Owner(s) Jean Fynn ▪ Viticulturist(s) Ian Fynn (2009) ▪ 3.5ha (chard, sauv, sem) ▪ PO Box 355 St Francis Bay 6312 ▪ jfynn@intekom.co.za ▪ **T +27 (0)42-294-0548**

☐ **Stilfontein** see Eerste Hoop Wine Cellar

Stoep

A label launched as part of Main Street Winery's garagiste portfolio by its owner, renowned for mentoring boutique wine start-ups, Stoep was taken over in 2010 as a stand-alone brand by 'planet-hopping' asset manager Gerrit Mars and two Swiss compatriots. It's now based in the Helderberg, where Romond's André Liebenberg vinifies occasional bottlings.

Location: Somerset West ▪ Est/1stB 2001 ▪ Tasting, sales & tours by appt ▪ Owner(s) Zelpy 1023 (Pty) Ltd: 3 share-holders Gerrit Mars (SA), Sven Haefner (Swiss) & Daniel Hofer (Swiss) ▪ Cellarmaster(s)/winemaker(s) André Liebenberg (Romond) & Gerrit Mars ▪ 50% red 50% white ▪ gerritmars@mweb.co.za ▪ **T +27 (0)82-352-5583**

Stofberg Family Vineyards

This is a family affair, from fiercest supporter oupa PJD (who lived to see the maiden vintage) to little Mia, after whom the first wines are named 'to symbolise new and small beginnings that will grow year by year'. Mom is 3rd-generation winemaker Mariette Coetzee (née Stofberg) while dad Deon and uncle Pieter care for the vineyards. The farm's Ou Stokery (distillery) has been renovated as a cellar, and plans include a family-friendly restaurant.

★★★★ Mia Shiraz Plumply ripe, dark berries & plums, plus spice, charcuterie & scrub on older-oak-matured **12** from Breedekloof grapes. Polished, balanced, with extended length.

Mia Chenin Blanc ★★★ Golden Delicious apples, white peach, focus in **14** is on freshness & elegance, which chenin delivers so well. Food-friendly minerality on the finish. WO W Cape. — CR, CvZ

Location: Rawsonville ▪ Map: Breedekloof ▪ WO: Breedekloof/Western Cape ▪ Est 2011 ▪ 1stB 2012 ▪ Tasting, sales & cellar tours Mon-Fri 7.30-5.30 Sat/Sun by appt only ▪ Closed all pub hols ▪ Owner(s) PJD Stofberg, M Coetzee & GJN Coetzee ▪ Cellarmaster(s)/winemaker(s) Mariëtte Coetzee (Nov 2011) ▪ Viticulturist(s) Pieter Jacobus Daniël Stofberg (Jan 1981), Andries de Wet (Jun 2002, consultant) & Gideon Jacobus Nicolaas Coetzee (Nov 2011) ▪ ±102ha (chenin) ▪ 11t/1,205cs own label 8% red 51% white 41% MCC ▪ PO Box 298 Rawsonville 6845 ▪ mariette@

stofbergfamilyvineyards.co.za ▪ www.stofbergfamilyvineyards.co.za ▪ S 33° 40' 17.24" E 019° 18' 37.27" ▪ F +27 (0)86-770-5138 ▪ **T +27 (0)82-867-6958**

☐ **Stonedale** *see* Rietvallei Wine Estate
☐ **Stonehaven** *see* Cape Point Vineyards

Stonehill

Tucked away in Stellenbosch's Devon Valley is Lorna Hughes' small vineyard, where, with husband Dave (an adviser to this guide), she indulges her passions for wine, rescue dogs and hiking. The wine-making is very hands-on, with interesting variations like her barrel-aged rosé, produced in boutique-scale volumes.

Dry Cabernet Sauvignon Rosé ⊗ ★★★★ Classy, lightly oaked **12** goes where few other rosés do: varietal character & body with real refreshment. Not retasted: **Bristle Red 08** ★★★ **Bristle White 11** ★★★★ — GdB

Location/WO: Stellenbosch ▪ Est 1990 ▪ 1stB 2003 ▪ Closed to public ▪ Owner(s)/vineyard manager(s) Lorna Hughes ▪ Winemaker(s) Mark Carmichael-Green ▪ 4ha/3.2ha (cab, shiraz) ▪ 70% red 30% white ▪ PO Box 612 Stellenbosch 7599 ▪ llhughes@telkomsa.net ▪ F +27 (0)21-865-2740 ▪ **T +27 (0)73-420-3300**

Stone Ridge Wines   ⓠ

The Eksteen family have been growing wine grapes on their 300-ha Voor Paardeberg property for 6 generations. Viticulturist Jan Eksteen keeps back parcels of prime red and white grapes to craft just 2,400 cases for the family label with advisers Bernard Smuts and JD Rossouw.

Location: Paarl ▪ Map: Paarl & Wellington ▪ Est 2002 ▪ 1stB 2003 ▪ Tasting by appt only ▪ Winemaker(s) Bernard Smuts & JD Rossouw (both consultants) ▪ Viticulturist(s) Jan Eksteen (2002) ▪ 300ha (cab, ptage, shiraz, chard, chenin, sauv) ▪ 20t/2,400cs own label 50% red 50% white ▪ PO Box 7046 Northern Paarl 7623 ▪ stoneridge@uitkijk.co.za ▪ S 33° 34' 19.72" E 018° 52' 45.48" ▪ F +27 (0)21-869-8071 ▪ **T +27 (0)82-324-8372**

☐ **Stone Road** *see* Louisvale Wines
☐ **Stones in the Sun** *see* Dunstone Winery

Stonewall Wines   ⓠ ⓜ ⓞ

The cellar behind the thick perimeter wall of this Helderberg property was built in 1828. Boutique owner-winemaker De Waal Koch, despite the tough economy, has taken care to renovate the white-gabled structure without sacrificing the 'olden times' atmosphere or the excellent original facilities, such as cement vats, from which emerge wines made in appropriately unshowy, olden-times style.

★★★★ **Rubér** ⊘ Blackcurrant fragrance on **12** blend of cab franc, merlot & cab. More complex than straight Cab & a little spicier & more tannic, but similar lightish feeling, similar supportive but uninsistent oaking. Improvement on **10** (★★★☆). No **11**.

Chardonnay ⓦ ★★★☆ Flavoursome aromas oatmeal & citrus on ripe, fresh, well-balanced & clean-finishing **13**; judiciously oaked. Also tasted: **Cabernet Sauvignon 12** ★★★★ Not tasted: **Valle Felice**. — TJ

Location: Somerset West ▪ Map: Helderberg ▪ WO: Western Cape ▪ Est 1828 ▪ 1stB 1997 ▪ Tasting & sales by appt Mon-Fri 10–5 Sat 10–1 ▪ Closed Easter Fri-Sun, Dec 25/26 & Jan 1 ▪ Refreshments by appt ▪ Helderberg wine festival ▪ Owner(s) De Waal Koch ▪ Cellarmaster(s) Ronell Wiid (Jan 2000, consultant) ▪ Winemaker(s) De Waal Koch (Jan 2000) ▪ Viticulturist(s) De Waal Koch (Jun 1984) ▪ 90ha/70ha (cabs s/f, merlot, ptage, shiraz, chard, pinot gris, sauv) ▪ 300t/4,000cs own label 80% red 20% white ▪ PO Box 5145 Helderberg 7135 ▪ stonewall@mweb.co.za ▪ S 34° 1' 59. 0" E 018° 49' 14.6" ▪ F +27 (0)21-855-2206 ▪ **T +27 (0)21-855-3675**

StoneyCroft

Home to the Stone family since 2000, this tiny property in Devon Valley produces quality shiraz, so much is expected from the young cabernet vines. Wines are made for businessman John Stone and his two daughters' own label by the Steytlers of nearby Kaapzicht.

★★★★ **Shiraz** ② **09** (★★★☆) sweet vanilla bouquet & plump berry palate well controlled by sappy grip & bitter-choc tail; ±15% alcohol perhaps just a little less balanced than **08** & previous. — CvZ

Location/map/WO: Stellenbosch ▪ Est 2000 ▪ 1stB 2001 ▪ Tasting by appt ▪ Owner(s) John Stone ▪ Winemaker(s) Danie Steytler (2001), with Danie Steytler jnr (both Kaapzicht) ▪ Viticulturist(s) Gary Probert (Jan 2010, consultant) ▪ 4ha/3.5ha (cab, shiraz) ▪ 20t/3,000cs own label 100% red ▪ PO Box 239 Koelenhof 7605 ▪ john@stoneycroft.co.za ▪ www.stoneycroft.co.za ▪ S 33° 53′ 24.41″ E 018° 48′ 19.78″ ▪ F +27 (0)21-865-2360 ▪ **T +27 (0)21-865-2301/ +27 (0)82-801-1804**

Stony Brook

It's 20 years since Nigel and Joy McNaught established their small Franschhoek winery. Much more recently, underlining the family nature of the concern, son Craig took over as chief winemaker. They produce a large array of wines off their multi-varietal vineyards, testifying to both enthusiasm and devotion to small-volume winemaking. A new cellar in time for the 2015 harvest, new plantings, a new Pinot (with a Chardonnay to come) all speak of continuing dynamism.

★★★★☆ **Ghost Gum** Handsome **09** single-vineyard cab tightly structured by remarkably well-absorbed all-new oak (32 months). Core of compact fruit & hint of mint in properly dry, savoury wine named for farm's 150-year-old bark-shedding gum.

★★★★ **Syrah Reserve** Savoury, complex **11** nicely matured & accessible after languishing in barrel for over 2 years. Not as fine as **10** (★★★★★) though plenty spicy black pepper & cured meats to pique interest.

★★★★ **The Max** ② Enticingly plush fruit in classy, well-constructed cab-led **10** blend with merlot convincingly delicious & thoroughly harmonious. Accessible now, though structured for keeping.

★★★★ **SMV** Floral, spicy **10**'s acidity somewhat unsettled in spicy, dark-fruited shiraz-led blend, with mourvèdre & splash co-fermented viognier.

★★★★ **Sauvignon Blanc** Firmly structured **13**, Elgin's racy, mineral acidity ensures bone-dry impression. Abundant fruit broadened by (perhaps a tad too much) extended lees-ageing.

★★★★ **Ghost Gum White** Barrel-fermented **13** an almost equal blend sauvignon, semillon. Subtle toasty edge to full, softly rich stonefruit flavours, fleshed out by time on lees. WO W Cape. **12** sold out untasted.

★★★★ **Lyle** ② Elegance & complexity return with **08**, after simplicity of **07** (★★★☆). Persistent, creamy MCC sparkling from own chardonnay & Stellenbosch pinot, raised in oak & with 58 months on lees.

★★★★ **V on A** ② Tank sample dessert-style **11** in fine form. Beautifully balanced sweetness & acidity in lusciously rich barrel-fermented & matured viognier. Excellent partner for mature cheeses.

Pinot Noir ⓝ ★★★★ Mineral core impresses in maiden **09**. Expressive, delicate savoury fruit somewhat overshadowed by oak, though only older barrels used. Coastal WO. Also tasted: **Shiraz 12** ★★★★ The **'J' 13** ★★★★ Occasional release: **Camissa, Snow Gum, Rosé.** Discontinued: **Semillon Reserve**. — IM

Location/map: Franschhoek ▪ WO: Franschhoek/Western Cape/Coastal/Elgin ▪ Est 1995 ▪ 1stB 1996 ▪ Tasting by appt ▪ Fee R50 ▪ Sales Mon-Fri 10—5 Sat 10-1; enquire about pub hols ▪ Self-catering cottages ▪ Owner(s) Nigel & Joy McNaught ▪ Winemaker(s) Craig McNaught (2011), with Michael Blaauw (Jan 2008) ▪ Viticulturist(s) Paul Wallace (consultant) ▪ 23ha/14ha (cab, malbec, merlot, mourv, p verdot, pinot, shiraz, tempranillo, chard, sem, viog) ▪ 100t/ 6,500cs own label 65% red 35% white ▪ ISO 14001:2003 ▪ PO Box 22 Franschhoek 7690 ▪ info@stonybrook.co.za ▪ www.stonybrook.co.za ▪ S 33° 56′ 28.7″ E 019° 7′ 4.1″ ▪ F +27 (0)86-664-2794 ▪ **T +27 (0)21-876-2182**

Storm Wines

Storm Wines is the story of two winemaking brothers, two continents and one grape: pinot noir. In Santa Barbara County, California, Ernst Storm since 2006 focuses on small lots from the Santa Rita Hills and Santa Maria Valley. Hannes, winemaker at Hamilton Russell, does likewise in the Hemel-en-Aarde and Upper Hemel-en-Aarde valleys. 'With three fantastic vintages in the bag, the first release has just landed on the shores of another continent,' says Hannes, promising further wine-focused sibling synergies, 'especially with pinot noir and its fascinating facets'.

Storm range (NEW)

★★★★☆ **Moya's Pinot Noir** Tiny Upper Hemel-en-Aarde Valley block, minuscule 1.5 T/ha yield, older oak; mulberries, raspberries, white pepper & forest floor in **12**; silky smooth, the fruit vivid in the flavours. Tannins just firm enough to add definition.

★★★★ **Vrede Pinot Noir** Hemel-en-Aarde Valley origin, similar to Moya's except for 25% new oak, more ripeness. **12** has classic tones, spice & red berries, notes of white pepper, earth. Palate is bright & refreshing, streamlined. — CR, CvZ

Location: Hermanus ▪ WO: Hemel-en-Aarde Valley/Upper Hemel-en-Aarde Valley ▪ Est 2011 ▪ 1stB 2012 ▪ Tasting by appt ▪ Closed Easter Fri/Sun, Ascension day, Dec 25/26 & Jan 1 ▪ Owner(s) Hannes Storm ▪ Winemaker(s)/viticulturist(s) Hannes Storm (Dec 2011) ▪ 3ha (pinot) ▪ 8t/1,200cs own label 100% red ▪ BWI, IPW ▪ PO Box 431 Hermanus 7200 ▪ hannes@stormwines.co.za ▪ **T +27 (0)82-325-4517**

Stoumann's Wines

A facilities upgrade at the Vredendal winery of conservation-minded Napoleon 'Nappies' Stoumann and wife Annalise was underway at press time. While no new vintages have been bottled, the 2010 reds should still be available to those stopping by for a taste and a close-up view of the endangered Cape Geometric Tortoise, to be seen in profusion at the visitor venue.

Vin de la Tortue ★★☆ **10** cab/shiraz combo has fruitcake appeal, is easy to drink. Not retasted: **Cabernet Sauvignon 10** ★★ **Shiraz 10** ★★☆ Not tasted: **Rosé Perlé Wine**. — DB, CvZ

Location: Vredendal ▪ Map/WO: Olifants River ▪ Est 1998 ▪ 1stB 2008 ▪ Tasting, sales & cellar tours Mon-Fri 8-5 Sat by appt ▪ Closed all pub hols ▪ Cheese platters/meals/braai available on request ▪ Tour groups ▪ Farm produce ▪ Conferences ▪ Owner(s)/cellarmaster(s)/winemaker(s) Napoleon Stoumann ▪ Viticulturist(s) CG Stoumann (Jan 2010) ▪ 100ha (cab, merlot, muscadel r/w, ptage, ruby cab, shiraz, chard, chenin, cbard, hanepoot) ▪ 1,040t/4,000cs own label 50% red 40% white 10% rosé + 800,000L bulk ▪ IPW ▪ PO Box 307 Vredendal 8160 ▪ stoumanns@cybersmart.co.za ▪ www.stoumanns.co.za ▪ S 31° 41' 20.5" E 018° 30' 23.3" ▪ F +27 (0)27-213-1448 ▪ **T +27 (0)27-213-2323/+27 (0)83-236-2794**

Strandveld Wines

A pioneer of the Elim Winegrowers group unlocking the viticultural potential of the vast, windswept Agulhas plain with its maritime climate, Strandveld boasts the continent's most southerly vineyards. Since the early-2000s collaboration between private investors and the Albertyns of Uintjieskuil (an 850ha sheep and wheat farm), the two-tiered selection, bolstered by exciting occasional additions, has earned acclaim for quality and value. As have environmental efforts through participation in the local farm-owner-driven Nuwejaars Wetland Special Management Area.

Strandveld range

★★★★ **Pinot Noir** **11** streamlined & suave, more restrained in youth than previous. Good core of fruit & acidity, with dry, fine-grained oak tannins still unfolding. Cool-climate pedigree evident, just needs time.

★★★★☆ **Syrah** A hint of viognier (1%) tempts **11** (★★★★) to show more, but syrah/shiraz fruit remains tightly coiled. Polished oak tannins & freshness confirm potential to age. No grenache or mourvèdre, as in more expressive **10**.

★★★★☆ **The Navigator** Shiraz & grenache (59/25) blend with mourvèdre & viognier, honouring Henry the Navigator. Fruit tightly woven into firm, muscular structure from cooler **12** vintage. A treasure chest for the future, currently best decanted. WO Cape South Coast.

★★★★☆ **Sauvignon Blanc Pofadderbos 13** (★★★★) from the 'Puff Adder Bush' single-vineyard, has hallmark flinty tension, with subtle asparagus & gooseberry flavours. Stern & steely restraint, needs time to unfurl. A shade off **12**.

★★★★☆ **Adamastor** **12** polished Bordeaux-style white blend dominated by oaked semillon's rich & waxy lemon tones. Unoaked sauvignon adds intensity & freshness. Elegant food wine, already appealing, but deserves cellar time to show true class.

Occasional release: **Anders Sparrman Pinot Noir**.

First Sighting range

Pinot Noir ★★★ Lighter & more accessible than senior version but not simple or insubstantial; **12** good varietal expression showing more savoury, leathery & red fruit nuances than sibling. **Shiraz-Grenache Rosé 14** tank sample too young to rate. Also tasted: **Shiraz 12** ★★★★ **Sauvignon Blanc 13** ★★★☆ — MW

Location: Elim ▪ Map: Southern Cape ▪ WO: Elim/Cape South Coast ▪ Est 2002 ▪ 1stB 2003 ▪ Tasting, sales & cellar tours Mon–Thu 8–5 Fri 8–4 Sat 10–3 ▪ Closed Good Fri & Dec 25 ▪ Farm produce ▪ BYO picnic ▪ Walks/hikes ▪ Mountain biking ▪ Conservation area ▪ Two self-catering cottages ▪ Owner(s) Strandveld Vineyards & Rietfontein Trust ▪ Winemaker(s) Conrad Vlok (Dec 2004), with Donovan Ackermann (Aug 2012) ▪ Viticulturist(s) Tienie Wentzel (Oct 2009) ▪ 850ha/ 70ha (pinot, shiraz, sauv, sem) ▪ 246t/24,000cs own label 43% red 57% white ▪ BWI, IPW ▪ PO Box 1020 Bredasdorp 7280 ▪ info@strandveld.co.za ▪ www.strandveld.co.za ▪ S 34° 39' 59.2" E 019° 47' 26.8" ▪ F +27 (0)28-482-1902/6 ▪ **T +27 (0)28-482-1902/6**

☐ **String of Pearls** see Francois La Garde

Strydom Vintners

This is an own label by leading husband-and-wife winemakers Louis and Rianie Strydom, both involved independently with prime Helderberg properties Ernie Els and Haskell/Dombeya respectively. Grapes grown on their small Simonsberg estate have gone into established brands to date, and they'll continue to sell off some fruit till they're ready to bottle their entire crop. They hope to welcome visitors for on-site tasting from the middle of this year.

★★★★☆ **Cabernet Sauvignon** (NEW) **12** has all hallmarks of quality cab from warmer part of Stellenbosch: generously structured, with muscle, grip & rich, dark fruit filling. Appealing freshness & complementary oak (20%). Cellaring will deliver more pleasures.

★★★★ **CWG Auction Reserve Pinot Noir** (NEW) Maiden CWG auction offering from Rianie Strydom, also a first for variety in WO Napier. **13** gorgeous pinot perfume & length in its red cherries & hint forest floor. Seductively supple but also good fresh backbone. 30% new oak well judged.

★★★★ **Syrah** (NEW) **12** bit forbidding at present with its dark spice richness, full body though nicely structured with fine, supple tannins, careful oaking (20% new) to benefit from cellaring.

★★★★ **Retro** (Ⓧ) Best wines of vintage determine blend; approachable **11** 50% merlot, equal parts cab, shiraz. Generous, fleshy mouthful of ripe, dark plummy fruit framed by seamless, fine tannins. No **10**. **09** (★★★★).

Also tasted: **The Freshman 14** ★★★ — AL

Location: Stellenbosch ▪ WO: Stellenbosch/Napier ▪ Est 2012 ▪ 1stB 2009 ▪ Closed to public ▪ Owner(s) Louis & Rianie Strydom ▪ Cellarmaster(s) Rianie Strydom ▪ 8.5ha/6.5ha (cab, merlot, shiraz, sauv, sem) ▪ ±30t/1,000cs own label 50% red 50% white ▪ IPW ▪ PO Box 1290 Stellenbosch 7599 ▪ rianie@strydomvineyards.com ▪ **T +27 (0)21-889-8553/+27 (0)82-290-6399**

☐ **Stubborn Man** see Retief Wines
☐ **Stumble Vineyards** see Flagstone Winery

☐ **Suikerbosch** *see* Zidela Wines

Sumaridge Wines

This increasingly impressive Hemel-en-Aarde producer is one of the longest established in the area, apart from the earliest pioneers. Gavin Patterson has been the winemaker and vineyard manager since 2005, learning 'the peculiarities of this region – the land, the climate and its people'. This has meant not only raising quality but also that he has been able to shift things, as he says, towards wines of individuality, expressive of the location (hence names like Epitome and Maritimus). Another significant move is that Sumaridge has now gained WIETA ethical trade accreditation - 'the first producer in the Walker Bay district,' he adds proudly.

★★★★ **Merlot** ⊘ Delicate, youthful **11** - even more restrained than **09** (no **10**). Vanilla-infused plum & cassis aromas lead to firm but unevolved palate. Good potential for further development.

★★★★☆ **Pinot Noir** Elegant yet powerful **12** (★★★★★) shows dark, spicy fruit interwoven with violets. The palate is energetic, with finely grained tannin, shows a seamless oak integration (30% new). Very Old World feel, culminating in a bone-dry finish. Like **11**, it needs time to open up.

★★★★ **Epitome** Crème de cassis, black pepper & plum notes emerge from densely packed **10** (★★★★☆) from pinotage & shiraz (**08** also included merlot). Partly naturally fermented & raised in 50% seamlessly integrated new oak. Concentrated flavours, yet with great lift & vigour, finishing long.

★★★★☆ **Chardonnay** Subtle yet rich **12** somehow expresses a maritime feel. Hazelnut, crushed stone & fine pear aromas lead to a dry palate which is broad but finely chiselled. Fine acid thread & notes of wet pebble & lime lingering on the satisfying finish. More exciting than **11** (★★★★); very fine **10** tasted ex tank.

★★★★ **Sauvignon Blanc** Classic green & mineral notes interwoven with lemongrass on **14**. Lean palate is zesty & sufficiently long, with a lipsmacking acidity.

★★★★ **Maritimus 12** (★★★★☆) similar interesting blend to **11**, with sauvignon, chardonnay, semillon & drop viognier. Aromas of ripe apple, cut grass, lanolin & smoked oyster lead to a complex palate which is broad yet focused, revealing extended fine lees-ageing & sensitive light oaking. Natural fermentation all round.

★★★★ **The Wayfarer 10** pink MCC sparkling from pinot noir, 36 months on lees before disgorged with zero dosage - yet with surprising richness. Fine mousse; initially shy nose of strawberry, brioche & spice.

Also tasted: **Rosé 14** ★★★☆ — JPf

Location: Hermanus ▪ Map: Elgin, Walker Bay & Bot River ▪ WO: Upper Hemel-en-Aarde Valley ▪ Est 1997 ▪ 1stB 2000 ▪ Tasting & sales daily 10—3 ▪ Tasting fee R25, redeemable on purchase ▪ Closed Easter Fri/Sun, Dec 25/26 & Jan 1 ▪ Seasonal tasting platter options plus kiddies platter ▪ Facilities for children ▪ Tour groups ▪ Conferences ▪ Weddings/functions ▪ Luxury self-catering lodge ▪ Conservation area ▪ Extensive nature trails ▪ Mountain biking ▪ Bass & fly fishing by arrangement ▪ Owner(s) Holly & Simon Bellingham-Turner ▪ Winemaker(s) Gavin Patterson (Jun 2005), with Reginald Maphumulo (Jun 2000) & Walter Pretorius (Jul 2013) ▪ 210ha/42ha (cab f, malbec, merlot, ptage, pinot, shiraz, chard, sauv, sem) ▪ 150t/20,000cs own label 45% red 50% white 5% rosé ▪ IPW, WIETA ▪ PO Box 1413 Hermanus 7200 ▪ info@sumaridge.co.za ▪ www.sumaridge.co.za ▪ S 34° 22' 1.6" E 019° 15' 18.6" ▪ F +27 (0)86-623-4248 ▪ **T +27 (0)28-312-1097**

☐ **Sumerton** *see* Zidela Wines

Summerhill Wines

⊘ ◎

The Dorpstraat Restaurant Theatre has closed down but soon will be replaced by a 'cellar theatre' and function venue. Meanwhile 2nd-generation owner Charles Hunting and wife Ingrid continue to welcome visitors to Summerhill boutique estate for tasting and sales. Winegrowing is deeply ingrained here: original grantee JG Snyman in the 1830s recognised the potential of the west-facing Simonsberg slopes and included vines in his blueprint for the farm.

Shiraz-Merlot ★★☆ Sappy fruit, some herbaceous notes despite shiraz's 80% dominance, but the flavours are where **12**'s main appeal lies - smooth & round ripe plums. WO W Cape. **Chenin Blanc** ⊘ ★★★ **14** bright-fruited pineapple & passionfruit, just enough freshness to lift the flavours, giving length & appeal. — CR

Location/map: Stellenbosch ▪ WO: Western Cape ▪ 1stB 2008 ▪ Tasting & sales Mon-Thu 9-4.30 Fri 9-2 ▪ Closed all pub hols ▪ Amenities: see intro ▪ Owner(s) Summerhill Wines cc, Charles R Hunting ▪ Winemaker(s) Hannes Meyer (whites, Simonsig) & Marius Malan (reds, Malanot Wines) ▪ Viticulturist(s) Paul Wallace (consultant) ▪ 15ha/3.5ha (merlot, shiraz, chenin) ▪ 24t/2,500cs own label 40% red 60% white ▪ PO Box 12448 Die Boord 7613 ▪ charles@summerhillwines.co.za, manager@summerhillwines.co.za, reception@summerhillwines.co.za ▪ www.summerhillwines.co.za ▪ S 33° 52' 57.71" E 018° 50' 49.39" ▪ F +27 (0)86-621-8047 ▪ **T +27 (0)21-889-5015**

Sumsaré Wines

Spell 'Sumsaré' backwards, and you get 'Erasmus', the Robertson family behind the brand. Patriarch Danie had an aha moment back in 2007 to bottle a commemorative wine for the home farm's 200th anniversary. The quixotic idea has since blossomed into a boutique wine and brandy business run by the 7th generation, daughters Francèl, Danielle and Janine, and son Johannes.

Location/map: Robertson ▪ Est 2008 ▪ 1stB 2007 ▪ Tasting, sales & tours by appt Mon-Fri 9–5 Sat 9–1 ▪ Closed Easter Fri-Mon, May 13, Pentecost, Dec 25/26 & Jan 1 ▪ Tour groups ▪ Facilities for children ▪ Farm produce ▪ BYO picnic ▪ Weddings ▪ Owner(s) Francèl Rabie, Johannes Erasmus, Danielle Jackson & Janine Joubert ▪ Winemaker(s) Lourens van der Westhuizen (Arendsig) ▪ Viticulturist(s) Briaan Stipp (Robertson Winery) ▪ 45ha/40ha (cab, ptage, ruby cab, shiraz, chard, chenin, cbard, muscadel w) ▪ 700t/±260cs own label 40% red 60% white ▪ PO Box 402 Robertson 6705 ▪ sumsare.wines@barvallei.co.za ▪ www.sumsarewines.co.za ▪ S 33° 54' 14.66" E 019° 40' 4.75" ▪ F +27 (0)86-505-8590 ▪ **T +27 (0)23-626-2152/+27 (0)82-221-6653**

☐ **Sunning Hill** see Vinopoly Wines
☐ **Sunshine** see Stellar Winery

Super Single Vineyards

Daniël and Ingrid de Waal's old Canettevallei farm in Stellenboschkloof is the base for Daniël's search for special viticultural sites (hence the brand name). The Pella label brings together wines from selected Stellenbosch vineyards (including one of SA's oldest pinotage vineyards, on the home farm). More radically, the Mount Sutherland wines are from well inland, near Sutherland in the Karoo. Daniël says it's 'the first true cool continental vineyard' in the country – 'the highest and coldest wine grow-ing region in Africa'. We're invited to share the exploration of classic and revolutionary Cape terroirs.

Pella Coastal Wines

★★★★ **Cabernet Sauvignon** Ⓥ After focused **08** (★★★★★), **09** has noble, dark & earthy Bor-deaux overtones with rich ripeness & lovely dry finish. Slightly gawky oak spices should integrate with time.

★★★★ **Merlot** Velvety yet structured **12** with dollop petit verdot; classic ripe berry & choc aromas lead to firm well-oaked palate - tight, but promising development. **11** (★★★☆) was simpler.

★★★★ **Thomas Se Dolland Pinotage** From 50 year old vines, concentrated **12** offers ripe aromas of black fruit, tar & allspice. Rich, round, fine-grained palate is well proportioned, with 50% new oak well absorbed.

Malbec (NEW) ★★★★ Big, ripe & succulent **12** displays leather, plums & liquorice. The bone-dry, supportively oaked palate is concentrated but needs time to develop complexity. **Petit Verdot** (NEW) ★★★★ **12**, with 15% cab, shows funky notes of reduction & underlying dark, spicy fruit. Rich & full flavoured, but a bit opaque & one dimensional mid-2014. Well-judged 25% new oak. Also tasted: **Sauvignon Blanc 13** ★★★★ Not retasted: **The Vanilla 12** ★★★★

Mount Sutherland Continental Wines

★★★★ Syrah Was 'Mount Sutherland Syrah' under previous range name. From extreme, high vineyards, elegant yet dense **12** (★★★★) raises bar on **11**. Meat, black pepper & blackberry aromas lead to intense palate with finely grained, ripe tannin & complex flavours. Will reward the patient.

Riesling **★★★★ 13** has zesty aromas of lime & green apple. Dry, lean palate should open up with year or two & develop complexity. **Sauvignon Blanc** (NEW) **★★★★** Crisp & vibrant **13** shows dusty aromas of greenpepper & fresh grass. The greener spectrum also dominates the lean palate, which has a lipsmacking finish. — JPf

Location/map: Stellenbosch ▪ WO: Stellenbosch/Sutherland-Karoo/Coastal ▪ Est/1stB 2004 ▪ Tasting Mon-Sat 10-5 (Oct-Apr)/by appt (May-Sep) ▪ Owner(s)/viticulturist(s) Daniël de Waal ▪ Winemaker(s) Daniël de Waal, with Kyle Zulch ▪ 60ha Canettevallei farm ▪ (cab, malbec, nebbiolo, p verdot, ptage, pinot, shiraz, tempranillo, riesling, sauv) ▪ 2,000cs own label 80% red 20% white ▪ PO Box 89 Vlottenburg 7604 ▪ marketing@ssvineyards.co.za ▪ www.supersinglevineyards.co.za ▪ S 33° 56' 29.73" E 018° 45' 15.20" ▪ F +27 (0)21-881-3026 ▪ **T +27 (0)72-200-5552 (Daniël)/+27 (0)82-556-0205 (Kyle)**

☐ **Sutherland** *see* Thelema Mountain Vineyards
☐ **Sutherland Continental** *see* Super Single Vineyards
☐ **Swallow** *see* Natte Valleij Wines

Swallow Hill Winery

One of a tiny handful of vineyards in Greyton, this 2 ha organic parcel is farmed and wines handcrafted with minimal intervention by Britons Di and Brian Dawes. Their debut 'natural blonde' Viognier has been joined by a tempranillo emulating the Spanish joven style ('young, light and smooth'). A tasting and sales area in the cellar is planned, along with tastings, and pairings of music, food and wine, in conjunction with local vintners.

Location: Greyton ▪ Map: Southern Cape ▪ Est 2009 ▪ 1stB 2013 ▪ Tasting, sales & cellar tours by prior arrangement ▪ Conservation area ▪ Owner(s) Di & Brian Dawes ▪ Cellarmaster(s) John Brian Dawes ▪ Winemaker(s) Di Dawes, with John Brian Dawes ▪ Viticulturist(s) Di Dawes & John Brian Dawes ▪ 21ha/2ha (tempranillo, viog) ▪ 2t own label 50% red 50% white ▪ IPW, SAWIS ▪ PO Box 299 Greyton 7233 ▪ swallowhill@thedawes.net ▪ www.thedawes.net, www.swallowhill.co.za ▪ S 34° 6' 10.10" E 019° 36' 35.46" ▪ **T +27 (0)82-423-9634**

☐ **Swartland Stories** *see* Pulpit Rock Winery

Swartland Winery

Established in 1948 as a co-operative, this large-scale producer has adapted to the winds of change that blew so dramatically over the region. The business has unbundled, and now leases the winemaking facilities to Leeuwenkuil, who, in turn, produce the Swartland ranges on contract. This allows them to concentrate on the marketing aspects, and to offer bottling and laboratory services to outside customers. Although the range is extensive, care is taken under wine coordinator Christo Koch to vinify special batches separately to provide regional character and well-defined tiers of quality.

Idelia range

★★★★ Cape Blend Label suggests pinotage content, but undisclosed blend in barrel-matured **10** (★★★★) offers intense fruit beneath acetone whiff. Last-tasted **08** was better. Swartland WO.

Swartland Bushvine range

★★★★ Shiraz **10** substantial, ripe & full bodied, but showing restraint.

Chenin Blanc ★★★★ Toasty oak & buttery pineapple, **12** full bodied, intensely flavoured, wholesome. Also tasted: **Pinotage 13 ★★★★** Not tasted: **Cabernet Sauvignon**. Swartland WO for all these.

For more information, visit wineonaplatter.com

Reserve range (NEW)

Pinotage ★★★ Nicely weighted & balanced **13** shows wild berry fruit & variety's acetone high notes. **Limited Selection Cabernet Sauvignon-Merlot** ⊘ ★★★ Light bodied, with juicy redberry fruit. Pleasant & easy-drinking **13**. Swartland WO for this range.

Swartland Winemakers Collection

★★★★ **Cape Vintage** (✷) Elegant **08** port-style from tinta & shiraz, with touriga. Rich primary berry fruit, hints of caramel & spicy brandy-oak highlights. Deftly handled. Swartland WO.

Cabernet Sauvignon ★★★ Sprightly unwooded **13**, with good fruit concentration. Swartland WO. **Shiraz** ★★★ Pleasantly juicy & fresh, cherry fruit with soft texture. Unwooded **13** improves on previous. **Chardonnay** ⊘ ★★★ Hint of salty lees minerality, **14** is well rounded, with soft acidity & lingering finish. **Chenin Blanc** ⊘ ★★★ Ripe peaches in nicely balanced, middleweight **14**, with just the right amount of freshness. **Cuvée Brut** ★★★ Fresh & light carbonated **NV** bubbly from sauvignon, with subtle flavour & hint of sweetness. **Hanepoot** ★★★☆ Rich & ripe **NV** fortified desert with intense muscat aromas, syrupy viscosity & fragrant finish. **Cape Ruby** ⊘ ★★★☆ Port-style tinta & shiraz, **NV** burnt sugar, malt & solid black plum core. Well-judged sweetness, appealing liquorice finish. Also tasted: **Merlot 13** ★★★ **Pinotage 13** ★★★ **Blanc de Noir** ⊘ **14** ★★★ **Sauvignon Blanc 14** ★★ **Red Jerepigo NV** ★★★ **White Jerepigo NV** ★★★ Not retasted: **Tinta Barocca 12** ★★★ **Dry Red NV** ★★ **Sparkling Rosè NV** ★★★ Not tasted: **Bukettraube**. Note: range previously listed as 'Swartland'.

Contours Collection

Merlot ★★ Fresh, minty, just off-dry **13** shows good fruit & flavour. **Moscato** ★★ Generous, sweetly spicy & aromatic **NV** from muscat d'Alexandrie, pétillant, with low alcohol. Also tasted: **Merlot-Cabernet Sauvignon 13** ★ **Chenin Blanc 14** ★★ **Sauvignon Blanc 14** ★★★

D' Vine range

Chenin Blanc-Sauvignon Blanc ★★ Fresher, fruitier than previous, light & crisp **NV** (**14**). Also tasted: **Cabernet Sauvignon-Merlot NV** ★★ Not retasted: **Rosé NV** ★★ — GdB

Location: Malmesbury ▪ Map: Swartland ▪ WO: Western Cape/Swartland ▪ Est/1stB 1948 ▪ Tasting & sales Mon–Fri 9–5 Sat 9–2 ▪ Closed Mar 21, Easter Fri/Sun, Dec 25/26 & Jan 1 ▪ Facilities for children ▪ Tour groups ▪ Farm produce ▪ Owner(s) 60 producers ▪ Wine coordinator Christo Koch (Feb 2014) ▪ Viticulturist(s) Claude Uren (Nov 2010) ▪ 2,689ha (cab, malbec, merlot, ptage, shiraz, chard, chenin, sauv) ▪ 20,000t 55% white 38% red 5% rosé 2% sparkling ▪ Brands for clients: Pick 'n Pay, Woolworths ▪ BRC, IFS, IPW, WIETA ▪ PO Box 95 Malmesbury 7299 ▪ susan@swwines.co.za ▪ www.swwines. co.za ▪ S 33° 27' 12.7" E 018° 45' 17.7" ▪ F +27 (0)22-482-1750 ▪ **T +27 (0)22-482-1134**

☐ **Sweet Darling** *see* Darling Cellars

SylvanVale Vineyards (Ⓥ)(¶)(⌂)(◎)(⒜)(♿)

Upmarket Louis Group Hotels are in the happy situation of owning an own wine brand but also own vineyards: the Sylvanvale grapes are vinified to spec by seasoned consultant Mark Carmichael-Green, while the vines share the scenic Stellenbosch premises of Devon Valley Hotel. Replanted chenin comes onstream this year, joining a line of characterful past vinifications (dry & sweet) of this variety.

SylvanVale range

★★★★ **Pinotage Reserve** Best decanted to remove sediment, **06** has matured beautifully, acquiring leather & star anise complexity while retaining bold fruit. Medium bodied yet rich, soft tannins. Not retasted: **Pinotage 06** ★★★ Not tasted: **Cabernet Sauvignon**, **Dry Cabernet Sauvignon Rosé**. Discontinued: **Family Reserve**.

For more information, visit wineonaplatter.com

Ghost Tree range

Three Colours White ★★★ Mostly chenin & two others on nearby Middelvlei, **14** is all apple pie on the nose, Granny Smith apple on the palate, crisp & dry with a long finish. Discontinued: **Sauvignon Blanc**. — JG

Location/map: Stellenbosch ▪ WO: Devon Valley ▪ Est 1997 ▪ 1stB 1998 ▪ Tasting & sales daily 11–7 ▪ Fee R25 ▪ Open pub hols ▪ Flavours Restaurant: 120 seater; Vineyard Terrace; Cedarwood Bar & Lounge ▪ The Devon Valley Hotel: 50 rooms ▪ Facilities for children ▪ Tour groups ▪ Conferences ▪ 6 banqueting venues (max capacity 98 pax) ▪ Walking/hiking trails ▪ Owner(s) Louis Group Hotels, Spas & Vineyards ▪ Winemaker(s) Mark Carmichael-Green (Sep 2003, consultant) ▪ Viticulturist(s) Lorna Hughes (1997, consultant) ▪ 8ha/4.3ha (cab, ptage, chenin) ▪ 6t/1,050cs own label 100% rosé ▪ PO Box 68 Stellenbosch 7599 ▪ info@sylvanvale.com ▪ www.sylvanvale.com ▪ S 33° 54' 12.5" E 018° 48' 57.7" ▪ F +27 (0)21-865-2610 ▪ **T +27 (0)21-865-2012**

☐ **Table Bay** *see* Ultra Liquors
☐ **Table Mountain** *see* Distell
☐ **Table View** *see* Rooiberg Winery

Taillard Family Wines

As anticipated last time, what was the Bernheim wine team have consolidated in Voor Paardeberg and rebranded, and chosen to reference the heritage of co-proprietor Pieter Taljaard, a financial director in the mining industry and owner of the Kersfontein home farm since 2006. Big hitter Teddy Hall is on board as winemaker and the wines, from a cellar dating from 1790, dedicated 'to those who dare to dream'.

Taillard range
The Bullion ★★★ Older-oak-aged **13** from 1999 pinotage bushvines; varietal mulberry & spice in fruit-forward expression. Great for pizza, pasta or BBQs, says winemaker. **Deep Level** ★★ Interesting dried spice, sweet leather & tobacco on **10** shiraz. Idiosyncratic honey oats & prunes; ready now for venison & roasts. **The Miner** ★★★ Dusty cab/merlot combo, splash cab franc, **12** capsicum, tealeaf & plums, with drying tannins; should be enjoyed soon. **Prospector's Cape Late Bottled Vintage** ★★★★ Port-style from shiraz, pinotage & petit verdot in pleasing **09**, 4 years old oak. Rich, warm & brooding; packed with fruit & enlivening acidity. Ready to drink now & for few years. — HJ

Location/WO: Paarl ▪ Map: Paarl & Wellington ▪ Tasting, sales & tours by appt ▪ Closed all pub hols ▪ Owner(s) Pacas Winery (Pty) Ltd (Pieter Taljaard, Hermann Helmbold, Anelise Taljaard) ▪ Cellarmaster(s)/winemaker(s) Teddy Hall ▪ Viticulturist(s) Morné van Greunen (Feb 2009) ▪ ±44ha (cabs s/f, merlot, p verdot, ptage, shiraz, chenin) ▪ 1,000cs own label 80% red 20% white ▪ BWI, IPW ▪ PO Box 7274 Noorder-Paarl 7623 ▪ rika@taillardwines.com ▪ www.taillardwines.com ▪ S 33° 35' 22.5" E 018° 52' 45.0" (VP) ▪ F +27 (0)21-869-8365 ▪ **T +27 (0)21-869-8384**

Tall Horse

Cheery labels and easy, fruit-forward style of this giraffe-themed DGB brand have clearly captured consumer tastes locally and overseas, where volumes are growing. Website www.tallhorsewines.com continues the quirky brand persona.

Tamboerskloof Wine – Kleinood Farm

The Afrikaans 'kleinood' means something small and precious - which is what boutique vintner/engineer Gerard de Villiers and wife Libby created in Stellenbosch's Blaauwklippen Valley. Libby harnessed tradition in the look and feel, while Gerard, with more than 150 winery process designs under his belt locally and abroad, handled the cellar. Their children's contribution is celebrated in the names of the Rosé and new Syrah. Inveterate surfer Gunter Schultz's focus on vineyard and wine is absolute, and environmentally sympathetic.

★★★★☆ **Syrah** Ripe berry aromas on plush **10** (★★★★), with spicy tobacco warmth. Richly balanced, with sweet fruit & strong molten tannin; but big 14.5% alcohol somewhat tiring. Splashes mourvèdre, viognier, as in **09**.

★★★★ **John Spicer Syrah** Deeper fruit than on standard Syrah, but **09** masked by a lot of oak (75% new), at least in youth - harmony might yet come. Ripe tannins; slightly warm finish, though alcohol just 14%.

★★★★ **Viognier** **13** a quiet expression of the variety, with subtle apricot & floral notes. Just a little supportive oak, with the stress on silky elegance & refinement - though there's no lack of flavour.

Also tasted: **Katharien Syrah Rosé 14** ★★★☆ — TJ

Location/map/WO: Stellenbosch ▪ Est 2000 ▪ 1stB 2002 ▪ Tasting, sales & cellar tours Mon-Fri by appt ▪ Closed all pub hols ▪ Owner(s) Gerard & Libby de Villiers ▪ Winemaker(s) Gunter Schultz (Sep 2007), with Julio Engelbrecht (Jan 2008) ▪ Viticulturist(s) Gunter Schultz (Sep 2007) ▪ 22ha/10ha (mourv, shiraz, rouss, viog) ▪ 80t/6,000cs own label 88% red 7% white 5% rosé ▪ BWI, IPW ▪ PO Box 12584 Die Boord 7613 ▪ admin@kleinood.com ▪ www.kleinood.com ▪ S 33° 59' 42.6" E 018° 52' 14.8" ▪ F +27 (0)21-880-2884 ▪ **T +27 (0)21-880-2527**

Tanagra Winery & Distillery

Visitors to Tanagra's mountainside guest cottages near McGregor can enjoy not only the small range of wines, vinified at Arendsig by Lourens van der Westhuizen, but the single-varietal grappa and eaux de vie, distilled on-site by German owner Robert Rosenbach. Robert, happily ensconced here with wife Anette since 2009, also crafts their red blend.

Location: McGregor ▪ Map: Robertson ▪ Est/1stB 2003 ▪ Tasting (wine/grappa), sales & cellar/distillery tours daily by appt ▪ Farm produce ▪ Boutique distillery (European style grappa & eaux de vie) ▪ Luxury farm accommodation in 6 cottages (self-catering/B&B) ▪ Adjoining Vrolijkheid Nature Reserve ▪ Owner(s) Robert & Anette Rosenbach ▪ Cellarmaster(s) Robert Rosenbach & Lourens van der Westhuizen ▪ Winemaker(s) Robert Rosenbach & Lourens van der Westhuizen ▪ Distiller(s) Robert Rosenbach ▪ Viticulturist(s) Lourens van der Westhuizen ▪ 78ha/12.5ha (cabs s/f, merlot, ptage, shiraz, cbard) ▪ 120t/1,600cs own label 90% red 10% blanc de noir ▪ BWI, IPW ▪ PO Box 92 McGregor 6708 ▪ tanagra@tanagra-wines.co.za ▪ www.tanagra-wines.co.za ▪ S 33° 55' 29.6" E 019° 52' 15.9" ▪ F +27 (0)23-625-1847 ▪ **T +27 (0)23-625-1780**

Tangled Tree

Two entwined Karee trees, symbols of the bond between Van Loveren founders and passionate gardeners Hennie and Jean Retief, inspire this eco-friendly label, packaged in light, robust, recyclable, low-carbon PET (plastic) bottles, perfect for active and outdoorsy winelovers. Off Robertson vines.

Chocolate Cabernet Sauvignon ⊘ ★★☆ Lightly oaked **13** super-friendly barbecue/campfire companion. **Tropical Sauvignon Blanc** ★★ Ripe mango & papaya fruit ensures **14** drinks easily. Also tasted: **Spicy Shiraz 13** ★★ **Moscato Rosé 14** ★★ **Butterscotch Chardonnay 14** ★★ — CvZ

Tanja Beutler Wine Collection

While waiting for her latest Red Tape merlots to be bottled, vigneron, marketer and garagiste nurturer Tanja Beutler has launched a sparkling in honour of daughter Juliet. 'At just 11 year old, she copes with a working mom who runs three businesses. She is so understanding and helps where she can.' Many things deserve to be celebrated with bubbly, adds Tanja, but a child is an excuse for a mom to celebrate every day.

Juliet Méthode Cap Classique range

★★★★ **Brut** Intensely savoury & salty from extended lees-ageing, **07** sparkling also shows yellow fruit & toasted almonds, persistent finish. Very food-friendly style, zero dosage. Mostly pinot noir & chardonnay, splash chenin.

Red Tape range

Not tasted: **Merlot, Merlot**. — CM

Location: Somerset West ▪ WO: Western Cape ▪ Est 2007 ▪ 1stB 2010 ▪ Sales by prior arrangement ▪ Owner(s) Tanja Beutler ▪ 650cs own label 87% red 13% MCC ▪ PO Box 804 Somerset Mall 7137 ▪ tanja@hiddengems.co.za ▪ F +27 (0)86-612-6118 ▪ **T +27 (0)21-855-4275**

Tanzanite Wines

As the name suggests, Wentzel and Melanie van der Merwe's boutique venture is a rare gem, focusing exclusively on handcrafting small parcels of champagne-method sparkling. Winemaker Melanie sources grapes and rents cellar space, and describes Tanzanite as 'minimalistic, passionate, reaching for the stars!'.

★★★★ **Méthode Cap Classique Brut Rosé** ② **NV (10)** bubbly with savoury, cranberry tone from 60% pinot noir & chardonnay. Retains delicacy & fresh refinement from 24 months on lees. Balanced, with good length.

★★★★☆ **Méthode Cap Classique** ② Latest **NV (08)** sparkler richer than previous, with 48 months on lees & focused chardonnay (80%), pinot noir blend. Clean lemon & slatey freshness, refined balance with lingering farewell. Winemaker's food/occasion match: 'Made to celebrate life, so enjoy daily!' — MW

Location: Worcester ▪ WO: Western Cape ▪ Est 2006 ▪ Tasting Mon-Sat by appt ▪ Owner(s) Wentzel & Melanie van der Merwe ▪ Cellarmaster(s) Melanie van der Merwe (Apr 2006) ▪ 800cs own label ▪ PO Box 5102 Worcester 6850 ▪ melanie@tanzanitewines.co.za ▪ www.tanzanitewines.co.za ▪ F +27 (0)86-694-0654 ▪ **T +27 (0)23-347-0018**

Tassenberg

Dry red affectionately known as 'Tassies'. Launched in 1936, the blend has varied over the years but not the affable persona. 750 ml, 2L & 5L. By Distell.

Tassenberg ⊘ ★★★ Soft & lightish **NV** ex unspecified grapes, easygoing all-rounder. — JPf

Taverna Rouge

Big-selling budget-priced red blend by Distell; available in 750 ml bottles and 2L packs.

Taverna Rouge ★★ Off-dry **NV** quaffer, earthy/spicy red berry flavour, appealing structure. — JPf

TCB Wines

The 6th generation to farm the Rawsonville property, Theunis Christoffel Basson (TCB) focuses on bulk wine production. Bird-like quantities of wine bottled as Swallow, Cape Sparrow and Wolfenberg have sold out, but winemaker Christo Basson assures there'll be more next time.

Location: Rawsonville ▪ Map: Breedekloof ▪ Est 2002 ▪ 1stB 2008 ▪ Tasting, sales & cellar tours Mon-Fri 8-5 ▪ Fee R10pp ▪ Closed all pub hols ▪ Tour groups ▪ BYO picnic ▪ Conferences ▪ Self-catering units ▪ Owner(s) / manager TC Botha ▪ Cellarmaster(s)/winemaker(s) Christo Basson (Oct 2008) ▪ Viticulturist(s) Johan Slabber (Feb 1999) ▪ 190ha (cab, merlot, ptage, ruby cab, shiraz, chenin cbard, nouvelle, sauv, sem) ▪ 1,800t/600cs own label 70% red 30% white + 200cs for clients ▪ IPW ▪ PO Box 56 Rawsonville 6845 ▪ basson.christo8@gmail.com ▪ S 33° 42' 5.63" E 019° 18' 21.92" ▪ F +27 (0)23-349-1325 ▪ **T +27 (0)23-349-1748**

Teddy Hall Wines

In 1992, Teddy Hall exchanged a career in financial services to study winemaking and soon made a name for himself — he was Diners Club Winemaker of the Year in 2001 when the featured category was chenin and he won the annual Chenin Blanc Challenge run by the now defunct Wine magazine four times. Teddy Hall Wines was born in 2006, his premium wines named after some of the more roguish characters of the early Cape (see website for full details).

Premium range

★★★★☆ **Hercùles van Loon Cabernet Sauvignon** ② Dense & brooding **09** includes 10% merlot. Rich & full but balanced, pleasantly austere on the finish.

★★★★☆ **Dr Jan Cats Chenin Blanc Reserve** ⓥ Refined **11** showing complexity & just enough texture to ensure that the acidity is nicely coated while the finish is long & dry.

★★★★ **Brut Méthode Cap Classique** ⓥ Pure & precise bottle-fermented sparkling from chardonnay. **NV** lemon & subtle brioche character, zippy acidity & lots of fine, long-lasting bubbles.

Jan Blanx Super White Cuvée ★★★★ Previously **NV**, latest is **13**, still sauvignon-dominated. A little richer than the Doreen version, with full, ripe flavours & a lipsmacking, succulent acidity, albeit no great intensity. Not retasted: **Sybrand Mankadan Chenin Blanc 12** ★★★★ **Blanc de Blancs Méthode Cap Classique 08** ★★★☆

Doreen range (NEW)

Sauvignon Blanc ★★★★ Forthcoming tropical & citrus notes on ripe **13**, with just an edge of grassier bite. Fresh, lively & well balanced.

Moments Collection

Summer Moments Chenin Blanc ★★★ Easygoing & pleasingly balanced **13** shows freshness & a nice, modest fruitiness. Follows particularly good **11** (★★★★). **12** sold out untasted. Not retasted: **Winter Moments Shiraz-Cabernet Sauvignon 11** ★★★★

Sgt Pepper range

Sgt Pepper ⓥ ★★★ Shiraz-led **10** is modest but likeable, with blackcurrant flavoured fruit-pastille quality about it. Juicy & fresh. — TJ

Location/WO: Stellenbosch ▪ Closed to public ▪ Owner(s)/cellarmaster(s)/winemaker(s)/viticulturist(s) Teddy Hall ▪ PO Box 2868 Somerset West 7129 ▪ teddy@teddyhallwines.com ▪ www.teddyhallwines.com ▪ F +27 (0)86-504-8178 ▪ **T +27 (0)83-461-8111**

☐ **Tembana Valley** *see* Rooiberg Winery

Tempel Wines ⓥ ⌂

Historically a place of worship for Jewish traders, this Berg River farm was planted with bushvines by its former Catholic Afrikaner owner to pioneer a kosher pinotage in 2003. The legacy of multiculturalism and experimentation continues with Swedish adman Alf Ljungqvist pleasing mainly Scandinavian buyers with non-kosher renditions including multi-variety co-fermentations.

Location: Paarl ▪ Map: Paarl & Wellington ▪ Est 2000 ▪ 1stB 2003 ▪ Tasting, sales & cellar tours by appt ▪ Fee R25 ▪ Guest lodge (B&B), with 5 cottages ▪ Owner(s)/winemaker(s) Alf Ljungqvist ▪ 6ha/4.2ha (ptage) ▪ 24t/1,700cs own label 85% red 15% white ▪ PO Box 7295 Noorder-Paarl 7623 ▪ sales@tempelwines.co.za ▪ www.tempelwines.co.za ▪ S 33° 40' 34.0" E 018° 58' 32.2" ▪ F +27 (0)21-872-3883 ▪ **T +27 (0)21-872-4065**

☐ **10 Chapters** *see* Thandi Wines
☐ **Terra Del Capo** *see* Anthonij Rupert Wyne
☐ **Terra Madre** *see* High Constantia Wine Cellar
☐ **Terre de Papillon** *see* Baratok Wines

Teubes Family Wines ⓥ 🍴 🥪 ⌂ ◎ 🅰 ♿

Co-owned by veteran viticultural consultant Johan Teubes, Houmoed's organically, ethically farmed vines supplemented by other cool-climate West Coast vineyards feed this emerging, steadily expanding boutique portfolio. Son Sybrand makes the wine in a converted tannery; mum Ella welcomes visitors with wildflower hikes, light lunches and the new 'Oeskoorsfees' (Harvest Fever Festival).

Teubes Family Collection

★★★★ **Sauvignon Blanc** Previewed **14** already shows complexity in its smoky 'fumé' & blackcurrant vinosity. Weighty & rich but energised by breathtaking natural West Coast freshness. Might rate (★★★★★) once bottled. No **13**.

Not tasted: **Pinotage Reserve**.

Lamberts Bay's Finest range

★★★★ **Sauvignon Blanc 14** reflective of Lamberts Bay's cool, coastal vineyards. Seabreeze fresh, good flavour intensity & weight without overt fruitiness. Balance, length, for few years ageing.

Limited Releases

Cabernet Sauvignon ⊘ ★★★★ Serious but approachable **10**, coconut-laced blackcurrant; evolved malty note & garnet hue suggest best enjoyed soon.

Malkopbaai range

Rosé (NEW) ★★ Semi-sweet **14** from pinotage with engaging natural fresh feel, wild strawberry & cream flavours. **Sauvignon Blanc** ★★★ Riper papaya/melon-style **14** refreshed by balanced zingy acid. WO W Cape. Not tasted: **Pinotage**. — AL

Location: Vredendal ▪ Map: Olifants River ▪ WO: Olifants River/Western Cape/Lamberts Bay ▪ Est 2010 ▪ 1stB 2011 ▪ Tasting & sales Mon-Fri 8-5 Sat 9.30-5 ▪ Fee R20 ▪ Closed Easter Sat/Sun, Dec 25 & Jan 1 ▪ Cellar tours by appt ▪ Tour groups (up to 40 pax) ▪ Facilities for children ▪ Farm produce ▪ Cheese platters & pizza ▪ BYO picnic ▪ Conferences ▪ Walks/hikes ▪ Bergkraal 4x4 trail ▪ Mountain biking ▪ Conservation area ▪ Guest cottages ▪ Owner(s) Johan & Ella Teubes ▪ Cellarmaster(s) Sybrand Teubes ▪ Winemaker(s) Sybrand Teubes & Elaine Conradie ▪ Viticulturist(s) Johan Teubes ▪ (cab, ptage, shiraz, chard, sauv) ▪ 300t ▪ PO Box 791 Vredendal 8160 ▪ sybrand@teubeswines.co.za ▪ www.teubeswines.co.za ▪ S 31° 43' 19.1" E 018° 30' 14.5" ▪ F +27 (0)27-213-3773 ▪ **T +27 (0)27-213-2377**

Thabani Wines

Jabulani Ntshangase started out in wine as a store assistant in New York City almost 4 decades ago, going on to co-found seminal Spice Route Winery, and mentoring young black winemakers. His own brand, Thabani ('Joyful'), is made to spec mostly for the on-trade. See under Highberry Wines for his new venture with vinegrower Andre Parker and ex-Waterkloof winemaker Werner Engelbrecht.

Location: Cape Town ▪ Closed to public ▪ Owner(s) Jabulani Ntshangase ▪ PO Box 1381 Stellenbosch 7599 ▪ jntshangase@aol.com ▪ www.thabani.co.za ▪ F +27 (0)86-648-3676 ▪ **T +27 (0)82-734-9409**

Thandi Wines   Ⓠ

Thandi was one of SA's earliest agricultural empowerment projects when 250 farm employee families took ownership of more than half the company in 1999. The vision of being socially and ethically responsible has remained steadfast, Thandi having the distinction of becoming the world's first Fairtrade accredited wine label in 2003, and any profits go towards upliftment initiatives.

Thandi Single Varietal range

Shiraz Rosé ★★★ Vermilion **14** candyfloss aroma & genteel crispness with soft red-fruit tones, balanced, dry. **Sauvignon Blanc** ⊘ ★★★ Missing the creamy breadth & fruit of previous, **14** is herbaceous, lean & crisp, a light summer quaffer. Not retasted: **Cabernet Sauvignon 11** ★★★ **Shiraz 11** ★★★★ **Shiraz Rosé Sparkling 13** ★★☆

Thandi Dual Varietal range

Shiraz-Cabernet Sauvignon ★★★ **13** 69/31 blend perfect braai mate: spicy, smoky & savoury, with rounded tannins. WO W Cape, as all these. **Chardonnay-Chenin Blanc** ⊘ ★★★★ Super al fresco/solo wine. **14** 50/50 blend attractive ripe pear & apple melange, fresh, tangy & very quaffable. Not retasted: **Cabernet Sauvignon-Merlot 10** ★★★ **Sauvignon Blanc-Semillon 11** ★★★

Discontinued: **Kumkani range**. — MW

Location/map: Stellenbosch ▪ WO: Stellenbosch/Western Cape ▪ Est 1995 ▪ Tasting & sales Mon-Thu 10-4 Fri 10-3 ▪ Fee R20pp ▪ Closed all pub hols ▪ Tour groups ▪ Owner(s) Thandi Wines (Pty) Ltd ▪ Fairtrade ▪ PO Box 597 Stellenbosch 7599 ▪ info@thandiwines.co.za ▪ www.thandiwines.co.za ▪ S 33° 57' 47.66" E 018° 47' 38.51" ▪ F +27 (0)86-561-0152 ▪ **T +27 (0)21-881-3290**

☐ **The 19th Wines** see 19th Wines

Thelema Mountain Vineyards

Pioneers of the 1990s revolution in SA winemaking, and still going strong, Gyles Webb and family continue to invest in and improve their farm and winery on the crest of Stellenbosch's Helshoogte Pass. New last year were six 5-ton stainless steel red-wine fermenters (which Gyles jokes cost more than building the original winery back in 1987!), and which will allow winemaker Rudi Schultz (marking 15 harvests here this year) to increase whole-bunch fermentation. The farm's Sutherland vineyards in cool-climate Elgin join the Stellenbosch estate in becoming members of the Biodiversity & Wine Initiative in their own right. It's all part of an ongoing commitment to preserving the natural advantages of their individual terroirs for future generations.

Thelema range

★★★★☆ **Cabernet Sauvignon** Elegant benchmark cab oozes class, authority & power with subtlety & grace. **10**, with soupçon petit verdot, perfumed black fruits give way to hints of dark chocolate, cedar spice - all underlined with perfectly integrated tannins & acidity. Glorious drinking now or keep for 10 years.

★★★★☆ **The Mint Cabernet Sauvignon** No surprises as to the name on **11** (★★★★), with fresh sweet spearmint & dark chocolate notes combining to rather overwhelm black fruit. Well-managed oak & softish tannins make for very pleasant drinking after better-balanced **10**.

★★★★ **Shiraz** Beautifully judged **11** balances black fruit nose (mulberries & black plums) with a meaty core flashed through with polish, leather & plenty of spice. Gritty texture smoothed by silky tannins.

★★★★★ **Rabelais** Darkly brooding **10**, mainly cab with 14% petit verdot; naturally fermented, 80% new oak. Intoxicating mix of cassis & perfume on the nose giving way to ripe (never jammy) blackberries, some tar, cedar & heady spices. Wrapped up in velvety tannins, a wine fit for the grandest occasions.

★★★★ **Chardonnay** Toasty notes slightly overdone on **13** (★★★☆) but almost enough creamy yellow fruit & ginger spice to balance. **12** was elegant & discreet.

★★★★ **Ed's Reserve Dry White** Layer upon layer of interesting flavours on **13** (★★★★☆), starting with trademark muscat nose of rosepetals before peaches, limes & cream take over, leading to lengthy, complex finish. From chardonnay, steps up on **12**.

★★★★ **Sauvignon Blanc** ⊘ Thoroughly lovely **14** (★★★★★) steps up on **13**, dancing delicately between perfume & nettles, gooseberries & grapefruits. Excellently integrated acidity & lengthy, positive finish. Very enjoyable now & will improve for next 2-3 years.

★★★★ **Blanc de Blancs MCC** ⓃⒺⓌ Great debut **11** sparkling from Elgin chardonnay shows lots of flowers & yeasty notes enlivened with bouncy acidity & frothy, persistent bubbles. Fresh citrus & nuts (despite 36 months on lees) twirl happily to floral, marzipan finish.

Mountain Red ★★★★ Excellent everyday quaffer, **12** spicy notes of fresh berries & leather. Mainly shiraz. Also tasted: **Merlot 11** ★★★★ **Muscat de Frontignan 14** ★★★ **Riesling 12** ★★★★ **Riesling Late Harvest 10** ★★★★ **Vin de Hel Muscat Late Harvest 12** ★★★ Not tasted: **Merlot Reserve**.

Sutherland range

★★★★ **Chardonnay** Breakfast notes on **12** of honey, oatmeal, creamy citrus. Well-integrated oak mixes happily with cooked apples & pears for harmonious, all-day everyday wine.

★★★★ **Sauvignon Blanc** Very flinty tank sample **14** starts out green - grass, hay & limes - before tropical notes, yellow citrus & balancing acidity take over. Needs & deserves some time to settle, should improve.

★★★★ **Viognier-Roussanne** Wonderful mouthful of rich & complex flavours on **11** - baked cling peaches, poached pears, all lifted by delicate aromas of marzipan & spice. Discreetly oaked, with lengthy though slightly warm finish.

Syrah ★★★★ Plum pudding & spice with smoked meat & bacon on **10**. Also tasted: **Cabernet Sauvignon-Petit Verdot 10** ★★★ **Grenache Rosé 14** ★★★ **Riesling 13** ★★★ Not retasted: **Pinot Noir 12** ★★★ — CM

Location/map: Stellenbosch ▪ WO: Stellenbosch/Elgin/Western Cape ▪ Est 1983 ▪ 1stB 1988 ▪ Tasting & sales Mon-Fri 9–5 Sat 10–3 ▪ Fee R25/6 wines, waived on purchase ▪ Owner(s) McLean & Webb Family Trusts ▪ Cellarmaster(s) Gyles Webb (1983) ▪ Winemaker(s) Rudi Schultz (Dec 2000), with Duncan Clarke (Jan 2009) ▪ 257ha/90ha (cab, grenache, merlot, p verdot, pinot, shiraz, chard, muscat d'F, riesling, rouss, sauv, viog) ▪ 1,000t/60,000cs own label 40% red 60% white ▪ BWI ▪ PO Box 2234 Dennesig Stellenbosch 7601 ▪ info@thelema.co.za ▪ www.thelema.co.za ▪ S 33° 54' 30.0" E 018° 55' 23.4" ▪ F +27 (0)21-885-1800 ▪ **T +27 (0)21-885-1924**

☐ **The Liberator** *see* Liberator
☐ **The Marais Family** *see* Wonderfontein
☐ **The Mason's Winery** *see* Mason's Winery

For more information, visit wineonaplatter.com

Thembi & Co

A black empowerment venture whose owner, medical nursing assistant turned entrepreneur Thembi Tobie, says is dependent for its long-term success on offering excellent products backed up by world-class service. 'I find people choose your wine because they like your label and what's in your bottle. That's all that matters.'

The Belief range
Pinotage ★★★ Blueberry & spice dusting on ex-tank **14**; flavourful & succulent drinking. **Sauvignon Blanc** **★★★** Gooseberry freshness on lively **14** preview. Also tasted: **Shiraz 14 ★★★ Chenin Blanc 14 ★★☆** Not tasted: **Chardonnay**.

Thembi range
Shiraz ★★★ 14 tank sample has black plums plus Christmas cake aromas, flavours. Slips down smoothly. **Chenin Blanc ★★★** Crisp **14** ex tank boasts tropical fruit, Granny Smith apple acidity. Also tasted: **Pinotage 14 ★★★ Sauvignon Blanc** **14 ★★☆** Not tasted: **Chardonnay**. — CR

Location: Paarl ▪ Est/1stB 2009 ▪ Tasting by appt ▪ Owner(s) Thembi Tobie ▪ Winemaker(s) Jaco Brand (Citrusdal Cellars) ▪ Fairtrade ▪ thembi@thembiwines.co.za ▪ www.thembiwines.co.za ▪ **T +27 (0)22-921-2235/+27 (0)83-277-5117**

☐ **Thembu** *see* House of Mandela
☐ **The Mentors** *see* KWV
☐ **The Observatory Cellar** *see* Observatory Cellar
☐ **The Old Man's Blend** *see* Groote Post Vineyards
☐ **The Pavillion** *see* Boschendal Wines
☐ **The Point** *see* Cape Point Vineyards
☐ **The Rhino of Linton Park** *see* Rhino of Linton Park
☐ **The Royal** *see* Valley Vineyards Wine Company
☐ **The Ruins** *see* Bon Cap Organic Winery
☐ **The Sadie Family** *see* Sadie Family Wines
☐ **The Saints** *see* DGB
☐ **The Spice Route Winery** *see* Spice Route Winery
☐ **The Stellenbosch Reserve** *see* Stellenbosch Reserve
☐ **The Three Foxes** *see* Three Foxes
☐ **The Tin Mine** *see* Zevenwacht
☐ **The Township Winery** *see* Township Winery
☐ **The Tree Series** *see* Bellingham

Theuniskraal ⓥ ⓹

Named after a son of one of the earliest families to settle in Tulbagh Valley (circa 1699), Theuniskraal has been farmed by the Jordaan family since 1927 and is recognised as SA's first white-wine estate.

Cape Riesling ★★★ Cape institution since 1948, from variety aka crouchen blanc. Bright & crisp **14**, with green apple hint. Modest alcohol, as all the whites. **Semillon-Chardonnay ★★★** Pleasantly fruity, light & fresh. **14** preview brisk acidity & upbeat finish. Also tasted: **Prestige 13 ★★★ Moscato Rosé 14 ★★★ Bouquet Blanc 14 ★★★** — GdB

Location/map/WO: Tulbagh ▪ Est 1705 ▪ 1stB 1947 ▪ Tasting & sales Mon-Fri 9–12 & 1–4, Sat 10–1 ▪ Closed Easter Sat/Sun, Dec 25 & Jan 1 ▪ Owner(s)/viticulturist(s) Jordaan family ▪ Cellarmaster(s) Andries Jordaan (1991) ▪ Winemaker(s) Andries Jordaan (1991) & Wagner Jordaan ▪ 140ha total ▪ BWI ▪ PO Box 34 Tulbagh 6820 ▪ tkraal@lando.co.za ▪ www.theuniskraal.co.za ▪ S 33° 13' 41.3" E 019° 8' 7.1" ▪ F +27 (0)23-230-2284 ▪ **T +27 (0)23-230-0687/89**

☐ **The Village Walk** *see* Franschhoek Cellar

- ☐ **The Warhorse** *see* Simonsig Landgoed
- ☐ **The Wine Fusion** *see* Wine Fusion
- ☐ **The Winery of Good Hope** *see* Winery of Good Hope
- ☐ **The Wingnut** *see* Chateau Naudé Wine Creation
- ☐ **The Wolftrap** *see* Wolftrap
- ☐ **Thierry & Guy** *see* Fat Bastard

Thokozani Wines

This Wellington empowerment partnership between Diemersfontein employees, external investors and Diemersfontein Wines is more than a range of wine. It owns land, offers event and hospitality facilities, provides professional training and development to its employees, and markets the Thokozani ('Celebration') wines - made by Diemersfontein - in Africa, Europe, America and Asia.

★★★★ **CCV** ⓥ Unwooded blend of chenin with dollops chardonnay & viognier; **12** (★★★★) citrus fruit given creamy texture by lees-ageing; tasty, but shade off last-tasted **10**.

Rosé ★★ Ruby-hued **14** laden with red berries, generous, styled for the sweeter tooth. Not retasted: **SMV 12** ★★★ — DS

Location/WO: Wellington ▪ Map: Paarl & Wellington ▪ Est/1stB 2005 ▪ Tasting & sales daily 10-5 ▪ Closed Dec 25 ▪ Cellar tours by appt ▪ Seasons Restaurant ▪ Tour groups ▪ Conferences ▪ Walks/hikes ▪ 4-star Thokozani Cottages ▪ Owner(s) Diemersfontein employees, external investors & Diemersfontein Wines ▪ Cellarmaster(s) Francois Roode (Sep 2003) ▪ Winemaker(s) Francois Roode (Sep 2003), with Lauren Hulsman (Nov 2011) ▪ Viticulturist(s) Waldo Kellerman (Aug 2007) ▪ 180ha/60ha (cabs s/f, grenache, malbec, mourv, p verdot, ptage, roobernet, shiraz, chenin, viog) ▪ 60t/8,000cs own label 40% red 40% white 20% rosé ▪ WIETA ▪ PO Box 41 Wellington 7654 ▪ info@thokozani. co.za ▪ www.thokozani.co.za ▪ S 33° 39' 41.1" E 019° 0' 31.1" ▪ F +27 (0)21-864-2095 ▪ **T +27 (0)21-864-5050**

Thorne & Daughters Wines

After qualifying in Viticulture & Oenology in the UK, and doing harvests around the world, John Seccombe and wife Tasha founded Thorne & Daughters at the end of 2012. (Thorne is John's middle name, in the family for centuries.). Their approach is to take on small parcels of exceptional grapes wherever they may be found, and the resulting maiden wines, while new to the guide, have been selling well locally and in 5 other countries. The plan is to build volumes and establish an own cellar. Meanwhile John continues to commute to Alsace, where he helps vinify grand cru riesling.

Thorne & Daughters range ⓝ

★★★★ **Tin Soldier Semillon 13** a true individual: copper gold colour from natural ferment on skins in oak of rare blend Franschhoek semillon gris & blanc. Green melon & wild honey, shortbread-savoury. Earthy, natural, pure.

★★★★☆ **Rocking Horse Cape White Blend** Roussanne-led multi-regional oaked blend with natural ferment & lees-ageing. **13** seduces with walnut, buttered toast & lemon/tangerine marmalade flavours. Offers layers of interest - savoury, earthy yet fruity, finishing creamy & long. — CR, CvZ

Location: Elgin ▪ WO: Western Cape/Franschhoek ▪ Est 2012 ▪ 1stB 2013 ▪ Closed to public ▪ Owner(s) John & Tasha Seccombe ▪ Cellarmaster(s)/winemaker(s)/viticulturist(s) John Seccombe (Dec 2012) ▪ 14t/1,600cs own label 5% red 95% white ▪ PO Box 96 Elgin 7180 ▪ john@thorneanddaughters.com ▪ www.thorneanddaughters.com ▪ F +27 (0)86-246-2923 ▪ **T +27 (0)76-036-7116**

- ☐ **1000 Miles** *see* Mulderbosch Vineyards

Three Foxes

After 11 vintages of vinifying fruit from different vineyards, the three foxes - Mullineux & Leeu cellarmaster Chris Mullineux and brothers Pascal and Olivier Schildt — say they've fallen so seriously in love with a parcel of old-vine clairette blanche on Wellington's Groenberg that they've decided to focus and make a white wine from it every year. 'Our red-wine offering will still be dynamic and changing each vintage though!'

Carignan (NEW) ⊛ ★★★☆ From Perdeberg unirrigated bushvines, delicious, characterful **12** smells & tastes like liquid youngberry jam. Supple, juicy, lovely piquant acidity lifting the tone, old oak & 25% bunch-pressing forming an invisible, supple structure. **Clairette Blanche** (NEW) ⊛ ★★★☆ Minuscule yield from Wellington dryland vines, intricately vinified (partly in oak), resulting in subtle, intriguing **13**, with glimpses of citrus, angelica & almond on a finely nuanced almost ethereal palate, the shadow of which lingers on in a long cider-like farewell. Not tasted: **Mourvèdre, Castillo Syrah**. — MW

Location: Riebeek-Kasteel ▪ WO: Swartland/Coastal ▪ Est/1stB 2004 ▪ Closed to public ▪ Owner(s) Pascal Schildt, Olivier Schildt, Mullineux & Leeu Family Wines ▪ Winemaker(s)/viticulturist(s) Chris Mullineux (Jan 2004) ▪ 1.2ha (carignan, mourv, syrah, chenin, clairette) ▪ 4t/400cs own label 80% red 20% white ▪ PO Box 369 Riebeek-Kasteel 7307 ▪ pascal.schildt@gmail.com ▪ www.the-three-foxes.com ▪ F +27 (0)86-720-1541 ▪ **T +27 (0)82-333-6888**

☐ **Three Graces** *see* Women in Wine
☐ **Three Peaks** *see* Mount Vernon Estate
☐ **Three Pines** *see* Stark-Condé Wines
☐ **Three Rivers** *see* Bon Courage Estate

Thunderchild

Bearing the motto 'In Aid of Humanity', Thunderchild is made pro bono by sympathetic Robertson wineries and sold from their cellardoors. After audited costs, all proceeds are ploughed into the education of the children of Die Herberg Home.

Thunderchild ⊗ ★★★★ Savoury Bordeaux red blend, naturally fermented, **09** is led by merlot (50%) with both cabs; dark berry & cocoa fusion, pliable tannins for easy imbibing. — TJ

Location/WO: Robertson ▪ Est 2003 ▪ 1stB 2008 ▪ Wines available from Rooiberg Winery, Ashton Cellar, Bon Courage, Robertson Winery, Ashton Wine Boutique, Affie Plaas Farmstall, Platform 62, Tanagra Winery, De Wetshof Winery & La Verne Wine Boutique - see individual cellars for opening times ▪ Owner(s) Thunderchild Wingerd Trust ▪ Cellarmaster(s) Various Robertson winegrowers ▪ 5ha (cabs s/f, merlot) ▪ PO Box 770 Robertson 6705 ▪ info@thunderchild.co.za ▪ www.thunderchild.co.za ▪ F +27 (0)23-626-3664 ▪ **T +27 (0)23-626-3661**

Tierhoek

This remote winery in Piekenierskloof's breathtaking landscape was established by Shelley and the late Tony Sandell in 2001. Huge boulders made way for new vineyards, but the 60-year-old ungrafted grenache and 40-year-old chenin, they say, 'still deliver amazing grapes with plenty of character'. The watchword is 'natural' – no pesticides or herbicides in the vineyards, and spontaneous fermentation and minimal use of sulphur. Carla Nieuwoudt joined the team as winemaker in 2014.

Tierhoek range

★★★★☆ **Grenache** ⊘ Characterful **12** from old vines shows fynbos, tar, olive & black fruits. The soft, intriguing palate, with long-lingering flavours of dried meat, dried flowers & tar, has intensity & warmth but also tension. Well framed by very fine tannin.

★★★★ **Syrah-Mourvèdre-Grenache** ⊘ Changing name reflects proportions of the grapes. Youthfully closed but promising **13** shows notes of fennel, dark cherries & Asian spice. Older oak allows the ripe yet fresh fruit & minerality to dominate on a complex but not showy palate.

★★★★ **Chardonnay 14** preview leans to the mineral spectrum, with yellow apple & stone. Natural ferment, light oaking. Fresh, vigorous & thirst quenching, with flinty tones & a twist of lemon to end. No **12**, **13** untasted.

★★★★ **Chenin Blanc** Refreshing & zesty **13** from 36 year old vines. Portion fermented & matured in oak to balance texture & freshness. Long, tightly woven palate, with lipsmacking acidity.

★★★★ **Sauvignon Blanc** New vintage tasted again as tank sample. Tending to minerality, **14** is elegant & finely chiselled, with subtle fruit aromas of granadilla & gooseberry. Looks promising.

★★★★☆ **Straw Wine** Usual generous richness offered by this **NV** dessert wine from air-dried chenin vinified in a solera. With nearly 300 grams of sugar & just 9.5% alcohol, the forceful, creamy palate offers quince, dark bread, dried mango, amongst other complexities, great persistence.

Sandveld range (NEW)

★★★★ **Sauvignon Blanc** ⊘ **13** tank sample shows vibrant characters of lemongrass, grapefruit & freshly mown lawn. Delicious, crisp & finely woven, with distinct mineral undertones. Potential to develop.

Piekeniers range

White ★★★☆ Fresh, satisfying **13** blend of sauvignon, chardonnay & viognier. Now bottled, is upbeat, crisp & bone-dry, with attractive mineral notes. Not tasted: **Red**. — JPf

Location: Citrusdal ▪ Map: Olifants River ▪ WO: Piekenierskloof ▪ Est 2001 ▪ 1stB 2003 ▪ Tasting, sales & cellar tours on the farm Mon-Fri 8.30-4.30 by appt ▪ Fee R20, waived on purchase ▪ Closed all pub hols ▪ BYO picnic ▪ Walks/hikes ▪ Conservation area ▪ Guest house (sleeps 9) ▪ Owner(s) Shelley Sandell ▪ Winemaker(s) Carla Nieuwoudt (Jan 2014) & Roger Burton (consultant), with Basie Snyers (Oct 2006) ▪ Viticulturist(s) Ryno Kellerman (Aug 2006) ▪ 700ha/16ha (grenache, mourv, shiraz, chard, chenin, sauv) ▪ 70t/6,000cs own label 40% red 60% white ▪ BWI, IPW ▪ PO Box 53372 Kenilworth 7745 ▪ info@tierhoek.com ▪ www.tierhoek.com ▪ S 32° 23' 27.49" E 018° 51' 24.14" ▪ F +27 (0)86-731-6351 ▪ **T +27 (0)21-674-3041/+27 (0)82-536-7132**

☐ **Tiger Horse** *see* Boutinot South Africa

☐ **Tin Cups** *see* Wineways Marketing

☐ **Tin Hill** *see* Signal Gun Wines

☐ **Tin Mine** *see* Zevenwacht

☐ **Titanic** *see* Louis

☐ **Title Deed** *see* Croydon Vineyard Residential Estate

☐ **Tobias** *see* Bryan MacRobert Wines

Tokara

Banker GT Ferreira, owner of this estate on the crest of the Helshoogte Pass outside Stellenbosch town, has been heard to proudly grumble about the absurdities of investment in wine – he famously spoke of 'return on ego' (versus return on investment). But then Tokara acquired two other farms, in the cooler-climate areas of Elgin and the Hemel-en-Aarde, to extend the range of terroirs expressed in his wines, so something convinced him, as it had many Tokara admirers, about real value. Miles Mossop has been in the cellar and Aidan Morton in the vineyards for some 15 years now, which could be something like a record in the Cape for a wine-producing team – let alone such a brilliantly effective one.

Reserve Collection

★★★★☆ **Pinotage** Polished **12** displays the light-footed elegance of previous. Alluring depth of perfumed fruit & unusual white pepper, enhanced by all-new oak. Harmonious balance & fine, supple tannins, tempered alcohol. Lingering & scented farewell.

★★★★ **Syrah** Departing from **10**'s expansively ripe profile, **11** (★★★☆) mere suggestion of red fruit enveloped in dry dusty tannins & muted by oak (2 years, 40% new). Might simply need time to integrate & fruit to reveal itself.

★★★★☆ **Director's Reserve Red** Classically styled **11** cab-led Bordeaux blend with petit verdot, merlot, cab franc & malbec (14/10/5/3). Shows youthful restraint with layers of flavour woven into fine chalky tannin structure. Balanced, with pedigree to age with distinction.

★★★★ **Stellenbosch Chardonnay 13** a shade off **12** (★★★★☆). Rich & flamboyant, with more new oak & alcohol than sibling, overshadowing the fruit kernel of lime & pear. Needs to harmonise.

★★★★☆ **Elgin Sauvignon Blanc** Polished **14**, more serious than Tokara version (both unoaked), showcases cooler Elgin provenance. Good fruit definition & freshness, some minerality & mid-palate weight. A fine food wine.

★★★★★ **Director's Reserve White** Seamless **13** (★★★★☆) sauvignon/semillon (71/29) blend, continues fine form of expressive **12**. Refined elegance, intense lemon & grapefruit freshness leavened by creamy beeswax nuance. Deft oaking (27% new) allows fruit to shine. Polished, with long finish.

★★★★☆ **Noble Late Harvest** Oak-fermented/matured **13** from sauvignon. Unctuously rich & viscous elixir, laced with glacé pineapple, barley sugar & lime. Focused intensity at 10.67% alcohol. Balanced & delicious on its own, perfect with dessert. WO Elgin.

Not tasted: **Walker Bay Chardonnay**, **Walker Bay Sauvignon Blanc**.

Tokara range

★★★★ **Cabernet Sauvignon** Less expressive than previous, but just as fine, in cooler-vintage **12**, with splashes petit verdot, merlot & cab franc. Cassis fruit core with dry food-friendly tannins still unfolding. Will reward cellaring.

★★★★ **Chardonnay 13** exuberant ripe pear & lime freshness, raises bar on **12** (★★★★). Brush new oak adds rich hazelnut nuance but fruit is the star in appealingly drinkable style. WO W Cape.

★★★★ **Sauvignon Blanc 14**, with a splash of semillon, continues in tangy & vivacious style. Lively passionfruit throughout, balanced & ready to enjoy now & over the next few years. WO W Cape.

Grenache (NEW) ★★★☆ With 12% shiraz, **12** restrained & hiding its charm — preferably give time to unfurl (potential is there!) or decant if curious/impatient to unlock some of the variety's fruity generosity. Walker Bay WO. Also tasted: **Grenache Rosé 14** ★★★ Not retasted: **Shiraz 11** ★★★★

Brandy range

5 Year Potstill (Ⓐ) ★★★☆ Attractive youthful mix dried fruit & floral notes, with nutty, clean oak support & a hint of sweetness. Smoothly bright, not too fiery. — WB, TJ, MW

Location/map: Stellenbosch ▪ WO: Stellenbosch/Elgin/Walker Bay/Western Cape ▪ 1stB 2001 ▪ Tasting & sales Mon-Fri 9–5 Sat/Sun 10–3 ▪ Closed Easter Fri/Mon & Dec 25 ▪ Tokara Restaurant Tue-Sun lunch 12.30-2.30 & dinner 7-9.30 ▪ Delicatessen Tue-Sun 10-4 ▪ Facilities for children ▪ Gift shop ▪ Art exhibitions ▪ Owner(s) GT & Anne-Marie Ferreira ▪ Winemaker(s) Miles Mossop (Jan 2000), with Dumisani Mathonsi (Jan 2004) ▪ Viticulturist(s) Aidan Morton (Nov 2000) ▪ 104ha (cabs s/f, grenache, malbec, merlot, mourv, p verdot, ptage, shiraz, chard, chenin, sauv, sem) ▪ 705t/100,000cs own label 40% red 59% white 1% rosé ▪ PO Box 662 Stellenbosch 7599 ▪ wine@tokara.com ▪ www.tokara.com ▪ S 33° 55' 2.9" E 018° 55' 13.7" ▪ F +27 (0)21-808-5911 ▪ **T +27 (0)21-808-5900**

☐ **Tooverberg** *see* Klein Parys Vineyards

Topaz Wine

The homemade wine from half a hectare of garden-grown pinot noir that inspired this venture in 2000 has become a diverse, highly rated range. But the essential element of having fun while making serious wine remains integral to the intrepid, creative and collaborative team, tweaked in 2013 and prevented by injury from harvesting in 2014.

★★★★ **Pinot Noir** (Ⓐ) Toasty, charry oak currently masks **12**'s bright, elegant sour cherry Elgin fruit; lively acidity gives structure & carries savoury mineral finish.

★★★★ **Shiraz** (Ⓐ) Previously 'Syrah' - last tasted by that name was elegant **07**. Smoothly textured spicy **12** (★★★★) exhibits Elgin's cool-climate pepperiness & finishes with appetising savoury acidity.

★★★★ **Custom Crush** (Ⓐ) Stern **11** (★★★★) from Wellington cab, latest offering under recession-beating label, not as plush & complex as **08** blend with cab franc.

★★★★ **Viognier** (Ⓐ) Rich, lightly oxidative **12** (★★★★) flaunts variety's ripe fleshiness & warmth, while happily retaining Elgin's trademark mineral edge. Like previous **09**, subtly oaked.

Not tasted: **Shiraz-Mourvèdre**. — GM

For more information, visit wineonaplatter.com

Location/map: Stellenbosch ▪ WO: Elgin/Wellington ▪ Est 2000 ▪ 1stB 2001 ▪ Tasting & sales Sat 10-2 (Sep-Apr), or by prior arrangement ▪ Owner(s) Topaz Wine Company (Pty) Ltd, shareholders Tanja Beutler, Anthony Hill & Christopher Cosgrove ▪ Winemaker(s) Topaz winemaking team ▪ 1,200cs own label 80% red 20% white ▪ IPW ▪ PO Box 804 Somerset Mall 7137 ▪ tanja@topazwines.co.za ▪ www.topazwineco.com ▪ S 33° 50' 55.67" E 018° 51' 26.19" ▪ F +27 (0)86-612-6118 ▪ **T +27 (0)21-855-4275**

Topiary Wines

This being a farm in Franschhoek ('French Corner'), it's appropriate that the new owners are from France, more so that both are steeped in wine: Philippe Colin, awarded vigneron in Burgundy's fabled Chassagne-Montrachet, and Serge Jaczynski, former sommelier and commercial agent for top French wineries, both frequent visitors to the SA winelands for more than 12 years. Chardonnay, in the form of a brilliant MCC sparkling, is the star performer here in the Wemmershoek Mountain foothills and, knowing a thing or two about the variety, and believing in its potential here, the proprietors are planting more.

★★★★ **Cabernet Sauvignon** Previewed **13** (★★☆) first since **08**, unoaked & showing plump & ripe, almost lush fruit yet also a hard tannic twist. Might gain more balance with time.

★★★★ **Shiraz** Unoaked **13**, pre-bottling, more elegant than last-made **08**. Great intensity of flavour with white pepper, cedar & wild scrub spicing to the polished fruit & fine-grained structure.

★★★★★ **Blanc de Blancs Brut** Méthode cap classique sparkling **11** (★★★★★) in a richer, more contemplative style than last-tasted, stellar **09**, which showcased chardonnay's zesty freshness. Layers of apple pie & brioche, with creamy richness from 30 months on lees, all with fine lime undertone & long, clean finish. One to savour.

Not retasted: **Cabernet Sauvignon-Shiraz 07** ★★★★ Not tasted: **Rosé**. — MW

Location/map/WO: Franschhoek ▪ Est 2005 ▪ 1stB 2006 ▪ Tasting & sales Mon-Fri 9-5 Sat 10-4 Sun by appt only ▪ Fee R20, waived on purchase ▪ Closed Easter Sun, Dec 24/25 & Jan 1 ▪ Meals/refreshments & cellar tours on special request ▪ BYO picnic ▪ Small tour groups ▪ 1.7km fynbos hiking trail ▪ Conservation area ▪ B&B ▪ Owner(s) Philippe Colin & Serge Jaczynski ▪ Cellarmaster(s)/winemaker(s) Philippe Colin (Aug 2014) ▪ Viticulturist(s) Dirk Wouter van der Merwe (Jan 2013) ▪ 63ha/20ha (cab, shiraz, chard) ▪ 44t/8,000cs own label 90% red 10% white ▪ IPW ▪ PO Box 108 La Motte 7691 ▪ topiarysales@telkomsa.net ▪ www.topiarywines.com ▪ S 33° 51' 52.2" E 019° 2' 39.0" ▪ F +27 (0)86-750-1742 ▪ **T +27 (0)21-867-0258**

☐ **Top Secret** *see* Ultra Liquors
☐ **Tormentoso** *see* MAN Family Wines
☐ **Torres Claude** *see* Crows Nest
☐ **Totus** *see* Trajan Wines
☐ **Touch of Oak** *see* Rijk's

Township Winery

Households in Philippi and nearby Cape Flats townships are finding new pride, dignity and 'hope for a better future for our children' (and bringing welcome splashes of green to the urban landscape) in this innovative community winegrowing project. Fruit from the families' homesteader vines is brought to a small Philippi Village cellar (open to the public for tasting) for vinification under the experienced eye of Tierhoek consultant winemaker Roger Burton. Original impetus for the venture came from low-income housing developer Kate Jambela, supported by Wellington-based wine entrepreneur Graham Knox (Wine Fusion).

Township Winery range

★★★★ **Philippi Merlot** **12** preview has ripeness & focus, with mulberry notes & creamy tannins. Impressive poise, weight & balance. Shows potential once settled.

Philippi Sauvignon Blanc ★★★★ Asparagus, grassy character beginning to dominate **10** on mid-2013 retaste. Roasted nuts & nettles spice up full, nicely balanced palate. Drink now. Not

For more information, visit wineonaplatter.com

retasted: **The Flats Pinotage 12 ★★★ Philippi Shiraz 12 ★★★☆ The Flats Viognier 12 ★★★**

Dido range
Pinotage ⊘ **★★★** Juicy **12** has faint mocha edge, fresh & easy for everyday drinking. Not retasted: **The Storm Mourvèdre-Shiraz 09 ★★★ Pinot Grigio 10 ★★★★** — IM

Location: Philippi ▪ Map: Cape Peninsula ▪ WO: Western Cape/Paarl ▪ Est 2009 ▪ 1stB 2010 ▪ Tasting Mon-Fri 10-4 ▪ Owner(s) The Township Winery cc ▪ Cellarmaster(s) Roger Burton (2014, consultant) ▪ 800cs own label 50% red 50% white ▪ PO Box 63 Philippi 7781 ▪ kate@jambela.co.za ▪ S 34° 0' 1.02" E 018° 35' 37.71" ▪ F +27 (0)21-447-4476 ▪ **T +27 (0)73-450-9516**

Trajan Wines

Established in 2005 by wine enthusiasts with dreams of an own brand and community service, Stellenbosch's Trajan latterly has focused on its premium range Totus ('Complete'). Fairtrade accredited, the brand funds a crèche/daycare school and helps fight child abductions by supporting Missing Children SA.

Totus range
Shiraz ★★★★ Swartland & Paarl grapes for **10**; high-toned berries, cherries, even some liquorice, to accompany the tobacco notes. Tannins evident in the flavours, savoury rather than harsh, this is a wine that would age well. **Sauvignon Blanc ★★★★ 13** from Elim achieves intensity without sacrificing elegance; has gooseberry freshness & a nice touch of minerality at the end. Not retasted: **Cabernet Sauvignon 09 ★★★★ Pinotage 09 ★★★ Shiraz-Mourvèdre 08 ★★★☆ Chenin Blanc 10 ★★★★** — CR

Location: Stellenbosch ▪ WO: Coastal/Western Cape ▪ Est 2005 ▪ 1stB 2008 ▪ Closed to public ▪ Owner(s) Trajan Wines (Pty) Ltd ▪ Winemaker(s) Mark van Schalkwyk (Sep 2005) ▪ Viticulturist(s) Mark van Schalkwyk ▪ 10,000cs own label 70% red 30% white ▪ Fairtrade ▪ PO Box 1498 Stellenbosch 7599 ▪ info@trajanwines.co.za ▪ www.trajanwines.co.za ▪ F +27 (0)86-299-4281 ▪ **T +27 (0)83-505-2681**

☐ **Travino** *see* Klawer Wine Cellars

Tread Lightly by Backsberg ⓠ

The team at forward-thinking Paarl estate Backsberg are focused on treading lightly on this planet, and showing the way with the use of eco-friendly, lightweight and shatterproof PET (plastic) bottles for this label. The packaging is one of many environmental initiatives by the Back family owners, from commissioning a biomass furnace to developing a protein farm from fly larvae for use as energy.

PET range
Merlot ★★★☆ 12 yields generous blackcurrant & mulberry flavour, ripe & concentrated. Structured, broad, offers good drinkability. **Chenin Blanc ★★★** Rich waxy orange & kumquat notes on **13**. Light, fresh & zesty, with clean, focused yet honeyed semi-dry finish. Also tasted: **Rosé NV ★★★ Sauvignon Blanc 13 ★★★** Not retasted: **Cabernet Sauvignon 10 ★★★★** — FM

Location: Paarl ▪ WO: Western Cape/Paarl ▪ Est/1stB 2010 ▪ Tasting, sales & cellar tours at Backsberg Estate (see entry) ▪ Owner(s) Michael Back & Simon Back ▪ Winemaker(s) Alicia Rechner (Jun 2012) ▪ Viticulturist(s) Clive Trent (Jul 1992) ▪ PO Box 537 Suider-Paarl 7624 ▪ info@backsberg.co.za ▪ www.backsberg.co.za ▪ S 33° 49' 42.9" E 018° 54' 56. 9" ▪ F +27 (0)21-875-5144 ▪ **T +27 (0)21-875-5141**

☐ **Tree Series** *see* Bellingham
☐ **Tribal** *see* Jacques Germanier

Trizanne Signature Wines

Initially sourcing grapes that met her sustainability standards but also offered terroir excellence from Elim and the Swartland, internationally experienced Trizanne Barnard has taken her wine business further afield. Grapes and wine are now also sourced to supply orders from offshore clients, including bulk wines - showing massive growth, here and as a category - but her signature wines still reflect her quest to find the spot that gives signature quality.

Trizanne Signature Wines range

★★★★ **Syrah-Grenache** Dark, savoury, bright fruit on juicily fresh Swartland blend. **13** balanced, with firm but gentle tannic grip, & (above all) delicious. Only older oak used, to keep fruit purity paramount.

★★★★ **Elim Sauvignon Blanc** Dash of oaked semillon on **13** to add weight & complexity. Fresh, interesting & individual, with floral & fynbos elements. Really nicely balanced, & textured.

★★★★ **Reserve Sauvignon Blanc-Semillon** Equal blend **13**; more sauvignon tropicality in youth but semillon lemon zest too. Forceful but crisp, elegant. Only old oak used for maturation, adding silky breadth.

Not tasted: **Coastal Syrah**.

Clearsprings Wines
Not tasted: **Sauvignon Blanc**. — TJ

Location: Cape Town ▪ WO: Elim/Swartland ▪ Est 2008 ▪ 1stB 2009 ▪ Closed to public ▪ Wine sales via website ▪ Owner(s)/winemaker(s) Trizanne Barnard ▪ 19,000cs own label 45% red 65% white + 2.5m L bulk wine export ▪ 14 van der Horst Avenue Kommetjie 7975 ▪ info@trizanne.co.za ▪ www.trizanne.co.za ▪ F +27 (0)86-669-0913 ▪ **T +27 (0)21-783-0617/+27 (0)82-383-6664**

Truter Family Wines

Small quantities of wine are made under the Agaat ('Agate') label of Wellington-based Hugo and Celeste Truter, both trained winemakers, who always wanted to produce handcrafted wines focusing on blends rather than 'boring' single cultivars.

Agaat range

★★★★ **Christina** Forthright sauvignon aromas in light-footed **14** (★★★★) blend with chenin, nouvelle & dash viognier. Immediate charm, with less weight than **12**. No **13**.

John David ⊘ ★★★★ Brightly fruited but also with cocoa powder perfume. **12** Cape Blend of cab, pinotage & shiraz is filled with youthful, fresh verve. — IM

Location: Wellington ▪ WO: Western Cape ▪ Est 2008 ▪ 1stB 2010 ▪ Closed to public ▪ Owner(s) Hugo & Celeste Truter ▪ Winemaker(s) Hugo Truter ▪ 1,000cs own label 50% red 50% white ▪ hugo@truterfamilywines.co.za ▪ www.truterfamilywines.co.za ▪ **T +27 (0)83-639-6288**

TTT Cellar Calitzdorp

Port Elizabeth electrical contractor Ashley Mason's hobby, assisting late 'port' supremo Tony Mossop at his Calitzdorp quinta, Axe Hill, has become a full-fledged winery on the Mason family farm nearby. Still commuting, but with resident help, Ashley dreams of retiring here. But 'TTT' (things take time)...

Viognier ★★ Melon preserve-toned semi-sweet **13**, quite rustic, lacks freshness & length.
Hanepoot ★★★ Now bottled, **13** combo hanepoot grape & ginger beer character, with tangy sweetness, extended finish. **Cape Ruby** ★★ Revisited as bottled wine, **NV (13)** port-style from touriga, tinta & souzão, ultra-ripe, broad beamed. Also tasted: **Cape White NV** ★★ Not retasted: **Cabernet Sauvignon 11 Dry Red NV** ★★ **Cape Vintage 13** ★★★ Not tasted: **Shiraz, Muscat d'Brigne, Red Muscadel**. — CR

Location/WO: Calitzdorp ▪ Map: Klein Karoo & Garden Route ▪ 1stB 2003 ▪ Tasting, sales & tours Mon-Fri 8-4 Sat 8-2 Sun by appt ▪ Closed Easter Fri-Mon, Apr 27, May 1, Dec 25 & Jan 1 ▪ Honey & olive oil ▪ BYO picnic ▪ Owner(s) Ashley & Pat Mason ▪ Cellarmaster(s)/viticulturist(s) Ashley Mason ▪ Winemaker(s) Ashley Mason, with Johan Julies ▪ 0.5ha (souzão, tinta, touriga, hanepoot) ▪ 4t/600cs own label 100% red ▪ PO Box 7067 Newton Park 6055 ▪ tttcellars@iafrica.com ▪ S 33° 31' 50.94" E 021° 41' 44.88" ▪ F +27 (0)44-213-3114 ▪ **T +27 (0)44-213-3114**

For more information, visit wineonaplatter.com

☐ **Tukulu** *see* Earthbound

Tulbagh Winery

Grower-owned Tulbagh Winery, with cellars in Tulbagh and Swartland's Piketberg, attributes dynamic management of its ranges to steady growth in exports (focused on China and Africa) and domestic sales (bolstered by listings like supermarket goliath Pick n Pay). Irreverently named Flippenice, flying off local shelves, welcomes a low-alcohol bottling from rare-bird white variety fernão pires, while niche red plantings from in-house Moravia Empowerment Project promise to spice up the future portfolio.

Klein Tulbagh Reserve range

Merlot ★★★☆ Plush plums, meaty chocolate notes, **13** is no pushover, & not a green nuance in sight. Merlot well handled: curvaceous body, the tannin a hidden support, nice combo fruit & savoury tones to finish. Also tasted: **Cabernet Sauvignon 12 ★★★★ Pinotage 13 ★★★** Not tasted: **Shiraz**.

Porter Mill Station range

Pinotage ⊕ ★★★ Ripe dark plums, a creamy richness in perfume, coupled with a juicy, smooth texture that will make many friends. **13** modern take on pinotage. WO W Cape. Also tasted: **Reserve Cabernet Sauvignon 13 ★★★** Not tasted: **Chenin Blanc**, **Sauvignon Blanc**. Discontinued: **Shiraz**.

Tulbagh range

Shiraz-Pinotage ★★☆ Good match, partners bring red & dark fruit, smoke, spice, rounded ripe flavours & body, plumped up by a touch of sweetness. **13** drinks easily & well. Coastal WO. **Rosé ★★** From pinotage, forthcoming strawberry scents, which fit this sweetish style. **NV** everyday quaffer. **Chardonnay ★★☆** Citrus with a gentle savoury thread, nothing overt, just easy, relaxed enjoyment. Unwooded **14** dry but fruity. **Sauvignon Blanc Brut ★★☆** Peardrops & litchi on latest dry **NV** sparkling, crisply refreshing. **Muscat Ottonel Doux ★★** Litchi-toned muscat flavours, friendly low alcohol (10.5%) & fruity sweetness on latest **NV**. Also tasted: **Merlot 13 ★★ Chenin Blanc 14 ★★ Sauvignon Blanc 14 ★★ Colombard-Chenin Blanc 14 ★★★ Pinotage Doux NV ★★ Sauvignon NV ★★** Not retasted: **Cabernet Sauvignon 11 ★★★ Shiraz 12 ★★★** Not tasted: **Pinotage**. Discontinued: **Port**.

Paddagang range

Paddapoot Hanepoot ⊘ ★★ Fortified sweetie **12** delivers lemon & honey fireside enjoyment. Not retasted: **Brulpadda Port NV ★★★** Not tasted: **Sopkoppie Rooi Muskadel**.

Flippenice range

Xtra Lite ⊜ ★★ Unusual fernão pires grape gives greengage flavours, an aromatic finish. **NV** bone-dry, just 9% alcohol. Coastal WO, as all. Also tasted: **Cabernet Sauvignon-Merlot NV ★★ Chenin Blanc-Sauvignon Blanc NV ★★**

Secluded Valley range

Shiraz-Pinotage ★★ Shiraz, pinotage blend, **NV** off-dry, softly rounded fruity sipper. In 3L bag-in-box, as all. Coastal WO, as for Chenin. Also tasted: **Chenin Blanc NV ★★** — CR

Location: Tulbagh/Porterville ▪ Map: Tulbagh ▪ WO: Tulbagh/Coastal/Western Cape ▪ Est 1906/2006 ▪ 1stB 1910 ▪ Tulbagh Cellar: Tasting & sales Mon-Fri 9–5 Sat & pub hols 9–1 Sun at Paddagang Wine Shop 11-3 ▪ Porterville Cellar: Tasting & sales Mon-Fri 9–5 ▪ Closed Easter Fri-Sun & Dec 25/26 ▪ Cellar tours by appt ▪ Gifts ▪ Farm produce ▪ BYO picnic ▪ Conferences ▪ Walks/hikes ▪ Mountain biking in the area ▪ Owner(s) 86 members ▪ Cellarmaster(s) /Production manager(s) Naude Bruwer (Jan 2010) ▪ Winemaker(s) Porterville: Rudi Wium (Aug 2011); Tulbagh: Helena Neethling (Jun 2010) ▪ Viticulturist(s) Elizabeth Cloete (Dec 2011) ▪ 1,230ha (cab, merlot, ptage, shiraz, chenin, chard, sauv) ▪ 14,500t/100,000cs own label 65% red 30% white 5% rosé & 8m L bulk + 40,000cs for clients ▪ Brands for clients: Grimont (Germany), Millberg (UK/France) ▪ IPW ▪ PO Box 85 Tulbagh 6820; PO Box 52 Porterville 6810 ▪ info@tulbaghwine.co.za ▪ www.tulbaghwine.co.za ▪ S 33° 15′ 8.8″ E 019° 8′ 36.5″ ▪ F +27 (0)23-230-1358; +27 (0)22-931-2171 ▪ T +27 (0)23-230-1001 (Tulbagh); +27 (0)22-931-2170 (Porterville)

☐ **Tullie Family Vineyards** *see* Lanner Hill
☐ **Tunnel** *see* Du Toitskloof Winery

Twee Jonge Gezellen Estate-House of Krone   ⓠ ⓞ

The old 'Two Young Companions' estate in Tulbagh was bought in 2012, after financially troubled times, by the major wine company Vinimark. Krones and their forbears had resided here since 1710 and the brand still bears the name of the family which had more latterly established it as an important house largely focusing on méthode cap classique sparkling wines. That tradition continues, but it will be on a grander scale now. Lavish expenditure has seen expansion and upgrading of the cellar and a substantial start (10 ha newly planted) to a major vineyard extension and revitalisation programme. Ambitions are high.

Krone range

★★★★ **Rosé Cuvée Brut 12** MCC sparkling refined step up on **09** (★★★★). Pinot noir (60%) & chardonnay, with delicate red fruit & rosepetal flavours, engaging piquancy to creamy texture. No **10**, **11** sold out.

★★★★ **Borealis Cuvée Brut** ⊘ Classically styled **12** MCC sparkler is chardonnay-led (60%) with pinot noir. Fresh & well structured, persistent. Touch more sugar than Rosé but still dry, with fine creamy bubbles. No **10, 11** sold out.

★★★★☆ **Nicolas Charles Krone Marque 1** ⓠ Standout **NV** multi-vintage (**01, 02, 03**) sparkling from 50/50 pinot noir/chardonnay; last-tasted disgorgement matured 7 years on lees. Restrained, with pinot richness, chardonnay freshness on palate, persistent bone-dry farewell.

Night Nectar ⓝⓔⓦ ★★★ Semi-sweet bubbles from 60% chardonnay & pinot noir; **11** delicate pineapple & honey favours; versatile: with dessert, bacony breakfast, sweeter-toothed anytimes. Also tasted: **Chardonnay-Pinot Noir 13** ★★★ — MW

Location/map: Tulbagh ▪ WO: Western Cape ▪ Est 1710 ▪ 1stB 1937 ▪ Tasting & sales Mon-Fri 10—4 Sat 10—2 ▪ Closed all pub hols ▪ Cellar tours Mon-Sat at 11 ▪ Annual festival: Christmas in Winter (Jun) ▪ Owner(s) TJG Estate (Pty) Ltd ▪ Winemaker(s) Stephan de Beer (2008) ▪ Viticulturist(s) Rosa Kruger ▪ PO Box 16 Tulbagh 6820 ▪ info@tjg.co.za ▪ www.houseofkrone.co.za ▪ S 33° 14′ 18.1″ E 019° 6′ 51.8″ ▪ F +27 (0)23-230-0686 ▪ T +27 (0)23-230-0680

Twelve Apostles Winery   ⓠ

Cape Town father-and-son team Chris and Charles Lourens describe themselves as 'garagiste winemakers in the true sense of the word; winelovers with a passion for the art and history of small-scale winemaking'. From basket-pressing hand-sorted grapes (sourced widely) to organising one-on-one tastings with winelovers, the civil engineer and online wine marketer swear by 'keeping it real by keeping it small, because when it becomes "work", the passion goes'.

Location: Cape Town ▪ Est/1stB 2009 ▪ Tasting by appt only ▪ Owner(s)/winemaker(s) Chris & Charles Lourens ▪ 3-5t/ ±650cs own label 50% red 50% white ▪ Brands for clients: Kanah Winery ▪ SAWIS ▪ PO Box 16007 Panorama 7506 ▪ info@twelveapostleswinery.co.za ▪ www.twelveapostleswinery.co.za ▪ F +27 (0)86-510-2431 ▪ T +27 (0)82-375-2884

☐ **24 Rivers** *see* Valley Vineyards Wine Company
☐ **21 Gables** *see* Spier
☐ **Twin's Peak** *see* Lateganskop Winery
☐ **II Centuries** *see* Nederburg Wines
☐ **Two Cubs** *see* Knorhoek Wines

Two Oceans

This best-selling Distell-owned brand, introduced in the early1990s and now available in 80 countries, covers all the bases, offering good value and meeting modern expectations in tastes and looks. Eco-minded lightweight bottles sport fresh livery that's even lighter and brighter than before. Low-alcohol wines are offered under the Quay 5 label (untasted).

Pinot Noir ⊘ ★★★☆ Well made & excellent value. **14** fruit-filled & lightish, with a spiced cherry finish, barely noticeable sweetness. Briefly oaked. **Shiraz Rosé** ★★☆ Pretty pink **14** is floral & dryish, with cherry & strawberry attractions that are hard to resist. **Pinot Grigio** ★★☆ Light & floral **14**, pleasant poolside refreshment with 15% colombard, dash sweetness for extra happiness. **Sauvignon Blanc** ★★★ Pleasant semi-dry & tropical-toned **14**, padded with 10% semillon, moderate alcohol & citrus tang for al fresco sipping. **Semillon-Chardonnay** ⊘ ★★★ Now bottled, **13** attractively fresh, orange fragrant & fruit filled, oaking a subtle sesame backdrop. **Fresh & Fruity White** ⊘ ★★★ 3-way marriage chenin, colombard & riesling for export. Fresh & fruity as advertised, **14** lightish pineapple-laced sweetness. Also tasted: **Pinotage** ⊘ **14** ★★★ **Shiraz** ⊘ **14** ★★★☆ **Chardonnay** ⊘ **14** ★★★ Not retasted: **Cabernet Sauvignon-Merlot 13** ★★★ **Soft & Fruity Red 13** ★★★ Not tasted: **Shiraz-Cabernet Sauvignon**, **Chenin Blanc-Sauvignon Blanc**, **Sauvignon Blanc-Chenin Blanc**. — GM

Location: Stellenbosch ▪ WO: Western Cape ▪ Owner(s) Distell ▪ Cellarmaster(s) Deon Boshoff & Andrea Freeborough ▪ Winemaker(s) Wim Truter, Pieter Badenhorst, Bonny van Niekerk & Elize Coetzee ▪ Viticulturist(s) Bennie Liebenberg, Annelie Viljoen & Drikus Heyns ▪ Distell PO Box 184 Stellenbosch 7599 ▪ info@distell.co.za ▪ www.twooceanswines.co.za ▪ T +27 (0)21-809-7000

☐ **Two Tunns** see Valley Vineyards Wine Company
☐ **Tygerberg** see Altydgedacht Estate
☐ **Uiterwyk Estate** see DeWaal Wines

Uitkyk Estate
(Ⓨ)(🍽)(📷)(👤)(♿)

Established in 1929 by Prussian nobleman Hans von Carlowitz, the elegant Lusan-owned Uitkyk Estate on prime Simonsberg slopes combines the 18th-century manor house's history with modern winemaking, eco-mindedness and varied family-friendly tourist attractions including pre-booked gourmet picnics on the lawns (boule or croquet optional). See also Flat Roof Manor entry.

Uitkyk Estate range
★★★★ **Carlonet** ② Venerable Old-Cape cab label given thoroughly modern styling in **10** (★★★★), with soupçon shiraz. Takes **09**'s ripeness & power to next level, with 14.7% alcohol, tannin that tightly grips blackberry fruit mid-2013, needing time.

Pinotage (NEW) ★★★★ Spicy, fruity-savoury aromas & flavours on **12**. Rich, juicy & full bodied (even burly, with nearly 15% alcohol), with well balanced oaking, but the acid a touch unintegrated. Also tasted: **Sauvignon Blanc 14** ★★★★ Not retasted: **Shiraz 10** ★★★☆ **Shiraz-Cabernet Sauvignon 09** ★★★ **Chardonnay 12** ★★★★ **Chenin Blanc 12** ★★★

Brandy range
★★★★ **10 Year Grand Reserve Brandy** ② Smart 10-year-matured pure postill estate brandy, unusually from clairette, cinsaut & chenin grapes. Plenty of oak vanillin & spice to accompany the fruit, though not great complexity. Smooth, rich, round & balanced. — WB, TJ

Location/map: Stellenbosch ▪ WO: Simonsberg–Stellenbosch/Stellenbosch ▪ Est 1712 ▪ 1stB 1957 ▪ Tasting & sales Mon-Fri 9–5 Sat/Sun 10–4 ▪ Tasting fees: R15/5 wines; R20/brandy & chocolate truffle; R40/brandy, chocolate truffle & fruit-cake ▪ Closed Good Fri & Dec 25 ▪ Facilities for children ▪ Tour groups ▪ Gift shop ▪ Cheese platters during tasting hours ▪ Gourmet picnic baskets, to be booked 24hrs in advance ▪ Conferences ▪ 4x4, hiking & mountain biking trails ▪ Conservation area ▪ Manor House museum ▪ Owner(s) Lusan Premium Wines ▪ Cellarmaster(s) Estelle Lourens (Oct 2000) ▪ Winemaker(s) Estelle Lourens (Oct 2000) ▪ Brandy master Estelle Lourens (Jan 2000) ▪ Viticulturist(s) Rudi Buys (2001) ▪

591ha/140ha (cab, shiraz, chard, pinot grigio, sauv) ▪ 772t/18,400cs 55% red 45% white (Uitkyk) & 71,000cs 53% red 45% white 2% rosé (Flat Roof Manor) ▪ BWI champion, WIETA ▪ PO Box 104 Stellenbosch 7599 ▪ info@uitkyk.co.za ▪ www.uitkyk.co.za ▪ S 33° 51' 24.8" E 018° 51' 50.7" ▪ F +27 (0)21-884-4717 ▪ **T +27 (0)21-884-4416**

☐ **Ukuzala** *see* Mountain River Wines

Ultra Liquors

Nationwide drinks retail chain with dynamic specialist wine division offering third-party brands and its own good-value Secret Cellar and Table Bay labels, plus new, somewhat higher-priced Top Secret bottlings.

Location: Cape Town ▪ Owner(s) Colin Robinson ▪ Winemaker(s) Various ▪ 426 Main Road Wynberg Cape Town 7800 ▪ marknorrish@ultraliquors.co.za, dale@bordelais.co.za ▪ F +27 (0)21-797-4351 ▪ **T +27 (0)21-797-4340**

☐ **Ulumbaza** *see* Springfontein Wine Estate

United Nations of Wine

Canadian born, locally resident David John Bate is a self-defined 'wine stylist' and maverick whose separately listed Leopard Frog brand is aimed at appreciators of classic, long-lived (though by no means conventional) wines, while these United Nations bottlings are prêt-à-porter, intended as 'fun, friendly and affordable'. Fairtrade, WIETA and carbon-neutral accreditation are 'a perfect trifecta'.

Frisky Zebras range

Captivating Cabernet Sauvignon ★★★ Supple, amenable style. **NV** bright, cheerful berry & herbaceous flavours with juicy farewell. Balanced, undemanding & ready to quaff. **Sultry Chenin Blanc ★★★★** Ripe, juicy melon & baked apple flavours plumped by touch sugar, **NV** is tangy (rather than sultry), exudes drinkability. Also tasted: **Mystic Merlot NV ★★ Seductive Shiraz NV ★☆ Sublime Chardonnay NV ★★★ Sensuous Sauvignon Blanc NV ★★★** Note: Dusty Rhino, G Spot, Harmony Tree & Luscious Hippos ranges untasted this edition. — MW

Location: Sandton ▪ WO: Western Cape ▪ Est/1stB 2005 ▪ Closed to public ▪ Owner(s) Dogwood Trust ▪ Cellarmaster(s)/winemaker(s) David John Bate (Jun 2005) ▪ 60,000cs own label 50% red 50% white ▪ Fairtrade; CarbonNeutral; WIETA ▪ 8 Royal Ascot Lane Sandown Sandton 2196 ▪ info@unitednationsofwine.com ▪ www. unitednationsofwine.com ▪ F +27 (0)11-883-0426 ▪ **T +27 (0)11-884-3304**

uniWines Vineyards

Diversity, ethical trade and innovation are key values of the 50 producer-shareholders contributing to this extensive Breedekloof winery (with cellars Groot Eiland, Nuwehoop and Daschbosch), and vinifying 45,000 tons of grapes. Hence their accreditation with Fairtrade, and support for initiatives such as creating computer rooms and after-school facilities. Production, mostly bulk, also features bottled wines like the top-tier Daschbosch reserves (with two new labels this edition), and Palesa, featuring eco-friendly pouches and a husk brandy.

Daschbosch range

Plicatilis (NEW) **★★★★** Mocha-scented **12** ripe shiraz, mourvèdre blend with splash viognier, a crowd pleaser in smooth, almost off-dry style. WO W Cape. **Exanimo** (NEW) **★★★** Seductively classy oak aromas, though **13** chenin, chardonnay, semillon blend doesn't deliver promise of depth, instead has brisk, somewhat hard finish. Not retasted: **Procavia Cabernet Sauvignon-Merlot 11 ★★★☆**

Ankerman range

The Referee (NEW) **★★★** Smooth, fruity, lightly oaked **13** blend shiraz, pinotage. **Nectar de Provision Red** (🍷) **★★★** Rosy red, sweet **NV** jerepigo, merlot-based version of Cognac's Pineau des Charentes. **Nectar de Provision White** (🍷) **★★★★** Deliciously sweet, solera-matured aperitif from colombard, fortified with matured brandy. Copper coloured **NV** good complexity, oxidative, nutty with nicely balanced conclusion. Also tasted: **The Foothold** (✓) **13 ★★★ The Whistle 14 ★★★**

Groot Eiland range

Shiraz-Pinotage ★★★★ Spicy & aromatic cooked fruit on **11** shows dominance of pinotage in this Cape Blend. Substantial & satisfying. Not retasted: **Cabernet Sauvignon 09 ★★☆ Merlot 09 ★★★ Pinotage 09 ★★★ Sauvignon Blanc 13 ★★★** Not tasted: **Shiraz**.

Meander range

Moscato ★★☆ Delightfully fizzy **14**, sweetly grapey & light (7% alcohol). From muscat d'Alexandrie, in bubbly bottle. Also tasted: **Merlot-Shiraz** ⊘ **13 ★★☆ Chenin Blanc-Sauvignon Blanc 14 ★★**

Palesa Fairtrade range

Shiraz Pouch (NEW) **★★** Smoky, savoury **13** lightly oaked & easygoing. 1.5L pouch. **Chenin Blanc Pouch** (NEW) **★★★** Conveniently packaged (1.5L pouch) **14** pleasantly fresh & tasty. **Husk Spirit** (NEW) ⊘ ★★★★ From cab, perfumed & smooth, easy & gentle. A fusion of sweet-berry perfume & integrated spirit. Also tasted: **Merlot** ⊘ **13 ★★★ Pinotage 13 ★★☆ Chenin Blanc 14 ★★★ Moscato NV ★★☆ Sauvignon Blanc 14 ★★** — WB, IM

Location: Rawsonville • Map: Breedekloof • WO: Breedekloof/Western Cape • Est/1stB 2007 • Tasting & sales Mon-Thu 8–5 Fri 8-4 Sat/pub hols 10–2 • Closed Easter Fri-Mon, Dec 25/26 & Jan 1 • Cellar tours Mon-Fri & by appt Sat/during harvest • Tour groups • BYO picnic • Conferences • Soetes & Soup festival (Jul) • Owner(s) 50 shareholders • Cellarmaster(s) Nicolaas Rust (Oct 2008) • Winemaker(s) WS Visagie (Nov 2010), Hattingh de Villiers (Sep 2010), Schalk van der Merwe (Dec 2007), Paul Burger (Dec 2013), Christo Smit (Jan 2001) & Madre Fullard (Apr 2013) • Viticulturist(s) Nicholas Bruyns (Jul 2013) • 6,000+ha/2,050ha (cab, cinsaut, merlot, ptage, shiraz, chard, chenin, cbard, sauv) • 45,000t/100,000cs own label 50% red 50% white + 50,000cs for clients • Brands for clients: Cape Promise, Fairtrade Original • ISO 22000:2008, BWI, Fairtrade, IPW, WIETA • PO Box 174 Rawsonville 6845 • info@uniwines.co.za • www.uniwines.co.za • S 33° 43' 16.7" E 019° 21' 0.0" • F +27 (0)86-529-1392 • **T +27 (0)23-349-1110**

☐ **Upington** see Orange River Wine Cellars

Upland Organic Estate Ⓠ ⓐ ⓞ

One of South Africa's first organic wine farms (official since 1994), secluded Upland is owned by scientist and veterinarian Edmund Oettlé and electrical engineer wife Elsie. Dedicated to self-sufficient, nature-friendly farming long before the sustainability trend, the practical partners produce sulphur- and animal product-free wines and spirits using re-tooled recycled equipment.

Upland Estate range

Cabernet Sauvignon Ⓠ ⓢ ★★★ Core of dark savoury fruit on **09** bridled by firm structure. Needs time & good hearty fare. Organic, & noted as sulphite free, as is the Cape Ruby. Not retasted: **Tandem Cape Ruby 07 ★★☆**

Brandy range

★★★★ Undiluted Cask Strength Potstill Brandy Ⓠ ⓢ 100% potstill, 13 years in oak. The only local brandy in this undiluted style (62% alcohol). Intense perfumed, fruit-rich nose; lovely, long flavours. Smooth despite the power. For small sips!

★★★★ Pure Potstill Brandy ⓢ Pure amber colour on 10 year old from chenin & crouchen blanc. Complex layers of dried pineapple, peach, citrus rind & vanilla mingle with hint of smoke. Full bodied, with a smooth richness & elegance, long-lingering aftertaste. New bottling tasted.

Husk Spirit range

★★★★ Grapé ⊘ ⓢ Another rare organic spirit. New bottling from pinot noir (last was cab); colourless offering teases with fragrant fynbos, nutty aromas; fresh herb & strawberry flavours combine for a smooth, understated mouthful. Fine expression. — WB, TJ

Location/WO: Wellington • Map: Paarl & Wellington • Est 1990 • 1stB 1996 • Tasting, sales & tours by appt • Closed Easter Fri-Mon & Dec 25 • Self-catering cottages • Distillery: brandy & grappa • Organic olives, olive oil, dried fruit &

nuts ▪ Craft workshop ▪ Owner(s) Edmund & Elsie Oettlé ▪ Cellarmaster(s) / brandy master(s) Edmund Oettlé ▪
Winemaker(s)/viticulturist(s) Edmund Oettlé ▪ 46ha/10ha (cab, chenin, cbard, crouchen) ▪ 20t/1,200cs own label
100% red & 2,200L brandy ▪ QCS organic certification ▪ PO Box 152 Wellington 7654 ▪ info@organicwine.co.za ▪
www.organicwine.co.za ▪ S 33° 40' 19.9" E 019° 2' 40.0" ▪ F +27 (0)21-873-5724 ▪ **T +27 (0)82-731-4774**

Usana ⓠ

Usana signifies 'new beginning' in Xhosa. Brothers JP and Pierre Winshaw, from a renowned winegrowing family, contract with Longridge to vinify the wines. They're determined, though, that 2015
will see the opening of a tasting room and deli on the Stellenbosch farm to show off not only wine
but also 'other products like our beef and eggs'.

★★★★ **The Fox Cabernet Sauvignon** Juicy **12** shows aromas of blackcurrant, plum & tobacco.
The vibrant palate is tight, with firm, mouth-puckering tannin structure - but enough fruit for maturation to soften it. **11** sold out untasted.

★★★★ **Sauvignon Blanc** ⓐ Unknit **13** tank sample unfair to rate conclusively last year. Satisfying
lees nutty creaminess, brisk acidity & full body. **12** was a gravelly mealtime companion.

Barrel Fermented Chenin Blanc ★★★ Naturally fermented **13** tank sample shows melon, mandarin & vanilla. The oak quite dominant (26% new) but should integrate better with a few years.
Elgin grapes. Also tasted: **Pinot Gris 14** ★★★ — JPf

Location/map: Stellenbosch ▪ WO: Stellenbosch/Elgin ▪ Est/1stB 2003 ▪ Tasting & sales by appt ▪ Owner(s) JP & Pierre
Winshaw ▪ Winemaker(s) Jasper Raats (2012, consultant), with Hendrien de Munck (2010, consultant) ▪ Viticultur-
ist(s) Deon Joubert, Nikki Joubert & Pierre Winshaw ▪ 300ha/60ha (cabs s/f, malbec, merlot, chard, pinot gris, sauv) ▪
29t/4,000cs own label 25% red 75% white ▪ PO Box 68 Lynedoch 7603 ▪ jp@usanawines.co.za, pierre@usanawines.
co.za ▪ www.usana.co.za ▪ S 33° 56' 29.7" E 018° 46' 16.3" ▪ **T +27 (0)83-650-9528**

Uva Mira Mountain Vineyards ⓠ ⓜ ⓞ ⓑ

Uva Mira, established in the late 1990s and especially noted for its Chardonnay, has recently undergone significant changes. Towards the end of 2012, Christiaan Coetzee came across from KWV as
winemaker and viticulturist, while the property - on a magnificent Helderberg viewsite - was
acquired mid-2014 by the CEO of Porsche South Africa, Toby Venter.

★★★★ **Merlot-Cabernet Sauvignon 09** (★★★) not up to complexity of previously previewed **08**.
Very ripe, with boiled sweet & tobacco notes. Only just dry, & the modest fruit a little insipid.

★★★★☆ **Red Blend 09** (★★★★) mostly cab with merlot, cab franc. Slightly fuller, spicier version of
the Merlot-Cabernet - this slightly drier, & with some green undertones to the light fruit. Last-tasted **07**
impressed more.

★★★★☆ **Single Tree Chardonnay** Previously 'Single Vineyard Chardonnay'. **13** (★★★★) in showy
style of **12**, though drier & more restrained. Aromas of spice, oatmeal & spicy oak (80% new) lead to
pleasantly balanced palate with good lemony acidity.

★★★★☆ **Chardonnay** ⓝ **13** still grand & imposing, but in rather lighter, more modern mode than
Single Tree, with less new oak (65%) in better balance, allowing more complex fruit to reveal itself.
Lovely integrated freshness, with a fine acidity threading through the richness, & a lingering finish.

★★★★ **Sauvignon Blanc 13** includes fruit from elsewhere, to give enticing aromas of blackcurrant
& passionfruit & a powerful, flavourful & lively palate, with flint & a satisfying green succulence.

★★★★☆ **Sauvignon Blanc Limited Release** ⓝ Elegant **13** is a touch riper, gentler & broader
than other version, with 6 months lees-ageing adding weight. But still with a bracing quota of freshness & verve despite lesser 'green' component. Should develop well a few years.

Not tasted: **Syrah**. — TJ

Location/map: Stellenbosch ▪ WO: Stellenbosch/Western Cape ▪ Est 1997 ▪ 1stB 1998 ▪ Tasting & sales Tue-Fri 10-4
Sat/Sun 10-6 (Sep-Mar)/Tue-Sun 10-4 (Apr-Aug) ▪ Fee R30 ▪ Closed Good Fri, Dec 25 & Jan 1 ▪ Artisan cheese platters & savoury meat platters ▪ Olive oil ▪ Tour groups ▪ Conservation area ▪ Owner(s) Toby & Jessica Venter ▪

Winemaker(s)/viticulturist(s) Christiaan Coetzee (2012) ▪ 140ha/30ha (cabs s/f, merlot, shiraz, chard, sauv) ▪ 100t/ 14,000cs ▪ IPW ▪ PO Box 1511 Stellenbosch 7599 ▪ info@uvamira.co.za ▪ www.uvamira.co.za ▪ S 34° 1' 31.3" E 018° 51' 26.1" ▪ F +27 (0)21-880-1682 ▪ **T +27 (0)21-880-1683**

Vaalvlei Wines

The Terblanche family farm near Stanford on the Walker Bay coastline lures fly-fishermen and shelters the endangered Western Leopard Toad, thanks in part to passionate conservationist and winemaker/ viticulturist Naas Terblanche.

Shiraz Reserve ⓥ ★★★ Displaying similar DNA of sweet fruit, vanilla, exotic spice & bold alcohol, vintage-boosted **11** is a notch up on previous. Not tasted: **Shiraz**, **Sauvignon Blanc**. — HJ

Location: Stanford ▪ Map: Elgin, Walker Bay & Bot River ▪ WO: Walker Bay ▪ Est 2005 ▪ 1stB 2008 ▪ Tasting & sales Mon-Sat 11-5 by appt ▪ Closed Good Fri & Dec 25 ▪ 2 self-catering cottages ▪ Fly-fishing ▪ Owner(s) Terblanche family ▪ Cellarmaster(s)/viticulturist(s) Naas Terblanche (Mar 2005) ▪ Winemaker(s) Naas Terblanche (Mar 2005) & Josef Dreyer (Aug 2005, Raka), advised by Charl van Teijlingen CWM (Mar 2008) ▪ 50ha/3ha (shiraz, sauv) ▪ 19t/650cs own label 40% red 60% white ▪ PO Box 92 Stanford 7210 ▪ info@vaalvlei.co.za ▪ www.vaalvlei.co.za ▪ S 34° 26' 56.11" E 019° 33' 07.05" ▪ **T +27 (0)28-341-0170/+27 (0)72-782-3431**

Val de Vie Wines

Created in the newly upgraded cellar on Val de Vie luxury wine-and-polo estate, the range reflects a special focus on the Rhône. The estate being part of a 17th century Huguenot land grant, however, suggests other French varieties and styles are welcome too, hence the new champagne-style bubbly. This being SA, after all, the rosé from pinotage is both apropos and delicious.

Val de Vie range

★★★★ **Shiraz** ⓥ **08**'s smoky mulberry & plum appeal follows similar **07**. Rounded yet muscled & firm. Dark char depth & density. Oak shows restraint, 70% new for 11 months. Long finish. WO Coastal.

★★★★ **Ryk Neethling** ⓥ Honouring the Olympic swimming gold medallist. Taut & toned **10** from shiraz, mourvèdre, carignan, grenache & cinsaut. Rich & savoury, with restrained black fruit wrapped around a firm body of tannin.

★★★★☆ **1783** Was 'Val de Vie'. Premium-priced flagship, mainly mourvèdre, shiraz & dabs grenache, carignan & cinsaut. Stunning **09** is rich, smooth, oozes ripe berry fruit, cured meat: concentrated yet elegant, with an earthy, savoury goodbye. Drinking well. No **08**.

★★★★ **GVC 11** (★★★) blend of grenache blanc, viognier & clairette blanche misses vivacity of **08**. Soft fruit, some oaky vanilla, fleeting flavours.

Cuvée de Vie ⓝⓔⓦ ★★★★ Méthode cap classique sparkling from chardonnay & pinots noir & meunier. Golden colour on **NV**, bruised apple & yeasty flavours. Frothy, broad, full; attractive without much persistence.

Polo Club range
Filly Rosé ★★★ Just-dry **14** from pinotage is bright pink, pungent strawberry fragrance, bright & zippy acid finish. Also tasted: **Craftsman 12 ★★★☆ Sauvignon Blanc 14 ★★★** Not tasted: **Cabernet Franc**, **Chenin Blanc**. — WB

Location: Paarl ▪ Map: Franschhoek ▪ WO: Western Cape/Coastal ▪ Est 2003 ▪ 1stB 2004 ▪ Tasting & sales Tue-Sun 11-4 ▪ Closed Good Fri, Dec 25 & Jan 1 ▪ Polo Club Restaurant ▪ Conservation area ▪ Owner(s) Val de Vie Wines (Pty) Ltd ▪ PO Box 6223 Paarl 7620 ▪ wine@valdevie.co.za ▪ www.valdevie.co.za ▪ S 33° 48' 15.0" E 018° 58' 4.0" ▪ F +27 (0)21-863-2741 ▪ **T +27 (0)21-863-6100**

Val du Charron

In converting their fruit farm, the Entwistle family planted 18 grape varieties, always intending to focus on blends - drawing on local history for the evocative names of their Theater of Wine range. A guest house and spa cater for visitors, who have access to the farm's many amenities, and for these there have been many plaudits, including the Cape Winelands District's New Tourism Business of the Year award.

Estate Reserve range

Chardonnay ★★★★ Uncomplex but juicy **14** shows succulent pear & ripe apple. Nicely dry, with a pleasing generosity. **Pinot Gris** ★★★★ Varietally typical **12** (tasted as preview last year) unusually is partly oak fermented. Citrus aromas intermixed with pear. Friendly & medium bodied. Also tasted: **Cabernet Sauvignon** 12 ★★★ **Shiraz** 12 ★★★★

Theater of Wine range

Erasmus ★★★★ **12** merlot-driven 5-way blend, now bottled, plentiful berry & spicy notes; enjoyable now & could further improve. Not tasted: **Black Countess**, **Four White Legs**. — JPf

Location/WO: Wellington ▪ Map: Paarl & Wellington ▪ Est 2007 ▪ 1stB 2009 ▪ Tasting daily 10-4 ▪ Sales Mon-Fri 8-5 Sat/Sun 10-4 ▪ Cellar tours during tasting hours ▪ Breakfast & lunch daily; dinner by appt ▪ Tour groups ▪ Conferences/functions (150 pax) ▪ Walks/hikes ▪ Mountain biking trail ▪ Spa ▪ 4-star guest house (stay@vdcwines.com) ▪ Owner(s) Val du Charron Wines (Pty) Ltd ▪ Winemaker(s) Bertus Fourie (Apr 2010, consultant) ▪ Viticulturist(s) Heinie Nel (Apr 2010, consultant) ▪ 43ha/21ha (cab, ptage, shiraz, chard, chenin) ▪ 200t ▪ Other export brands: Girlfriends Wine, Goldcoast 3L BIB ▪ IPW ▪ PO Box 890 Wellington 7654 ▪ ce@vdcwines.com ▪ www.vdcwines.com ▪ S 33° 37' 28.14" E 019° 2' 55.32" ▪ F +27 (0)86-509-4865 ▪ **T +27 (0)21-873-1256**

☐ **Valley Green** *see* Hannay Wines
☐ **Valley Road Vintners** *see* Ross Gower Wines

Valley Vineyards Wine Company

Wine partners Richard James and Richard Addison, specialists in Argentina and South Africa respectively, combine their knowledge and long experience to select wines from mainly those countries for their United Kingdom merchant house. Recently they opened new export markets in South America and Asia, and had success with private label development. Their South African brands include Lion Ridge, Millbrook, Mischief Maker, Post Tree, Short Street, The Royal, 24 Rivers and Two Tunns.

Location: Riebeek-Kasteel ▪ Est/1stB 2009 ▪ Closed to public ▪ Owner(s) Richard Addison & Richard James ▪ ±100,000cs own label 40% red 40% white 15% rosé 5% other ▪ Other export brands: see intro ▪ PO Box 2175 Riebeek-Kasteel 7307 ▪ raddison@valleyvineyardswine.com ▪ www.valleyvineyardswine.com ▪ **T +27 (0)71-238-6765**

Van Biljon Wines

Anton and Julia van Biljon's boutique winery on Stellenbosch's Polkadraai Hills last edition launched to favourable reviews in this guide and elsewhere, prompting consulting winemaker/viticulturist Chris Keet (Keet Wines) to note: 'The year ahead sees new focus and energy to fine-tune the vineyards even more, create an even better blend with all five varieties - and generate some cashflow!'

★★★★☆ **Cinq** Fine Bordeaux red debuted in **11** without five varieties promised in name. Missing petit verdot included in **12** (★★★★). Ripe, sweet fruit (but bone-dry). Big, even bold, with tannins a touch awkward now; warm glow from 14.4% alcohol. Needs time. — TJ

Location/map/WO: Stellenbosch ▪ Est 2004 ▪ 1stB 2013 ▪ Tasting, sales & cellar tours Mon-Sat by appt ▪ Closed all pub hols ▪ Self-catering Tarentaal Cottage ▪ Owner(s) Anton & Julia van Biljon ▪ Winemaker(s) Christopher Keet (Oct 2008, consultant), with Anton van Biljon (Jan 2011) ▪ Viticulturist(s) Christopher Keet (Oct 2008, consultant) ▪ 7ha/3ha (cabs s/f, malbec, merlot, p verdot) ▪ 15t/500cs own label 100% red ▪ IPW ▪ PO Box 1292 Hermanus 7200 ▪ info@vanbiljonwines.co.za ▪ www.vanbiljonwines.co.za ▪ S 33° 58' 4.98" E 018° 45' 8.39" ▪ F +27 (0)28-313-0435 ▪ **T +27 (0)21-882-8445**

Van Loveren Family Vineyards

Just one wine made up this dynamic Robertson farm's range when brothers Nico and Wynand Retief launched their Premier Grand Cru in 1980. Today it's difficult to keep up with the extensive range, which includes many innovations in keeping with the family's promise to offer 'a wine for each palate

and every occasion'. This promise generates positive results: the PET (plastic bottle) range, Tangled Tree, launched as recently as 2013, is already the top seller on the market. Newcomers to the range are a wine-based liqueur (untasted) and pinot noir. To accommodate this burgeoning list, both vineyards and cellar capacity have been extended. See also Tangled Tree and Vinopoly Wines entries.

Christina Van Loveren Limited Releases

★★★★ **Sauvignon Blanc** 13 offers satisfying vinosity, lipsmacking acidity & creamy length for solo or dinner table enjoyment. As vibrant & poised as **12** (★★★★) but with greater gravitas. Drier, higher alcohol than standard bottling. WO W Cape.

★★★★ **Méthode Cap Classique Brut** Traditional-method sparkling. Latest **NV** appealing apple pie & cream bouquet, lemon freshness from chardonnay (93%), weight & fruitiness ex pinot noir, tiny bubble & faint brioche from 9 months lees-ageing. More complex than citrus-infused predecessor.

Chardonnay Ⓥ ★★★★ Barrel-fermented & lees-aged, 5 months in **13**. Genteel lemon/lime aromas & flavours, spice & butter background notes; better integrated than previous. Also tasted: **Shiraz 12** ★★★★ Not tasted: **Cabernet Sauvignon**, **Noble Late Harvest Rhine Riesling**.

Van Loveren range

Blue Velvet Pinot Noir ★★★ Only older barrels for **13**'s pure cherry fruit. Stalky, but less gawky than **12**, as sippable & reasonably priced. **African Java Pinotage** ★★ With the expected big mocha aromas, touch of sugar, spicy mulberry fruitiness, oak-staved **14** successfully rides the 'coffee pinotage' train. **Neil's Pick Colombar** ⊘ ★★★ Honours viti man Neil Retief. **14** pungent guava/sweat aroma (which you either love or hate), ruby grapefruit flavour & pithy texture, pleasant off-dry conclusion. **Pinot Grigio** ★★★ Back-on-track **14** characterful sipper with peardrop aroma, pithy texture. Bone-dry, modest 12% alcohol for long al fresco lunches. **Sauvignon Blanc** ★★ Subtle grass & 'wet pebble' appeal on zesty, lightly flavoured **14**. **Red Muscadel** ★★★★ Fortified dessert for winter firesides. **14** signature red fruit pastille character, tealeaf & molasses; delightfully clean & uncloying end. Also tasted: **Merlot 13** ★★ **Blackberry Cabernet Sauvignon-Shiraz 13** ★★★ **Blanc de Noir Shiraz 14** ★ **Blanc de Noir Red Muscadel Blush 14** ★★ **Chenin No. 5 14** ★★ **Blanc de Blanc 14** ★ Not retasted: **Cape Ruby NV** ★★★ Not tasted: **Cramond Cabernet Sauvignon-Merlot**, **River Red**, **Chardonnay**, **Cramond Sauvignon Blanc-Chardonnay**, **Special Late Harvest Gewürztraminer**. Discontinued: **Cape Riesling**.

Four Cousins range

Dry Red Ⓖ ★★ From ruby cab & merlot, charmingly rustic unoaked **NV** braai companion. **Extra Light White** Ⓖ ★ Lemony & light **NV** gets the nod from Weigh-Less. Not retasted: **Dry White NV** ★★ **Natural Sweet Red NV** ★★ **Sweet Rosé NV** ★★ **Light Natural Sweet Rosé NV** ★★ **Natural Sweet White NV** ★☆

Five's Reserve range

Merlot Rosé ★★ Sunset-hued, bone-dry **14** slimmer's friend with sweet-sour appeal. Also tasted: **Cabernet Sauvignon 13** ★★ **Pinotage 13** ★☆ **Chenin Blanc 14** ★☆

Papillon Sparkling range

Brut Ⓖ ★★☆ Latest **NV** uncomplex but easy & charming celebratory sparkler. Not retasted: **Vin Doux NV** ★★ **Demi-Sec NV** ★☆

Four Cousins Sparkling range

Sauvignon Blanc Brut ★★★ Latest **NV** (**14**) sparkler as fresh & invigorating as a seabreeze with 'wet beach' minerality, seaweed salinity & zesty dry tail. Not retasted: **Red NV** ★★ **Blush NV** ★★ **White NV** ★★

Brandy range

Brandy ⓐ ★★★ 5 year old blended brandy (50% potstill) from chenin & colombard. Peaches & caramel flavours - cheerful & charming, some dry elegance. Good on the rocks. — WB, TJ, CvZ

Location/map: Robertson ▪ WO: Robertson/Western Cape ▪ Est 1937 ▪ 1stB 1980 ▪ Tasting & sales Mon-Fri 8.30-5 Sat 9.30-3 Sun 11-2 ▪ Closed Easter Fri/Sun, Dec 25 & Jan 1 ▪ Cellar tours ▪ Garden tours ▪ Food & wine tasting platters ▪ Fish Eagle hiking trail ▪ MTB trails (bike rental available) ▪ Self-catering farm cottage ▪ Christina's @ Van Loveren bistro (closed Tue) ▪ Owner(s) Nico, Wynand, Phillip, Hennie, Bussell & Neil Retief ▪ Cellarmaster(s) Bussell Retief ▪ Winemaker(s) Danelle Conradie (Jan 2007), with Malcolm Human (Jan 2012) ▪ Viticulturist(s) Neil & Hennie Retief ▪ 500ha (cab, merlot, mourv, muscadel r/w, ptage, pinot noir/gris, ruby cab, shiraz, touriga nacional, chard, chenin, cbard, gewürz, morio muscat, nouvelle, sauv, sem, viog) ▪ 7,700t/2,400,000cs own label 33% red 33% white 34% rosé ▪ Brands for clients: Woolworths ▪ BWI, Fairtrade, IPW ▪ PO Box 19 Klaasvoogds 6707 ▪ info@vanloveren.co.za ▪ www.vanloveren.co.za ▪ S 33° 52' 31.3" E 020° 0' 9.1" ▪ F +27 (0)23-615-1336 ▪ **T +27 (0)23-615-1505**

Van Ryn

Van Ryn distillery was established by a Dutch immigrant in 1905, and soon began bringing home awards for its cognac-style brandies. That international recognition continues today, with its regular taking of World's Best Brandy trophy. Owned by Distell, it is situated in century-old visitor-friendly premises outside Stellenbosch, with its own cooperage on site. Custodian Marlene Bester reports to production director Johan Venter, a globally recognised spirits expert. Regular tours show the distillation and maturation process, and a variety of tastings matched to gourmet food are available to introduce visitors to brandy's versatility.

★★★★☆ **Vintage 10 Year** ⓐ Testimony to the quality possible for a Vintage Brandy - that is, with a component of matured (not potstill) spirit. Youthful, with a showy array of fruit aromas, plus some sandalwood & vanilla from oak. The mature & fruity parts marry appealingly. Assertive, rich, lively.

★★★★★ **12 Year Distillers Reserve** ⓐ 100% potstill brandy, like all below. Deep colour, with mahogany gleam. Fragrant, delicate aromas of fruit, herbs, flowers lead to full, richly powerful but gentle palate, then a long, sustained finish. Complete, balanced, triumphant.

★★★★☆ **15 Year Fine Cask Reserve** ⓐ Delicate & penetrating aromas - rather less fruit, but more floral notes than 12YO (rose, violet, lavender), & rather more restrained in effect though still in the richer style of this house. Refined, complex finish. These all from chenin & colombard, widely sourced.

★★★★★ **20 Year Collectors Reserve** ⓐ Concentrated nose of dark berries, dried fruit & spice. Spice, especially, repeated on the palate along with apricot & prune amidst the complexity. Reminiscences of oak but never intrusive. Mellow, silky & very rich, with forthright finish.

★★★★★ **Au.Ra** ⓐ South Africa's longest-matured - & by a long way rarest & priciest - brandy: 30 year minimum maturation. Even smoother, more sumptuously mouthfilling than others in range, but retaining elegance. Full spicy, dried fruit complexity splendidly supported by oak. Sets a local standard for excellence. — WB, TJ

Location/map: Stellenbosch ▪ Est 1905 ▪ Tasting & sales Mon-Fri 9-5 (May-Sep) 9-6 (Oct-Apr) Sat 9-4 Sun (Oct-Apr only) 11-4 ▪ Van Ryn's tasting R35 (with tour R50); brandy, coffee & chocolate pairing R75 (with tour R90); Van Ryn's Florentine Collection Reserve tasting R80 (with tour R95) ▪ Closed Good Fri, Dec 25 & Jan 1 ▪ Cellar tours Mon-Fri 10, 11.30 & 3 Sat 10, 11.30 & 1 ▪ Light meals, artisan charcuterie & cheese platters ▪ Tour groups ▪ Gift shop ▪ Conference & boardroom facilities ▪ Exhibitions & special events ▪ Museum collection of historical brandies on display ▪ Owner(s) Distell ▪ Brandy master(s) Marlene Bester (Jul 2009) ▪ ISO 9001:1995 ▪ Van Ryn Road Vlottenburg Stellenbosch 7604 ▪ info@vanryns.co.za ▪ www.vanryn.co.za ▪ S 33° 57' 43.26" E 018° 48' 4.87" ▪ F +27 (0)21-881-3127 ▪ **T +27 (0)21-881-3875**

☐ **Vansha** *see* Ridgeback
☐ **Van Zijls Family Vintners** *see* Imbuko Wines

Van Zylshof Estate

The Van Zyls have run a steady ship on this small family estate just outside Bonnnievale since oupa Andries built the cellar in 1940, making white wine for wholesale. Son Chris and grandson Andri, having introduced an own label and added reds to the mix, eagerly await young crewman Dirk, finding his sea legs elsewhere.

Chenin Blanc ★★★ Peachy **14** very pleasant, finishing dry with persistent peach stone dryness.
Sauvignon Blanc ★★★ Floral & fresh hay notes lead to tropical fruit flavours of zesty **14**. Also tasted: **Rosé 14 ★★★** **Chardonnay 13 ★★☆** **Riverain Unwooded Chardonnay 14 ★★★** Not retasted: **Cabernet Sauvignon-Merlot 12 ★★★** — JG

Location: Bonnievale ▪ Map/WO: Robertson ▪ Est 1940 ▪ 1stB 1994 ▪ Tasting & sales Mon-Fri 9–5 Sat 9–1 ▪ Closed Good Fri, Ascension day, Dec 25 & Jan 1 ▪ Cellar tours by appt ▪ Owner(s) Van Zylshof Trust ▪ Cellarmaster(s)/winemaker(s)/viticulturist(s) Andri van Zyl (Mar 1993) ▪ 37ha/32ha under vine ▪ 450t/±8,000cs own label 15% red 80% white 5% rosé ▪ PO Box 64 Bonnievale 6730 ▪ vanzylshof@lando.co.za ▪ www.vanzylshof.co.za ▪ S 33° 56' 18.5" E 020° 6' 23.4" ▪ F +27 (0)23-616-3503 ▪ **T +27 (0)23-616-2401**

Vaughan Johnson's Wine & Cigar Shop

Vaughan Johnson's Wine & Cigar Shop has long been a landmark at Cape Town's V&A Waterfront. Proprietor Vaughan Johnson is a champion of customer service, and his belief that 'three times the price is not always three times the quality' is evident in his own modestly priced range.

Good Everyday Cape Red **★★☆** Dark-fruited & eminently drinkable **NV** Bordeaux blend from cab franc, merlot, cab & petit verdot. Not tasted: **Good Everyday Cape White**. — JG

Location: Cape Town ▪ Map: Cape Peninsula ▪ WO: Paarl ▪ Est/1stB 1985 ▪ Sales Mon-Fri 9–6 Sat 9–5 Sun 10–5 ▪ Open pub hols ▪ Gifts, souvenirs, spirits & beer available ▪ Owner(s) Vaughan Johnson ▪ PO Box 50012 Waterfront 8002 ▪ vjohnson@mweb.co.za ▪ www.vaughanjohnson.co.za ▪ S 33° 54' 19.15" E 018° 25' 10.68" ▪ F +27 (0)86-509-6401 ▪ **T +27 (0)21-419-2121**

Veenwouden Private Cellar

There has been a change in the holding company and emphasis of this boutique venture between Wellington and Paarl. It is now solely dedicated to wine and there is no-one better placed to ensure focus and continuity than Marcel van der Walt, ex golfing professional, who took over the winemaking after Veenwouden's maiden vintage in 1993. He continues to make classically styled quality wines, with potential to age elegantly.

Reserve Collection
★★★★ Merlot ⓧ **12**, with splash cab franc, shows refinement despite 14.5% alcohol. Cool red fruit & mint, deftly oaked. Balanced, silky tannins already tempting, with charm for 4-6 years.
★★★★ Syrah ⓧ Similar fresh spicy tone to **11**, but preview of **12** (**★★★☆**) shows less fruit intensity. Bright & sappy, with supple tannins.
★★★★ Classic ⓧ Cab-led quintet of Bordeaux varieties, **10** more restrained than **09**. Tart savoury fruit sheathed in chalky tannins. Refined, all elements in place, just needs time's smoothing hand.
Not retasted: **Chardonnay 11 ★★★☆**

Hugh Masekela Collection
★★★★ Hugh Masekela ⓧ Harmonious merlot-based **10** blend with cab, shiraz. Invitingly rich, savoury with caressing velvet feel, gentle grip.

Premium Collection
Pinot Noir ⓧ **★★★★ 12** elegant, but taut & introverted in youth. Time & decanting will reveal greater charm. Not tasted: **Chardonnay**.

Vivat Bacchus Collection

Red ⓥ ★★★★ Approachable merlot-based **11** with a little shiraz; spicy flavours polished with French oak. WO Coastal, as next. Not retasted: **Sauvignon Blanc-Chenin Blanc 12** ★★★ — MW

Location: Paarl • Map: Paarl & Wellington • WO: Paarl/Coastal • Est 1989 • 1stB 1993 • Tasting, sales & cellar tours by appt • Fee R100, waived on purchase • Owner(s) 5 W Wineries (Pty) Ltd, t/a Veenwouden • Cellarmaster(s) Marcel van der Walt • Winemaker(s) Marcel van der Walt, with Faried Williams • Viticulturist(s) Marcel van der Walt, with Sias Louw • 14ha/12.5ha (cabs s/f, malbec, merlot, p verdot, pinot) • ±100t/11,000cs own label 90% red 10% white • PO Box 7086 Northern Paarl 7623 • admin@veenwouden.com • www.veenwouden.com • S 33° 41' 7.0" E 018° 57' 52.4" • F +27 (0)21-872-1384 • **T +27 (0)21-872-6806**

☐ **Veldt** *see* Robertson Wide River Export Company
☐ **Velo** *see* Wildehurst Wines

Vendôme

Farmed by the Le Roux family for 10 generations, this Berg riverside property in Paarl was named to honour their Huguenot heritage and ancestral home in central France. Vigneron Jannie le Roux focuses on Bordeaux blends, red and white, none ready for tasting.

Location: Paarl • Map: Paarl & Wellington • Est 1692 • 1stB 1999 • Tasting & sales by appt • Closed all pub hols • Conferences/functions (up to 150 pax) • Owner(s)/winemaker(s)/viticulturist(s) Jannie le Roux • 40ha (cabs s/f, merlot, shiraz, chard, chenin, cbard, sauv, sem) • 5t/600cs own label 50% red 50% white • PO Box 36 Paarl 7645 • lerouxjg@icon.co.za • www.vendome.co.za • S 33° 45' 27.8" E 018° 58' 42.4" • F +27 (0)21-863-0094 • **T +27 (0)21-863-3905**

☐ **Vera Cruz Estate** *see* Delheim Wines

Vergelegen Wines

The first Frenchman to set foot in Vergelegen's octagonal cellar - a lone sentry on a hill, flanked by dramatic mountains - was Baron Eric de Rothschild of Bordeaux's Château Lafite, when he opened the multi-level, largely subterranean building. Now there's new French eminence in the cellar, with renowned oenologist Michel Rolland advising longtime winemaker André van Rensburg, to bring a further dimension to the award-winning wines. World-class, too, is the Vergelegen estate at Somerset West, its myriad attractions helping secure the Great Wine Capitals Best of Wine Tourism Award 2014. With views of wind-buffeted Schaapenberg vineyard and False Bay beyond, the property is planted with not only vines but also fruit trees belonging to an empowerment enterprise. Near the historic manor house are 300+ year old camphor trees, National Monuments since 1942, 17 gardens (including a children's play area), modern winetasting centre and two fine restaurants.

Flagship range

★★★★★ **Vergelegen V** Premium-priced flagship, 100% cab with 23 months all-new oak, **11** is more savoury than Reserve Cab, tightly knit, made for the long haul. Cigarbox & blackcurrants, lead pencils, firm but ripe tannin as foundation. Accessible but still an infant. No **10**.

★★★★★ **Vergelegen GVB Red** Masterly Bordeaux blend always fine & dry with measured tannic grip. Cab dominant in **09**, with merlot, cab franc. Cassis & morello cherries, cedar dusting, the 100% new oak well judged, approachable now but the best is yet to come.

★★★★★ **Vergelegen GVB White** Pioneering barrel-fermented/aged semillon & sauvignon blend. Toasted almond & gentle lemon bouquet in **13**, but flavours richer, dried fig & preserved citrus peel, mouthfilling, hedonistic, back to **11**'s styling. Would reward cellaring.

Reserve range

★★★★★ **Cabernet Sauvignon 09** is seamless, has such integration of fruit & oak that it's difficult to pick out a single flavour element. Boasts with plush silky tones, sleek musculature for a long distinguished future. With a dash merlot, cab franc.

For more information, visit wineonaplatter.com

★★★★☆ **Merlot** Consistently one of the Cape's finest. **11** now 100% merlot, first since **94**. Creamy plums, Belgian chocolate, slight dusting white pepper, a lesson in harmony, the perfect balance makes it enjoyable now, also has ageing potential.

★★★★☆ **Shiraz** Black pepper, red berry perfume, hint of scrub, **12** shows lovely ripeness, round, smooth & succulent. As many of these reds, harmonious, tannin a hidden structure. Savoury spicing a nice counterpoint to the plush berries.

★★★★☆ **DNA** Cab franc leads merlot & cab in serious nod to Bordeaux, with **10**'s 100% new French oak, the elegance, restraint. Lead pencils, herbaceous whiffs, opening up in the glass to plush red berries. Seamless, polished, great finesse. For savouring.

★★★★ **Chardonnay** Most serious of chardonnays, 45% new oak giving **12**'s citrus peel an oat biscuit, hazelnut tone, the flavours quite savoury. Elegant, bone-dry & individual, no New World pandering.

★★★★☆ **Sauvignon Blanc Schaapenberg** Named for 24 year old hillside vineyard overlooking False Bay. Signature minerality, oystershell tones to **14** (1st wine with Michel Rolland advising), just-right acidity adds stiffening, ageing potential. Similar **13**, also tasted, a touch leafier, retaining the mineral core. Both distinctive, classic & classy.

★★★★☆ **Semillon** Lime & fennel, a hint of sage, **13** (★★★★★) shows striking purity & focus, the oak a gentle buttered toast shading, allowing the fruit to shine. Polished, svelte, admirable. No **12**. **11** heralded departure from more savoury & oxidative styling.

★★★★ **MMV** ⓥ Individual MCC sparkler from chardonnay & pinot noir. **08** biscuity, savoury & austere; not as creamy as many others. WO W.Cape.

★★★★☆ **Semillon Straw Wine** ⓥ Shimmering gold dessert from vine- & pallet-dried grapes, fermented on skins/stems, aged 14 months older barrels. Nuts, glacé pineapple & varietal lanolin on hedonistic **11**. Bolt of tangy lime cuts sweetness for a clean, lingering finish. 375 ml.

Premium range

★★★★ **Shiraz** Black pepper & scrub, meat extract, **11**'s red fruit showing more in the flavours. Succulent, streamlined & misleadingly accessible, has the credentials to age well.

★★★★ **Cabernet Sauvignon-Merlot** ⓥ Drops cab franc from name (but not from blend; also dab petit verdot); **10** highly perfumed with lavender, plum. Fruitier than **09**, soft & rounded for easy drinking with friends.

★★★★ **Chardonnay** Only part oaked to showcase the fruit flavours, **13**'s orange/lemon & buttered toast styling puts it back on track after **12** (★★★★). Elegant, with a lifting freshness.

★★★★ **Sauvignon Blanc 14** bouquet of pear & green apple, a nettle nuance, this & the flavours showing the cool terroir, vibrantly fresh, staying long after the glass is empty. — CR

Location: Somerset West ▪ Map: Helderberg ▪ WO: Stellenbosch/Western Cape ▪ Est 1987 ▪ 1stB 1991 ▪ Tasting & sales daily 9.30–4.30 (gate closes at 4) ▪ Estate closed Good Fri, May 1 & Dec 25 ▪ Daily heritage & gardens tour at 10; cellar tours at 11.30 & 3 ▪ All tours R20pp (reservations advised) ▪ Tasting R30/6 wines (excl flagship wines), R10 each for flagship wines ▪ Camphors Restaurant, Stables Bistro & Camphor Forest Picnic ▪ Facilities for children ▪ Gift shop ▪ Historic Cape Dutch homestead ▪ Library ▪ Exhibition corridor ▪ 315 year old camphor trees (National Monuments since 1942) ▪ Conservation area ▪ 17 gardens including Camellia garden of excellence & children's adventure garden & maze ▪ Owner(s) Anglo American plc ▪ Winemaker(s) André van Rensburg (Jan 1998) ▪ Viticulturist(s) Dwayne Lottering (Nov 2003) ▪ 3,000ha/158ha (cab, merlot, sauv) ▪ 900t/120,000cs own label 58% red 42% white ▪ ISO 9001, ISO 14001, ISO 22000, OSHAS 18000, BWI champion, WIETA ▪ PO Box 17 Somerset West 7129 ▪ info@vergelegen.co.za ▪ www.vergelegen.co.za ▪ S 34° 4' 38.33" E 018° 53' 30.03" ▪ **T +27 (0)21-847-1334**

Vergenoegd Wine Estate ⓥ ⓦ ⓞ ⓐ ⓑ

Just 5 km from False Bay, Vergenoegd ('Satisfied') is one of the oldest farms in Stellenbosch and owned by the Faure family since 1820. Sixth-generation John Faure is the current cellarmaster, honouring tradition while meeting the demands of the modern market. Passionate about birds since childhood, John recently created a pair of hides at the estate so fellow birders can experience at first hand the amazing extent and diversity of Vergenoegd's avian life. He's also initiated a project with Government and conservation groups to strengthen indigenous waterbird populations and improve the hydrology and water quality of the Cape's agricultural landscape.

Vintage Collection

★★★★ **Cabernet Sauvignon** Ⓠ Keep **01** (we advised at the time), while drinking **02** (★★★★): lighter, less intensity, also tannic but not the same rich fruit. ±20 months oak, ± 60% new.

★★★★ **Shiraz** Ⓠ Back on song in burly, firm-structured **00**, with dark plums & herbs. Oaking tweaked to 2 years, 86% new. On review needed few years chance.

★★★★☆ **Estate Blend** Ⓠ Forceful cab-based blend, resisting market pressure for showy, simple fruitiness. **00**, with spicy cherry scents, previously noted as still rather formidably tannic, but dark, savoury fruit carries the weight. 39% merlot, few drops cab f.

Classic range

★★★★ **Cabernet Sauvignon** Distinctive, stalwart SA cab with emphasis on structure, reined-in fruit. **08** still taut - good few more years to go. Includes dab cab franc instead of ripe **07**'s touriga.

★★★★ **Merlot 08** elegant & refreshing glassful, thanks to zesty acidity, moderate alcohol & judicious new oak. Drops of malbec & cab franc aid complexity.

★★★★ **Shiraz** Ⓠ Lush **06** with 8% touriga. Game, truffle & leather undertones; attractively rustic palate shows intensity & weight, with a nice warming finish. Drink soon.

★★★★ **Estate Blend** Ⓠ **06** Bordeaux-style blend rewards the patient. Usual firm structure & earthy tones uplifted by fresh redcurrant, tar & spicy plum.

★★★★☆ **Old Cape Colony Cape Vintage 07** (★★★★) tinta, touriga offering less convincing than powerful & elegant **06**. Has Xmas cake richness, fiery conclusion, oxidative headiness.

Also tasted: **Terrace Bay 07** ★★★

Runner Duck range

Red ★★★ Interesting combo of touriga, cab franc, malbec & tinta, 18 months older oak. Smoke, farmyard top notes on fruity, early-drinking **12**. Also tasted: **Rosé 14** ★★ **White 14** ★★★

Limited Edition range

Tawny Port Ⓠ ★★★ Sweetly rich & rustic once-off **99** from tinta barocca tasted a few years back. Not tasted: **Cabernet Franc**. — CvZ

Location/map: Stellenbosch ▪ WO: Stellenbosch/Western Cape ▪ Est 1696 ▪ 1stB 1972 ▪ Tasting & sales Mon-Fri 9—5 Sat/Sun 9.30—4 ▪ Fee R35 ▪ Closed Good Fri, Dec 25 & Jan 1 ▪ Cellar tours by appt ▪ Facilities for children ▪ Tour groups ▪ Wine-related gifts ▪ Fresh duck eggs in spring ▪ 6 boule courts ▪ Guided historical walks & duck tours by appt ▪ Bird hides ▪ Conservation area ▪ Pomegranate Restaurant open for lunch Tue-Sun, dinner by appt ▪ Owner(s) Vergenoegd Trust ▪ Cellarmaster(s) John Faure (Nov 1983) ▪ Winemaker(s) Marlize Jacobs (Dec 2007) ▪ Viticulturist(s) Marlize Jacobs (Dec 2007), advised by Drikus van der Westhuizen (2004) ▪ 300ha/66ha (cabs s/f, malbec, merlot, p verdot, shiraz, tinta, touriga) ▪ 500t ▪ 94% red 3% white 3% rosé ▪ BWI, IPW, WIETA ▪ PO Box 1 Faure 7131 ▪ info@vergenoegd.co.za ▪ www.vergenoegd.co.za ▪ S 34° 2' 2.8" E 018° 44' 20.1" ▪ F +27 (0)21-843-3118 ▪ **T +27 (0)21-843-3248**

Verlieft Wines

The Roos family, boutique brand owners in Stellenbosch, enjoy collaborations - like using New York artist Jason Oliva's depiction of an astronaut on the label for Verlieft's Astronaut blend. Word got round, says Dirk Roos, 'and the wine ended up being served during the 2014 Hall of Fame inauguration gala dinner at the Kennedy Space Centre'. The 2011 vintage was due for release late 2014.

Location: Stellenbosch ▪ Est 2010 ▪ Tasting & sales by appt ▪ Closed Easter Fri-Mon, Dec 25/26 & Jan 1 ▪ Owner(s) Roos Family Wines ▪ Cellarmaster(s) Dirk Roos ▪ PO Box 104 Stellenbosch 7605 ▪ dirk@verlieftwines.com ▪ www.verlieftwines.com ▪ **T +27 (0)82-904-6886**

For more information, visit wineonaplatter.com

Versailles

Owner Annareen de Reuck is the scion of the Malan family which helped establish the Wellington grower-owned cellars now merged into Wellington Wines. Small parcels of her Versailles grapes are vinified in the old estate cellar. Current releases '13 Merlot and '14 Sauvignon Blanc untasted.

Location: Wellington ▪ Map: Paarl & Wellington ▪ Est/1stB 2004 ▪ Tasting, sales & tours by appt ▪ Conservation area ▪ Owner(s) Annareen de Reuck (Malan) ▪ Vineyard manager(s) M Joseph ▪ 100ha (cab, cinsaut, merlot, shiraz, chenin, cbard, riesling) ▪ ±1,200t ▪ PO Box 597 Wellington 7654 ▪ adereuck@ezinet.co.za, orders@versailleswines.co.za ▪ www.versailles.co.za ▪ S 33° 37' 34.98" E 018° 59' 37.11" ▪ F +27 (0)86-502-1482 ▪ **T +27 (0)21-873-2618/+27 (0)82-898-9314**

☐ **Versus** *see* Stellenbosch Vineyards
☐ **Vet Rooi Olifant** *see* Kaapzicht Wine Estate

Viceroy

One of SA's most enduring blended brandies, with the added fillip of 5 years' barrel maturation (unusual in its category), Viceroy has historic ties to what was once the Van Ryn Wine & Spirit Company, dating back to the mid-1800s. It subsequently became part of Distell's extensive brandy stable.

5 Year ⦿ ★★★★ A more serious blended brandy (30% potstill), & smoother & more complex than 5 years ageing would usually imply. Pleasing whether sipped or diluted. — WB, TJ

☐ **Victoria Bay** *see* Darling Cellars

Vierkoppen

Anticipating a bright future for their hilly Klaasvoogds part of Robertson — a happening place 'with several small wineries, tourist attractions, great restaurants and accommodation' - Britons David and Daphne Briscoe are building a boutique-scale cellar on the vineyard holding they bought in 2008 and since upgraded extensively, and intend taking over the reins from contract winemakers. (They grew 2,000 bottles a year of white and sparkling wines back in England.) Emphasis will remain on limited-release premium reds and on exports (currently to Europe and Asia).

★★★★☆ **Cabernet Sauvignon** With dash cab franc. Cassis & coconut spicing from 2 years French oak but **11** has other layers of interest as well, a bit of scrub, forest floor. Polished, silky, with aristocratic elegance, outclasses jammy, less complex **10** (★★★★), labelled 'Weavers Nest'.

Pinotage ★★★☆ Plums & blueberries, showcasing the appeal of good fruit given a spice dusting from French/American oak. Lovely balance, **11** has succulence, freshness, integrated tannins. Already accessible but also promises a future. **Sauvignon Blanc** ★★★ Grapefruit core, with the softening effect of gooseberries, straddles minerality & fruit ripeness. **13** elegant structure, crisp & dry. — CR, CvZ

Location/map/WO: Robertson ▪ Est 2008 ▪ 1stB 2009 ▪ Tasting & sales by appt ▪ Fee R50pp ▪ Closed Dec 25 & Jan 1 ▪ Owner(s) David & Daphne Briscoe ▪ Cellarmaster(s) David Briscoe (Mar 2008) ▪ Winemaker(s) Kobus Burger & Alkie van der Merwe (2009/2014, both consultants) ▪ Viticulturist(s) Philip Swart (Apr 2013, consultant) ▪ 32ha/10ha (cab, durif, merlot, ptage, ruby cab, sauv) ▪ 100t/1,700cs own label 80% red 20% white ▪ PO Box 950 Robertson 6705 ▪ vierkoppen@gmail.com ▪ www.vierkoppen.com ▪ S 33° 48' 1.52" E 019° 58' 55.76" ▪ **T +27 (0)78-413-1733**

Vierlanden Boutique Family Cellar

The four garagistes vinifying small parcels from selected terroirs in a thatched cellar in Durbanville's Vierlanden area - Danel van Tonder, wife Esther, younger brother Marius and winemaker friend PJ Geyer - liken their personalities to the four elements, saying: 'Our combined efforts and energy produce balanced wines of great expression and character that pair beautifully with food.'

Chardonnay ⦿ ★★★ Pleasant **12** from Franschhoek, with nutty & pickled lime notes. Juicy, with a loose structure & strong hint of sweetness. **Sauvignon Blanc** ⦿ ★★★★ **14** ex Elgin difficult to rate ex-tank, but shows plenty of flavour intensity, with succulence & attractive fruitiness, supported by fresh grippy acidity. Also tasted: **ThatchRoof 11** ★★☆ — TJ

Location: Durbanville ▪ Map: Durbanville, Philadelphia & Darling ▪ WO: Swartland/Elgin/Franschhoek ▪ Est 2009 ▪ 1stB 2010 ▪ Tasting, sales & cellar tours Mon-Sat by appt ▪ Fee R55 ▪ Closed all pub hols ▪ Conferences ▪ Owner(s) Vierlanden Boutique Wines cc ▪ Cellarmaster(s) Esther van Tonder (Jan 2009) ▪ Winemaker(s) Esther van Tonder (Jan 2009), Marius van Tonder & PJ Geyer ▪ 1ha/0.25ha (cab) ▪ 4t/±650cs own label 60% red 40% white ▪ Le Petit Jem, 137 on Murray, Vierlanden Heights, Durbanville 7550 ▪ vierlandencellar@gmail.com ▪ www.vierlandencellar.com ▪ S 33° 48' 21.44" E 018° 39' 35.36" ▪ F +27 (0)21-975-7286 ▪ **T +27 (0)21-975-7286**

Vilafonté

The establishment of Vilafonté in the mid 1990s, with two eminent US wine people investing, represented a signal mark of confidence in Cape terroir. Phil Freese, who consults to some of California's grand wineries (and some SA ones), designed and continues to direct their Paarl vineyards while Zelma Long, with an illustrious reputation as a winemaker, is in charge of the cellar on the outskirts of Stellenbosch town. Both are frequent visitors and fully involved (as the plush elegance, rather Napa-like, of the two red wines perhaps attests), with the help of Martin Smith as resident winemaker and the redoubtable Mike Ratcliffe (also of Warwick), the managing partner in the venture.

★★★★☆ **Series C** Seductive Bordeaux blend, cab-based as name hints, with merlot & malbec (26/14), drops **10**'s cab franc in bold & concentrated **11** (★★★★★). Classic claret markers - ripe cassis, graphite & spice (courtesy 80% new oak). Smoothly delicious now & more so given time.

★★★★☆ **Series M** M is now for malbec, having overtaken (just) merlot in beautifully perfumed & fruited **11** Bordeaux blend with cab (51/46/3). Firm dark flavours, with liquorice nuance, & a stately structure for long ageing. Less new oak (only 20%) here than sibling or similarly spicy, elegant **10**. — GM

Location/map: Stellenbosch ▪ WO: Paarl ▪ Est 1996 ▪ 1stB 2003 ▪ Tasting, sales & tours by appt only ▪ Owner(s) Mike Ratcliffe, Zelma Long & Phil Freese ▪ Winemaker(s) Zelma Long & Martin Smith (May 2010) ▪ Viticulturist(s) Phil Freese & Edward Pietersen (2006) ▪ 17ha (cabs s/f, malbec, merlot) ▪ 60t/4,000cs own label 100% red ▪ Unit 7C Lower Dorp Street Bosman's Crossing Stellenbosch 7600 ▪ info@vilafonte.com ▪ www.vilafonte.com ▪ S 33° 56' 26.8" E 018° 50' 49.8" ▪ F +27 (0)21-883-8231 ▪ **T +27 (0)21-886-4083**

Viljoensdrift Wines & Cruises

The 5th generation to grow and make wine here (historically for sale in bulk), brothers Manie and Fred Viljoen started bottling under their own label in 1999. They optimised their farm's location beside the bucolic Breede with scenic riverboat cruises offering onboard gourmet picnics to add to the enjoyment of visitors' tasting experience. Still producing wine for clients, they have increased own-label bottlings while recently consolidating and streamlining the three-tier portfolio.

Viljoensdrift range

★★★★ **Villion** Much-improved méthode cap classique sparkling from chardonnay, 5 years on lees; **08** golden patina, lovely lightness to fresh-bread profile, svelte extra-dry finish. Last was **NV** (★★★).
Muskapino Sweet Sparkling Rosé ★★ **13** sweet, frothy, low-alcohol pink party starter. Muscat de Frontignan & pinotage, as name suggests. Not retasted: **Cape Vintage Reserve 09** ★★

River Grandeur range

Merlot ★★★ Piquant cranberry profile of supple **12** suggests versatile food accompaniment. **Cape Blend** ★★★ **12** now pinotage with a third shiraz, very tropical — banana, pine & coconut profile, generous 14.6% alcohol. **Sauvignon Blanc** ★★ Cut grass & capsicum edge to crisp **14**, for picnic pouring. Also tasted: **Cabernet Sauvignon 12** ★★★☆ **Pinotage 13** ★★ **Shiraz 12** ★★★ Not retasted: **Chardonnay 13** ★★★

For more information, visit wineonaplatter.com

Anchor Drift range (NEW)

Dry Red ★★ **NV** from merlot, beefy & savoury rather than berried, gentle tannins for ease of access.
Dry White ★★ Thatch & hay notes in lightish, modest **13**, semillon with third sauvignon. — DS

Location/map/WO: Robertson ▪ Est/1stB 1998 ▪ Tasting, sales & river cruises at Riverside venue Mon-Fri 9—5 Sat 10-4 & 1st Sun/month 10-3; open 7 days/week during peak season ▪ Closed Good Fri, Dec 25 & Jan 1 ▪ Deli - create your own picnic ▪ Tour groups ▪ Conferences ▪ Owner(s) Fred & Manie Viljoen ▪ Winemaker(s) Fred Viljoen, with Zonia Lategan ▪ Viticulturist(s) Manie Viljoen ▪ 240ha/120ha (cab, ptage, shiraz, chard, chenin, sauv) ▪ 2,000t/±160,000cs own label 55% red 40% white 4% rosé 1% port + 15,000L for clients ▪ Other export brands: Elandsberg, Riverscape, Vuurgloed ▪ BWI, IPW, WIETA ▪ PO Box 653 Robertson 6705 ▪ rivercruises@viljoensdrift.co.za ▪ www.viljoensdrift.co.za ▪ S 33° 52' 8.4" E 019° 59' 13.6" ▪ F +27 (0)23-615-3417 ▪ **T +27 (0)23-615-1901 (cellar)/+27 (0)23-615-1017 (tasting/cruises)**

☐ **Village Walk** *see* Franschhoek Cellar
☐ **Villa San Giovanni** *see* Zandvliet Wine Estate & Thoroughbred Stud

Villiera Wines

There's always been more to the wine business than just wine at this quintessential family estate at the edge of Stellenbosch district, since it was founded by cousins Jeff and Simon Grier over 30 years ago. Good value to go with the quality, for a start. But Villiera has long been known for its sustainability initiatives, eco and social, and those efforts are now better communicated through updated packaging. Ever attuned to trends, they've launched the new Jasmine label to slake the growing thirst for aromatic, slightly sweeter white wine. And as leading bubbly exponents for many years, Jeff and the team feel well positioned to take advantage of expected renewed growth in the méthode cap classique category.

Villiera Wines range

★★★★ **Cabernet Sauvignon** ⊘ **12** successfully fuses blackcurrant fruit, graphite minerality & spice aromas from year in oak (25% new); generous & rounded, with lingering conclusion. A step up on herbal **11** (★★★☆).

★★★★ **Monro** Ⓐ Nicely matured, plush-textured & accessible **09** merlot-led Bordeaux blend with both cabs; sweet expressive ripe dark fruit both structured & softened by 2 years in all-new barrels. No **08** made.

★★★★ **Traditional Barrel Fermented Chenin Blanc** Barrel-fermented (50% new) **14** classically structured & flavoured. Rich but not showy, gains delicious apricot nuance from 3% botrytised portion, pine nut complexity & enlivening acid seam. **12**, **13** not made.

★★★★ **Bush Vine Sauvignon Blanc** From single-vineyard, low-yielding untrellised vines, complex, kaleidoscopic **14** billows herbs & grass, kiwi & gooseberry, plus capsicum, in nicely toned body with sufficient substance & life to reward few years in bottle.

★★★★☆ **Inspiration** Ⓐ Botrytised chenin, riesling dessert. Last-tasted **10**'s fresh acid controls richness.

Sauvignon Blanc ★★★☆ Harmonious **14**, light & fresh, appealing tropical/green crossover style. Always a great seafood match, or try with fresh asparagus. WO W Cape. **Jasmine** (NEW) ★★★ Name perfectly captures perfumed character of light, gently sweet blend of 4 aromatic varieties. **14** Turkish Delight wafts, crisp acidity ensures drinkability. Also tasted: **Merlot 12** ★★★ **Pinotage 12** ★★★ **Chenin Blanc 14** ★★★ Discontinued: **Gewürztraminer, Rhine Riesling**.

Méthode Cap Classique range

★★★★ **Brut Natural** Quietly-spoken charm in clean, delicate **10** sparkler from chardonnay. Bone-dry, 3 years on lees for refined mousse, subtle weight & aroma. Soft & smooth, seamless finish. No sulphur added.

★★★★☆ **Monro Brut** Classy, deliciously creamy & persistent **08** barrel-fermented chardonnay-pinot sparkling softer than much-lauded cool-vintage **07** (★★★★★), shows great dimension & complexity from 4 years on lees.

★★★★ **Tradition Brut** Ever-popular **NV** bubbles from chardonnay, pinot noir & pinotage (50/30/20). Dry yet creamy, with red fruit & citrus highlights. Latest disgorgement steps up, & still perfectly partners seafood.

Also tasted: **Tradition Brut Rosé NV** ★★★☆ **Starlight Brut NV** ★★★

Down to Earth range

Red ★★★ Easygoing sipper with tempting perfume, touriga, shiraz blend, **13** cinnamon & cedarwood spice to plum & mulberry fruit. Also tasted: **White 14** ★★★ — GM

Location/map: Stellenbosch ▪ WO: Stellenbosch/Western Cape ▪ Est/1stB 1983 ▪ Tasting, sales & self-guided cellar tours Mon-Fri 9–5 Sat 9–3 ▪ Closed Good Fri, Dec 25 & Jan 1 ▪ MCC & nougat pairings; cheese platters & soft drinks ▪ Wildlife sanctuary ▪ Game drive safaris & birding R170pp (R85 for children under 15) incl tasting & self-guided tour of cellar, book ahead ▪ Owner(s) Grier family ▪ Cellarmaster(s) Jeff Grier (1983) ▪ Winemaker(s) Christiaan Visser (Dec 2008) ▪ Viticulturist(s) Simon Grier ▪ 180ha (cab, merlot, ptage, pinot, shiraz, chard, chenin, sauv) ▪ 1,800t/120,000cs own label 28% red 37% white 35% MCC ▪ Brands for clients: Woolworths (local); Marks & Spencer (export) ▪ HACCP, WIETA ▪ PO Box 66 Koelenhof 7605 ▪ wine@villiera.com ▪ www.villiera.com ▪ S 33° 50' 14.4" E 018° 47' 34.4" ▪ F +27 (0)21-865-2314 ▪ **T +27 (0)21-865-2002/3**

Villiersdorp Cellar

The farms of Villiersdorp Cellar's 40 grower-owners are situated in four distinct geographical regions around Villiersdorp town, and these terroirs are highlighted, along with the winery's founding date, in the new Since 1922 brand. The red and white listed below, along with an untasted rosé, are available from the characterful visitor centre, which includes a tractor museum open on request.

Since 1922 range
Bossieveld Cabernet Sauvignon-Merlot ★★★ Pocket-pleasing **13** preview, plump-fruited pizza & pasta mate. **Van Der Stel Sémillon-Sauvignon Blanc** ★★★☆ Ex tank, **14** unoaked 60/40 combo zesty & sweet fruited, with hints of wax, lemon & grass.

Villiersdorp Cellar range
Treintjiewyn Hanepoot Jerepiko ★★★ 'Little Tractor' **NV** fortified dessert oozes orange rind, watermelon & sunshine. Slippery & luscious. Not retasted: **Cape Ruby NV** ★★ — CvZ

Location/map: Villiersdorp ▪ WO: Western Cape ▪ Est 1922 ▪ 1stB 1974 ▪ Tasting & sales Mon-Fri 8–5 Sat 9-1 ▪ Fee R10 for groups of 7+ ▪ Closed Easter Fri-Mon & Dec 25/26 ▪ Cellar tours by appt ▪ Kelkiewyn Restaurant ▪ Farm produce ▪ Walks/hikes ▪ Mountain biking & 4x4 trails ▪ Tractor museum open on request ▪ Owner(s) 40 growers ▪ Winemaker(s) Christo Versfeld, with André Bruyns (Dec 2009) ▪ Viticulturist(s) André Bruyns (Dec 2009) ▪ 300ha (merlot, chenin, sauv) ▪ 3,600t/19,000cs own label 30% red 30% white 30% rosé 10% fortified ▪ BWI, IPW ▪ PO Box 14 Villiersdorp 6848 ▪ marketing@slowine.co.za ▪ www.villiersdorpcellar.co.za ▪ S 33° 59' 11.2" E 019° 17' 48.5" ▪ F +27 (0)28-840-1833 ▪ **T +27 (0)28-840-1120**

☐ **Vinay** *see* Slanghoek Winery

Vin du Cap International

Grapes and wine for Vin du Cap's main brands, Vrede, Charmé and Jabari, are sourced from own vineyards on Stellenbosch's Vrede farm as well as selected contracted growers. Attractively and classically attired, each wine is intended to be 'a voyage of discovery'.

Vrede Vineyard Select range
Cabernet Sauvignon ★★ Naturally fermented **13** more red than typical black fruit, toffee hints on medium body. Ready now. Not retasted: **Syrah 10** ★★★ **Lourentius van Andringa 10** ★★★
Andrea 10 ★★★

Charmé range
Sauvignon Blanc (NEW) ★★ From Durbanville, **13** gently tropical fruit & greenpepper glassful, brief grassy farewell. Also tasted: **Shiraz 11** ★★ Not retasted: **Cabernet Sauvignon 11** ★★

Jabari range (NEW)
Shiraz ★★★ **11**'s red fruits mingle happily with dark chocolate & spice; well-judged oaking gives smooth & savoury enjoyment. WO W Cape for this range. Also tasted: **Cape Red 12** ★★★ — GM

Location/map: Stellenbosch ▪ WO: Stellenbosch/Western Cape/Durbanville ▪ Est 2011 ▪ Tasting & sales strictly by appt ▪ Owner(s) LvA Bellingan, Andrea Lubbe & Christa Calitz ▪ 90% red 10% white ▪ PO Box 7271 Stellenbosch 7599 ▪ christa@vinducap.com ▪ www.vinducap.com ▪ S 33° 50' 37.8" E 018° 48' 31.4" ▪ F +27 (0)21-851-8475 ▪ **T +27 (0)82-929-2894**

Vinimark

Wine merchants marketing, selling and distributing various ranges with local partners, including Robertson Winery, Kleindal, Long Beach and Silversands, some listed separately.

Stellenbosch ▪ Closed to public ▪ Directors Tim Rands, Cindy Jordaan, Geoff Harvey, Gys Naudé, Rudiger Gretschel & Guy Pause ▪ Exports: Geoff Harvey ▪ geoff@vinimark.co.za ▪ PO Box 441 Stellenbosch 7599 ▪ www.vinimark.co.za ▪ F +27 (0)21-886-4708 ▪ **T +27 (0)21-883-8043/4**

Vinopoly Wines

Bonnievale-based Vinopoly is a fledgling negociant and brand owner established by the Retief family of Van Loveren to access the value-for-money segment of the wineloving public. Supplying house brands to a variety of retailers, including Pick n Pay (SunningHill) and Food Lover's Market (Wine Lover's), it recently added Jonkheer brands Bakenskop and Es La Vida to the stable. With rapid local and export growth, its bright red delivery fleet emblazoned with the mission, 'Making Wine Sense', is a common sight on roads linking the small town to SA's distribution hubs.

Bakenskop range
Pinotage ⊘ ★★★★ **12** is juicy, fruity, with touch of oak & decent grip for good balance. Smoky whiff on finish. **Chardonnay** ★★ Unwooded **14** fresh & uncomplicated with soft marshmallow texture, crisp apple on finish. **White Muscadel** ★★★ **14** fortified dessert with interesting sweet melon, dried apricot tang, pleasant grip. Robertson WO. Also tasted: **Cabernet Sauvignon 12** ★★ **Merlot 12** ★★ **Sauvignon Blanc 14** ★★ **Red Muscadel 14** ★★★ Not retasted: **Shiraz 11** ★ **Es La Vida Rosa NV** ★★ **Es la Vida Blanca NV** ★★

Cape Auction range
Rosé (Ⓩ) ★★ Muscatty **NV** rosé for the sweet-toothed. Not retasted: **Red NV** ★★ **White NV** ★★

SunningHill range (NEW)
Red ★★ **NV** allsorts blend offering dusty fruit, soft & light in all departments. **Rosé** ★★ Pretty pink **NV**, fragrant strawberry aromas & flavours. Semi-sweet but with a nice zip. **White** ★★ Semi-dry fun **NV** from sauvignon, chenin & muscadel. Fragrant, light as a feather, soft fruit flavours. — WB

Location: Bonnievale ▪ WO: Western Cape/Robertson ▪ Closed to public ▪ Owner(s) Van Loveren Vineyards ▪ PO Box 92 Bonnievale 6730 ▪ info@vinopoly.co.za ▪ www.vinopoly.co.za ▪ F +27 (0)23-616-3146 ▪ **T +27 (0)23-616-2137/8/9**

☐ **Vins d'Orrance** see Dorrance Wines
☐ **Vinum** see Winery of Good Hope
☐ **Vior** see Malanot Wines

Virgin Earth

About 320 km distant from its West Coast sibling property, Havana Hills, the Virgin Earth home farm is situated on the foothills of the Langeberg. Most of the 13,000 ha estate has been kept natural, and a game park established where wild antelope roam. Winemakers Piet Kleinhans and Joseph Gertse have been experimenting extensively with natural fermentations and, in the vineyard, some 3,000 cubic metres of trucked-in natural compost have yielded excellent results. New pinot noir, chardonnay and chenin blocks have been established.

★★★★ **High 5** ⊘ Seamless, elegant **11**, five Bordeaux reds in harmonious blend, back on form after **10** (★★★★). Pure, ripe red fruit given sufficient grip by well-integrated third new oak, slightly sweet finish.

★★★★ **Pepper Tree Sauvignon Blanc** ⊘ Pale, aromatic **14**, few grains sugar perfect foil for rapier-like acidity. Vibrant, rich fruit provides ample drinking pleasure.

★★★★ **Noble Late Harvest** ② From semillon, last **08** ticked all the boxes: deeply rich & full-flavoured; apricot, pineapple, good length. Deliciously easy to drink. 30% in seasoned barrels. 500 ml.

Pinot Noir ★★★☆ Pale, light-footed & savoury **12** from Philadelphia offers plenty juicy cherry fruit in refreshing spicy sipper. **Sauvignon Blanc-Semillon** ⊘ ★★★★ Mouthwatering acidity structures austere **14** blend, steeliness softened by some residual sweetness. 'Try with something exotic & sensual' say the team. Also tasted: **Chenin Blanc** ⊘ **14** ★★★★ Not retasted: **Pinotage 10** ★★★★ **Lost Barrel Shiraz 07** ★★★ **Shiraz-Viognier 11** ★★★ **Viognier MCC 08** ★★★ Not tasted: **Succulent**. — IM

Location: Riversdale ▪ WO: Langeberg-Garcia/Philadelphia/Coastal/Overberg ▪ Est 2002 ▪ 1stB 2003 ▪ Closed to public ▪ Owner(s) Kobus du Plessis ▪ Winemaker(s) Piet Kleinhans (Sep 2008) & Joseph Gertse (Jan 2000) ▪ Viticulturist(s) Rudi Benn (Jan 2001) & Hendrik Otto (2004) ▪ 13,000ha/21ha (cabs s/f, merlot, p verdot, pinot, shiraz, chard, chenin, sauv, sem, verdelho, viog) ▪ 70,000cs own label 40% red 45% white 15% rosé ▪ Fairtrade, organic in conversion, WIETA ▪ PO Box 451 Melkbosstrand 7437 ▪ sales@havanahills.co.za ▪ www.havanahills.co.za ▪ F +27 (0)21-972-1105 ▪ **T +27 (0)21-972-1110**

Virginia

For over 4 decades, a consistent semi-sweet white, widely sourced, by Distell. 2 & 5L.

Virginia ★ Like its front label, sweetish **NV** is straightforward & unvarying from year to year. — AL

☐ **Vivat Bacchus** *see* Veenwouden Private Cellar

Vleiland Wines

While winemaking remains a passion for Vredendal-based Nico Laubscher jnr, he hasn't found time for much beyond a small cab-shiraz bottling (the latest '12 untasted). He and father Nico grow grapes for Namaqua Wines and have been extending the family landholding for cultivation of more vines, as well as squashes, cucumbers and tomatoes.

Location: Vredendal ▪ Map: Olifants River ▪ Est 2004 ▪ 1stB 2005 ▪ Tasting & sales by appt Mon-Fri 8-5 Sat 8-12 ▪ Closed Easter Fri-Mon, Dec 25 & Jan 1 ▪ BYO picnic ▪ Walks/hikes ▪ 4x4 & mountain bike trails ▪ Owner(s) Nico Laubscher snr, Alette Laubscher, Nico Laubscher jnr ▪ Winemaker(s)/viticulturist(s) Nico Laubscher ▪ 60ha (cab, ptage, shiraz, chenin, cbard, sauv) ▪ 790t/560cs own label 100% red ▪ PO Box 627 Vredendal 8160 ▪ alzanne@mylan.co.za ▪ S 31° 44' 42.24" E 018° 32' 8.16" ▪ F +27 (0)27-213-2825 ▪ **T +27 (0)27-213-2525/+27 (0)82-905-1640**

Vondeling

High on the agenda for this British-owned property is conservation and sustainability. There can be only a handful of Cape farms that employ a full-time botanist, as Vondeling does, to geo-tag, catalogue and fingerprint endangered fynbos on its biodiverse Voor Paardeberg land. However, wine definitely gets its due. The cellar team is encouraged to be creative and one of the results is a rare, just-released méthode ancestrale sparkling wine. Though labour intensive, fraught with difficulty and reliant on very precise timing, the venture is deemed 'exciting, with enormous potential!'

★★★★ **Cabernet Sauvignon** Molten dark plums, loads of spice, **12** is hard to ignore, its 18 months in French/Hungarian barrels apparent in the flavours but tannins are supple, drinkability assured.

For more information, visit wineonaplatter.com

★★★★ **Erica Shiraz** ⓥ With soupçons 4 other Rhône varieties, **10** has all the right touches, scrub, white pepper, hint of chocolate, folded into plush dark fruit. Supple tannins give a platform for ageing.

★★★★ **Chardonnay** Bunch pressed, wild yeast barrel ferment/ageing year. **13** shows citrus peel & white peach, nutty savoury overlay, lemon-fresh elegance. Also-tasted **12**'s citrus freshness & svelte lines as attractive.

★★★★ **Sauvignon Blanc** Leafy, fynbos top note to **14**'s mineral character, the crisp lemony acidity an ideal match with seafood, oysters. Lovely Old World austerity, another take on sauvignon.

★★★★☆ **Babiana** Chenin-led with 3 others, natural ferment/ageing in barrel. Melon & quince in **12**, savoury shortbread oak spicing, the freshness given a sweet/sour edge from a touch of sugar. Distinctive, delicious, ageworthy.

★★★★ **Rurale Méthode Ancestral** ⑭ Ancient method where fermenting juice is bottled & conversion to bubbly takes place in it, in one process. **13** from chardonnay, great lemony intensity, long zesty finish, can age.

★★★★☆ **Sweet Carolyn** An occasional release, ambrosial vine-dried muscat de Frontignan. Like **06**, **11** is stellar, hedonistic, the grapey perfume not preparing you for the flavour intensity: molten apricots & pineapple, riveting freshness underpinning the richness. Improves on last **09** (★★★★).

Rosé ⑭ ★★★ Red berries with herbaceous overtones, **14** from merlot is light & dry, the styling a great match for creative salads, tapas. Also tasted: **Baldrick Shiraz 13** ★★★★ **Petit Rouge 13** ★★★ **Petit Blanc 14** ★★★ — CR

Location: Paarl ▪ Map: Paarl & Wellington ▪ WO: Voor Paardeberg ▪ Est 2001 ▪ 1stB 2005 ▪ Tasting & sales Mon-Fri 10-5 Sat/pub hols by appt ▪ Wedding/function/conference venue ▪ St Clement's Chapel ▪ Owner(s) Richard Gower, Julian Johnsen & Anthony Ward ▪ Winemaker(s) Matthew Copeland (Jul 2007), with Emile van der Merwe (Dec 2011) ▪ Viticulturist(s) Magnus Joubert (Jul 2012) ▪ 115ha (cabs s/f, carignan, grenache r/w, malbec, merlot, mourv, p verdot, shiraz, chard, chenin, muscat de F, sauv, viog) ▪ 1,200t/90,000cs own label 40% red 40% white 20% rosé ▪ Other export brand: Signal Cannon ▪ BWI champion ▪ PO Box 57 Wellington 7654 ▪ admin@vondelingwines.co.za ▪ www.vondelingwines.co.za ▪ S 33° 35' 22.50" E 018° 52' 45.00" ▪ F +27 (0)21-869-8219 ▪ **T +27 (0)21-869-8595**

☐ **Vrede** see Vin du Cap International

Vrede en Lust Wine Farm ⓔ ⓜ ⓗ ⓘ ⓐ ⓑ

The ambitious Buys family owners continue to develop this venerable Simonsberg property as a wine tourism and business hub. Besides adding three new wines (two from the family's Elgin farm) to its portfolio, there are plans for another 10 guest rooms and more conference facilities.

Location: Paarl ▪ Map: Franschhoek ▪ Est 1688 ▪ 1stB 2002 ▪ Tasting & sales daily 10–5 ▪ Closed Good Fri & Dec 25 ▪ Tours 10–4 by appt ▪ Lust Bistro & Bakery ▪ Guest accommodation in deluxe suites & manor house ▪ Tour groups by appt ▪ Conferences, functions & weddings ▪ Play area for children ▪ Pétanque courts ▪ Owner(s) Buys family ▪ Winemaker(s) Susan Erasmus (2006), with Ansoné Stoffberg (2009) ▪ Viticulturist(s) Etienne Buys (Jun 1998) ▪ 275ha total ▪ Vrede en Lust: 66ha (cab, grenache, malbec, merlot, p verdot, shiraz, chard, viog); Casey's Ridge, Elgin: 88.9ha (cabs s/f, merlot, shiraz, chard, chenin, pinots g/n, riesling, sauv, sem, viog); Ricton: 127ha (cab, cinsaut, ptage, shiraz, chard) ▪ 800t/45,000cs own label ▪ WIETA ▪ PO Box 171 Groot Drakenstein 7680 ▪ info@vnl.co.za ▪ www.vnl.co.za ▪ S 33° 50' 15.9" E 018° 57' 13.4" ▪ F +27 (0)21-874-1859 ▪ **T +27 (0)21-874-1611**

☐ **Vredehoek** see Koopmanskloof Wingerde

Vredenheim Wines ⓔ ⓜ ⓗ ⓘ ⓑ

Family-owned Vredenheim with its trademark antelope enclosure is also home to an African Big Cats Park among many visitors' offerings. These include a range of wines led by flagship red blend dedicated to 'gracious lady' Rikie Bezuidenhout and a chardonnay honouring late husband 'M'Lord' Coen, who bought the farm in 1986.

For more information, visit wineonaplatter.com

Pinotage ★★☆ Ripe banana & plums with hints of spice, fine tannin on uncomplicated, juicy **13**.
Gracious Lady (NEW) ★★★★ Bordeaux-style cab (80%) & merlot blend, **11** straightforward red fruit with touch of Asian of spice. Undemanding midweek sipper. **M'Lord Chardonnay** (NEW) ★★★ Typical chardonnay character with subtle oaking, **12** notes of melon & lemon, understated & soft. WO W Cape. **Sauvignon Blanc** ★★★ Thirst-quenching **14** an easy quaffer with green & tropical notes, vibrant acidity. Also tasted: **Rosé NV** ★★ **Sparkling Wine Off-Dry NV** ★★★ Not retasted: **Cabernet Sauvignon 10** ★★★ **Merlot 11** ★★★ **Shiraz 11** ★★★ Discontinued: **Reserve**. — JPf

Location/map: Stellenbosch ▪ WO: Stellenbosch/Western Cape ▪ Tasting & sales Mon-Sat 9-4.45 ▪ Closed Good Fri, Dec 25 & Jan 1 ▪ Restaurant Barrique T +27 (0)21-881-3001 ▪ Hudson's Coffee Shop T +27 (0)21-881-3590 ▪ Conferences/functions ▪ Vredenheim Angus Stud ▪ Big Cats Park ▪ Jaguar cars for hire ▪ Curio shop ▪ Guesthouse ▪ Owner(s) Bezuidenhout family ▪ Winemaker(s) Kowie du Toit ▪ Viticulturist(s) Kalie Kirsten ▪ 80ha under vine ▪ 20,000cs own label 60% red 40% white ▪ PO Box 369 Stellenbosch 7599 ▪ wine@vredenheim.co.za ▪ www.vredenheim.co.za ▪ S 33° 57' 38.2" E 018° 48' 29.4" ▪ F +27 (0)21-881-3296 ▪ **T +27 (0)21-881-3637**

Vredevol Private Wine Cellar

While a new barrel maturation cellar at their Klawer winery and an Out of Region range are still on the agenda, boutique vignerons Johan and Anne-Mari le Hanie's melot-cab is still from Coastal fruit vinified at Stellenbosch's Blue Creek. The current release is '12, untasted by us.

Location: Klawer ▪ Est 2007 ▪ 1stB 2008 ▪ Closed to public ▪ Owner(s) Johan & Anne-Mari le Hanie ▪ Cellarmaster(s)/ winemaker(s) Johan van Wyk (Jul 2010) ▪ 30ha ▪ 1,000cs own label 50% red 50% white ▪ PO Box 12695 Die Boord 7613 ▪ vredevol.wines@vodamail.co.za ▪ F +27 (0)21-887-1288 ▪ **T +27 (0)21-887-1277**

Vriesenhof Vineyards

Rugby legend Jan 'Boland' Coetzee bought his farm on the slopes of Stellenbosch Mountain, just outside the town, in 1980, but purchases, long leases, land swaps and new plantings have changed its shape over the years. Working with Nicky Claasens in the cellar, Jan's winemaking approach remains resolutely traditional, avoiding upfront fruitiness and maintaining a proper dryness in their adherence to a model of classic austerity. The celebratory Pinot Noir Blend debuting this edition was made in 2011, exactly 30 years after the estate's first bottling under the Paradyskloof label.

Vriesenhof range

★★★★ **Cabernet Sauvignon** Estate's best cab bottled in magnum, just 980 of **10** available. More fruit intensity than muted & savoury **09** (★★★★). Still tightly coiled & brooding, with a dense fruit core & firm tealeaf tannins. Deserves cellar time.

★★★★☆ **Grenache** Limited bottling from Piekenierskloof. **12** supremely elegant, silky & balanced. Initially understated, grows in savoury & perfumed red-fruited intensity. A real sophisticated beauty. Also-tasted **13** more overt fruit & perfume, more vivacious, outgoing. Same pedigree & good structure but not as balanced, needs more time to harmonise. Both also sold in magnum.

★★★★ **Pinot Noir** Ⓩ **09** released after **10** (tasted last year). Most attractive cherry & berry fruit, though not showy or intense; well balanced, with mild tannins & fresh acidity. **11** (★★★★) also well structured, but more earthy, with the fruit a little dulled.

★★★★ **Chardonnay 13** less steely & restrained than previous but retains elegance. Layers of nutty lime flavours in supportive, older oak framework. Lovely freshness, with a creamy conclusion.

Pinotage ★★★ Classic Vriesenhof expression in **10**; unshowy savoury-sweet, polished leather tone & texture, lengthy oaking (18 months 2nd fill) integrated into ample savoury-toned fruit. Not retasted: **Kallista 09** ★★★★

Paradyskloof range

Pinot Noir Blend (NEW) ★★★★ Well-crafted **11** marks 30 years of Paradyskloof wines. Blend of pinotage & its parents - pinot noir (85%) & cinsaut. Bright, balanced & juicy, savoury red-fruited flavours in very supple framework. Ready to celebrate. **Grenache Rosé** (NEW) ★★★ Pale onion skin **14**, lightish, crisp & dry, with clean prosciutto & cranberry flavours. Friendly sunset quaffer. Also tasted: **Pinotage 12** ★★★ **Chardonnay 13** ★★★ Not retasted: **Cabernet Sauvignon 10** ★★ Not tasted: **Pinot Noir**. Discontinued: **Grenache-Malbec-Shiraz, Muscat d'Alexandrie**. — MW

Location/map: Stellenbosch ▪ WO: Stellenbosch/Piekenierskloof ▪ Est 1980 ▪ 1stB 1981 ▪ Tasting & sales Mon-Thu 10—4 Fri 10—3.30 Sat by appt ▪ Fee R25 ▪ Closed all pub hols ▪ Cellar tours by appt ▪ Owner(s) Landgoed Vriesenhof (Pty) Ltd ▪ Cellarmaster(s) Jan Coetzee ▪ Winemaker(s) Nicky Claasens (2008), with Richard Phillips (2001) ▪ Viticulturist(s) Coetzee Ehlers ▪ 60ha/45ha (cabs s/f, grenache, merlot, pinot, ptage, chard) ▪ 300t/34,000cs own label 90% red 10% white ▪ PO Box 155 Stellenbosch 7599 ▪ info@vriesenhof.co.za ▪ www.vriesenhof.co.za ▪ S 33° 58' 16.7" E 018° 52' 2.8" ▪ F +27 (0)21-880-1503 ▪ **T +27 (0)21-880-0284**

Vruchtbaar Boutique Winery

Production at this boutique cellar owned by father and son Alwyn and Francois Bruwer has always been minuscule — under 1,000 cases, some vintages a mere 100 — as their grapes have been sought after by Robertson Winery. Francois eschews modern winemaking equipment, convinced that his 'primitive' methods have stood the test of time.

★★★★ **Chenin Blanc Limited Edition** (ⓘ) In contrast to sinuous **08**, bold **09** (★★★★) not for the faint-hearted: ripe tropical tones lashed with buttery oak, warming 15% alcohol.
Not retasted: **Island Red NV** ★★★ Not tasted: **Cabernet Sauvignon, Pinotage, Chardonnay, Chenin Blanc Unwooded, Noble Late Harvest**. — CvZ

Location/map/WO: Robertson ▪ Est/1stB 2001 ▪ Tasting, sales & cellar tours Mon-Sat by appt ▪ Closed all pub hols ▪ Owner(s) Alwyn & Francois Bruwer ▪ Cellarmaster(s)/winemaker(s) Francois Bruwer ▪ Viticulturist(s) Briaan Stipp (consultant) ▪ 35ha (cab, merlot, ptage, ruby cab, chard, chenin, sauv) ▪ 400t/±874cs own label 62% red 38% white ▪ PO Box 872 Robertson 6705 ▪ vruchtbaar@mweb.co.za ▪ S 33° 48' 17.7" E 019° 51' 43.6" ▪ F +27 (0)23-626-2334 ▪ **T +27 (0)82-739-5553/+27 (0)82-335-1152**

☐ **Vry Burger** see Group CDV
☐ **Vusani** see House of Mandela

Vuurberg

During a 2000 kite-surfing holiday to the Cape, Dutchman Sebastiaan Klaassen acquired a vineyard on the Helshoogte Pass and has slowly been establishing Vuurberg as a top boutique winery ever since. Donovan Rall, known for non-conformist yet highly acclaimed wines under his own label, came on board in 2010, making this surely a label to watch.

★★★★ **Vuurberg Reserve** Naturally fermented, powerful **10**, notch up on **09** (★★★★). Mix of cab, malbec, petit verdot & merlot shows fynbos & blackcurrant verve with tannin grip. Tail a tad warm with 15.5% alcohol.

★★★★ **White** Chenin reigns in bold **13** six-part blend. Complex melange of ripe stonefruit. Vibrant & lively with focused acidity & broad, nuanced palate from natural ferment & mainly older oak. Also-tasted **12**, similar, creamy; both a step up on 7-way **11** (★★★★). Coastal WO. — FM

Location/map: Stellenbosch ▪ WO: Stellenbosch/Coastal ▪ Tasting, sales & cellar tours by appt ▪ Closed all pub hols ▪ Owner(s)/cellarmaster(s) Sebastiaan Klaassen ▪ Winemaker(s) Donovan Rall (Oct 2010) ▪ 8ha (cabs s/f, malbec, merlot, p verdot, chenin, viog) ▪ 2,000cs own label 50% red 50% white ▪ PO Box 449 Stellenbosch 7599 ▪ info@ vuurberg.com ▪ www.vuurberg.com ▪ S 33° 54' 28.9" E 018° 56' 52.7" ▪ **T +27 (0)72-182-7571**

☐ **Vuurgloed** see Viljoensdrift Wines & Cruises
☐ **W** see Whalehaven Wines

Waboomsrivier Wine Cellar

Situated in the mountain and river wonderland of the upper Breede River Valley, grower-owned Waboomsrivier has carried out upgrades to its production facilities, installing new crushers and decanters. Small volumes appear under the Wagenboom own label, not ready for tasting this edition.

Location: Worcester ▪ Map: Breedekloof ▪ Est 1949 ▪ Tasting & sales Mon-Fri 8-5 ▪ Closed all pub hols ▪ Cellar tours by appt during harvest ▪ Cellarmaster(s) Bennie Wannenburg (Sep 2005) ▪ Winemaker(s) Wim Viljoen (Sep 1991), with André Landman (Jan 2013) ▪ Viticulturist(s) Pierre Snyman (Vinpro) ▪ ±1,106ha ▪ 19,872t ▪ ISO 22000:2011 ▪ PO Box 24 Breërivier 6858 ▪ sales@wabooms.co.za ▪ www.waboomsrivier.com ▪ S 33° 31' 43.08" E 019° 12' 35.24" ▪ F +27 (0)23-355-1731 ▪ **T +27 (0)23-355-1730**

Wade Bales Wine Society

Long-established Wade Bales Wine Society is a specialist merchant sourcing fine-wine from producers and selling directly to private clients based on their individual needs and preferences. The Society is also a negociant, bottling and marketing exclusive and limited-release wines under the Bales Choice and Wade Bales Winemaker Selection labels to its clients.

Location: Constantia ▪ Map: Cape Peninsula ▪ Est 1992 ▪ Tasting & sales Mon-Fri 8.30-5 ▪ Closed all pub hols ▪ Owner(s) Wade Bales ▪ 10,000cs own label ▪ Private Bag X2 Constantia 7848 ▪ info@thewinesociety.co.za ▪ www.wadebaleswinesociety.co.za ▪ S 34° 2' 5.43" E018° 25' 32.98" ▪ F +27 (0)21-794-2821 ▪ **T +27 (0)21-794-2151**

☐ **Wagenboom** *see* Waboomsrivier Wine Cellar

Waka Waka Wines

Invoking Shakira's catchy theme song for FIFA World Cup 2010, this joint venture between Perdeberg Winery and REH Kendermann is for export only, mainly to the US and Germany. New releases of the Shiraz-Cabernet, Sauvignon and Sauvignon-Chenin not ready for tasting.

Location: Paarl ▪ Est 2011 ▪ 1stB 2010 ▪ Tasting & sales at Perdeberg Winery (see entry) ▪ Owner(s) REH Kendermann & Perdeberg Winery ▪ Cellarmaster(s) Albertus Louw (Oct 2008) ▪ Winemaker(s) Riaan Möller (Dec 2006) & Carla Herbst (Jun 2008) ▪ Viticulturist(s) Jaco Engelbrecht (Nov 2011) ▪ PO Box 214 Paarl 7620 ▪ info@perdeberg.co.za ▪ www.perdeberg.co.za ▪ F +27 (0)21-869-8245 ▪ **T +27 (0)21-869-8244**

Walker Bay Vineyards

Lovers of wine, beer, spring water and food are all catered for at this family-cordial estate outside Stanford, with a cellar, Birkenhead micro-brewery, water-bottling plant and restaurant on the premises. Wine production is up, and a new-look logo and label have improved sales and brand awareness, according to winemaker, viticulturist and GM Reinhard Odendaal.

Rosé ★★★ 13 from shiraz & sauvignon. Flavoursome, dry, lightish - refreshing warm-weather sipping. **Chardonnay Unoaked ★★** Refreshing, dry **13**, with some light nutty appeal. Also tasted: **Sauvignon Blanc 13 ★★** Not retasted: **Cabernet Sauvignon 11 ★★★ Amesteca 10 ★★★** Not tasted: **Chardonnay**. — AL

Location: Stanford ▪ Map: Elgin, Walker Bay & Bot River ▪ WO: Walker Bay ▪ Est 1997 ▪ 1stB 2007 ▪ Tasting & sales Mon-Sat 10-5 Sun 11-4 ▪ Fee R20 wine/beer ▪ Closed Good Fri & Dec 25/26 ▪ Cellar tours by appt ▪ Micro brewery ▪ Restaurant ▪ BYO picnic ▪ Facilities for children ▪ Tour groups ▪ Owner(s) Birkenhead Holdings Ltd (Isle of Man) ▪ GM Reinhard Odendaal ▪ Winemaker(s)/viticulturist(s) Reinhard Odendaal ▪ 300ha/24ha (cab, merlot, p verdot, pinot, shiraz, chard, sauv, sem) ▪ 100t/14,000cs own label 40% red 60% white ▪ PO Box 530 Stanford 7210 ▪ info@birkenhead.co.za ▪ www.walkerbayestate.co.za ▪ S 34° 26' 30.5" E 019° 27' 40.5" ▪ F +27 (0)28-341-0196 ▪ **T +27 (0)28-341-0183**

Wandsbeck Wyne Koöp Bpk

Freshening up of this Agterkliphoogte grower-owned winery continues. The new face belongs to winemaker Hugo Conradie, who'll be handling increased tonnage for bulk and bottled wine due to two more growers having joined. Back-up comes in the form of recently upgraded and enlarged cellar facilities and full-time viticulturist Hennie Visser.

Cabernet Sauvignon ★★☆ Walnut & crushed dark berry in easy-drinking, well-oaked **13**.
Muscadel ★★★ Fortified & ultra-sweet **13** red muscadel shows grapey & floral notes & a lush, viscous palate. Also tasted: **Revelation Red 12** ★★★ **Symphony 13** ★★ **Sauvignon Blanc 14** ★★ Not retasted: **Revelation White 13** ★★★ — JPf

Location/map/WO: Robertson ▪ Est 1965 ▪ 1stB 1986 ▪ Tasting & sales Mon-Fri 8–5 Sat/Sun by appt ▪ Closed all pub hols ▪ Cellar tours by appt ▪ Facilities for children ▪ Owner(s) 21 members ▪ Cellarmaster(s) Jacques du Toit (Jun 2008) ▪ Winemaker(s) Hugo Conradie (Aug 2013) ▪ Viticulturist(s) Hennie Visser ▪ 516ha (cab, cinsaut, merlot, ruby cab, shiraz, chenin, chard, cbard, sauv) ▪ 8,000t/4,000cs own label 43% red 29% white 14% rosé 14% other + 6M L bulk ▪ IPW ▪ PO Box 267 Robertson 6705 ▪ info@wandsbeckwyne.co.za ▪ www.wandsbeckwyne.co.za ▪ S 33° 55' 60.0" E 019° 36' 34.4" ▪ F +27 (0)23-626-3329 ▪ **T +27 (0)23-626-1103**

☐ **Warhorse** *see* Simonsig Landgoed

Warwick Estate

Women feature strongly at Warwick: 6 wines have female names, it all having started with matriarch Norma Ratcliffe. Husband Stan bought the farm 50 years ago, planting cabernet, which still forms the backbone of the reds. Pioneer female winemaker, Cape Winemakers Guild member/former chair, Norma still plays an active role on the farm, its supervising winemaker, involved in strategic planning and as PR personality par excellence locally and abroad. This is very much a family business, for 2nd generation head of the estate is son Mike Ratcliffe, who puts his Adelaide University wine marketing qualification to good use by connecting with consumers through social media, and continually offering lifestyle value. There are so many different activities on offer that Tripadvisor, the biggest travel website, continually names Warwick the #1 Stellenbosch winery to visit.

★★★★ **The First Lady Cabernet Sauvignon** A slightly sterner First Lady in **12** (★★★★), from 100% cab & missing the softening effect of **11**'s 15% shiraz component. Though firmer, & for heartier food, **12** will still drink earlier than other reds in line-up. WO W Cape.

★★★★☆ **Blue Lady** 100% cab, a vineyard & barrel selection. **11** (★★★★), like **10**, demands to be taken seriously given its plush cassis & mocha fruit, serious 20 months French oaking, youthfully firm tannins, yet not quite as fine, impressive; more regent than monarch.

★★★★★ **Cabernet Franc** Matriarch Norma Ratcliffe's signature grape flying high, showing suppleness, complexity & generosity, plus restraint & the promise of development. **11**'s leaf-seamed youngberry fruit, massaged tannins & precise oaking (45% new) still helps set the bar for the variety.

★★★★ **Old Bush Vines Pinotage 12** (★★★★) reflects estate's blueberry succulence but fruit somewhat hemmed in by tarry nuance & firm tannins, latter less supportive & well judged than in **11**.

★★★★ **The Black Lady Syrah 12** initial reductive note blows off to reveal perfumed bouquet of cranberries & lilies, pliant spicy tannins grant early access with promise of few years' development.

★★★★☆ **Trilogy** Cab-led Bordeaux-style red blend & flagship, **11** a classic Cape expression marrying cassis fruit, exotic spice & fine tannins. Seriously wooded - 2+ years French barrels, 60% new - setting the stage for a grand future.

★★★★ **Three Cape Ladies** Cape Blend with pinotage (40%), equal cab & shiraz working well together in **12**, as in **11**. Creamy dark fruit, touch of liquorice & well structured palate.

★★★★☆ **White Lady Chardonnay** Lots of care taken: wild yeast ferment/maturation in 40% new French wood, 11 months. Lime seam, stony minerality, exceptional length among **13**'s myriad attractions. Seductive, classy & poised.

★★★★ **The First Lady Unoaked Chardonnay** With small but active drop viognier, this delivers more flavour, character, than most unwooded versions. **13** (★★★★) tropical rather than **12**'s citrus tones, tasty if unlingering fruit flavours. WO W Cape.

★★★★☆ **Professor Black Sauvignon Blanc** 13's (★★★★) initial brimstone notes yield to peachy, tropical aromas & flavours courtesy 14% home-grown viognier. Lacks **12**'s thrilling mineral freshness from soupçon semillon ex Durbanville. — CvZ

Location/map: Stellenbosch ▪ WO: Simonsberg–Stellenbosch/Western Cape ▪ Est 1964 ▪ 1stB 1983 ▪ Tasting & sales daily 10–5 ▪ Cellar tours by appt ▪ 'Big 5' vineyard safari & 'Big 5' vineyard safari on horseback ▪ Gourmet picnics in summer; tapas inspired winter menu ▪ Facilities for children ▪ Gifts ▪ Conferences ▪ Conservation area ▪ Owner(s) Ratcliffe family ▪ Winemaker(s) Nic van Aarde (May 2011) ▪ Viticulturist(s) Ronald Spies (Nov 2001) ▪ 110ha/70ha (cabs s/f, merlot, ptage, shiraz, chard, sauv) ▪ 300t/80,000cs own label 60% red 40% white ▪ BWI, WIETA ▪ PO Box 2 Elsenburg 7607 ▪ info@warwickwine.com ▪ www.warwickwine.com ▪ S 33° 50' 27" E 018° 51' 54.0" ▪ F +27 (0)21-884-4025 ▪ **T +27 (0)21-884-4410**

Waterford Estate

This stylish property in Stellenbosch's Blaauwklippen Valley was founded when IT magnate Jeremy Ord and wife Leigh bought a sizeable section of the old Stellenrust farm. Eminent winemaker Kevin Arnold was a partner (and cellarmaster) from the beginning, establishing new vineyards and resurrecting old ones, and planning the grand new winery. The sizeable number of wines is deftly divided into four ranges, the most original of which is the Library Collection: small parcels of mature and/or experimental wines, mostly one-offs, reflecting continuing exploration of possibilities in the cellar. The flagship is The Jem (named for Jeremy Ord), a blend of many of the estate's 11 red grape varieties, making for an unusually comprehensive reflection of the farm's soils, aspects and climates.

Waterford Estate range

★★★★☆ **Cabernet Sauvignon** Elegant, svelte & lithe **11** has gentle cherry tobacco & blackcurrant edge. Generous, ripe yet structured, complex & layered - truly an iron fist in velvet glove! Great harmony & integration. Lingers long. Includes drops merlot & cab franc; 30% new oak. **10** untasted.

★★★★☆ **The Jem** Melange of rich dark fruit in **10** 8-way cab-led blend. Taut, textured & modern in style, it offers ample succulence tempered by firm dry tannin & oak spice (40% new). Balanced, lissom & supple, it keeps on giving. Will reward patient cellaring.

★★★★☆ **Reserve Chardonnay** ⓥ Single-vineyard, natural ferment **11** less forthcoming in mid-2012 than standard version, but subtly exudes quality. Restrained but forceful, with oaky note over the citrus & fruit intensity veined by insistent acidity - really well balanced. Will benefit from ageing.

★★★★ **Chardonnay** Right on trend, **13** is statuesque with perfect balance of citrus verve & oak (25% new). Creamy, rich, long & poised. Lovely lime acid tang (no malo) keeps things fresh throughout.

★★★★ **Sauvignon Blanc** 14 (★★★★) tank sample has tart lemongrass & sherbet hit. Light flint & herb nuance, zesty freshness but lean & somewhat less impressive than last-tasted **11**.

Also tasted: **Rose Mary 14** ★★★

Library Collection

★★★★☆ **Edition: 3BB** ⓥ Cab-based **09** with cab franc & merlot is serious, even stern. Forthright tannins should soften & harmonise in 5+ years. Decant now & drink with food.

★★★★ **Edition: BW** ⓥ More severity than easy charm on unwooded **09** 'Bordeaux White'; lemony, waxy semillon firmly in charge, hints of aromatic sauvignon. Fruit intensity should allow for few years in bottle.

Edition: Riesling (NEW) ★★★★ Vibrant apple & lime curd on dry **13** from Elgin, fresh acidity & focus. Needs time to develop & show true potential. **Edition: VRC** (NEW) ★★★★ Peach blossom vies with light nut, stonefruit & bitter marmalade edge on **13** viognier-led mix with riesling & chardonnay. Breadth, palate weight & structure. A bit ponderous. WO W Cape, as for VSBC. **Edition: VSBC** (NEW) ★★★ Big, bold & brash **13** viognier-led blend of sauvignon blanc & chenin. White pepper & grapefruit, with phenolic nuance. Not retasted: **Edition: MB 04** ★★★★

Waterford range

★★★★☆ **Kevin Arnold Shiraz** Seamless integration & texture on sleek yet powerful **10**. Ripe black berry fruit with a crack of pepper & squeeze of dry, spicy tannin from combo of dab mourvèdre (10%) and older oak. Refined & smart but with a wild glint in youth.

★★★★ **Elgin Sauvignon Blanc 14** keeps up stellar quality of previous in its vibrant, zingy lime acidity with mineral underpinning. Complex, focused, taut, & yet refreshingly dry & long.

★★★★ **Heatherleigh Family Reserve** Heady muscat scent seduces on solera-aged **NV** (unfortified) dessert from muscat d'Alexandrie, with chenin & chardonnay. Complex layering of flavour but gentle, delicate & clean with superb length.

Méthode Cap Classique Brut ⑲ ★★★★ Creamy, oxidative & rich **06** sparkling from near-equal chardonnay & pinot noir. Full bodied & weighty, with nutty, broad, structured palate. Good freshness & long finish. Also tasted: **Elgin Pinot Noir 12** ★★★★

Pecan Stream range

Pebble Hill ★★★☆ Spicy fruit drives dark, brooding 5-way red blend of **11**. Tobacco flavour vies with black pepper & spice. Fresh & rewarding. WO W Cape, as all these. Also tasted: **Chenin Blanc 14** ★★★ **Sauvignon Blanc 14** ★★★ — FM

Location/map: Stellenbosch ▪ WO: Stellenbosch/Western Cape/Elgin ▪ Est/1stB 1998 ▪ Tasting, sales & cellar tours Mon-Fri 9—5 Sat 10—5 ▪ Tasting fees: R45/standard; R50/chocolate; R50/The Jem (current vintage only); R200/reserve; R250/wine walk & R550/wine drive, pre-booking essential ▪ Closed Good Fri, Dec 25 & Jan 1 ▪ Tea/coffee/soft drinks & chocolates ▪ 14ha BWI conserved land ▪ Owner(s) Jeremy & Leigh Ord; Kevin Arnold (partner) ▪ Cellarmaster(s) Kevin Arnold (1998) ▪ Winemaker(s) Mark le Roux (Jul 2009) ▪ Viticulturist(s) David van Schalkwyk (Jun 2014) ▪ 120ha/60ha (barbera, cabs s/f, grenache, malbec, merlot, mourv, p verdot, sangio, shiraz, tempranillo, chard, sauv) ▪ 503t/80,000cs own label 51% red 45% white 3% rosé 1% other ▪ PO Box 635 Stellenbosch 7599 ▪ info@waterfordestate.co.za ▪ www.waterfordestate.co.za ▪ S 33° 59' 54.6" E 018° 52' 12.7" ▪ F +27 (0)21-880-1007 ▪ **T +27 (0)21-880-5300**

☐ **Waterhof** *see* Waterstone Wines

Waterkloof

This handsome property on Schapenberg Hill near Somerset West was acquired by British wine industry figure Paul Boutinot — following a classic apprenticeship in the UK wine trade in the early 1970s, Paul launched his own successful wine import business in 1980, which he sold in 2013. Waterkloof was the culmination of a long worldwide search to discover somewhere capable of 'truly fine wine with a defining sense of origin', and viticulture and winemaking is very much orientated to the traditional — vines are farmed biodynamically, nearly all the wines fermented without inoculation and not acidified. The cellar itself, however, is housed in an ultra-modern facility alongside a tasting room and deluxe restaurant with spectacular vistas of False Bay — well worth a visit.

Waterkloof range

★★★★☆ **Sauvignon Blanc** Bottled without fining, bunch-pressed & naturally fermented (as all below), **12** offers layer upon layer of rich apricot & peach with a squeeze of lime, lots of depth & breadth, weight & length.

Circle of Life range

★★★★ **Red** Bordeaux meets Rhône in seamless **10** (★★★★★) with 51% merlot adding fruitcake richness supported by dash petit verdot while 38% shiraz & splashes mourvèdre & grenache provide fresh red fruit & spice. Even more elegant than stylish **09**.

★★★★ **White** ⑫ **12** 56% sauvignon, rest chenin, chardonnay & semillon, is intellectual & mid-2013 not ready with its favours. Notes of lime, peach & spice before savoury finish.

Seriously Cool range

★★★★☆ **Cinsault** ⊘ Was 'Cinsaut Noir'. New range name reflects much-improved image of SA's 'Cinderella red' as well as recommended serving temperature (lightly chilled). Fynbos-perfumed **13** has red berry fruit purity & medium body. Soft & seriously sippable.

Circumstance range

★★★★ **Cabernet Franc** ⓃⒺⓌ Whiff of clove on inky **12**, ripe black plum & berry flavours with dark chocolate & liquorice spice from 30% new French oak. Big, with soft ripe tannins.

★★★★☆ **Syrah** ② **10** as usual a star of the range, flaunting its floral-spicy charm. Quietly assertive, succulent & satisfying. Approachable, but should respond well to ±5 years in bottle.

★★★★ **Sauvignon Blanc** Older-oak-fermented **13** calls for clams & crayfish, pinch of turmeric adding savoury intrigue to peach & tangy apricots, lovely purity & length.

Chardonnay ★★★☆ Soft & approachable **13** has honeysuckle & peardrop notes, creamy texture, but not at all flabby due to balanced acidity. Also tasted: **Cape Coral Mourvèdre Rosé 14** ★★★★ **Chenin Blanc 13** ★★★☆ Not retasted: **Cabernet Sauvignon 10** ★★★☆ **Merlot 10** ★★★☆ **Viognier 12** ★★★ — JG

Location: Somerset West ▪ Map: Helderberg ▪ WO: Stellenbosch ▪ Est 2004 ▪ 1stB 2005 ▪ Tasting & sales daily 10-5 ▪ Fee: standard R30/6 wines, premium R40/6 wines ▪ Closed Dec 25 & Jan 1 ▪ Healey's cheese tasting ▪ Waterkloof platters R130 with selection of cheese, olives, meat terrine, gherkins, pickles, chutney & bread ▪ Cellar tours by appt ▪ The Restaurant at Waterkloof ▪ Walking/hiking/horse riding trails ▪ Conservation area ▪ Art collection on display ▪ Tutored horse riding & biodynamic walking tours with ploughman's platter & wine tasting ▪ Owner(s) Paul Boutinot ▪ Cellarmaster(s)/winemaker(s) Nadia Barnard (Jan 2013) ▪ Viticulturist(s) Christiaan Loots (Jan 2010) ▪ 149ha/56ha (cabs s/f, grenache, merlot, mourv, p verdot, shiraz, chard, chenin, sauv, sem, viog) ▪ 450t/20,000cs own label 50% red 45% white 5% rosé ▪ BWI champion ▪ PO Box 2093 Somerset West 7129 ▪ info@waterkloofwines.co.za ▪ www. waterkloofwines.co.za ▪ S 34° 5' 55.4" E 018° 53' 22.8" ▪ F +27 (0)21-858-1293 ▪ **T +27 (0)21-858-1292**

☐ **Waterlilly** *see* Bloemendal Estate

Waterstone Wines

Founded almost a decade ago, internationally active negociant house Waterstone Wines is increasing its global footprint 'by sure determination', says co-owner Reino Kruger. 'Attention to detail, focus on quality and knowledge of market requirements give us the edge.' A landmark development sees its primary production capacity augmented and relocated to Stellenbosch's Bottelary area, where tastings and many other visitor facilities are available.

Africa Five Collection

Pinotage ⓦ ★★★★ Espresso & chocolate tones add to the black cherry richness of **09** preview. Age-softened oak tannins a pleasure to drink, harmonious, but there's a good future ahead. Stellenbosch WO for all these. **Shiraz Reserve** ★★★ From barrel, piquant red berries, ripe plums, sweet spice, & just enough tannin grip to give definition; **10** a fruity wine designed to please, & does. Also tasted: **Cabernet Sauvignon-Shiraz 12** ★★★

Africa Five range

Pinotage ★★★ Crushed red berries, the body remaining juicy & lively, oak in gentle support. **12** off-dry in style. **Chardonnay** ★★★ Gentle melon & peach flavours, plumped up by a bit of sweetness, good fresh finish on unwooded **13**. **Chenin Blanc** ★★☆ Some tropical notes in just-dry **13**, softly fruity easy-drinker. Not retasted: **Cabernet Sauvignon 12** ★★ **Merlot 12** ★★★ **Shiraz 11** ★★ **Cape Premier Red NV** ★★ **Sauvignon Blanc 12** ★★☆

Africa range

Bomvu ★★★ Red berries, touch of sweet spice, **12** cab/shiraz blend is smooth textured, has appealing drinkability. Not retasted: **Ifula 12** ★★

Cape Discovery range

Magic Red (NEW) ★★★ Colourful label on frosted bottle, as for White. **NV** high-toned berries, a piquant fruitiness in the flavours but there's a serious undertone, year+ barrel ageing giving a savoury dimension. **Magic White** (NEW) (symbol) ★★★ Multi-regional **NV** blend (as for Red) shows fresh herbaceous apple notes, a tangy-crisp acidity that begs for a second glass. Not retasted: **Cabernet Sauvignon NV** ★★ **Merlot NV** ★★ **Pinotage NV** ★★ **Shiraz NV** ★ **Chardonnay NV** ★ **Sauvignon Blanc NV** ★★

Pride of Kings range (NEW)

Cabernet Sauvignon ★★★ Blackcurrants & dark cherries hold centre stage on **13**, with tannin support & savoury flavouring from French oak maturation. **Merlot** (symbol) ★★★ Plush red berries, smoky savoury overlay from oaking without interfering with the juicy, smooth—textured appeal of **13**. **Pinotage** (symbol) ★★★ Creamy coffee & dark cherries, Belgian chocolate, the tannins assimilated leaving no edges, just a smooth savoury effect. Drink **11** over the next 4-5 years. **Shiraz** (symbol) ★★★ Red berries, a herbaceous tone, white pepper, nice juicy texture, there is plenty to keep you interested in **13**. **Rosé** ★★★ Mainly sauvignon, dab of pinotage for colour. **13** leafy aromas becoming more fruity on the palate, aided by some sweetness.

Zulu 8 range

Pinotage ★★ Mocha-toned black cherries, tannins a firm foundation, **13** will soften over next 2–3 years. **Cabernet Sauvignon-Shiraz** ★★★ Perfume of smoky, savoury spice, dark plums, with the fruit taking a dominant role in **12**'s flavours, juicy & vibrant. Not retasted: **Cabernet Sauvignon 11** ★★ **Merlot 11** ★★ **Shiraz 11** ★★ **Sauvignon Blanc 11** ★★

Cape Royale range

Shiraz (symbol) ★★ **NV** leans towards savoury in olive/saline character, lots of wood evident throughout. Not retasted: **Cabernet Sauvignon NV** ★★ **Merlot NV** ★ **Sauvignon Blanc NV** ★

KFK range

Cabernet Sauvignon (symbol) ★★★★ Satisfying **10**, precise tannin & bright acidity provide counterpoint to vanilla-infused dark fruit. Warm but quite juicy. Stellenbosch WO, as for all these. Not retasted: **Shiraz 07** ★★★ **Chardonnay 11** ★★★ **Sauvignon Blanc 10** ★★★★

Opener's range

Merlot (symbol) ★★★ Fun, fruity **12**, with obvious sweetness, appealing red/purple fruits & touch of herbs. **Chenin Blanc** (symbol) ★★★ Grain sugar plumps the palate of tropical & orchard fruit in **12**, bright & fresh, nice pithy grip. Not retasted: **Shiraz 12** ★★★ **Rosé 13** ★★ **Sauvignon Blanc 12** ★★ **Cabernet Sauvignon 12** ★★ Not tasted: **Dry Red**.

Sonata range

Cabernet Sauvignon (symbol) ★★★ Improved **10** raspberry & clean leather wafts, rounded tannins; neat dinner companion. Stellenbosch vines, as all these. **Sauvignon Blanc** (symbol) ★★★ **11** offers nettles, fresh hay; palate-cleansing sweet-sour acidity. Not retasted: **Shiraz 11** ★★★ **The Ludwig 04** ★★ **Chenin Blanc 11** ★★★

Waterhof range

Sauvignon Blanc Reserve (symbol) ★★★★ Showing good varietal character & balance at moderate alcohol, **10** still standout in range. WO Stellenbosch, as all these. Not retasted: **Cabernet Sauvignon Reserve 10** ★★★★ **Shiraz Reserve 07** ★★★ **Chardonnay Reserve 11** ★★★ — CR

Location/map: Stellenbosch ▪ WO: Western Cape/Stellenbosch ▪ Est/1stB 2007 ▪ Tasting, sales & cellar tours on Hazendal Estate ▪ Amenities: see Hazendal entry ▪ Owner(s) Reino Kruger & De Lijster family ▪ Winemaker(s) Annamarie Fourie & Burger Badenhorst ▪ 41ha (cab, merlot, ptage, shiraz, chard, chenin, sauv) ▪ 200,000cs own label 75% red 25% white ▪ PO Box 1560 Somerset West 7129 ▪ info@waterstonewines.co.za ▪ www.waterstonewines.co.za ▪ S 33° 54' 2.7" E 018° 43' 9.1" ▪ F +27 (0)86-505-8691 ▪ **T +27 (0)21-842-2942**

Waverley Hills Organic Wines & Olives ⓘ ⓘ ⓘ ⓘ ⓘ ⓘ

The Du Toit family owners of Brenn-O-Kem (recycler of winery waste into natural products for industry re-use) run their Tulbagh farm as a model of eco-friendly productivity. Vineyards established in 2000 produce a plethora of wines (including a new ultra low-alcohol option, untasted) certified organic and sustainable. A wellness spa and farmstall may join the many food-for-the-soul offerings.

★★★★ CW Reserve Shiraz ⊘ From tiny parcel yielding smaller-than-usual grapes & bunches. Vivacious & poised **11** for solo sipping or mealtime enjoyment. As intense as **10** (★★★★) but with complex graphite & lily aromas, red berry & tobacco flavours, lingering velvet finish.

Cabernet Sauvignon ⊘ ★★★ Intense plum & tobacco, whiff tar & meat on very sippable, long **13**. **Grenache** ⊘ ⊘ ★★★ Retasted as bottled wine, **13** soft & pliant, peppery & herbaceous notes from smidgens shiraz & viognier. Easy to see why **12** recognised by Grenaches du Monde. **Cabernet Sauvignon-Merlot** ⊘ ★★★ Cab-led **13** plumped by 27% merlot, spiced with dollop shiraz & drop mourvèdre. Supple & succulent. 'Perfect with our restaurant's choc dessert' say the team. **Viognier-Semillon-Chardonnay** ⊘ ★★★★ Bottled version of **12** lives up to last year's promise. Smooth & lively, with aromas of sandalwood, pine needles & flowers; good freshness. Older oak aged, portion cask fermented. Also tasted: **Shiraz** ⊘ **11** ★★★ **Shiraz-Mourvèdre-Viognier** ⊘ **11** ★★★ **Cabernet Sauvignon-Shiraz** ⊘ **12** ★★★ **Pinot Grigio** ⊘ **13** ★★ **Rooi Jerepiko** ⊘ **13** ★★★ Not retasted: **Méthode Cap Classique Brut 11** ★★★★ Not tasted: **Cabernet Sauvignon No Added Sulphites**, **Rosé**, **Sauvignon Blanc-Semillon**. — CvZ

Location/map/WO: Tulbagh ▪ Est 2006 ▪ 1stB 2004 ▪ Tasting, sales & cellar tours Mon-Fri 8-5 Sat 10-4 Sun 11-3 ▪ Closed Easter Fri/Mon & Dec 25 ▪ Restaurant Tue-Fri 9-4 Sat 10-4 Sun 11-3 & Wed/Fri evenings ▪ Picnic baskets by appt; or BYO picnic ▪ Facilities for children ▪ Tour groups ▪ Farm produce ▪ Conferences ▪ Wedding venue & chapel ▪ Walks/hikes ▪ Mountain biking ▪ Conservation area ▪ Fynbos nursery & eco-centre ▪ Owner(s) Brenn-O-Kem (Pty) Ltd ▪ Cellarmaster(s) Johan Delport (Oct 2008) ▪ Winemaker(s) Elizma Visser (Sep 2013), with Andre Ewerts (Jul 2008) ▪ Viticulturist(s) Johan Greeff (May 2012) ▪ 80ha/30ha (cab, grenache, merlot, mourv, shiraz, chard, pinot gris, sauv, sem, viog) ▪ 230t/20,000cs own label 75% red 15% white 5% rosé 5% MCC ▪ Other export brand: Dixon's Peak ▪ BWI champion, WIETA ▪ PO Box 71 Wolseley 6830 ▪ info@waverleyhills.co.za ▪ www.waverleyhills.co.za ▪ S 33° 24' 21.2" E 019° 14' 19.6" ▪ F +27 (0)23-231-0004 ▪ **T +27 (0)23-231-0002**

Wavescape Wines (NEW)

This is a joint marketing venture between Grangehurst winemaker Jeremy Walker and Wavescape surf reporter Steve Pike, who met at the Vintners Surf Classic (an annual surfing competition for wine people) and decided to combine their passions for wine and waves by creating 'vibrant blends of surfing and winemaking' under the Red Barrel and (untasted) White Curl labels. 'In typical surf speak, you are invited to pull in and chill out with these wines.'

Red Barrel ★★★★ Fruit-forward, easygoing **09** a cab-shiraz blend with drop mourvèdre. Gobs of red fruit with leathery undertones; open-knit palate, fine soft tannin. Ready to chill out. — JPf

Location: Stellenbosch ▪ WO: Coastal ▪ Est 2014 ▪ 1stB 2009 ▪ Closed to public ▪ Sales by telephone or mail order via Wavescape & Grangehurst website ▪ Owner(s) Grangehurst Winery (Jeremy Walker) & Wavescape (Steve Pike) ▪ Cellarmaster(s) Jeremy Walker ▪ ±1,200cs own label 50% red 50% white ▪ PO Box 206 Stellenbosch 7599 ▪ jeremy@grangehurst.co.za, spike@wavescape.co.za ▪ www.wavescape.co.za ▪ F +27 (0)86-710-6067 ▪ **T +27 (0)21-855-3625**

☐ **Weathered Hands** see Dewaldt Heyns Family Wines

Webersburg Wines ⓘ ⓘ ⓘ ⓘ ⓘ

Helderberg-based businessman Fred Weber has devoted himself to the restoration and preservation of venerable Cape Dutch property Groenerivier since acquiring it in 1996. The late 18th-century buildings offer stylish accommodation, functions, food and Webersburg wine, crafted by Matthew van Heerden, building on foundations laid by classicist Giorgio Dalla Cia, former winemaker and adviser.

★★★★☆ **Cabernet Sauvignon** Classically moulded **12** (first tasted since **09**), restrained aroma of pencil shaving, cassis & integrated toasty oak. Finely structured palate with ripe yet fresh flavours framed by beautiful fine-grained tannin. A Stellenbosch classic which will reward the patient.

★★★★ **Webersburg** Cab-based blend with merlot & petit verdot true to restrained house style. **11** underlying tomato bush, redpepper notes; a touch mouth drying & angular - allow few years to harmonise. Last tasted was **05**. Also available in magnum, like Cabernet.

★★★★ **Webersburg MCC Brut** Adds 'MCC' to name. 3-variety **NV** sparkler tasted last year; intense citrus & honey biscuit styling, seam of acidity giving freshness. Elegant & lengthy. WO W Cape, like Rosé.

Also tasted: **Webersburg MCC Brut Rosé NV ★★★★** Not tasted: **Sauvignon Blanc**. — JPf

Location/map: Stellenbosch ▪ WO: Stellenbosch/Western Cape ▪ Est 1995 ▪ 1stB 1996 ▪ Tasting, sales & cellar tours Mon-Fri 10—5 Sat/Sun 10-4 ▪ Fee R40 ▪ Closed Dec 25/26 & Jan 1 ▪ French country bistro ▪ Tour groups ▪ Historic buildings: Manor House 1786; cellar & Jonkershuis 1796 ▪ 5-star Cape Dutch guesthouse ▪ Conferences ▪ Weddings/functions ▪ Owner(s) Fred Weber ▪ Winemaker(s)/viticulturist(s) Matthew van Heerden ▪ 20ha/5ha (cab) ▪ 30t/4,000cs own label 80% red 20% white ▪ PO Box 3428 Somerset West 7129 ▪ info@webersburg.co.za ▪ www.webersburg.co.za ▪ S 34° 0' 22.1" E 018° 50' 34.5" ▪ F +27 (0)21-881-3217 ▪ **T +27 (0)21-881-3636**

Wederom Boutique Winery

Philip du Toit makes wine chiefly for wholesale, but since 2003 has bottled some of his favourite shiraz 'mainly for family and visitors', says daughter Joyce. From the '11 vintage, it's just been one under the Giovanni Salvadori label, Philip's tribute to Italian POWs who tended the vines here in the 1940s.

Giovanni Salvadori Shiraz ★★★ Toasty, pepper-spiced **11** a friendly glass of juicy fruit & pliable tannins. 'All-day everyday wine' says winemaker. Discontinued: **Shiraz**. — CvZ

Location/map: Robertson ▪ WO: Western Cape ▪ Est 2002 ▪ 1stB 2003 ▪ Tasting, sales & cellar tours by appt ▪ Fee R20pp tasting/tour ▪ Closed Good Fri & Dec 25 ▪ Meals by appt ▪ Tour groups ▪ Gifts ▪ Farm produce ▪ Conferences ▪ Weddings/functions ▪ Hikes ▪ Conservation area ▪ Italian prisoner of war museum ▪ Hanepoot Huisies guesthouse ▪ Owner(s) Philip & Almien du Toit ▪ Cellarmaster(s)/winemaker(s)/viticulturist(s) Philip du Toit ▪ 111ha/±17ha (cinsaut, merlot, shiraz) ▪ ±130t/838cs own label 100% red + 42t grapes for clients ▪ IPW ▪ PO Box 60 Robertson 6705 ▪ wederom@myisp.co.za ▪ www.wederom.co.za ▪ S 33° 49' 5.5" E 019° 47' 15.8" ▪ F +27 (0)23-626-3306 ▪ **T +27 (0)23-626-4139**

☐ **Wedgewood Wines** *see* Nordic Wines

Welbedacht Wine Estate

Welbedacht and neighbour farm Af-en-Toe were bought by the Burger family in the 1990s, though both properties date back to the 1800s. Encouraged by the success of other producers who made award-winning wines from their grapes, Schalk Burger snr and his family in 2005 decided to restore the old cellar and start making wine, enjoying similar success under their own label. Exports to Japan are set to rise following Schalk jnr's move to top Tokyo rugby football club Suntory Sungoliath. Brother and GM Tiaan expects to be 'selling a lot more', with club owners Suntory Group among the biggest alcoholic beverage distributors in that country.

Schalk Burger & Sons Proprietors Reserve range

★★★★ **No. 6**  Striking shiraz-led 6-way mix. **06** (★★★★★) plush fruitcake & plum spice, big & bold but harmonious, lithe as a flank brushing off a tackler. 2 years older French oak. Step up on **05**.

★★★★ **Myra**  Last tasted was **07** viognier, chenin, chardonnay blend. Oxidative styling, rich & satiny.

Mon René ★★★★ NV MCC sparkling from 100% chardonnay, latest 2nd bottling unoaked. Expressive citrus, ginger biscuit notes, soft creamy mousse & refreshing dryness. Named for Burger daughter.

Welbedacht Estate range

★★★★ Merlot Barrique Select Delayed release has imbued **09** (★★★★) with interesting savoury evolution. Still some red plum flesh too but hint drying tannins suggest drink sooner rather than later. **08** was stylish, refined.

★★★★ Bohemian Syrah 10 illustrates viability of variety with these Wellington vineyards. Big but supple, rich & savoury with well-integrated fine tannin. Oak, just 10% new, aids harmony, extra dimension. **09** sold out untasted.

★★★★ Cricket Pitch Cab-based Bordeaux quintet; **10** retains freshness, lightness of touch, allowing focus on well-layered fruit, gentle rounded grip. Ready, but will drink well for further few years. **09** sold out untasted.

★★★★ Hat Trick ② Concentrated **10**, first since **07**, absorbs 75% new oak. Harmonious mix pinotage & grenache with merlot, their rich, dark fruit still embraced by firm yet balanced tannins.

★★★★ Old Bush Vine Chenin Blanc Was 'Chenin Blanc Barrel Fermented'. Vines into their 5th decade; tentatively rated tank sample **12** as sun-rich in colour as in its tempting ripe fruit; a gentle oxidative richness adds to its individuality. Older French oak. **10** (★★★★) was promising. **11** untasted.

Patriot ★★★☆ Previewed **12**, first made since **08**, switches from Bordeaux to cab-led Cape Blend with pinotage & merlot. Less of a style change, still showy, with evident oak (30% new). Underlying ripe fruit may harmonise once bottled. Also tasted: **Cabernet Sauvignon Barrique Select 12** **★★★☆ Pinotage 11 ★★★☆ Chardonnay Barrel Fermented 11 ★★★☆** Not retasted: **Sauvignon Blanc 12 ★★★**

Meerkat range

Pinotage ★★★ 13 offers charm & drinkability in its scented spiced raspberry fruit, rounded tannins & medium body. **Unwooded Chardonnay** (NEW) **★★★ 14** breadth, concentration of ripe lemons, oranges with nutty hint provides good aperitif & versatile food partner. 12.5% alcohol. Also tasted: **Burrow Blend 13 ★★★ Pinotage Rosé 14 ★★☆ Chenin Blanc 14 ★★★ Sauvignon Blanc 14 ★★★** Not retasted: **Sun Angel Semi-Sweet NV ★★** — AL

Location/WO: Wellington ▪ Map: Paarl & Wellington ▪ Est/1stB 2005 ▪ Tasting, sales & cellar tours Mon-Fri 9–5 Sat 9–1 ▪ Fee R15 ▪ Closed Easter Fri-Mon, Dec 25 & Jan 1 ▪ No. 6 Restaurant @ Welbedacht ▪ Picnics ▪ Facilities for children ▪ Tour groups ▪ Gifts ▪ Conferences ▪ Welbedacht Cricket Oval ▪ Bradgate Manor House ▪ Owner(s) Schalk Burger Family Trust ▪ Winemaker(s) Chris Joubert & Kajo Malek ▪ Viticulturist(s) Tony Julies (Jan 2007, consultant) ▪ 140ha/130ha (19 varieties r/w) ▪ 1,300t ▪ 75% red 20% white 5% rosé ▪ IPW ▪ PO Box 51 Wellington 7654 ▪ tiaan@welbedacht.co.za ▪ www.meerkatwines.co.za, www.schalkburgerandsons.co.za ▪ S 33° 34' 39.8" E 019° 1' 12.8" ▪ F +27 (0)86-669-5641 ▪ **T +27 (0)21-873-1877**

Welgegund Wines

Changes at this venerable Wellington farm see the Brimacombe family as new owners with former Doolhof winemaker Friedrich Kühne as manager. Situated at the foot of the Limietberg, the vineyards are ideally suited to Rhône varieties. These now dominate, where once, as part of Rhodes Fruit Farms, apricots and tobacco were the main crops.

★★★★ Pinotage ② Bright hue, buchu & cherry aromas mark **10**. Silkiness clipped by fine, freshening tannins; long savoury tail. Like next, tasted a few years back.

★★★★☆ Chiara ② Grenache blanc joins chenin, chardonnay, sauvignon & viognier in **10** oaked blend. Haunting complexity on aromas & suave, smooth-textured palate. WO Paarl.

Not retasted: **Ricco 09 ★★★☆** — AL

Location: Wellington ▪ Map: Paarl & Wellington ▪ WO: Wellington/Western Cape/Paarl ▪ Est 1800 ▪ 1stB 1997 ▪ Tasting & sales by appt ▪ Carignan B&B cottages with pool, tennis court & walks ▪ Owner(s) Brimacombe family ▪ Farm manager Friedrich Kühne ▪ Winemaker(s) Daniël Langenhoven (Jun 2008) ▪ 35ha/15ha (carignan, cinsaut, grenache,

For more information, visit wineonaplatter.com

shiraz, chard, chenin, viog) ▪ 1,000cs 75% red 25% white ▪ PO Box 683 Wellington 7654 ▪ sales@welgegund.co.za ▪ www.welgegund.co.za ▪ S 33° 39' 38.3" E 019° 2' 13.6" ▪ **T +27 (0)21-873-2123**

Welgeleë Boutique Wedding & Wine Farm

Chris and Lidea Meyer ceased circumnavigating the world's oceans to settle on this small Paarl wine estate, tapping into the market for winelands weddings, country conferences and, latterly, team building programmes. Contributing to the farm's charm – it's home to the couple's two children, pack of dogs and field full of horses – is a handmade shiraz.

Location: Paarl ▪ Map: Paarl & Wellington ▪ Est 1999 ▪ 1stB 2003 ▪ Tasting & sales daily 9–5 ▪ Picnics by appt ▪ Function venues (±45 & 160 pax): weddings, conferences & team building ▪ Owner(s) Liris Trust (Chris & Lidea Meyer) ▪ Winemaker(s) Chris Meyer ▪ Viticulturist(s) Chris & Lidea Meyer ▪ 26ha/3ha (shiraz) ▪ 600cs own label 100% red ▪ PO Box 439 Klapmuts 7625 ▪ chris@welgelee.com ▪ www.welgelee.com ▪ S 33° 47' 45.3" E 018° 53' 35.4" ▪ F +27 (0)86-590-4632 ▪ **T +27 (0)21-875-5726**

Welgemeend Estate

The young, enthusiastic team running Welgemeend, once home to Billy Hofmeyr, maker of the first commercial Cape Bordeaux blend, is widening the heretofore red-only range with two whites (the sauvignon untasted) under the estate label, and a soon-to-debut second tier featuring a red, white and sparkling rosé. Farm upgrades are being completed, and local and export markets expanded.

Estate Reserve ★★★☆ Classic savoury character with restrained fruit expression on merlot-led **09** blend with cab & cab franc. The house's dry tannins more than support the modest flavour intensity. Like all the reds, shows some austere elegance. **Chenin Blanc** ⓃⒺⓌ **★★★** Flavoursome, forceful **13** is lightly rich & well balanced, with good typicity. Also tasted: **Douelle 09 ★★★☆ Soopjeshoogte 08 ★★★ Amadé 12 ★★★** — TJ

Location: Paarl ▪ Map: Paarl & Wellington ▪ WO: Paarl/Coastal ▪ Est 1974 ▪ 1stB 1979 ▪ Tasting, sales & cellar tours Mon-Fri 10–4 Sat 10–2/by appt in winter ▪ Closed all pub hols ▪ Owner(s) Welgemeend Estate (Pty) Ltd ▪ Winemaker(s) Lizette Steyn-James (Mar 2007), advised by Louis Nel ▪ Viticulturist(s) Lizette Steyn-James (Mar 2007) ▪ 16ha/11ha (cabs s/f, grenache, malbec, merlot, ptage, shiraz) ▪ 27t own label 50% red 50% white ▪ PO Box 1408 Suider-Paarl 7624 ▪ info@welgemeend.co.za ▪ www.welgemeend.co.za ▪ S 33° 47' 50.8" E 018° 53' 8.5" ▪ F +27 (0)86-654-3806 ▪ **T +27 (0)21-875-5210**

☐ **Welgevallen Cellar-Stellenbosch University** *see* Stellenbosch University Welgevallen Cellar

Welgevallen Wines

Named after the farm on which Stellenbosch's prestigious Paul Roos Gymnasium was built in 1866, this is a selection of wines donated by old boys who have gone on to become winemakers and estate owners. Sales generate funds enabling talented boys from economically disadvantaged families to attend the school.

Pinotage ⓐ **★★★☆ 09** succulent & smooth, worth seeking out as much for palate appeal as for noble (fund-raising) intentions. Not tasted: **Cabernet Sauvignon-Merlot.** — CvZ

Location/map/WO: Stellenbosch ▪ Est/1stB 2000 ▪ Visits Mon-Fri 10–2 ▪ Closed pub & school hols ▪ Owner(s) Paul Roos Gymnasium Old Boys Union ▪ Winemaker(s)/viticulturist(s) Wouter Pienaar & Tinnie Momberg (consultants) ▪ 800cs own label 75% red 25% white ▪ c/o Paul Roos Gymnasium Old Boys Union Suidwal Stellenbosch 7600 ▪ oldboys@prg.wcape.school.za ▪ www.paulroos.co.za ▪ S 33° 56' 31.2" E 018° 51' 41.1" ▪ F +27 (0)21-883-8627 ▪ **T +27 (0)21-883-8627**

Wellington Wines

Wellington has stepped out from under the shadow of Paarl as a Wine of Origin district, and the formation of Wellington Wines by merging neighbours Wamakersvallei and Wellington Cooperative and, more recently, Bovlei Cellar has added impetus to the enterprise. The marketing focus is on

taking the wine to the people, with harvest festivals, food-and-wine pairings, art exhibitions and other public events in the mix. The Bovlei visitor venue is due for an upgrade, while the nearby facility in Wellington town will be used for smaller/private functions.

La Cave range

★★★★ **Cabernet Sauvignon 11** (★★★★) is both big (over 15% alcohol) & sweetly rich (just off-dry), though balanced & pleasant, with a softly firm structure. But little in the way of character or depth is possible with such ripeness. **10** was more elegant.

★★★★ **Cape Blend 11** nearly half pinotage, with shiraz & cab. Rich & powerful, but touch drier, more restrained than Cab. Juicy, sweet fruit, tasty & succulent, well built - will benefit from a few years. Not retasted: **Shiraz 10** ★★★★ **Méthode Cap Classique 11** ★★★☆ Not tasted: **Pinotage**.

Wellington Wines range

Pinotage ★★★ Bright red fruit & customary mocha sheen on supple & plush **12** with a modicum of tannic grip. **Moscato Frizzante** ★★ What's not to be charmed by on frivolous, sweet, lightly fizzy & fresh, apricot-grapey? Low 8.1% alcohol too on latest **NV** from hanepoot. Also tasted: **Cabernet Sauvignon 12** ★★★ **Chenin Blanc 14** ★★★ Not retasted: **Chardonnay 13** ★★☆ Not tasted: **Shiraz**.

Bain's Way range

Fishermans Jerepigo ★★★ Golden, grapey lusciousness on latest very sweet but not cloying **NV** from hanepoot. Packed with flavour. Also tasted: **Jagters Port NV** ★★★ Not retasted: **Merlot 12** ★★★ **Rosé NV** ★★☆

Bovlei Vineyard Selected range

Merlot Ⓥ ★★★★ Focused, richly fruity **10** offers elegance, balance & good varietal character. Laudable effort at the price. Not retasted: **Cabernet Sauvignon 10** ★★★★ **Pinotage 10** ★★★☆ **Shiraz 10** ★★★☆ Not tasted: **Shiraz-Mourvèdre**.

Bovlei Winemakers Selection

Pinotage Rosé Ⓥ ★★★ Lightish, off-dry **12** is crisply fruity & cheerful. **Chenin Blanc** ★★☆ Light-fruited, very easy, balanced, & pleasantly juicy but dry **14**. **Gewürztraminer** ★★ Off-dry **13** gushes forth rosepetal & litchi scents & flavours. **Sauvignon Blanc** ★★★ Crisp, dry **14** has lots of flavour - nicely mixing tropical & green notes - but little intensity. Also tasted: **Chardonnay 13** ★★★ **Beaukett NV** ★★ **Special Late Harvest 13** ★★ Not retasted: **Cabernet Sauvignon 11** ★★★ **Merlot 12** ★★★ **Pinotage 11** ★★★ **Vin Rouge NV** ★★ **Vin Blanc NV** ★★ **Cape Ruby NV** ★★☆ Not tasted: **Shiraz, Rosé, Sparkling Pinotage Rosé Secco**. Discontinued: **Sparkling Brut, Hanepoot Jerepiko**.

Mad Hatter's range

Roussanne-Grenache Blanc Ⓥ ★★★☆ Refreshingly different Rhône-style white blend, **12** has lean stylish body & texture with convincing varietal character. Not retasted: **Barbera 12** ★★★ **Carignan 12** ★★★ **Malbec 12** ★★★ **Mourvèdre 12** ★★★ **Sangiovese 12** ★★☆ — TJ

Location: Wellington ▪ Map: Paarl & Wellington ▪ WO: Western Cape/Wellington ▪ Est 1941 ▪ Tasting & sales Mon-Fri 9–5; Sat 9-1/pub hols 9-5 (only Bovlei tasting room) ▪ Cellar tours by appt ▪ BYO picnic ▪ Owner(s) 70 shareholders ▪ Production manager Gert Boerssen (Oct 1980) ▪ Winemaker(s) Pieter-Niel Rossouw (Jun 2009), Chris Smit (Nov 2005) & Fritz Smit (Jan 2009) ▪ Viticulturist(s) Marko Roux (Nov 2008) ▪ 2,400ha ▪ 27,000t 60% red 40% white ▪ BWI, BRC, Fairtrade, IPW, WIETA ▪ PO Box 509 Wellington 7654 ▪ sales@wellingtonwines.com ▪ www.wellingtonwines.com▪ S 33° 38' 17.7" E 018° 59' 20.6" (Wellington), S 33° 38' 18.4" E 019° 1' 54.2" (Bovlei) ▪ F +27 (0)21-873-3194/+27 (0)21-864-1483 ▪ **T +27 (0)21-873-1582**

Welmoed

Well-priced easy-drinking range named for the property whose 17th-century owner, Jacobus van der Heyden, resisted government corruption and earned the people's admiration for his fortitude. The site is now home to brand owner Stellenbosch Vineyards.

Shiraz ★★☆ Floral **13** meaty, spicy & sweet-fruit flavours. Softly gripping & easy. **Sauvignon Blanc** ⊘ ★★★☆ Dependable, well-priced label, epitomised by **14**. Perfect al fresco partner: cool, green fruited, characterful with smooth acidity. **Viognier** ★★★ Light & fresh **14** dried apricots dusted with spice (though unwooded), amiable anytime companion. Also tasted: **Cabernet Sauvignon 13** ★★ **Merlot 13** ★★ **Pinotage 13** ★★★ **Rosé 14** ★★ **Chardonnay 14** ★★★ **Chenin Blanc 14** ★★★ Not retasted: **Sparkling Brut NV** ★★★ — WB

Weltevrede Estate

Chardonnay has long been the focus – in still and sparkling form – of the Bonnievale estate farmed by the Jonker family for more than a century. Ever-thoughtful cellarmaster Philip Jonker revels in the diversity of soils in Robertson, and the proximity to the Breede River. The Jonkers share their bounty with guests, offering wedding, function and conference facilities, and accommodation. The family also share with employees via the Weltevrede Aanspringtrust, an empowerment initiative.

Estate range

Place of Rocks Chardonnay ★★★★ Balanced & lively **13** ticks all varietal boxes; appealing brioche aroma, subtle oak-brushed apple & pear flavour, all livened by clean limy acidity. Not retasted: **Bedrock Black Syrah 12** ★★★★ Not tasted: **Poet's Prayer Chardonnay**. Discontinued: **Gewürztraminer**.

Philip Jonker Brut Cap Classique Collection

★★★★ **Entheos** ⊘ Aptly named sparkler ('Energy of Spontaneous Laughter'). Dry **NV** from chardonnay (60%) & pinot noir is fruitier, less rich, than vintage-dated sibling. Lively & fresh.

★★★★ **The Ring** ⊘ Improved **09** celebratory bubbles from chardonnay. Like **07** (★★★★), impressive leesy richness despite being bone-dry, fine mousse completes the package. No **08**.

Lindelize ⊘ ★★★★ Pinot noir **NV** bubbly named for Philip Jonker's wife. Gorgeous sunset pink colour, fine bead with some creaminess, lovely refreshing acidity. Flavoursome & highly quaffable.

Simplicity range

Vanilla Chardonnay ★★★ **13** oaked chardonnay billows vanilla spice, zested with lime & touch of pear. Clean, tangy, balanced for easy quaffing. WO W Cape, as most. Also tasted: **Cherrychoc Merlot 13** ★★★ **Trop!co Sauvignon Blanc 13** ★★ Not retasted: **Cigarbox Shiraz 12** ★★★

Heritage range

Oupa se Wyn ★★★★ **12** 'Grandfather's Wine' fortified dessert from muscat de Hambourg, delightful fireside treat. Not retasted: **Ouma se Wyn 12** ★★★ — MW

Location: Bonnievale ▪ Map: Robertson ▪ WO: Robertson/Western Cape ▪ Est 1912 ▪ 1stB 1945 ▪ Tasting & sales Mon-Fri 8–5 Sat 9–3.30 ▪ Closed Easter Fri/Sun, Dec 25/26 & Jan 1 ▪ Cellar tours & underground tasting by appt ▪ Walks/hikes ▪ Conservation area ▪ Weddings/functions ▪ 4 self-catering guest cottages ▪ Owner(s) Lourens Jonker ▪ Cellarmaster(s) Philip Jonker (Jan 1997) ▪ Viticulturist(s) Francois Viljoen (consultant) ▪ 360ha/106ha (cab, merlot, pinot, shiraz, chard, cbard, gewürz, sauv) ▪ 1,300t/50,000cs own label 15% red 75% white 10% other ▪ Brands for clients: Woolworths ▪ BWI ▪ PO Box 6 Bonnievale 6730 ▪ info@weltevrede.com ▪ www.weltevrede.com ▪ S 33° 56′ 30.9″ E 020° 3′ 4.4″ ▪ F +27 (0)23-616-2460 ▪ **T +27 (0)23-616-2141**

Welvanpas

Welvanpas owner and cellarmaster (and proud new father) Dan Retief is a descendant of Great Trek leader Piet Retief, so it's fitting that this Wellington wine estate offers pre-booked 'history packages' featuring interesting chats about local lore over lunch at onsite Die Ou Meul coffee shop.

Pinotage (NEW) ★★ **12** gentle plummy, mulberry flavours, rounded plump palate, balanced easy-drinking style with a brush of oak (from staves) & smoky farewell. **Revival Red** ★★☆ **12** blend of cab, merlot & shiraz has cab's herbaceous aromas, & spicy stewed red-fruit flavours. Balanced despite 14.5% alcohol, finishes fresh. Also tasted: **De Krakeelhoek Rood 12** ★★ **Chardonnay 12** ★★ Not tasted: **Cabernet Sauvignon**, **Shiraz**, **Suzanne Rosé**, **Sauvignon Blanc**, **Amity**. — MW

Location/WO: Wellington ▪ Map: Paarl & Wellington ▪ Est 1704 ▪ 1stB 1994 ▪ Tasting & sales Tue-Fri 8–5 Sat/Sun 8–3 ▪ Fee R10pp ▪ Closed Easter Fri-Mon, Dec 16-Jan 2 ▪ Die Ou Meul coffee shop open daily ▪ Facilities for children ▪ Tour groups ▪ History package incl lunch & talk on Piet Retief family, booking required ▪ Farm produce ▪ BYO picnic (day permit R20pp) ▪ Walks/hikes ▪ Bains mountain bike trails ▪ Owner(s)/viticulturist(s) Dan Retief ▪ Cellarmaster(s) Dan Retief (Jan 1993) ▪ Winemaker(s) Dan Retief (Jan 1990), with Neels Kruger (Jan 1999) ▪ 260ha/50ha (11 varieties r/w) ▪ 25t own label 80% red 15% white 5% rosé ▪ PO Box 75 Wellington 7654 ▪ welvanpas@gmail.com ▪ S 33° 37' 59.9" E 019° 4' 12.5" ▪ F +27 (0)21-864-1239 ▪ **T +27 (0)21-864-1239**

☐ **Weskus** *see* Winkelshoek Wine Cellar

Whalehaven Wines

Whalehaven, at the entrance to the Hemel-en-Aarde Valley, was established in 1995 without vineyards of its own, one of the earliest wineries in the area after the pioneers. Since the Bottega family (of Idiom Wines) acquired it in 2003, much changed, quite apart from visitor friendliness. Notably, the range expanded greatly, with many of the grapes sourced elsewhere – but, happily, the Chardonnay and Pinot Noir, signature varieties, once more celebrate home terroir.

Whalehaven range

★★★★ **Merlot** **11** a rung above **10** (★★★) in intense black fruit concentration, velvet texture, warm spice & supple tannin structure, savoury goodbye.

★★★★ **Pinot Noir** Improved **12** from Upper Hemel-en-Aarde is savoury, earthy, with gorgeous strawberry wafts; medium body, fresh acidity, integrated tannins. Sweet vanilla oak better managed than in Elgin-sourced **10** (★★★). No **11**.

★★★★ **Chardonnay** What a step up! **12** from Upper Hemel-en-Aarde trumps Elgin-sourced **11** (★★★) with focused, intense citrus fruit, creamy vanilla oak backbone, firm structure to last.

Also tasted: **Pinotage 11** ★★★ **Sauvignon Blanc 14** ★★★★ Not retasted: **Cabernet Franc 09** ★★★ **Viognier-Chardonnay 12** ★★★ Discontinued: **Sauvignon Blanc-Semillon**.

W range

Old Harbour Red ★★☆ Gluggable merlot-driven **11**, easy, fruity fun. Coastal WO for these. Not retasted: **Pinotage Rosé 13** ★★★ — WB

Location: Hermanus ▪ Map: Elgin, Walker Bay & Bot River ▪ WO: Coastal/Upper Hemel-en-Aarde Valley/Elgin ▪ Est/1stB 1995 ▪ Tasting & sales Mon-Fri 9.30–5 Sat/Sun 10.30–2.30 ▪ Fee R30pp for wine tastings, R60pp for paired tastings with fine floral chocolates & aromatic jams ▪ Tours by appt ▪ Tour groups (up to 40 pax) ▪ Private tasting room can be booked for small functions/corporate events (up to 12 pax) ▪ Owner(s) Bottega family ▪ Winemaker(s) Reino Thiart ▪ 120t capacity ▪ Private Bag X14 Hermanus 7200 ▪ wine@whalehaven.co.za, info@bottegafamilywine.co.za ▪ www.whalehaven.co.za, www.bottegafamilywine.co.za ▪ S 34° 24' 36.9" E 019° 11' 60.0" ▪ F +27 (0)28-316-1640 ▪ **T +27 (0)28-316-1633**

☐ **Whispering Jack** *see* Flagstone Winery
☐ **White River** *see* Bergsig Estate
☐ **Wilde Haf** *see* Carmel Wines

Wildehurst Wines

Joanne Hurst happily chose to plant shiraz and viognier rather than olives in her 'garden' at the foot of the Koringberg, in the heart of the vast Swartland. Other varieties are brought in to the tiny winery there. Winemaking is as passionate and non-interventionist as you'd expect from a member of Swartland Independent Producers.

Wildehurst range

★★★★ Red 🍷 **10** from shiraz & mourvèdre, with drop viognier for fragrance. Characterful & different, with light-footed charm; sweet-fruited but ends dry. Fine structure.

★★★★ Chenin Blanc 🍷 Lightly oaked **12** from Perdeberg grapes. A winning combo of silky richness & subtle fruit - with peachy notes from a drop of viognier. Long-lingering finish.

Velo range

Blanc (NEW) **★★★★ 13** from colombard, chenin & viognier. Slightly earthy pear flavour. Fresh, lightish, unpretentious, with modest alcohol. Also tasted: **Red 12 ★★★★ Rosé 13 ★★★★** — TJ

Location: Koringberg ▪ Map/WO: Swartland ▪ Est 2006 ▪ 1stB 2009 ▪ Tasting & sales daily at The Wine Kollective, Riebeek-Kasteel ▪ Closed Dec 25 & Jan 1 ▪ Cellar tours & tasting by appt at 1 Main Road, Koringberg ▪ Guest accommodation ▪ Owner(s) Chris & Joanne Hurst ▪ Winemaker(s) Sheree Nothnagel (Dec 2013) ▪ Viticulturist(s) John Loxton (2006, consultant) ▪ 0.5ha/±0.3ha (shiraz, viog) ▪ 10t ▪ own label 45% red 45% white 10% rosé ▪ PO Box 103 Koringberg 7312 ▪ wildehurst@gmail.com ▪ www.wildehurst.co.za ▪ S 33° 01' 10.10" E 018° 40' 26.42" ▪ F +27 (0)22-423-8396 ▪ **T +27 (0)22-423-8396 (winery)/+27 (0)60-374-9267**

Wildekrans Wine Estate

Since this extensive Bot River farm was established just over 20 years ago, tracking varieties that perform best in its many different soils and micro-climates has been an ongoing task. Vines include relatively scarce pinot noir and riesling but also pinotage, winner of many awards for the estate. Contributing to its success are two clones, bushvine and trellised, shale soils, careful canopy management and winemaker William Wilkinson's love of the variety. Fruit from employees' own block has also been channelled into the pinotage wines.

Barrel Selection Reserve range

★★★★ Pinotage Very ripe **12** (★★★☆) most immediately ingratiating of the reds, with sweet fruit, tobacco & spice, softly firm tannins, & (like Cape Blend) nearly off-dry levels of sweetness. **11** also oaky.

★★★★ Cape Blend Equal parts pinotage & shiraz on **12** (★★★★), with 6% cab (**11** had 20%). Smooth & rich, ripe & sweetish flavours tempered by serious tannins & firm - though as yet slightly unintegrated - acidity.

Chenin Blanc ★★★★ Friendly, flavourful **13**, with a few grams of sugar adding smooth richness & pointing up the fruit (though less sugar than previously), while the supportive oak (30% new) adds complexity & a touch of tannic grip. Also tasted: **Shiraz 12 ★★★★ Sauvignon Blanc 14 ★★★**

Méthode Cap Classique range

Brut Rosé (NEW) **★★ 11** sparkling from pinotage with 17% pinot noir. Pleasant, if muted, berry notes & a good acidic thrust which becomes a little lemony-sour on the finish. Also tasted: **Méthode Cap Classique** ⊘ **11 ★★★** — TJ

Location/WO: Bot River ▪ Map: Elgin, Walker Bay & Bot River ▪ Est/1stB 1993 ▪ Tasting, sales & cellar tours Mon-Fri 8. 30–5 Sat/Sun 11-3 ▪ Closed Dec 25 ▪ Tour groups ▪ Picnics to order ▪ Conferences/functions ▪ Walks/hikes ▪ Mountain biking ▪ Birding ▪ Conservation area ▪ Self-catering cottages ▪ Owner(s) Wildekrans Trust ▪ Winemaker(s) William Wilkinson (2006) ▪ Viticulturist(s) Braam Gericke (2008) ▪ 1,015ha/70ha (ptage, pinot, chard, chenin) ▪ 350t own label 55% red 40% white 5% rosé; ±13,200cs for clients ▪ WIETA ▪ PO Box 31 Botriver 7185 ▪ wines@wildekrans.com ▪ www.wildekrans.com ▪ S 34° 9' 42.6" E 019° 0' 36.0" ▪ F +27 (0)21-413-0967 ▪ **T +27 (0)28-284-9902**

☐ **Wild Olive** see Grape Grinder

William Everson Wines

William Everson, 'proud to be a garagiste', makes his wines literally in the garage of his Grabouw home, the range depending on what varieties he sources where. He says the wine forms a nice balance with his artisan apple and pear ciders. All available at several farmstalls and restaurants in and around Grabouw, Hermanus and Cape Town.

Paarl Shiraz ② ★★★★ Fruity & rounded **08** abounds with dark ripe berries & warm plums. **Shiraz-Mourvèdre** ② ★★★ From two Elgin farms, **10** offers leathery dark chocolate & a pleasant firmness. Not retasted: **Stellenbosch Cabernet Sauvignon 09** ★★★ **Elgin Shiraz 09** ★★★ Not tasted: **Poplar Overberg Cabernet Sauvignon**, **Poplar Overberg Shiraz**. — GM

Location: Grabouw ▪ Map: Elgin, Walker Bay & Bot River ▪ WO: Elgin/Stellenbosch/Paarl ▪ Est/1stB 2001 ▪ Tasting, sales & tours by appt ▪ Self-catering accommodation (www.mentmor.co.za) ▪ Owner(s)/winemaker(s) William Everson ▪ 4t/800cs own label 60% red 40% white ▪ 2281 Essenhout Avenue Klipkop Grabouw 7160 ▪ william@eversonwine.co.za, william@eversoncider.com ▪ www.eversonwine.co.za, www.eversoncider.com ▪ S 34° 8' 44.01" E 019° 1' 1.21" ▪ F +27 (0)86-662-4045 ▪ **T +27 (0)82-554-6357**

☐ **Willowbrook** *see* Wine-of-the-Month Club
☐ **Willow Way** *see* Overhex Wines International

Windfall Wine Farm

Formerly owned by late cricketing legend Eddie Barlow, Windfall farm in Agterkliphoogte Valley has been transformed by KwaZulu-Natal property developer Robert Alexander, daughters Bianca Weingartz and Sarah Alexander, and partner Jaco de Wet. They have overseen vineyard replanting, infrastructure rebuilding, cellar and storage construction, farmhouse renovation, and latterly, self-catering accommodation - all backing up a boutique offering of wines (this edition a special bottling for Randgold Resources CE Mark Bristow), potstill brandy and olive oil.

Kibali (NEW) ★★★ Shiraz with other Rhône varieties & cab in **11**. Pleasant meaty, ripe soft berry aromas; assertively fresh, contrasting sweetish tail. **Barrel 41** ★★★ Tinta roriz/tempranillo new partner to shiraz/cab in **12**. Generously spiced with balanced freshness, lively grip. **Mendola** ★★★ Méthode cap classique bubbly from 100% chardonnay showing nuttiness from several years on lees. **08** brisk, refreshing sparkle, mellow 19 grams sugar. Also tasted: **Cabernet Sauvignon 13** ★★★ **Shiraz 11** ★★ **Sauvignon Blanc 14** ★★★ — AL

Location/map/WO: Robertson ▪ Est 1998 ▪ 1stB 2006 ▪ Tasting, sales & tours by appt ▪ Closed all pub hols ▪ Picnics by appt; or BYO picnic ▪ 5 self-catering cottages (sleeps between 2 & 4 people) R295pppn ▪ Owner(s) Bianca Weingartz, Sarah Alexander & Jaco de Wet ▪ Cellarmaster(s) Kobus van der Merwe (Jan 2006, consultant) & Jaco de Wet ▪ Winemaker(s) Kobus van der Merwe (Jan 2006, consultant), with Van Zyl de Wet (Jan 2009, consultant) ▪ Viticulturist(s) Jaco de Wet (Jan 2003) ▪ 300ha/42ha (cab, merlot, pinot, ruby cab, chard, chenin, sauv) ▪ 840t/1,250cs own label 75% red 25% white ▪ PO Box 22 Robertson 6705 ▪ info@windfallwine.co.za ▪ www.windfallwine.co.za ▪ S 33° 56' 33.37'' E 019° 38' 42.98'' ▪ F +27 (0)86-743-4162 ▪ **T +27 (0)83-320-8473**

Windmeul Cellar

A lengthening list of medals and excellent ratings in this guide speak eloquently of the fruit quality produced by grower-owned Windmeul Cellar's Agter Paarl vines. The Reserve range of varietals and blends, in particular, offers stellar quality but also value for money. These gems and the other Windmeul bottlings feature at monthly farmers' markets, celebrating the winery's origins as a collaborative agricultural venture.

Reserve range

★★★★ **Cabernet Sauvignon** Excellent varietal character in **11**, molten berries counter the bold tannins, give a smoothly textured effect with a liqueur-like finish. Great value!

For more information, visit wineonaplatter.com

★★★★☆ **Pinotage** Fragrant **13** oozes succulent cocoa-dusted blueberries, fynbos & cinnamon spice from new French barrels (as for other reds in range). Generous & elegant, with a polished tannin structure built for 8+ years. Benchmark pinotage.

★★★★ **Shiraz** A serious wine, **11** needs time. Ripe, big with spicy fruit & dusty oak tannins. Smooth & filling mouthfeel with a dark berry intensity & long savoury fynbos finish.

★★★★☆ **The Legend** Cab-led (with petit verdot & merlot) Bordeaux-style blend **12** boasts lovely notes of tobacco, crushed herbs & cedar, overlying a rich rounded palate of blackcurrant fruit. Harmonious & ageworthy.

★★★★☆ **Cape Blend** Voluptuous **13** only a shade off spectacular **12** (★★★★★), with ripe & rich black plum fruit, fleshy body & dense, strapping tannins. Mostly pinotage (55%), supported by cab, merlot & dollop petit verdot.

★★★★ **Chardonnay** Concentrated citrus & buttered toast on **12**. Though mouthfilling & rich, bright acid balances the overall structure & fresh, zesty finish. Will reward ageing few years. Paarl WO.

★★★★ **Chenin Blanc** Knockout citrus & tropical aromas mingle with sweet vanilla oak (100% new French). **13** (★★★★★) ups the ante on **12** with incredible depth of intense, concentrated & focused fruit & vanilla flavour, yet elegant & complex.

Windmeul range

★★★★ **White Muscadel** Fragrant, vibrant orange peel on fresh **10** fortified dessert. Slippery, dense & concentrated, with a delicious alcohol grip balancing sweetness.

Cabernet Sauvignon-Merlot ★★★ **12** up a notch. Smooth, harmonious & easy picnic fare. **Chenin Blanc** ★★★ **14** fresh, fruity, with zippy acid & modest alcohol. Dependable, great value. Also tasted: **Cabernet Sauvignon 12** ★★★ **Pinotage 12** ★★★ **Sauvignon Blanc 14** ★★☆ Not retasted: **Merlot 12** ★★★ **Port 09** ★★★ Not tasted: **Shiraz**, **Chardonnay**. — WB

Location: Paarl = Map: Paarl & Wellington = WO: Coastal/Paarl = Est 1944 = 1stB 1945 = Tasting & sales Mon-Fri 9–5 Sat 9–3 = Closed all pub hols = Cellar tours by appt = Farmers' market every 1st Sat of each month, with fresh produce & meals = Owner(s) 42 members = Cellarmaster(s) Danie Marais (Oct 1999) = Winemaker(s) Francois van Niekerk (Dec 2004) = Viticulturist(s) Anton Laas (Oct 2007) = 1,700ha = 13,500t/12,000cs own label 54% red 44% white 1% rosé 1% fortified + 800cs for clients = PO Box 2013 Windmeul 7630 = windmeul@iafrica.com = www.windmeulwinery.co.za = S 33° 40' 18.1" E 018° 54' 30.6" = F +27 (0)21-869-8614 = **T +27 (0)21-869-8100/8043**

☐ **Winds of Change** *see* Jacques Germanier

Wine Concepts

Derick Henstra and Peter Fehrsen, co-owners of Wine Concepts specialist wine shops in Cape Town and Johannesburg, themselves make wine with the help of Nabygelegen's James McKenzie from grapes sourced from high-lying vineyards. Their first release Black Block Pinot Noir '13 is available from all three stores.

Location: Cape Town/Johannesburg = Tasting & sales Mon-Fri 9–7 Sat 9–4 Sun (Blu Bird only) 9-2 = Owner(s) Newlands: Michael Bampfield-Duggan; Kloof Street: Neil & Sue Proudfoot; Blu Bird: Corlien Morris, Derick Henstra & Peter Fehrsen = Winemaker(s) Derick Henstra & Peter Fehrsen = Cardiff Castle cnr Kildare & Main St Newlands 7700 = newlandshop@wineconcepts.co.za = www.wineconcepts.co.za = F +27 (0)21-671-9031/+27 (0)88-021-426-4401/+27 (0)11-440-5398 = **T +27 (0)21-671-9030 (Newlands)/+27 (0)21-426-4401 (Gardens)/+27 (0)11-440-5498 (Blu Bird, Jhb)**

Wine Fusion

In an innovative take on entrepreneurial wine-selling, Wellington-based Graham Knox gathers a team of winemakers to produce singular and evocatively named wines, bottled offshore.

★★★★ **Linley's Pure Chardonnay-Viognier** Peach, tangerine, zesty citrus lead to soft creamy palate. **11**'s off-dry appeal balanced by crisp acid, giving a rounded richness. Only a splash viognier.

The Alabama Pinotage-Zinfandel Ⓠ ★★★★ Lively & fresh **12** mostly from pinotage (75%), but has juicy & spicy support from zinfandel component. WO Wellington. Not retasted: **Vermeulen & Knox High Hills Pinot Noir 11** ★★★ **The Grid Single Vineyard Optenhorst Pinotage 10** ★★★★ **Desert & Dunes Shiraz 11** ★★★ **The Puddingstone 11** ★★★★ — CR

Location: Wellington ▪ WO: Western Cape/Wellington ▪ Est 2007 ▪ Closed to public ▪ Cellarmaster(s) Graham Knox (Dec 2007) ▪ Winemaker(s) various ▪ 1.5M L bulk 60% red 40% white ▪ c/o Wine Masterpieces (Pty) Ltd PO Box 1209 Wellington 7654; TWF 90 London Rd London SE16LN UK T +44 2077171569 ▪ graham@thewinefusion.com ▪ F +27 (0)21-447-4476 ▪ **T +27 (0)21-447-4476/+27 (0)83-625-2865**

☐ **Winemaster's Reserve** *see* Nederburg Wines

Wine-of-the-Month Club

Wine-of-the-Month Club, South Africa's original and still leading wine mail-order business, distributes third-party wines selected by its expert panel as well as its own labels such as Berg en Dal, Giant's Peak, Montebello, Semara, Steenhuis and Willowbrook.

Location: Cape Town ▪ Est 1986 ▪ MD Tai Collard ▪ Private Bag X2 Glosderry 7702 ▪ wineclub@wineofthemonth.co.za ▪ www.wineofthemonth.co.za ▪ F +27 (0)86-674-4690 ▪ **T +27 (0)21-709-6300**

Winery of Good Hope

This Stellenbosch-based winery continues to move in the direction of a more natural, non-interventionist approach to winemaking, with the goal always to make (as founder and MD Alex Dale puts it) 'fresher, more aromatic and lighter wines – red and white'. This does not just involve less manipulation in the cellar, but also improving viticulture, to allow for picking fruit at lower levels of sugar-ripeness. While the winery's specialisation has long been pinot noir and chenin blanc, this has not by any means excluded other varieties – gamay (naturally made, of course) is the latest grape to find a place here. Social concerns are also central, with the Land of Hope range going entirely to support a trust benefiting previously disadvantaged employees and their families.

Radford Dale range

★★★★☆ **Merlot** Ⓠ Good, ripe aromas & flavours on **10** (★★★★), with herbal twist to sweet fruit; forceful, dense-textured & big, but perhaps less intense than **09** so slightly drying oak tannins less harmonised.

★★★★☆ **Freedom Pinot Noir 13** made for maturation rather than early charm, as was **12**. But already shows depth of flavour & some complexity, along with fresh, bright refinement & liveliness. Finely structured; poised acidity & ripe, taut tannin. Natural ferment. Both pinots ex Elgin.

★★★★☆ **Pinot Noir AD** This version, made in best vintages, released after 3 years, designed to mature 'for a good number of years'. **11** not made. **12** has more earthy, smoky notes than Freedom, even a little funkiness, above a depth of more intense raspberry fruit & more of a tannic tug. Look forward to trying again in 5+ years!

★★★★ **Frankenstein Pinotage** As always, **13** more perfumed than monstrous. Well balanced & fresh, with bright berry flavours. Serious tannin controls the sweet fruit to a satisfying dry finish. One of the more elegant pinotages; best give it a few years.

★★★★ **Nudity** Syrah/shiraz from organic Voor Paardeberg vines in spirit of 'natural wine'. Early picking means modest alcohol, freshness & herbaceous note to pure red fruit on **13**. Light but forceful tannins. Unsulphured.

★★★★ **Syrah** Hints of lilies, spice & scrubby warm hillsides on **12** (★★★★★). With energetic vibrancy, but not at the expense of balance, ripe fruit warmth, depth & emerging complexity. Good length, savoury finish. Supportive integrated oak; a quarter new barrels. More harmonious even than **11**.

★★★★ **Black Rock** Immediately appealing, pure-fruited & spicy aromas on **12** shiraz-led 5-way blend from Swartland. Well balanced fruit & structure, juicy but also fresh & rather elegant. Mostly older barrels used.

★★★★☆ **Gravity** ⓥ Forceful, forward **10** from shiraz, cab, merlot offering spice & bright red & black berries on a firmly structured base. Successfully balances the claims of fresh fruitiness & savoury depths to give some early complexity supported by good oaking. Will benefit from some years in a cool dark place.

★★★★☆ **Chardonnay** A little toast accompanies the refined cool citrus on **13** in youth, though mostly older barrels used. Stony minerality & subtlety ensure big distance from fat, caricatured chards. A satisfying, silky glide all the way to lingering, mouthwatering finish. Bone-dry & just 12.5% alcohol.

★★★★☆ **Renaissance Chenin Blanc** Another wine with stony, understated intensity & finesse. The oak on **13** from old, unirrigated bushvines broadens & adds to the texture, supporting the clean fruit flavours. The elegant, serene highpoint from this chenin specialist.

★★★★☆ **Vine Dried Viognier** ⓥ Intense but not overdone **11** dessert wine; subtle oaking, fresh acidity & modest 12% alcohol in good balance with rich texture & fine mineral tension.

★★★★ **Vine Dried Chenin Blanc** (NEW) Rich, honeyed, raisiny **13** dessert wine (tank sample). Full of flavour, including blue orangeskin notes. Fairly high alcohol level; vein of acidity controls much cloy on medium-length finish. 375 ml.

Also tasted: **Shiraz-Merlot 12** ★★★☆ Discontinued: **Viognier**.

Land of Hope range

★★★★☆ **Cabernet Sauvignon** ⓥ Adds 'Reserve' with **11** (★★★★), previewed few years ago. Solid ripe fruit & long finish hint at future complexity, but dominated in youth by oak & drying tannin. Followed plush **09**.

★★★★ **Reserve Pinot Noir** ⓥ Enticing red-fruit & savoury scents on **11** from Elgin & Stellenbosch. Less intensity than Radford Dales, but lovely cherry fruit, savoury elegance & light, firm grip.

★★★★ **Reserve Chenin Blanc** Behind its lovely, meaningful label, **13** is as charming as ever - gentle, full of ripe apple fruit. Technically dry, but only hints at pleasing sweetness; nor does it flaunt its oak.

Vinum range

★★★★ **Cabernet Sauvignon** As usual, the firmly serious structure of **12** should ensure few years' development. Warm, savoury, generous, ripe fruit flavour too, though, complemented by judicious oaking.

★★★★ **Chenin Blanc** Perhaps the most forthcoming of the chenins here. **13** has sweet melony flavours & notes of tropical ripeness, but less concentrated than **12** (★★★★★) & showing its oaking a little more.

Winery of Good Hope range

★★★★ **Granite Ridge Reserve** Varying blend with shiraz. **12** (★★★☆) has pinotage & 3 others, mostly ex Stellenbosch. Big & bold, less easygoing than previous **09**. Tannic power, juicy fruit, solid dry finish.

Bush Vine Chenin Blanc ★★★☆ There's some depth & character as well as straightforward fruity easiness on firm & tasty **13** - it's properly dry, too. Also tasted: **Unoaked Chardonnay 13** ★★★ Not retasted: **Bush Vine Pinotage 12** ★★★☆ **Mountainside Shiraz 12** ★★★ **Oceanside Cabernet Sauvignon-Merlot 12** ★★★ Not tasted: **Pinot Noir Reserve**. — TJ

Location: Stellenbosch ▪ Map: Helderberg ▪ WO: Stellenbosch/Swartland/Western Cape/Elgin/Stellenbosch ▪ Est/ 1stB 1998 ▪ Tasting & sales Mon-Fri 9-5 by appt ▪ Closed all pub hols ▪ Owner(s) Alex Dale, Andrew Openshaw, Yalumba, Edouard Labeye, Cliff Roberson, Ben Radford, Heather Whitman ▪ Cellarmaster(s) Edouard Labeye (1998) ▪

Winemaker(s) Jacques de Klerk (Oct 2009), with Bernhard Bredell (2013) & Tubby May (2002) ▪ Viticulturist(s) Edouard Labeye, Jacques de Klerk, Gus Dale & Bernhard Bredell ▪ ±100ha (cab, carignan, cinsaut, gamay, grenache, mourv, ptage, pinot, syrah, chard, chenin) ▪ 600t/80,000cs own label 50% red 50% white ▪ Brands for clients: Pick's Pick ▪ Level 3 BEE, IPW, WIETA ▪ Postnet Suite 124 Private Bag X15 Somerset West 7129 ▪ thewineryofgoodhope@ thewineryofgoodhope.co.za ▪ www.thewineryofgoodhope.com ▪ S 34° 0' 57.5" E 018° 49' 2.6" ▪ F +27 (0)21-855-5529 ▪ **T +27 (0)21-855-5528**

Wines of Cape Town

A negociant business based in Bellville, Wines of Cape Town specialises in mainly red private-label wines for clients in Asia and Africa. It also exports its own brand of 'good-value, well-made wines', Dolphin Sands, available in 6L packaging with branded dispenser that chills the contents optimally.

Location: Bellville ▪ Map: Durbanville, Philadelphia & Darling ▪ Est 2007 ▪ Tasting by appt ▪ Owner(s) DS Sarnia (Pty) Ltd ▪ 80% red 20% white ▪ Other export brand: Dolphin Sands ▪ Brands for clients: Diamond Creek, Bushman's Creek, Dolphin Bay ▪ 71 Sonneblom Street Stellridge Bellville 7530 ▪ sales@winesofcapetown.com ▪ www. winesofcapetown.com ▪ F +27 (0)21-876-3486 ▪ **T +27 (0)21-876-2129**

Wine Village-Hermanus

Realising a dream to bring together the fine wines of South Africa under one roof, Paul and Cathy du Toit opened Wine Village at the entrance to the Hemel-en-Aarde Valley in 1998. Daughter Ulla now joins the team to manage events and the popular annual Hermanus Wine & Food Festival. Are We Having Fun Yet? is their house brand.

Are We Having Fun Yet? ★★★ Shiraz & merlot, dash petit verdot. As name says, this about enjoyment, which **13** delivers. Flavourful, juicy, rounded, & just enough tannin grip for food. — CR, CvZ

Location: Hermanus ▪ Map: Elgin, Walker Bay & Bot River ▪ WO: Walker Bay ▪ Est 1998 ▪ 1stB 2004 ▪ Open Mon–Fri 9–6 Sat 9–5 Sun 10–3 ▪ Closed Good Fri & Dec 25 ▪ Owner(s) Paul & Cathy du Toit ▪ ±2,000cs 50% red 50% white ▪ PO Box 465 Hermanus 7200 ▪ winevillage@hermanus.co.za ▪ www.winevillage.co.za ▪ S 34° 24' 40.7" E 019° 12' 1.9" ▪ F +27 (0)86-509-4931 ▪ **T +27 (0)28-316-3988**

Wineways Marketing

Negociant business Wineways Marketing buys grapes from Stellenbosch, Swartland and elsewhere for vinification by Leeuwenkuil's Pieter Carstens. Marketed under the brand names Black Box, Black Tie, Coral Reef, Tin Cups, Mountain Shadows and Moods. They're available locally as well as throughout Africa, the Indian Ocean Islands and Middle East.

Location: Kuils River ▪ Est 2000 ▪ Closed to public ▪ Owner(s) Carl Schmidt, Stephen Vermeulen & Fanie Marais ▪ Winemaker(s) Pieter Carstens (Leeuwenkuil) & Bernard Claassen (Stellenbosch Vineyards) ▪ 400,000cs own label 60% red 40% white ▪ Plot 689, Zinfandel Street, Saxenburg Park 2, Blackheath 7580 ▪ info@wine-ways.co.za ▪ www. wine-ways.co.za ▪ F +27 (0)86-509-9587 ▪ **T +27 (0)21-905-7713/6/9**

☐ **Wingnut** *see* Chateau Naudé Wine Creation

Winkelshoek Wine Cellar

Available for tasting and sale from the visitor centre at Piketberg on the West Coast, Winkelshoek's offering now includes a pair from its sibling label Schenkfontein, listed and rated separately, plus the Schenkfontein unwooded chardonnay which missed our tasting deadline. Winkelshoek's own easy-drinking wines, unreviewed as usual, include Weskus Dry Red, Sweet Rosé, Grand Cru, Blanc de Blanc and Late Harvest; and Cap Vino Red (unwooded) and White (chenin).

Location: Piketberg ▪ Map: Swartland ▪ Tasting & sales Mon-Fri 9–4 Sat 9–12 ▪ Gifts ▪ Owner(s) Hennie Hanekom & Jurgens Brand ▪ Cellarmaster(s) Hennie Hanekom ▪ Winemaker(s) Hennie Hanekom (1984) ▪ PO Box 395 Piketberg 7320 ▪ info@winkelshoek.co.za ▪ S 32° 54' 22.4" E 018° 46' 2.0" ▪ F +27 (0)22-913-1095 ▪ **T +27 (0)22-913-1092**

Winters Drift

The Winters Drift brand is homed at characterfully renovated Elgin train station, a nascent hub of wine, food and family entertainment. The wines are crafted by eminent Kobie Viljoen and Koen Roose. The vines are on Glen Elgin and surrounding farms owned by the non-profit, community- and conservation-conscious Molteno Brothers Trust, legacy of 19th-century farmers Edward and Harry.

★★★★ **Pinot Noir 13** (★★★★) continues bright-fruited, elegant style of maiden **12**, with oak playing supportive role. Nicely balanced & accessible, for shorter-term enjoyment.

Sauvignon Blanc ★★★ Retains fuller styling with 3 months on lees & short bottle-maturation providing soft, well rounded, creamy mouthfeel. **13** ripe & generous, styled for food. Also tasted: **Shiraz 12** ★★★ **Chardonnay 13** ★★★★ Not retasted: **Rosé 12** ★★★ — HJ

Location/WO: Elgin ▪ Map: Elgin, Walker Bay & Bot River ▪ Est 2004 ▪ 1stB 2010 ▪ Tasting Tue-Fri 9-4 Sat 10-4 & every first Sun of the month ▪ Platform 1 eatery ▪ Facilities for children ▪ Boule court ▪ Conservation area ▪ Owner(s) Molteno Brothers (Pty) Ltd ▪ Cellarmaster(s) Kobie Viljoen (shiraz, consultant) & Koen Roose (pinot/chard/rosé/sauv, Spioenkop) ▪ Viticulturist(s) Christiaan Cloete (Jan 2011) & Francois Viljoen (Vinpro) ▪ 1,600ha/±54ha (grenache, merlot, mourv, pinot, shiraz, chard, sauv, sem, viog) ▪ 460t/7,000cs own label 40% red 50% white 10% rosé ▪ PO Box 128 Elgin 7180 ▪ gerhard@wintersdrift.com ▪ www.wintersdrift.com ▪ S 34° 08' 59.42" E 019° 02' 22.61" ▪ F +27 (0)21-859-4893 ▪ **T +27 (0)21-859-3354**

Withington

Having long marketed the wines of vaunted Cape names, Charles Withington relishes introducing his personal selection — now including a potstill brandy — to wine 'drinkers' rather than 'thinkers' at his Darling wine shop. This varies vintage to vintage, as he sources wines widely, though preferably from his viticulturally acclaimed home turf.

Withington range

Malbec ⓃⒺⓌ ★★★ Cheery, smoky blue-fruit entry to **13**, charcoal & liquorice grip on firm tail. Also tasted: **NBC Chardonnay 13** ★★★★ Not retasted: **Shiraz-Cabernet Sauvignon 09** ★★★ Discontinued: **Carignan**, **Semillon**.

Darlington range

Malbec ⓄⒷ ★★★ Juicy raspberry & blueberry vibrancy to **12**. Light, gentle & uncomplicated, with clean dry finish. Not retasted: **Chardonnay 12** ★★★ Not tasted: **Pinotage**.

Greendale range

In abeyance: **Chenin Blanc-Chardonnay**.

Living Rock range

Not tasted: **Cinsaut-Ruby Cabernet**. In abeyance: **Chenin Blanc-Chardonnay**.

Brandy range ⓃⒺⓌ

★★★★ **Voorkamer** Literally 'Living Room', & intended for convivial occasions there, 7-year potstilled colombard is genteel, with a smooth creamy texture, spiced orchard fruit & a lingering balanced citrus conclusion. A delight. — WB, FM

Location: Darling ▪ Map: Durbanville, Philadelphia & Darling ▪ WO: Darling/Paarl ▪ Est 2001 ▪ 1stB 2003 ▪ Tasting & sales at Darling Wine Shop Mon-Sat 10-6 (10-7 in summer) Sun 11-2 ▪ Closed Mar 21, Easter Fri/Sun & Dec 25/26 ▪ Fresh West Coast oysters served when available ▪ Owner(s) Withington family ▪ 6,000cs own label 70% red 30% white + 8,000cs for clients ▪ Brands for clients: Cape Diversity, Greendale ▪ PO Box 236 Darling 7345 ▪ mail@withington.co.za ▪ www. withington.co.za ▪ S 33° 22' 28" E 018° 22' 38" ▪ **T +27 (0)22-492-3971/+27 (0)74-194-1711**

Withoek

In the red hills on the fringe of Calitzdorp village, the Geyser family vineyards share space with fruit orchards, self-catering cottages and a cellar dating from the 1940s, where Fanie Geyser makes his boutique wines, keeping things simple and traditional.

Fick's Cape Ruby ② ★★ Raisin & dusty spices on **NV** 'port'. **Geyser Cape Ruby** ② ★★ Rustic **NV** port-style fireside sipper. Not tasted: **Cabernet Sauvignon**, **Shiraz**, **Sauvignon Blanc**, **Kairos Muscadel**, **Geyser Cape Vintage**. — CE, JP

Location/WO: Calitzdorp ▪ Map: Klein Karoo & Garden Route ▪ Est/1stB 1996 ▪ Tasting, sales & cellar tours by appt ▪ Self-catering cottages ▪ Walks ▪ Conservation area ▪ Owner(s) Geyser family ▪ Winemaker(s) Fanie Geyser ▪ Viticulturist(s) Johannes Mellet ▪ 454ha/30ha (cab, p verdot, ruby cab, shiraz, tinta, touriga, chenin, cbard, hanepoot, muscadel) ▪ ±300t/800cs own label 50% red 50% fortified ▪ PO Box 181 Calitzdorp 6660 ▪ withoek@telkomsa.net ▪ www.withoek.blogspot.com ▪ S 33° 32' 24.1" E 021° 40' 59.8" ▪ F +27 (0)86-628-7853 ▪ **T +27 (0)44-213-3639**

☐ **Witklip** *see* Eerste Hoop Wine Cellar

Woestkloof Estate

Located high up on Groenberg Mountain, this is the Hoogenhout family's 'new' estate, their ancestors having farmed in Wellington since the 1800s. Today Simon Obholzer and Celia Hoogenhout-Obholzer tend 'a wonderful old block' of syrah and merlot, combining their first names to create the Simelia range of 'wines that best celebrate the Boland'. Consultant Louis Nel completes their 'small team of highly passionate people', with luxury self-catering accommodation offered at Casa Simelia.

Simelia range

Merlot ★★★★ Blackcurrants, a whiff of mint resting on a bed of firm tannin, **13** an ideal food match or give it a few years. **Syrah** ★★★ Deep dark fruit, liquorice & spice, the tannins still brusque; give **13** time to meld or serve with rich casseroles. — CR, CvZ

Location/WO: Wellington ▪ Est farm circa 1837/wine brand 2012 ▪ 1stB 2013 ▪ Closed to public ▪ Casa Simelia luxury self-catering house ▪ Hiking/walking trails ▪ Owner(s) BM Hoogenhout Trust (farm); Simon A Obholzer & Celia Hoogenhout-Obholzer (wine brand) ▪ Winemaker(s) Louis Nel (Nov 2012, consultant) ▪ 42ha/2.2ha (merlot, syrah) ▪ 8t/±1,016cs plus ±100 magnum btls own label 100% red ▪ info@simelia.co.za ▪ www.simelia.co.za ▪ F +27 (0)86-637-2920 ▪ **T +27 (0)21-424-7261**

☐ **Wolfenberg** *see* TCB Wines

Wolfkloof

Jan Kannemeyer's boutique vintning story began in 2004 when he concluded he couldn't call himself a vinegrower and not make wine. Merlot - all of one barrel - was his first attempt and the variety is still his favourite. Production from his estate just outside Robertson has reached 10 tons, all made as naturally as possible and bottled under his JC Kannemeyer label.

Location/map: Robertson ▪ Est 1883 ▪ 1stB 2004 ▪ Tasting, sales & cellar tours by appt ▪ Meals by appt; or BYO picnic ▪ Tour groups ▪ Conferences (40 pax) ▪ Weddings/functions (100 pax) ▪ Hiking trail ▪ Owner(s)/cellarmaster(s)/winemaker(s) Jan Kannemeyer ▪ Viticulturist(s) Hennie Visser (consultant) ▪ 360ha/4ha (merlot, chard) ▪ 10t/1,000cs own label 40% red 40% white 20% rosé + 180cs for clients ▪ PO Box 40 Robertson 6705 ▪ info@wolfkloof.co.za ▪ www.wolfkloof.co.za ▪ S 33° 47' 28.1" E 019° 52' 1.4" ▪ F +27 (0)86-554-4894 ▪ **T +27 (0)74-339-5008**

Wolftrap

Ever more successful Wolftrap is made by the eminent Boekenhoutskloof winery from widely sourced fruit — Breede River and Wellington being new areas since last edition. Volumes are high - 190,000 cases of the red alone - but meticulous and thoughtful winemaking (much of the white is naturally fermented, the new rosé is vinified saignée-style from red Rhône grapes) and ungreedy pricing make this a truly exceptional entry-level offering.

For more information, visit wineonaplatter.com

The Wolftrap ⊘ ★★★☆ Syrah, mourvèdre, viognier blend ratchets up quality in **13**. Juicy & soft, with defined body yet pliable blackberry & cocoa generosity. WO W Cape, as all. **The Wolftrap Rosé** (NEW) ⊙ ★★★ Candyfloss & blueberry/plum vibrancy on maiden **14**, syrah/shiraz with dabs grenache & cinsaut. Textured, dry, crisp & refreshing. Thinking man's pink. **The Wolftrap White** ⊘ ★★★☆ **13** once more a broad, deep intriguing mix of viognier, chenin & grenache blanc that overdelivers. Rich stonefruit & cream yet lively & fresh to long tail. Intelligently oaked. — FM

Wolvendrift Private Cellar

This Robertson farm has been in the Klue family for more than 100 years, and 4 generations have made wine in its cellar. Hospitality is a particular focus, and the child-friendly facilities and attractions include a vineyard deck with mountain views, pre-booked meals on the lawns beside the Breede River, and weddings in the cellar itself.

Location/map: Robertson ▪ Est 1903 ▪ Tasting & sales Mon-Fri 8.30–4.30 Sat 11–2 ▪ Closed Easter Fri-Mon, May 1, Dec 25/26 & Jan 1 ▪ Cellar tours by appt ▪ Refreshments/meals by pre-booking ▪ Facilities for children ▪ Tour groups ▪ Walking/hiking trails ▪ Conservation area ▪ Weddings & functions ▪ Owner(s) Michael Klue ▪ Winemaker(s) Jan Klue (Jan 2003) ▪ Viticulturist(s) Jan Swart (Jan 2000) ▪ 120ha (cab, merlot, chard, chenin, cbard, sauv) ▪ 45% red 45% white 10% fortified ▪ PO Box 24 Robertson 6705 ▪ info@wolvendriftwines.co.za ▪ www.wolvendriftwines.co.za ▪ S 33° 55′ 0.1″ E 020° 0′ 9.0″ ▪ F +27 (0)23-616-2396 ▪ **T +27 (0)23-616-2890**

Women in Wine

Women in Wine was established by a group of black female professionals inspired by quality wines and the empowerment of women in the winelands. Their portfolio consists of two labels: Women in Wine (Cabernet, Chardonnay and Sauvignon) and Three Graces Reserve (Euphrosyne Cabernet, Thalia Merlot and Aglaia Chardonnay).

Location: Paarl ▪ Closed to public ▪ PO Box 12869 Die Boord Stellenbosch 7613 ▪ info@womeninwine.co.za ▪ www.womeninwine.co.za ▪ F +27 (0)21-872-8967 ▪ **T +27 (0)21-872-8967**

Wonderfontein

The boutique wine label of Wonderfontein's 5th-generation grape-growing Marais family, bolstered by the acquisition of two neighbouring farms, is focusing on MCC bubblies, riddled in an underground storeroom sometimes used for making honey. Same creativity, different product, ancestor Kosie Marais is credited with pioneering South Africa's iconic Klipdrift brandy in the early 1900s.

★★★★ Paul René MCC Brut NV bottle-fermented sparkling from chardonnay holds head high in a valley respected for the style. Lively mousse, lemon vibrancy, elegant dry conclusion.
La Bonne Vigne Sauvignon Blanc ★★★ Melange of grass, greenpepper & scrub on zesty & satisfying **14** anytime sipper. Not retasted: **The Marais Family Merlot 10 ★★☆ La Bonne Vigne Merlot 11 ★★ La Bonne Vigne Shiraz 11 ★★★ La Bonne Vigne Rosé NV ★★★ Wonderfontein Red Muscadel 11 ★★★★ White Muscadel 12 ★★★** — CvZ

Location/map/WO: Robertson ▪ Est ca 1884 ▪ Tasting by appt only ▪ Sales Mon-Fri 9–5.30 Sat 9–1 ▪ Tour groups ▪ Conferences/events (40-80 guests), picnic facilities, 4×4 trail & other attractions ▪ Owner(s) Paul René Marais ▪ Winemaker(s) Stefan Bruwer ▪ Viticulturist(s) Gert Visser & Gerald Stemmet ▪ 310ha (cab, merlot, ptage, pinot, ruby cab, shiraz, chard, chenin, sauv) ▪ 5,500t/6,000cs own label 10% red 80% white 1% rosé 9% fortified ▪ PO Box 4 Robertson 6705 ▪ henk@wonderfonteinestate.co.za ▪ www.wonderfonteinestate.co.za ▪ S 33° 49′ 3.5″ E 019° 52′ 2.1″ ▪ F +27 (0)23-626-2669 ▪ **T +27 (0)23-626-2212**

Woolworths

Woolworths celebrates 30 years of selling wine in 2015. Far from resting on their laurels, the wine department team at this upmarket retail network, Allan Mullins and Ivan Oertle, are pursuing new ideas to sustain and grow their customer base. From the popular Coffee Pinotage and Chocolate Shiraz, now joined by Blackberry Cabernet and Peachy Chenin Blanc, via more imports from Spain, Chile and France, to single-serve wine cups and magnums, so the range expands. The Store Profile & Space Team are responsible for getting the right stock in the right place for the right customer. That now includes the newer Super Woolies outlets, large food and wine 'theatre' stores. Wine education for staff and more focus on customer service are high on the agenda.

Cabernet Sauvignon range

★★★★ **Exclusive Cabernet** 09 from Grangehurst displays classic red fruit & tomato cocktail aromas. Like unshowy 08, firmly structured, with fine tannin, & attractively restrained. Good partner to a variety of meat dishes.

★★★★ **Single Vineyard The Hutton Cabernet Sauvignon** Named for main Groenekloof vineyard soil type. 12 a 'wow' wine! Tight, tense & tannic in youth, it's packed with cassis & promises much, & much more than slighter 11 (★★★★). By Spier.

★★★★ **Cabernet Sauvignon Reserve** ⓘ Full, rich 11 measured blackcurrant fruit woven with ripe, pliable tannin. Understated tobacco & herbal notes, & the firm grip of its Diemersfontein origin.

★★★★ **Cabernet Sauvignon Reserve** 12 dense & intense blackcurrant fruits rest in very fine tannins, dark & brooding in youth. Beautifully textured but needs time to show its all. 60% new oak 18 months. Crafted at Spier.

Blackberry Cabernet Sauvignon ⓝ ★★★ Latest in series of 'flavour'-named wines from Diemersfontein. 13 steps beyond frivolity of peers (Coffee Pinotage & Chocolate Shiraz) with more serious styling. **Stellenbosch Cabernet Sauvignon** ⓝ ★★★ Blackcurrant fruit from first sniff to last swallow, Spier's regional expression in 12 attractively unfettered by obvious oak (only 20% new). Also tasted: **NSA Organic Running Duck Cabernet Sauvignon** ⓞ 14 ★★★ Not retasted: **Longmarket Cabernet Sauvignon** 12 ★★★ **House Cabernet Sauvignon** 12 ★★☆

Merlot range

★★★★ **Merlot Reserve** ⓘ Firmly structured 09 from Morgenhof shows dark cherries, blackberries, & slight herbaceous note. Powerful, with integrated acidity but warmish finish ex 14.8% alcohol.

★★★★ **Exclusive Selection Merlot** ⓘ Carefully made, Jordan's 11 has the cassis & dark chocolate notes you'd expect, plus a sleekly curvaceous body, ending dry & food friendly.

★★★★ **Organic Merlot** ⓞ With some Voor Paardeberg grapes, organic 13 maintains pace set by velvety 12, & shows juicy core of inky fruit in neatly tailored, suave tannin framework. Dapper & flavoursome, with clean dry farewell. By Laibach.

★★★★ **Shannon Merlot** ⓘ Plummy, honeyed 12's plush palate has a hint of oak char, sufficient tannic grip to extend the finish. Concentrated but vivacious, like also-tasted 11 by Shannon Vineyards.

Stellenbosch Merlot ⓝ ★★☆ Ripe, warmly welcoming 12 from Delheim is easygoing but firm, dry & respectable. **Blackcherry Merlot** ⓝ ★★★ Smoky dark fruit & cocoa nuance on 13 from Weltevrede. Supple & juicy style for attractive easy drinking, pleasing dry farewell. Also tasted: **Single Vineyard Koffie Klip Merlot** 12 ★★★★ **Merlot** 13 ★★★ **Longmarket Merlot** 12 ★★☆ **House Merlot** 14 ★★★ **Light Merlot** 13 ★★ Not retasted: **NSA Organic Swooping Falcon Merlot** 13 ★★ Discontinued: **Breath Merlot**.

Pinot Noir range

★★★★ **Pinot Noir Reserve** From Paul Cluver, 12 returns to form in better vintage. Greater depth of fruit than 11 (★★★★), similar fresh earth & leather tones with smooth tannins. Polished, elegant & balanced; tempting now, could age 3-5 years.

★★★★ **Limited Release CM Pinot Noir** Like 12, elegant restraint & silky texture that epitomise Catherine Marshall's wines evident on 13. Perfumed red fruit from 4 sites, balanced by bright acidity. Could grace a table now but best to wait few years.

Single Vineyard Le Petit Shannon Pinot Noir ⓝ ★★★☆ Naturally fermented **13** slightly high-toned & sappy, & very individual; drinks well & easily but expect a walk on the (positive) wilder side! Also tasted: **DMZ Pinot Noir 13** ★★★★ Discontinued: **Longmarket Pinot Noir**.

Pinotage range

★★★★ **Simonsig Pinotage** ⓟ **12** (★★★☆) dense & brimming with berry compote fruitiness. High-toned aroma spices up well-structured & focused body. Follows **10**. **11** untasted.

Coffee Pinotage ★★☆ Close your eyes & **13** tastes of, well, coffee, with a sweet feel for an easy glide. From Diemersfontein. **House Pinotage** ⓥ ★★★★ Made by Ken Forrester, **13** bursts with mulberries, cherries & plums. Juicy, with fine tannins & slight hint of liquorice. Also tasted: **NSA Organic Glowing Firefly Pinotage** ⓦ **14** ★★ **Exclusive Selection Pinotage 13** ★★★ Not retasted: **Light Pinotage 13** ★ **Longmarket Pinotage 12** ★★★ **Pinotage Reserve 12** ★★★★ Discontinued: **Pinotage**.

Shiraz range

★★★★ **Syrah Reserve** ⓝ Warm, ripe-fruited, smoky, spicy fragrance on **12** from Winery of Good Hope's Radford Dale. Plummy flavours, structured by gentle tannins & very firm acidity, lead to good dry finish. Unfined/filtered.

NSA Organic Diving Hawk Shiraz ⓝ ⓦ ★★☆ Translucent **14** vibrant & crunchy, 14% alcohol balanced by fresh fruit; similar to also-tasted **13**, slightly more concentrated; both lightly wooded for early accessibility. Fairtrade certified. From Stellar Winery. **House Shiraz** ⓝ ★★★★ Typical plum spice with lurking liquorice depth on soft, approachable **13** by Porcupine Ridge/Boekenhoutskloof. Also tasted: **Chocolate Shiraz 13** ★★★ Not retasted: **Longmarket Redstone Shiraz 12** ★★☆ Discontinued: **Shiraz Reserve**, **Organic Hunting Owl Shiraz**, **Hercules Paragon Shiraz**, **Light Shiraz**.

Niche Red Cultivars

★★★★ **Granite Blocks Cabernet Franc** Pungent & powerful **12** shows plushy black berries & soft tannins. Satisfying depth of flavour, soft & balanced. No **11**. By cab franc specialists Raats Family.

★★★★ **Nederburg Grenache** ⓥ Deep, earthy & rich but bright red berries, fynbos & sprinkling of nutmeg, **13** ticks all the drinkability boxes. With dollop carignan for complexity.

★★★★ **Limited Release Malbec** By Bellevue, **11** in similar form to excellent **10** with deep plum fruit, cherry tobacco notes & solid but rounded tannin base. For now or keeping few years.

★★★★ **Malbec Reserve** ⓟ Perfumed **12** proffers nutmeg & blackcurrant profile contrasted & balanced by sleek tannin. 12 months 60% new oak; needs few years to unfurl. By Diemersfontein.

Also tasted: **Cabernet Franc Reserve 12** ★★★☆

Red Blends

★★★★ **Cabernet Sauvignon-Merlot Reserve** More fruit opulence on this delicious blend (including a little cab franc) than on Neil Ellis's own-label wines, but same elegance. **12** supportive oak, good supple structure for similar accessibility to **11**.

★★★★ **Warwick Cape Lady** ⓟ Shiraz-led with pinotage, 3 others, **11**'s hedonistic spiced dark fruit & fleshy palate designed to please. Not for long ageing, but why resist something so delicious?

★★★★ **Grenache-Shiraz-Mourvèdre** ⓥ Ken Forrester's accessible, medium-bodied **10** brims with red cherry fruit, the mourvèdre component rising to 32% (**09**: 12%) to add richness to nutmeg & pepper complexity.

Longmarket Cabernet Sauvignon-Merlot ⓝ ★★★ Sweet-fruited **13** is smooth, juicy, with hint of mocha on finish. Ex Simonsvlei. **Longmarket Syrah-Mourvèdre-Viognier** ⓝ ★★★☆ Rounded mouthfeel & soft juicy approachability to maiden **13**, from Wolftrap/Boekenhoutskloof.

Cape Red ⓥ ★★★ Smoky, gently fruity aromas introduce lightish but ripe, juicy & tasty **NV** blend from Wellington Wines. **Cabernet Sauvignon-Shiraz Reserve** ★★★☆ Sound structure, rich savoury fruit harmonised in older oak provides current satisfaction in La Motte's unshowy **12**. **The Portuguese Connection** ✓ ★★★☆ **12** by Boplaas, mainly touriga/tinta with tweak of cab makes for a meaty, chunky nose given lightness by perfumed notes & soft tannins. Appetisingly lipsmacking! Also tasted: **Grand Rouge 12** ★★★ **Cabernet Sauvignon-Merlot 12** ★★★★ **Juicy Red NV** ★★★ **Natural Sweet Red 13** ★★ **Bel Rosso NV** ★★ Not retasted: **Exclusive Selection Cabernet Sauvignon-Merlot 11** ★★★★ **Longmarket Shiraz-Pinotage 12** ★★ Discontinued: **Allan Mullins Red 'My Song', Parlotones Giant Mistake, Shiraz-Cabernet Sauvignon, Goshawk's Chant**.

Rosé Wines

Light Pinot Noir Rosé ★★☆ Just-dry, zingy **13**, pomegranate & appealing wet earth flavours. From Villiera, for chilled summer drinking. Only 9.8% alcohol. Also tasted: **Pinotage-Shiraz Rosé 14** ★★ **Cape Rosé NV** ★★ Not retasted: **Natural Sweet Rosé 13** ★ Discontinued: **Longmarket Blanc de Noir, Longmarket Rosé, Zesty Rosé, Parlotones We Call this Dancing**.

Chardonnay range

★★★★ **Chardonnay Reserve 12** blooms in glass to reveal well-knit & poised wine, with citrus curd & white flower flavours, delicate oak spicing. Shows De Wetshof's mastery of the variety.

★★★★ **Single Vineyard Block 2A Chardonnay** (NEW) Lime, oatmeal & oak spice on rich & mouthfilling **13** from a Paul Cluver single-vineyard. Generous texture streamlined by clean citrus-toned acidity. Good weight for food pairing.

★★★★ **Exclusive Selection Chardonnay** ⊘ Tropical fruit & limy freshness give **13** ex Jordan taste appeal, offers a good alternative to wooded chardonnay.

Organic Feeding Duck Chardonnay ⊘ ★★★ Lime acidity perks up lightly oaked, lemon-toned **14**'s buttery softness. Real crowd pleaser. Fairtrade credited. By Stellar Winery. **Vanilla Chardonnay** ★★★ **13** oaked chardonnay billows vanilla spice, with a zest of lime & subtle pear tones. Clean & tangy for attractive easy drinking, from Weltevrede. **DeWetshof Unwooded Chardonnay** ★★★☆ Made-for-oysters **13** shows clean lime aromas, crisp citrus notes & elegant minerality. Also tasted: **Longmarket Chardonnay 14** ★★☆ **The Ladybird Chardonnay** ⊘ **13** ★★★ **House Chardonnay 14** ★★★ **Light Chardonnay 13** ★ Discontinued: **Abacus Chardonnay**.

Chenin Blanc range

★★★★ **Exclusive Collection Chenin Blanc Sur Lie** ⊘ Classy unwooded **13** from Simonsig deserves attention heaped on stylish & complex **12**. Lees rich, as name suggests, with ripe, layered tropical fruit. Delicate floral nuances, taut minerality on finish.

★★★★ **Chenin Blanc** ⊘ Buttered toast richness (14 months oak, 45% new) to fruit-filled **12** from Spier. Tasty, but obvious sweetness (7.4 g/l RS) makes you wish for a bite more acidity.

★★★★ **Noble Late Harvest Chenin Blanc** ⊘ By Ken Forrester, unctuous **11** nutty toffee nuances from 18 months oak, tastes like toasted hazelnuts & pine nuts sprinkled on caramelised pineapple.

Private Collection (NEW) ★★★★ A glossy show stealer! Spier's **13** in full, bold style; oak sheen, grain of sugar & friendly alcohol will find many fans. **Granite Blocks Chenin Blanc** (NEW) ★★★★ Fragrant & delicate unwooded **13**, aromas of yellow citrus, spanspek melons & grass. By Raats Family. Also tasted: **Chenin Blanc Reserve 13** ★★★★ **House Chenin Blanc 13** ★★★ **Longmarket Chenin Blanc 14** ★★☆ **Light Chenin Blanc 13** ★

Sauvignon Blanc range

★★★★ **Exclusive Selection Sauvignon Blanc** Cape Point Vineyards' **13** is WO Cape Peninsula, more forceful, pungent than restrained **12** from Durbanville vines. Still crisp, elegant & mineral driven, with velvety texture & appealing finish.

★★★★ **Exclusive Selection Nitida Sauvignon Blanc** **14** has 7% semillon adding soft, silky mouthfeel to naartjie & gooseberry zest. From Durbanville & Darling fruit, only slightly herbaceous. **13** sold out untasted.

★★★★ **Single Vineyard Windy Peak** (NEW) From high-altitude Helderberg block on Tukulu soil, **14** bolts out of the blocks with intense green fig & pea features adding flesh to rapier-like grassy freshness. Long, tempered tail. By Spier.

Durbanville Sauvignon Blanc (NEW) ★★★★ Diemersdal's **14** full of refreshing citrus & passionfruit flavour. Appetising & showing a wide spectrum of green & tropical fruit. **White Rock** (NEW) ★★★☆ Convincing dusty/mineral layers on **14**, gooseberry notes & bracing freshness but a cushion of creamy lees ensures drinkability. Multi-region blend with splash semillon, from Delaire Graff. Also tasted: **Organic Swooping Swallow Sauvignon Blanc** (symbol) **14** ★★☆ **Longmarket Sauvignon Blanc 14** ★★☆ Not retasted: **Light Sauvignon Blanc 13** ★ **House Sauvignon Blanc 13** ★★★ Discontinued: **Wet Rocks Sauvignon Blanc**, **Breath Sauvignon Blanc**.

Niche White Cultivars

★★★★ **Exclusive Selection Gewürztraminer** (symbol) Charming, light & perfumed **13** from Paul Cluver. Delicate intensity effortlessly achieved. Rose & litchi flavours with fresh balancing acidity. Semi-dry & step up on **12** (★★★★).

★★★★ **Ferricrete Riesling** Grown on ferricrete soils by Paul Cluver, **13** is clean & creamy, with per-fumed lime & kiwi. Tangy fruit & acid (masking 19 grams sugar), appealing low 10.6% alcohol, but shade off the thrilling tension & intensity of **12** (★★★★☆).

Longmarket Pinot Grigio ★★☆ Back-on-track **14** bone-dry weight watcher's friend with modest alcohol. Characterful sipping, with telltale peardrop aroma, pithy texture. By Van Loveren. Also tasted: **Moscato Light 13** ★★★ Not tasted: **Exclusive Selection Viognier**.

White Blends

★★★★☆ **DMZ White** (symbol) **12** echoes viognier, roussanne, chenin blend (no chardonnay) of **11** in bigger, firmer style. Slightly riper dried fruit, spice features, too, but well offset by freshness, tangy dry conclusion. Natural ferment in older oak. By DeMorgenzon.

★★★★ **Nitida Cellars Sauvignon Blanc-Semillon Reserve** (symbol) Gooseberry- & leaf-toned white Bordeaux blend from Nitida, **12** has nervy elegance; fresh & focused. Portion oak fermented.

Longmarket Chardonnay-Viognier ★★☆ Uncluttered everyday enjoyment from Spier. Lick of oak gives gloss to **13**, with cling peach lift. **Chenin Blanc-Pinotage** ★★★ Quirky chenin-led white blend, dry, unwooded. Faintly floral **14**, crisp, fresh & fruity. By Simonsig. **Natural White** ★★☆ Aro-matic, citrus blossom & ginger nose showing citrus on **14**'s palate, tangy, dry & light. Riesling & char-donnay, naturally fermented. By Villiera. **Zesty White** (NEW) ★★★ Tropical-fruited chenin-sauvignon **NV** blend from Wellington Wines with a little aromatic hanepoot. Light bodied, just off-dry, thor-oughly easygoing. Also tasted: **Cape White NV** ★★★ **Longmarket Sauvignon Blanc-Semillon** (symbol) **14** ★★★ Not retasted: **NSA Organic Fluttering Butterfly White 13** ★ **Longmarket Sau-vignon Blanc-Chenin Blanc 13** ★★★ **Bianca Light 13** ★★ **Cape Sweet Wine NV** ★★ **Natu-ral Sweet White 13** ★★ Discontinued: **Allan Mullins White My Song**, **Parlotones Push Me To The Floor**.

Méthode Cap Classique Sparkling range

★★★★☆ **Exclusive Selection Pinot Noir Rosé NSA** **13** (★★★★) from Simonsig is crisper, fresher than **12**, but still seriously conceived. Dry & silky, showing wispy brioche aromas mingled with baked apple & strawberries.

★★★★ **Brut** (symbol) Ever-popular, consistent **NV** bubbles ex Villiera get engaging red fruit from pinot & pinotage, zesty finish from chardonnay, smooth fine mousse thanks to 18 months on lees.

★★★★ **Brut Natural** From chardonnay, no added sulphur. Latest disgorgement is **NV (10)**, as charming as delicate **09**. Bone-dry, yet shows a soft, refined edge with brioche accents from 3 years on lees. Persistent mousse, pure citrus finish. By Villiera.

Ladybird Brut Méthode Cap Classique ⓥ ★★★ From Laibach, organic sparkling from pinotage & chardonnay; **12** is savoury, with subtle cranberry flavours from pinotage, a fine brisk mousse for easy sipping. Also tasted: **Brut Rosé** ⓥ **NV** ★★★★ Discontinued: **Blanc de Blancs Brut**.

Sparkling Wines
Spumante Rosé ★★ **NV** from Rooiberg pretty, pink & sweet, packed with strawberry appeal. Also tasted: **Spumante Brut NV** ★★ **Organic Sauvignon Blanc Brut** ⓥ **NV** ★★ **Spumante Doux NV** ★★

1L Box range
Dry Red ★★ Allsorts **NV** for easy sipping. By Simonsvlei, as all these. **Sweet Rosé** ★★ Bright, juicy, berry-fruited **NV**. Serve chilled. Also tasted: **Crisp White NV** ★★ **Light White NV** ★ **Semi-Sweet NV** ★★

2L Box range
Longmarket Cabernet Sauvignon-Merlot ★★★ Improved **13** has ripe berry tones & nice grip. Ideal picnic companion. By Simonsvlei. **Longmarket Sauvignon Blanc** ★★★ Tangy lemon zest & pepper ease to fresh **14** from Robertson Winery. Lowish alcohol an added bonus. Also tasted: **Longmarket Merlot 13** ★★★ **Longmarket Chardonnay 14** ★★★ Discontinued: **Longmarket Pinot Grigio**.

3L Box range
Light Red ★★ Off-dry **NV** party starter, mainly shiraz, low ±9% alcohol. By Simonsvlei, as for all. **Crisp White** ★★ Softly dry **NV** from chenin, bright & zippy. Also tasted: **Dry Red NV** ★★ **Light Rosé NV** ★★ **Light White NV** ★

5L Box range
Dry Red ★★ Undemanding smooth & spicy **NV** quaffer. By Simonsvlei, as all these. Also tasted: **Crisp White NV** ★★ **Semi Sweet NV** ★★ — Various tasters

WO: Various ▪ Selector Allan Mullins T +27 (0)21-407-2777 AllanMullins@woolworths.co.za ▪ Buying manager Ivan Oertle T +27 (0)21-407-2762 IvanOertle@woolworths.co.za ▪ Wine product developer Rebecca Constable T +27 (0)21-407-3162 RebeccaConstable@woolworths.co.za ▪ Owner(s) Woolworths Holdings ▪ Woolworths House 93 Longmarket Street Cape Town 8000 ▪ www.woolworths.co.za ▪ F +27 (0)21-407-3958 ▪ **T +27 (0)21-407-9111**

☐ **Workhorse (Marks & Spencer)** *see* Ken Forrester Wines
☐ **Wyma Vineyards** *see* Cape Hutton
☐ **Xaro** *see* Stellenrust
☐ **Xenna** *see* Annex Kloof Wines
☐ **Y** *see* Yonder Hill

Yardstick Wines

The collaboration between two Cape creatives at the top of their game - Mulderbosch winemaker Adam Mason and chef Peter Tempelhoff from boutique hotel group The McGrath Collection - searches for 'exceptional sites' to provide grapes for wines made specifically to work with food. The new names and packaging for the Mavelous range are meant to convey a sense of the wines' personality.

Yardstick range
★★★★ **Pinot Noir** Density & concentration on yielding yet sinewy **13**, from Elgin & Ceres like standout **12** (★★★★★). Delicate smoky cherry ripeness balanced by light tannin from older oak. Portion carbonic maceration.

For more information, visit wineonaplatter.com

★★★★ **Chardonnay** Mandarin vibrancy & creamy breadth two-step in elegant harmony on subtle oak stage in **13**. Silky smooth, harmonious & integrated, with lovely marmalade length & richness. 4 different sites, including Ceres.

Marvelous range

★★★★ **Blue** Was 'Kaboom!' Dried thyme nuance to fruitcake generosity on merlot-led 4-way Bordeaux blend in now-bottled **12** from Elgin, portion Stellenbosch. Seamless, complex, succulent all the way to long, rewarding finish. Up on last-tasted **10** (★★★★).

★★★★ **Yellow** Was 'Ka-Pow!' Complex melange of white grapes, some rare & old vines, but chenin leads on now-bottled **13**. Vibrant, fresh & broadly creamy, it remains focused & poised. Complex & rewarding. Step up on **12** (★★★).

Red ★★★★ Was 'Shazam!' Inviting cherry & plum compote on **12**, now-bottled syrah-led cinsaut, mourvèdre & grenache mix. Ripe, broad, juicy & dry. — FM

Location/map: Stellenbosch ▪ WO: Western Cape ▪ Est/1stB 2009 ▪ Tasting by appt ▪ Owner(s) Peter Tempelhoff, Charles Banks & Adam Mason ▪ Winemaker(s) Adam Mason ▪ Yardstick 3,400cs & Marvelous 8,000cs ▪ 70% red 30% white ▪ adam@marvelouswines.com, peter@marvelouswines.com ▪ www.yardstickwines.com, www.marvelouswines.com ▪ S 33° 53' 22.8" E 018° 49' 8.3" ▪ F +27 (0)21-881-3372 ▪ **T +27 (0)82-924-3286 (Adam)/+27 (0)82-578-5320 (Peter)**

Yonder Hill

After working at Eikendal, Kanonkop, Simonsig, Lievland and Darling Cellars, Abé Beukes has returned to the Helderberg foothills where his winemaking career began 30 years ago to consult to Naudé-family-owned Yonder Hill. As cellarmaster/winemaker, Abé oversees a mostly red-wine range focused on Bordeaux varieties, from a combination of own, recently replanted blocks and selected parcels further afield (the 2014 sauvignon is from Durbanville's Diemersdal).

Premium range

★★★★ **Merlot** Chunky, solid **12** has herbal notes with sweet berry fruit - riper-tasting than 13% alcohol would suggest. Grippy, dry tannins, partly from oaking with a generous new component, need time to settle.

★★★★ **Nicola** Cab-led Bordeaux blend in established blockbuster style, **10** has intense fruit & all-new oak to match. Well balanced, apart from the oak, & should develop well - needs 5+ years to show its best.

Also tasted: **Inanda 13** ★★★★

Y range

Sauvignon Blanc ★★★ Rather delicious **14** tank sample packed with flavour; crisply balanced. Not retasted: **Shiraz 13** ★★★ Not tasted: **Merlot**. — TJ

Location: Somerset West ▪ Map: Helderberg ▪ WO: Stellenbosch/Western Cape ▪ Est 1989 ▪ 1stB 1993 ▪ Tasting & sales Mon-Fri 9–4 Sat (Oct-Mar) 10-2 ▪ Closed all pub hols ▪ Tour groups ▪ Gift shop ▪ Olives & olive oil tasting ▪ Owner(s) Naudé family ▪ Cellarmaster(s)/winemaker(s) Abé Beukes (2014) ▪ Viticulturist(s) Francois Hanekom ▪ 14ha/10ha (cabs s/f, merlot, p verdot) ▪ 50t/15,000cs own label 95% red 5% white ▪ PO Box 914 Stellenbosch 7599 ▪ wines@yonderhill.co.za ▪ www.yonderhill.co.za ▪ S 34° 2' 22.5" E 018° 49' 40.2" ▪ F +27 (0)21-855-1006 ▪ **T +27 (0)21-855-1008**

☐ **ZAHarmonie Wine Cellar** *see* Snowfield Boutique Winery

☐ **Zalze** *see* Kleine Zalze Wines

Zanddrift Vineyards - Chapel Cellar

Owned by retired Singapore architect Koh Seow Chuan, Zanddrift boutique winery near Paarl is the day-to-day responsibility of Christo Jacobs, who cares for the ±9 ha under vine and the cellar. The

mostly exported wines, a cabernet and shiraz, are labelled Chapel Cellar, acknowledging the chapel-like visitor locale built from stone excavated by Italian prisoners of war.

Location: Paarl ▪ Map: Paarl & Wellington ▪ Est 1995 ▪ 1stB 2006 ▪ Tasting & sales Mon-Fri 9-1 & 2-5 ▪ Function venue ▪ Owner(s) Windsharp Trading 23, Koh Seow Chuan (Singapore) ▪ Winemaker(s)/viticulturist(s) Christo Jacobs ▪ 8.5ha (cab, shiraz) ▪ PO Box 1302 Suider-Paarl 7624 ▪ zanddrift@telkomsa.net ▪ S 33° 45' 39.20" E 018° 59' 11.41" ▪ F +27 (0)86-530-1892 ▪ **T +27 (0)21-863-2076/+27 (0)82-256-5006**

Zandvliet Wine Estate & Thoroughbred Stud

The De Wet family of Zandvliet in Robertson Valley share their twin passions - wine and horses - with growing numbers of fans. Winemaker Jacques Cilliers is now hitting his straps with his 4th vintage, and relishing working with shiraz, the estate's signature variety, in particular. First crops of complementary varieties such as grenache, carignan and mourvèdre are due this year. Helping spread the word about these and other happenings is new brand ambassador Werner Els.

Zandvliet Estate range

★★★★ **Kalkveld Chardonnay** Ⓐ 100% new French oak sets this apart from standard bottling. **10** restrained & savoury, some earthy notes.

Kalkveld Shiraz ★★★★ 09 vintage ripeness shows in plum & black cherry perfume, flavours, given an appealing cigarbox tone by well-judged oaking. A food-friendly savoury ending, with touch of scrub adding interest. **Shiraz ★★★** Plush dark fruit well spiced, juicy enough to drink solo but **10** has tannin grip for a few years cellaring. Also tasted: **Chardonnay 13 ★★★ VLW Cape Vintage Shiraz 12 ★★★★**

Le Bistro range

Chardonnay Unwooded ★★★ 14 friendly alcohol (11.8%), yellow peach flavours, refreshed by zesty acidity. Also tasted: **Cabernet Sauvignon 11 ★★★** Discontinued: **Crème**.

My Best Friend range

Cape Red ★★ Was 'Red'. Unspecified blend, **11** off-dry & unoaked. Ripe plummy flavours, smooth palate. Designed to avoid the mystique & just enjoy with friends. **Cape Muscat** Ⓝ **★★★ 14** Natural Sweet, with powerful grapiness, limy acidity offsetting the high sugar, & a remarkably light 7.6% alcohol. Delicious. Also tasted: **Shiraz Rosé 14 ★★ Sauvignon Blanc** ⊘ **14 ★★★ Cape White 14 ★★** Discontinued: **Semi-Sweet**. — CR

Location: Ashton ▪ Map/WO: Robertson ▪ Est 1867 ▪ 1stB 1975 ▪ Tasting & sales Mon-Fri 9–5 Sat 10-2 ▪ Closed Easter Fri/Sun, Dec 25/26 & Jan 1 ▪ Tour groups ▪ BYO picnic ▪ Owner(s) Paul & Dan de Wet ▪ Cellarmaster(s) Paul de Wet (1971) ▪ Winemaker(s) Jacques Cilliers (Dec 2011) ▪ Viticulturist(s) Dan de Wet (1993) ▪ 830ha/144ha (cab, shiraz, chard, cbard, sauv) ▪ 1,134t/90,000cs own label 47% red 49% white 5% rosé + 4,000cs for clients ▪ Export brands: Enon, Cogmanskloof ▪ Ranges for clients: Cogmanskloof, Rijckholt (Netherlands); Villa San Giovanni ▪ PO Box 36 Ashton 6715 ▪ info@zandvliet.co.za ▪ www.zandvliet.co.za ▪ S 33° 50' 50.7" E 020° 2' 13.7" ▪ F +27 (0)23-615-1327 ▪ **T +27 (0)23-615-1146**

Zevenwacht

Winemaking remains the main focus at this property just outside Kuils River, with spectacular views of Table Mountain and the ocean. However, when Harold Johnson became owner 23 years ago he declared: 'I want this to become a people-friendly farm'. Zevenwacht has become exactly that - a tourist, family and business hub, offering a wide range of hospitality, entertainment and conferencing services. Jacques Viljoen, winemaker the past 10 years, also loves viticulture, with a particular soft spot for the old gewürztraminer block which yields exceptional fruit. He continues to hone in his skills with advice from top vine and wine man Chris Keet.

Flagship range

★★★★ **Merlot** 11 (★★★) effusive red berry & spicy oak aromas but less flavoursome on palate, with oak somewhat dominant. Chunky & unknit mid-2014, shade off balanced **10**.

★★★★ **Syrah** Savoury, smoky dark fruit & tobacco lead-in to 11 (★★★★), pliable tannin structure with new wood better absorbed than Merlot. Solidly made wine in a difficult vintage, but misses **09**'s quality. **10** sold out untasted.

★★★★ **Sauvignon Blanc** Retasted after a year in bottle, **13** retains fresh, clean-cut profile but shows more mid-palate fruit intensity & weight. Understated & elegant food wine. **12** (★★★★) was softer.

Also tasted: **Cabernet Sauvignon** 12 ★★★★ **Chardonnay** 13 ★★★ **Chenin Blanc** 13 ★★★

Z-Collection

★★★★ **Grenache** (NEW) Two select barrels make up the maiden **12** vintage, from lofty vineyards. Already charming, with scented fruit & lithe silky tannins. Elegant & fresh, with underlying seriousness.

★★★★ **CMC** (🍷) **10** elegant, cab-led Bordeaux blend with merlot & cab franc, has a good core of cassis & spice, interwoven with fine-grained tannins. Shows inherent balance & ageing potential.

★★★★ **SG Rhône Style** Was 'SGM' but loses mourvèdre component in **11**, seamless mix of shiraz & grenache (60/40) ex 4 blocks. Appealing layers of dark & spicy flavour in a balanced oak framework, easily carries 14.5% alcohol. Ageworthy.

★★★★☆ **Gewürztraminer** Continues unusual oaked styling in naturally fermented **13**, returning to form after **12** (★★★★). From low-yielding 27 year old vines, variety's litchi & rosepetal charm infused in rich & viscous but texture. Dry, uncloying despite naturally low acidity.

★★★★ **360° Sauvignon Blanc** Name refers to lofty sea-facing viewsite. Oak-brushed **13** (★★★★) misses some of the intensity & freshness of standout **12** (★★★★★) & **11**. Broader textured, with pithy grip & greengage/peach flavours, dash semillon adds some flesh. A table mate.

Tin Mine Collection

★★★★ **Red** (✓) Flavoursome shiraz-led blend with grenache & mourvèdre (50/30/20) in **12**, with spicy, savoury tone. Open textured, smooth & generous, showing lively balance. Enjoy now & over the next few years.

★★★★ **White** (✓) Wooded blend of chardonnay, viognier, chenin & roussanne (50/28/21/1). Aromatic **13** (★★★★) similar to **12** but shade less fresh, creamier, showing more oak. Still an appealing drink.

7even range

Pinotage ★★★ Rich & heartwarming style, although alcohol in sync with dense fruit of **13**. Generous, ripe & juicy, ready to entertain. **Rosé** ★★★ From cab franc in **14**, unwooded & now dry. Clean & refreshing summer quaffer, bright cherry & cranberry flavours with savoury twist on the tail. Also tasted: **Rood** 12 ★★★ Not retasted: **Sauvignon Blanc** 13 ★★ **Bouquet** 13 ★★★ — MW

Location: Kuils River ▪ Map/WO: Stellenbosch ▪ Est 1980 ▪ 1stB 1983 ▪ Tasting & sales Mon-Fri 8.30–5 Sat/Sun 9.30–5 ▪ Fee R35 incl glass ▪ Closed Dec 25 ▪ Cellar tours by appt ▪ Restaurant ▪ Picnics in summer ▪ Facilities for children ▪ Gift shop ▪ Conferences ▪ Weddings/banqueting ▪ Walking & mountain biking trails ▪ 4x4 trail by appt ▪ Conservation area ▪ Mangwanani spa ▪ 4-star country inn ▪ Owner(s) Harold Johnson ▪ Winemaker(s) Jacques Viljoen (May 2005), with Charles Lourens (Jun 2014) ▪ Viticulturist(s) Eduard van den Berg (Jan 2001) ▪ 473ha/100ha (cabs s/f, grenache, merlot, mourv, ptage, primitivo, shiraz, chard, chenin, gewürz, muscat de F, rouss, sauv, sem, viog) ▪ 657t/

100,000cs own label 48% red 48% white 4% rosé ▪ BWI, IPW ▪ PO Box 387 Kuils River 7579 ▪ info@zevenwacht.co.za ▪ www.zevenwacht.co.za ▪ S 33° 55' 46.0" E 018° 43' 38.2" ▪ F +27 (0)21-903-3373 ▪ T +27 (0)21-900-5700

Zidela Wines

Family-owned Stellenbosch negociant Zidela, its co-owners well versed in wine buying, production and marketing, continues to grow. Providing bulk and bottled wine for buyers' own brands as well as under the proprietary labels below (some available locally), the business is moving beyond the more traditional European markets to tap into the US, China and Russia.

Mooiberg range

Sauvignon Blanc ⊘ ★★★ Passionfruit aromas & flavours on nicely balanced, easygoing **14**. Also tasted: **Cabernet Sauvignon** ⊘ **13** ★★★

New World Collection (NEW)

Pinotage ★★ Berried aromas on **13** lead quickly, via a slightly severe palate, to a tart, red-fruited conclusion. Unwooded, as for all ranges. **Sauvignon Blanc** ★★ Suggestions of ripe tropical fruit on dryish **14** quaffer.

Suikerbosch range

Cabernet Sauvignon (NEW) ⊘ ★★★ Fruit outpaces structure on juicy, tasty **14** - rather rare in these ranges. A touch drier than some, too. **Merlot** (NEW) ★★ **13** is grippy, lean & tart, with a herbaceous tone to the modest fruit. **Chardonnay** (NEW) ★★ Light-flavoured **14** has pleasant varietal aromas, but quick-vanishing flavour. Also tasted: **Shiraz-Merlot 13** ★★ **Rosé 14** ★★ **Chenin Blanc 14** ★★ **Golden Muscat 14** ★ Discontinued: **Reserve Shiraz**, **Reserve Chardonnay**.

Sumerton range

Cabernet Sauvignon-Pinotage ★★ Powerful **13**, with tart & herbal edge to the modest fruit. **Sauvignon Blanc** ★★ Pleasant tropical notes on **14**, with short, sweetish finish.

Zidela range

Rosé (NEW) ★★ Unassuming red-berry fragrance on lowish-alcohol, off-dry **14**. **Chenin Blanc** ⊘ ★★★ Friendly, mildly flavourful **14** rounded by a few grams of sugar. Not tasted: **Cabernet Sauvignon**, **Merlot**, **Pinotage**, **Shiraz**, **Bouquet Blanc**, **Sauvignon Blanc**. — TJ

Location: Stellenbosch ▪ WO: Western Cape ▪ Est 2001 ▪ 1stB 2002 ▪ Closed to public ▪ Owner(s) Danie Kritzinger, Herman Nell, Jaco Kritzinger & Erik Kritzinger ▪ 60% red 30% white 10% rosé ▪ 11 million litres for clients ▪ PO Box 3021 Matieland 7602 ▪ info@zidelawines.co.za ▪ www.zidelawines.co.za, www.privatewinelabel.co.za ▪ F +27 (0)21-880-2937 ▪ T +27 (0)21-880-2936

Zonnebloem

The latest generation of winemakers at this historic Distell-owned wine brand gives a youthful and modern air to one of SA's most enduring labels. Led by Deon Boshoff, they have over 300 different vineyard parcels of hand-picked grapes to choose from, allowing them to create wines of 'grace matched with power', and winning a new generation of fans. Building on the contemporary vibe is their collaboration with designer Haldane Martin, creating wine service tables, decanters and retail merchandising units.

Limited Editions

★★★★ **Pinotage** ⊘ Very lovely **10** is a welcome return after absence. Perfumed nose, moist plumcake flavours, chewy pliable tannins. Plenty of elegance & polish. All-new oak.

★★★★ **Shiraz** Pungent **11** pleases with lots of polish, leather & spice on the nose before dense, dark, baked black fruit surges through on the palate. 1st & 2nd fill French & American oak.

★★★★ **Sauvignon Blanc** Waxy lemons & herbal honey notes on **13**. Showing some age but great fruit intensity & good levels of acidity ensuring pleasant drinking for a further few years. Coastal WO.

★★★★ **Semillon** Pungent pine needles, peppers & limes on the nose of elegant, unwooded **13**. From a single vineyard in Malmesbury, racy citrus acidity is balanced by creamy intensity. Plenty more to come here.

★★★★ **Sauvignon Blanc-Semillon** Delicious drinking on **12**, showing some development mid-2013 but should be more to come as layered, complex finish hints. Coastal WO.

Also tasted: **Cabernet Sauvignon 11** ★★★ In abeyance: **Chenin Blanc**.

Zonnebloem range

★★★★ **Shiraz-Mourvèdre-Viognier** ⊘ A real cracker, **11** is thoroughly appetising with savoury/ gamey notes vying with soft red cranberries & juniper berries in a juicy, accessible mouthful with lovely texture & length. Even better than **10** (★★★☆).

★★★★ **Lauréat 11** improves on **10** (★★★☆) as 5% each of shiraz, mourvèdre & petit verdot add spice, leather & chewy black fruit to cab/merlot blend. Elegant tannins, firm finish. A cut above every-day wine.

Blanc de Blanc ⊛ ★★★ Delightful **14** tingles with gooseberries, grapefruit & hint of sherbet for dry, easy-drinking summery pleasure. WO W Cape. Also tasted: **Cabernet Sauvignon 12** ★★★ **Merlot 12** ★★★ **Pinotage 12** ★★★★ **Shiraz 12** ★★★★ **Chardonnay 13** ★★☆ **Sauvignon Blanc 14** ★★★ — CM

Location: Stellenbosch ▪ WO: Stellenbosch/Coastal/Western Cape ▪ Est 1893 ▪ Wine sales at Die Bergkelder Wine Centre ▪ Owner(s) Distell ▪ Cellarmaster(s) Deon Boshoff (Feb 2010) ▪ Winemaker(s) Bonny van Niekerk (reds, Oct 2007) & Elize Coetzee (whites, Jun 2010), with Bradley van Niekerk, Praisy Dlamini, Michelle Louw & James Ochse ▪ Viticulturist(s) Annelie Viljoen (Jun 2008) ▪ (cab, merlot, shiraz, chard, sauv, sem) ▪ 9,000t/±440,000cs own label 59% red 41% white ▪ ISO 9002, Fairtrade ▪ PO Box 184 Stellenbosch 7599 ▪ info@zonnebloem.co.za ▪ www.zonnebloem.co.za ▪ F +27 (0)21-886-4879 ▪ **T +27 (0)21-809-7000**

☐ **Zonneweelde** *see* Slanghoek Winery

Zonquasdrift Estates   ⊘

When Alexander and Antoinette Mettenheimer bought Swartland's Zonquasdrift farm in 2001, they realised the value of the 50+ year old chenin vines. A precious 100 cases (sold out at press time) are made at nearby Riebeek Cellars, with tastings and tours by appointment, and sales at Riebeek.

Location: Riebeek-Kasteel ▪ Map: Tulbagh ▪ Est 2001 ▪ 1stB 2009 ▪ Tasting Mon-Fri by appt ▪ Closed all pub hols ▪ Sales at Riebeek Cellars ▪ Owner(s) Alexander & Antoinette Mettenheimer ▪ Cellarmaster(s) Zakkie Bester (Riebeek Cellars) ▪ Winemaker(s) Eric Saayman (Riebeek Cellars) ▪ Viticulturist(s) Gustav Andrag (Sep 2005) ▪ 360ha/53ha (mourv, shiraz, chard, chenin, cbard, grenache blanc, muscadel) ▪ 600t/100cs own label 100% white ▪ HACCP, IPW ▪ PO Box 7 Riebeek-Kasteel 7307 ▪ info@zonquasdrift.co.za ▪ S 33° 20' 35.00" E 018° 58' 32.00" ▪ F +27 (0)86-606-2049 ▪ **T +27 (0)22-448-1078/+27 (0)82-896-4430**

Zorgvliet Wines

It's appropriate that Zorgvliet owner Mac van der Merwe's winery has the Silver Myn range – he made his fortune in mining. Hospitality is another key enterprise for the self-made man whose family is involved in all aspects of the multi-pronged business. Accommodation, functions and conferences, deli and picnic facilities, and wine are all available – but it's the 'amazing terroir' and location in Banhoek Valley outside Stellenbosch, with different elevations and cool southerly aspects, which excite new winemaker Bernard le Roux. With restraint his watchword, he's keen to apply some of the skills he learned working with California luminary Zelma Long at Vilafonté.

Zorgvliet range

★★★★ **Cabernet Sauvignon** All-new French oak makes **10** spicier than velvety soft **09**, more grippy from 18 months ageing too. Vibrant fruitcake appeal to ripe fruit.

★★★★☆ **Richelle** Red flagship **10** (★★★★) sees Bordeaux blend change to 75% cab & petit verdot; no merlot & cab franc as in **09**. Inky cassis flavour with rich plum succulence. Bold but restrained & lithe, as befits its status.

★★★★ **Single Vineyard Sauvignon Blanc 13** was structured & taut - as is **14** (★★★★) tank sample. Tangy & crisp, with tropical granadilla & fig ripeness rather than typical zest.

★★★★ **Simoné** Light, bright & delicate, semillon still leads sauvignon in **12** (★★★★) flagship wooded white blend. Less dense than **11**.

★★★★ **Natural Sweet Sauvignon Blanc** Echoes of last-tasted **10** (★★★★☆) grapefruit marmalade freshness in improved **12** preview, naturally fermented in barrel. Clean, crisp & focused, with zesty lime cordial finish. No **11**.

Not retasted: **Blanc de Blancs 10** ★★★★ Not tasted: **Cabernet Franc**, **Petit Verdot**.

Silver Myn range
Sauvignon Blanc ★★★ White pepper bite to gooseberry-laden **14** tank sample. Like **13**, (unwooded) semillon adds interest & texture - but boosted to 13%. Also tasted: **Argentum 12** ★★★ In abeyance: **Cabernet Franc Rosé**. — FM

Location/map: Stellenbosch ▪ WO: Banghoek ▪ Est/1stB 2000 ▪ Tasting & sales Mon-Fri 9–5 Sat/Sun 10–5 pub hols 10–4 ▪ Closed Good Fri, Dec 25 & Jan 1 ▪ Fee R20pp, waived on purchase ▪ Cellar tours by appt ▪ Zorgvliet Picnic Sep-Apr ▪ Facilities for children ▪ Tour groups ▪ Gifts ▪ Conferences ▪ Walks/hikes ▪ Zorgvliet Country Lodge (17 rooms) ▪ Owner(s) Van der Merwe family ▪ Winemaker(s) Bernard le Roux (Dec 2013), with Ruben Adams ▪ Viticulturist(s) Hannes Jansen van Vuuren ▪ 131ha/46ha (cabs s/f, merlot, p verdot, shiraz, tannat, chard, chenin, sauv, sem, viog) ▪ 300t/30,000cs own label 25% red 45% white 27% rosé 3% MCC + 200t for clients ▪ Other export brand: Enigma by Zorgvliet ▪ PO Box 1595 Stellenbosch 7599 ▪ cellar@zorgvliet.com ▪ www.zorgvlietwines.com ▪ S 33° 54' 41.7" E 018° 56' 32.0" ▪ F +27 (0)21-885-1318 ▪ **T +27 (0)21-885-1399**

☐ **Zulu 8** *see* Waterstone Wines

This Year's Ratings Summarised

Here we summarise the wines featured in the A–Z section, with their ratings, sorted first by wine style, in alphabetical order, and then by producer or brand. New wines in **bolder type**. **NS** = no star; **NT** = not tasted; **NR** = tasted but not rated; **D** = discontinued. Where wineries produce more than one version of a particular style, the number of versions is indicated in brackets after the name. A number of wines were tasted as pre-bottling barrel or tank samples, and therefore ratings are provisional. Refer to the A–Z for details.

Barbera

★★★★ Merwida

★★★☆ Altydgedacht, Fairview, Hofstraat ★★★ Wellington Winery **NT** Idiom

Biodynamic

★★★★★ Reyneke (Sauvignon blanc wooded)

★★★★☆ Reyneke (4) (Shiraz/syrah, Shiraz/syrah, Chenin blanc wooded, dry, Sauvignon blanc wooded)

★★★★ Reyneke (2) (Pinotage, Red blends, Cape Bordeaux)

Blanc de noir

★★★★ Aaldering, Mellasat, **Olifantsberg**

★★★☆ Antebellum, Maison, Nieuwedrift, **Springfontein** ★★★ Altydgedacht, Arra, Blaauwklippen, Boschendal, Buitenverwachting, Eaglevlei, Groot Constantia, Lovane, Lynx, Meinert, Peter Falke ★★★ Asara, Flagstone, Landskroon, Lemberg, Swartland ★★ **Ameera**, Landskroon, Van Loveren ★★ Boucheron, De Redley, Deux Frères ★ Van Loveren **NT** Aan de Doorns, Lovane, Signal Hill, Tempel **D** Klawer, Woolworths

Brandy

★★★★★ Boplaas, **KWV** (3), Oude Meester, Van Ryn (3)

★★★★☆ Blaauwklippen, **Boplaas** (3), **Elsenburg**, Klipdrift , KWV, Oude Meester (2), Oude Molen, Van Ryn (2)

★★★★ Avontuur, Backsberg (2), Flight of the Fish Eagle, **Gentleman Spirits** (2), Kaapzicht, KWV (2), Ladismith, Mons Ruber, **Napier**, Nederburg, Oude Molen (2), Richelieu, **Robertson**, Uitkyk, Upland (2) (Organic), **Withington**

★★★☆ Backsberg, Barrydale (2), Blaauwklippen, **Boplaas** (2), Collisons, **Die Mas**, **Grundheim**, Klipdrift (2), KWV, Oude Meester, Oude Molen, **Robertson**, Tokara, Viceroy ★★★ Chateau, **Die Mas**, **Grundheim** (2), Kingna Distillery, Limosin,

Louiesenhof (2), Olof Bergh, Van Loveren ★★☆ D'Aria, **Grundheim**, Mons Ruber, Richelieu

Bukettraube

★★★ Cederberg ★★☆ Seven Sisters **NT** Swartland **D** Nuweland

Cabernet franc

★★★★★ Warwick

★★★★☆ Buitenverwachting, **Cape Chamonix**, Hermanuspietersfontein, Nelson, Raats, Rainbow's End, Raka, Stellenrust

★★★★ Camberley, CK Wines, Doolhof, Hillcrest, Knorhoek, Mont du Toit, Môreson, Oldenburg, Ormonde, Raats, Rainbow's End, Ridgeback, **Waterkloof**, Woolworths

★★★☆ Claime d'Or, Druk My Niet, **Holden Manz**, Woolworths ★★★ Audacia, Avontuur, Bushmanspad, **Haut Espoir**, Lynx, **Osbloed**, Signal Hill, Spookfontein , Whalehaven ★★☆ **Onderkloof NT** Benguela Cove, BLANKbottle, Hannay, High Constantia, Idiom, Lovane, Maison de Teijger (2), My Wyn, Val de Vie, Vergenoegd, Zorgvliet **D** La Petite Ferme

Cabernet sauvignon

★★★★★ Groot Constantia, Le Riche, Nederburg, Oldenburg, Stark-Condé

★★★★☆ Bartinney, Bilton, Boekenhoutskloof, Buitenverwachting, Cederberg, Darling Cellars, Delaire (2), Edgebaston, Eikendal, Ernie Els (2), Flagstone, Fleur du Cap, Glen Carlou, Glenelly, Graham Beck, Grangehurst, Guardian Peak, House of Mandela, Jordan, Kanonkop, Kleine Zalze (2), Knorhoek, **La Petite Vigne**, Laibach, Le Bonheur, Le Riche, Meerlust, Nederburg, Neil Ellis, **PaardenKloof**, Restless River, Rickety Bridge, Rudera (2), Rust en Rede, Rustenberg, Springfield, Springfontein, Stark-Condé, Stony Brook, **Strydom**, Teddy Hall, Thelema, Vergelegen (2), **Vierkoppen**, Waterford, Webersburg

★★★★ Akkerdraai, Alto, Annandale, Arra (2), Backsberg, Bayede!, Belfield, Bergsig, Bilton, Bon Courage, Botanica, Brenaissance, Cape Hutton, **Cape Point**, Capelands, Cederberg, Chateau Naudé, De Meye, De Wetshof, Delheim, Devonvale, DeWaal, Dornier, Druk My Niet, Edgebaston, Eerste Hoop, Excelsior, Glen Carlou, Glenelly, Goedverwacht, Graceland, Graham Beck, Groenland, Guardian Peak, Hartenberg, Hoopenburg, Jakob's Vineyards, Journey's End, Kaapzicht, Katbakkies, Kloovenburg, L'Avenir, La Bri, La Motte, La Petite Ferme, Landskroon, Lanzerac, Le Riche, Louis, M'hudi, Marianne, Meinert, Miravel, MolenVliet, Mont du Toit, **Mooiplaas** (2), Morgenhof, **Muratie**, Napier, Nederburg, Neil Ellis, Niel Joubert, Nitida, Noble Hill, Org de Rac (Organic), Osbloed, Overgaauw, Perdeberg, Post House, Rainbow's End, Raka, **Rannoch**, Remhoogte, Rickety Bridge, Ridgeback, Robertson, Rust en Vrede, Savanha, Saxenburg, Silvermist, South Hill, **Spier**, Springfield, Stellekaya, Stellenzicht, Sterhuis, Super Single Vineyards, Thelema, Tokara, Usana, Vergenoegd, Villiera, Vondeling, Vriesenhof , Warwick, Windmeul, Winery of Good Hope (2), Woolworths (4) (Light & low-alcohol), Zorgvliet

★★★☆ Amani, **Ameera**, Anura, Arra, Asara, Avontuur, **BABISA**, Beau Joubert, Blaauwklippen, **Bloemendal**, Boland, Bon Courage, Bon Terroir, Bonview, Boschheim, Boschkloof , **Boschrivier**, Bosman, Butcher Shop, Carisbrooke, Chennells, Claime d'Or, Clovelly, Conviction, Dalla Cia, Devonair, **Domaine Coutelier**, Dormershire (2), Eaglevlei, Entre Nous, Fairview, Fat Bastard, Feiteiras, Fernskloof (Organic), Fort Simon, Goose Wines, Groenland, Haut Espoir, Helderberg, Hildenbrand, Jacques Smit, Klawer, Klein Roosboom , Koopmanskloof (Fairtrade), Kyburg, Leopard's Leap, Linton Park (2), Longridge, Lourensford, Lovane (2), Lutzville, Lyngrove, Lynx, MAN Family, Marklew, Meerendal, Middelvlei, Mimosa, **Mitre's Edge** (2), Mont Rochelle, Morgenster, Mount Rozier, Mountain Ridge, Nederburg, Neethlingshof, Opstal, Ormonde, Peter Falke, Plaisir, Porcupine Ridge, Rooiberg, Sijnn, Simonsig, Simonsvlei, Slaley, Spier, Stellenrust, Stonewall, Teubes, Trajan, Tread Lightly, Tulbagh Winery, Uitkyk, Vergenoegd, Viljoensdrift, Warwick, Waterkloof,

Waterstone (2), Welbedacht, Wellington Winery (2), Zevenwacht ★★★ Abbottshill, African Pride, Allesverloren, Altydgedacht, Alvi's Drift, Annex Kloof, Ayama, Beau Joubert, Bellingham, Bergsig, Bergwater, Blue Crane, Boland, Bonnievale, Bonview, Boplaas (2), Boschheim, Botha, Brampton, Bushmanspad, Cape Dreams, Cloof, Conradie, Darling Cellars, David Frost, De Bos (Fairtrade), De Meye, De Wet, Desert Rose, Die Mas, Diemersfontein, Domaine Brahms, Doolhof, Drostdy-Hof, Du Preez, Du Toitskloof , Durbanville Hills, Earthbound (Organic, Fairtrade), Eikehof, Elgin Vintners, Fairview, False Bay, **Flagstone**, Fleur du Cap, Galleon, Goede Hoop, Grande Provence, Hathersage, Havana Hills (Fairtrade), Hills, Holden Manz, Hoopenburg, Hunneyball, Joubert-Tradauw, Kanu, Kleine Zalze, Kranskop, L'Olivier, La Chaumiere, Landskroon, Le Manoir de Brendel, **Leipzig**, Linton Park (2), Lovane, Maastricht, MAN Family, Merwida, Mostertsdrift, **Mountain Ridge**, Namaqua, Napier, **Nederburg** (3) (Fairtrade), Obikwa, Olifantsberg, Orange River, Org de Rac (Organic), Ormonde (2), Painted Wolf, Phizante Kraal, Pulpit Rock (2), **Retief**, Rhino of Linton Park, Riebeek, Robertson (4), Roodezandt, **Rosendal**, Sauvignon.com, Seal Breeze, **Ses'Fikile**, Seven Sisters, Simonsvlei, Slanghoek, Slowine, Southern Sky, Stellenbosch Hills, Swartland, Thandi (Fairtrade), United Nations, Upland (Organic), Val du Charron, Vredenheim, **Waterstone** (2), Waverley Hills (Organic), Wellington Winery (2), Windfall, Windmeul, **Woolworths** (3), Zandvliet, Zonnebloem (2)

★★☆ Baccarat, Bayede!, Brandvlei, Cape Dreams, Clairvaux, De Krans, Desert Rose, Douglas Green, Du Preez, **Du Toitskloof** , **Dusty Heath**, Eagle's Cliff, Excelsior, Franschhoek Cellar, Goudini, Group CDV, Hofstraat, House of Mandela (2) (Fairtrade), Jacobsdal, **Jakkalsvlei**, Kleine Draken (Kosher), La Petite Provence, Libby's Pride, Lutzville, Malanot, Manley, Montagu Wine Cellar, Namaqua, New Beginnings, Niel Joubert, Overhex, Place in the Sun (Fairtrade), Riebeek, Rooiberg, Ruitersvlei, Saam, Simonsvlei, Somerbosch, Somerset Wines, Spier, Spookfontein , Steenberg, Stellar (2) (Organic, Fairtrade), **Stellenbosch Family Wines**, **Stettyn**, Tangled Tree, Topiary, Tulbagh Winery (2), uniWines, Walker Bay Vineyards, Wandsbeck, William

Everson, Woolworths (2) (Organic, Light & low-alcohol, Fairtrade), **Zidela** (2) ★★ Bergwater, Blomendahl, **Clive Torr**, Cranefields, De Breede (Organic), Het Vlock Casteel, Imbuko, Kleine Draken (Sacramental, Light & low-alcohol, Kosher), Long Mountain, Louisvale, Lovane, **M'hudi**, Mountain River, **Namaqua**, Oude Compagnies Post, Southern Sky, Stoumann's, Van Loveren (Fairtrade), Vin du Cap (2), Vriesenhof, Waterstone, Welmoed ★★ African Pride, Ashton, Nuy, Southern Sky, Vinopoly, Waterstone (3) ★ Long Mountain **NS** TTT Cellar **NT** AlexKia, Audacia, Benguela Cove, Berrio, Blomendahl, Breëland, Calitzdorp, Camberley, Cape Rock, Catch Of The Day, Constantia de Tulbagh, Crows Nest, De Doorns, De Trafford, Devon Hill, Devonair, DuVon, Esau, Goedvertrouw, Govert, Herold, High Constantia, Hout Bay, Juno, Klein Parys, Knorhoek, La Kavayan, Landzicht (2), **Louis**, Lovane, Maison de Teijger (3), Maske, MC Square, McGregor, Miravel, Mont Rochelle, Montpellier, Mooi Bly, Mountain River, Neil Ellis Meyer-Näkel, Nietvoorbij, Nuweland, Nuy, Oldenburg, Onderkloof, Perdeberg, Rico Suter, Rosendal, Savanha, Schalkenbosch, Snowfield (2), Spier, Stark-Condé, Stellendrift (3), Stone Ridge, Swartland, SylvanVale, Valley Vineyards, Van Loveren, Vruchtbaar, Waverley Hills (Organic), Welvanpas, William Everson, Withoek, Zanddrift, Zidela **NR** Fairvalley **D** Cape Chamonix, Dombeya, Durbanville Hills, Escapades, Hildenbrand, Org de Rac

Cape Riesling
★★★ Theuniskraal **NT** Calais **D** Van Loveren

Carignan
★★★★ Blackwater

★★★☆ Three Foxes ★★★ BLANKbottle, Koopmanskloof, Wellington Winery **NT** Fairview **D** Withington

Chardonnay unwooded
★★★★☆ Springfield

★★★★ Cape Chamonix, De Wetshof (2), GlenWood, Groote Post, Woolworths

★★★★ **Baleia Bay**, Bellpost, Bouchard Finlayson, **Brunia**, **Claime d'Or**, Constantia Uitsig, De Wetshof, Delheim, Diemersdal, Eikendal, False Bay, Franschhoek Cellar, Glen Carlou, Glenelly, Goudini, Kloovenburg,

Meerendal, Môreson, **Retief**, Seven Springs , Signal Gun, Sterhuis, Warwick, Withington, Woolworths ★★★ AlexKia, Arendskloof, Ayama, **Boucheron**, Butcher Shop, Cape Dreams, De Bos (Fairtrade), De Meye, **De Wetshof**, Doolhof, Eaglevlei, **Fram**, Jordan, Kleine Zalze, La Petite Ferme, Landskroon, Louisvale, Lourensford, McGregor, Middelvlei, Neethlingshof, New Beginnings, Niel Joubert, Org de Rac (Organic), Ormonde, Plettenvale, Rooiberg, Swartland, Vriesenhof , Waterstone, Winery of Good Hope, Woolworths ★★★ Backsberg (Kosher), Blomendahl, Boland, Brampton, Cloof, Cloverfield, Die Mas, Eerste Hoop, Graham Beck, Hoopenburg, Koopmanskloof (Fairtrade), La Couronne, Obikwa, Place in the Sun (Fairtrade), Rhino of Linton Park, Riebeek, Savanha, Tulbagh Winery, United Nations, Van Zylshof, Waterstone, **Welbedacht**, Wellington Winery (2), Zandvliet ★★ African Pride, Ashton, Bon Courage, Burgershof, Calais, Hildenbrand, **Observatory**, Vinopoly, Walker Bay Vineyards, Welbedacht ★☆ Group CDV (3), Leopard's Leap, Libby's Pride, **Zidela** ★ Long Mountain, Waterstone, Woolworths **NT** Hill & Dale, Jean Daneel, Karusa, Leeuwenberg, Malanot, Mont Rochelle, Mostertsdrift, Re'Mogo, Somersbosch, Stone Ridge, United Nations, Valley Vineyards (2) **NR** De Krans **D** Boplaas, Nuweland, Org de Rac (Organic), Stellenzicht

Chardonnay wooded
★★★★★ **DeMorgenzon**, Iona, Richard Kershaw, Sterhuis

★★★★☆ Ataraxia, Bartinney, Boschendal, Bouchard Finlayson, Buitenverwachting, Cape Chamonix (2), Cape Point, **Clayton**, Constantia Uitsig, Creation, Crystallum (2), De Wetshof (2), Dorrance, Edgebaston, Eikendal, Fleur du Cap, Glen Carlou, GlenWood (2), Groot Constantia, Hamilton Russell, Hartenberg, Haskell, Jordan (2), Journey's End, Julien Schaal, Koelfontein, Lanzerac, Longridge, Môreson, Mulderbosch, Neil Ellis, Newton Johnson, Paul Cluver, Restless River, Rupert & Rothschild, Rustenberg, Saxenburg, Springfield, Sumaridge, Thelema, Uva Mira, Warwick, Waterford, Winery of Good Hope

★★★★ Alvi's Drift, Anura, Babylonstoren, Badsberg, Baleia Bay, Bergsig, Bloemendal, Bon Courage, Boschendal, Bouchard Finlayson (2),

Capelands, Corder, Dalla Cia, **De Grendel**, De Wetshof, Delaire, Delheim, DeMorgenzon, Domaine Coutelier, Dombeya, Durbanville Hills, Elgin Vintners, Glen Carlou, Glenelly, Grande Provence, Groote Post, Haut Espoir, Havana Hills, JH Meyer, Jordan, Joubert-Tradauw, Journey's End, Kleine Zalze, Kloovenburg, La Motte, La Petite Ferme, Lanzerac, Lourensford, Maison, Marklew, Meerlust, Meinert, Migliarina, Mulderbosch, Muratie, Newton Johnson, Oldenburg, Ormonde, Plaisir, Quoin Rock, Rhebokskloof, Robertson, Rooiberg, **Rosendal**, Savanha, Scrucap, Seven Springs , Stellenrust, Thelema, Tierhoek, Tokara (2), Uva Mira, Vergelegen (2), Vondeling, Vriesenhof , Waterford, Whalehaven, Windmeul, **Woolworths** (2), Yardstick, Zandvliet

★★★★☆ Aaldering, Almenkerk, Amani, Backsberg, Bayede!, Boland, **Bridge**, Brothers, Callender, Chateau Naudé, Clos Malverne, De Wet, Diemersdal, Domaine des Dieux, Doolhof, **Entre Nous**, Ernst Gouws, Fairview, Flagstone, Fort Simon, Four Paws, Freedom Hill, Goedverwacht, Goudini, Graham Beck, Hartenberg, House of Mandela, Journey's End, Kanu, **Klein Constantia**, Kloovenburg, Kranskop, La Bri, La Vierge, Le Bonheur, Linton Park, Lord's, Lothian, Louiesenhof, Louisvale (2), Lourensford, Lyngrove, Mellasat, Merwida, Mimosa, Morgenhof, Mountain River, Nabygelegen, Nederburg, Niel Joubert, Nitida, Noble Hill, Nuy, Oak Valley, Olsen, Org de Rac (Organic), Ormonde, Overgaauw, **Paserene**, Rhebokskloof, Rickety Bridge, Simonsig, Slaley, Spier, Stanford Hills, Steenberg, Stellenrust, Stonewall, Thelema, Uitkyk, Val du Charron, Van Loveren, Veenwouden, Waterkloof, Welbedacht, Weltevrede, Winters Drift ★★★ **Altydgedacht**, Anura, Ashton, Avontuur, **Barista**, Bellingham, Boschendal, Boschkloof , Brandvlei, Cape Classics, Claime d'Or, Credo, Darling Cellars, Drostdy-Hof, Du Toitskloof , Durbanville Hills, Elgin Heights, Excelsior, Fairvalley (Fairtrade), Fairview, Fat Bastard, Fleur du Cap, Goede Hoop, Goedvertrouw, Hildenbrand, Holden Manz, Hoopenburg, Klawer, Kumala, La Chaumiere, **Leopard Frog**, Linton Park, Louiesenhof, Lutzville, Meerendal, Mount Rozier, Nederburg, Newstead, Orange River, Overhex, Passages, Pulpit Rock, Robertson, Simonsig, Simonsvlei,

Slanghoek, Spier, Springfontein, **Stellenbosch Family Wines**, Two Oceans, **Vierlanden**, Viljoensdrift, **Vredenheim**, Welmoed, Withington, Woolworths (Organic), Zandvliet, Zevenwacht ★★★ Asara, **Barrydale**, Eikehof, Goedverwacht, Groot Parys (Organic), House of Mandela (Fairtrade), Klein Parys, **L'Olivier**, **Ladismith**, **Leipzig**, MAN Family, Osbloed, Pulpit Rock, Riebeek, Robertson (3), Schalkenbosch, Stellar (Organic, Fairtrade), Van Zylshof, Waterstone, Weltevrede, Woolworths (4) (Organic), Zonnebloem ★★ Bonnievale, Cloverfield, De Zoete Inval, Hathersage, Lorraine, **Stellar** (Organic, Fairtrade), Tangled Tree ★☆ Kleine Draken (Kosher), Welvanpas ★ Long Mountain **NT** Alkmaar, Brenaissance, Buffalo Creek, Calitzdorp, Clovelly, Crows Nest, Douglas Green, Du Preez, Eerste Hoop, Felicité, Fernskloof (Organic), Galleon, Hermit on the Hill, Hillock, Imbuko, Kingsriver, Ladera, Lazanou (Organic), Le Riche, Lutzville, MC Square, Mont Rochelle (2), Montpellier, Mooi Bly, Mountain Oaks (Organic), Napier, Nederburg, Nelson, Nietvoorbij, Olifantsberg, Onderkloof , Paul Cluver, Rosendal, Rustenberg, Stellenbosch University, Stoumann's, Thembi & Co (2), Tokara, Van Loveren, Veenwouden, Vruchtbaar, Walker Bay Vineyards, Weltevrede, William Everson, Windmeul **D** Springfontein, Thandi, Woolworths, Zidela

Chenin blanc off-dry/semi-sweet (w & u/w)
★★★★★☆ DewaldtHeyns, Ken Forrester
★★★★ Diemersfontein, **Kanu** (2), Katbakkies, Knorhoek, Lammershoek, Perdeberg, Slanghoek, Woolworths

★★★★ Simonsig, Trajan ★★★ Cape Classics, Kanu, Landskroon, **Nederburg** (2), Tread Lightly ★★☆ Botha, Breëland, **Cloof** (Fairtrade), False Bay, **Goede Hoop**, Goudini, Hoopenburg, Ken Forrester, **Mountain Ridge**, Nuweland, Waterstone ★★ Bon Courage, Bottelary ★☆ Bonnievale (2) (Perlé), Cloverfield, Kupferberger Auslese, Leopard's Leap, Seven Sisters (Perlé, Light & low-alcohol), Tulbagh Winery, Woolworths (2) ★ Woolworths **NT** Hillock, Ken Forrester, Landskroon, Landzicht, Saam, Valley Vineyards **D** Groot Parys (Organic), Zandvliet

Chenin blanc unwooded dry
★★★★★☆ Bayede!, Fledge & Co, Old Vines

★★★★ Babylon's Peak, Babylonstoren, Beaumont, Black Pearl, **Blackwater**, Cederberg, **DeanDavid**, Luddite, Maison, **Perdeberg**, Raats, Woolworths

★★★★ Alvi's Drift, Annex Kloof, Arra, Barton, Boland, Chateau Naudé, **Delaire**, Ernie Els, Fairview, Groote Post, Kleine Zalze, Kumala, La Chataigne, Liberator, Mooiplaas, Neethlingshof, Nieuwedrift, Olsen, Oude Denneboom, Scrucap, Simonsig, Simonsvlei, Slowine, United Nations, Virgin Earth, Winery of Good Hope, **Woolworths**

★★★ Ayama, Backsberg, Badsberg, Bellingham, Blaauwklippen, Boschendal, Brandvlei, **Cavalli**, Cloof, Darling Cellars (2) (Light & low-alcohol), De Bos (Fairtrade), De Meye, Domaine Brahms, **Doolhof**, Dornier, Drostdy-Hof, Du Toitskloof, Eagle's Cliff, **Eaglevlei**, Earthbound (Organic, Fairtrade), Fairview, Fish Hoek, Flagstone, Grape Grinder, Groenland, **Groot Parys** (Organic), Hawksmoor, **Jordan**, Kaapzicht, Ken Forrester, Kleine Zalze (2), Knorhoek, Koopmanskloof (2) (Light & low-alcohol, Fairtrade), La Petite Ferme, Laibach, Landskroon, Leeuwenkuil, Leopard's Leap, Lyngrove, **M'hudi**, MAN Family, Mellasat, Nederburg, Nelson, Ormonde (2), Overhex, Phizante Kraal, Rickety Bridge, Robertson (2), Saam, Somerbosch, Spier, Stellekaya, Stellenbosch Hills, **Stofberg**, Summerhill, Swartland, Teddy Hall, Van Zylshof, **Welgemeend**, Wellington Winery, Welmoed, Windmeul, Woolworths ★★☆ Ayama, Baccarat, **Barrydale**, Bergsig, Blomendahl, Croydon, De Krans, De Wet, Diemersfontein, Eagle's Cliff, Fairvalley (Fairtrade), False Bay, Franschhoek Cellar, **Grape Grinder**, Klawer, Knorhoek, **Ladismith**, Lutzville, MAN Family, McGregor, Monterosso, New Beginnings, Niel Joubert, Nuy (2), Obikwa, Onderkloof, Orange River, Pulpit Rock, Rhebokskloof, Rhino of Linton Park, Riebeek, Roodezandt, Rooiberg, **Rosendal**, **Simonsvlei**, Skilpadvlei, Somerset Wines, Thembi & Co (2), **uniWines** (2) (Fairtrade), Waterstone, Welbedacht, Wellington Winery, Woolworths, Zidela ★★ Aan de Doorns, Ashton (2), **Bayede!**, Botha, Cape Dreams, DeWaal, Hills, **Imbuko**, **Leipzig**, Long Mountain, Montagu Wine Cellar, **Namaqua**, Robertson (Light & low-alcohol), Savanha, Slanghoek, Tulbagh Winery, Van Loveren ★★ African Pride, Bottelary, House

of Mandela (Fairtrade), Long Mountain, Swartland, Van Loveren (Fairtrade), Waterstone, Woolworths (3), Zidela ★ Woolworths (2) (Light & low-alcohol) **NT** Bayede!, Calais, Catch Of The Day, Delheim, Douglas Green, Dragonridge, DuVon, Freedom Hill, Halala, Jacques Smit, Klein Parys (2), L'Avenir, Lazanou (Organic), Lula, Maske, Mason's Winery, Montpellier, Mooi Bly, Mountain River, Napier, Perdeberg, Robert Stanford, Ruitersvlei, Stellar, Stoumann's, TTT Cellar, Tulbagh Winery, United Nations, Valley Vineyards (3), Vaughan Johnson, Versailles, Vruchtbaar, Waboomsrivier, Zonnebloem, Zonquasdrift **D** Bergsig, Diners Club Bartho Eksteen , Glenview, Groot Parys (Organic), Group CDV (2)

Chenin blanc wooded, dry
★★★★★ **Alheit**, **Fram**, **Kaapzicht**

★★★★☆ AA Badenhorst, Beaumont, Bellingham, Bosman (Fairtrade), Botanica, Cederberg, David & Nadia Sadie, DeMorgenzon, Donkiesbaai, **Edgebaston**, **Intellego**, Jean Daneel, **Keermont**, Kleine Zalze, **Miles Mossop**, Mount Abora, Mulderbosch (2), **Mullineux** (2), Nederburg, Opstal, Raats, Remhoogte, Reverie, Reyneke (Biodynamic), Rudera, Sadie, Spice Route, **Spioenkop**, Stellenrust, Teddy Hall, Windmeul, Winery of Good Hope

★★★★ AA Badenhorst, Allée Bleue, **Alvi's Drift**, Avondale (Organic), BLANKbottle, Boland, Bryan MacRobert, Catherine Marshall, Credo, Dagbreek, De Trafford, Delaire, **Delheim**, Domaine Brahms, Doran, **Glen Carlou**, Graham Beck, **Grande Provence**, Groot Parys (2) (Organic), Intellego, Jordan, Ken Forrester, Kleine Zalze, **Kulsen**, L'Avenir (2), **Leeuwenkuil**, Longridge, Lutzville, Maison, **Migliarina**, Mooiplaas, Mulderbosch (2), Mullineux, Old Vines, Paardebosch, Post House, Remhoogte, Rickety Bridge, Ridgeback, Rijk's (3), Rudera, Saltare (2), Signal Hill, Spier, Spioenkop, Springfontein (2), Sterhuis, Tierhoek, Villiera, Welbedacht, Wildehurst, Winery of Good Hope (2)

★★★☆ Andy Mitchell, Antebellum, Anura, Beaumont, Bellevue, Crios Bríde, DeMorgenzon, Dornier, Fleur du Cap, **Groot Parys** (Organic), **Kleine Zalze**, MAN Family, Morgenhof, **Mount Pleasant**, Nabygelegen, **Observatory**, Oldenburg, Painted Wolf (2), Raka, Riebeek, Rudera, **Schenkfontein**, Star Hill, Stark-Condé,

Stellenrust, Super Single Vineyards, Swartland, Teddy Hall, Vruchtbaar, Waterkloof, Wildekrans, **Woolworths** (2) ★★★ **Asara**, Beau Joubert, **Bryan MacRobert**, Damarakloof, Druk My Niet, Graham Beck, Groot Parys (Organic), **Hofstraat**, Orange River, Uitkyk, Usana, Villiera, Waterford, Zevenwacht ★★★ Koelenhof ★★ Hildenbrand **NT** Aeternitas, Alheit, Andy Mitchell, Fort Simon, Hawksmoor (2), Jacaranda, Jean Daneel, Liberator, Linton Park, Malanot, Robert Stanford, Sadie, Stellenbosch Vineyards, Stone Ridge, Val de Vie **NR** Chateau Naudé **D** M'hudi, Perdeberg

Cinsaut

★★★★★ Sadie

★★★★☆ **AA Badenhorst**, Mount Abora, Waterkloof

★★★★ Stellenrust

★★★☆ **Elsenburg**, **MAN Family**, Osbloed, **Rico Suter** ★★★ BLANKbottle ★★ Landskroon **NT** Howard Booysen

Clairette blanche

★★★☆ **Three Foxes**

Colombard

★★★ Bon Courage, Orange River, Van Loveren
★★☆ **Cape Dreams**, McGregor, Micu Narunsky, Nuy, Rooiberg ★★ **Ses'Fikile** ★★ Goedverwacht, Hartswater (2), Montagu Wine Cellar ★ Woolworths **NT** Stellar **NR** Aan de Doorns

Fairtrade

★★★★☆ Bosman (Chenin blanc wooded, dry)
★★★★ Nederburg (Red blends, shiraz/syrah-based), Winery of Good Hope (Shiraz/syrah), Bosman (2) (Red blends, shiraz/syrah-based, White blends, wooded, dry, Light & low-alcohol), Stellar (Vin de paille, Organic), Goats do Roam (Red blends, shiraz/syrah-based), Rivendell (Sauvignon blanc unwooded), Bosman (Pinotage), Township Winery (Merlot), Virgin Earth (2) (Red blends, Cape Bordeaux, Sauvignon blanc unwooded)

★★★☆ Thandi (Shiraz/syrah), Fairview (Pinotage), Thandi (White blends, unwooded, dry), De Bos (Pinot noir), Goats do Roam (3) (Red blends, shiraz/syrah-based, Rosé dry, White blends, unwooded, dry), Koopmanskloof (2) (Cabernet sauvignon, Shiraz/syrah), **uniWines** (Husk spirit/grappa-styles), Place in the Sun

(Sauvignon blanc unwooded), Rivendell (Rosé dry), Township Winery (Shiraz/syrah), Virgin Earth (Pinot noir) ★★★ **Nederburg** (2) (Cabernet sauvignon, Pinotage, Light & low-alcohol), Thandi (2) (Cabernet sauvignon, Red blends, Cape Bordeaux), **Overhex** (Red blends, shiraz/syrah-based, White blends, unwooded, dry), **Havana Hills** (3) (Cabernet sauvignon, Sangiovese, Shiraz/syrah, Light & low-alcohol), De Bos (3) (Cabernet sauvignon, Chardonnay unwooded, Chenin blanc unwooded dry), Earthbound (3) (Cabernet sauvignon, Chenin blanc unwooded dry, Sauvignon blanc unwooded, Organic), Fairvalley (3) (Pinotage, Chardonnay wooded, Sauvignon blanc unwooded), **Koopmanskloof** (5) (Merlot, Pinotage, Chenin blanc unwooded dry, Chenin blanc unwooded dry, Sauvignon blanc unwooded, Light & low-alcohol), uniWines (Merlot), Place in the Sun (2) (Merlot, Shiraz/syrah), Township Winery (Pinotage) ★★★ **Woolworths** (3) (Cabernet sauvignon, Shiraz/syrah, Sauvignon blanc unwooded, Organic), **Stellar** (7) (Pinot noir, White blends, unwooded, dry, Cabernet sauvignon, Pinotage, Shiraz/syrah, Chardonnay wooded, Sauvignon blanc unwooded, Organic, Light & low-alcohol), **Cloof** (Chenin blanc off-dry/semi-sweet (w & u/w)), Stellar (Cabernet sauvignon, Organic), Thandi (3) (Rosé dry, Sauvignon blanc unwooded, Sparkling, Non-MCC, rosé, dry, Light & low-alcohol), **Stellar** (3) (Pinotage, White blends, off-dry/semi-sweet (w & u/w), Sweet red, Organic), Thandi (2) (Red blends, shiraz/syrah-based, White blends, unwooded, dry, Light & low-alcohol), Stellenrust (3) (Red blends, with pinotage, Rosé dry, White blends, unwooded, dry), **House of Mandela** (6) (Cabernet sauvignon, Merlot, Pinotage, Shiraz/syrah, Chardonnay wooded, Sauvignon blanc unwooded), Earthbound (2) (Pinot noir, Pinotage, Organic), Fairvalley (Chenin blanc unwooded dry), Savanha (2) (Red blends, shiraz/syrah-based, White blends, unwooded, dry), United Nations (Sauvignon blanc unwooded), Koopmanskloof (2) (Rosé dry, Chardonnay unwooded), **uniWines** (4) (Pinotage, Chenin blanc unwooded dry, Chenin blanc unwooded dry, Hanepoot unfortified, Perlé, Light & low-alcohol), Place in the Sun (2) (Cabernet sauvignon, Chardonnay unwooded, Light & low-alcohol), Township Winery (Viognier) ★★ **Stellar** (Chardonnay wooded, Organic), Van Loveren (2) (Cabernet sauvignon, Rosé dry), Stellar (9) (Merlot, Rosé dry, White blends, unwooded, dry, Merlot, Pinotage, Shiraz/syrah, Rosé dry, Rosé off-dry/semi-sweet, White blends, unwooded, dry, Organic), De Bos (Sauvignon blanc unwooded), **uniWines** (2) (Shiraz/syrah, Sauvignon blanc unwooded) ★★ Van Loveren (2) (Pinotage, Chenin blanc unwooded dry), **Stellar** (Sparkling, Non-MCC, rosé, off-dry/semi-sweet), House of Mandela (Chenin blanc unwooded dry), De Bos (Merlot), United Nations (Shiraz/syrah), Havana Hills (2) (Rosé dry, Sauvignon blanc unwooded) ★ Woolworths (Colombard) **NT** Nederburg (Sauvignon blanc unwooded) **NR** Fairvalley (Cabernet sauvignon) **D** Overhex (3) (Shiraz/syrah, Rosé dry, Pinot gris/grigio)

Fernão pires
★★★ BLANKbottle ★★ Tulbagh Winery

Gamay noir
★★★ Kleine Zalze ★★ Asara

Gewürztraminer
★★★★☆ Paul Cluver, Zevenwacht
★★★★ Neethlingshof, Woolworths
★★★☆ Altydgedacht, Nederburg, Simonsig
★★★ Bergsig, Delheim ★★☆ Bon Courage ★★ Wellington Winery **NT** Montpellier **D** Group CDV, Villiera, Weltevrede

Grenache blanc
★★★★★ Foundry
★★★★ Bosman, Signal Hill

Grenache noir
★★★★☆ AA Badenhorst, David & Nadia Sadie, Neil Ellis, Sadie, Tierhoek, Vriesenhof
★★★★ Diemersdal, Momento, **Painted Wolf** (Organic), Signal Hill, **Spice Route**, Woolworths, **Zevenwacht**
★★★☆ BLANKbottle, Lynx, Saronsberg, **Tokara**
★★★ Waverley Hills ★★☆ Franki's, Hermit on the Hill **NT** Esau, Hermit on the Hill, Nederburg **D** Nuweland

Grüner veltliner
★★★★ Diemersdal

Hanepoot fortified
★★★★☆ Goudini, Muratie, Signal Hill

★★★★ Aan de Doorns, Boplaas, Constantia Uitsig, Klawer, Opstal, Orange River
★★★★ Badsberg, De Wet, Du Preez, Goudini, **Jakkalsvlei**, Kaapzicht, **Nuweland**, Slanghoek, SoetKaroo, Swartland ★★★ Boplaas, Clairvaux, Die Mas, Domein Doornkraal, Du Toitskloof , Koelenhof, TTT Cellar, Villiersdorp ★★☆ Grande Provence ★★ Bergwater, Landzicht, Tulbagh Winery **NT** Calitzdorp (2), Stoumann's, Waboomsrivier **D** Eaglevlei, Nuweland, Vriesenhof , Wellington Winery

Hanepoot unfortified
★★★★ Hofstraat ★★★ Du Toitskloof , Overhex, uniWines (2) (Perlé, Light & low-alcohol, Fairtrade) ★★ Cape Classics, Riebeek (Perlé, Light & low-alcohol), Swartland (Light & low-alcohol), Wellington Winery ★ Zidela **D** Boplaas

Hárslevelü
★★★★ Lemberg

Husk spirit/grappa-styles
★★★★★☆ Dalla Cia (2)
★★★★★ Dalla Cia (3) (Organic), **Gentleman Spirits** (4), **Mont Destin**, **Org de Rac** (Organic), Upland
★★★★ Dalla Cia, **uniWines** ★★★ Iona, Klein Constantia ★★☆ **Gentleman Spirits**

Icewine
★★★ Kaapzicht

Jerepigo red
★★★★★ Blaauwklippen
★★★★ Badsberg, De Krans
★★★★☆ Avontuur, Orange River, Solms-Delta
★★★ Domein Doornkraal, Grundheim, Simonsvlei, Slanghoek, Swartland, uniWines
★★★☆ Botha, Hartswater, Waverley Hills ★★ Die Mas **NT** Camberley, Feiteiras, Landzicht, Stonewall, Stoumann's **D** Grundheim, Nuweland

Jerepigo white
★★★★☆ Signal Hill
★★★★ Botha
★★★★☆ Backsberg, **Lateganskop**, Niel Joubert, Opstal, Orange River, Riebeek, uniWines ★★★ Die Mas, Domein Doornkraal, Namaqua, Sedgwick's Old Brown, Wellington Winery ★★☆ Chateau Naudé, Swartland ★★ Brandvlei, Hartswater, Ship **NT** Calitzdorp, Feiteiras **D** Nuweland

Kosher

★★★ Backsberg (2) (Merlot, Pinotage) ★★☆ Backsberg (2) (Chardonnay unwooded, Sparkling, Méthode cap classique, white, dry), Kleine Draken (Cabernet sauvignon) ★★ Backsberg (Sweet red, Sacramental), Kleine Draken (5) (Cabernet sauvignon, Merlot, Red blends, Cape Bordeaux, Sparkling, Non-MCC, white, off-dry/semi-sweet, Natural Sweet, white, Sacramental, Light & low-alcohol) ★★ Kleine Draken (3) (Chardonnay wooded, Sauvignon blanc unwooded, Natural Sweet, red, Light & low-alcohol) **NT** Kleine Draken (Rosé off-dry/semi-sweet)

Late Harvest

★★★★ Thelema (2) (Light & low-alcohol) ★★★ Montagu Wine Cellar ★★ **Drostdy-Hof**, Kellerprinz, Overmeer Cellars, Robertson **NT** Landau du Val, Nederburg

Light & low-alcohol

★★★★☆ Paul Cluver (Noble Late Harvest), Tierhoek (Vin de paille), Namaqua (Noble Late Harvest), Neethlingshof (Noble Late Harvest), Fleur du Cap (Noble Late Harvest), De Wetshof (Noble Late Harvest), Vondeling (Vin de paille) ★★★★ Paul Cluver (Riesling), **Laibach** (Natural Sweet, white)

★★★☆ De Trafford (Vin de paille), Altydgedacht (Noble Late Harvest), **Hofstraat** (Hanepoot unfortified), Thelema (Late Harvest) ★★★ Woolworths (White blends, off-dry/semi-sweet (w & u/w)), Leopard's Leap (Muscadel, white, unfortified), Villiera (Sparkling, Méthode cap classique, white, dry), Klawer (Sparkling, Non-MCC, rosé, off-dry/semi-sweet), Somerset Wines (Natural Sweet, white), **Zandvliet** (Natural Sweet, white) ★★★☆ Woolworths (Rosé dry), Overhex (Rosé off-dry/semi-sweet), **Du Toitskloof** (Sparkling, Non-MCC, red, off-dry/semi-sweet), 4th Street (Natural Sweet, white), Orange River (Sparkling, Non-MCC, white, off-dry/semi-sweet), Solms-Delta (Sparkling, Non-MCC, red, off-dry/semi-sweet), Badsberg (Sparkling, Non-MCC, white, off-dry/semi-sweet), Cold Duck (5th Avenue) (Sparkling, Non-MCC, rosé, off-dry/semi-sweet), De Grendel (Noble Late Harvest), Grünberger (Natural Sweet, white), **Somerset Wines** (3) (Sparkling, Non-

MCC, rosé, dry, Natural Sweet, red, Natural Sweet, rosé), uniWines (Hanepoot unfortified, Perlé), Alvi's Drift (2) (Sparkling, Non-MCC, rosé, off-dry/semi-sweet, Sparkling, Non-MCC, white, off-dry/semi-sweet), Obikwa (Muscadel, white, unfortified), uniWines (Hanepoot unfortified, Perlé, Fairtrade), Imbuko (Muscadel, white, unfortified) ★★ Robertson (11) (Natural Sweet, rosé, Natural Sweet, red, Natural Sweet, rosé, Natural Sweet, white, Rosé dry, Chenin blanc unwooded dry, Sauvignon blanc unwooded, Sparkling, Non-MCC, red, off-dry/semi-sweet, Sparkling, Non-MCC, rosé, off-dry/semi-sweet, Sparkling, Non-MCC, white, off-dry/semi-sweet, Natural Sweet, rosé), Overhex (3) (White blends, off-dry/semi-sweet (w & u/w), Sweet red, Sparkling, Non-MCC, white, off-dry/semi-sweet), Robertson (Natural Sweet, white), **Du Toitskloof** (2) (Rosé off-dry/semi-sweet, Sweet red), Viljoensdrift (Sparkling, Non-MCC, rosé, off-dry/semi-sweet), Swartland (Hanepoot unfortified), **Tulbagh Winery** (Fernão pires), **4th Street** (2) (Natural Sweet, red, Natural Sweet, rosé, Perlé), Robertson (2) (Natural Sweet, red, Natural Sweet, rosé), Wellington Winery (Hanepoot unfortified, Perlé), **Eaglevlei** (Sauvignon blanc unwooded), Fleur du Cap (White blends, off-dry/semi-sweet (w & u/w)), Rooiberg (Sparkling, Non-MCC, rosé, off-dry/semi-sweet), **Long Mountain** (Sparkling, Non-MCC, rosé, off-dry/semi-sweet), Badsberg (Muscadel, white, unfortified, Perlé), De Krans (Muscadel, white, unfortified, Perlé), De Wet (Muscadel, white, unfortified, Perlé), Flat Roof Manor (Rosé off-dry/semi-sweet), Grünberger (Natural Sweet, rosé), Kleine Draken (3) (Cabernet sauvignon, Sparkling, Non-MCC, white, off-dry/semi-sweet, Natural Sweet, white, Sacramental, Kosher), Riebeek (Hanepoot unfortified, Perlé), Drostdy-Hof (2) (Natural Sweet, rosé, Natural Sweet, white), House of JC le Roux (2) (Sparkling, Non-MCC, red, dry, Sparkling, Non-MCC, white, off-dry/semi-sweet) ★★ Woolworths (3) (Merlot, Natural Sweet, red, Rosé off-dry/semi-sweet), Robertson (2) (White blends, unwooded, dry, Merlot), Woolworths (2) (White blends, off-dry/semi-sweet (w & u/w), Natural Sweet, white), Van Loveren (4) (Natural Sweet, red, Natural Sweet, rosé, Natural Sweet, rosé, Natural Sweet, white), Douglas Green (Natural Sweet, rosé), Group CDV

(Natural Sweet, white), Overhex (Sparkling, Non-MCC, rosé, off-dry/semi-sweet), Simonsvlei (Natural Sweet, rosé), Robertson (Sauvignon blanc unwooded), Woolworths (2) (Red blends, shiraz/syrah-based, Rosé off-dry/semi-sweet), Botha (White blends, off-dry/semi-sweet (w & u/w), **4th Street** (3) (Natural Sweet, white, Natural Sweet, red, Natural Sweet, rosé, Perlé), Conradie (Rosé off-dry/semi-sweet, Perlé), Swartland (Rosé off-dry/semi-sweet), Bonnievale (Chenin blanc off-dry/semi-sweet (w & u/w), Perlé), Vinopoly (2) (Rosé off-dry/semi-sweet, Muscadel, white, unfortified, Perlé), Kleine Draken (Natural Sweet, red, Kosher), Drostdy-Hof (Natural Sweet, red), Rooiberg (Sauvignon blanc unwooded), Seven Sisters (Chenin blanc off-dry/semi-sweet (w & u/w), Perlé), House of JC le Roux (Sparkling, Non-MCC, red, off-dry/semi-sweet), Slanghoek (Natural Sweet, rosé) ★ Woolworths (5) (Pinotage, Natural Sweet, rosé, Chardonnay unwooded, Chenin blanc off-dry/semi-sweet (w & u/w), Sauvignon blanc unwooded), Van Loveren (White blends, unwooded, dry), Robertson (White blends, unwooded, dry), Woolworths (2) (Chenin blanc unwooded dry, Chenin blanc unwooded dry), Bonnievale (Ruby cabernet, Perlé), Landzicht (Natural Sweet, white), Riebeek (Sweet red) ★ Drostdy-Hof (White blends, unwooded, dry), Riebeek (Rosé off-dry/semi-sweet) **NT** Lutzville (3) (Natural Sweet, red, Natural Sweet, rosé, Natural Sweet, white), Perdeberg (Sparkling, Non-MCC, rosé, off-dry/semi-sweet)

Malbec

★★★★ Anura, Bellevue, **Black Elephant**, Diemersfontein, Druk My Niet, Hillcrest, Mooi Bly, Paul Wallace, Woolworths (2) (Light & low-alcohol)

★★★☆ Annex Kloof, **Bloemendal**, Doolhof, Dornier, Fairview, Flagstone, **Glen Carlou**, Hildenbrand, La Couronne, Neethlingshof, Raka, **Super Single Vineyards** ★★★ Bushmanspad, Ormonde, **Withington** (2) ★★☆ Blaauwklippen, Maison de Teijger, Malanot, Wellington Winery ★★ **Kleine Zalze NT** High Constantia, Maison de Teijger (3), Signal Hill, Vergenoegd **D** Giant Periwinkle, Paardebosch

Merlot

★★★★☆ Barton, Bein (2) (Light & low-alcohol), Catherine Marshall, Eagles'Nest, Eikendal, Laibach (Organic), Meerlust, Nederburg, Shannon, Vergelegen

★★★★ Amani, Anura, Bayede!, Buitenverwachting, Butcher Shop (2) (Light & low-alcohol), Creation, **De Trafford** (2), De Wetshof, Delaire, DeWaal, Dombeya, Fleur du Cap, Glenelly, GlenWood, Graceland, Groenland, Hartenberg, Hillcrest, Jordan, La Petite Ferme, **Landskroon**, Linton Park, Marianne, Morgenhof, Nabygelegen, Noble Hill, Overgaauw, Rainbow's End, Remhoogte, Rickety Bridge, Rust en Vrede, Rustenberg, Saxenburg, Slaley, Stellekaya, Sumaridge, Super Single Vineyards, Township Winery (Fairtrade), Veenwouden, Vergenoegd, Whalehaven, Winery of Good Hope, Woolworths (4) (Organic), Yonder Hill

★★★☆ Akkerdal, Altydgedacht, Annandale, Ayama, Backsberg, Bein, Blaauwklippen, Boland (2), Boschkloof , Botanica, Cloof, Clos Malverne, Darling Cellars, De Breede (Organic), Diemersdal, Doolhof, Dornier, Eaglevlei, Elgin Vintners, Ernie Els, Ernst Gouws, Fairview, False Bay, Fort Simon, Guardian Peak, Hout Bay, Journey's End, Kaapzicht, Ken Forrester, Kloovenburg, Knorhoek, Kyburg, L'Avenir, La Bri, Lanner Hill, Lanzerac, Linton Park, Longridge, Lourensford, Lyngrove, Marklew, Meinert, Miravel, Morgenster, Muratie, Nederburg, Nico van der Merwe, Niel Joubert, Oldenburg, Ormonde (2), Passages, Plaisir, Porcupine Ridge, Post House, Raka, Ridgeback, Rooiberg, Seal Breeze, Signal Gun, Somerbosch, Spier, Spookfontein , Steenberg, Sterhuis, Thelema, Tread Lightly, Tulbagh Winery, Waterkloof, Welbedacht, Wellington Winery, **Woestkloof**, Woolworths ★★★ Anura, **Audacia**, Backsberg (Kosher), Bellpost, Bilton, Bloemendal, Blue Crane, Boschendal, Botha, Brenaissance, Cape Classics, D'Aria, De Grendel, De Meye, Delheim, DeWaal, **Domaine Coutelier**, Du Preez, Dunstone, Durbanville Hills, Excelsior, Fairview, **Fernskloof** (Organic), Fish Hoek, Flagstone (2), Fleur du Cap, Fort Simon, Glen Carlou, Goede Hoop, Graham Beck, Groote Post, Group CDV, Hathersage, Havana Hills, Holden Manz, Hoopenburg, House of Mandela, Jordan, Klein Parys, Kleine Zalze, Koelenhof, **Koopmanskloof**

(Fairtrade), L'Auberge, Laibach, Lievland, Lomond, Lutzville, Manley, Mont du Toit, Mount Rozier, Mzoli's, Nederburg, Neethlingshof, **Nuweland**, Org de Rac (2) (Organic), Ormonde, Overhex, Place in the Sun (Fairtrade), Retief, Riebeek, Robertson (3), **Rosendal**, Ruitersvlei, **Scrucap**, Slowine, Stellenrust, uniWines (Fairtrade), Viljoensdrift, Villiera, **Waterstone** (2), Wellington Winery (2), Windmeul, **Woolworths** (2), Zevenwacht, Zonnebloem ★★★ **Alvi's Drift**, Arra, Asara, Audacia, Badsberg, Bellingham, Blomendahl, Bonnievale, Boplaas, Butcher Shop, Desert Rose, Douglas Green, Drostdy-Hof, Du Preez, Du Toitskloof , Eikehof, Flat Roof Manor, **Fort Simon**, Franschhoek Cellar, **Goede Hoop**, Goudini, Group CDV, Het Vlock Casteel, **House of Mandela** (Fairtrade), Kanu, Klein Roosboom , Kranskop, La Chataigne, La Couronne, La Petite Provence, Le Manoir de Brendel, Leopard's Leap, MAN Family, Namaqua, Niel Joubert, Rhino of Linton Park, Riebeek, Schalkenbosch, Simonsvlei, Slanghoek, Spier, **Stellenbosch Family Wines**, Stellenbosch Hills, **Stettyn**, Swartland, uniWines, Vredenheim, Wandsbeck, Waterstone, Weltevrede, Wonderfontein, **Woolworths** (4) ★★ African Pride, Bayede!, Bellingham, Bergwater, Boland, Bonview, Bottelary, **Bridge**, Burgershof, Cape Dreams, Glenview, Goedverwacht, Group CDV, Halala, Hill & Dale, Hoopenburg, Klawer, Kleine Draken (Kosher), Long Mountain, Louisvale, Lula, **Nicholson Smith**, Obikwa, Robertson, Rooiberg, Seven Sisters, Stellar (2) (Organic, Fairtrade), Stellendrift, Swartland, Tulbagh Winery, United Nations, Van Loveren, **Viljoensdrift**, Waterstone, Welmoed, Woolworths ★★ Cranefields, De Bos (Fairtrade), Libby's Pride, Pulpit Rock, Robertson (Light & low-alcohol), Vinopoly, Waterstone, Wonderfontein, Woolworths (Light & low-alcohol), **Zidela** ★ Waterstone **NT** AlexKia, Buffalo Creek, Calais, Calitzdorp, Camberley, Catherine Marshall, Devon Hill, Die Mas, Domaine Brahms, Durbanville Hills (2), Excelsior, Groot Constantia, Herold, High Constantia (2), Hofstraat, Klein Parys, Landskroon, Landzicht, **Leeuwenberg**, Linton Park, Lourensford, Maison de Teijger (3), Maske, Meerendal (2) (Light & low-alcohol), **Mitre's Edge**, Mont Rochelle, My Wyn,

Nietvoorbij, Oude Compagnies Post, Painted Wolf, Perdeberg, Re'Mogo, Rosendal, Savanha, Snowfield, Stellendrift, Stone Ridge, Tanja Beutler (2), Thelema, Valley Vineyards (2), Versailles, Yonder Hill, Zidela **NR** Bergwater, Old Vines **D** Asara, Blaauwklippen, Escapades, Fraai Uitzicht 1798 (2), Lynx, M'hudi, Nuweland, Pulpit Rock, Quoin Rock, Woolworths

Mourvèdre

★★★★ Fairview, **Grangehurst**, Raka, Signal Hill, Spice Route

★★★★ **Almenkerk**, Arra, Boschheim, Hermit on the Hill ★★★ MAN Family, Wellington Winery ★★★ Arra ★★ Idiom **NT** Hawksmoor, Oude Compagnies Post, Spice Route, Three Foxes **NR** Beaumont

Muscadel, red, fortified

★★★★★ Boplaas, Nuy

★★★★ Allesverloren, Badsberg, Boplaas, Calitzdorp, **Nuweland**, Nuy, Orange River, Rooiberg

★★★★ Aan de Doorns, Bon Courage, **Boplaas**, Clairvaux, De Wet, Du Toitskloof , Excelsior Vlakteplaas, Karusa, Klawer (2), **SoetKaroo**, Van Loveren, Weltevrede, Wonderfontein ★★★ Boland, Boplaas, **Jakkalsvlei**, Landzicht, McGregor, Namaqua, Reiersvlei, Roodezandt ★★★ **Conradie**, Die Mas, Grundheim, Slanghoek, Vinopoly, Wandsbeck ★★ Ashton **NT** BurCon, Klein Parys, Montagu Wine Cellar, Robertson, TTT Cellar, Tulbagh Winery, Wolvendrift **D** Nuweland

Muscadel, red, unfortified

★★ Landzicht

Muscadel, white, fortified

★★★★★ Alvi's Drift, Nuy

★★★★ Boplaas (2) (Light & low-alcohol), Calitzdorp, De Krans, Monis, Orange River

★★★★ Bon Courage, De Wet, Domein Doornkraal, Graham Beck, Lutzville, Windmeul ★★★★ Clairvaux, Klawer, Merwida, Namaqua ★★★ Boplaas, De Wetshof, Die Mas, Excelsior Vlakteplaas, McGregor, Vinopoly, Weltevrede ★★★ Wonderfontein ★★ Grundheim **NT** Landzicht, Montagu Wine Cellar, Mostertsdrift, Robertson, Withoek **D** De Krans, La Couronne

Muscadel, white, unfortified

★★★★ Elsenburg, Fledge & Co

★★★ Karusa (2), Leopard's Leap ★★★ Imbuko (Perlé, Light & low-alcohol), Obikwa (Light & low-alcohol), Thelema ★★ Badsberg (Perlé, Light & low-alcohol), De Krans (Perlé, Light & low-alcohol), De Wet ★★ Vinopoly

Muscat de Hambourg fortified
★★★ Stellenbosch Hills

Muscat Ottonel unfortified
NT Zidela

Natural Sweet, red
★★★★☆ Adoro

★★★ Blomendahl (2) ★★☆ Arra, **Goudini**, Somerset Wines ★★ 4th Street (Perlé, Light & low-alcohol), Robertson (2) (Light & low-alcohol), Rooiberg ★★ 4th Street (Light & low-alcohol), Drostdy-Hof (Light & low-alcohol), Kanu, Kleine Draken (Light & low-alcohol, Kosher), Van Loveren (Light & low-alcohol), Woolworths **NT** Bosman, Cape Hutton, Lutzville

Natural Sweet, rosé
★★★★ Groot Constantia

★★★ Nelson, Orange River, Seven Sisters, Somerset Wines ★★ 4th Street (Perlé, Light & low-alcohol), Drostdy-Hof (Light & low-alcohol), Grünberger (2) (Perlé, Light & low-alcohol), **Rhino of Linton Park**, Robertson (4) (Light & low-alcohol), Rooiberg ★★ 4th Street (Light & low-alcohol), Douglas Green (Light & low-alcohol), Landzicht, Simonsvlei (Light & low-alcohol), Slanghoek (Light & low-alcohol), Van Loveren (2) (Light & low-alcohol) ★ Woolworths **NT** Lutzville

Natural Sweet, white
★★★★☆ Badsberg, Jordan, Klein Constantia, Nederburg, Perdeberg

★★★★ Edgebaston, Glen Carlou, **Laibach** (Light & low-alcohol), Quoin Rock, Ridgeback, Stony Brook, Zorgvliet

★★★☆ Delheim, Rickety Bridge ★★★ Rooiberg, Somerset Wines (Light & low-alcohol), **Zandvliet** ★★★ 4th Street (Light & low-alcohol), Arra, Grünberger (Light & low-alcohol), Theuniskraal ★★ Douglas Green, Drostdy-Hof (Light & low-alcohol), Goudini, Kleine Draken (Light & low-alcohol, Kosher), Lord's, Orange River, Robertson (3) (Light & low-alcohol) ★★ 4th Street (Perlé, Light & low-alcohol), Group

CDV (Light & low-alcohol), Van Loveren (Light & low-alcohol), Woolworths ★ Landzicht **NT** Dornier, Highlands Road, Lutzville (Light & low-alcohol), Meerendal, Quando **D** Cloof

Nebbiolo
★★★★☆ Steenberg
★★★★ Dagbreek, Idiom, Morgenster
★★★☆ Du Toitskloof

Noble Late Harvest
★★★★★ Delheim, Signal Hill

★★★★☆ Asara, Boekenhoutskloof, Boschendal, Buitenverwachting, De Wetshof (Light & low-alcohol), Durbanville Hills, Fleur du Cap (Light & low-alcohol), Hermanuspietersfontein, Ken Forrester, Lourensford, Lutzville, Miles Mossop, Namaqua (Light & low-alcohol), Nederburg (2), Neethlingshof, Paul Cluver (Light & low-alcohol), Post House, Rudera, **Spier**, Springfontein, Tokara, Villiera

★★★★ Badsberg, Beaumont, Blaauwklippen (2), **Bloemendal**, Bon Courage, **D'Aria**, Fort Simon, **Gabriëlskloof**, Joostenberg (Organic), Kanu, L'Illa, Longridge, Mulderbosch, Shannon, Signal Hill, Simonsig, Slaley, Slanghoek, Stellenrust, Virgin Earth, Woolworths

★★★★ Altydgedacht (Light & low-alcohol), Blaauwklippen ★★★ Hildenbrand ★★★ De Grendel **NT** Avontuur, Badsberg, Cape Point, Darling Cellars, Delaire, Du Toitskloof , Hartenberg, Kranskop, Morgenhof, Nitida, Signal Hill (2), Van Loveren, Vruchtbaar

Non-muscat, white, fortified
★★★★ Haute Cabrière

Nouveau
★★★ Groot Parys (Pinotage) ★★ Asara (Gamay noir)

Nouvelle
★★☆ Boland

Organic
★★★★★ Porseleinberg (Shiraz/syrah)

★★★★☆ Avondale (2) (White blends, wooded, dry, Sparkling, Méthode cap classique, white, dry), Laibach (Merlot), Lazanou (Shiraz/syrah), Hughes Family (White blends, wooded, dry), Scali (White blends, wooded, dry), Silvermist (Sauvignon blanc unwooded)

★★★★ Woolworths (Merlot), Avondale (2) (Red blends, shiraz/syrah-based, Chenin blanc wooded, dry), Org de Rac (3) (Cabernet sauvignon, Shiraz/syrah, Sparkling, Méthode cap classique, white, dry, Light & low-alcohol), **Painted Wolf** (Grenache noir), La Motte (Sauvignon blanc unwooded), Stellar (Vin de paille, Fairtrade), **Org de Rac** (Husk spirit/grappa-styles), Upland (2) (Brandy, Brandy), **Dalla Cia** (Husk spirit/grappa-styles), De Breede (Shiraz/syrah), Groot Parys (2) (Chenin blanc wooded, dry, Chenin blanc wooded, dry), Elgin Ridge (Sauvignon blanc unwooded), Upland (Husk spirit/grappa-styles), Laibach (Red blends, Cape Bordeaux), Joostenberg (2) (Shiraz/syrah, Noble Late Harvest), Silvermist (Red blends, other), Waverley Hills (Shiraz/syrah)

★★★★ Avondale (2) (Shiraz/syrah, Red blends, Cape Bordeaux), **Bellingham** (Shiraz/syrah), **Org de Rac** (2) (Chardonnay wooded, Red blends, other), Bon Cap (2) (Red blends, with pinotage, Sparkling, Méthode cap classique, white, dry), De Breede (Merlot), **Groot Parys** (2) (Chenin blanc wooded, dry, Sparkling, Méthode cap classique, white, off-dry/semi-sweet), **Elgin Ridge** (Pinot noir), Fernskloof (Cabernet sauvignon), Laibach (White blends, wooded, dry), Lammershoek (White blends, unwooded, dry), Lazanou (2) (Red blends, shiraz/syrah-based, Viognier), **Matzikama** (Pinot noir), Mountain Oaks (Pinotage), Joostenberg (2) (Red blends, shiraz/syrah-based, White blends, unwooded, dry), Scali (Sparkling, Méthode ancestrale), Waverley Hills (2) (White blends, wooded, dry, Sparkling, Méthode cap classique, white, dry)

★★★ Woolworths (Chardonnay wooded), Avondale (Rosé dry), Van Loveren (Port-style, red), Woolworths (Sparkling, Méthode cap classique, red, dry), Org de Rac (Merlot), Stellar (Red blends, with pinotage), **Org de Rac** (5) (Cabernet sauvignon, Merlot, Shiraz/syrah, Chardonnay unwooded, Red blends, Cape Bordeaux), Bon Cap (Port-style, red), **Groot Parys** (4) (Pinotage, Rosé dry, Chenin blanc wooded, dry, Chenin blanc unwooded dry, Nouveau), Earthbound (3) (Cabernet sauvignon, Chenin blanc unwooded dry, Sauvignon blanc unwooded, Fairtrade), **Fernskloof** (4) (Merlot, Pinotage, Red blends, shiraz/syrah-based, Rosé dry, Light &

low-alcohol), Lammershoek (2) (Pinotage, Rosé dry), **Matzikama** (Shiraz/syrah), Mountain Oaks (Red blends, Cape Bordeaux), **Reyneke** (2) (Red blends, shiraz/syrah-based, White blends, unwooded, dry), Bon Cap (Sauvignon blanc unwooded), **Scali** (Pinotage), **Groot Parys** (Red blends, with pinotage), Upland (Cabernet sauvignon), Waverley Hills (5) (Cabernet sauvignon, Grenache noir, Shiraz/syrah, Red blends, shiraz/syrah-based, Red blends, other) ★★★
Woolworths (4) (Cabernet sauvignon, Shiraz/syrah, Chardonnay wooded, Sauvignon blanc unwooded, Fairtrade), Stellar (White blends, unwooded, dry, Fairtrade), **Org de Rac** (Red blends, shiraz/syrah-based), Stellar (7) (Cabernet sauvignon, Pinotage, Shiraz/syrah, Chardonnay wooded, Sauvignon blanc unwooded, Sparkling, Non-MCC, white, dry, Cabernet sauvignon, Fairtrade), Org de Rac (Red blends, Cape Bordeaux), Stellar (2) (Pinotage, White blends, off-dry/semi-sweet (w & u/w), Fairtrade), **De Breede** (2) (Red blends, Cape Bordeaux, Red blends, Cape Bordeaux), Groot Parys (Chardonnay wooded), Earthbound (2) (Pinot noir, Pinotage, Fairtrade), Joostenberg (Rosé dry), Bon Cap (2) (Rosé off-dry/semi-sweet, White blends, unwooded, dry), Upland (Port-style, red), Waverley Hills (2) (Red blends, other, Jerepigo red) ★★
Woolworths (2) (Merlot, Pinotage), **Stellar** (11) (Chardonnay wooded, Pinot noir, Merlot, Rosé dry, White blends, unwooded, dry, Merlot, Pinotage, Shiraz/syrah, Rosé dry, Rosé off-dry/semi-sweet, White blends, unwooded, dry, Light & low-alcohol, Fairtrade), De Breede (Cabernet sauvignon), Mountain Oaks (Red blends, with pinotage) ★★ Woolworths (Sparkling, Non-MCC, white, dry), De Breede (Red blends, Cape Bordeaux), Waverley Hills (Pinot gris/grigio) ★ Woolworths (Colombard) **NT** Org de Rac (Rosé dry), Bon Cap (Viognier), Groot Parys (Vin de paille), Fernskloof (Chardonnay wooded), Lammershoek (Shiraz/syrah), Lazanou (3) (Chardonnay wooded, Chenin blanc unwooded dry, White blends, unwooded, dry), Mountain Oaks (3) (Rosé dry, Chardonnay wooded, White blends, unwooded, dry), Bon Cap (2) (Red blends, shiraz/syrah-based, Sparkling, Non-MCC, white, dry), Waverley Hills (3) (Cabernet sauvignon, Rosé dry, White blends, wooded, dry) **D** Woolworths (

Shiraz/syrah), Org de Rac (3) (Cabernet sauvignon, Rosé dry, Chardonnay unwooded), Groot Parys (3) (Chenin blanc off-dry/semi-sweet (w & u/w), Rosé dry, Chenin blanc unwooded dry), Reyneke (White blends, wooded, dry)

Perlé Wines

★★★ Group CDV (White blends, off-dry/semi-sweet (w & u/w), Perlé), Autumn Harvest Crackling (Rosé off-dry/semi-sweet, Perlé), **Calitzdorp** (White blends, off-dry/semi-sweet (w & u/w), Perlé), Grünberger (White blends, off-dry/semi-sweet (w & u/w), Perlé), uniWines (2) (Hanepoot unfortified, Hanepoot unfortified, Perlé, Light & low-alcohol, Fairtrade), Imbuko (Muscadel, white, unfortified) ★★ Asara (Gamay noir, Perlé, Nouveau), Ashton (White blends, off-dry/semi-sweet (w & u/w), Perlé), **4th Street** (2) (Natural Sweet, red, Natural Sweet, rosé, Perlé, Light & low-alcohol), Wellington Winery (Hanepoot unfortified, Perlé, Light & low-alcohol), Badsberg (Muscadel, white, unfortified, Perlé, Light & low-alcohol), Capenheimer (White blends, off-dry/semi-sweet (w & u/w), Perlé), De Krans (Muscadel, white, unfortified, Perlé, Light & low-alcohol), De Wet (2) (Rosé off-dry/semi-sweet, Muscadel, white, unfortified, Perlé, Light & low-alcohol), Grünberger (Natural Sweet, rosé, Perlé), Riebeek (Hanepoot unfortified, Perlé, Light & low-alcohol), Wandsbeck (Rosé off-dry/semi-sweet) ★★ **4th Street** (Natural Sweet, white, Perlé, Light & low-alcohol), Conradie (Rosé off-dry/semi-sweet, Perlé, Light & low-alcohol), Bonnievale (Chenin blanc off-dry/semi-sweet (w & u/w), Perlé, Light & low-alcohol), Autumn Harvest Crackling (White blends, off-dry/semi-sweet (w & u/w), Perlé), Vinopoly (2) (Rosé off-dry/semi-sweet, Muscadel, white, unfortified, Perlé, Light & low-alcohol), **Jakkalsvlei** (Rosé off-dry/semi-sweet, Perlé), Seven Sisters (Chenin blanc off-dry/semi-sweet (w & u/w)) ★ Bonnievale (Ruby cabernet, Perlé, Light & low-alcohol), Autumn Harvest Crackling (Sweet red, Perlé), Riebeek (Sweet red) ✭ Riebeek (Rosé off-dry/semi-sweet) **NT** Bergsig (White blends, off-dry/semi-sweet (w & u/w), Perlé), Louiesenhof (Rosé off-dry/semi-sweet) **D** Du Toitskloof (2) (Rosé off-dry/semi-sweet, White blends, off-dry/semi-sweet (w & u/w), Perlé)

Petit verdot

★★★★★ **Flagship**

★★★★ **Almenkerk**, Anura, Nederburg, Raka, Springfontein

★★★★ Doolhof, Hillcrest, Lovane, **Pulpit Rock**, **Super Single Vineyards** ★★★ Bellevue, Maison de Teijger ★★★ Definitum **NT** Asara, Calais, Du Preez, Havana Hills, Maison de Teijger, My Wyn, Rico Suter, Signal Hill, TTT Cellar, Zorgvliet **D** Haut Espoir, Stellenzicht

Petite sirah/durif

★★★★✩ Fairview

★★★★ Black Elephant

★★★★ Spotswood ★★★ Karusa

Pinot gris/grigio

★★★★ Arendskloof

★★★★ De Grendel, Nederburg, Township Winery, Val du Charron ★★★ Fairview, Hill & Dale, Idiom, **Overhex**, Stettyn, Usana ★★★ Flat Roof Manor, Robertson, Spring Grove, **Stellekaya**, Two Oceans, Van Loveren, Woolworths ★★ Obikwa ★★ Waverley Hills **D** Overhex (Fairtrade), Woolworths

Pinot noir

★★★★★ Creation, Crystallum, Newton Johnson, Sumaridge

★★★★★✩ Blackwater, Botanica, Bouchard Finlayson, Cape Chamonix, Cederberg, **Crystallum** (2), **Edgebaston**, Litigo, Meerlust, Newton Johnson (3), **Stark-Condé**, **Storm**, Winery of Good Hope (2)

★★★★ Bouchard Finlayson, **Brunia**, **Butcher Shop**, **Cape Chamonix**, Catherine Marshall (2), Clouds, **Craven**, Creation, Crystallum, De Grendel, De Wetshof, **Donkiesbaai**, Driehoek, Edgebaston, Glen Carlou, Groote Post, Hamilton Russell, Iona, Jasper Raats, JH Meyer, La Chaumiere, La Vierge, **Lieben**, Lothian, **Meinert**, Muratie, **Nederburg**, Newton Johnson, Oak Valley, Paul Cluver (2), Scrucap, Seven Springs , Signal Hill, **South Hill**, **Storm**, Strandveld, **Strydom**, Topaz, Whalehaven, Winery of Good Hope, Woolworths (2), Yardstick

★★★★✩ **Altydgedacht**, Andy Mitchell, Arendskloof, Backsberg, Baleia Bay, Blackwater, Boschendal, Boschheim, Claime d'Or, **Clive Torr**, De Bos (Fairtrade), **Elemental Bob**, **Elgin Ridge** (Organic), Elgin Vintners, **Fat Bastard**, Felicité,

Fryer's Cove, **Giant Periwinkle**, Grande Provence, Haute Cabrière, Herold, Karusa, Kleine Zalze, La Vierge, **Laibach**, Lomond, Maison de Teijger, **Matzikama** (Organic), Meerendal, Nabygelegen, Ormonde, **Paul Cluver, Paul Wallace**, Stark-Condé (2), **Sterhuis, Stony Brook**, Two Oceans, Veenwouden, Virgin Earth (Fairtrade), Vriesenhof , Waterford, Winters Drift, **Woolworths** (2) ★★★ Avontuur, **BLANKbottle**, Bon Courage, **Clive Torr, De Wetshof**, Domaine des Dieux, Ernst Gouws, Glen Carlou, Haute Cabrière, Highlands Road, Hoopenburg, Lemberg, Lord's, Maastricht, **Namaqua**, Ormonde, **Packwood**, Peter Falke, Quando, Robertson, Sophie & Mr P, **Springfield**, Strandveld, Thelema, Van Loveren, Wine Fusion ★★☆ **Carmel**, Earthbound (Organic, Fairtrade), Kranskop, **Nabygelegen, Osbloed, Overhex, Stellar** ★★ Goedvertrouw, Stellar (Organic), **Stellenbosch Family Wines NT** Andy Mitchell, AntHill, Dalla Cia, Flagstone, Herold, Hills, Longbarn, Maison de Teijger (6), Malanot, Paul Cluver, Shannon, Signal Hill, Spookfontein , Stellekaya, Strandveld, Vriesenhof , Winery of Good Hope **D** Beau Joubert, Woolworths

Pinotage
★★★★★ Flagstone, Kanonkop
★★★★☆ **Beeslaar**, Beyerskloof, Cape Chamonix, Cecilia, Chateau Naudé, DeWaal (2), Diemersfontein, Fairview, Grangehurst, Kaapzicht (2), Kanonkop, L'Avenir, Lanzerac, Meerendal, Môreson, Nederburg, Pulpit Rock, Rijk's, Simonsig, Spier, Spioenkop, Tokara, Windmeul
★★★★ Allée Bleue, Anura, Arendskloof, Arra, Bayede!, Bellevue, Bellingham, Beyerskloof, Bosman (Fairtrade), Clos Malverne, Conradie, De Zoete Inval, **Delheim**, Diemersdal (2), Eaglevlei, Eikendal, Escapades, Flagstone, Four Paws, Groot Constantia, Karusa, Kleine Zalze, L'Avenir, Lanzerac, Lemberg, Longridge, Lyngrove, M'hudi, Neethlingshof, Neil Ellis, Nuy, Paardebosch, Painted Wolf (2), Perdeberg, Remhoogte, Reyneke (Biodynamic), Rijk's, Rooiberg, Scali, Slaley, Southern Right, Spice Route, **Spioenkop, Springfontein** (3) (Light & low-alcohol), Stellenrust, Stellenzicht, Super Single Vineyards, SylvanVale, Welgegund, Winery of Good Hope, Zonnebloem

★★★★ Aaldering, Altydgedacht, Annex Kloof, Anura, Badsberg, Barista, Beaumont, Bellevue, Bergsig, Beyerskloof, **Bloemendal**, Boland, Camberley, Cape Dreams, Clos Malverne, Croydon, **DeanDavid**, Delheim, **DewaldtHeyns**, Die Mas, Diemersfontein, Ernst Gouws, Fairview (Fairtrade), False Bay, Fat Bastard, Flagstone, **Fram**, Franschhoek Cellar, Goede Hoop, Graham Beck, Hidden Valley, Hofstraat, Hornbill , **Kanonkop**, Ken Forrester, Kleine Zalze, Knorhoek, Lemberg, Lutzville, M'hudi, Maastricht, Malanot, MAN Family, Manley, Marklew, Meerendal, Meinert, Middelvlei, Miravel, Mooiplaas, Mountain Oaks (Organic), Mountain River, Nederburg, Olifantsberg, Olsen, Passages, Raka, Rhebokskloof, Rico Suter, Rijk's, Robertson, Romond, Saxenburg, Silkbush, Simonsvlei, Slaley, **Spier** (2), Springfontein, Stanford Hills, Stellekaya, Stellenbosch Vineyards, Stellenrust, Swartland, **Uitkyk, Vierkoppen**, Vinopoly, Virgin Earth, Warwick, Waterstone, Welbedacht, Welgevallen, Wellington Winery, Wildekrans, Wine Fusion, Winery of Good Hope, Woolworths (3), Zonnebloem ★★★ Allée Bleue, Amani, **Ayama** (2), Backsberg (Kosher), Bellingham, Bergsig, Blomendahl, Boland, Bon Courage, **Brampton**, Chateau Naudé, Cloof, Darling Cellars (3), DeWaal, Doran, Dornier, Douglas Green, Drostdy-Hof, Du Toitskloof , Durbanville Hills, Eagle's Cliff, Fairvalley (Fairtrade), Fairview, Fernskloof (Organic), Fish Hoek, Fort Simon, Galleon, Grape Grinder, Groot Parys (Organic, Nouveau), House of Mandela, Imbuko, Jacobsdal, Klawer, Koopmanskloof (Fairtrade), L'Auberge, Laibach, Lammershoek (Organic), Louiesenhof, Lyngrove, **M'hudi**, Merwida, Morgenhof, **Namaqua**, Nederburg (2) (Fairtrade), Neethlingshof, New Beginnings, Obikwa, Overhex, Painted Wolf, Pulpit Rock, Rickety Bridge, Riebeek, Robertson, Saam, **Scali** (Organic), Schalkenbosch, Simonsig, Simonsvlei, Slanghoek, **Slowine**, Somerbosch, Stanford Hills, Stellendrift, **Swartland** (2), SylvanVale, **Taillard**, Thembi & Co (2), Township Winery (2) (Light & low-alcohol, Fairtrade), Trajan, Tulbagh Winery (2), Two Oceans, uniWines, Villiera, Vriesenhof (2), **Waterstone**, Welbedacht, Wellington Winery, Whalehaven, Windmeul, Woolworths ★★☆ Aan de Doorns, Alvi's Drift, Anura, Arra, Avontuur, Backsberg,

Barnardt Boyes, **Bellingham**, Bon Cap, Boplaas, Botha, Cape Dreams, **David Frost**, Earthbound (Organic, Fairtrade), Fleur du Cap, Goudini, Graham Beck, Hill & Dale, Hoopenburg, House of Mandela (Fairtrade), **Jakkalsvlei**, Kleine Zalze, Koopmanskloof, La Couronne, Landskroon, Lateganskop, Le Manoir de Brendel, **Leipzig**, Long Mountain, Lutzville, MAN Family, McGregor, Namaqua (2), Niel Joubert, Rhebokskloof, Rhino of Linton Park, Rooiberg (2) (Light & low-alcohol), **Rosendal**, **Signal Gun**, Spier, Stellar (2) (Organic, Fairtrade), Stellenbosch Hills, uniWines (Fairtrade), Vredenheim, Waterstone, Wellington Winery, Welmoed, Woolworths (2) (Light & low-alcohol), Zevenwacht ★★ Bayede!, Bergheim, Boland, Breëland, Group CDV (2), Riebeek, **Ses'Fikile**, Simonsvlei, Stellar (Organic, Fairtrade), Van Loveren, Viljoensdrift, Waterstone (2), **Welvanpas**, Woolworths (Organic), **Zidela** ★★ African Pride, Ashton, Blomendahl, Long Mountain, Mountain River (2), Oude Compagnies Post, Van Loveren (Fairtrade), Wellington Winery ★ Woolworths **NT** Aaldering, Alkmaar, Black Elephant, Buffalo Creek, Burgershof, Calais, Calitzdorp, De Zoete Inval, Devon Hill, Devon Rocks, Domaine Brahms, Doolhof, Doran, Durbanville Hills, Freedom Hill (2), Govert, Group CDV, **Halala**, Hawksmoor (3), Imbuko, Klein Parys (3), Knorhoek, Koelenhof, L'Avenir, Long Mountain, **Lula**, Malanot (2), Marianne, Neil Ellis, Nietvoorbij, Nuweland, Old Vines, Onderkloof , Orange River, Oude Compagnies Post, Perdeberg, Re'Mogo, Reiersvlei, Ruitersvlei, Stellenbosch University (2), Tempel, Teubes (2), Tulbagh Winery, United Nations, Valley Vineyards, Vruchtbaar, Waboomsrivier, Wellington Winery, Withington, Zidela **D** Cloof, De Wet, Nitida, Nuy, Perdeberg, Stellenzicht, Thandi, Woolworths

Port-style, pink
★★★ Boplaas ★★★ De Krans, **Peter Bayly**

Port-style, red
★★★★★ Axe Hill, Boplaas (2) (Light & low-alcohol), De Krans, JP Bredell
★★★★★ Boplaas (3) (Light & low-alcohol), **De Krans** (2), Muratie

★★★★ Anura, Beaumont, Bergsig, Boplaas (2), De Krans, De Wet (2), Delaire, JP Bredell, **Kloovenburg**, Landskroon, Lieben, Monis, Morgenhof, Muratie, Overgaauw, Peter Bayly, Simonsig, Swartland
★★★★ Aan de Doorns, Alto, Annandale, Axe Hill, Backsberg, Bergsig (2), Beyerskloof, Boplaas, Calitzdorp, Domein Doornkraal, Douglas Green, Du'SwaRoo, **Elsenburg**, Flagstone, Grundheim, Jacques Smit, Kaapzicht, **Lieben**, Louiesenhof, Monis, **Spier**, **Spookfontein** , Swartland, **Taillard**, Vergenoegd, Zandvliet ★★★ Anura, **Axe Hill**, Badsberg, Boland, Bon Cap (Organic), Botha, Calitzdorp, Catherine Marshall, Clairvaux, De Zoete Inval, Die Mas, Druk My Niet, Du Toitskloof , Holden Manz, Koelenhof, Louiesenhof, Orange River, Riebeek, Rooiberg, Slanghoek, **Stettyn**, TTT Cellar, Van Loveren (Organic), Vergenoegd, Windmeul ★★★ Bon Courage, Grundheim, Hofstraat, Peter Bayly, Somersbosch, Tulbagh Winery, Upland (Organic), Wellington Winery (2) ★★ Allée Bleue, Highlands Road, Karusa, Klawer, **Namaqua**, Reiersvlei, Viljoensdrift, Villiersdorp, Withoek (2) ★★ Bergwater, Landzicht, TTT Cellar ★ McGregor **NT** Allesverloren, Beau Joubert, Boplaas, De Zoete Inval, Goede Hoop, Groot Constantia, Grundheim, Lovane, Maison, Montpellier, My Wyn, Nietvoorbij, Robertson, Snowfield, SoetKaroo (2), Withoek **D** Bonnievale, De Krans, Du'SwaRoo, Knorhoek, Tulbagh Winery

Port-style, white
★★★★ Axe Hill ★★★ Boplaas, Grundheim, Karusa, Peter Bayly ★★ TTT Cellar **NT** My Wyn **D** De Krans

Red blends, Cape Bordeaux
★★★★★ Hartenberg, Thelema, Vilafonté
★★★★★ Allée Bleue, Bartinney, Barton, Beaumont, Beyerskloof, Buitenverwachting, Butcher Shop, Cape Chamonix, Constantia Glen (2), Dalla Cia, Darling Cellars, De Toren (2), **De Trafford**, Delheim, Diemersdal, Dornier, Druk My Niet, **Du Toitskloof** , Eikendal, Epicurean, Ernie Els, Fleur du Cap, Grangehurst, Hermanuspietersfontein, Hidden Valley, Hillcrest, Jordan (2), Journey's End, Kaapzicht, Kanonkop, Keet, Klein Constantia, Laibach, **Longridge**, Lourensford, Meerlust, Miles Mossop, Môreson, Morgenster (2), Mulderbosch, Muratie, Mvemve Raats, Nabygelegen, Napier,

Neethlingshof, Nico van der Merwe, Nitida, Ormonde, Overgaauw, Raats, **Rainbow's End**, **Raka**, Remhoogte, Romond, Rupert & Rothschild, Simonsig, **Spier**, Stellenbosch Reserve, Stellenrust, Tokara, Vergelegen (2), Vergenoegd, Vilafonté, Warwick, Waterford, Windmeul

★★★★ Arra, Asara, **BABISA**, Backsberg, Beau Constantia, Belfield, Bellevue, Bilton, BLANKbottle, Boschkloof, Butcher Shop, Camberley (2), CK Wines, Cloof, Constantia Uitsig, Creation, Damarakloof, **Darling Cellars**, DeMorgenzon, DeWaal, Dombeya, Dornier, Drift Farm, Elgin Vintners, Gabriëlskloof, Glen Carlou, Grande Provence, Grangehurst (2), Groot Constantia, Hermanuspietersfontein, High Road, Holden Manz, Idiom, JP Bredell, Kanu, Knorhoek, La Bri, La Motte, La Petite Ferme, La Vierge, Laibach (Organic), Le Riche, Leeuwenberg, Leopard's Leap, Lovane, Lynx, Malanot, Meerlust, MolenVliet, Mooiplaas, Morgenhof, Namaqua, Nederburg (2), Neil Ellis, Nelson, Noble Hill, Peter Falke, Raka, Reyneke (Biodynamic), Ridgeback, Robert Stanford, Saltare, Spier, Spookfontein , Springfield, **Star Hill**, Stellekaya, Stellenbosch Vineyards, Stonewall, Stony Brook, Van Biljon, Veenwouden, Vergelegen, Vergenoegd, Villiera, Virgin Earth (Fairtrade), Vuurberg, Webersburg, Welbedacht, Woolworths, Yardstick, Yonder Hill, Zevenwacht, Zorgvliet

★★★★ Aaldering, Allée Bleue, Amani, Anura, Avondale (Organic), Avontuur, **Babylon's Peak**, Black Oystercatcher, Boschkloof , Buitenverwachting, Butcher Shop, Cape Chamonix, **Capelands**, Claime d'Or, Cloof, Clos Malverne, D'Aria, De Grendel, De Toren, **Delavia Estate**, Diemersdal, Domaine Brahms, **Doolhof** (2), Dornier, Emineo, Equitania, Four Fields, Gabriëlskloof, Goudini, Hathersage, Havana Hills, High Road, Hillcrest, Jordan (2), Journey's End, Klein Constantia, Klein Roosboom , La Petite Ferme, Linton Park, Louis, Louisvale, Malanot, Marianne, Mimosa, Miravel, Mzoli's, Neethlingshof, Nelson, Nick & Forti's, Noble Savage, Oak Valley, Old Vines, Oldenburg, Rainbow's End, Rustenberg, Saronsberg, Schalkenbosch, Scrucap, Southern Sky, Steenberg, Stellekaya, Sterhuis, Thunderchild, Topaz, uniWines, **Vredenheim**, Vriesenhof , Welgemeend (2),

Woolworths (2), Yonder Hill ★★★ Alkmaar, Ashton, Audacia, Avontuur, Bayede!, Beyerskloof, Blomendahl, Boschendal, Brenaissance, Cape Classics, **De Wet**, Diemersdal, Diemersfontein, Doolhof (2) (Light & low-alcohol), Eagle's Cliff, Eagles' Nest, **Entre Nous**, **Fort Simon** (3), Goedverwacht, Hathersage, Jacaranda, Klein Parys, Kleine Zalze, Leopard Frog, Leopard's Leap, Louiesenhof, Lourensford, MolenVliet, Monterosso, Morgenhof, Mostertsdrift, Mountain Oaks (Organic), Opstal, Orange River, **Org de Rac** (Organic), Passages, Rhebokskloof, Rooiberg, Rosendal, **Signal Gun**, Simonsvlei, Slaley, Spier, Steenberg, Stellendrift, **Swartland**, Thandi (Fairtrade), Thelema, Two Oceans, uniWines, Uva Mira, Vin du Cap, Vondeling, Walker Bay Vineyards, Welbedacht, Welgemeend, Windmeul, Winery of Good Hope, **Woolworths** (2), Zorgvliet ★★★ Akkerdal, **AntHill**, Anura, Asara, Beau Joubert, Bonnievale, Darling Cellars, **De Breede** (2) (Organic), Diemersfontein, Doran, **Dusty Heath**, Glen Carlou, **Halala**, La Petite Provence, **Lula**, McGregor, Mooiplaas, Morgenhof, **Nicholson Smith**, Org de Rac (Organic), Overgaauw, Riebeek, Schalkenbosch, Simonsig, Slanghoek, Somerset Wines, Stellendrift, **Taillard**, Van Zylshof, Vaughan Johnson, Vierlanden, **Villiersdorp**, Woolworths ★★ **Ayama**, Bon Courage, Douglas Green (2), **Dusty Heath**, Havana Hills, Kleine Draken (Kosher), La Couronne, Landskroon, **Nicholson Smith**, Nuy, Overhex, Robertson, Saxenburg, **Stellenbosch Family Wines**, Tulbagh Winery ★★ De Breede (Organic), **Mountain Ridge**, Swartland ★ Lathithá, Swartland **NT** Akkerdal, Alto, Amani, Beau Constantia, Camberley, Crows Nest, Doran, Durbanville Hills, Equitania, Fernskloof, Govert, High Constantia, Hillock, Hoopenburg, Ken Forrester, Le Joubert, Maison de Teijger (2), Montpellier, Môreson (2), Natte Valleij, Nederburg, Nico Vermeulen, Nietvoorbij (2), Noble Hill, Nomada, Perdeberg, Rosendal (2), Ruitersvlei, Russo, Saronsberg, Snowfield, Springfontein, Stellendrift, Van Loveren, Vendôme (2), Versailles, Vredevol, Welgevallen, Wolvendrift **D** Eagles' Nest, MC Square, Painted Wolf, Rico Suter, Sterhuis, Woolworths

Red blends, other
★★★★★ Delaire, Ernie Els

★★★★☆ Adoro, Anwilka, Arendskloof, **Dalla Cia**, De Trafford, Druk My Niet, Graham Beck, Haskell, Ken Forrester, Mont du Toit, **Mount Abora**, **Nederburg** (3), Rust en Vrede, Val de Vie, Waterford, Waterkloof, Winery of Good Hope

★★★★ Akkerdal, **Allesverloren**, Alto, Amani (2), Anatu, Annandale (2), Backsberg (2), Beau Joubert, Bergsig, **Boplaas**, Bouchard Finlayson, **Bramon**, Bryan MacRobert, Butcher Shop, **Capaia** (2), **Crows Nest**, **Darling Cellars**, De Krans, De Meye, Eikendal, Ernie Els, Fairview (2), Glen Carlou, Goose Wines, Graceland, Groenland, Keermont, Klein Gustrouw, Le Bonheur (2) (Light & low-alcohol), Lingen, **Mellasat**, Micu Narunsky, Mont du Toit (2) (Light & low-alcohol), Nabygelegen, Neil Ellis Meyer-Näkel, Nietgegund, Osbloed, **Paserene**, Perdeberg, Plaisir, Rustenberg, Silvermist (Organic), Somerbosch, Steenberg, Strydom, Veenwouden, Woolworths, Zonnebloem

★★★★ Akkerdal, **Ameera**, **Arumdale**, Ataraxia, Axe Hill, Babylonstoren, Badgerberg, Badsberg, Blaauwklippen, Boplaas, **Boschheim** (2), Brampton, Capaia, Casa Mori, Cederberg, Desert Rose, Deux Frères, Dormershire, Escapades, Faraway House, GlenWood, Goats do Roam, Guardian Peak, Hartenberg, Haut Espoir, Havana Hills, Hill & Dale, **Holden Manz** (2), Jacques Smit, Joostenberg, Kanu, Kyburg, La Vierge, Leopard Frog, Lynx, Mary Le Bow, Micu Narunsky, Morgenster, Napier, Nederburg, Neil Ellis, **Org de Rac** (Organic), Osbloed, Peter Bayly, Peter Falke, Plaisir, Remhoogte, Rhebokskloof, Rico Suter, Schalkenbosch, **Spier**, **Springfontein**, Stellekaya, Swartland, Topiary, Uva Mira, Veenwouden, **Wavescape**, Wildehurst, Woolworths (2) ★★★ Allée Bleue, Arra, Audacia, Axe Hill, Backsberg, Blaauwklippen, Blomendahl, Bon Courage, **Boucheron**, **Calitzdorp**, Chateau Libertas, **Chennells**, Cloof, Clos Malverne, Delheim, Dornier, Du Toitskloof , **Du'SwaRoo**, **Esau**, Franki's, Graceland, Groote Post, Hermanuspietersfontein, Hermit on the Hill, Hills, **Keermont**, Koelenhof, Koopmanskloof, Kumala (2), Mont Rochelle, Nederburg, Nuweland, **Onderkloof**, Raka, Rhino of Linton Park, Robertson, Saxenburg, Simonsig, Skilpadvlei, Somerset Wines, **Sonklip**, **Spier**, Stonehill, Township Winery, Vergenoegd (2), Villiera, **Waterstone**,

Waverley Hills (Organic), Windfall ★★★ Aan de Doorns, Almenkerk, Barnardt Boyes, Bellingham, **Blaauwklippen**, Blouvlei, Boland, Bonnievale, Botha, Brandvlei, Burgershof, Camberley, Darling Cellars, De Zoete Inval, **Esau**, Highlands Road, Idiom, Kanu, Kumala, Landskroon, Leeuwenberg, **M'hudi**, Mitre's Edge, Mzoli's, Oude Compagnies Post, **Rhebokskloof**, Rustenberg, Stettyn, Stoumann's, Tassenberg, Theuniskraal, uniWines, Van Loveren, **Vin du Cap**, Waterstone (3), Waverley Hills (Organic), Welvanpas, Whalehaven, Woolworths ★★ Ashton, Beaumont, Bergwater (2) (Light & low-alcohol), Bonnievale, Calais, Cranefields, **Du'SwaRoo**, Grande Provence, Kumala (2), Landskroon (2) (Light & low-alcohol), **Leopard Frog**, Leopard's Leap, Montagu Wine Cellar, Robertson (2), **RobinHood**, Simonsvlei, Sophie & Mr P, Southern Sky, **Stellenbosch Family Wines**, Stellenbosch Hills, Swartland, Taverna Rouge, Waterstone, Zandvliet ★★ **Kumala**, Van Loveren, **Vinopoly**, Welvanpas, Woolworths (3) **NT** Abbottshill, Akkerdal, Ashton, Bayede! (2), BLANKbottle, Blue Crane, Boplaas, Buffalo Creek, Bushmanspad, Calais, Cape Rock, Crows Nest, Gilga, Goudini, Govert, Herold, Idiom, Jean Daneel, Klein Parys, La Kavayan, Main Street, Mont du Toit, Mountain River, Natte Valleij, Nederburg, Osbloed, Rosendal, Signal Hill, Stony Brook (2), TCB Wines, Tierhoek, TTT Cellar (2), Van Loveren, Vleiland, Waterstone, Withington **D** Avontuur, Du'SwaRoo (2), Durbanville Hills, Group CDV, Klein Constantia, Quoin Rock, Rico Suter, Vriesenhof , Woolworths

Red blends, shiraz/syrah-based

★★★★☆ AA Badenhorst, Anatu, Arra, Bellingham, Boekenhoutskloof, Cape Rock, Creation, David & Nadia Sadie, **DeMorgenzon**, Fable, Glenelly, Haskell, Hermanuspietersfontein, Hidden Valley, Jean Daneel, Ken Forrester, La Motte, Lammershoek, Luddite, **Newton Johnson**, Nico van der Merwe, Rall, Rust en Vrede, Sadie, Saronsberg, Savage, Sequillo, Strandveld, Sumaridge, Welbedacht

★★★★ AA Badenhorst, Akkerdal, Annex Kloof, Anwilka, Asara, Avondale (Organic), Babylon's Peak, Barton, Beau Constantia, Beaumont, Black Oystercatcher, Black Pearl, Blackwater, **Blake**, **BLANKbottle**, Boschendal, Bosman (Fairtrade), Brothers, Bushmanspad, Crios Bríde, Deux Frères,

Du Toitskloof , Edgebaston, Emineo, Ernie Els, Goats do Roam (Fairtrade), Graceland, Grangehurst, Guardian Peak, Hermit on the Hill, Hoopenburg, Hout Bay, Hughes Family, Iona, Kaapzicht, Ken Forrester, Kleine Zalze, Kloovenburg, Kronendal, Landskroon, Leopard's Leap, **Lomond**, Marianne, MolenVliet (2), Mont Destin, Mullineux, Nederburg (Fairtrade), Newton Johnson, Nico Vermeulen, Painted Wolf, Paradisum, Post House, Ridgeback, Scrucap, Sijnn, Simonsvlei, Solms-Delta, **South Hill**, Spice Route, Spier, Stellenbosch Hills, Stony Brook, Tierhoek, **Trizanne**, Val de Vie, Wildehurst, Winery of Good Hope, Zevenwacht (2), Zonnebloem

★★★☆ Alkmaar, **Antebellum**, Ayama, Babylon's Peak, **Barton**, Beaumont, Bilton, **Black Elephant**, **Boutinot**, **Bryan MacRobert**, **Butcher Shop** (2), Credo, Darling Cellars, Diemersfontein, Edgebaston, **Elemental Bob**, Esau, Feiteiras, Flagstone, Flat Roof Manor, Four Paws, Goats do Roam (Fairtrade), Grape Grinder, Heron Ridge, Idiom, Jean Daneel, Joostenberg (Organic), Karusa, Lazanou (Organic), Leeuwenkuil, Leopard's Leap, Lievland, Louis, Lourensford, Lynx (2), Mount Babylon, Naughton's, Neil Ellis, Nico van der Merwe, Ormonde, **Oude Compagnies Post**, Painted Wolf, Porcupine Ridge, Post House, Rickety Bridge, **Rico Suter**, Rosendal, **Saam**, Schalkenbosch, Sijnn, Simonsig, Skilpadvlei, Spier, Stettyn, Teddy Hall, Thelema, Trajan, **uniWines** (2), Val de Vie, Waterford (2), Welgegund, Winery of Good Hope, Wolftrap, **Woolworths**, Yardstick ★★★ Arra, Beau Joubert, **Boschendal** (2), D'Aria (2), Darling Cellars (2), DeMorgenzon, Domaine des Dieux, Drostdy-Hof, Eagle's Cliff, **Fernskloof** (Organic), Graham Beck (2), Groenland, Hermanuspietersfontein, **Journey's End**, Juno, Kanu, Kleine Zalze, Kumala, Leeuwenjacht, Lourensford, MAN Family, Manley, Mont Destin, Muratie, Nederburg (2), Noble Hill, Old Vines, **Oude Compagnies Post**, **Overhex** (Fairtrade), **Post House**, Reyneke (Organic), Ridgeback, Somersbosch (2), Stellenrust, Teddy Hall, Thokozani, Uitkyk, Waverley Hills (Organic), William Everson, Wine Village-Hermanus, Withington ★★☆ Andy Mitchell, **Boschendal** (2), **Boutinot** (2), Dorrance, Drostdy-Hof, Excelsior, Groenland, Kaapzicht, Karusa, Klawer, Kleine Zalze, Leopard

Frog, Longridge, Maske, **Org de Rac** (Organic), Overhex, Retief, Ridgeback, Riebeek, Savanha (Fairtrade), Schalkenbosch, Simonsvlei, Summerhill, Thandi (Fairtrade), Tulbagh Winery, **uniWines**, Virgin Earth, **Windfall**, Zevenwacht ★★ Allesverloren, Ayama, Barnardt Boyes, Domaine Brahms, Kleine Zalze, Pulpit Rock, Savanha, Tulbagh Winery, Zidela ★★ **Group CDV**, TTT Cellar, Woolworths **NT** Abbottshill, Akkerdal, AntHill, Auction Crossing, BABISA, Bon Cap (Organic), Brenaissance, Cape Rock, Cecilia, Freedom Hill, Govert, Havana Hills, Hawksmoor (2), Hoopenburg, Jacaranda, Jean Daneel, Joostenberg, La Motte, Le Joubert (2), Liberator (2), Malanot (2), Noble Hill, Orangerie, Oude Compagnies Post (2), Oude Denneboom, Reiersvlei, Robert Stanford, Saam, Spice Route, Topaz, Two Oceans, Val du Charron, Valley Vineyards (2), Waka Waka, Wellington Winery **D** De Wet, Doolhof, Du'SwaRoo, Vredenheim, Woolworths

Red blends, with pinotage

★★★★☆ Beaumont, Beyerskloof, Bosman, **Grangehurst**, Kaapzicht (2), Lanzerac, Meinert, **Rhebokskloof**, Spier, Windmeul

★★★★ Alvi's Drift, Anura, Ashbourne, Beyerskloof, Bon Cap, Clos Malverne (2), Croydon, **Doolhof** (2), Emineo, Flagstone, Goede Hoop, Grangehurst, Idiom, Lyngrove, Meerendal, Middelvlei, Post House, Raka, Simonsig, Stellenrust, Warwick, Welbedacht, Wellington Winery, Woolworths

★★★☆ Bon Cap (Organic), Clovelly, Croydon, Eaglevlei, Esau, Hawksmoor (2), Hornbill , Kaapzicht, L'Avenir, Lateganskop, Lorraine, Lutzville, Lyngrove, **Pulpit Rock**, Remhoogte, Rooiberg, Rupert & Rothschild, Slaley, Solms-Delta, **Spier**, Stellekaya (2), Stellenbosch University, Truter Family, Val du Charron, **Vriesenhof** , Welbedacht, Wildekrans, Wine Fusion, Winery of Good Hope ★★★ Anura, Arra, Bellevue, Bergsig, **Carrol Boyes**, Cloof, Die Mas, Domein Doornkraal, Doolhof, Du Toitskloof (2), Flagstone, **Goats do Roam**, Groot Constantia, **Groot Parys** (Organic), Hillock, Kanonkop, Knorhoek, L'Avenir, **Leipzig**, Leopard Frog, **Marianne**, Meinert, Mellasat, Middelvlei, Mostertsdrift, Skilpadvlei, Stellar (Organic), Two Oceans, Viljoensdrift, Vin du Cap ★★☆ Cloof, Conradie, **D'Aria**, Douglas Green,

Dragonridge, Du Preez, Faraway House, **Jakkalsvlei**, **Kumala** (3), Lemberg, Louiesenhof, **Namaqua**, **New Beginnings**, Savanha, Seven Sisters, Slaley, Spekulasie, Stellenbosch Hills, Stellenrust (Fairtrade), Vruchtbaar, Welgemeend, Woolworths ★★ Asara, BurCon, Clairvaux, Douglas Green, Koelenhof, Mountain Oaks (Organic), Overhex, Roodezandt, Rooiberg, Savanha, Stellendrift, Vinopoly, Waterstone, Woolworths, Zidela ★★ African Pride, De Doorns, **Definitum**, Drostdy-Hof, Overmeer Cellars, Slanghoek **NT** Altydgedacht, Clos Malverne, Devon Hill, Fernskloof, Freedom Hill (2), Klein Parys, Marklew, Maske, Mellasat, Oude Compagnies Post, Re'Mogo, Stellendrift, Waboomsrivier **D** Cloof, De Krans, Durbanville Hills, Marianne (2), Observatory, Stellenzicht, SylvanVale, Woolworths

Riesling

★★★★☆ Nitida, Spioenkop

★★★★ Drift Farm, Hartenberg, Jordan, Paul Cluver (2) (Light & low-alcohol), Scrucap, Woolworths

★★★★ Altydgedacht, BLANKbottle, **Darling Cellars**, De Wetshof, Groote Post, Howard Booysen, **Spier**, **Super Single Vineyards**, Thelema, **Waterford** ★★★ Carmel, Fairview, Lothian, Meinert, Nederburg, Osbloed, Thelema ★★ La Vierge **NT** Hartenberg, Howard Booysen, Klein Constantia, Rosendal **D** Villiera

Rosé dry

★★★★ Bramon, Cape Rock, Solms-Delta

★★★★ AA Badenhorst, Allesverloren, Anatu, Arumdale, BLANKbottle, **Botanica**, Cederberg, **Cloof**, Croydon, Desert Rose, Drift Farm, Goats do Roam (Fairtrade), Grangehurst, Haute Cabrière, Hermanuspietersfontein, L'Avenir, Leopard's Leap, Morgenster, Noble Savage, **Paardebosch**, **Perdeberg**, Rivendell (Fairtrade), Romond, Signal Gun, Sijnn, South Hill, Stonehill, Sumaridge, Tamboerskloof, Waterkloof, Wildehurst ★★★ **Aaldering**, Almenkerk, Anatu, Andy Mitchell, Asara, Avondale (Organic), Babylonstoren, Barton, Beaumont, Beyerskloof, Bloemendal, Blomendahl, Boschendal, Brampton, Butcher Shop, De Grendel, De Krans, De Meye, Delaire, DeMorgenzon, Dornier, Elgin Vintners, **Ernie Els**, Feiteiras, Fernskloof (Organic), Fish Hoek,

Grande Provence, Groot Parys (Organic), Hawksmoor, Herold, Hillcrest, Jacaranda, Jordan, Kanonkop, Klein Constantia, Klein Dauphine, Kleine Zalze, La Petite Ferme, La Petite Vigne, Lammershoek (Organic), Lourensford, Meerendal, Mulderbosch, Nelson, Noble Hill, Opstal, **Painted Wolf** (2), Quando, Rainbow's End, Raka, Schalkenbosch, Scrucap, Thelema, Tokara, Val de Vie, Waterford, Whalehaven, **Wolftrap** ★★★ **Asara**, **Avontuur**, **Baccarat**, Bein, Blaauwklippen, Black Oystercatcher, **Boschendal**, Claime d'Or, Diemersdal, Dragonridge, Dunstone, Durbanville Hills, Escapades, **Excelsior**, Fairview, Felicité, Foothills, **Graham Beck**, Highlands Road, Hill & Dale, Holden Manz, Joostenberg (Organic), Ken Forrester, Kleine Zalze, Kloovenburg, Koopmanskloof (Fairtrade), Leopard Frog, Marianne, Niel Joubert, Rickety Bridge, Riebeek, Saronsberg, Slaley, Slowine, Spekulasie, **Spier**, Spotswood, Stellenrust (Fairtrade), Thandi (Fairtrade), Two Oceans, Van Zylshof, **Vondeling**, **Vriesenhof** , Walker Bay Vineyards, Woolworths (Light & low-alcohol), Zevenwacht ★★ African Pride, **Cavalli**, Cloof, Darling Cellars, **Doolhof**, Doran, Drostdy-Hof, Eerste Hoop, False Bay, Franschhoek Cellar, La Couronne, Leeuwenkuil, Lord's, Mellasat, Mitre's Edge, Mont Rochelle, Mooiplaas, Mountain River, Muratie, Oude Compagnies Post, Overhex, Pulpit Rock, Rhebokskloof (2), Robertson (Light & low-alcohol), Savanha, Sophie & Mr P, **Spier**, **Springfontein**, Steenberg, Stellar (2) (Organic, Fairtrade), Van Loveren (Fairtrade), Vergenoegd, Welmoed, Zandvliet ★★ **Bryan MacRobert**, Havana Hills (Fairtrade), **Spookfontein** ★ Hildenbrand, Leopard's Leap **NT** Abbottshill, Beau Joubert, Blomendahl, Bosman, Bushmanspad, Cape Dreams, Dormershire, Du'SwaRoo, Fort Simon, Group CDV, Hawksmoor, High Constantia (2), **Hoopenburg**, Hout Bay, Knorhoek, La Chataigne, Land's End, Leeuwenberg, Mountain Oaks (Organic), Nederburg, New Beginnings (2), Org de Rac (Organic), Perdeberg, Plettenvale, Robert Stanford, Signal Hill, Stellenbosch University, Stony Brook, SylvanVale, Topiary, Waverley Hills (Organic), Zorgvliet **NR** Strandveld **D** Avontuur, Ayama, Blouvlei, Doolhof, Feiteiras, Groot Parys (Organic), Group CDV (3), Haut Espoir, Hoopenburg, Joostenberg, Koelenhof,

Koopmanskloof, Le Bonheur, Leeuwenjacht, Nuweland (2), Org de Rac (Organic), Overhex (Fairtrade), Ridgeback

Rosé off-dry/semi-sweet

★★★ Allée Bleue, Anura, **Baleia Bay**, Karusa, Lanzerac, Merwida, **Onderkloof** , Winters Drift, Wonderfontein ★★★ Autumn Harvest Crackling (Perlé), Backsberg, Blomendahl, Bon Cap (Organic), Delheim, Gabriëlskloof, Goedverwacht, Kumala, Lorraine, Lutzville, Morgenhof, Nederburg, Obikwa, Overhex (Light & low-alcohol), Rhino of Linton Park, Theuniskraal, Tread Lightly, **Waterstone**, Welbedacht, Wellington Winery (2) ★★ Amani, Bellingham, Bergsig, Bergwater, Bon Courage, Botha, Bottelary, Brandvlei, Calitzdorp, D'Aria, De Wet (Perlé), Douglas Green, **Du Toitskloof** (Light & low-alcohol), Eagle's Cliff, Flat Roof Manor (Light & low-alcohol), Goudini, Graça, Grande Provence, Imbuko, Kanu (2), **Kleine Draken**, Koelenhof, **Kumala** (2), Lathithá, **Ses'Fikile**, Stellar (Organic, Fairtrade), Tangled Tree, **Teubes**, Thokozani, Tulbagh Winery, **Vinopoly**, Wandsbeck (Perlé), Waterstone, Woolworths (2) ★★ Cellar Cask, Conradie (Perlé, Light & low-alcohol), Darling Cellars, Hartswater, **Jakkalsvlei** (Perlé), Overmeer Cellars, **RobinHood**, Swartland (Light & low-alcohol), Vinopoly (2) (Perlé, Light & low-alcohol), Vredenheim, Woolworths (2) (Light & low-alcohol), **Zidela** (2) ★ Ashton, Long Mountain ☆ Riebeek **NT** Badsberg, Benguela Cove, Buffalo Creek, Devon Rocks, Hillock, **Kanu**, Kleine Draken (Kosher), Louiesenhof (Perlé), McGregor, Mostertsdrift, Mzoli's, Nietvoorbij, Saxenburg, Stoumann's, Wellington Winery, Welvanpas **D** Boland, Du Toitskloof (Perlé), MAN Family, Nuweland, Rooiberg, Woolworths (3)

Roussanne
★★★★☆ Bellingham, Foundry, **Hermit on the Hill**, Ken Forrester

★★★★ Painted Wolf, **Simonsig**

★★★★ Fairview **NT** Rustenberg, Simonsig

Ruby cabernet
★★★★ Bellpost ★★★ Orange River, Robertson (2) (Light & low-alcohol) ★★ Barrydale, Ladismith, Ses'Fikile ★★ Hartswater, McGregor ★ Bonnievale (Perlé, Light & low-alcohol),

Nuweland ☆ Long Mountain **NT** Kingsriver, Lutzville **D** Nuweland

Sacramental Wines
★★ Backsberg (Sweet red, Sacramental, Kosher), Kleine Draken (Cabernet sauvignon) ★☆ Landzicht (Muscadel, red, unfortified)

Sangiovese
★★★★ Anura, Spring Grove

★★★☆ Dragonridge, Idiom, Monterosso, Morgenster ★★★ Fairview, **Havana Hills** (Fairtrade), **Kleine Zalze**, Raka ★★★ Wellington Winery ★★ Koelenhof **D** Fairview

Sauvignon blanc unwooded
★★★★★ Buitenverwachting

★★★★☆ Berrio, Boschendal, Bramon, Buitenverwachting, Cederberg, Constantia Glen, De Grendel, Diemersdal (2), Flagstone, Fleur du Cap, Graham Beck, Groot Constantia, Groote Post, Hillcrest (2), **Jean Daneel**, Kleine Zalze, Nederburg, Neil Ellis, Silvermist (Organic), **Spice Route**, Spioenkop, Thelema, Tokara, **Uva Mira**, Vergelegen

★★★★ Aaldering, Allée Bleue, Arendskloof, Ataraxia, Bartinney, Black Oystercatcher, Boplaas, Boschendal, Bouchard Finlayson (2), Brunia, Butcher Shop, Cape Chamonix, Cape Hutton, Cederberg, Constantia Mist, Constantia Uitsig, Corder, Darling Cellars, De Grendel, De Wetshof, Diemersdal, Driehoek, Durbanville Hills, Elgin Heights, Elgin Ridge (Organic), **Fryer's Cove**, Garden Route, Hartenberg, Havana Hills, Hermanuspietersfontein (2), Hidden Valley, Jasper Raats, Jordan, **Klein Constantia** (2), Klein Gustrouw, La Motte (2) (Organic), Lanner Hill, Le Bonheur, Lemberg, Lomond, Meinert, Merwida, Mulderbosch, Nederburg, Neethlingshof, Nitida (2) (Light & low-alcohol), **PaardenKloof**, Phizante Kraal, Plaisir, Rivendell (Fairtrade), Robertson, Saxenburg, Scrucap, Sir Lambert, Skaap, South Hill, Southern Right, Spice Route, Spier, Spioenkop, Springfield, Sterhuis, Stony Brook, Strandveld, Sumaridge, **Teubes** (2), Thelema, Tierhoek, Tokara, Uva Mira, Van Loveren, Vergelegen, Villiera, Virgin Earth (Fairtrade), Vondeling, Waterford, **Woolworths** (3), Zevenwacht, Zonnebloem

★★★☆ Adoro, African Pride, Almenkerk, Altydgedacht, Alvi's Drift, **AntHill**, Arumdale,

Asara, Avontuur, Ayama, Barton, Bayede!, Benguela Cove, Bergsig, Bloemendal, Blomendahl, Boplaas, Brampton, Capaia, Claime d'Or, Clos Malverne, Creation, Crios Bríde, D'Aria, Dalla Cia, Delaire, Dombeya, Doolhof, Durbanville Hills, Eagles' Nest, Edgebaston, Elgin Vintners, **Elsenburg**, Ernie Els, Excelsior, Fish Hoek, Fort Simon, Franschhoek Cellar, Gabriëlskloof, Giant Periwinkle, GlenWood, Grande Provence, Groenland, Groote Post, Hout Bay, Imbuko, Journey's End, Kaapzicht, Karusa, Klein Constantia, Kleine Zalze, Kloovenburg, La Petite Ferme, Land's End, Lanzerac, Le Bonheur, Lomond (2), Lutzville, Maastricht, **Manley**, Meerendal, Mooiplaas, Morgenhof, **Morgenster**, Neethlingshof, Newstead, Nico Vermeulen, Noble Hill, Oak Valley, Ormonde (3) (Light & low-alcohol), **Paul Wallace**, Place in the Sun (Fairtrade), Quando, Raka, Rare Earth, Rosendal, Saronsberg, Scrucap, Seven Springs , Signal Gun (2), **Silvermist**, Simonsig, Simonsvlei, Spier, Spring Grove, Springfield, Springfontein, Stellendrift, Stellenrust, Strandveld, **Super Single Vineyards**, **Teddy Hall**, Township Winery, Trajan, Uitkyk, **Vierlanden**, Villiera, Warwick, Waterford, Waterstone (2), Welmoed, Whalehaven, **Woolworths** (2), Zorgvliet ★★★ Almenkerk, Anura, Backsberg, Badgerberg, Bellingham, Bilton, Blaauwklippen, Boland, Bon Cap (Organic), Boschendal, Boschkloof , **Boschrivier**, Breëland, Butcher Shop, Cape Classics, Cape Point, Cloof, Conradie, Darling Cellars, De Wetshof, Delheim, DeWaal, Dornier, Du Toitskloof , Durbanville Hills, Earthbound (Organic, Fairtrade), Ernst Gouws, Fairvalley (Fairtrade), Fairview, False Bay (2), Fat Bastard, Fleur du Cap, Foothills, Fort Simon, Four Paws, **Gantouw**, Glen Carlou, Goedverwacht, Goose Wines, Graham Beck, Guardian Peak, Hathersage, Helderberg, Herold, Hill & Dale, Hoopenburg, **Jakkalsvlei**, Ken Forrester, Klawer, **Kleine Zalze**, Koopmanskloof (Fairtrade), Kranskop, L'Avenir, La Chataigne, Lievland, Longbarn, Lord's, Louis, Louisvale, Lutzville, Lyngrove, MAN Family, **Marklew**, Miravel, Monterosso, Mount Rozier, Nabygelegen, Nederburg (2), Nelson, Niel Joubert, Onderkloof , Overgaauw, Overhex, PaardenKloof, Packwood, **Perdeberg** (2), Peter Falke, Porcupine Ridge, Rhino of Linton Park,

Rickety Bridge, Ridgeback, Seal Breeze, Seven Sisters, **Signal Gun**, Simonsig, Skilpadvlei, Slanghoek, Sophie & Mr P, Spier, Stanford Hills, Stellenbosch Hills, Teubes, Tread Lightly, uniWines, Val de Vie, Van Zylshof, **Vierkoppen**, Waterford, Welbedacht, Winters Drift, Wonderfontein, Woolworths, Yonder Hill, Zandvliet, Zonnebloem, Zorgvliet ★★☆ African Pride, Andersons, Asara, Ashton, Badsberg, Baleia Bay, **Barnardt Boyes**, Bon Courage, Bonnievale, Boplaas, Burgershof, Calitzdorp, Clairvaux, **Clive Torr**, Cloverfield, David Frost, **De Doorns**, De Wet, Die Mas, Diemersdal, Domaine des Dieux, Du Preez, Eagle's Cliff, Eikehof, Excelsior, Fairview, Flagstone, **Fort Simon**, Glenview, Goede Hoop, Goedvertrouw, Highlands Road, Hoopenburg, House of Mandela (Fairtrade), Juno, Kanu, Klein Parys, Klein Roosboom , Knorhoek, Koelenhof, L'Olivier, La Couronne, Landskroon, Libby's Pride, Linton Park, Louiesenhof, **M'hudi**, Mountain River (2), Muratie, Noble Savage, Nuweland, Obikwa, Orange River, Reiersvlei, Robertson (4), Roodezandt, Sauvignon.com, **Simonsvlei**, Slaley, Slowine, Somerbosch, Somerset Wines, Stellar (Organic, Fairtrade), Stellenzicht, Stettyn, Thandi (Fairtrade), **Thembi & Co** (2), Two Oceans, United Nations (Fairtrade), Vredenheim, Waterstone (2), Welbedacht, Wellington Winery, Windfall, Windmeul, Woolworths (3) (Organic, Light & low-alcohol, Fairtrade), Zidela ★★ Beau Joubert, Blue Crane, Boland, Brandvlei, Calais, Cape Dreams, D'Aria, De Bos (Fairtrade), Drostdy-Hof, Eagle's Cliff, **Eaglevlei** (Light & low-alcohol), Flat Roof Manor, **Goede Hoop**, Goudini, Grande Provence, Koelenhof, Lateganskop, **Leipzig**, Leopard's Leap, Lorraine, Lourensford, McGregor, Mountain Ridge, **Nicholson Smith**, Nuy, Rhebokskloof, Riebeek, Robertson (Light & low-alcohol), Rooiberg, Ruitersvlei, Savanha, Steenberg, Swartland, Tangled Tree, Tulbagh Winery, uniWines (Fairtrade), Van Loveren, Viljoensdrift, Walker Bay Vineyards, Wandsbeck, Waterstone, Weltevrede, Zevenwacht, **Zidela** (2) ★☆ Aan de Doorns, Bergwater (2), Corder, Havana Hills (Fairtrade), Imbuko, Kleine Draken (Kosher), Robertson (Light & low-alcohol), Rooiberg (Light & low-alcohol), Stellenbosch Hills, **Vin du Cap**, Vinopoly, Waterstone (2) ★ Long Mountain, Waterstone, Woolworths **NT**

Akkerdal, Bayede! (2), Bellevue, Blouvlei, Botha, Brenaissance, Brothers, Buffalo Creek, Bushmanspad, Camberley, Catch Of The Day, Devon Hill, Dormershire, Douglas Green, Du Preez, Dunstone, DuVon, Freedom Hill, Fryer's Cove (2), Galleon, Het Vlock Casteel, High Constantia (2), Hillock (2), Izak van der Vyver, Ken Forrester, Kingsriver, Klein Constantia, Klein Roosboom , Knorhoek, Linton Park, LuKa, Mimosa, Montpellier, Môreson (2), Nederburg (2) (Fairtrade), Noble Hill, Nomada, Old Vines, Ormonde, Robert Stanford, Rosendal (2), Rustenberg, Saam, Seven Steps, Spier, Star Hill, Stellenbosch University, Stoumann's, TCB Wines, Tokara, Trizanne, Tulbagh Winery, United Nations, Vaalvlei, Valley Vineyards (2), Versailles, Waboomsrivier, Waka Waka, Webersburg, Welgevallen, Welvanpas, Withoek, Wolvendrift, Zidela **NR** Flagstone, Usana **D** Boplaas (2), Fryer's Cove, Longridge, Montagu Wine Cellar, Nuweland, Post House, Rico Suter, SylvanVale, Thandi, Woolworths (2)

Sauvignon blanc wooded
★★★★★ **Diners Club Bartho Eksteen** , Reyneke

★★★★☆ Bloemendal, Cederberg, Delaire, Diemersdal, **Giant Periwinkle**, Hermanuspietersfontein, Hermit on the Hill, Iona, **Klein Constantia**, Mulderbosch, Nederburg, Quoin Rock, Reyneke (Biodynamic), Waterkloof

★★★★ Anura, Black Oystercatcher, **Boutinot**, Buitenverwachting, Butcher Shop, Cape Point, Catherine Marshall, D'Aria, Diners Club Bartho Eksteen , Eikendal, Goose Wines, Jordan, **La Petite Ferme**, La Vierge, Louis, Newton Johnson, Paul Cluver, Rickety Bridge, Steenberg, Tierhoek, Trizanne, Waterkloof

★★★☆ Backsberg, DeMorgenzon, Escapades, Glen Erskine, Hannay, Lourensford, Marianne, **Miravel**, Quoin Rock, **Spier**, Steenberg (2), Zevenwacht ★★★ Amani, Avontuur, Black Elephant, Opstal, Stark-Condé, Wildekrans ★★★ Schalkenbosch, Swartland ★★ Namaqua **NT** Cape Point, Hermit on the Hill, Lourensford, Meerendal, Mont Rochelle, Painted Wolf, Shannon, Stone Ridge

Semillon unwooded
★★★★ Lutzville, Zonnebloem

★★★☆ **Brunia** ★★★ Ormonde **NT** Nederburg **D** Withington

Semillon wooded
★★★★★ Vergelegen

★★★★☆ Bloemendal, Boekenhoutskloof, **Cederberg** (2), Constantia Uitsig, Fairview, **Mullineux**, **Sadie**

★★★★ **BLANKbottle**, **Boutinot**, Escapades, Fleur du Cap, Franschhoek Cellar, GlenWood, Haut Espoir, Landau du Val, Nitida, Rickety Bridge, Steenberg, **Thorne & Daughters**

★★★☆ Eaglevlei, Hathersage ★★★ Hildenbrand, La Chataigne **NT** Dornier, Lanner Hill, My Wyn, Shannon **D** Stellenzicht, Stony Brook

Sherry-Styles
★★★★ KWV (2), Monis

★★★★ Douglas Green (3), **Karusa**, Monis (2) ★★ Landzicht

Shiraz/syrah
★★★★★ Boekenhoutskloof, Boschendal, De Trafford, Fable, Porseleinberg

★★★★☆ Arra, Black Pearl, Boschendal, Boschkloof , Cederberg, Cirrus, D'Aria, De Grendel, De Trafford, Delheim, **DeMorgenzon**, **Diners Club Bartho Eksteen** , Dorrance, Eagles' Nest, Fairview (4), Flagstone, Foundry, GlenWood, Graham Beck, Groote Post, Hartenberg (3), Haskell (2), **Hidden Valley**, Hilton, Julien Schaal, **Keermont** (2), Kleine Zalze, La Motte, Lazanou (Organic), Lomond, Luddite, Metzer, Mont Destin, **Mullineux** (4), Muratie, Nederburg, Nico van der Merwe, Quoin Rock, Raka, Reyneke (2) (Biodynamic), **Richard Kershaw**, Rijk's, Robertson, Rust en Vrede (2), Saronsberg (2), Saxenburg (2), Schultz Family, Signal Hill, Sijnn, Simonsig (2), Super Single Vineyards, Vergelegen, Waterford, Waterkloof, Winery of Good Hope

★★★★ Aaldering, Aeternitas, Akkerdal, Almenkerk, Andreas, Annandale, **Annex Kloof**, Anura (2), Arra, Backsberg, **Beau Belle**, Bellingham, Bilton, Blaauwklippen, **Bloemendal**, Boland, Bon Courage, Bonnievale, Boschrivier, Butcher Shop, Cederberg, **Cloof** (2), Creation, Darling Cellars, De Breede (Organic), DeanDavid, Delheim, DeMorgenzon, Diners Club Bartho Eksteen , Domaine Brahms, Dombeya, Driehoek, Dunstone, Edgebaston, Elgin Vintners, Ernie Els, Fort Simon, Franschhoek Cellar, GlenWood,

Groenland, Groot Constantia, Hartenberg, Hermit on the Hill (2), Heron Ridge, Hildenbrand, Hilton, **Holden Manz**, Hoopenburg, House of Mandela, Joostenberg (Organic), Jordan, **Journey's End** (2), Katbakkies, Keermont, Kleine Zalze, Kloovenburg, La Bri, Ladera, Lammershoek, Land's End, Landskroon, Leeuwenberg, **Leeuwenkuil**, Lomond (2), Lyngrove, Lynx, M'hudi, Maison, Malanot, Metzer, Migliarina, Mimosa, MolenVliet, Mooiplaas, Nabygelegen, Nederburg, Nick & Forti's, Nico van der Merwe, Niel Joubert, Nuy, Org de Rac (Organic), Ormonde, PaardenKloof, Perdeberg, Porcupine Ridge, Quoin Rock, Rainbow's End, Remhoogte, Rhebokskloof, Rickety Bridge, Riebeek, Rijk's, Robert Stanford, Robertson, Rooiberg, **Rosendal**, Rudera, Saltare, Schultz Family, Spier, Star Hill, Stark-Condé (2), Steenberg, Stellekaya, Stellenrust, Stellenzicht, **Stofberg**, Stony Brook, Strandveld, **Strydom**, Swartland, **Tamboerskloof** (2), Thelema, Topiary, Val de Vie, Vergelegen, Vergenoegd (2) (Light & low-alcohol), Vondeling, Warwick, Waverley Hills (Organic), Welbedacht, Windmeul, Winery of Good Hope (Fairtrade), **Woolworths**, Zonnebloem

★★★☆ African Pride, Allegria, Allesverloren, **Alte Neffen**, Alto, Altydgedacht, Andy Mitchell, **Auction Crossing**, Avondale (Organic), Avontuur, Ayama, Babylonstoren, **Beau Belle**, Beau Joubert, Belfield, **Bellingham** (Organic), Benguela Cove, Bergheim, Bizoe, Blaauwklippen, Black Elephant, Blackwater, Bloemendal, Boland, Boplaas, Boschheim, Brenaissance, Brothers, Butcher Shop, Cape Dreams, Cape Point, Credo, Crows Nest, Darling Cellars, De Meye, Delaire, Devonvale, Diemersdal, Diemersfontein, Doolhof, **Drostdy-Hof**, Eerste Hoop, **Elana**, Elgin Heights, Ernst Gouws, Excelsior, Fairview (2), Faraway House, Fish Hoek, Fleur du Cap, Freedom Hill, Gabriëlskloof (2), Garden Route, Glen Carlou, Glenelly, Goede Hoop, Graham Beck, Grande Provence, Groenland, Hartenberg, **Hawksmoor** (2), Heron Ridge, Hout Bay, **Intellego** (2), Jacques Smit, Jordan, Joubert-Tradauw, Kaapzicht, Karusa, Katbakkies, Koelfontein, Koopmanskloof (Fairtrade), Kumala, Kyburg, La Chaumiere, La Petite Ferme, La Vierge, Linton Park (2), Louiesenhof, Lourensford, Lutzville, Lyngrove,

Maastricht, MAN Family, Marianne, Meerendal (2), Metzer, Middelvlei, Mont du Toit, Mont Rochelle, Mount Pleasant, **Mountain Ridge**, Namaqua, Naughton's, Nederburg, Neethlingshof, Nelson (2), Niel Joubert, Nieuwedrift, Nitida, Noble Hill, Oldenburg, Olifantsberg, Oude Denneboom, Peter Falke, Plaisir, Post House, **Rhebokskloof** (2), Ridgeback, Riebeek, Rivendell, Rustenberg, Scali, Seal Breeze, Seven Springs , Seven Steps, Signal Gun (2), Simonsig, Simonsvlei (3) (Light & low-alcohol), Skaap, Slaley, Spekulasie, **Spice Route**, Spring Grove, Stellendrift, Stellenrust, StoneyCroft, Stony Brook, Strandveld, Thandi (Fairtrade), Thelema, Tokara (2) (Light & low-alcohol), Topaz, Township Winery (Fairtrade), Trajan, Two Oceans, Uitkyk, Val du Charron, Van Loveren, Veenwouden, Vondeling, Wellington Winery (2), Weltevrede, Wildekrans, William Everson, **Woolworths**, Zandvliet, Zevenwacht, Zonnebloem ★★★ Abbottshill, Allée Bleue, Alvi's Drift, Amani, Annex Kloof, Antebellum, Asara, Audacia, Axe Hill, **Backsberg**, Bayede!, Bellevue, Bergheim, Blaauwklippen, Blue Crane, Bon Courage, Boschendal, Botha, Brampton, **Bridge**, Brunia, Bushmanspad, Cape Dreams, Cape to Cairo, **Carrol Boyes**, **Cavalli**, Chateau Naudé, Chennells, Claime d'Or, **Clive Torr**, **Conradie**, David Frost, Desert Rose, Doran, Dormershire (2), Du Toitskloof , Durbanville Hills, Foothills, **Fort Simon** (2), **Four Paws**, Fraai Uitzicht 1798, **Fram**, Freedom Hill, Giant Periwinkle, Goose Wines, Graceland, Grape Grinder, Guardian Peak, Havana Hills (2) (Fairtrade), Hills, Hofstraat, Holden Manz, Hoopenburg, Kanu, Klawer, Klein Roosboom , Kranskop, La Terre La Mer, Landskroon, Lanzerac, Le Fût, Lemberg, Leopard's Leap, Lievland, Londinium, Lord's, Lutzville, **M'hudi**, Malanot, MAN Family, Manley, **Marianne**, **Matzikama** (Organic), Mount Rozier, Mountain Ridge, Nederburg, Neil Ellis, **Nuweland**, Orange River, Org de Rac (Organic), Ormonde (2), Overhex, Place in the Sun (Fairtrade), Rhino of Linton Park, Riebeek, Rijk's, Robertson (3), Rooiberg, **Rosendal**, **Schenkfontein**, Scrucap, Silkbush, Simonsvlei, Slaley, Slanghoek, Slowine, Somersbosch, Southern Sky, Spier, Spotswood, Stellenzicht, **Stettyn**, Swartland, Thembi & Co (2), Tulbagh Winery, Vaalvlei, Viljoensdrift, Vin du Cap, Virgin Earth,

Vredenheim, **Waterstone** (5), Waverley Hills (Organic), Weltevrede, William Everson, Wine Fusion, Winters Drift, **Woestkloof**, Woolworths, Yonder Hill, Zandvliet ★★★ African Pride, Arra, Asara, Ashton, Ayama, **Baleia Bay**, **Barrydale**, Bayede!, Bellingham, Bellpost, Bergwater, Blomendahl, Bonview, **Clive Torr**, Corder, De Meye, De Wet, DeWaal, Die Mas, Douglas Green, Du Preez, Du'SwaRoo, Dunstone, Eerste Hoop, Excelsior, False Bay (2) (Light & low-alcohol), Fat Bastard, Four Secrets, Franschhoek Cellar, Goedverwacht, Goudini, Haut Espoir, Het Vlock Casteel, Hill & Dale, House of Mandela (2) (Fairtrade), Imbuko, Juno, Klein Parys, Koelenhof, La Couronne, **Ladismith**, Le Manoir de Brendel, Leeuwenkuil, Liberator, Mason's Winery, Mellasat, Mitre's Edge, **Nicholson Smith**, Phizante Kraal, Pulpit Rock (2), Rhebokskloof, Roodezandt, **Ses'Fikile**, Somerset Wines, **Stanford Hills** (2), Stellar (Organic, Fairtrade), Stellenbosch Hills, Stoumann's, **Vin du Cap**, Waterstone, Wederom, Welmoed, Winery of Good Hope, Wonderfontein, **Woolworths** (2) (Organic, Fairtrade) ★★ African Pride, **Bergwater**, Blomendahl, Bonnievale, Brandvlei, Calitzdorp, Clairvaux, Devonvale, Du Preez, Eikehof, Kumala, **Leipzig**, Libby's Pride, Mountain River (2), Namaqua, Obikwa, **Olsen**, Oude Compagnies Post, Reiersvlei, Savanha, Stellar (Organic, Fairtrade), **Taillard**, Tangled Tree, **uniWines** (Fairtrade), Vin du Cap, Waterstone (2), Windfall ★★ Axe Hill, Cranefields, Libby's Pride, Schalkenbosch, United Nations (Fairtrade), Waterstone ★ Long Mountain, McGregor, Vinopoly, Waterstone **NT** Andy Mitchell, AntHill, Arumdale, Boplaas, Calais, Camberley, Cape Rock, Catch Of The Day, Cloof, Clovelly, Cloverfield, Corder, Devon Hill, DewaldtHeyns, Doran, Durbanville Hills, DuVon, Eagle's Cliff, Fernskloof, Galleon, Gilga, Halala, Hawksmoor, Hermit on the Hill, Hillock, Kingsriver, Knorhoek, Lammershoek (Organic), Le Manoir de Brendel, Linton Park, Longridge, Lorraine, Lourensford, Lula, Mason's Winery, MC Square, Montpellier, Mooi Bly, My Wyn, Neil Ellis, New Beginnings, Nietvoorbij, Oak Valley, Onderkloof , Painted Wolf, Perdeberg, Rosendal, Ruitersvlei, Rustenberg, Saam (2), Signal Hill, Sijnn, Sir Lambert, Solms-Delta, Spotswood, Stellenbosch University, Stone Ridge (2),

TCB Wines, Three Foxes, Trizanne (2), TTT Cellar, Tulbagh Winery, United Nations (3), uniWines, Uva Mira, Vaalvlei, Versailles, Wellington Winery (2), Welvanpas, William Everson, Windmeul, Withoek, Zanddrift, Zidela **D** Babylon's Peak, Drostdy-Hof, Du'SwaRoo, Escapades, GlenWood, Group CDV, Observatory, Overhex (Fairtrade), Perdeberg, Rico Suter, Signal Hill, Spice Route, Thandi, Tulbagh Winery, Wederom, **Woolworths** (4) (Organic), Zidela

Sparkling, Méthode ancestrale
★★★★ Vondeling

★★★☆ AA Badenhorst, Scali

Sparkling, Méthode cap classique, red, dry
★★★ Nitida, Woolworths **NT** Camberley

Sparkling, Méthode cap classique, rosé, dry

★★★★☆ Ambeloui, Bon Courage, CharlesFox
★★★★ Chateau Naudé, **Clos Malverne**, Colmant, De Wetshof, Fairview, Graham Beck (2), Lourensford, Mount Babylon, Rickety Bridge, Saltare, Silverthorn, Simonsig, Steenberg, Sumaridge, Tanzanite, Twee Jonge/Krone, Woolworths

★★★☆ Allée Bleue, **Arendskloof**, Ayama, Barrydale, Boplaas, Boschendal, House of JC le Roux, Klein Optenhorst, L'Avenir, Ladismith, **Longridge**, Pongrácz, **Signal Gun**, Villiera, Webersburg, Weltevrede, Woolworths ★★★ Domaine des Dieux, Groote Post, Haute Cabrière, House of JC le Roux, Karusa, Leopard Frog, Packwood, Plettenvale ★★★ Namaqua ★★ **Wildekrans NT** Chabivin, Du Preez, Francois La Garde, **Môreson** (2), Ross Gower

Sparkling, Méthode cap classique, rosé, off-dry/semi-sweet
★★ Tulbagh Winery

Sparkling, Méthode cap classique, white, dry

★★★★★ Graham Beck

★★★★☆ Ameloui, Avondale (Organic), Boschendal, Cederberg, Colmant (2), De Wetshof, Graham Beck, House of GM&AHRENS, Klein Constantia, Longridge, Lourensford, Pongrácz, **Saltare**, Silverthorn (2), Simonsig, Tanzanite, Topiary, Twee Jonge/Krone, Villiera

★★★★ **Alvi's Drift**, Anura, Avontuur, Ayama, Bon Courage (2), Boschendal, Bramon, Buitenverwachting, CharlesFox, Constantia Uitsig, Darling Cellars, De Grendel, De Wet, Domaine des Dieux, Genevieve, Graham Beck, **Hildenbrand**, Hoopenburg, House of JC le Roux (2), **House of Mandela**, Hout Bay, **Kleine Zalze**, La Motte, Meerendal, Mooiplaas, Morgenhof, Muratie, **Newstead**, Nico van der Merwe, Niel Joubert, Org de Rac (Organic), **Perdeberg**, Pongrácz, Quoin Rock, **Rare Earth**, Rhebokskloof, Roodezandt, Saltare (2), Saronsberg, Saxenburg, Scrucap, Signal Hill, Simonsig, Steenberg, Sterhuis, Stony Brook, **Tanja Beutler**, Teddy Hall, **Thelema**, Twee Jonge/Krone, Van Loveren, Vergelegen, Viljoensdrift, Villiera (2), Webersburg, Weltevrede (2) (Light & low-alcohol), Wonderfontein, Woolworths (2)

★★★★ Allée Bleue, **Andy Mitchell**, Ayama, Backsberg, Badgerberg, Bon Cap (Organic), Boschendal, **Bramon**, Butcher Shop, Chabivin, Crios Bríde, **DeMorgenzon**, Diners Club Bartho Eksteen , Glen Carlou, Graham Beck, House of JC le Roux, Huis van Chevallerie, Kanu, Klein Parys, Klein Roosboom , **L'Avenir**, **Lateganskop**, Leopard's Leap, **Longridge**, Lord's, Môreson, Nitida, Perdeberg, Rickety Bridge, Ross Gower, Spier, **Spookfontein** , Teddy Hall, **Val de Vie**, **Waterford**, Waverley Hills (Organic), Welbedacht, Wellington Winery, Zorgvliet ★★★ Altydgedacht, Francois La Garde, Haute Cabrière, Highlands Road, Karusa, Ken Forrester, La Chaumiere, Leopard Frog, **Maison**, Plaisir, Riebeek, Robertson, Villiera (Light & low-alcohol), Virgin Earth, Wildekrans, Windfall ★★★ Backsberg (Kosher), **Domaine Coutelier**, Koelenhof, Nieuwedrift **NT** Cape Chamonix, Chabivin (3), De Zoete Inval, Du Preez, Elgin Heights, Francois La Garde, Groot Constantia, High Constantia, Klein Parys, Lovane, MC Square, Montpellier, Môreson, My Wyn, Old Vines, Re'Mogo, Saxenburg, Schalkenbosch, Skaap, Somerbosch **D** Haute Cabrière (3), Thandi, Woolworths

Sparkling, Méthode cap classique, white, off-dry/semi-sweet
★★★★ Colmant

★★★★ Groot Parys (Organic), South Hill ★★★ Graham Beck ★★★ House of JC le Roux

Sparkling, Non-MCC, red, dry
★★ House of JC le Roux (Light & low-alcohol), Van Loveren

Sparkling, Non-MCC, red, off-dry/semi-sweet
★★★ Four Secrets ★★★ Du Toitskloof (Light & low-alcohol), Solms-Delta ★★ Robertson ★★ House of JC le Roux

Sparkling, Non-MCC, rosé, dry
★★★ Boplaas, Kloovenburg ★★★ Somerset Wines (Light & low-alcohol), **Stellar**, Thandi ★★ **Mountain Ridge NT** Knorhoek

Sparkling, Non-MCC, rosé, off-dry/semi-sweet
★★★ Klawer, **Rhebokskloof**, Swartland ★★★ Aan de Doorns, Alvi's Drift (Light & low-alcohol), Bergwater, Cold Duck (5th Avenue) (Light & low-alcohol), Goedverwacht, Orange River, Stellenbosch Hills, Vredenheim ★★ Bon Courage, **Long Mountain** (Light & low-alcohol), Robertson (Light & low-alcohol), Rooiberg (Light & low-alcohol), Van Loveren (2), Viljoensdrift (Light & low-alcohol), Woolworths ★★ Koelenhof, Overhex (Light & low-alcohol), **Stellar** ★ Ashton **NT** Bayede!, Perdeberg (Light & low-alcohol), Wellington Winery **D** Rhebokskloof

Sparkling, Non-MCC, white, dry
★★★★ Hermit on the Hill ★★★ Clos Malverne, Du Toitskloof , House of JC le Roux, Nederburg, Orange River, **Steenberg**, Swartland ★★★ Bergwater, Botha, Obikwa, Riebeek, Robertson, Stellar (Organic), Tulbagh Winery, Van Loveren, Welmoed ★★ Alvi's Drift, Bonnievale, Goudini, Overhex, Slanghoek, Woolworths ★★ Woolworths **NT** Bergsig, Bon Cap (Organic), Merwida, Perdeberg **D** Wellington Winery

Sparkling, Non-MCC, white, off-dry/semi-sweet
★★★ Twee Jonge/Krone ★★★ Alvi's Drift (Light & low-alcohol), Badsberg (Light & low-alcohol), **Eaglevlei**, Koelenhof, Nuy, Opstal, Orange River (Light & low-alcohol), Van Loveren, Woolworths ★★ House of JC le Roux (Light & low-alcohol), Kleine Draken (Light & low-alcohol, Kosher), Overhex (Light & low-alcohol), Robertson (Light & low-alcohol), Rooiberg (2), Slanghoek, Tulbagh Winery, Van Loveren ★★ De Doorns, Grand Mousseux, Van Loveren

Special Late Harvest

★★★★ Nederburg

★★★☆ Backsberg, Drostdy-Hof ★★★ Badsberg, Robertson, Roodezandt ★★☆ Bon Courage, Fairview, Slanghoek ★★☆ Wellington Winery **NT** Bergsig, Van Loveren

Sweet red

★★★☆ Dormershire ★★★ Fairview, Perdeberg, **Simonsig**, **Stellar** ★★ Backsberg (Sacramental, Kosher), Bottelary, Cape Classics, Darling Cellars, **Du Toitskloof** (Light & low-alcohol), Louiesenhof, Overhex (Light & low-alcohol), RED ESCape, Robertson, Somerset Wines, Waterstone, Woolworths ★★ Cloverfield, Hartswater, Imbuko, Kumala, Robertson, **RobinHood**, Tulbagh Winery ★ Autumn Harvest Crackling (Perlé), Cellar Cask, **Kumala**, Riebeek **NT** Lynx, Signal Hill

Sylvaner

NT Overgaauw

Tannat

★★★☆ Fairview, Glen Carlou, Mooi Bly

Tempranillo/tinta roriz

★★★ De Krans, Dornier

Tinta barocca

★★★★☆ Sadie

★★★★ Momento

★★★☆ Boplaas, De Krans, Nuweland ★★★ Allesverloren, BLANKbottle, Jeu, Swartland ★★☆ Boplaas **NT** Reiersvlei **D** De Krans

Touriga nacional

★★★★☆ Sijnn

★★★★ De Krans

★★★☆ MAN Family, Overgaauw ★★★ Allesverloren, Bergsig, Boplaas, Dagbreek, Reiersvlei ★★☆ Calitzdorp

Verdelho

★★★★ Feiteiras ★★★ Flagstone

Vin de paille

★★★★★ Mullineux

★★★★☆ Druk My Niet, Fairview, Keermont, Meinert, Nuweland, Rustenberg, Tierhoek (Light & low-alcohol), Vergelegen, Vondeling (Light & low-alcohol), Winery of Good Hope

★★★★ Boplaas, Donkiesbaai, Goede Hoop, Lemberg, Maison, Saronsberg, Stellar (Organic, Fairtrade), **Winery of Good Hope**

★★★☆ Asara, De Trafford (Light & low-alcohol), **Fledge & Co**, Môreson, Orange River, Signal Hill, Simonsig, **Stettyn** ★★★ Mellasat, Naughton's **NT** Fairview, Groot Parys (Organic), La Motte

Viognier

★★★★☆ Buitenverwachting, Eagles' Nest, Elgin Vintners, Foundry, Ridgeback

★★★★ Alvi's Drift, Backsberg, Beau Constantia, Creation, Diemersfontein, Fairview, Flagstone, Four Paws, **Grande Provence**, Idiom, Kanu, La Petite Ferme, Mellasat, Nick & Forti's, Painted Wolf, Spice Route, Tamboerskloof

★★★☆ Arra (2), Babylonstoren, Bellingham, Bilton, Black Elephant, Cloof, De Grendel, **Elsenburg**, Fledge & Co, Gabriëlskloof, Glen Erskine, Hermit on the Hill, Katbakkies, Klawer, Kranskop, La Bri, Lazanou (Organic), Lynx, **Mitre's Edge**, Noble Hill, Rhebokskloof, Saronsberg, Star Hill, Stonehill, Topaz ★★★ Anura, Auction Crossing, Calais, Chennells, **Clive Torr**, Corder, Excelsior, Fairview, Fort Simon, Graham Beck, Karusa, Katbakkies, Maison, Riebeek, Robertson, Schalkenbosch, Silkbush, Waterkloof ★★☆ **Ayama**, Eerste Hoop, **Fraai Uitzicht 1798**, Lynx, Spotswood, Township Winery (Fairtrade), Welmoed ★★ Arra, **Leipzig** ★☆ TTT Cellar **NT** Bon Cap (Organic), High Constantia (2), Hilton, Le Joubert, Lorraine, Lourensford, Lutzville, Montpellier, My Wyn, Naughton's, Nederburg, Niel Joubert, Spring Grove, Stellenbosch University, Woolworths **D** Ayama, Blaauwklippen, Boplaas, DeWaal, Fleur du Cap, Nuweland, Winery of Good Hope

White blends, off-dry/semi-sweet (w & u/ w)

★★★★ BLANKbottle, Butcher Shop, Painted Wolf, Solms-Delta, Waterford, Wine Fusion

★★★☆ Amani, **Bramon**, Virgin Earth ★★★ Altydgedacht, Bellpost, Boland, De Wetshof, Edgebaston, Havana Hills, Kanu, Onderkloof , Opstal, Robertson, **Signal Gun**, Villiera, Woolworths ★★☆ Boschendal, **Calitzdorp** (Perlé), Douglas Green, Drostdy-Hof, Du Toitskloof , Grande Provence, Group CDV (Perlé), Grünberger (Perlé), Leeuwenjacht, **Overhex** (2), **RobinHood**,

Stellar (Organic, Fairtrade), Stellenrust, Tulbagh Winery, Two Oceans, Zevenwacht ★★ Ashton (Perlé), Capenheimer (Perlé), Darling Cellars, Fleur du Cap (Light & low-alcohol), Graça, Koelenhof, Overhex (Light & low-alcohol), Overmeer Cellars, Robertson (3), Slanghoek, Swartland, Tulbagh Winery, Vinopoly, Waterstone ★★ Autumn Harvest Crackling (Perlé), Botha (Light & low-alcohol), Cellar Cask, **Kumala** (2), Robertson, **Vinopoly**, Wellington Winery, Woolworths (2) (Light & low-alcohol) ★ Drostdy-Hof, Virginia **NT** Bayede!, Bergsig (Perlé), Bonnievale, Imbuko, Landzicht, Montpellier, TTT Cellar, Virgin Earth, Waka Waka **D** Buitenverwachting, Du Toitskloof (Perlé), Rooiberg, Woolworths

White blends, unwooded, dry

★★★★☆ Ashbourne, Berrio

★★★★ Barton, **Boplaas**, Bouchard Finlayson, Grande Provence, **Kaapzicht**, Spier, Waterford, Woolworths, Zonnebloem

★★★☆ Allée Bleue, Ayama, Barton, Beaumont, Buitenverwachting, Creation, Elgin Vintners, Flagstone, Foothills, Goats do Roam (Fairtrade), Groot Constantia, Groote Post, Haute Cabrière, Jean Daneel, Joostenberg (Organic), Lammershoek (Organic), **Leeuwenberg**, **Lynx**, Quando, Teddy Hall, Thandi (Fairtrade), Thokozani, Tierhoek, Truter Family, Wellington Winery, **Wildehurst**, Wine Fusion ★★★ Ashbourne, Ayama, Boschendal, Darling Cellars, De Zoete Inval, Diemersfontein, Douglas Green, **Eikehof**, Glen Carlou, Imbuko, Jordan, Karusa, Koopmanskloof, Kumala, Lanzerac, Leeuwenjacht, Longridge, **Mellasat**, Mooiplaas, Nabygelegen, Napier, Nederburg, Neil Ellis, Noble Hill, Old Vines, Opstal, **Overhex** (2) (Fairtrade), Post House, **Reyneke** (Organic), **Saronsberg**, Saxenburg (2), Slowine, Solms-Delta, Stettyn, **SylvanVale**, Theuniskraal, uniWines, Vergenoegd, Villiera, Vondeling, Wandsbeck, Whalehaven, Woolworths (2), Zonnebloem

★★★ Asara, Beau Joubert, Bellingham, Beyerskloof, **BLANKbottle**, Bon Cap (Organic), Bon Courage, Boschendal, **Boutinot** (2), Brandvlei, Cloof, Darling Cellars, Diemersfontein, Doolhof, Dorrance, **Du Toitskloof**, Group CDV, **Jakkalsvlei**, Kumala (2), Landskroon, Louisvale, Morgenhof, Nabygelegen, Namaqua, Pulpit

Rock, Rustenberg, Savanha (Fairtrade), Simonsvlei, Spier, **Springfontein**, Stellar (Organic, Fairtrade), Stellenbosch Hills, Stellenrust (Fairtrade), Thandi (Fairtrade), Veenwouden, **Villiersdorp**, **Waterstone**, **Woolworths** (4) (Light & low-alcohol) ★★ African Pride, Hathersage, Kanu, Kumala (2), **Nicholson Smith**, Rhino of Linton Park, Robertson (2), Savanha, Schalkenbosch (2), Somerset Wines, Stellar (2) (Organic, Fairtrade), uniWines, Van Loveren, **Viljoensdrift**, Zandvliet ★★ Drostdy-Hof, **Kumala**, Leopard's Leap, Nuy, Robertson (Light & low-alcohol), Simonsvlei, Wellington Winery ★ Overmeer Cellars, Robertson (2) (Light & low-alcohol), Van Loveren (2) (Light & low-alcohol) ✦ Drostdy-Hof (Light & low-alcohol), Oom Tas **NT** Doran, Four Paws, Group CDV, Joostenberg, Klein Parys, Lazanou (Organic), Môreson, Mountain Oaks (Organic), Mountain River, Nederburg, Nico Vermeulen, Oude Denneboom, Re'Mogo, Somerbosch, Stellendrift, Two Oceans (2), Van Loveren, Vendôme, **Wavescape**, Welvanpas, Withington **D** Avontuur, Doolhof, Jordan, Kaapzicht, Knorhoek, Rico Suter, Whalehaven, Zandvliet

White blends, wooded, dry

★★★★★ Constantia Uitsig, David & Nadia Sadie, DeMorgenzon, Flagstone, Miles Mossop, Oak Valley, Sadie (2)

★★★★☆ AA Badenhorst, Adoro, Alheit, Anatu, Avondale (Organic), **Bergsig**, Bizoe, Black Oystercatcher, Bloemendal, Cape Chamonix, Cape Point (2), Cape Rock, Cederberg, Constantia Glen, Delaire, Dornier, Dorrance, Ernst Gouws, Fable, Fairview, Hermanuspietersfontein, Hughes Family (Organic), Lammershoek, Lemberg, Lourensford, **Momento**, Môreson, Mullineux, Muratie, Nederburg, Newton Johnson, Nico van der Merwe, Nitida, **Olifantsberg**, Rall, Sadie, Savage, Scali (Organic), Sequillo, Sijnn, **Simonsig**, Solms-Delta, Steenberg, Sterhuis, Strandveld, Sumaridge, **Thorne & Daughters**, Tokara, Vergelegen, Vondeling, Welgegund, Woolworths

★★★★ AA Badenhorst, Allée Bleue, Alvi's Drift, Backsberg, Bellingham, **BLANKbottle** (2), Bosman (Fairtrade), Celestina, Darling Cellars, Du Toitskloof, **Elemental Bob**, Escapades, Gabriëlskloof, **Grande Provence**, Groot Constantia, Keermont, Leeuwenkuil, **Liberator**,

Lomond (2), Morgenster, **Mulderbosch**, **Nabygelegen**, Neethlingshof, Neil Ellis, **Rickety Bridge**, Sterhuis, Stony Brook, Thelema, **Trizanne**, Vuurberg, Waterkloof, Welbedacht, Yardstick

★★★☆ Alvi's Drift, Anatu, Anura, Bergheim, **Black Elephant**, **Blake**, **Cavalli**, Eerste Hoop, **Fijndraai**, Glen Erskine, Highlands Road, **Hildenbrand**, Idiom, Joostenberg, Laibach (Organic), Malanot, Metzer, Nuweland, Porcupine Ridge, Stellenbosch Hills, Stellenbosch Vineyards, Stony Brook, **Waterford**, Waverley Hills (Organic), Wolftrap, Zevenwacht, Zorgvliet

★★★ Beau Constantia, Doolhof, Hildenbrand, Karusa, Kumala, **Leipzig**, Leopard's Leap, Nederburg, **Perdeberg**, Raka, Ridgeback, Stark-Condé, Twee Jonge/Krone, Two Oceans, **uniWines**, Val de Vie, **Waterford** ★★★ Bergheim, Kumala (2), Namaqua (2), Savanha, Strydom, Woolworths ★★ Kumala **NT** Altydgedacht, AntHill, Babylon's Peak, D'Aria, Dragonridge, Gilga, Hermit on the Hill, Hillock, Jean Daneel, Klein Parys, Lanner Hill, Liberator, Mountain Oaks, My Wyn, Nederburg (2), Nomada, Orangerie, Osbloed, Steenberg, Val du Charron, Waverley Hills (Organic), Withington **D** De Grendel, Drostdy-Hof, Fleur de Cap, Klein Constantia, Manley, Observatory, Olifantsberg, Paardebosch, Perdeberg, Quoin Rock, Reyneke (Organic), Woolworths

Zinfandel/Primitivo
★★★☆ Blaauwklippen (2), Glen Carlou, **Grande Provence**, Idiom

The Industry

Overview

According to the latest available data (2013), South Africa is the 9th largest wine-producing nation by volume. Italy, with 16.2% of global production, is the new number one producer, followed by Spain (15.4%) and France (15.1%). South Africa, with ±1,097m litres (excluding grape juice and grape juice concentrate), in 2013 maintained its 4% contribution to global volume, though the number of wine-grape growers in South Africa continued to decline (3,323 compared with 3,440 the previous year).

The overall number of wine cellars crushing grapes dipped, to 564, as did the number of private cellars, from 509 in 2012 to 493, reversing a long-term trend. (Producing wholesalers crushing grapes again were slightly down, to 21, while co-operatives — 'producer cellars' in officialese — were steady at 50). Though their number continued to decline in 2013, to 240, micro-cellars vinifying fewer than 100 tonnes still constituted ±43% of all producers and thus remained a potent force in the industry.

Vineyards

Adjusted official figures reveal a significant decline in new vineyard establishment over the past decade, from 5,958 ha to just 1,987 in 2013

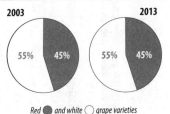

Red ● and white ○ grape varieties
as % of total area

(the rate of uprooting remained fairly steady at an average of ±4,000 ha per annum).

In 2013, planting for white wine overtook that for red (1,032 ha vs 955), and white-wine grape chenin retained its entrenched position as most-planted variety (388 ha added). Colombard remained the second most-planted white-wine variety, with 237 ha, followed by sauvignon (96) and chardonnay (69). Pinotage, with 310 ha, again outpaced shiraz (154) as most-planted red-wine variety, followed by ruby cab (125) and cab (119).

As ever, much more chenin was uprooted than planted, but the variety still led the overall hectareage table, with 18% of the total 99,680 ha under vine. Cab, with ±12%, remains the leading red. The percentage of very young vines (under

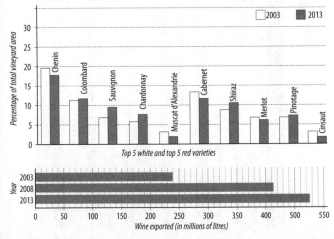

South African Wine Industry — Ten-Year Overview

	2004	2005	2006	2007	2008	2009	2010	2011	2012	2013
Number of wineries	561	581	576	560	585	604	573	582	582	564
Total vine area (excl sultana) (hectares)	100 207	101 607	102 146	101 957	101 325	101 259	101 016	100 568	100 093	99 680
Producing area 4 yrs & older (excl sultana) (hectares)	85 331	87 284	89 426	91 326	92 503	93 285	93 198	92 621	91 867	91 972
Avg yield (tons/hectare)	15.38	13.42	14.55	14.80	15.41	14.45	13.53	14.06	15.40	16.30
Avg grape price — producer cellars/co-ops (R/ton)	1458	1387	1362	1434	1522	1918	1814	1933	1981	not avail
Avg grape price — excl producer cellars/co-ops (R/ton)	4133	3593	3128	2971	3173	3917	3949	3801	3930	not avail
Grapes crushed (millions of tons)	1.31	1.17	1.30	1.35	1.43	1.35	1.26	1.30	1.41	1.50
Total production (millions of litres)	1015.7	905.2	1013.0	1043.5	1089.0	1033.4	984.8	1012.8	1097.0	1156.9
Domestic sales (millions of litres)	338.4	334.2	337.4	355.5	355.8	338.3	346.4	353.3	363.0	369.4
Consumption per capita (litres SA wine)	7.26	7.13	7.12	7.43	7.31	6.86	6.93	6.98	7.01	6.97
Export volume (millions of litres)	267.7	281.1	271.7	312.5	411.7	395.6	378.5	357.4	417.2	525.6
Stock (millions of litres)	363.7	339.4	403.1	425.2	357.2	361.7	351.0	417.5	433.0	401.9
Stock : sales ratio	0.60:1	0.55:1	0.66:1	0.64:1	0.47:1	0.49:1	0.48:1	0.59:1	0.55:1	0.45:1

4 years) decreased fractionally in 2013 to 7.7%, while 19.2% are older than 20, slightly more than previously.

Exports

Exports continued to rebound in 2013 to reach a new ten-year high of 525,6 m litres, or ±57% of South Africa's total wine production. Chenin and sauvignon (overtaking chardonnay) topped the list of most-exported varietal wines (bottled and bulk), with in-vogue pinks, cab, shiraz, pinotage and merlot also in demand. France edged the US out of the the top five markets for SA wine (packaged and bulk) in 2013, with stalwarts UK and Germany, and fast-growing Russia in the top three slots. When it comes to packaged wine only, UK, Sweden, Germany, the Netherlands and US top the list.

Local wine consumption

South African domestic per-capita wine consumption in 2013 decreased fractionally for the first time in four years, to 6.97L.

While wine's combined market share (natural, fortified and sparkling) increased slightly to 16.5% in 2013, it remained substantially lower than beer (56.5%). Brandy's 5.3% share continued to decline, while whisky's 6.6% represented steady incremental growth.

Of natural wine sold in South Africa during 2013 (including locally bottled imports), 50.3% was in glass, of which about half was in the standard 750 ml bottle. Wine in bag-in-box accounted for a steady ±27% of total sales, plastic containers ±21% and Tetra packs ±2%. Foil bags — the notorious *papsakke*, now carefully regulated — represented only 0.7%.

Note

Statistical data was provided by SA Wine Industry Information & Systems.

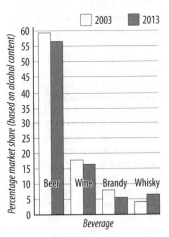

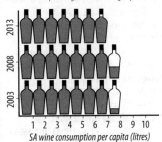

SA wine consumption per capita (litres)

Wine Industry Organisations

African Vintners Alliance Marketing: Vivian Kleynhans ▪ **T +27 (0)71-049-4109** ▪ ava@africanrootswines.com
Established to create an enabling environment for emerging black-owned wineries.

Agricultural Ethical Trade Initiative (WIETA) CEO: Linda Lipparoni ▪ **T +27 (0)21-880-0580** ▪ F +27 (0)21-880-0580 ▪ linda@wieta.org.za; info@wieta.org.za ▪ www.wieta.org.za
Multi-stakeholder, non-profit, voluntary

organisation established in 2002 to promote ethical trade in wine, fruit, cut flowers and general agriculture. WIETA has adopted a code of labour standards for the industry, and its main task is to support, enhance and promote members' ethical performance and best practice through training, technical assessments and ethical inspections to assess compliance. WIETA recently adopted an ethical seal which has been endorsed by the wine industry in recognition of wine supply chains' ethical commitment to good working conditions on farms and in cellars.

ARC Infruitec-Nietvoorbij Acting research institute manager: Hennie du Plessis ▪ Public relations officer: Derusha Rangasamy ▪ **T +27 (0)21-809-3100** ▪ F +27 (0)21-809-3400 ▪ infocape@arc.agric.za ▪ www.arc.agric.za Internationally regarded one-stop research institute, committed to provide sustainable technologies to the developing and commercial agricultural sectors in South Africa, through leading and dynamic research, technology development and technology transfer.

Biodiversity & Wine Initiative (BWI) See WWF-SA Biodiversity & Wine Initiative.

Cape Port Producers' Association Chair: Carel Nel ▪ **T +27 (0)44-213-3326** ▪ F +27 (0)44-213-3750 ▪ boplaas@mweb.co.za

Cape Vintner Classification Manager: Charl Theron ▪ info@cvc1659.co.za ▪ www.cvc1659.co.za Independent body committed to the accreditation, governance, representation and promotion of distinctive regional site-specific Cape wines.

Cape Winemakers Guild (CWG) Chair: Andries Burger ▪ General Manager: Kate Jonker ▪ **T +27 (0)21-852-0408** ▪ F +27 (0)21-852-0409 ▪ info@capewinemakersguild.com ▪ www.capewinemakersguild.com Independent, invitation-only association, founded in 1982 to promote winemaking excellence among its members. Since 1985, the CWG has held a highly regarded annual public auction. Established in 1999, the Nedbank CWG Development Trust supports social development in the winelands through its Protégé Programme, which plays an active role in transformation of the wine industry, ensuring its long-term health and sustainability. The Guild also offers Billy Hofmeyr AGRI Seta bursaries to final year Viticulture & Oenology students.

Chardonnay Forum of South Africa Chair: Matthew van Heerden ▪ matthew@webersburg.co.za ▪ **T +27 (0)21-881-3636 / +27 (0)82-520-9338** ▪ F +27 (0)21-881 3217

Chenin Blanc Association (CBA) Chair: Ken Forrester ▪ **T +27 (0)21-855-2374 / +27 (0)82-783-7203** ▪ F +27 (0)21-855-2373 ▪ ken@kenforresterwines.com ▪ www.chenin.co.za ▪ Manager: Ina Smith ▪ T +27 (0)82-467-4331 ▪ F +27 (0)86-672-8549 ▪ ina.smith@iafrica.com ▪ @CheninBlancAsso

Fairtrade Africa - Southern Africa Network (FTA-SAN) Regional head: Faith Muisyo ▪ **T+27 (0)21-448-8911** ▪ f.muisyo@fairtradeafrica.net ▪ www.fairtradeafrica.net. FTA-SAN represents Southern African Fairtrade producers in the global Fairtrade system on issues related to governance, new price setting, standards consultation and making standards more relevant to local farming practices. FTA-SAN supports producers with their development program, market access and promotes south-south trade and intra-Africa trade.

Fairtrade Label South Africa (FLSA) Executive director: Arianna Baldo ▪ **T +27 (0)21-448-8911** ▪ info@fairtradesa.org.za ▪ www.fairtradesa.org.za FLSA was established in 2009 to create a Fairtrade market in South Africa, and increase awareness about Fairtrade and ethical farming practices among local businesses and consumers. Wine is one of the key Fairtrade products, and an increasing number of local farms and wineries choose Fairtrade as endorsement for their sound ethical and environmental practices.

Garagiste Movement Coordinator: Tanja Beutler ▪ **T +27 (0)21-855-4275** ▪ F +27 (0)86-612-6118 ▪ tanja@topazwines.co.za

Institute of Cape Wine Masters Chair: Winifred Bowman ▪ **T +27 (0)83-702-3665** ▪ Secretary: Margaret Fry ▪ T +27 (0)83-628-6511 ▪ F +27 (0)86-611-7150 ▪ capewinemasters@gmail.com ▪ www.capewinemasters.co.za Successful completion of examinations set since 1983 by the Cape Wine & Spirit Education Trust and, latterly, the Cape Wine Academy, have qualified 91 Cape Wine Masters. Their Institute runs tasting workshops, charts trends and names a Wine Personality of the Year.

Integrated Production of Wine (IPW) Manager: Daniël Schietekat ▪ **T +27 (0)21-889-6555** ▪ F +27 (0)866-903-224 ▪ daniel@ipw.co.za ▪ www.ipw.co.za Innovative, widely supported initiative aimed at producing wine in an environmentally sustainable, profitable way by means of guidelines for both farm and cellar, embracing all aspects of grape production, winemaking and biodiversity conservation. See also WWF-SA Biodiversity & Wine Initiative and Sustainable Wine South Africa.

Méthode Cap Classique Producers' Association Chair: Peter Ferreira ▪ bubblesferreira@gmail.com ▪ Admin: Elsabe Ferreira ▪ **T +27(0)21-863-1599** ▪ F +27 (0)21-863-1552 ▪ info@capclassique.co.za

Muscadel SA Chair: Henri Swiegers ▪ **T +27 (0)23-344-3021** ▪ F +27 (0)86-617-9443 ▪ winemaker@badsberg.co.za ▪ Vice-chair: André Scriven ▪ **T +27 (0)23-626-1664** ▪ andres@rooiberg.co.za

Pinotage Association Chair: Beyers Truter ▪ T +27 (0)21-865-1235 ▪ F +27 ()21-865-2683 ▪ reception@beyerskloof.co.za ▪ Manager: Elsabe Ferreira T +27 (0)21-863-1599 ▪ F +27 (0)21-863-1552 ▪ admin@pinotage.co.za ▪ www.pinotage.co.za

Sauvignon Blanc Interest Group of South Africa (SBIG) Admin: Elsabe Ferreira ▪ **T +27 (0)21-863-1599** ▪ F +27 (0)21-863-1552 ▪ elsabe@efpromosies.co.za

Shiraz South Africa Chair: Edmund Terblanche ▪ **T +27 (0)82-770-2929** ▪ F +27 (0)21-876-3446 ▪ et.cellar@la-motte.co.za ▪ Secretary: Sandra Lotz ▪ **T +27 (0)82-924-7254** ▪ F +27 (0)86-267-4333 ▪ info@shirazsa.co.za

South African Black Vintners Alliance See African Vintners Alliance

South African Port Producers' Association (SAPPA) See Cape Port Producers' Association

South African Sommelier Association (SASA) Chair: Neil Grant ▪ Vice-chair: David Clarke ▪ info@sommeliers.org.za, membership@sommeliers.org.za ▪ www.sommeliers.org.za
Membership-driven, non-profit, voluntary private organisation established in 2012 to promote a culture of fine wine, food and service excellence in South Africa; formalise the profession of sommelier; and provide a forum for dialogue, exchange of ideas, knowledge and skills.

South African Wine Industry Information & Systems (SAWIS) Executive Manager: Yvette van der Merwe ▪ **T +27 (0)21-807-5703** ▪ F +27 (0)86-559-0274 ▪ info@sawis.co.za
Responsible for the collection, processing and dissemination of industry information. Administers the Wine of Origin (WO) system and manages the Information Centre, a comprehensive information resource base for the South African wine and brandy industry.

South African Wine Industry Trust (SAWIT) Chair: Sharron Marco-Thyse ▪ CEO: Charles Erasmus ▪ **T +27(0)21-889-8101** ▪ F +27 (0)86-503-6222 ▪ sawit@live.co.za ▪ www.sawit.co.za
The vision of SAWIT is the creation of a transformed wine industry that is sustainable and vibrant, populated by an empowered worker community that shares equitably in growth and prosperity.

Southern Africa Fairtrade Network (SAFN) See Fairtrade Africa Southern Africa Network

Sustainable Wine South Africa
www.swsa.co.za ▪ Contact details as for individual organisations.
Alliance between the Wine & Spirit Board (WSB), Integrated Production of Wine (IPW), Biodiversity & Wine Initiative (BWI) and Wines of South Africa (WOSA), driving the industry's commitment to sustainable, eco-friendly production.

Wine & Spirit Board Chair: Matome Mbatha ▪ Secretary: Hugo van der Merwe ▪ **T +27 (0)21-889-6555** ▪ F +27 (0)21-889-5823 ▪ hugo@wsb.org.za
Mainly administers the Wine of Origin, Estate Brandy and Integrated Production of Wine (IPW) schemes.

Wine & Agricultural Ethical Trade Association (WIETA) See Agricultural Ethical Trade Initiative.

Wines of South Africa (WOSA) Chair: Michael Jordaan ▪ michael@bartinney.co.za ▪ CEO: Siobhan Thompson ▪ **T +27 (0)21-883-3860** ▪ F +27 (0)21-883-3861 ▪ info@wosa.co.za ▪ www.wosa.co.za
Generic marketing organisation, responsible for raising the profile of SA wine in key export markets.

Wine Industry Development Association (WIDA) Executive Manager: Henry Petersen ▪ **T** +27 (0)21-872-9181 ▪ F +27 (0)2-872-4560 ▪ henry@wida.co.za, sally@wida.co.za ▪ www.wida.co.za

Promotes transformation through social development, human resource development and training, economic empowerment, and industrial relations, and protects the interests of vulnerable communities in the industry.

Wine Industry Network of Expertise & Technology (WINETECH) Executive manager: Gerard Martin ▪ **T** +27 (0)21-276 0498 ▪ F +27 (0)86-611-7846 ▪ marting@winetech.co.za

Coordinates the research, training and technology transfer programmes of participating institutions and individuals, to improve the competitiveness of the wine industry.

WWF-SA Biodiversity & Wine Initiative (BWI) bwi@wwf.org.za ▪ www.wwf.org.za/bwi ▪ Programme manager: Martin Albertus ▪ **T** +27 (0)21-882-9085 ▪ F +27 (0)865-359-433 ▪ malbertus@wwf.org.za ▪ Senior extension officer: Joan Isham ▪ **T** +27 (0)21-886-4080 ▪ F +27 (0)865-359-433 ▪ jisham@wwf.org.za

Pioneering conservation partnership between the wine industry and conservation sector, aiming to protect places of outstanding conservation value and iconic species, and to maintain living and productive landscapes. This is achieved by steering expansion away from threatened natural vegetation and fostering a culture of sustainable production through ecologically-sound land use practices. Demonstrating laudable commitment and buy-in, producers have set aside highly threatened natural areas well in excess of the industry's 99,680 ha vineyard footprint. Today, thanks to the WWF Biodiversity & Wine Initiative (BWI), South African wines lead the world in production integrity, environmental sustainability and conservation. Consumers can support accredited BWI members by buying wines displaying the colourful 'conservation in action' logo, depicting a sugarbird and a protea. See also Integrated Production of Wine and Sustainable Wine South Africa.

Winegrowing Areas

From modest beginnings in the Dutch East India Company's 17th-century gardens below Table Mountain, South Africa's vineyards now cover 99,680 ha and more than 100 official appellations. Changes to the Wine of Origin (WO) scheme of 1972/3 saw 'geographical units' incorporated into the WO classification alongside 'regions', 'districts' and 'wards' (the latter have the

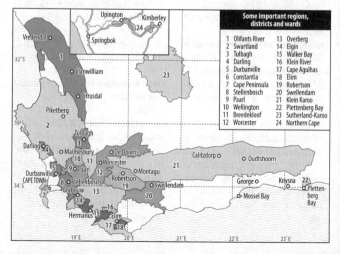

Some important regions, districts and wards			
1	Olifants River	13	Overberg
2	Swartland	14	Elgin
3	Tulbagh	15	Walker Bay
4	Darling	16	Klein River
5	Durbanville	17	Cape Agulhas
6	Constantia	18	Elim
7	Cape Peninsula	19	Robertson
8	Stellenbosch	20	Swellendam
9	Paarl	21	Klein Karoo
10	Wellington	22	Plettenberg Bay
11	Breedekloof	23	Sutherland-Karoo
12	Worcester	24	Northern Cape

The Industry

smallest footprint of the WO areas, following earlier amendments to the 'estate' legislation). Below are brief notes on the most important grape cultivation zones. Information supplied by Wines of South Africa (WOSA) and SA Wine Industry Information & Systems (SAWIS), and reflects 2013 data for the WO areas. *Note:* Area maps are not to the same scale.

Breedekloof Large (12,870 ha) Breede River Valley district producing mainly for brandy industry and merchant trade, but also featuring some quality-focused boutiques and family estates with reputations for pinotage, chenin, chardonnay and semillon. Major varieties (ha): chenin (2,778), colombard (1,898), chardonnay (981), sauvignon (955), pinotage (919). See under Robertson for climate, geology etc.

Cape Peninsula Recently enlarged (to 454 ha) and renamed (from 'Cape Point'), cool-climate district with wards Hout Bay and Constantia (see below). Vineyards mainly on western and eastern mountain slopes, and inner-city Cape Town. Recognised for sauvignon and semillon. Sauvignon (195), cab (44), merlot (41), shiraz (27), chardonnay (26).

Cape Point See Cape Peninsula

Cape South Coast 'Umbrella' region (2,738 ha) for Cape Agulhas, Elgin, Overberg, Plettenberg Bay, Swellendam and Walker Bay districts, and Herbertsdale, Napier and Stilbaai East wards.

Cederberg 70 ha ward in the Cederberg Mountain range, with some of South Africa's remotest and highest vineyards (950-1,100 m). Best known for shiraz (14 ha) and sauvignon (11). Also chenin (9) chardonnay (8), cab (7).

Central Orange River

This ward along the Orange River (Gariep) is a production zone within the Northern Cape Geographical Unit. Altitude: 500-1,000 m; temp 25.3°C; rain: 250/208 mm; geology: granite, dolorite, shale, alluvial. Overwhelmingly a white-grape area but red plantings are increasing. Sultana (6,758), colombard (2,290), chenin (962), villard blanc (200), muscat d'Alexandrie (150).

Constantia Premier viticultural ward on the eastern flank of the Cape Peninsula, cooled by south-easterly sea breezes. Recognised for whites generally, notably sauvignon, semillon and muscat. Altitude: 100-300 m; temp (Mean February Temperature, MFT) 20.6°C; rain: total/summer 1,056/335 mm; geology: granite (sandstone). Major varieties: sauvignon (177), merlot (41), cab (38), chardonnay (25), shiraz (22).

Darling District (2,781 ha) encircling the eponymous West Coast town, best known for the wines from its higher-lying ward, Groenekloof, long the source of top sauvignon; growing reputation for reds, especially shiraz. Groenekloof: cab (470), shiraz (344), sauvignon (326), pinotage (194), merlot (175).

Durbanville Ward within the Tygerberg district, with solid reputation for striking merlot and sauvignon. The latter (431) is the dominant variety, followed by cab (240), merlot (227), shiraz (211) and chardonnay (93). Altitude: 150-350 m; temp 22.4°C; rain: 481/140 mm; geology: shale.

Elgin Cool upland district within the Cape South Coast region, yielding aromatic whites and elegant reds. Altitude: 200-250 m; temp 19.7°C; rain: 1,011/366 mm; geology: shale (sandstone). Sauvignon (330), pinot noir (111), chardonnay (101), shiraz (76), cab (56).

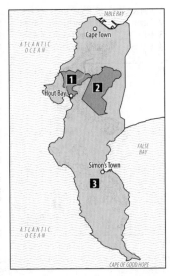

1 Hout Bay 2 Constantia 3 Cape Peninsula

Elim Maritime ward within the Cape Agulhas district, its 143 ha of vineyards are arrayed around the old mission village of Elim near Africa's most southerly point. Sauvignon (80), shiraz (32), pinot noir (11), semillon (11), cab (3).

Franschhoek Valley A district with 1,226 ha under vine, recognised for cab and semillon. Sauvignon (186), chardonnay (178), cab (177), shiraz (169), merlot (117).

Hemel-en-Aarde See Walker Bay

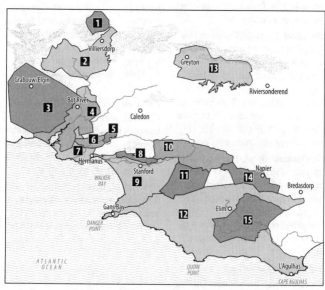

1 Elandskloof	5 Hemel-en-Aarde Ridge	9 Walker Bay	13 Greyton
2 Theewater	6 Upper Hemel-en-Aarde	10 Klein River	14 Napier
3 Elgin	7 Hemel-en-Aarde Valley	11 Sunday's Glen	15 Elim
4 Bot River	8 Stanford Foothills	12 Cape Agulhas	

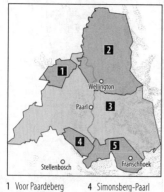

1 Voor Paardeberg	4 Simonsberg-Paarl
2 Wellington	5 Franschhoek
3 Paarl	

1 Polkadraai Hills	5 Stellenbosch
2 Bottelary	6 Simonsberg-Stellenbosch
3 Devon Valley	7 Jonkershoek Valley
4 Papegaaiberg	8 Banghoek

The Industry

Klein Karoo Scrubby semi-arid region (2,478 ha), reliant on irrigation. Recognised for excellent 'ports', and fortifieds generally. Calitzdorp district: muscat d'Alexandrie (84), colombard (68), chenin (31), cab (23), merlot (15). Tradouw ward: chardonnay (15), merlot (11), shiraz (10), colombard (8), sauvignon (8). Interesting stirrings in tiny Langeberg-Garcia district (40), and Upper Langkloof (54) and Tradouw Highlands (10) wards.

Northern Cape See Central Orange River.

Olifants River Quality moves are afoot in this north-westerly Cape grape-growing region (9,958 ha), particularly in the Bamboes Bay 'micro-ward' (just 6 ha) and Lutzville Valley district (3,082) nearer the coast, as well as the cool upland ward of Piekenierskloof (482). Inland, a climate conducive to organic cultivation is being exploited to that end. Altitude: 20-100 m; temp 23°C; rain: 139/47 mm; geology: mainly schist and alluvial deposits. Koekenaap ward (Lutzville Valley): chenin (299), colombard (216), sauvignon (167), cab (66), muscat d'Alexandrie (38). Piekenierskloof: pinotage (68), chenin (51), palomino (49), grenache noir (47), sauvignon (38).

Orange River See Central Orange River

Paarl This district has many mesoclimates, soils and aspects, and thus succeeds with a variety of styles and grapes. Altitude: 100-300 m; temp 23.2°C; rain: 945/273 mm; geology: granite and shale. Paarl proper is recognised for shiraz and, more recently, viognier and mourvèdre grown on warmer slopes. Chenin (1,470), cab (937), shiraz (929), pinotage (576), chardonnay (394). The following are wards: Simonsberg-Paarl, on the warmer slopes of the Simonsberg, recognised for red blends, shiraz and chardonnay. Cab (317), chardonnay (212), sauvignon (187), shiraz (180), merlot (115). Voor Paardeberg, long an uncredited source of top-quality grapes, now becoming a star in own right. Cab (377), shiraz (320), chenin (230), merlot (203), pinotage (188).

Philadelphia A ward of Tygerberg, cooled by the Atlantic air and noted for cab, merlot and Bordeaux-style reds. Cab (225), sauvignon (139), shiraz (65), merlot (65), chardonnay (37). See under Durbanville for climate, geology etc.

Robertson Traditionally a white-wine district, increasingly recognised for shiraz and cab. Chardonnay, sauvignon and sparkling remain standouts. Altitude: 150-250 m; temp 23°C; rain: 280/116 mm; geology: shale and alluvial. Colombard (2,181), chardonnay (2,036), chenin (1,656), cab (1,505) sauvignon (1,503).

Stellenbosch To many, this intensively farmed district is the wine capital of South Africa. Key contributors to quality are the cooler mountain slopes, varied soil types and breezes off False Bay which moderate summer temperatures. Altitude: 200-400 m; temp 21.5°C; rain: 713/229 mm; geology: granite (sandstone). Jonkershoek Valley, a ward east of Stellenbosch town, is recognised for cab and cab blends. Cab (62), merlot (24), shiraz (19), chardonnay (17), sauvignon (15). Simonsberg-Stellenbosch, in the south-western foothills of the Simonsberg Mountain, is especially recognised for cab, cab blends and pinotage, and reds generally. Cab (333), sauvignon (182), merlot (168), shiraz (147), chardonnay (123). North-west of Stellenbosch town are

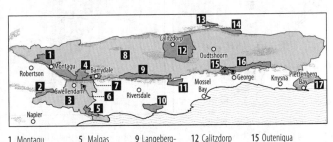

1 Montagu
2 Stormsvlei
3 Swellendam
4 Tradouw Highlands
5 Malgas
6 Buffeljags
7 Tradouw
8 Klein Karoo
9 Langeberg-Garcia
10 Still Bay East
11 Herbertsdale
12 Calitzdorp
13 Prince Albert Valley
14 Swartberg
15 Outeniqua
16 Upper Langkloof
17 Plettenberg Bay

four adjoining wards: Papegaaiberg - chardonnay (28), sauvignon (22), chenin (21), pinot gris (12), cabernet (12); Devon Valley, recognised mainly for red blends - merlot (141), cab (121), sauvignon (120), shiraz (71), pinotage (67); Bottelary, noted for pinotage, shiraz and warmblooded blends - chenin (438), cab (357), sauvignon (305), shiraz (277), pinotage (252); the most westerly ward, Polkadraai Hills - sauvignon

(162), cab (151), shiraz (130), merlot (90), chenin (70); and Banghoek, the mountain amphitheatre above the village of Pniel - cab (75), shiraz (44), merlot (30), sauvignon (28), chardonnay (24). The remainder of the Stellenbosch district, as yet officially undemarcated, includes Stellenboschberg, Helderberg and Faure, recognised for red blends, chenin and sauvignon. Cab

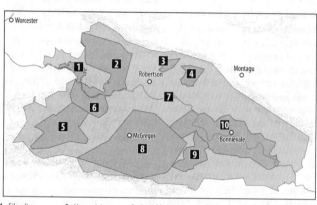

| 1 Eilandia | 3 Hoopsrivier | 5 Agterkliphoogte | 7 Robertson | 9 Boesmansrivier |
| 2 Vinkrivier | 4 Klaasvoogds | 6 Le Chasseur | 8 McGregor | 10 Bonnievale |

1 Swartland	4 Durbanville	7 Tulbagh
2 Darling	5 Malmesbury	
3 Philadelphia	6 Riebeekberg	

1 Lutzville Valley	6 Olifants River
2 Bamboes Bay	7 Citrusdal Mountain
3 Lamberts Bay	8 Citrusdal Valley
4 Vredendal	9 Piekenierskloof
5 Spruitdrift	10 Cederberg

The Industry

(1,640), shiraz (1,211), sauvignon (1,054), merlot (937), chenin (677).

Swartland Traditionally associated with full-bodied reds, but latterly also with chenin and Mediterranean-style red and white blends, this sunny district north of Cape Town has two wards, Malmesbury and Riebeekberg, plus a large unappellated area. Riebeekberg: chenin (213), shiraz (180), pinotage (179), chardonnay (132), cab (103). Malmesbury: cab (715), shiraz (565), pinotage (488), chenin (472), sauvignon (318). 'Swartland': chenin (1,756), shiraz (877), cab (747), pinotage (733), chardonnay (383). Altitude: 100-300 m; temp 23.3°C; rain: 523/154 mm; geology: granite and shale.

Tulbagh Inland district, traditionally known for sparkling and lightish whites, acquiring reputation for quality reds and serious white blends. Altitude: 160-400 m; temp 24°C; rain: 551/175 mm; geology: sandstone boulderbeds and shale. Chenin (225), colombard (161), shiraz (131), cab (117), chardonnay (73).

Walker Bay Highly regarded maritime district south-east of Cape Town, recognised for pinot noir, pinotage, sauvignon and chardonnay. Altitude: 100-250 m; temp 20.3°C; rain: 722/322 mm; geology: shale, granite and sandstone. Sauvignon (266), shiraz (133), pinot noir (131), chardonnay (105), cab (77). Bot River, Hemel-en-Aarde Ridge, Hemel-en-Aarde Valley, Stanford Foothills, Sunday's Glen and Upper Hemel-en-Aarde Valley are wards.

Wellington District in the Coastal region increasingly reputed for shiraz and gutsy red blends. Chenin (958), cab (767), shiraz (622), pinotage (435), chardonnay (317).

Worcester District producing chiefly for the brandy industry and merchant trade, but small quantities bottled under own labels often represent good quality/value. Recognised for everyday reds/whites and fortifieds. Chenin (1,889), colombard (1,101), chardonnay (528), shiraz (427), pinotage (394). See under Robertson for climate, geology etc.

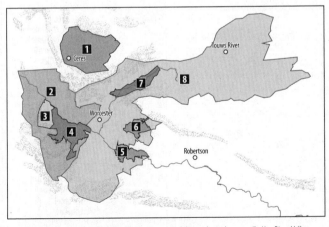

1 Ceres Plateau	3 Slanghoek	5 Scherpenheuvel	7 Hex River Valley
2 Breedekloof	4 Goudini	6 Nuy	8 Worcester

Wine of Origin-defined production areas

(New appellation/s in **bold**.)

Geographical Unit	Region	District	Ward
Eastern Cape	—	—	St Francis Bay
KwaZulu-Natal	—	—	—
Limpopo	—	—	—
Northern Cape	—	Douglas	—
	—	—	Central Orange River
	—	—	Hartswater
	—	—	Rietrivier (Free State)
	—	Sutherland-Karoo	—
Western Cape	Breede River Valley	Breedekloof	Goudini
			Slanghoek
		Robertson	Agterkliphoogte
			Boesmansrivier
			Bonnievale
			Eilandia
			Hoopsrivier
			Klaasvoogds
			Le Chasseur
			McGregor
			Vinkrivier
		Worcester	Hex River Valley
			Nuy
			Scherpenheuvel
	Cape South Coast	Cape Agulhas	Elim
		Elgin	—
		Overberg	Elandskloof
			Greyton
			Klein River
			Theewater
		Plettenberg Bay	—
		Swellendam	Buffeljags
			Malgas
			Stormsvlei
		Walker Bay	Bot River
			Hemel-en-Aarde Ridge
			Hemel-en-Aarde Valley
			Stanford Foothills
			Sunday's Glen
			Upper Hemel-en-Aarde Valley
		—	Herbertsdale
		—	Napier
		—	Stilbaai East
	Coastal	Cape Peninsula	Constantia
			Hout Bay
		Darling	Groenekloof
		Franschhoek Valley	—
		Paarl	Simonsberg-Paarl
			Voor Paardeberg
		Stellenbosch	Banghoek
			Bottelary
			Devon Valley
			Jonkershoek Valley

Geographical Unit	Region	District	Ward
Coastal (*continued*)	Stellenbosch (*continued*)		Papegaaiberg
			Polkadraai Hills
			Simonsberg–Stellenbosch
		Swartland	Malmesbury
			Riebeekberg
			St Helena Bay
		Tulbagh	—
		Tygerberg	Durbanville
			Philadelphia
		Wellington	—
	Klein Karoo	Calitzdorp	—
		Langeberg-Garcia	—
		—	Montagu
		—	Outeniqua
		—	Tradouw
		—	Tradouw Highlands
		—	Upper Langkloof
	Olifants River	Citrusdal Mountain	Piekenierskloof
		Citrusdal Valley	—
		Lutzville Valley	Koekenaap
		—	Bamboes Bay
		—	Spruitdrift
		—	Vredendal
—	—	—	Cederberg
	—	Ceres Plateau	Ceres
	—	—	Lamberts Bay
	—	—	Prince Albert Valley
	—	—	Swartberg

Boberg (fortified wines from Franschhoek, Paarl and Tulbagh). Source: SAWIS

Grape Varieties

Below are brief notes on some of the grape varieties mentioned in the guide, and their contribution to the national vineyard (statistics from SA Wine Industry Information & Systems — SAWIS). See under Winegrowing Areas for details of the most widely planted and best-performing varieties in the major vine cultivation zones.

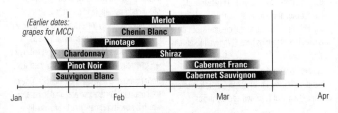

Approximate ripening dates in the Stellenbosch area for some important grape varieties

Red-wine varieties

Cabernet sauvignon Adaptable and internationally planted black grape making some of the world's finest and longest-lasting wines. And retaining some of its inherent qualities even when overcropped in less suitable soils and climates. Can stand alone triumphantly, but frequently blended with a wide range of other varieties: traditionally, as in Bordeaux, with cab franc, merlot and a few minor others, but also in SA sometimes partnering varieties such as shiraz and pinotage. Number of different clones, with differing characteristics. ±12% of total vineyard area.

Cabernet franc Like its descendant cabernet sauvignon, with which it is often partnered, a classic part of the Bordeaux blend, but in SA and elsewhere — particularly in the Loire — also used for varietal wines. Tiny, stable vineyard area (±1%).

Carignan Hugely planted in the south of France, where it is not much respected. But there, as in SA, older, low-yielding vines can produce pleasant surprises. Insignificant vineyard area.

Cinsaut (noir) 'Cinsault' in France. Another of the mass, undistinguished plantings of southern France, which only occasionally comes up trumps. Used to be known locally as hermitage, the name reflected in its offspring (with pinot noir), pinotage. About 2% of vineyard area.

Gamay noir Although it produces some serious long-lived wines in Beaujolais, its use for (mainly) early- and easy-drinking 'nouveau' wines there, often using carbonic maceration, is the model mostly copied in SA. Insignificant vineyard area.

Grenache (noir) The international (ie French) name for the Spanish grape garnacha. Widespread in Spain and southern France, generally used in blends (as in Rioja and Châteauneuf), but occasionally solo. A favourite for rosés. When vigour restrained, capable of greatness, but this is rare. Tiny plantings here. (White/pink versions also occur.)

Malbec Once a significant part of Bordeaux's blend, now most important in Cahors in western France (where it is known as cot), and as Argentina's signature variety. In SA a few varietal and blended examples; very small plantings.

Merlot Classic blending partner (as in Bordeaux) for cabernet, fashionable around the world, where it tends to be seen as an 'easier' version of cab — although this is perhaps because it is often made in a less ambitious manner. Merlot varietal wines increasingly common in SA too. ±6% of vineyard area.

Mourvèdre Internationally known by its French name, though originally Spanish (monastrell). In Australia and California also called mataro. Particularly successful in some serious southern French blends, and increasingly modish internationally. Minuscule plantings here.

Nebbiolo Perhaps the greatest red grape to have scarcely ventured from its home — Piedmont in this case, where it makes massive, tannic, long-lived wines. Minute plantings here.

Petit verdot Use of this excellent variety in the Médoc limited by its late ripening. Now appearing in some local blends, and a few varietals. 0.8% of vineyard area.

Pinotage A 1920s cross between pinot noir and cinsaut ('hermitage'). Made in a range of styles, from simply fruity to ambitious, well-oaked examples. 7.2% of vineyard area, increasing.

Pinot noir
Notoriously difficult grape to succeed with outside its native Burgundy, but South Africa, along with the rest of the New World, now produces some excellent examples. Just over 1% of the vineyard.

Ruby cabernet US cross between cabernet sauvignon and carignan, designed for heat tolerance. Rather rustic, used mostly in cheaper blends. ±2% of vineyard area.

Shiraz Better known as syrah outside South Africa and Australia (and on some local labels too). Internationally increasing in popularity, with northern Rhône and now also Australia as its major domiciles. Made here in a variety of styles — generally wooded. ±11% of vineyard area.

Tinta barocca Elsewhere spelt 'barocca'. One of the important Portuguese port-making grapes, which is now its primary role in SA, usually blended. Also used for some varietal unfortified wines, and namelessly in some 'dry reds'. 0.2% of vineyard area.

Touriga nacional Important Portuguese port-making grape, now usefully grown here for similar ends, along with tinta barocca, tinta roriz (tempranillo) and souzão. Tiny plantings.

Zinfandel The quintessential Californian grape (of European origin, and the same as Italy's primitivo), used here in a small way for some big wines. Tiny plantings.

White-wine varieties

Chardonnay In SA, as elsewhere, many new vineyards of this grape have come on-stream, with wines showing a wide range of styles, quality and price. Generally used varietally, but also in blends, and for sparkling. (Heavily) wooded in more ambitious wines. ±8% of vineyard area.

Chenin blanc SA has more chenin (locally also called steen) than even France's Loire Valley, the variety's home. Used here for everything from generic 'dry white' to ambitious sweet wines, to brandy. Increasing numbers of table-wine successes in recent years, as well as inexpensive but flavoursome easy drinkers. ±18% of vineyard area.

Colombar(d) One of the mainstays of brandy production in South Africa, colombard (usually without the 'd' in SA) is also used for numerous varietal and blended wines, ranging from dry to sweet — seldom wooded. Steady ±12% of vineyard area.

Gewürztraminer Readily identifiable from its rosepetal fragrance, best known in its Alsatian guise. In South Africa usually made off-dry. Insignificant vineyard area.

Hanepoot Traditional Afrikaans name for muscat d'Alexandrie, South Africa's most planted muscat variety (see also muscadel below). ±2%

of vineyard area (some for raisins and table grapes), slowly declining.

Muscadel Name used here for both muscat de Frontignan and muscat blanc à petits grains (both red and white versions). The grape associated with the famous Constantia dessert wines of the 18th century today is used chiefly for dessert and fortified wines and for touching up blends. Red and white versions total about 1% of vineyard area.

Muscat See Hanepoot and Muscadel.

Riesling The name by itself now refers to the great German grape (as it does in this guide). Previously, the grape had to carry the prefix 'Rhine' or 'weisser', and the 'riesling' was an official SA synonym for the inferior crouchen blanc, also known as Cape riesling and mostly used anonymously in blends, occasionally varietally. Rhine riesling often off-dry here, in blends or varietally, some excellent botrytised dessert examples. Crouchen: 0.5% of vineyard area, steady; Rhine: small but steady 0.2%.

Sauvignon blanc Prestigious vine most associated with eastern Loire regions, Bordeaux and New Zealand — whose wines have helped restore fashionability to the grape. The SA version no longer a poor relation of these. Usually dry, but some sweet wines; sometimes wooded, more often not (former sometimes called fumé blanc/blanc fumé). ±9% of vineyard area.

Semillon
Spelt sémillon in French. Sometimes heavily wooded, sometimes sweet, more often in blends. ±1% of vineyard area, including rare red version.

Viognier Increasingly fashionable variety internationally, spreading out from its home in the northern Rhône, now showing promise here. Usually wooded. Still tiny plantings.

Competitions, Challenges & Awards

An increasing number of wine competitions, awards and challenges are run by liquor industry bodies, independent companies, publishing houses and individuals. Below are the main national events:

Absa Top Ten Pinotage Competition Run annually by the Pinotage Association and a major financial institution to help set international quality targets for growers of pinotage.

Local/overseas judges. See under Industry Organisations for contact details.

Amorim Cap Classique Challenge Annual competition to appoint SA's top bottle-fermented sparkling wines. Mostly local judges. ▪ admin@capclassique.co.za ▪ www.capclassique.co.za ▪ **T +27 (0)21-863-1599** ▪ F +27 (0)21-863-1552

Best Value Wine Guide SA judges gather annually to select the best-value wines under a predetermined price point based on quality. Results are published in the Best Value Wine Guide, distributed with Getaway magazine. ▪ kathryn.frew@ramsaymedia.co.za ▪ www.greenwineawards.com ▪ **T +27 (0)21-530-3308**

CAPPA Cape Port & Wine Challenge Organised by the Cape Port Producers' Association to award best in class and gold medals in each of the port categories, and select the Top 10 Portuguese-style wines. Local judges. ▪ info@boplaas.co.za ▪ www.capeportproducers.co.za ▪ **T +27 (0)44-213-3326** ▪ F +27 (0)44-213-3750

Christian Eedes Cabernet Sauvignon Report Founded 2012 and presented by Sanlam Private Investments, the Cabernet Sauvignon Report scrutinises the category's 60 frontrunners, included by invitation only. Local tasters. ▪ christian.eedes@gmail.com ▪ www.whatidranklastnight.co.za ▪ **T +27 (0)83-454-3644**

Christian Eedes Chardonnay Report Launched 2011 in association with Sanlam Private Investments, the Chardonnay Report follows the format of the Christian Eedes Cabernet Sauvignon Report. See that entry for details and contact numbers.

Classic Wine Trophy See Taj Classic Wine Trophy

Diners Club Winemaker of the Year Inaugurated in 1981, this prestigious competition features a different category each year. The Young Winemaker of the Year recognises the winning entrant aged 30 years or younger. Local panel with some overseas representation. ▪ winemaker@dinersclub.co.za ▪ www.dinersclub.co.za ▪ **T +27 (0)21- 795-5400** ▪ F +27 (0)21-794-8185

Getaway Ultra Liquors Best Value Wine Awards See Best Value Wine Guide

Michelangelo International Wine & Spirits Awards sponsored by Collotype Labels Well-established competition (1997) of which judging panels consist of solely internationally accredited experts from around the globe. Foreign as well as South African wines, brandies and liqueurs compete under OIV rules for 16 trophies as well as Platinum awards and Gran d'Or, gold and silver medals. The Liqueur Awards were introduced in 2014 and a panel of liqueur specialists brought from Europe to judge the inaugural entries. ▪ lorraine@michelangeloawards.com ▪ www.michelangeloawards.com ▪ T +27 (0)82-5568679 / +27 (0)21 856 0059 ▪ F +27 (0)86-555-8061

Muscadel Award for Excellence Annual competition aimed at raising consumer awareness and recognising quality in the creation, packaging and promotion of SA's muscadel wines. Local judges. ▪ winemaker@badsberg.co.za, andres@rooiberg.co.za ▪ **T +27 (0)23-344-3021 / +27 (0)23-626-1664** ▪ F +27 (0)23-344-3023

Nedbank Green Wine Awards A three-part competition, recognising the best wine made from certified organically grown grapes, wines made from BWI certified farms and the producer with the best environmental practices. Results are published in the Nedbank Green Wine Awards booklet. Local judges. ▪ kathryn.frew@ramsaymedia.co.za ▪ www.greenwineawards.com ▪ **T +27 (0)21-530-3308**

Old Mutual Trophy Wine Show Convened by Michael Fridjhon and sponsored by Old Mutual. Seeks to identify the best wines in SA and award trophies to the top gold medal winner in the major classes, as well as the top producer overall. Local and international judges. ▪ alex@outsorceress.co.za ▪ www.trophywineshow.co.za ▪ **T +27 (0)11-482-5936** ▪ F +27 (0)86-532-5177

Perold Absa Cape Blend Competition Launched in 2011 and aimed at creating a signature style for Cape Blends (see SA Wine Styles section). Local judges. Contacts as for Absa Top Ten Pinotage.

SAPPA Port Challenge See Cape Port Challenge

Shiraz SA Wine Challenge Recent (2013) annual competition to identify the 12 best varietal shirazes and 3 best shiraz blends across all regions and styles. Local/international judges. ▪ info@shirazsa.co.za ▪ www.shirazsa.co.za ▪ **T** +27 (0)82 924 7254 ▪ F +27 (0)86-267 4333

South African Airways (SAA) Wine Awards Annual selection of wines to fly with the national carrier (drinkability in flight conditions an important consideration). The top red, white, bubbly and port each receive a trophy. Local and overseas palates. ▪ BongiSodladla@flysaa.com, YolandeSchutte@flysaa.com ▪ **T** +27 (0)11-978-9304 / +27 (0))11-978-3982 ▪ F +27 (0)11-978-3115

SA National Bottled Wine Show See Veritas

South African Terroir Wine Awards Only wines that truly portray a specific terroir can enter, making this a highly exclusive competition. The best wines certified as from single vineyards, units registered for the production of estate wine, wards in SA's officially recognised winegrowing areas, as well as small districts that are not divided into wards, are awarded. SA's top 5 estate wines are also honoured. Novare Trophies for SA Terroir Top Wine Area, Top Wine Estate and Top Producer are also awarded. Seven local judges. ▪ mlab@iafrica.com ▪ www.terroirwineawards.co.za ▪ **T** +27 (0)21-975-8166

South African Wine Tasting Championship (SAWTC) In the spirit of ongoing education, and in an attempt to encourage new converts to wine, the South African Wine Tasting Championship (SAWTC) offers all winelovers the chance to put their talents to the test and be the centre of a local wine event, with an opportunity to compete internationally. ▪ ridon@iafrica.com ▪ www.sawtc.co.za ▪ **T** +27 (0)21-422-5206 ▪ F +27 (0)21-422-5238

South African Young Wine Show Inaugurated 1975 to gauge the quality of embryo wines, prior to finishing and bottling, thereby also recognising wineries which sell their products in bulk. The grand champion receives the General Smuts Trophy. Local judges. ▪ information@veritas.co.za ▪ www.youngwineshow.co.za ▪ **T** +27 (0)21-863 1599 ▪ F +27 (0)21-863-1552

TAJ Classic Wine Trophy Established in 1998 to recognise ageworthy, elegant and well-made SA wines. Staged in partnership with the TAJ Hotel Cape Town and La Revue du Vin de France. Overseas judges. ▪ info@classicwinetrophy.co.za ▪ www.classicwinetrophy.co.za ▪ **T** +27 (0)21-683-7479 ▪ F +27 (0)86-588-2989

Top 100 South African Wines National fine-wine challenge that aims to identify the best 100 wines of South Africa using mainly Master of Wine (MW) qualified judges. The winning wines are showcased in a bespoke app available free for Android and iOS devices from www.top100sawines.com Winning wines can be tasted at events around the world. ▪ info@top100sawines.com ▪ www.top100sawines.com

Triton Express Winemakers' Choice Awards Gives winemakers from all wine regions the opportunity to judge the products of their peers. A Diamond Award is given to all winning wines; trophies and cash prizes to the value of R25,000 are also awarded to the best white and red on show. ▪ robyn@winemakerschoice.co.za ▪ www.winemakerschoice.co.za ▪ **T** +27 (0)21-8872377 / +27(0)82-301-4509

Trophy Wine Show See Old Mutual Trophy Wine Show

Veritas SA's biggest competition for market-ready wines, awarding double-gold, gold, silver and bronze medals across a wide range of categories. Local palates with some overseas input. ▪ information@veritas.co.za ▪ www.veritas.co.za ▪ **T** +27 (0)21-863 1599 ▪ F +27 (0)21-863-1552

Winemakers' Choice Awards See Triton Express Winemakers' Choice Awards

Wine Education

Cape Wine Academy Founded by the wine industry in 1979, CWA is the wine education body for the industry, tertiary colleges, hospitality and the public in South Africa.

Offices in Stellenbosch and Johannesburg with satellites in Durban, Pretoria, Bloemfontein, Kenya, Zimbabwe, London and Florida. Runs wine theory and tasting educational courses with examinations, from the South African Wine Course (level 1) through to Cape Wine Master's Program as well as the registered Cape Sommelier program. Also fun, edutainment and team building with Wine & Food, Wine & Cheese and corporate tastings. Stellenbosch: **T+27 (0)21-889-8844** ▪ F +27 (0)21-889-7391 ▪ michelle@capewineacademy.co.za ▪ Johannesburg: **T+27 (0)11-024-3616** ▪ F +27 (0)86-559-7329 ▪ busi@capewineacademy.co.za ▪ www.capewineacademy.co.za

University of Stellenbosch Garagiste Winemaking Course The premium short course for people interested in producing quality small-scale wines at home or simply expanding their wine knowledge. Attendees receive a set of notes; observe the use of garagiste winemaking equipment; taste different vinifications; bottle their own wine; and receive a certificate from Stellenbosch University. ▪ wdutoit@sun.ac.za ▪ **T +27 (0)21-808-2022** ▪ F +27 (0)21-808-4781

Wine Judging Academy Run by Michael Fridjhon in association with the University of Cape Town's Graduate School of Business, this intensive 3-day tasting and wine judging course aims to increase the number of competent wine judges at work in the local industry. ▪ crossley@reciprocal.co.za

WSET in South Africa Founded in 1969 and the industry standard for wine education in 62 countries, the UK-based Wine & Spirit Education Trust's (WSET) courses cater for enthusiastic amateurs and wine industry professionals alike. In-situ training for front-of-house staff is also offered and, for those wanting to take their wine education to the highest level, WSET is the direct path to the Master of Wine (MW) qualification. Standalone spirits courses also available. WSET are the only internationally recognised wine courses available and offered throughout Africa. ▪ info@thewinecentre.co.za ▪ www.thewinecentre.co.za ▪ **T +27 (0)72-390-9166**

Service Excellence Training Runs wine courses for staff in the licensed restaurant trade to improve their knowledge of viticulture and wine service. ▪ mfine@icon.co.za ▪ www.bevtrainsa.co.za ▪ **T +27 (0)82-932-9430 / +27 (0)21-782-5472**

A-Code Numbers & Codes

Many wines appear on the market under brand names, with, at first glance, no reference to their producers or purveyors. However, consumers need not buy 'blind', and may trace a wine's provenance by checking the official 'A-number' which appears on the bottle or pack. This identity code tells you either who produced the wine, or who sourced it for resale. In the latter case, an enquiry to the merchant should elicit the source. The list keeps growing and being revised, and is too lengthy to reproduce in this guide. Via the online SAWIS portal (**www.sawis.co.za**), it is possible however to search the list of A-codes, as well as the certification codes issued for each wine by the Wine & Spirit Board, for details about the production area, variety and vintage.

Styles & Vintages

Recent South African Vintages

South African wines do not exhibit the major vintage variations seen in some winegrowing areas. There are, nevertheless, perceptible differences from year to year. Dry, hot summers are the norm but a variety of factors make generalisations difficult and possibly misleading.

2014 Later, slightly smaller and unusually cool, among wettest pre-seasons in years. Seemingly lighter, less powerful wines; potential for fine concentration and elegance if picked judiciously.

2013 Biggest crop to date; moderate conditions yielded good to very good reds and whites, lighter alcohol levels.

2012 Unusually dry, hot January strained unirrigated vineyards; otherwise good to very good vintage for both reds and whites; moderate alcohol levels.

2011 Yet more variable than the last, impossible to generalise. As in 2010, producer's track record should guide the buying/cellaring decision.

2010 A real test of the winegrower's savvy, and one of the toughest recent harvests to call. Be guided by producer's track record.

2009 Perhaps one of the greatest vintages. Late, gruelling, but whites and reds both stellar.

2008 Long, wet, late and challenging but also unusually cool, favouring elegance in reds and whites.

2007 Elegant, structured whites; smaller red-grape berries gave intense colour and fruit concentration.

2006 Perhaps the best white-wine vintage in a decade — particularly expressive sauvignon and chenin. Fleshy, mild-tannined reds, with lower alcohols.

2005 Particularly challenging. Concentrated if alcoholic reds; mostly average whites, some exceptions.

2004 Cooler dry conditions yielded elegant, often ageworthy wines with lower alcohols, softer tannins.

2003 Outstanding, especially for reds — concentrated and structured, and often slow to show their best.

Older Vintages

2002 Challenging and patchy, but top producers show fine concentration and moderate alcohols. **2001** Some excellent reds — fruity and concentrated, best are long lived. Flavourful if alcoholic whites. **2000** Powerful, concentrated reds, befitting a hot year; the best have kept very well. Whites generally less impressive, not for long ageing. **1999** Fat, alcoholic reds with ripe fruit for earlier drinking. Generally not too much excitement among the whites. **1998** Excellent red vintage with enough fruit for extended cellaring; whites generally not for keeping. **1997** Among coolest and latest vintages on record. Supple, elegant reds; some excellent and stylish whites. **1996** Generally awkward reds, not for keeping; whites, except for top NLHs, best drunk up. **1995** For many, the vintage of the 90s. Concentrated reds, some still maturing spectacularly.

1994 Hottest, driest vintage in decades; variable quality; new-clone cabs and early ripening reds fared well. **1993** Without serious mishaps; some excellent sauvignons; above-average reds. **1992** Coolish season, favouring whites, especially sauvignon; the reds (notably pinotage) very good; **1991** Dry, warm to hot, favouring early to mid-season ripeners; some long-lasting reds. **1990** Uneven year, alternately cool and warm; average whites and reds; not for further ageing. **1980s**: even years ('82, '84, '86) usually more favourable for reds; uneven years, marginally cooler, favoured whites, but 'white' years '87 and, especially, '89 produced remarkable reds. **1970s**: again, even years generally favoured reds. Best was '74; but top wines from some other vintages are still delicious. **1960**s and earlier yielded some astonishingly long-lived wines.

South African Wine Styles

Blanc de blancs White wine made from white grapes only; also used for champagne and méthode cap classique.

Blanc fumé or **fumé blanc** Dry white from sauvignon, usually but not necessarily wooded (nor smoked, smoky).

Blanc de noir A pink wine (shades range from off-white through peach to pink) made from red grapes. See also Rosé.

Blend See Varietal wine and Cape Blend.

Brut See Sugar or sweetness, and Sparkling wine.

Cap classique See Sparkling wine.

Cape Blend Evolving term, increasingly used to denote a (red) blend with pinotage, the 'local' grape making up a significant part of the assemblage; sometimes simply a blend showing a distinct 'Cape' character; occasionally used for chenin-based blends.

Carbonated See Sparkling wine.

Cultivar Grape variety (a contraction of 'cultivated variety').

Cuvée French term for the blend of a wine.

Demi-sec See Sugar or sweetness.

Dessert wine A sweet wine, often to accompany the dessert but sometimes pleasurably prior, as in the famous Sauternes/foie gras combo.

Dry to sweet See Sugar or sweetness.

Estate wine Term now reserved for wine originating from an officially registered 'unit for the production of estate wine' (see www.sawis.co.za for current list).

Fortified wines Increased in alcoholic strength by the addition of spirit, by SA law to minimum 15% alcohol by volume.

Grand cru See Premier Grand Cru.

Jerepiko or **jerepigo** Red or white wine, produced without fermentation; grape juice is fortified with grape spirit, preventing fermentation; very sweet, with considerable unfermented grape flavours.

Kosher See Winemaking terms section.

Late Harvest Sweet wine from late-harvested and therefore sweeter grapes. See Sugar or sweetness.

Méthode cap classique (MCC) See Sparkling wine.

Noble Late Harvest (NLH) Sweet dessert wine (still, perlé or sparkling) exhibiting a noble rot (botrytis) character, from grapes infected by the *botrytis cinerea* fungus. This mould, in warm, misty autumn weather, attacks the skins of ripe grapes, causing much of the juice to evaporate. As the berries wither, their sweetness and flavour become powerfully concentrated. SA law dictates that grapes for NLH must be harvested at a minimum of 28° Balling and residual sugar must exceed 50g/L.

Nouveau Term originated in Beaujolais for fruity young and light red, usually from gamay and made by the carbonic maceration method. Bottled soon after vintage to capture the youthful, fresh flavour of fruit and yeasty fermentation.

Perlant, perlé, pétillant Lightly sparkling, usually carbonated wine.

Port Fortified dessert with excellent quality record in South Africa since late 1980s, partly through efforts of Cape Port Producers' Association which has adopted 'Cape' to identify the local product. Following are CAPPA-defined styles: **Cape White**: non-muscat grapes, wood-aged min 6 months, any size vessel; **Cape Pink**: non-muscat varieties, pink hue, barrel/tank-aged min 6 months; **Cape Ruby**: full bodied, fruity; min 50% barrel/tank-aged 6-36 months; **Cape Vintage**: fruit of one harvest; dark, full-bodied; tank/cask-aged min 1 year; must be certified, sold in glass, vintage dated; **Cape Vintage Reserve**: as for Vintage, but 'superior quality'; **Cape Late Bottled Vintage** (LBV): fruit of single year, full-bodied, slightly tawny colour, barrel/bottle aged min 3 years (of which min 2 years in oak); **Cape Tawny**: min 80% wood matured, amber-orange (tawny) colour, smooth, slightly nutty taste; **Cape Dated Tawny**: single-vintage tawny.

Premier Grand Cru Unlike in France, not a quality rating in SA — usually an austerely dry white.

Residual sugar See Sugar or sweetness.

Rosé Pink wine, made from red or a blend of red and white grapes. The red grape skins are removed before the wine takes up too much colour.

Single-vineyard wine Classification for wines from officially registered vineyards, no larger than 6ha in size and planted with a single variety.

Sparkling wine Bubbly, or 'champagne', usually white but sometimes rosé and even red, given its effervescence by carbon dioxide — allowed to escape in the normal winemaking process.

Champagne undergoes its second fermentation in the bottle. Under an agreement with France, SA does not use the term, which describes the sparkling wines from the Champagne area. Instead, **méthode cap classique** (MCC) the SA term to describe sparkling wines made by the classic method. **Charmat** undergoes its second, bubble-forming fermentation in a tank and is bottled under pressure.

Carbonated sparklers are made by the injection of carbon dioxide bubbles (as in fizzy soft drinks). See also Sugar or sweetness.

Special Late Harvest (SLH) SA designation for a lighter dessert-style wine. There is no legal stipulation for residual sugar content, but if the RS is below 20g/L, the label must state 'extra dry', 'dry', 'semi-dry' or 'sweet', as the case may be. The minimum alcohol content is 11% by volume.

Stein Semi-sweet white wine, usually a blend and often confused with steen, a grape variety (chenin blanc), though most steins are at least made partly from steen grapes.

Sugar or sweetness In still wines: extra-dry or bone-dry wines have less than 2.5g/L residual sugar, undetectable to the taster. A wine legally is dry up to 5g/L. Taste buds will begin picking up a slight sweetness, or softness, in a wine — depending on its acidity — at about 6g/L, when it is still off-dry. By about 8–9g/L a definite sweetness can usually be noticed. However, an acidity of 8–9g/L can render a sweet wine fairly crisp even with a sugar content of 20g/L plus. Official sweetness levels in SA wine are listed in the table opposite. (* Recent amendments allow for higher sugar levels for dry (9g/L) and semi-dry (18g/L) if

the total acidity is within 2g/L or 10g/L respectively of the sugar level.

Varietal wine From a single variety of grape. Legislation requires the presence in the wine of 85% of the stated variety or vintage. Blends may name component parts only if those components were vinified separately, prior to blending; then they are listed with the larger contributor(s) named first. If any one of the blend partners is less than 20%, percentages for all the varieties must be given. Blends may be vinified separately in any recognised WO area; component areas may be named, as above except the threshold is 30%.

Vintage In SA primarily used to denote year of harvest. Not a quality classification (a 'vintage' port in Europe means one from an officially declared great port-grape year).

Wine	Sugar (g/l)
Still wines	
Extra-dry	≤ 2.5
Dry*	≤ 5
Semi-dry*	5 ≤ 12
Semi-sweet	> 5 <30
Late Harvest	≥ 20
Special Late Harvest (SLH)	—
Natural Sweet (or Sweet Natural)	> 20
Noble Late Harvest (NLH)	> 50
Naturally dried grape wine (straw wine)	> 30
Sparkling wines	
Brut nature	<3
Extra brut	<6
Brut	<12
Extra-dry	12–17
Dry	17–32
Semi-sweet	32–50
Sweet	> 50

Brandy, Husk Spirit & Sherry-styles

Brandy and Husk Spirit

South African brandy is divided into three main stylistic categories. Put simply and reductively these are as follows:

- **Blended Brandy** must by law contain at least 30% brandy distilled in a potstill and aged for at least three years in oak barrels. The remaining component will be of unmatured wine spirit (made in a continuous still). More often than not, these brandies are intended to partner mixers or to play a role in cocktails.

The alcohol by volume (ABV) content must be at least 43% (in practice it usually is 43%).

- **Vintage Brandy** (a small category) bottled after 31 December 2013 must have at least 30% potstill brandy aged minimum eight years. Up to 70% wine spirit is permitted but it too must be matured at least eight years.
- **Potstill Brandy** bottled after 31 December 2013 may no longer contain up to 10% neutral wine spirit. As for Vintage Brandy, the ABV

level must be at least 38% (and tends in practice to vary between 38% and 41%).

Estate Brandy is brandy in any of the above categories in which all stages of production, from vineyard to maturation, have taken place on one property (as for 'estate' wine).

Sherry-Style Fortified Wines

There are eight classes of sherry-style wines described in South Africa's Liquor Products Act.

The colour of these wines must range – depending on the class – from pale straw to amber. Their aromas and flavours must be 'nutty' and 'woody'.

Five of the eight classes must have a discernible flor yeast and/or wood character. In addition, these classes should:

- In the case of **Fino**, the residual sugar shall not exceed 20 g/l, and the alcohol content must not exceed 16%. It should have an almond flavour.
- The alcohol content of an **Amontillado** must be at least 16%, and it should have a flavour of hazelnuts.
- **Oloroso** must have rich, nutty flavours; a minimum of 50 g/l residual sugar, and at least 16% alcohol by volume.
- The residual sugar content of a **Pale Dry** wine cannot exceed 30 g/l, and its alcohol content should exceed 16%.

Husk Spirit will have an ABV level of at least 43% and not be matured; Premium Husk Spirit must be at least 40% ABV, and be matured in oak for between three and six months.

- Similarly, the alcohol content of a **Pale Cream** must exceed 16%, but its residual sugar can only range between 30 g/l and 80 g/l.
- The remaining three classes need only exhibit a discernable wood character.
- In addition, the residual sugar and alcohol content of a **Medium Cream** must be between 80 g/l and 115 g/l, and above 16% respectively.
- A **Full Cream** wine must have at least 115 g/l residual sugar, and an alcohol content above 16%.
- A muscat character and an aldehyde content of at least 80 mg/l, a residual sugar content of at least 100 g/l, and at least 16% alcohol by volume is necessary for an **Old Brown**. This may also only be sweetened with concentrated must, or with fortified wine with a residual sugar content of at least 180 g/l.

Words & Phrases

Winetasting Terms

Short of a ready description? Here are a few frequently-used words, phrases and explanations that may be helpful. See also Winemaking terms; SA wine styles.

Accessible, approachable Flavours and feel of the wine are harmonious, easily recognised; it is ready to drink.

Aftertaste The lingering flavours and impressions of a wine; its persistence — the longer, the better.

Alcoholic 'Hot' or, in excess, burning character caused by imbalanced or excessive alcohol. Also simply spiritous.

Astringent Mouth-puckering sensation, associated with high tannin (and sometimes acid); also bitter, sharp.

Aroma Smells in the bouquet, or nose, especially the odours associated with the grape rather than the winemaking process.

Attack First sensations on palate/nose — pungent, aggressive, quiet etc.

Austere Usually meaning unyielding, sometimes harsh. Sometimes, more favourably, to imply a notable restraint/refinement.

Backbone The wine is well formed, firm, not flabby or insipid.

Baked 'Hot', earthy quality. Usually from scorched/shrivelled grapes which have been exposed too long to the sun, or from too warm a barrel fermentation, especially in some whites.

Balance Desirable attribute. The wine's chief constituents — alcohol, acid, tannin, fruit and wood (where used) — are in harmony.

Bead Bubbles in sparkling wine; a fine, long-lasting bead is the most desirable. See also Mousse.

Big Expansive in the mouth, weighty, full-bodied, as a result of high alcohol or fruit concentration.

Bite or **grip** Imparted by tannin, acid and/or alcohol, important in young wines designed for ageing. If overdone can impart undesirable bitterness, harshness or spiry 'glow'.

Bitter Sensation perceived mainly on the back of the tongue, and in the finish of the wine. Usually unpleasant, though an accepted if not immediately admired character of certain Italian wines. Sometimes more positively associated with the taste of a specific fruit or nut, such as cherry-kernel or almond.

Body Fullness on the palate.

Botrytis/ed Exhibits a noble rot/botrytis character, from grapes infected by the *botrytis cinerea* fungus.

Bottle-age Negative or positive, depending on context. Positively describes development of aromas/flavours (ie complexity) as wine moves from youth to maturity. Much-prized attribute in fine whites and reds. Negatively, bottle age results in a wine with stale, empty or even off odours.

Buttery Flavour and texture associated with barrel-fermented white wines, especially chardonnays; rich, creamy smoothness.

Claret Another name for a dry red Bordeaux or Bordeaux-like red.

Classic Showing characteristics of the classics of Bordeaux, Burgundy etc; usually implying balance, elegance, subtlety.

Coarse Rough, unbalanced tannins, acid, alcohol or oak.

Complexity Strong recommendation. A complex wine has several layers of flavour, usually developing with age/maturation. See Bottle age.

Concentration See Intensity.

Confected Over-elaborately constructed, artificial, forced; sometimes overly sweet.

Corked, **corky** Wine is faulty; its flavours have been tainted by yeast, fungal or bacterial infections, often but not necessarily from the cork. It smells damp and mouldy in its worst stages — but sometimes it's barely detectable. In a restaurant, a corked wine should be rejected and returned immediately; producers are honour-bound to replace corked wine.

Creamy Not literally creamy, of course; more a silky, buttery feel and texture.

Crisp Refers to acidity. Positively, means fresh, clean; negatively, too tart, sharp.

Deep and **depth** Having many layers; intense; also descriptive of a serious wine.

Dense Well-padded texture, flavour packed.

Deposits (also sediment or crust) Tasteless and harmless tartrates, acid crystals or tannin in older red wines. Evidence that wine has not been harshly fined, filtered or cold-stabilised.

Dried out Bereft of fruit, harder constituents remaining; tired.

Earthy Usually positive, wine showing its origins from soil, minerals, damp leaves, mushrooms etc.

Easy Undemanding (and hopefully inexpensive).

Elegant Stylish, refined, 'classic'.

Esters Scents and smells usually generated by alcohols and acids in wine. A wine may be 'estery' when these characteristics are prominent.

Extract An indication of the 'substance' of a wine, expressed as sugar-free or total extract (which would include some sugars). 18g/L would be low, light; anything much above 23g/L in whites is significant; the corresponding threshold for reds is around 30g/L.

Fat Big, full, ample in the mouth.

Finesse Graceful, polished. Nothing excessive.

Finish The residual sensations — tastes and textures — after swallowing. Should be pleasant (crisp, lively) and enduring, not short, dull or flat. See also Length.

Firm Compact, has good backbone.

Flabby Usually, lacking backbone, especially acid.

Flat Characterless, unexciting, lacks acid. Or bubbly which has lost its fizz.

Fleshy Very positive, meaning a wine is well fleshed out with texture and grape flavours.

Flowery, **floral** Flower-like (ie the smell of rose, honeysuckle, jasmine etc). Distinct from 'fruity' (ie smell/taste of papaya, cantaloupe, grape! etc).

Forward rather than shy; advancing in age too; mature.

Fresh Lively, youthful, invigorating. Closely related to the amount of acid in the wine and absence of oxidative character: a big, intensely sweet dessert without a backbone of acidity will taste flat and sickly; enough acid and the taste is fresh and uncloying.

Fruity See Flowery.

Full High in alcohol and extract.

Gamey Overripe, decadent, not universally unattractive; also meaty, 'wild'.

Gravel/ly With suggestions of mineral, earthy quality; also firm texture.

Green Usually unripe, sour; also herbaceous; sometimes simply youthful.

Grip Gripping, firm on palate, in finish. Acid, tannin, alcohol are contributors.

Heady Usually refers to the smell of a wine. High in alcohol; intense, high-toned.

Herbaceous Grassy, hay-like, heathery; can also indicate under-ripeness.

Hollow Lacking substance, flavours.

Honey or **honeyed** Sometimes literally a honey/beeswax taste or flavour; a sign of developing maturity in some varieties or more generally a sign of bottle-age.

Hot Burning sensation of alcohol in finish.

Intensity No flab, plenty of driving flavour; also deep colour.

Lean Thin, mean, lacking charm of ample fruit; also, more positively, compact, sinewy.

Lees/leesy Taste-imparting dead yeast cells (with grape skins and other solid matter) remaining with wine in tank/barrel (or bottle in the case of *méthode champenoise* sparkling wines) after fermentation. The longer the wine is 'on its lees' (*sur lie*) the more richness and flavour it should absorb.

Light/lite Officially wines under 10% alcohol by volume; also light in body (and often short on taste); a health-conscious trend in both reds and whites.

Lively Bouncy, fresh flavours.

Long or **length** Enduring; wine's flavours reverberate on the palate long after swallowing.

Maderised Oxidised and flat; colour is often brownish. Over-mature.

Meaty Sometimes suggesting a general savouriness; but also literally the aroma of meat — raw, smoked etc.

Mousse Fizz in sparkling wines; usually refers also to quality, size and effervescence of the bubbles. See also Bead.

Mouthfeel, mouthfilling Texture, feel; racy, crispness (fine with appropriate dishes) or generous, supple, smooth.

Neutral What it says, neither here nor there.

New World Generally implies accessible, bold, often extrovert (in terms of fruit and use of oak). **Old World** embraces terms like subtle, complex, less oaky, more varied and generally more vinous (than fruity). See also Classic.

Oaky Having exaggerated oak aromas/flavours (vanilla, spice, char, woodsmoke etc). Oak balanced by fruit in young wines may lessen with age, but over-oaked young wines (where fruit is not in balance) will become over-oaked old wines.

Palate Combination of flavour, taste and texture of a wine.

Pebbly See Gravelly.

Perfumed or **scented** Strong fragrances (fruity, flowery, animal etc)

Plump Well fleshed in a charming, cherubic way.

Porty Heavy, over-ripe, stewed; a negative in unfortified wine.

Rich Flavourful, intense, generous. Not necessarily sweet.

Robust Strapping, full-bodied (but not aggressive).

Rough Bull-in-a-china-shop wine, or throat sand-papering quality.

Round Well balanced, without gawkiness or jagged edges.

Sharp or **tart** All about acid, usually unbalanced. But occasionally sharpish, fresh wine is right for the occasion.

Short or **quick** Insubstantial wine, leaving little impression.

Simple One-dimensional or no flavour excitement.

Stalky Unripe, bitter, stemmy.

Stewed Over-ripe, cooked, soft, soggy fruit.

Structure Vague word, usually refers to the wine's make up (acid, tannin, alcohol) in relation to its ageing ability; if a wine is deemed to have 'the structure to age' it suggests these principal preservatives are in place.

Stylish Classy, distinguished; also voguish.

Supple Very desirable (not necessarily subtle), yielding, refined texture and flavours. See also Mouthfeel.

Tannic Tannins are prominent in the wine, imparting, positively, a mouth-puckering, grippy, tangy quality; negatively, a harsh, unyielding character.

Tension Racy, nervous fruity-acid play on the palate.

Terpene(s)/terpenoid Strong, floral compounds influencing the aromas of especially riesling, gewürztraminer and the muscats; with bottle-age, terpenes often develop a pungent resinous oiliness.

Texture Tactile 'feel' in the mouth: hard, acidic, coarse and alcoholic; or, smooth, velvety, 'warm'.

Toasty Often used for barrel-fermented or -aged wines showing a pleasant biscuity, charry character.

Vegetal Grassy, leafy, herby — in contrast to fruity, flowery, oaky. Overdone, a no-no.

Yeasty Warm bakery smells, often evident in barrel-fermented whites and *méthode champenoise* sparkling wines, where yeasts stay in contact with the wine after fermentation.

Winemaking Terms

A few brief reference explanations. See also sections Winetasting Terms, SA Wine Styles.

Acid and **acidity** The fresh — or, in excess, sharp or tart — taste of wine. Too little acid and the wine tastes dull and flat. In SA, winemakers are permitted to adjust acidity either by adding acid — at any stage before bottling — or by lowering the acid level with a de-acidifier. See also Volatile acid and Malolactic.

Alcohol Essential component of wine, providing fullness, richness and, at higher levels, sometimes an impression of sweetness. Also a preservative, helping keep wines in good condition. Produced by yeasts fermenting the sugars in the grape. Measured by volume of the total liquid. Most unfortified table wines in SA have between 11% and 14.5% alc by vol; fortifieds range from ±16% to 21%. A variation of up to 1% between the strength stated on the label and the laboratory analysis is permitted by local law. Various techniques (such as reverse osmosis and 'spinning cone', also the addition of water) exist to address the increasingly important issue of high alcohol levels in wine, and some are legal in SA (though not for export to, eg, Europe).

Barrels (**barrel-aged**; **barrel-fermented**) Wines are transferred into barrels to age, pick up oaky flavours etc. When must or fermenting must is put into barrels, the resulting wine is called barrel-fermented. A barrel or cask is generally a 225–500L oak container; *barrique* is a French word for a 225L barrel; a pipe, adapted from the Portuguese *pipa*, usually indicates a vessel of 530–630L; vat is a term generally used for larger (2,000–5,000L) wooden vessels.

Batonnage See Lees.

Biodynamic See Organic.

Blend A wine made from two or more different grape varieties, vintages, vineyards or containers. Some of the world's finest wines are blends.

Bottles While the 750ml (75cl) bottle is now the most widely used size of container for wine, it is by no means the only one. Smaller bottles (375 & 500ml) are popular with restaurants and airlines, and larger sizes are prized by collectors because of their novelty value and/or their tendency to promote slower wine ageing. The following are the larger bottle sizes (note: some no longer in production):

Capacity		Bordeaux	Champagne/Burgundy
litres	bottles		
1.5	2	Magnum	Magnum
3	4	Double magnum	Jéroboam
4.5	6	Jéroboam	Rehoboam
6	8	Impériale	Methuselah
9	12	—	Salmanazar
12	16	—	Balthazar
15	20	—	Nebuchadnezzar

Brettanomyces or **'brett'** Naturally occurring yeast, usually associated with red wine and regarded as a spoilage factor, because its growth triggers the formation of volatile acids, phenols and other compounds which, in sufficient concentration, impart a range of unpleasant characters, from barnyard to sweat to cheese. At low concentrations, can enhance complexity and character.

Carbonic maceration or **maceration carbonique** Method of fermenting wine without first crushing the grapes. Whole clusters with stalks etc are put into closed vat; intracellular fermentation occurs within the grape berries, which then burst.

Chaptalisation Originally French term for the addition of sugar to grape must to raise the alcohol of a wine. Selectively legal in northern Europe, where acid adjustments are not allowed as they are in SA. Winemakers in both hemispheres bend the rules.

Charmat Method of making sparkling wine in a sealed tank (*cuvée close*) under pressure. Easier, cheaper than *méthode champenoise*.

Chips See Oak chips.

Cold ferment 'Cold' is a relative term; applied to fermentation of mainly white wines in temperature-controlled tanks, it refers to a temperature around usually 13–16°C. The benefits, especially important in a warm country, include conserving the primary fruit aromas and ensuring fermentation is carried out steadily and thoroughly.

Cold soak or **cold maceration**. Red winemaking method carried out prior to fermentation. Skins and juice are held, usually for a few days, at a sufficiently cool temperature to prevent fermentation. The theory is that this extracts more favourable colour and aromas than after fermentation.

Cold stabilisation Keeping a wine at about −4°C for a week or more to precipitate tartaric acid and 'clean up' the wine, preventing later formation of (harmless) tartrate crystals in bottle. Some winemakers believe this process damages flavour and prefer to avoid it.

Disgorgement (*dégorgement* in French) Important stage in the production of traditionally fermented sparkling where accumulated sediment (or lees), which could cloud the finished wine, is removed from the neck of the bottle.

Dosage The sugar added to sparkling wine after the second fermentation.

Fermentation The conversion of sugar in grapes into alcohol and carbon dioxide, a function of enzymes secreted by yeasts. Wild yeasts occur in vineyards and wineries, but in modern Cape winemaking cultured yeasts are normally added to secure the process. Beyond about 15% of alcohol, yeasts are overwhelmed and fermentation ceases, although it usually is stopped (for instance by cooling, filtration or the addition of alcohol) before this stage. See also Malolactic.

Filtration Removes last impurities including **yeast** cells. Done excessively, can thin a wine. Some traditionalists bottle without cold- or protein-stabilisation or filtration.

Fining and **protein stabilisation** Fining is ridding wine of suspended particles by adding substances that attract and draw the particles from the wine.

Flash-pasteurisation See Kosher.

Free run After grapes have been de-stalked and crushed, juice runs freely.

Garage wine Generic term for wine made in minuscule quantities, sometimes literally in a garage; a grower of such wine is sometimes called a *garagiste*.

Glycerol Minor product of alcoholic fermentation; from the Greek for sweet. Has an apparent sweetening effect on even dry wines and also gives a viscous, mouthfilling character.

Icewine Sweet, concentrated wine from grapes picked and pressed while frozen. Not a recognised category for SA wine production.

Kosher Wine made 'correctly', i.e. under rabbinical supervision, to be suitable for use by religious Jews. Vinification and any initial movement of the wine must be done by an observant Jew. Flash-pasteurisation, increasingly by means of new flavour-preserving processes such as Thermoflash, renders the resulting *meshuval* wine (literally 'boiled' or 'cooked') fit for handling by non-Jews.

Leafroll virus Virus (or complex of viruses), widespread throughout the winegrowing world, which causes the vine to perform below its potential and thereby produce wine which is lower in colour, body and flavour than that derived from virus-free or 'cleaned-up' plants.

Lees Spent yeast cells and other matter which collect at the bottom of any container in winemaking. Yeast autolysis, or decomposition, can impart richness and flavour to a wine, sometimes referred to as leesy. Lees stirring or *batonnage* involves mixing the bed of lees in a

barrel or tank through the wine, which is said to be *sur lie*; it is employed primarily on barrel-fermented white wines. The main effects of mixing lees and wine are to prevent off-odours developing from lack of oxygen, to limit the amount of wood tannin and oak character extracted, and to increase flavour.

Malolactic fermentation (malo) Occurs when bacteria convert malic into lactic acids. This reduces the acidity of a wine, a normal and healthy process, especially in reds — provided, of course, it occurs before bottling.

Maturation Ageing properties are closely related to tannin and/or fixed acid content of a wine. A relatively full red wine with tannin has lasting power. With age, it may develop complexity, subtlety and smooth mellowness. Lighter wines with lower tannins are drinkable sooner but probably will not reach the same level of complexity. A number of Cape whites mature well over several years, but most are best drunk in their fruity youth, up to 18 months.

Méthode champenoise Classic method of making champagne by inducing secondary fermentation in the bottle and producing fine bubbles. Due to French restrictions on terminology, Cape sparkling wines made in this way are called méthode cap classique (MCC).

Micro-oxygenation Technique enabling introduction of precise, controlled doses of oxygen to must/wine. Advocates claim softer tannins, more stable colours and other advantages.

Oak chips, either in older barrels or stainless steel tanks, are used increasingly in SA, as are oak **staves**. Still frowned on by some purists, the 'additives' approximate the flavour effects of a new barrel, far more cheaply, more easily handled.

Oak-matured See Barrels.

Organic viticulture/winemaking Increasingly popular alternative to 'conventional' or 'industrialised' winegrowing, emphasising natural and sustainable farming methods and cellar techniques. A variant is biodynamic viticulture, influenced by anthroposophy, focused on improving wine quality through harmony with nature and its rhythms.

Oxidation Change (usually for the worse) due to exposure to air, in whites often producing dark yellow or yellowish colour (called maderisation), altering, 'ageing' the taste. Controlled aeration is used to introduce acceptable and desirable development in wine.

Pasteurisation See Kosher.

pH A chemical notation, used in winemaking and evaluation. The pH of a wine is its effective, active acidity — not in volume but by strength or degree. The reading provides a guide to a wine's keepability. The optimum pH in a wine is somewhere between 3.1 and 3.4 — which significantly improves a wine's protection from bacterial spoilage, so permitting it to mature and develop if properly stored.

Racking Drawing or pumping wine off from one cask or tank to another, to leave behind the deposit or lees.

Reductive Wine in an unevolved, unoxidised state is said to be 'reductive'; usually with a tight, sometimes unyielding character. The absence of air (in a bottled wine) or the presence of substantial sulphur dioxide (anti-oxidant) levels, will inhibit both oxidation and reduction processes, which are linked and complementary.

Reverse osmosis A specialised filtration technique, now permitted in SA for various purposes, including the removal of water from wine. See also Alcohol.

Skin contact After crushing and de-stemming, white grapes may be left for a period with the juice, remaining in contact with skins (before being moved into the press, from which the grape juice is squeezed). Some winemakers believe the colours and flavours in and under the grape skins should be maximised in this way; others believe extended (or any) contact can lead to coarseness, even bitterness.

Spinning cone See Alcohol.

Sulphur dioxide (SO₂) Sterilising agent and preservative, near-ubiquitous in winemaking since antiquity, now strictly controlled. In SA, max total SO₂ level for dry wines is 150–160mg/L; for wines with 5+ g/L sugar it is 200mg/L; and botrytis-style wines 300 mg/L.

Any wine with more than 10mg/L total SO₂ must carry the warning 'Contains sulphites' (or 'sulfites') on the label.

Sur lie See Lees.

Tannin Vital preservative in wine, derives primarily from the grape skins. Necessary for a red wine's longevity. A young wine's raw tannin can give it a harshness, but no red wine matures into a great one without tannin, which itself undergoes change, combines with other substances and mellows. Tannin leaves a mouth-puckering dryness about the gums, gives 'grip' to a wine. A wooded wine will usually also contain some wood tannin.

Tartrates Harmless crystals formed by tartaric acid precipitating in non-cold-stabilised wine. Because of lack of public acceptance, usually avoided through cold stabilisation.

Terroir Important, controversial (and in SA overused) French term embracing soil, climate, topography and other elements which constitute the natural environment of a vineyard site and give it a unique character.

Thermovinification/Thermoflash See Kosher.

Unfiltered See Filtration.

Virus or **virused** See Leafroll.

Volatile acid (VA) The part of the acidity which can become volatile. A high reading indicates a wine is prone to spoilage. Recognised at high levels by a sharp, 'hot', vinegary smell. In SA, most wines must by law be below 1.2g/L of VA; in practice, the majority are well below 1g/L.

Whole-bunch pressing or **cluster pressing** Some SA cellars use this age-old process of placing whole bunches directly in the press and gently squeezing. The more usual method is to de-stem and crush the berries before pressing. Whole-bunch pressing is said to yield fresher, cleaner must, and wine lower in polyphenols which, in excess, tend to age wines faster and render them coarser.

Wood-fermented/matured See Barrels.

Yeasts Micro-organisms that secrete enzymes which convert or ferment sugar into alcohol. See fermentation.

Touring Wine Country

Wine Routes, Trusts & Associations

For localised information about regional official wine routes and wineries, contact these organisations:

Breedekloof Wine & Tourism ▪ T +27 (0)23-349-1791 ▪ F +27 (0)23-349-1720 ▪ info@breedekloof.com ▪ www.breedekloof.com

Constantia Valley Wine Route ▪ T +27 (0)83-679-4495 (Carryn Wiltshire) ▪ info@constantiafoodandwine.co.za ▪ www.constantiawineroute.com

The Darling Wine & Art Experience ▪ +27 (0)22-492-3971 ▪ wine@darlingwine.co.za ▪ www.darlingtourism.co.za

Durbanville Boutique Wine Association ▪ T +27 (0)83-357-3864 ▪ F +27 (0)21-948-6666
info@durbanvilleboutiquewine.co.za ▪ www.durbanvilleboutiquewine.co.za

Durbanville Wine Valley Association ▪ T +27 (0)83-310-1228 ▪ info@durbanvillewine.co.za ▪ www.durbanvillewine.co.za

Elim Winegrowers ▪ T +27 (0)28-482-1902/ +27 (0)82-328-3824 (Conrad Vlok) ▪ conrad@strandveld.co.za

Franschhoek See Vignerons de Franschhoek

Green Mountain Eco Route (Elgin/Bot River) ▪ T +27 (0)28-284-9827 ▪ info@greenmountain.co.za ▪ www.greenmountain.co.za

Helderberg See Stellenbosch

Hermanus Wine Route & Hemel-en-Aarde Winegrowers Association ▪ T +27 (0)83-305-7319 (Frieda Lloyd) ▪ frieda@hermanuswineroute.com ▪ T +27 (0)28-312-3862 (Bevan Newton Johnson) ▪ bevan@newtonjohnson.com ▪ www.hermanuswineroute.com

Klein Karoo Wine Route ▪ T +27(0)44-272-7492 / +27 (0)82-214-5910 ▪ F +27 (0)86-528-4055 (Ellen Marais) ▪ info@kleinkaroowines.co.za ▪ www.kleinkaroowines.co.za

Northern Cape Wine Association See Orange River Wine Route

Olifants River Vodacom Wine Route ▪ See West Coast Wine Route

Orange River Wine Route ▪ T +27 (0)54-337-8800 (Marlé Nel) ▪ F +27 (0)54-332-4408 ▪ info@orangeriverwines.com

Paarl Wine Route ▪ T +27 (0)21-863-4886 / +27 (0)82-787-4118 ▪ F +27 (0)21-863-4883 ▪ info@paarlwine.co.za ▪ www.paarlwine.co.za

Robertson Wine Valley ▪ T +27 (0)23-626-3167 / +27 (0)83-701-5404 ▪ F +27 (0)23-626-1054 ▪ manager@robertsonwinevalley.com ▪ www.robertsonwinevalley.com

Stellenbosch American Express Wine Routes ▪ T +27 (0)21-886-4310 ▪ F +27 (0)21-886-4330 ▪ info@wineroute.co.za ▪ www.wineroute.co.za

Santam Swartland Wine & Olive Route ▪ T +27 (0)22-487-1133 ▪ F +27 (0)22-487-2063
swartlandinfo@westc.co.za ▪ www.swartlandwineandolives.co.za

Tulbagh Wine Route ▪ T/F +27 (0)23-230-1348/75 ▪ tulbaghinfo@lando.co.za ▪ www.tulbaghwineroute.com ▪ www.tulbaghtourism.co.za

Vignerons de Franschhoek ▪ T +27 (0)21-876-2861 ▪ F +27 (0)21-876-2768 ▪ marketing@franschhoek.org.za, office@franschhoek.org.za ▪ www.franschhoek.org.za

Walker Bay Wine Wander ▪ T +27 (0)28-316-3988 ▪ F +27 (0)86-509-4931 ▪ wine@hermanus.co.za

Wellington Wine Route ▪ T +27 (0)21-864-2479 ▪ wine@wellington.co.za ▪ www.wellington.co.za

West Coast Wine Route ▪ T +27 (0)82-611-3999 / +27 (0)27-201-3376 / F +27 (0)27 213 4819 ▪ monika@namaquawestcoast.com ▪ www.namaquawestcoast.com

Worcester Wine Route ▪ T +27 (0)23-342-8710 ▪ F +27 (0)86-771-4468 ▪ info@worcesterwineroute.co.za ▪ www.worcesterwineroute.co.za

Winelands Tourism Offices

For additional accommodation options, brochures and local advice, contact the information offices and/or publicity associations of the wine areas you plan to visit.

Breedekloof Wine & Tourism • T +27 (0)23-349-1791 • F +27 (0)23-349-1720 • info@breedekloof.com • www.breedekloof.com

Calitzdorp Tourism • T +27 (0)44-213-3775 • F +27 (0)86-569-1447 • tourism@calitzdorp.org.za • www.calitzdorp.org.za

Cape Town Tourism • Contact Centre: T +27 (0)86-132-2223

Cape Town Tourism (Head-Office) • T +27 (0)21-487-6800 • F +27 (0)21-487-6859 • capetown@capetown.travel

Somerset West • T +27 (0)21-840-1400 • F +27 (0)21-840-1410 • somersetnwest@capetown.travel

Elgin Valley Tourism T +27 (0)21-848-9838 • F +27 (0)86-660-0398 • info@elginvalley.co.za • www.elginvalley.co.za

Franschhoek Wine Valley • T +27 (0)21-876-2861 • F +27 (0)21-876-2768 • info@franschhoek.org.za, office@franschhoek.org.za • www.franschhoek.org.za

Hermanus Tourism Bureau • T +27 (0)28-312-2629 • F +27 (0)28-313-0305 • hermanustourism@hermanus.co.za • www.hermanustourism.info

McGregor Tourism • T +27 (0)23-625-1954 • info@tourismmcgregor.co.za • www.tourismmcgregor.co.za

Northern Cape Tourism • T +27 (0)53-832-2657 • F +27 (0)53-831-2937 • info@experiencenortherncape.com • www.experiencenortherncape.com

Paarl Tourism • T +27 (0)73-708-2835 • F +27 (0)86-590-871 • info@paarlonline.com • www.paarlonline.com

Paarl Tourist Information Centre • T +27 (0)21-872 4842 • F +27 (0)21-872-9376 •

paarlinfo@drakenstein.gov.za • www.drakenstein.gov.za

Robertson Tourism Association • T +27 (0)23-626-4437 • F +27 (0)23-626-4290 • info@robertson.org.za • www.robertsontourism.co.za

Route 62 • T +27 (0)23-616-3563 • F +27 (0)23-616-3422 • info@route62.co.za • www.route62.co.za

Saldanha Bay Tourism Organisation • marketing@sbto.co.za, tourismmanager@sbto.co.za • www.capewestcoastpeninsula.co.za
Saldanha: T +27 (0)22-714-2088 • saldanha@sbto.co.za
Hopefield: T/F +27 (0)22-723-1720 • hopefield@sbto.co.za
Langebaan: T +27 (0)22-772-1515 • F +27 (0)22-772-1531 • langebaan@sbto.co.za
Vredenburg: T +27 (0)22-715-1142 • F +27 (0)22-715-1141 • vredenburg@sbto.co.za
Paternoster: T/F +27 (0)22-752-2323 • paternoster@sbto.co.za
St Helena Bay: T +27 (0)22-736-2374 • sthelenabay@sbto.co.za
Jacobs Bay: T +27 (0)22-714-2088 • saldanha@sbto.co.za

Stellenbosch 360 • T +27 (0)21-883-3584 • F +27 (0)21-882-9550 • info@stellenbosch360.co.za • www.stellenbosch.travel

Wellington Tourism • T +27 (0)21-873-4604 • info@wellington.co.za • www.wellington.co.za

West Coast Peninsula Tourism Bureau See Saldanha Bay Tourism Organisation

Worcester Tourism Association • +27 (0)23-342-6244 / +27 (0)76-200-8742 • info@worcestertourism.com • www.worcestertourism.com

Specialist Wine Tours

Adamastor & Bacchus Cape Gourmet Wine & Culinary Tours • English, Afrikaans, Dutch, Norwegian, German • www.adamastorbacchus.com • johnford@iafrica.com, jarche@iafrica.com • T +27 (0)21-439-3169 / +27 (0)83-229-1172

African Story Wine Tours • English • info@africanstorytours.com • www.africanstorytours.com • T +27 (0)73-755-0444 / +27 (0)79-694-7915

African Trax Tours ▪ English ▪ africantrax@telkomsa.net ▪ www.africantrax.co.za ▪ T +27 (0)83-692-8873

African Wonder Tours ▪ Afrikaans, English, French, Italian, German ▪ info@africanwonder.co.za ▪ www.africanwonder.co.za ▪ T +27 (0)82-325-1485

Amber Tours ▪ English ▪ lesley@ambertours.co.za ▪ www.ambertours.co.za ▪ T +27 (0)83-448-7016

Bizoe Wine Tours ▪ Afrikaans, English ▪ info@bizoe.co.za ▪ www.bizoe.co.za ▪ T +27 (0)21-843-3307 / +27 (0)83-709-3957 ▪ F +27 (0)86-653-8186

Capefuntours ▪ English ▪ capefuntours@icon.co.za ▪ www.capefuntours.co.za ▪ T +27 (0)21-782-5472 / +27 (0)82-932-9430 ▪ F +27 (0)21-782-5472

Cape Fusion Tours ▪ English ▪ cazcape@mweb.co.za, info@capefusion.co.za ▪ www.capefusiontours.com ▪ T +27 (0)21-461-2437 / +27 (0)83-235-9777 ▪ F +27 (0)86-672-5877

'C' the Cape Tours ▪ English, Afrikaans ▪ cheryl.scott@ballmail.co.za, cheryl.dawnscott@gmail.com ▪ www.cthecapetours.co.za ▪ T +27 (0)21-433-2545 / +27 (0)83-698-5483 ▪ F +27 (0)86 654 5989

Double Gold Wineland Tours ▪ English • throughkimseyes210@gmail.com • **T +27 (0)82-293-3176**

D'Vine Wine & Dine ▪ pauline.nel@dvinewinedine.co.za ▪ www.dvinewineanddine.co.za ▪ +27 (0)73-972-7830 / +27 (0)21-975-4851 ▪ +27 (0)86-601-1238

Exclusively African Tours ▪ English, Dutch (German, Swedish, French on request) ▪ ian@travelxa.com ▪ www.holidaystosouthafrica.co.uk ▪ T +27 (0)21-5314887 ▪ F +27 (0)86-609-0896

Franschhoek Wine Tours ▪ English, Afrikaans ▪ info@winelandstours.com ▪ www.franschhoekwinetours.com ▪ +27 (0)83-301-6774

Go Cape Tourism Services Private Wine Tours ▪ English, Afrikaans & German on request ▪ john@gocape.co.za ▪ www.gocape.co.za ▪ T +27 (0)72-630-7907

Go! Shuttles & Tours • English, German, Afrikaans, French and Italian ▪ info@goshuttle.co.za, nic@gotours.co.za ▪ www.gotours.co.za ▪ T +27 (0)72-368-3455 ▪ F +27 (0)86-548-2375

Gourmet Travels ▪ English, German ▪ rainer@gourmettravels.co.za ▪ www.gourmettravels.co.za ▪ T +27 (0)82-449-7666 ▪ F +27 (0)86-542-0542

Gourmet Wine Tours ▪ English ▪ sflesch@iafrica.com ▪ www.gourmetwinetours.co.za ▪ T +27 (0)21-705-4317 / +27 (0)83-229-3581 ▪ F +27 (0)86-241-1685

Greatest Africa • English, French ▪ richard@greatestafrica.com • www.greatestafrica.com • T +27 (0)21-855-5244 / +27 (0)83-650-5661

Happy Holiday Wine Tours See Go Cape Tourism

Janet Malherbe ▪ English, German, French & Flemish ▪ janetm@mweb.co.za ▪ www.janetmalherbe.webs.com ▪ T +27 (0)82-553-8928 ▪ T/F +27 (0)21-862-1484

Judy Krohn Personal Itineraries & International Wine Experience ▪ English, German ▪ judithk@lantic.net ▪ www.judykrohn.co.za ▪ T +27 (0)84-500-1941 / +27 (0)21-851-7009

Klaus Schindler See Schindler's Africa

Luhambo Tours ▪ English, Afrikaans, German ▪ info@luhambotours.com ▪ www.luhambotours.com ▪ T +27 (0)21-551-0467 / +27 (0)82-306-4141

Ocean & Vine Adventures & Tours ▪ English, translator on request ▪ wayne@wine.co.za, oceanv@netactive.co.za ▪ www.prowinetours.co.za ▪ T +27 (0)21-559-6906 / +27 (0)82-900-6999 ▪ F +27 (0)21-559-6906

Percy Tours ▪ English, Afrikaans & some French & German ▪ travel@percytours.com ▪ www.percytours.com ▪ T +27 (0)72-062-8500 / +27 (0)28-316-4871

Redwood Tours ▪ English, Afrikaans ▪ info@redwoodtours.co.za ▪ www.redwoodtours.co.za ▪ T +27 (0)21-886-8138 / +27 (0)82-443-6480

Schindler's Africa ▪ German, English ▪ schindler@kapstadt.de ▪ www.kapstadt.de/schindlers-africa ▪ T +27 (0)83-270-3449

Southern Destinations ▪ English ▪ info@southerndestinations.com, vanessa@southerndestinations.com ▪ www.southerndestinations.com ▪ T +27 (0)21-671-3090 ▪ F +27 (0)21-674-7481

Taste The Cape Travel & Tours ▪ English, other languages upon request ▪ info@tastethecape.co.za ▪ www.tastethecape.co.za ▪ T +27 (0)21-788-1649 / +27 (0)79-812-0220

Tri Active Events Management (Green Mountain Eco Route) ▪ English, Afrikaans ▪ info@triactive.co.za ▪ www.triactive.co.za ▪ T +27 (0)21-844-0975 / +27 (0)83-456-2181 ▪ F +27 (0)21-844-0970

Tsiba Tsiba Wine Tours & Travel ▪ Dutch, English, French, German, Spanish ▪ info@tsibatsiba.co.za ▪ www.tsibatsiba.co.za ▪ T +27 (0)82-956-8104

Vineyard Ventures English, Afrikaans, German; other languages on request ▪ vinven@iafrica.com ▪ www.vineyardventures.co.za ▪ T +27 (0)21-434-8888 / +27 (0)82-920-2825 ▪ F +27 (0)86-579-9430

Walker Bay Wine Wander ▪ English, Afrikaans, French, German ▪ wine@hermanus.co.za, travel@percytours.com ▪ T +27 (0)28-316-3988 / +27 (0)72-062-8500 ▪ F +27 (0)86-509-4931

Wanderer Wines ▪ English, German, French, Italian ▪ wines@wanderer.co.za ▪ www.wanderer.co.za ▪ T +27 (0)82-878-1176 ▪ F +27 (0)86-648-0352

Wellington Wine Walk ▪ English, Afrikaans ▪ info@winewalk.co.za ▪ www.winewalk.co.za ▪ T +27 (0)82-335-8132 / +27 (0)83-235-5570

Wine Desk ▪ Scheduled (small group) and private day tours led by specialist wine guides. Available in most languages for private tours ▪ info@winedesk.co.za, ligia@winedesk.co.za ▪ www.winedesk.co.za ▪ T +27 (0)21-424-6364 / +27 (0)82-822-6127 ▪ F +27 (0)86-607-2980

Wine Escapes ▪ info@wineescapes.co.za ▪ www.wineescapes.co.za ▪ T +27 (0)83-453-2670

WineFairy ▪ English ▪ info@winefairy.co.za, katie@winefairy.co.za ▪ www.winefairy.co.za ▪ T +27 (0)79-892-2859

Wine & Whales Tours ▪ English ▪ wineandwhales@telkomsa.net ▪ T +27 (0)72-019-4456 / +27 (0)21-852-6545

Winemaker-led Tasting Tours ▪ English; translators on request with sufficient notice ▪ vitis@mweb.co.za ▪ www.winetastingtours.co.za ▪ T +27 (0)82-322-3733

Disabled Access in SA Wineries

The Accessibility for All initiative, launched in conjunction with Guy Davies' Disability Solutions team in the 2002 guide, continues to be funded by Platter's in the interests of inclusive wine tourism.

The aim is to verify that venues which are open to the public at set times, and claim to be disabled friendly, are in fact accessible. Accessibility for All means that any person with a special need, not only wheelchair users (as the international wheelchair icon seems to suggest) is provided safe access at venues where the icon is displayed in the guide.

The special needs community is broad and accounts for about 15% of the population. It includes people who are visually impaired,

hearing impaired, elderly, mothers with prams and others.

The 2002 book featured 104 wineries that had been assessed and shown as accessible. That number now stands at 208, illustrating the willingness of the wine industry to make the effort to be inclusive of a wider audience.

We believe the right attitude to accommodating visitors at venues is very important, with 'friendly' being the key word. Wine tourism is an integral part of South Africa's tourism offering, in which service is king. Accessibility should be seen as a core service.

The assessments in brief:
▪ Jeremy Hazell, Disability Solutions' leg-man for this edition, visits only wineries that consider

their facilities to be disabled friendly. The evaluations cover both new and recently upgraded venues, and the results are incorporated into the relevant producer entries in the A-Z section of this book, in the form of the universally recognisable 'wheelchair' icon, as well as in the look-up tables which accompany the maps.

- Wineries open only by appointment are excluded, as it is felt that in these cases visitors can ascertain their individual requirements when making an appointment.

- The assessments cover four aspects: parking, the tasting area, toilet facilities and cellar tours, if offered. The focus is on the tasting area, however, and in the A-Z we display the icon for wineries whose tasting area is considered accessible.

- All assessments are concluded with suggestions to wineries on how to improve access, where necessary, in all four of the above aspects.

- Many wineries have perfectly accessible toilet facilities but others have toilets that are either in the process of renovation or not spacious

enough for all wheelchair users. We suggest that wineries are phoned in advance to determine if their toilet facilities are adequate.

- Bear in mind that wineries which are not flagged as accessible in the A-Z or the maps table do not necessarily have deficient or non-existent facilities for people with disabilities; it might simply be that we are not yet in a position to comment on them.

- With Jeremy criss-crossing the winelands every year with his wheelchair and hand-controlled car, assessments are a work in progress. So we invite readers who have any comments and suggestions about the project to please contact him through our offices or directly on his mobile phone +27 (0)82-377-3498 or email jeremy@disabilitysolutions.co.za.

- While Guy and Jeremy base their assessments on the principles of Universal Design (making things safer, easier and more convenient for everyone), they try to be sensitive to the practical implications for each winery. In agricultural, rural and historical settings it is often a real challenge for wineries to ensure that access conforms to international standards.

Winelands Maps

The maps in this section show locales where wine is available for tasting/sale either at set times or by appointment. The larger-scale map below shows the areas covered by the maps, and the table starting on the next page lists some details for prospective visitors.

Areas covered by the maps

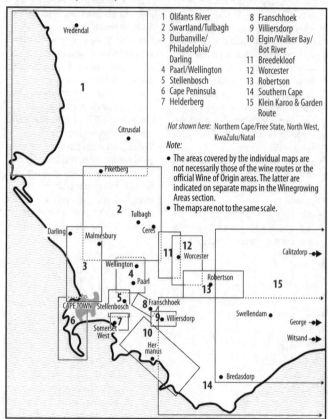

1 Olifants River
2 Swartland/Tulbagh
3 Durbanville/
   Philadelphia/
   Darling
4 Paarl/Wellington
5 Stellenbosch
6 Cape Peninsula
7 Helderberg

8 Franschhoek
9 Villiersdorp
10 Elgin/Walker Bay/
   Bot River
11 Breedekloof
12 Worcester
13 Robertson
14 Southern Cape
15 Klein Karoo & Garden
   Route

Not shown here: Northern Cape/Free State, North West, KwaZulu/Natal

Note:
- The areas covered by the individual maps are not necessarily those of the wine routes or the official Wine of Origin areas. The latter are indicated on separate maps in the Winegrowing Areas section.
- The maps are not to the same scale.

Some distances from Cape Town (kilometres)

Calitzdorp	370	Paarl	60	Tulbagh	120
Franschhoek	75	Robertson	160	Vredendal	300
Hermanus	120	Stellenbosch	45	Worcester	110

Key for maps

═══ Main access roads		R62 R60 ═	Road numbers
─── Roads		◢ ●	Towns
⋯⋯⋯ Gravel roads			

The tables below are intended to facilitate winery visits by providing summary information about all the winetasting venues which are open to the public, either at set times or by appointment, and appear on our winelands maps. Venues are listed by region, and details provided include a **map grid-reference**, if applicable; whether the particular venue is **open only by appointment** (T); **open on Saturdays and/or Sundays** (✓ = at set times; T = by appointment); **open on public holidays** (× = closed all public holidays; otherwise assume open all or some holidays); and whether **meals/refreshments are available** (BYO = bring your own picnic). Other details include availability of **accommodation**, **cellar tours** and **facilities for children**.

Venues which have tasting facilities **friendly to individuals with reduced mobility**, as audited by our disability consultants, are highlighted. **Other languages spoken** (besides English and Afrikaans) are also noted (Danish = da, Dutch/Flemish = nl, French = fr, German = de, Hebrew = he, Hungarian = hu, Italian = it, Japanese = ja, Mandarin = mdr, Norwegian = nn, Portuguese = pt, Romanian = ro, Russian = ru, Setswana = tn, Spanish = sp, Swedish = sv, Swiss = gsw, isiXhosa = xh, isiZulu = zu). For more information, **particularly items marked with an asterisk**, see the A–Z and Restaurants/Accommodation sections. For **GPS coordinates**, where known, for wineries open to the public, see the relevant A–Z entries.

	Grid reference	Open by appt. only	Open Saturdays	Open Sundays	Open public holidays	Meals/refreshments	Accommodation	Cellar tours	Disabled friendly	Child friendly	Languages spoken
Breedekloof Map											
Aufwaerts Co-operative		T									
Avondrood Vineyards			T			T/BYO*	✓	✓		✓	
Badsberg Wine Cellar			✓		×	BYO		✓*		✓	
Bergsig Estate			✓			✓		T		✓	
Botha Wine Cellar			✓			BYO		T			
Breëland Winery		T*				T/BYO*	✓	T			
Dagbreek		T			×	BYO		T			
De Breede Organic Vineyards		T									
Du Preez Estate			✓		×	BYO		T*			
Du Toitskloof Winery			✓			**		T			de
Goudini Wines			✓			✓*		T			
Jason's Hill Private Cellar			✓			✓		T	✓	✓	
Kirabo Private Cellar			T		×	T/BYO		✓		✓	
Ladera Artisan Wines		T*				T*		T			sp
Lateganskop Winery								T			
Lorraine Private Cellar					×	T/BYO*		✓			
Merwida Winery			✓				✓				
Mountain Oaks Organic Winery		T						T			
Mountain Ridge Wines					×	BYO				✓	
Olifantsberg Family Vineyards		T*									

	Grid reference	Open by appt. only	Open Saturdays	Open Sundays	Open public holidays	Meals/refreshments	Accomodation	Cellar tours	Disabled friendly	Child friendly	Languages spoken
Opstal Estate			✓	T		✓*		✓*		✓	
Rico Suter Private Cellar		T					✓	T			de/fr/it
Slanghoek Winery			✓			T*		T			de
Stofberg Family Vineyards			T	T	×			✓*			
TCB Wines					×	BYO	✓	✓			
uniWines Vineyards			✓			BYO		✓*			
Waboomsrivier Wine Cellar					×			T*			
Cape Peninsula Map											
Ambeloui Wine Cellar		T									
Beau Constantia			✓	✓							
Buitenverwachting			✓		×	✓		T			
Cape Point Vineyards			✓	✓		✓*			✓	✓	
Cape to Cairo Wines		T									
Constantia Glen			✓	✓		✓*					
Constantia Mist		T*				BYO	✓				
Constantia Uitsig			✓	✓		✓*			✓		
Dorrance Wines						✓					fr
Eagles' Nest			✓	✓		✓			✓		
Emineo Wines		T									
Groot Constantia Estate			✓	✓		✓		✓		✓	de/fr/nl
High Constantia Wine Cellar			✓			T/BYO		✓			
Hout Bay Vineyards		T						T		✓	de
Klein Constantia Estate			✓	✓*							fr/sv
Mzoli's Wines			✓	✓		✓					xh
New Beginnings Wines		T									fr
Signal Hill Wines			✓*		×	✓*		✓			fr
Silvermist Vineyards			✓	✓		✓*	✓				
Steenberg Vineyards			✓	✓		✓	✓	✓			
Township Winery											
Vaughan Johnson's Wine & Cigar Shop											
Wade Bales Wine Society					×						
Durbanville, Philadelphia & Darling Map											
Altydgedacht Estate			✓			✓		T		✓	
Bloemendal Estate			✓	✓		✓					
Capaia Wine Estate			✓*	✓*		✓		✓		✓	de
Cloof Wine Estate			✓			✓*		T		✓	
D'Aria Winery			✓	✓		✓	✓				nl

	Grid reference	Open by appt. only	Open Saturdays	Open Sundays	Open public holidays	Meals/refreshments	Accomodation	Cellar tours	Disabled friendly	Child friendly	Languages spoken
Darling Cellars			✓					T		✓	xh
De Grendel Wines			✓	✓		✓		T			
Diemersdal Estate			✓	✓		✓		T			
Durbanville Hills			✓	✓		✓*		✓*		✓	
Groote Post Vineyards			✓	✓		✓*		✓		✓	
Hillcrest Estate			✓	✓		✓		T			
Klein Roosboom			✓	✓		✓*		✓		✓	
Kronendal Boutique Winery		T				✓*		T	✓		
Lanner Hill		T*									
Maison de Teijger		T									
Meerendal Wine Estate			✓	✓		✓*	✓	T		✓	xh/zu
Nitida Cellars			✓	✓		✓				✓	
Nomada Wines			✓	✓							
Nuweland Wynkelder			✓	✓		✓		T		✓	
Ormonde Private Cellar			✓			T/BYO*		T*		✓	
Phizante Kraal			✓			✓					
Russo Family Vintners			T		X			✓			
Signal Gun Wines			✓	✓		✓					
Vierlanden Boutique Family Cellar		T*			X			T*			
Wines of Cape Town		T									
Withington			✓	✓							
Elgin, Walker Bay & Bot River Map											
Alheit Vineyards		T									
Almenkerk Wine Estate			✓	✓		**		✓*			nl/fr
Arumdale Cool Climate Wines			✓	✓							
Ashbourne		T						T			
Ataraxia Wines			✓	✓*							
Barry Gould Family Wines		T				T*	✓	T		✓	
Barton Vineyards			✓				✓	✓	✓		
Beaumont Wines			✓				✓	✓			
Belfield Wines		T					✓	T			
Benguela Cove			✓	✓							
Blomendahl Vineyards		T									de
Boschrivier Wines: NJT Boerdery			✓			*	✓				
Bouchard Finlayson			✓		X	**		✓			de/fr
Carmel Wines		T									
Catherine Marshall Wines		T				T		T			

	Grid reference	Open by appt. only	Open Saturdays	Open Sundays	Open public holidays	Meals/refreshments	Accomodation	Cellar tours	Disabled friendly	Child friendly	Languages spoken
Charles Fox Cap Classique Wines			✓	✓				✓		✓	
Corder Family Wines			T	T	×						
Creation Wines			✓	✓		✓		✓	✓	✓	de/fr
Dispore Kamma Boutique Winery		T						T			
Domaine des Dieux			✓	✓							
Eerste Hoop Wine Cellar		T*						T			
Elgin Ridge		T*				**		T*			fr
Elgin Vintners			✓	✓			*				
Feiteiras Vineyards		T									pt
Gabriëlskloof			✓			✓		T		✓	
Glen Erskine Estate		T				BYO		T			de
Goedvertrouw Estate		T				T	T			✓	
Hamilton Russell Vineyards			✓					T			tn/xh
Hannay Wines		T				T/BYO		T			
Hermanuspietersfontein Wynkelder			✓	✓*		✓*	✓	T			
Highlands Road Estate			✓	✓		✓		✓		✓	
Hornbill Garagiste Winery			✓			✓	✓	✓			
Iona Vineyards			T		×			✓			
Jakob's Vineyards		T									
La Vierge Private Cellar			✓	✓		✓		T			fr
Lothian Vineyards		T*					✓				sp
Luddite Wines		T						T			nl
Mofam Wines			✓	✓		✓	✓			✓	
Mount Babylon Vineyards		T						T			
Newton Johnson Vineyards			✓	×		✓					
Oak Valley Wines			✓	✓		✓	✓				it/fr
Oneiric Wines		T				BYO					
Oude Molen Distillery			T	T	T			✓*			
PaardenKloof		T*						T			xh
Paul Cluver Estate Wines			✓	✓*		✓*					
Paul Wallace Wines		T*	✓*			✓*					
Raka			✓			BYO		T			
Restless River		T			×	T/BYO*		T			
Richard Kershaw		T									
Rivendell			✓	✓		✓*				✓	
Robert Stanford Estate			✓	✓		✓*				✓	
Ross Gower Wines		T					✓				fr/de

	Grid reference	Open by appt. only	Open Saturdays	Open Sundays	Open public holidays	Meals/refreshments	Accomodation	Cellar tours	Disabled friendly	Child friendly	Languages spoken
Shannon Vineyards		T									de/sp
South Hill Vineyards			✓	✓		✓*	✓				
Southern Right			✓					✓			
Spioenkop Wines		T			×	BYO	✓	T		✓	fr/nl
Spookfontein Wines			✓	✓			✓				
Springfontein Wine Estate			✓	✓		*	✓	✓			
Stanford Hills Winery			✓	✓		✓*	✓		*		
Sumaridge Wines			✓	✓		✓*	✓			✓	
Vaalvlei Wines		T*					✓				
Walker Bay Vineyards			✓	✓		*		T		✓	
Whalehaven Wines			✓	✓				T			
Wildekrans Wine Estate			✓	✓		T*	✓	✓			
William Everson Wines		T					✓	T			
Wine Village-Hermanus			✓	✓							
Winters Drift			✓	✓*		✓				✓	
Franschhoek Map											
Akkerdal Wine Estate					×		✓				
Allée Bleue Wines			✓	✓		✓	✓	T		✓	de
Anthonij Rupert Wyne			✓	✓*		✓					
Babylonstoren			✓	✓		✓*	✓	✓			
Backsberg Estate Cellars			✓	✓		*		T*		✓	
Bellingham			✓	✓		✓*					
Black Elephant Vintners		T						T			
Boekenhoutskloof Winery		T			×						xh
Boschendal Wines			✓	✓		✓		✓		✓	
Cape Chamonix Wine Farm			✓	✓		✓	✓	T			
Colmant Cap Classique & Champagne											fr
Dieu Donné Vineyards			✓	✓		✓		T*			
Eikehof Wines			✓			✓*		✓			
Four Paws Wines		T									
Franschhoek Cellar			✓	✓		**					
Freedom Hill Wines			✓	T	T						
GlenWood			✓*	✓*		✓*		✓*			
Grande Provence Heritage Wine Estate			✓	✓		✓	✓	✓*		✓	
Haut Espoir		T			×			T			
Haute Cabrière			✓	✓		✓		✓*			fr/de
Holden Manz Wine Estate			✓	✓		✓	✓	✓			de

	Grid reference	Open by appt. only	Open Saturdays	Open Sundays	Open public holidays	Meals/refreshments	Accomodation	Cellar tours	Disabled friendly	Child friendly	Languages spoken
House of GM&AHRENS		T			×	T		T			
La Bri Estate			✓			✓*		✓			
La Chataigne			✓	✓	×			✓			sv
La Chaumiere Estate		T						T			
La Couronne Wines			✓	✓		✓*	✓			✓	
La Motte			✓			✓				✓	xh
La Petite Ferme Winery		T*				✓	✓	✓			
La Petite Vigne		T						T			
Landau du Val		T									
Le Manoir de Brendel			✓	✓			✓			✓	
Leopard's Leap Family Vineyards			✓	✓		✓				✓	
Lynx Wines			T	T	T			✓*			de/sp
Maison			✓	✓		✓					
Mont Rochelle Hotel & Vineyards			✓	✓		✓	✓	✓			
Môreson			✓	✓		✓		✓			
My Wyn			T	T	T	T*		✓			
Noble Hill Wine Estate			✓	✓		✓		T		✓	fr
Plaisir de Merle			✓	T*		✓*	*	✓		✓	de
Rickety Bridge Winery			✓	✓		✓	✓	✓		✓	
Rupert & Rothschild Vignerons			✓					✓			
Solms-Delta			✓	✓		✓*		T			
Stony Brook		T*					✓				
Topiary Wines			✓	T		T/BYO	✓	T			fr
Val de Vie Wines			✓	✓		✓					
Vrede en Lust Wine Farm			✓	✓		✓	✓	T*		✓	
Helderberg Map											
Aeternitas Wines		T			×						
Anatu Wines		T			×			T			fr/he
Avontuur Estate			✓	✓		✓		T			de/pt
BLANKbottle		T*									
Cape Classics		T									
Cavalli Wine & Stud Farm			✓	✓		✓*					
Chennells Wines		T*			×			T			de/sp
Clive Torr Wines		T									
Conspirare		T									
Croydon Vineyard Residential Estate			✓					T	*	✓	
Eikendal Vineyards			✓	✓		✓*	✓	✓		✓	de

	Grid reference	Open by appt. only	Open Saturdays	Open Sundays	Open public holidays	Meals/refreshments	Accomodation	Cellar tours	Disabled friendly	Child friendly	Languages spoken
Equitania		T			×	BYO					
Fish Hoek Wines											
Flagstone Winery			✓					T			
Foothills Vineyards		T				T	✓				
Grangehurst			✓*	✓*			✓				
Hathersage		T*			×						
Heron Ridge		T			×	T*		T			
Highberry Wines		T									
Idiom Collection		T*									it
Jasper Raats Signature Wines		T									
Journey's End Vineyards		T*				T/BYO*		T			
JP Bredell Wines		T									
Ken Forrester Wines			✓	✓*		✓*					
Kumala											
Le Riche Wines			T		×			✓			de
Lithos Wines		T*			×			T			
Longridge Wine Estate			✓			✓		T			
Lourensford Wine Estate			✓	✓		✓		✓			
Lyngrove		T	✓	✓		✓*	✓				
Miravel		T			T	T	✓				nl/fr
Morgenster Estate			✓	✓							
Mount Rozier Estate		T*						T			
Onderkloof		T					✓	T			
Osbloed Wines		T*						T*			
Pfeifer's Boutique Wines		T									gsw/de
Post House Vineyards			T		×	BYO	✓	✓			
Romond Vineyards		T*					✓	T*			
Skaap Wines						T*	✓			✓	nl
Somerbosch Wines			✓	✓		✓		T		✓	
Somerset Wines			✓		×						
Stonewall Wines		T*				T					
Vergelegen Wines			✓	✓		✓		✓*		✓	
Waterkloof			✓	✓		✓*		T			
Winery of Good Hope		T			×						fr/sv
Yonder Hill			✓*		×						
Klein Karoo & Garden Route Map											
Andersons Wines		T			×						

	Grid reference	Open by appt. only	Open Saturdays	Open Sundays	Open public holidays	Meals/refreshments	Accomodation	Cellar tours	Disabled friendly	Child friendly	Languages spoken
Axe Hill		T						T			
Baleia Bay			✓					T			
Barrydale Winery & Distillery			✓			BYO		T			
Bergwater Winery			✓	✓		T/BYO	✓	T			
Boplaas Family Vineyards			✓	✓				T		✓	
Bramon Wines			✓	✓		✓		T		✓	
Calitzdorp Cellar			✓			T/BYO		T			
De Krans			✓			**				✓	
Domein Doornkraal			✓			✓*	✓				
Du'SwaRoo		T*			X						
Excelsior Vlakteplaas		T									
Fernskloof Wines			✓	T*		BYO	✓			✓	sp
Garden Route Wines			✓*								
Goose Wines		T				T					
Grundheim Wines			✓								
Herold Wines			✓			✓*	✓	✓		✓	
Hillock Wines			✓	✓		✓	✓	✓			
Jakkalsvlei Private Cellar			✓			*					
Joubert-Tradauw Wingerde & Kelder			✓			✓	✓	✓		✓	
Karusa Vineyards			✓			✓					
Kingna Distillery			✓	✓		BYO	✓	✓			de
Lieben Wines		T									
LuKa Wine Estate											
Mimosa Boutique Wines			✓	✓		✓	✓		✓		de/gsw
Mons Ruber Wine Estate			✓		X	BYO					
Montagu Wine Cellar					X						
Newstead Lund Family Vineyards			✓			T*		T			zu
Packwood Wines			T	T	T	T*	✓				
Peter Bayly Wines		T						T			
Plettenvale Wines		T					✓				
Rare Earth Wines		T				T*	✓				
Reiersvlei			✓			T*		✓			
SoetKaroo Wine Estate			✓								de
St Francis Point Vineyards						✓					
Star Hill			✓	✓		✓	✓	T		✓	
TTT Cellar Calitzdorp			✓	T		BYO		✓			
Withoek		T					✓	T			

	Grid reference	Open by appt. only	Open Saturdays	Open Sundays	Open public holidays	Meals/refreshments	Accommodation	Cellar tours	Disabled friendly	Child friendly	Languages spoken
KwaZulu-Natal Map											
Abingdon Wine Estate		T*	√	√		√*		T			
Highgate Wine Estate		T				√		T		√	de
Northern Cape, Free State & North West Map											
Bezalel-Dyasonsklip Wine Cellar			√			√*		√		√	nl
Die Mas van Kakamas			T	T		T/BYO*	√	√*		√	
Douglas Wine Cellar					X			T			
Hartswater Wine Cellar								T			
Landzicht GWK Wines					X	T		T*			
Orange River Wine Cellars			√		X			√*			
Olifants River Map											
Bellpost		T						T			
Cape Rock Wines		T				BYO		T			
Cecilia Wines		T									
Cederberg Private Cellar			√	√*		BYO	√				
Desert Rose Wines		T									
Driehoek Wines			√			BYO	√			√	
Fryer's Cove Vineyards			√			**		√			
Klawer Wine Cellars			√			BYO				√	
Lutzville Cape Diamond Vineyards			√			√		√			de
Matzikama Organic Cellar		T									
Melkboomsdrift Wines						√*	√				
Namaqua Wines			√			√*		√*		√	
Seal Breeze Wines			√			T/BYO		√		√	
Sir Lambert Wines		T*				**	√			√	
Stellar Winery					X			T			
Stoumann's Wines			T		X	T		√			
Teubes Family Wines			√			**	√	T		√	
Tierhoek		T*			X	BYO	√	T*			
Vleiland Wines		T*				BYO					
Paarl & Wellington Map											
Alkmaar Boutique Vineyard	G2		√					T			
Andreas Wines	G1	T*			X		√	T			sv
Anura Vineyards	C7		√	√		√		√			de
Arra Vineyards	C8		√								
Avondale	F6	T*						T		√	
Ayama Wines	B2	T			X	T/BYO					it

	Grid reference	Open by appt. only	Open Saturdays	Open Sundays	Open public holidays	Meals/refreshments	Accomodation	Cellar tours	Disabled friendly	Child friendly	Languages spoken
Baratok Wines	E5	T			×	✓					
Bayede!	E6		T	T	×						
Bergheim	E6	T									
Black Pearl Vineyards	D5	T*					✓	T*			
Blouvlei Wyne	G2		T		×			✓*			de
Boer & Brit	E5		✓			✓					de/fr/nl/sp/xh
Boland Kelder	E4		✓					T			
Bosman Family Vineyards	G1	T*						T			
Calais Wine Estate	F4	T*					✓				
Crows Nest	D3		T	T	T	T/BYO		✓*		✓	
Damarakloof	A7	T*									
David Frost Wines	E5		✓								
De Villiers Wines	E6	T									
De Zoete Inval Estate	E6	T									
Diemersfontein Wines	F2		✓	✓		✓	✓	T			
Diners Club Bartho Eksteen Academy	G3	T						T			
Domaine Brahms Wineries	G3	T			T			T			
Doolhof Wine Estate	H1		✓	✓		✓*	✓	T			
Doran Vineyards	D1	T*	✓	✓							
Druk My Niet Wine Estate	F4	T			×	T/BYO	✓	T			de
Dunstone Winery	H1		✓	✓		✓	✓	✓*		✓	
Eenzaamheid	B5	T									
Esau Wines	E6	T									
Fairview	D6		✓	✓		✓					
Glen Carlou	D7		✓	✓		✓		T		✓	de
Groot Parys Estate	E5	T									nl
Hawksmoor at Matjieskuil	A7	T*				T*	✓				fr/de/ja
Hildenbrand Wine, Olive & Art Estate	G2		✓	T*			✓				de
Imbuko Wines	F4		T		×	T*					
Jacaranda Wine & Guest Farm	F1		✓			T*	✓				fr/de/mdr
Jacques Germanier	G1	T*			×			T			fr
Jacques Smit Wines	F2	T						T		✓	
Joostenberg Wines	A7	T*				✓	✓	T		✓	
Juno Wine Company	E5		✓			✓					
Klein Optenhorst	H1	T									
Klein Parys Vineyards	E5		✓	✓				✓		✓	
Kleine Draken	D6				×	T*		T			

	Grid reference	Open by appt. only	Open Saturdays	Open Sundays	Open public holidays	Meals/refreshments	Accomodation	Cellar tours	Disabled friendly	Child friendly	Languages spoken
KWV	E6		√	√		√*		√			de
La Ferme Derik	D3	T						T			
Laborie Wine Farm	E6		√	√		√	√				de
Landskroon Wines	D6		√*			BYO	√	T*		√	
Lazanou Organic Vineyards	F1	T*				T*					
Le Fût	F5	T									
Le Joubert	E4	T									
Linton Park Wines	G1	T*			X	T		T*			
Longbarn Winery	F2							T			
Maske Wines	G2	T				BYO					de
Mason's Winery	E6	T				√*					
Mellasat Vineyards	G5		√	√		T*		T			
Mitre's Edge	F1	T*					√	T			
Mon Rêve Estate	D7	T						T		√	fr/de
Mont du Toit Kelder	G2		T		X	BYO*	√	√*			de
Mooi Bly Winery	F3	T				BYO	√	T			nl
Mount Vernon Estate	C7		√					√			
Nabygelegen Private Cellar	H1		√		X		√	√			
Napier Winery	G2		√			√*		√			
Nederburg Wines	F5		√	√*		√*		√			de
Nelson Family Vineyards	D3	T			X		√	T		√	
Niel Joubert Estate	C8	T*			X						
Olsen Wines	G5	T				T*					
Oude Denneboom	C2	T					√				
Painted Wolf Wines	E6	T*				T*					fr
Perdeberg Winery	B3		√			T/BYO*		T*			xh
Retief Wines	E4		√	√		√					
Rhebokskloof Wine Estate	D3		√	√		√		T		√	
Ridgeback	D3		√	√		√	√	T		√	
Ruitersvlei Wines	D6		√	√		√	√				
Scali	C1	T*			X		√	T			
Simonsvlei International	D7		√	√*		*		T		√	
Southern Sky Wines	E5	T									
Spice Route Winery	D6		√	√		√					
Stone Ridge Wines	D1	T									
Taillard Family Wines	D1	T			X			T			
Tempel Wines	E3	T					√	T			de/fr/sv

	Grid reference	Open by appt. only	Open Saturdays	Open Sundays	Open public holidays	Meals/refreshments	Accommodation	Cellar tours	Disabled friendly	Child friendly	Languages spoken
Thokozani Wines	F2		✓	✓		✓	✓	T			
Upland Organic Estate	G3	T			T			✓	T			de
Val du Charron	G1		✓	✓		✓	✓	✓	✓		
Veenwouden Private Cellar	E3	T						T			
Vendôme	E6	T			×						
Versailles	E1	T						T			
Vondeling	C1		T		T						
Welbedacht Wine Estate	F1		✓			✓	✓	✓		✓	de
Welgegund Wines	G2	T					✓				
Welgeleë Boutique Wedding & Wine Farm	D7		✓	✓		T					
Welgemeend Estate	C7		✓*		×			✓			
Wellington Wines	E2		✓*			BYO		T			
Welvanpas	H1		✓	✓		*				✓	nl
Windmeul Cellar	D3		✓		×			T			
Zanddrift Vineyards – Chapel Cellar	E6										
Robertson Map											
Arendsig Handcrafted Wines		T				T/BYO	✓	T			
Ashton Kelder			✓					T		✓	
Bon Cap Organic Winery				✓		✓	✓			✓	
Bon Courage Estate			✓			✓				✓	
Bonnievale Wines			✓			✓*				✓	
Buffalo Creek Wines			✓	T				✓*			
BurCon Wines		T*				✓	✓		✓		
Bushmanspad Estate						BYO	✓				nl
Cape Dreams		T						T			
Clairvaux Private Cellar					×	BYO		T			
Cloverfield Private Cellar											
De Wetshof Estate			✓					T*	*		
DuVon Private Cellar		T					✓	T			
Esona Boutique Wine			✓			✓		✓		✓	
Excelsior Estate			✓			**	✓			✓	
Fraai Uitzicht 1798			✓	✓		✓*	✓				de
Goedverwacht Wine Estate			✓			T/BYO*		✓			
Graham Beck Wines			✓	✓							
Kingsriver Estate			✓	✓		✓	✓	T			nl
Kleinhoekkloof		T*									
Kranskop Wines			✓			BYO		✓			de

	Grid reference	Open by appt. only	Open Saturdays	Open Sundays	Open public holidays	Meals/refreshments	Accomodation	Cellar tours	Disabled friendly	Child friendly	Languages spoken
Langverwacht Wynkelder					X			✓			
Le Grand Chasseur Wine Estate		T			X						
Lord's Wines			✓	T				✓			
Major's Hill Estate			✓				✓	T		✓	
McGregor Wines			✓			BYO		T			
Quando Vineyards & Winery		T			X						de
Rietvallei Wine Estate			✓			✓*		T			
Robertson Winery			✓	✓				T			
Roodezandt Wines					X			T*		✓	
Rooiberg Winery			✓			✓				✓	
Rosendal Winery			✓	✓		✓	✓	✓			nn
Springfield Estate			✓			BYO		T			
Sumsaré Wines		T*				BYO		T*		✓	
Tanagra Winery & Distillery		T*					✓	T			de
Van Loveren Family Vineyards			✓	✓		✓*	✓	✓			
Van Zylshof Estate			✓					T			
Vierkoppen		T									
Viljoensdrift Wines & Cruises			✓	✓*		✓*					fr
Vruchtbaar Boutique Winery		T			X			T			
Wandsbeck Wyne Koöp Bpk			T	T	X			T		✓	de
Wederom Boutique Winery		T			T	T	✓	T			de
Weltevrede Estate			✓				✓	T			
Windfall Wine Farm		T			X	T/BYO*	✓	T			
Wolfkloof		T				T/BYO		T			
Wolvendrift Private Cellar			✓			T		T		✓	
Wonderfontein		T*									
Zandvliet Wine Estate & Stud			✓			BYO					
Southern Cape Map											
Andy Mitchell Wines		T						T			
Berrio Wines		T									
Black Oystercatcher Wines			✓	✓		✓*	✓	✓		✓	
Brunia Wines		T*				✓*					
Giant Periwinkle		T									
Jean Daneel Wines		T				✓		T			de
Lismore Estate Vineyards		T								✓	
Lomond		T*			X	✓	✓				
Sijnn			✓*		X						

Details of Locales Shown on Maps

	Grid reference	Open by appt. only	Open Saturdays	Open Sundays	Open public holidays	Meals/refreshments	Accomodation	Cellar tours	Disabled friendly	Child friendly	Languages spoken
Strandveld Wines			✓			BYO	✓	✓			
Swallow Hill Winery		T						T			de/fr/sp
Stellenbosch Map											
Aaldering Vineyards & Wines	D4		✓*		X			✓	T		
Akkerdraai	E8		✓								de
Allegria Vineyards	C6	T						✓			nl/de/gsw
Alto Wine Estate	E8		✓	✓		T*					
Amani Vineyards	B6	T									
Ameera	D7	T									nl/fr/de
Annandale Wines	E8		✓			BYO		✓			
Asara Wine Estate & Hotel	D6		✓	✓		✓	✓	T	✓		de
Audacia Wines	E7		✓	✓	X	✓*				✓	
Bartinney Private Cellar	H5				X			T			
Beau Belle	C7	T*				T/BYO*	✓	T*			
Beau Joubert Vineyards & Winery	B6		T		X	BYO	✓	T			
Bein Wine Cellar	B6	T						T			de/fr
Bellevue Estate Stellenbosch	C3		✓								
Beyerskloof	E3		✓			✓		T			
Bilton Wines	E8		✓	✓				T*	✓		
Blaauwklippen Vineyards	E7		✓	✓		✓		✓*	✓		de
Bonfoi Estate	C5	T			X	BYO					
Boschheim	E5	T									de
Boschkloof Wines	C6		✓			*		✓			
Botanica Wines	D4	T*				✓*	✓				
Boutinot South Africa	H4	T			X			T			
Brampton	F5		✓			✓*					
Brenaissance	D4		✓	✓		✓	✓			✓	
Camberley Wines	H4		✓	✓		T/BYO	✓	T			
Cape Hutton	E7	T						T			
Carisbrooke Wines	C6				X						
Casa Mori	D3	T					✓	T			it/fr
Chabivin Champagne & MCC House	E7		✓	✓							fr
Cirrus Wines	E8		✓	✓							
Clos Malverne	D4		✓	✓		✓		✓*			
Clouds Wine Estate	G5		✓			✓*	✓				
Clovelly Wines	D4	T						T			
Dalla Cia Wine & Spirit Company	E5		✓			✓					it

Details of Locales Shown on Maps

	Grid reference	Open by appt. only	Open Saturdays	Open Sundays	Open public holidays	Meals/refreshments	Accomodation	Cellar tours	Disabled friendly	Child friendly	Languages spoken
De Meye Wines	E1	T*	✓	✓		✓*		T*			
De Toren Private Cellar	B6	T						T			
De Trafford Wines	G8		✓		×			✓*			
Delaire Graff Estate	G5		✓	✓		✓	✓	T*			
Delheim Wines	F2		✓	✓		✓	✓	✓		✓	de
DeMorgenzon	C5		✓	✓				T			
Deux Frères Wines	E3	T*				BYO					
Devon Rocks	D3	T					✓	T			de/sv
Devonair	D3	T			×		✓				
Devonvale Golf & Wine Estate	D3	T*				✓	✓				de/fr
DeWaal Wines	C5		✓*								
Die Bergkelder Wine Centre	E5		✓					✓			
Domaine Coutelier	D4	T			×			T			fr
Dombeya Wines	F8		✓	✓		✓*	✓	T	✓	✓	
Donkiesbaai	E8		✓	✓							
Dormershire Estate	A5	T			×			T			
Dornier Wines	F7		✓	✓		✓*	✓	T		✓	
Eaglevlei Wine Estate	E1		✓	✓		✓*				✓	
Edgebaston	F3	T									
Elgin Heights	C6	T									
Entre Nous	H5	T			T	BYO		T			
Ernie Els Wines	E8		✓			✓*		✓			
Ernst Gouws & Co Wines	D1		✓							✓	de
Escapades Winery	B4	T									
Fort Simon Wine Estate	C4		✓		×	✓*		T			
Foundry	B8	T			×			T			
Francois La Garde	E5	T									
Gentleman Spirits	E7		✓	✓				T			de
Gilga Wines	D5	T					✓				
Glenelly Estate	F4		✓					T			de/fr
Goede Hoop Estate	C3		✓			T/BYO*		✓			
Graceland Vineyards	E7	T*			×						
Groenland	B3		✓			BYO*		T		✓	
Guardian Peak Wines	E8		✓	✓		✓					
Hartenberg Estate	C4		✓	✓*		✓*		T		✓	de
Haskell Vineyards	F8		✓	✓		✓*	✓	T		✓	
Hazendal	B3		✓	✓		✓		✓*		✓	de/ru

	Grid reference	Open by appt. only	Open Saturdays	Open Sundays	Open public holidays	Meals/refreshments	Accomodation	Cellar tours	Disabled friendly	Child friendly	Languages spoken
Hidden Valley Wines	E8		✓	✓		✓*		T			
High Road	E5	T			×						
Hills	D4	T									
Hoopenburg Wines	E1				×	BYO	✓	✓			
House of JC le Roux	D4		✓	✓		✓		✓*			
Jacobsdal	B6	T*									
Jordan Wine Estate	C5		✓	✓		✓*		T*			
Kaapzicht Wine Estate	B4		✓				✓	T			de
Kanonkop Estate	F2		✓			T/BYO*					
Kanu Wines	E3				×						
Katbakkies Wine	D5	T*			×						
Keermont Vineyards	G8	T						T			
Klein DasBosch	F7	T*				✓					
Kleine Zalze Wines	E6		✓	✓		✓	✓				
Knorhoek Wines	F3		✓	✓		✓*	✓	✓	✓		
Koelenhof Winery	D1		✓			*				✓	de
Kyburg Wine Estate	D4	T					✓				fr/de
L'Avenir Vineyards	E3		✓				✓	T		✓	fr
L'Olivier Wine & Olive Estate	D5	T					✓				
Laibach Vineyards	F1		✓*				✓	T			
Lanzerac Wine Estate	G5		✓	✓		✓	✓	✓			
Le Bonheur Wine Estate	F1		✓	✓		✓*					
Lievland Estate	F1	T				T*	✓	T			
Louiesenhof Wines	E4		✓	✓		✓*	✓			✓	de
Louisvale Wines	D4				×	BYO		✓			
Lovane Boutique Wine Estate	D6		✓	✓	×			✓	✓		
Marianne Wine Estate	G1		✓	✓		✓	✓	✓			de/fr
Marklew Family Wines	F1	T						T			
Meerlust Estate	B8		✓		×			T			
Meinert Wines	D4	T*			×						de
Middelvlei Estate	E4		✓	✓		✓*	✓	T		✓	
MolenVliet Wine & Guest Estate	H4	T					✓				
Mont Destin	G1	T			×			T			de/fr
Monterosso Estate	E4	T			T			T			it/zu
Mooiplaas Estate & Private Nature Reserve	B4		✓	✓		T*	✓				
Morgenhof Wine Estate	F3		✓	✓		✓	✓	T		✓	de/fr
Mostertsdrift Noble Wines	E4	T				T*		T		✓	

Details of Locales Shown on Maps

	Grid reference	Open by appt. only	Open Saturdays	Open Sundays	Open public holidays	Meals/refreshments	Accomodation	Cellar tours	Disabled friendly	Child friendly	Languages spoken
Mulderbosch Vineyards	C6		✓	✓		✓*					fr
Muratie Wine Estate	F2		✓	✓		✓*	✓	T			
Mvemve Raats	B6	T			×						
Natte Valleij Wines	F1	T			×		✓	T		✓	
Neethlingshof Estate	D5		✓	✓		✓*		✓		✓	de
Neil Ellis Wines	G5		✓			✓*			✓		
Nico van der Merwe Wines	B6	T									fr/de
Nietvoorbij Wine Cellar	F4				×						
Oldenburg Vineyards	H5		✓*			✓*	*		✓		
Origin Wine	D3	T									fr/de
Overgaauw Wine Estate	D5		✓			✓*					
Peter Falke Wines	E8		✓	✓		✓*		T			
Quoin Rock Winery	F3					✓*					
Raats Family Wines	B6	T			×						
Rainbow's End Wine Estate	H6	T						T			
Re'Mogo Wines	E4		T*								
Remhoogte Wine Estate	F3		✓			T*	✓	T			
Reyneke Wines	B6		T		T			✓*			
Rudera Wines	G6	T									
Rust en Vrede Estate	E8		✓			✓		✓			
Rustenberg Wines	G4		✓	✓							
Saltare	F5	T*						T			
Saxenburg Wine Farm	A5		✓	✓		✓*	✓				
Seven Sisters	C7	T									
Simonsig Landgoed	E2		✓	✓		✓		✓*		✓	
Skilpadvlei Wines	C6		✓	✓		✓	✓			✓	
Slaley	E2		✓	✓		✓		T			
Sonklip Wine	G5	T*						T			
Spier	C7		✓	✓		✓	✓			✓	de/xh
Spotswood Wines	F7	T									
Spring Grove Wines	H4	T									
Stark-Condé Wines	G6		✓	✓		✓					ja
Stellekaya Winery	E5				×	T*		✓			zu
Stellenbosch Family Wines	D1	T									
Stellenbosch Hills Wines	D6		✓		×						
Stellenbosch Reserve	E8		✓	✓							
Stellenbosch University Welgevallen Cellar	F5				×						

	Grid reference	Open by appt. only	Open Saturdays	Open Sundays	Open public holidays	Meals/refreshments	Accomodation	Cellar tours	Disabled friendly	Child friendly	Languages spoken
Stellenbosch Vineyards	C7		✓	✓		✓				✓	xh
Stellendrift – SHZ Cilliers/Kuün Wyne	C7	T						T			
Stellenrust	E7		✓			**		T			xh
Stellenzicht Vineyards	F8		✓	✓		BYO		T			
Sterhuis	C4	T						T		✓	
StoneyCroft	D3	T									
Summerhill Wines	E3				×						
Super Single Vineyards	C5		✓*								
SylvanVale Vineyards	D4		✓	✓		✓	✓			✓	de/xh
Tamboerskloof Wine – Kleinood Farm	F7	T*			×			T*			
Thandi Wines	D6				×				✓		
Thelema Mountain Vineyards	G4		✓								
Tokara	G4		✓	✓		✓				✓	
Topaz Wine	F2		✓*								de/fr
Uitkyk Estate	F2		✓	✓		✓*				✓	
Usana	C8	T									
Uva Mira Mountain Vineyards	E8		✓	✓		✓					
Van Biljon Wines	B6	T			×		✓	T			
Van Ryn	D6		✓	✓*		✓		✓*			
Vergenoegd Wine Estate	B8		✓	✓		✓*		T		✓	xh
Vilafonté	E5	T						T			
Villiera Wines	D1		✓			✓*		✓			fr
Vin du Cap International	D1	T									
Vredenheim Wines	D6		✓			✓	✓				
Vriesenhof Vineyards	F7		T		×			T			
Vuurberg	H4	T			×			T			
Warwick Estate	F1		✓	✓		✓*		T		✓	
Waterford Estate	F7		✓					✓			
Waterstone Wines	B3		✓	✓		✓		✓			
Webersburg Wines	E8		✓	✓		✓	✓	✓			
Welgevallen Wines	F5				×			✓			
Yardstick Wines	C6	T									
Zevenwacht	B5		✓	✓		✓	✓	T		✓	xh
Zorgvliet Wines	H4		✓	✓		T*	✓	T		✓	
Swartland Map											
AA Badenhorst Family Wines		T			×		T	T			
Abbottshill		T				BYO		T			

	Grid reference	Open by appt. only	Open Saturdays	Open Sundays	Open public holidays	Meals/refreshments	Accomodation	Cellar tours	Disabled friendly	Child friendly	Languages spoken
Allesverloren			✓			✓*		T	✓	✓	
Annex Kloof Wines			✓	✓		BYO		T			
Antebellum Winery		T									
Babylon's Peak Private Cellar		T				T/BYO*	✓	T	✓		
Bryan MacRobert Wines		T			X						
David & Nadia Sadie		T									
Dragonridge		T				T/BYO*	✓	T		✓	
Franki's Vineyards		T*			X	T/BYO	✓	T*			
Het Vlock Casteel			✓			T*			✓		
Hofstraat Kelder		T						T			
Hughes Family Wines		T									sp
Huis van Chevallerie		T									de/fr/it
Kloovenburg Wine & Olives			✓	✓*		BYO	✓	✓*			
Lammershoek Winery		T				T/BYO		T			de
Mullineux & Leeu Family Wines		T						T			
Nieuwedrift Vineyards			✓			T/BYO		✓		✓	
Observatory Cellar		T						T			de
Orangerie Wines		T						T			
Org de Rac			✓			T/BYO		✓			de
Paardebosch Wines		T			X	BYO					
Pulpit Rock Winery			✓			BYO	✓	T			
Riebeek Cellars			✓	✓		BYO		T			
Sadie Family Wines		T									
Santa Cecilia			✓	✓		✓*	✓				
Sequillo Cellars		T			X						
Spekulasie Landgoed		T			T	T	✓	T		✓	
Swartland Winery			✓							✓	
Wildehurst Wines			✓	✓			✓	T*			
Winkelshoek Wine Cellar			✓								
Tulbagh Map											
Constantia de Tulbagh		T						T			
Drostdy-Hof Wines			✓								
Fable Mountain Vineyards		T						T			
Koelfontein			✓		X	BYO	✓				
Lemberg Wine Estate			✓	✓		T/BYO*	✓	✓			
Manley Private Cellar			✓			✓	✓	T			
Montpellier			✓	✓		✓*	✓	✓		✓	

	Grid reference	Open by appt. only	Open Saturdays	Open Sundays	Open public holidays	Meals/refreshments	Accomodation	Cellar tours	Disabled friendly	Child friendly	Languages spoken
Oude Compagnies Post Private Cellar		T						T			
Rijk's			✓				✓	T			
Saronsberg			✓			BYO	✓	T			
Schalkenbosch Wines		T			×		✓	T			de
Theuniskraal			✓								
Tulbagh Winery			✓*	✓*		BYO		T			
Twee Jonge Gezellen Estate-House of Krone			✓		×			✓			de
Waverley Hills Organic Wines & Olives			✓	✓		**		✓		✓	
Zonquasdrift Estates		T*			×						
Villiersdorp Map											
Badgerberg Estate		T									
Cranefields Wine		T									
Faraway House Wine Estate		T									
Slowine			✓			✓					
Villiersdorp Cellar			✓			✓		T			
Worcester Map											
Aan de Doorns Cellar			✓		×			T*			
Alvi's Drift Private Cellar		T			×			T			
Auction Crossing Private Cellar			✓		×	✓		T		✓	
Brandvlei Cellar			✓		×			T	✓		
Conradie Family Vineyards			✓	✓		*	✓	✓		✓	
De Doorns Wynkelder (Koöp) Bpk			✓								
De Wet Cellar			✓		×	BYO		T			
Eagle's Cliff Wines-New Cape Wines					×	✓*				✓	
Leipzig Winery			✓			✓*	✓	✓*		✓	ru
Nuy Wine Cellar			✓								
Overhex Wines International			✓	✓		✓*		T		✓	
Stettyn Cellar			✓*		×	BYO		T*		✓	

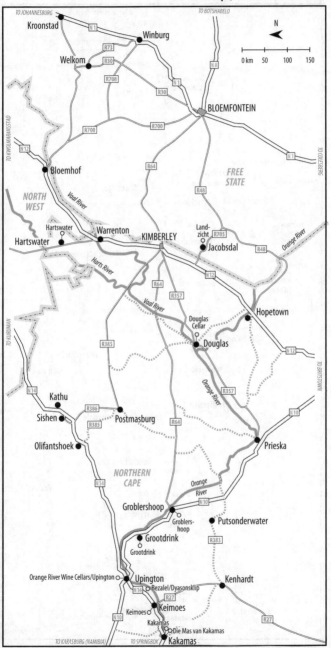

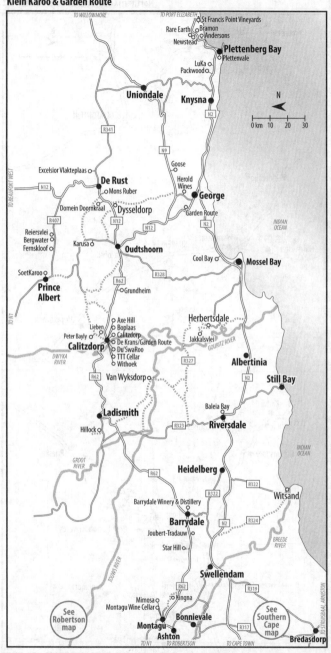

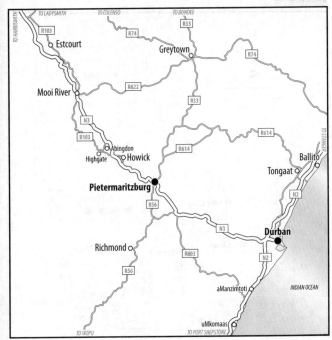

KwaZulu-Natal

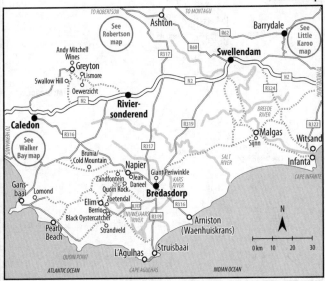

Southern Cape

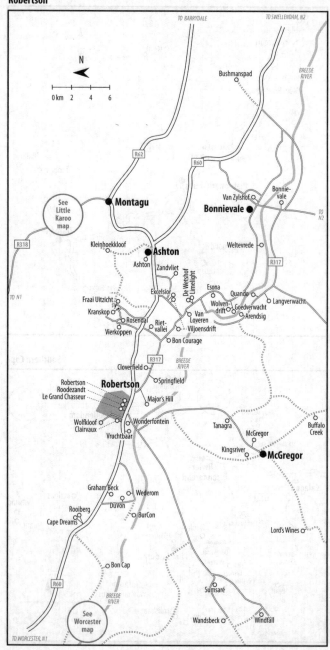

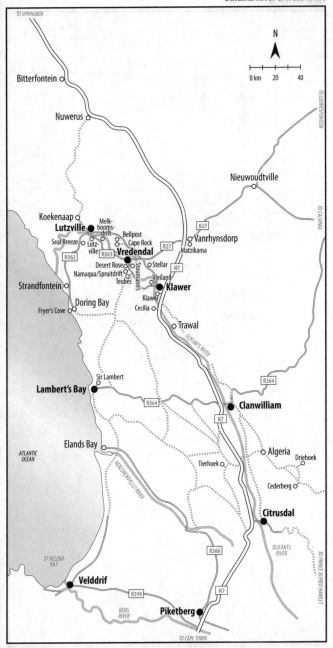

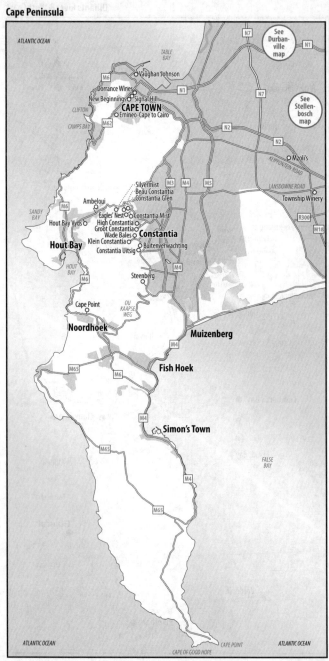

Cape Peninsula

ATLANTIC OCEAN

N7

N1

See Durbanville map

N1

TABLE BAY

See Stellenbosch map

M6 ○ Vaughan Johnson

Dorrance Wines ○
New Beginnings ○ ○ Signal Hill

N7

N7

CAPE TOWN
CLIFTON

M62 ○ Emineo-Cape to Cairo

N2

N2

CAMPS BAY

M6

KLIPFONTEIN ROAD

○ Mzoli's

M3 M4 M5

LANDSDOWNE ROAD

SANDY BAY

Silvermist
Beau Constantia
Constantia Glen

Township Winery

Ambeloui ○

R300

Eagles' Nest ○ ○ Constantia Mist

M18

Hout Bay Vyds ○

High Constantia ○
Groot Constantia ○ ○ **Constantia**
Wade Bales ○

Klein Constantia ○ ○ Buitenverwachting
Constantia Uitsig ○

M6

Hout Bay

HOUT BAY

M6

○ Steenberg

M4

OU KAAPSE WEG

Cape Point ○

Noordhoek

Muizenberg

M4

M65

M6

Fish Hoek

M4

M65

⌂ **Simon's Town**

FALSE BAY

M4

M65

ATLANTIC OCEAN

CAPE POINT
CAPE OF GOOD HOPE

ATLANTIC OCEAN

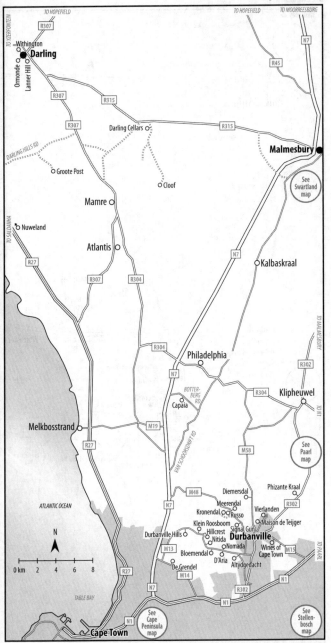

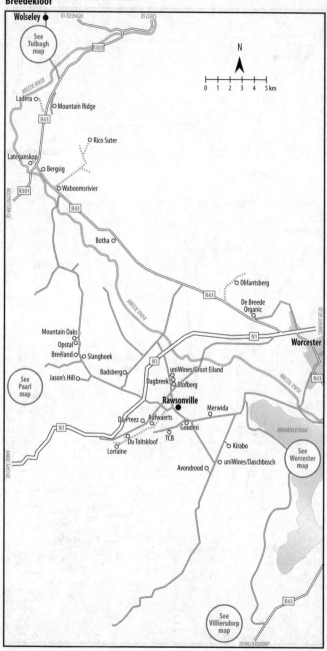

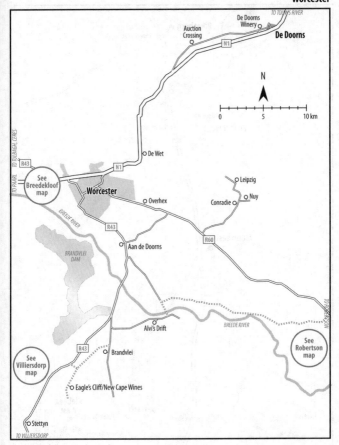

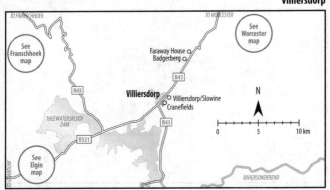

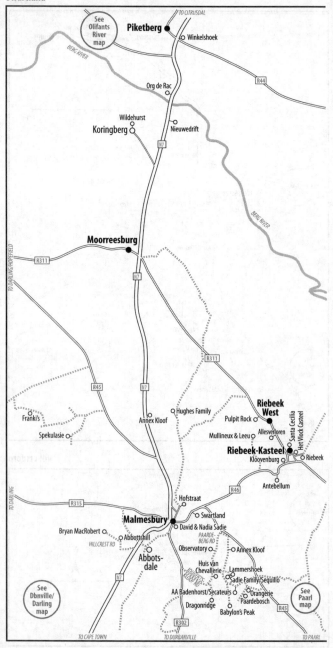

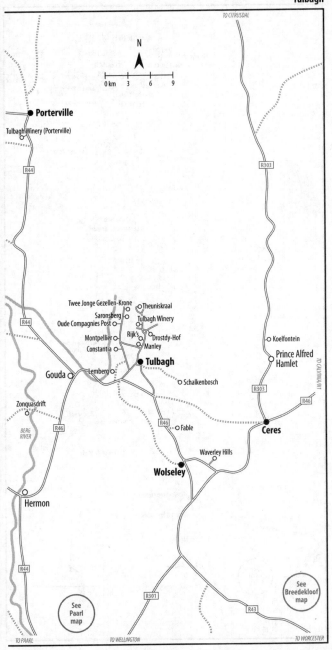

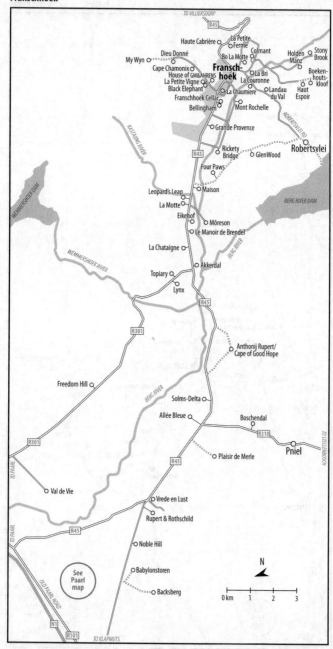

TO VILLIERSDORP

R45

Haute Cabrière
La Petite
Ferme
Colmant

My Wyn
Dieu Donné
Bo La Motte
Holden
Manz
Stony
Brook

Cape Chamonix
House of GM&AHRENS
Franschhoek
La Bri
Boeken-
houts-
kloof

La Petite Vigne
La Couronne

Black Elephant
Landau
du Val
Haut
Espoir

Franschhoek Cellar
La Chaumiere

Bellingham
Mont Rochelle

Grande Provence

R45
Rickety
Bridge
GlenWood
Robertsvlei

Four Paws
ROBERTSVLEI RD

KASTEELBERG RIVER

Leopard's Leap
Maison

La Motte
BERG RIVER DAM

Eikehof
Môreson

Le Manoir de Brendel

La Chataigne

WEMMERSHOEK DAM

Akkerdal

Topiary

Lynx

WEMMERSHOEK RIVER

R45

BERG RIVER

Anthonij Rupert/
Cape of Good Hope

R301

Freedom Hill

BERG RIVER

Solms-Delta

Allée Bleue
Boschendal

R310
TO STELLENBOSCH

Pniel

TO PAARL

R301

Plaisir de Merle

R45

Val de Vie

Vrede en Lust

Rupert & Rothschild

TO PAARL

R45

Noble Hill

See
Paarl
map

Babylonstoren

Backsberg

N

0 km   1   2   3

OLD PAARL ROAD

N1

R101

TO KLAPMUTS

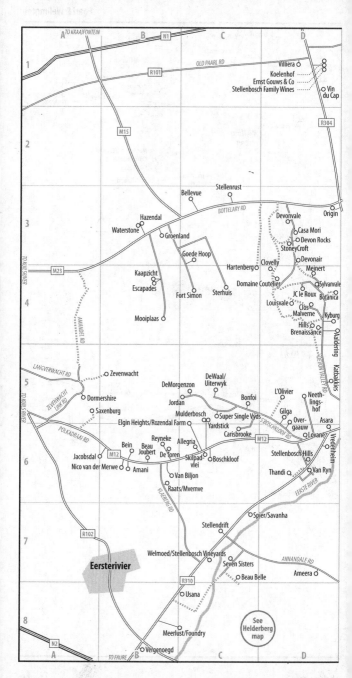

Winelands Maps

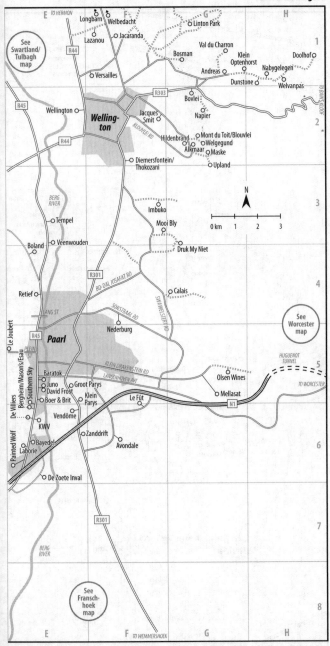

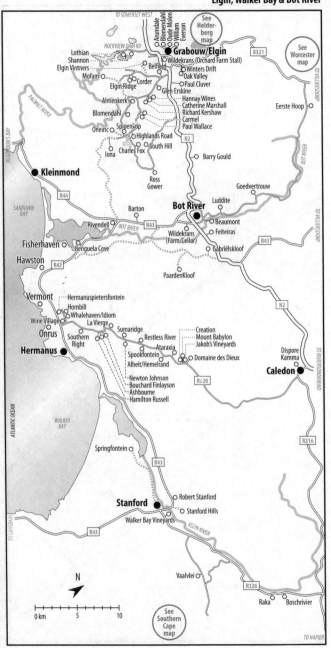

See Helderberg map

See Worcester map

TO SOMERSET WEST

Arundale
Blomendahl
Oude Molen
William
Everson

ROCKVIEW DAM RD

Grabouw/Elgin

R321

TO VILLIERSDORP

Lothian
Shannon
Elgin Vintners
Mofam

Belfield

Wildekrans (Orchard Farm Stall)
Winters Drift
Oak Valley
Paul Cluver

Elgin Ridge

Corder

Glen Erskine
Hannay Wines
Catherine Marshall
Richard Kershaw
Carmel
Paul Wallace

Almenkerk

Blomendahl

Eerste Hoop

Oneiric

Spioenkop

Highlands Road

South Hill

Iona

Charles Fox

Barry Gould

N2

Ross
Gower

BOT RIVER

FALMSET RIVER

TO GORDON'S BAY

Kleinmond

R44

SANDOWN BAY

Goedvertrouw

Luddite

Bot River

Barton

Beaumont
Feiteiras

Rivendell

BOT RIVER

R43

Wildekrans
(Farm/Cellar)

Gabriëlskloof

R43

TO VILLIERSDORP

Fisherhaven

Benguela Cove

PaardenKloof

Hawston

R43

Vermont

Hermanuspietersfontein
Hornbill
Whalehaven/Idiom

Wine Village

La Vierge

Sumaridge

Restless River

Creation
Mount Babylon
Jakob's Vineyards

Onrus

Southern
Right

Ataraxia

Spookfontein

Domaine des Dieux

N2

Caledon

Hermanus

Alheit/Hemelrand

Newton Johnson
Bouchard Finlayson
Ashbourne
Hamilton Russell

R320

Dispore
Kamma

TO RIVIERSONDEREND

ATLANTIC OCEAN

*WALKER
BAY*

R316

Springfontein

R43

Stanford

Robert Stanford

Stanford Hills

Walker Bay Vineyards

KLEIN RIVER

TO GANSBAAI

N

Vaalvlei

R326

Raka

Boschrivier

0 km   5   10

See
Southern
Cape map

TO NAPIER

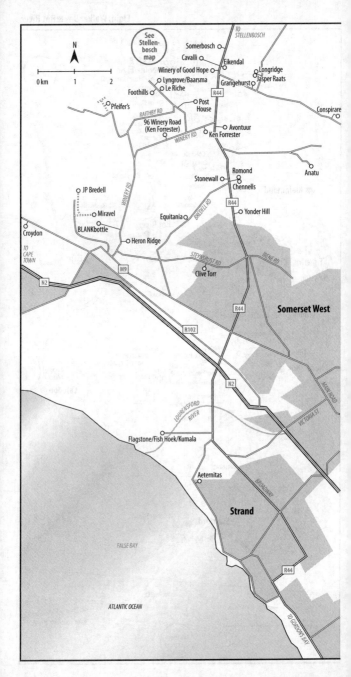

See Stellenbosch map

N

0 km 1 2

TO STELLENBOSCH

Somerbosch
Cavalli
Eikendal
Winery of Good Hope
Longridge
Jasper Raats
Grangehurst
Lyngrove/Baarsma
Le Riche
Foothills
Conspirare
Pfeifer's
RAITHBY RD
Post House
96 Winery Road (Ken Forrester)
WINERY RD
Avontuur
Ken Forrester
WINERY RD
Romond
Stonewall
Chennells
Anatu
JP Bredell
BREDELL RD
R44
Yonder Hill
Miravel
Equitania
BLANKbottle
Croydon
TO CAPE TOWN
Heron Ridge
STEYNSRUST RD
IRENE RD
M9
Somerset West
N2
Clive Torr
R102
R44
MAIN ROAD
N2
LOURENSFORD RIVER
VICTORIA ST
Flagstone/Fish Hoek/Kumala
BROADWAY
Aeternitas
FALSE BAY
Strand
R44
TO GORDON'S BAY
ATLANTIC OCEAN

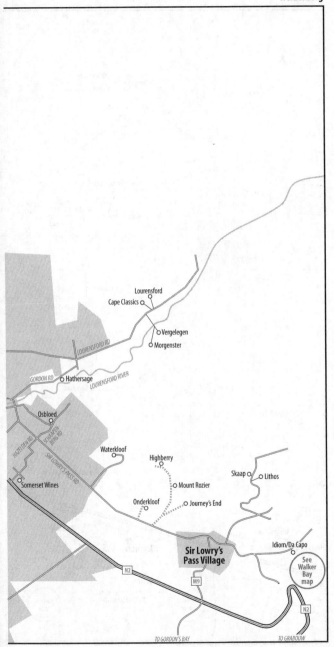

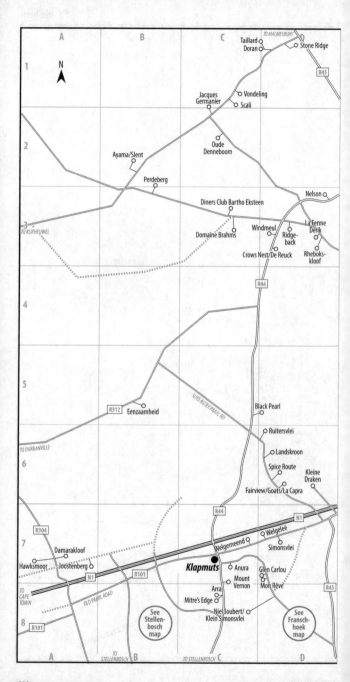